Histopathologic Technic

and

Practical Histochemistry

By
R. D. LILLIE

Department of Pathology
Louisiana State University
School of Medicine
New Orleans, Louisiana

Third Edition

The Blakiston Division
McGRAW-HILL BOOK COMPANY
New York   Toronto   Sydney   London

HISTOPATHOLOGIC TECHNIC
AND PRACTICAL HISTOCHEMISTRY

" ὅταν δὲ ἔλθῃ ἐκεῖνος, το πνεῦμα τῆς ἀληθείας,

ὁδηγήσει ὑμᾶς εἰς την ἀλήθειαν πᾶσαν." Ιω. xvi–13

δίδασκε ἡμᾶς, κύριε, γνῶναι ταύτην ἀλήθειαν.

Preface

Since the previous edition was written, there has been a great deal of active investigation of histochemical procedures. I have endeavored to bring selected variants of the newer methods into this book, and to amend them so that the methods may be followed without personal instruction by one who has had previous experience, or a good deal of experimentation to find optimal times, temperatures, pH levels and reagent concentrations. This has entailed in many instances a considerable amount of experimentation in arriving at workable conditions.

I am indebted to Drs. J. H. Peers, G. Laqueur, G. Brecher, B. Highman, R. W. Mowry, J. B. Longley, G. G. Glenner, S. S. Spicer, H. Fullmer, P. R. Gilmer and others of the staff for their suggestions and cooperation in evolving these variants, and to Miss A. Laskey, Mrs. J. Greco Henson, Mrs. H. Burtner, R. Henderson, M. Abadie and Mr. A. Gutierrez for their active help in performance and evaluation of procedures.

I also acknowledge my indebtedness to my predecessors and colleagues from whose works I have borrowed freely. Such of these borrowings as have been taken directly from their original publications are usually so cited in the text, but many have been taken, often in modified form, from other laboratory manuals. These texts are usually cited simply by the author's name, except that in the case of Ehrlich's *Encyklopädie* I have often cited the contributor's name. This last text I have often preferred as a source of those older methods which are still used in unmodified form. The texts listed on the following page have been thus used, as well as earlier editions of some of them.

R. D. LILLIE

v

General References

AM. ASSOC. TEXTILE CHEMISTS AND COLORISTS: "Yearbook," 1939–1949, Howes, N.Y.

BARKA, T., and ANDERSON, P. S.: "Histochemistry, Theory, Practice and Bibliography," Hoeber Medical Division, Harper & Row, Publishers, Incorporated, New York, 1963.

"COLOUR INDEX," 2d ed., Society of Dyers and Colourists, Bradford, Yorkshire, England, and American Association of Textile Chemists and Colorists, Lowell, Mass., 1956; suppl., 1963.

CONN, H. J.: "Biological Stains," 7th ed., The Williams & Wilkins Company, Baltimore, 1961.

CONN, H. J.: "Biological Stains," 4th, 5th and 6th eds. Biotech Publications, Geneva, N.Y., 1940, 1946, 1953.

CONN, H. J., and DARROW, M. A.: "Staining Procedures," Biotech Publications, Geneva, N.Y., 1943–1945, 1947–1949.

COWDRY, E. V.: "Microscopic Technique in Biology and Medicine," The Williams & Wilkins Company, Baltimore, 1943, 1948.

DAVENPORT, H. A.: "Histological and Histochemical Technics," W. B. Saunders Company, Philadelphia, 1960.

EHRLICH, P., et al.: "Encyklopädie der mikroskopischen Technik," Urban & Schwarzenberg, Berlin, Munich, 1903.

FEIGL, F.: "Qualitative Analysis by Spot Tests," 3d ed., Elsevier Publishing Company, New York and Amsterdam, 1946.

FEIGL, F.: "Chemistry of Specific Selective and Sensitive Reactions," Academic Press, Inc., New York, 1949.

FEIGL, F.: "Spot Tests in Organic Analysis," 5th ed., Elsevier Publishing Company, Amsterdam and New York, 1956.

FEIGL, F.: "Spot Tests in Inorganic Analysis," 5th ed., Elsevier Publishing Company, Amsterdam and New York, 1958.

GATENBY, J. B., and BEAMS, H. W.: Bolles Lee's "The Microtomist's Vade Mecum," McGraw-Hill Book Company, New York, 1950.

GLICK, D.: "Techniques of Histo- and Cytochemistry," Interscience Publishers, Inc., New York, 1949.

GOMORI, G.: Histochemical Staining Methods, in M. B. Visscher (ed.), "Methods in Medical Research," The Year Book Medical Publishers, Inc., Chicago, 1951.

GOMORI, G.: "Microscopic Histochemistry, Principles and Practice," The University of Chicago Press, Chicago, 1952.

HICKINBOTTOM, W. J.: "Reactions of Organic Compounds," 2d ed., Longmans, Green & Co., Inc., New York, 1948; 3d ed., 1957.

HUECK, W.: Pigmentstudien, *Zieglers Beitr. path. Anat.* **54**:68–232, 1912.

HUECK, W.: Die pathologische Pigmentierung, chap. 6 in Kraehl-Marchands (ed.), "Handbuch der allgemeimen Pathologie, 1921.

JONES, RUTH McCLUNG: "McClung's Handbook of Microscopical Technique," Paul B. Hoeber, Inc., Harper & Row, Publishers, New York, 1950.

KARRER, P.: "Organic Chemistry," 4th ed., Elsevier Publishing Company, New York and Amsterdam, 1950.

KRAJIAN, A. A., and GRADWOHL, R. B. H.: "Histopathological Technic," 2d ed., The C. V. Mosby Company, St. Louis, 1952.

KRAUS, GERLACH and SCHWEINBURG: "Lyssa bei Mensch und Tier," Urban & Schwarzenberg, Berlin, Munich, 1926.

LANGE, N. A.: "Handbook of Chemistry," 9th and 10th eds., McGraw-Hill Book Company, New York, 1956–1961.

LANGERON, M.: "Précis de microscopie," 5th ed., Masson et Cie, Paris, 1934, 1949.

LEE, A. B.: in J. B. Gatenby and T. S. Painter (eds.), "The Microtomist's Vade-Mecum," 10th ed., McGraw-Hill Book Company, New York, 1937.

LILLIE, R. D.: "Histopathologic Technic," The Blakiston Company, Philadelphia and Toronto, 1948.

LILLIE, R. D.: "Histopathologic Technic and Practical Histochemistry," 2d ed., McGraw-Hill Book Company, New York, 1954.

LISON, L.: "Histochimie animale," Gauthier-Villars, Paris, 1936.

LISON, L.: "Histochimie et cytochimie animales," 2d ed., Gauthier-Villars, Paris, 1953; 3d ed., 1960.

LONG, C.: "Biochemists' Handbook," D. Van Nostrand Company, Inc., Princeton, N.J., 1961.

MELLORS, R. C., (ed.): "Analytical Cytology," 2d ed., McGraw-Hill Book Company, New York, 1959.

MALLORY, F. B.: "Pathological Technic" W. B. Saunders Company, Philadelphia, 1938.

McCLUNG, C. E.: "Handbook of Microscopical Technique," Hoeber Medical Division, Harper & Row, Publishers, Incorporated, 1929.

McLEAN, R. C., and COOK, W. R. I.: "Plant Science Formulae," The Macmillan Company, New York, 1941.

McMANUS, J. F. A., and MOWRY, R. W.: "Staining Methods, Histological and Histochemical," Hoeber Medical Division, Harper & Row, Publishers, Incorporated, New York, 1960.

"THE MERCK INDEX OF CHEMICALS AND DRUGS," 7th ed., P. G. Stecher (ed.), Merck & Co., Inc., Rahway, N.J., 1960.

PEARSE, A. G. E.: "Histochemistry, Theoretical and Applied," Little, Brown and Company, Boston, 1953; 2d ed., 1960.

RAMÓN Y CAJAL, S.: "Histology," translated by M. Fernán-Nuñez, William Wood & Company, Baltimore, 1933.

ROMEIS, B.: "Taschenbuch der mikroskopischen Technik," 13th ed., R. Oldenbourg, Munich and Berlin, 1932.

ROMEIS, B.: "Mikroskopische Technik," Leibnitz Verlag, Munich, 1948.

ROULET, F.: "Methoden der pathologischen Histologie," Springer-Verlag, Vienna, 1948.

ROWE, F.: "Colour Index," 1st ed. and suppl., 1924 and 1928. See "Colour Index."

SCHMORL, G.: "Die pathologisch-histologischen Unterschungsmethoden," 15th ed., Vogel, Leipzig, 1928.

Contents

xi

Chapter 1

Microscopy

I do not propose to enter into any theoretical discussion of the optics concerned in the use of the compound microscope. Rather, the purpose of this chapter is to bring in certain practical points in the use of the microscope in which I have found it necessary to instruct technicians and physicians in training in pathology.

LIGHT

The advice in older manuals about the necessity for north windows for microscopic work, the avoidance of direct sunlight, and the preferability of a white cloud as a source of illumination is still applicable for the monocular microscope. However, daylight seldom gives adequate lighting for binocular microscopes or for more than low powers; hence some form of artificial lighting generally is necessary for microscopic work. Such lighting has the further advantage of not being subject to variations in the weather.

A tungsten filament electric lamp gives satisfactory illumination for most purposes. The slightly yellowish color of the light can be corrected by insertion of a thin blue glass disk into the microscope substage, by the use of blue glass daylight bulbs, or by the interposition of a water filter containing a weak solution of copper sulfate to which sufficient ammonia water has been added to change its color from green to blue. In form this water filter may be a cell with flat parallel sides such as the microscope lamp manufacturers often supply, or it may be spherical, such as a 500 cc Florence flask. The latter serves also as a converging lens.

Filament images, which give rise to uneven illumination of the microscopic field, are avoidable by the use of ground glass disks placed in the microscope substage, by the use of frosted or milky glass bulbs, or, in more elaborate lamps, by the use of a homogeneous light source large enough to fill the field completely, such as the 6 volt ribbon filament lamp.

In all lamps which do not possess a focusing or condensing device to produce parallel or converging light rays, it must be borne in mind that the intensity of the illumination is inversely proportional to the square of the distance of the light source from the object. The same law applies when a ground glass disk is inserted in the path of a parallel or converging light beam, since this ground glass surface acts as though it were the light source, and the available illumination diminishes with the distance from the disk to the object.

With the larger microscope lamps, which employ lens systems to focus the light accurately on the condenser of the microscope, it is advisable to mount both lamp and microscope in permanent positions on a baseboard, so that once proper optical alignment is established, it need not be disturbed. In this case it is desirable to have a cloth bag or some form of rigid cover to place over the microscope when it is not in use, in order to protect it from dust. The old-fashioned bell jar functioned well in this respect, but it was heavy and breakable. A cylinder of cellophane or similar transparent plastic, of sufficient diameter and height to cover the microscope readily and with a handle on top, makes a very satisfactory lightweight, transparent substitute which is not readily broken.

The baseboard on which the microscope and lamp are mounted may be made of sufficient thickness to support the microscope at a level such that the eyepieces are at the most convenient height for the individual observer. Among 7 workers in one laboratory the most convenient height of the eyepieces above a table 76 cm (30 in.) high varied from 33 to 40 cm (13–15¾ in.). A swivel chair with adjustable height may also be used to bring the user's eyes to the approximate level of the eyepieces. Larger lamps with large light sources and focused beams are needed for critical work at high magnifications, for dark field work, and, principally, for photomicrography. Of late years many of the microscope manufacturers have been furnishing integrated lighting systems attached to the microscope, usually in the substage area. Description of these systems and statements as to the type of illumination furnished are to be found in the manufacturer's catalogs. Some of them include devices for polarized light and dark field illumination and for substitution of phase contrast optics.

As with other projection lamp bulbs, it is often profitable to purchase bulbs of somewhat higher voltage rating than specified by the lamp manufacturer, and to operate the lamp at a slightly lower voltage than the stated rating of the bulbs employed. When used this way the bulbs last much longer, and the difference in color value of the light is scarcely appreciable.

THE MICROSCOPE

For the average worker, the use and care of the microscope are adequately described in the booklets furnished by the manufacturers. Only a few practical points will be discussed here. As Schmorl aptly states, the microscope should be obtained from a reputable manufacturer, and from personal experience I would recommend that when possible the manufacturer's plant be in the same country as the user. Necessary repairs and adjustments are greatly expedited if it is not necessary to send instruments or lenses out of one's own country.

When practical, it is preferable to have a binocular microscope with inclined ocular tubes, so that wet mounts may be studied without standing up over the instrument. The binocular instrument furthermore lessens the fatigue of prolonged use, as compared with the monocular. By training both eyes to observe, it also guards against incapacity during temporary losses of the use of one eye.

Either achromatic or apochromatic objectives may be selected. The former are corrected for 2 colors only, and are considerably cheaper. They give quite satisfactory service for almost all visual work. The latter are corrected for 3 colors and are preferable for photomicrography, especially in color photomicrography.

The Abbé test plate is a glass slide with a thin film of metallic leaf through which a series of parallel lines has been scored so as to leave clear lines bounded by narrow, opaque, metallic bands with jagged edges. This film is covered by a long, narrow coverslip which varies progressively in thickness from about 90 μ at one end to 230 μ at the other. At the side of this coverslip are graduations indicating the approximate coverglass thickness at any point.

This test plate is used for testing objectives for chromatic aberration, for spherical aberration, for sharpness of definition, and for flatness of field. A complete substage with a device for oblique illumination is needed. Low power objectives should be tested between 150 μ and 200 μ equivalent coverglass thickness. No. 1 coverglasses average about 150 μ, No. 2 about 210 μ in thickness. Test 4 mm apochromats with correction collars at at least 2 points, with corresponding adjustment of the correction collar. Immersion objectives should be tested immersed in their proper immersion fluids.

With oblique illumination, achromatic objectives give relatively broad fringes of complementary colors on the edges of the metallic strips. With apochromats, these fringes are narrower—often almost inappreciable.

When sharply focused with the condenser centered and properly focused, a good objective should continue to give sharply defined points on the edges of the metallic bands when the illumination is decentered across the direction of the bands. Similar performance should be obtained in the central and peripheral portions of the field.

Relative flatness of field can be judged by the amount of focusing necessary to give sharp definition respectively in the center and at the periphery of the field. It should be borne in mind that lenses with the greatest resolving power in the center of the field ordinarily do not give so flat a field as some others inferior in resolving power. This property of flatness of field is more important with lower powers and for photographic purposes.

Resolving power may be tested on various test slides. For instance, the diatom *Pleurosigma angulatum* at 250 × should show three distinct striation systems. One runs perpendicular to the median rib; the other 2 cross obliquely at an angle of about 58°. At higher magnification the striae appear as material between rounded globules which is dark at high and low focus, bright at normal focus. The wing scales of *Epinephele janira* ♀ show longitudinal striation at 40 ×. Between these striae a fine cross striation is seen at 150 ×. At 800–1000 × the longitudinal striae are doubly contoured and contain round granules. (The material for this paragraph was derived from Romeis. For a fuller account consult Langeron.)

The objectives to be selected for a microscope naturally vary widely with the purpose to which each is to be put. For general pathology the following seem the most desirable. An achromat of about 3–6 × initial magnification is almost essential for general views of sections. Achromats or apochromats of 10 and 20 × (16 and 8 mm) are needed for more detailed study. A 31 × (5.5 mm) achromat has proved quite useful in practice. It is similar in performance to the English ¼ in. objective. I have found dry achromats of 45 × and even 60 × very useful on occasion, especially when the use of oil is inconvenient. An immersion objective of 60 or 90–100 × initial magnification (3 or 2 mm) is required for very high magnification. These last are available in three grades: achromatic, fluorite and apochromatic, in ascending grades of performance and cost. The second will serve almost all purposes; the last are somewhat better for photography and maximum resolution. The 4 mm apochromat is in practice rather unsatisfactory because of the necessity for adjustment of the correction collar for variations in thickness of coverslips and of film of the mounting medium. An oil immersion objective of 4 mm (40–45 ×) has been found very useful for differential cell counts of leucocytes in thin blood films, because of the larger field afforded. This magnification is still adequate for identification of ordinary blood leucocytes, but for marrow films a 2 or 3 mm (90 × or 60 ×) objective is required.

Among eyepieces the 7.5 ×, 10 × and 12.5 × seem the most useful. Visual impairment in the user may be partly compensated for with 15 or 20 × oculars. In selecting oculars it should be remembered that objectives do not give effective magnifications of over 1000 times their numerical aperture (NA). Hence a 60 × objective with NA 1.40 can be used with 15 × oculars, giving about 900 diameters final magnification; but a 90 ×, NA 1.30 objective will accept only a 12.5 × eyepiece, giving 1125 diameters; or, perhaps better, a 10 × eyepiece, yielding 900 diameters.

Attempts to obtain higher magnifications by use of higher oculars result in blurring of detail.

For apochromatic objectives, compensating eyepieces should be used. For achromats, the Huygenian type is satisfactory. For fluorite objectives, eyepieces should be either compensating or of an intermediate grade designated as hyperplane or planoscopic. These last can also be used with achromatic objectives and even with apochromats, though they are not recommended for the latter.

Generally 2 eyepieces separated by 5 × in magnification are adequate. For the binocular instruments, only matched pairs should be used, at a constant interpupillary distance which one may determine by trial for himself. Both should be brought to focus on some individual detail in a microscopic field by means of the focusing collar on one of the ocular tubes.

In regard to the question of parallel or converging ocular tubes, both have their defenders and either seems to be satisfactory to the individual observer when he has become accustomed to it. Changing from one to the other is difficult. Note that the parallel design has been adopted by 3 of the 4 manufacturers whose microscopes have been commonly used in the United States.

Condensers are commonly used in the substage of microscopes to bring to bear on the object a sufficient amount of light at an adequate angular aperture to illuminate the field adequately. For work with ordinary transmitted light, the usual Abbé condenser serves for routine work with achromatic objectives. For apochromatic and fluorite objectives an aplanatic or achromatic condenser is necessary, whose numerical aperture should approximate the highest numerical aperture of the objectives likely to be used.

ILLUMINATION

To obtain the best results with any suitable combination of optical components, it is necessary to relate them to one another in a definitely prescribed way. This principle is generally understood with respect to the focusing on the object of the parts above the microscope stage, and it is hardly less important with respect to the components below the stage. The necessary adjustments are (1) alignment of the optical axes of the condenser and illuminator with that of the objective and ocular, (2) focusing of the substage and illuminator condenser, and (3) regulation of the iris diaphragms of the system. If these procedures are not carried out correctly the most elaborate equipment is no better than the plainest, and is frequently worse.

Dim and uneven illumination is the most frequent consequence of faulty axial alignment. To avoid this, align the equipment as described in the following paragraphs.

Focus the microscope on a slide placed on the stage, then move the slide to obtain an empty field. Remove the ocular and observe the back lens of the objective through a pinhole eyepiece. Close the condenser diaphragm until it begins to restrict the lighted disk seen. Move the condenser by means of its centering screws until the restriction is evenly distributed around the edge of the disk. The condenser is now centered. (The pinhole eyepiece required for this operation can be made by making a needle hole through the center of a cardboard cap fitted over the tube after the eyepiece is removed.)

Before aligning the illuminator with the microscope, the centration of the light source itself with respect to the illuminator condenser should be checked. If the illuminator is aimed horizontally at a nearby wall and the image of the lamp filament is focused upon it, the center of the filament image should be at a level with the center of the illuminator condenser. If the housing has a reflector behind the filament, the direct and reflected images of the filament should fall on top of one another, except that with filaments composed of multiple parallel coils, the two images should be displaced just enough to alternate the coils in the combined image.

To align the illuminator with the microscope, place it in a convenient position in front of the microscope and aim it roughly at the flat side of the substage mirror. Close the illuminator diaphragm, and with the microscope still focused as for centering the condenser, move the mirror and adjust the height of the substage condenser until the aperture in the illuminator diaphragm is seen sharply focused in the center of the field. Place a piece of white paper in the substage filter holder. Examine the image of the lamp filament projected on it. Adjust the lamp position to center the image on the condenser axis. The image should be large enough to cover the lower lens of the condenser. Remove the paper and again center the image of the diaphragm in the visual field by moving the mirror. Replace the paper, and should it be necessary to adjust the lamp position again, repeat the mirror adjustment also. The optical system will be in axial alignment. In addition, after this procedure the substage and illuminator are also correctly focused for critical microscopy. (This method of aligning the lamp is essentially that of Galbraith, *Quart. J. Micr. Sci.* **96**:515, 1955.)

The arrangement described, with illuminator condenser imaged in the plane of the object, is often referred to as "Köhler illumination" and is distinguished from "critical illumination," in which the light source is imaged in the plane of the object. These terms are unfortunate because both methods are suitable for critical work; furthermore, Köhler did not discover the method referred to here, but did devise another quite different method, also named after him, for evenly illuminating very large fields, such as are required with very low power objectives.

"Critical illumination," in the sense of imaging the actual incandescent light source in the object plane, is rarely used because it requires a large and uniformly luminous filament. Using this arrangement with standard equipment, even the ribbon filament can fill only the restricted fields of higher power objectives. However, since for visual microscopy it is necessary to reduce the intensity and correct the color of the light from the usual incandescent sources, it is usual to place a blue ground glass diffuser in front of the lamp condenser. This diffuser in effect becomes the light source, and since, if the procedure recommended above is used, it is imaged by the condenser in the object plane of the microscope, the arrangement becomes the equivalent of "critical illumination." When a diffuser *is* inserted in this way in the system described above, the lamp condenser should be moved as close to the light as possible, as this results in the most uniform illumination of the ground glass. It is important to secure axial alignment of the system whether a diffuser is to be used or not because even the diffused light is preferentially radiated in the axial direction. Some observers feel that a diffuser detracts from the quality of the illumination.

Finally, before actual observation is begun, the lamp and substage diaphragms should be adjusted. It is especially important that correct use be made of the latter, as it controls the numerical aperture of the condenser. In theory any objective can achieve its maximum resolution only if it is used with a condenser adjusted to equal it in numeral aperture; if the condenser diaphragm is opened too wide, light which the objective cannot use will pass, and some of it, reaching the objective as stray reflections and refractions, will degrade the visual image; if the condenser aperture is reduced too far, resolution will be sacrificed and excessive diffraction may also degrade the image. In practice the most satisfactory image seems to be obtained if the substage diaphragm is closed slightly more than theory requires. At this point a slight restriction of the lighted area may be seen by examining the back lens of the objective with the ocular removed. The adjustment of the lamp, or field, diaphragm is a relatively minor matter, but for critical work, if it is closed so as just to avoid encroaching on the visual field, it may improve the image slightly by excluding a small amount of stray light.

In view of the foregoing considerations it should not be necessary to warn against controlling the brightness of the image by closing the condenser diaphragm. Brightness can be controlled satisfactorily by equipping the lamp with a rheostat, by inserting neutral filters in the light path, or by inserting two sheets of polaroid film in the light path and varying their relative alignment. So long as both polaroids are on the same side of the object the birefringence of collagen, striated muscle, or other anisotropic tissue components will not interfere with the dimming effect.

The practice of controlling image brightness by lowering the condenser is also to be discouraged. It not only throws the condenser out of proper focus but also reduces its effective numerical aperture, thereby sacrificing resolution and introducing diffraction effects. Lowering the condenser to illuminate the whole field of a low power objective may be justified on grounds of expedience if it is being used simply to locate objects for critical study at higher magnifications, but for really adequate lighting with such objectives other measures are required. Some microscopes provide auxiliary condenser lens which may be swung into the light path to enlarge the image of the light source; others achieve the same result by the use of a variable focus "split" condenser. Removal of the top element of the condenser is also satisfactory; a swinging top element is a built-in feature of some condensers.

It was assumed above that every microscopist knows when the objective of his microscope is focused. Unfortunately this is not the same as saying that every microscopist knows how to focus his objective. One simple precaution insures against damage to slides and equipment while focusing: *focus up!* After placing a slide on the microscope stage, lower the tube slowly by means of the coarse adjustment while watching the space between slide and objective. When it is certain that the objective is below its focused position, look into the microscope and raise the tube slowly until the specimen appears. When using immersion objectives the tube should be lowered before the immersion medium is applied, the objective being rotated to the side to permit application of the medium after the tube has been brought to a suitable level. When the objectives in a nosepiece have been adjusted to be a parfocal this precaution is necessary only when bringing the object into focus for the first time. However, when relying on this feature one should be on guard against thick coverslips or inverted slides, either of which will interfere with the use of the higher powers.

I am indebted to Dr. James B. Longley, now at the University of Louisville, for contributing the foregoing section on illumination. I have little to add to it.

About focusing of the several objectives, try if possible to have them adjusted so as to be parfocal. It is especially valuable to be able to focus sharply with a 20, 30 or 45 × dry lens, center the area desired for examination, swing the first lens out of position, apply a drop of immersion oil and swing the immersion lens into position and find the field sufficiently visible to permit sharp focusing with a small movement of the fine adjustment.

It helps also to learn which way to focus on your own microscope on changing objectives. Many objectives have incorporated in them devices for altering their focus, so that they can be rendered parfocal. Learn from the local representative of your microscope manufacturer how to do this, or have him do it for you. Unstained sections sometimes present special problems in finding the focal plane. In such cases the plane can be found with phase equipment, or by use of a mounting medium of quite low refractive index, so that the unstained section is readily visible grossly. Or one may place a small dot of India ink or black slide marking ink on the lower surface of the coverglass, to one side of the specimen in the course of mounting. Two ink lines drawn transversely and longitudinally on the surface of smear preparations which are to be studied with oil immersion without coverslips serve the same purpose of locating the focal plane.

Generally the microscope can be used without eyeglasses except when the wearer's optical defect includes a considerable degree of astigmatism or is extreme in grade. A mere 10 diopter spherical correction is readily adjusted for by focusing. So-called *high point* oculars are essential for persons who find it necessary to wear their spectacles while working at the microscope. These oculars are now readily available. Or individual caps carrying small lenses of the worker's eyeglass prescription may be procured from the microscope manufacturers and placed over the microscope eyepieces.

Objectives, eyepieces and condensers should be cleaned by breathing on the glass and wiping with the lens paper made for that purpose. Immersion oil should be cleaned off daily at least, or when the use of that objective is finished for the time being. To do this it is well to dampen a spot on a piece of lens paper with a drop of xylene and wipe first with this damp spot, then with the remaining dry lens paper in a single movement.

For **immersion objectives** it is preferable to use one of the nondrying oils now made for the purpose. These are available in high and low viscosities and may be blended according to the particular need of the user. Low viscosities are better when rapid motion of the slide is to be used with short working distances, and when fresh wet preparations are being studied under a coverglass. The most practical oil for routine use may be an equal volume mixture of the 2 grades. On one occasion it was found necessary to make immersion oil of a very low viscosity by mixing approximately 4 volumes of light mineral oil with 1 volume of α-bromonaphthalene. If it is necessary to make such mixtures, they should be checked for index of refraction with a refractometer if possible. The index of refraction should be between nΔ 1.515 and 1.520.

If the refractometer is not available, the proper index of refraction may be approximated by immersing a white glass slide (or a glass rod of the proper refractive index) in the mineral oil and then gradually adding α-bromonaphthalene until the glass can no longer be seen through the oil.

If one persists in the use of thickened cedar oil for immersion, the utmost care should be taken to have it cleaned off the immersion lenses at least daily. Dry balsam or cedar oil is probably best removed by carefully chipping off the outer portion with a knife, avoiding contact with either metal or glass, and then removing the remainder with lens paper or a soft cloth moistened with benzene or xylene. Alcohol should be avoided, since it softens the cement in which the front lenses of many older immersion objectives were mounted.

Immersion oil is conveniently removed from coverglasses covering fresh resinous or glycerol-gelatin or similar mounts by first inverting the slide on a blotter and pressing down lightly. This absorbs the bulk of the oil. The small residue is readily removed by gently wiping on a blotter wet with xylene, or by dragging a piece of lens paper moistened with xylene across the soiled area, steadying the coverglass with a finger on one corner if necessary.

Blood films may be cleaned of cedar oil by dipping repeatedly in a jar of xylene, or by dropping xylene slowly on the slanted slide just above the oil drop until it runs off the edge of the film. The nondrying mineral oils may be removed in the same manner; but it is not necessary to remove them from blood films, since they apparently do not cause fading of Romanovsky stains, as did cedar oil. In fact, it appears that this type of oil may even act to better preserve Giemsa and Wright stains.

When the utmost resolution is required with lenses of a numerical aperture above 1.0, and for dark field work, a drop of oil is also placed between condenser and slide. Usually this procedure is unnecessary and (if much movement of the slide is required) both troublesome and messy.

If after immersion contact has been made and focus has been attained, a grayish haze appears moving in from one side to obscure the image, a tiny air bubble in the immersion fluid is probably responsible. The trouble is remedied by swinging the objective out laterally to break the immersion contact, and then back in again without changing the focus.

OBLIQUE ILLUMINATION

Oblique illumination is used to make more prominent the lineal details transverse to the plane of oblique lighting. It is obtained by excluding light from all but one side of the under surface of the condenser. A device for this purpose is included in research model microscopes, and a similar device may be improvised for student microscopes by sliding a piece of cardboard gradually across the undersurface of the condenser from the desired side. Utilization of this type of lighting materially increases the resolving power of the objective in the plane of the oblique illumination.

DARK FIELD ILLUMINATION

Dark field illumination is a device of essentially similar nature, but it provides oblique illumination from all sides while excluding directly transmitted light. Particulate matter in a fluid medium is thus caused to glow against a dark background, and particles materially smaller than can be discerned by direct transmitted light are thus rendered visible.

Dark field illumination can be simply achieved for low magnifications by inserting beneath the condenser a disk or stop which shuts off light from the center of the condenser while admitting it to most of the periphery. For immersion work a special dark field condenser is needed. An immersion objective with a numerical aperture somewhat below 1.0 is required. The usual immersion objective of NA 1.25–1.40 may be used if a funnel stop designed for the purpose is inserted into the upper side of the objective before screwing it into the nosepiece. More convenient are immersion objectives with normal numerical apertures which are equipped with an iris diaphragm for reducing the aperture. For routine use, the objectives specially built for dark field work are desirable. Also very convenient are dark field illumination units which may be attached directly to the dark field condenser. This eliminates the troublesome centering of illumination.

Both condenser and objective must be immersed. Otherwise the desired extremely oblique rays are lost by reflection from the undersurfaces of the slide and the objective.

I have on one occasion observed a sample of one of the modified mineral oil type of immersion oils which although perfectly satisfactory for bright field work gave unsatisfactory dark field illumination when used for immersion of the condenser. Focusing on the oil film revealed large numbers of minute bright particles. These were not removed by filtration. A mixture of 4 parts heavy mineral oil and 1 part α-bromonaphthalene proved free of these particles and was quite satisfactory.

POLARISCOPY

The use of polarized light in histology is particularly valuable in the detection and identification of certain crystalline substances and of certain lipids, and in the study of such tissues as cross-striated muscle, collagen and myelinated nervous tissue. Polarized light may be obtained by disks of polaroid material, by interposition of series of obliquely placed thin glass plates such as coverglasses or by the use of a Nicol prism. The polarizing device may be set at any convenient place between the light source and the object under study. In research microscopes a place is usually provided for a polarizer just beneath the condenser. For observation, a second polarizing device is required, and this is usually placed over the microscope ocular. This is called the analyzer.

The first Nicol prism, or polarizer, permits passage of light vibrating in a single plane. When the second prism, or analyzer, is in the optically identical position, the light which passed through the polarizer passes also through the analyzer, and the field of the microscope is bright. Now if one of the prisms is rotated 90° on its long axis relative to the other, light which passed through the first prism is unable to pass through the second, and the field is dark. In this dark field such substances as rotate the plane of polarized light are seen to glow. Such substances are referred to as anisotropic or doubly refractile. When the slide is rotated about the axis of the light beam, the bright material fades and brightens 4 times during a complete rotation. By inserting the mica disks supplied with polarizing outfits, color changes are substituted for the lightening and darkening. For this purpose a rotating circular stage carefully centered is almost essential, though it is possible to achieve the same results by simultaneously rotating both polarizer and analyzer in opposite directions with thumb and forefinger. This is fairly easily done with a little practice, so that the overall darkness of the field is maintained.

In using polarizing equipment in an inclined monocular tube microscope, the polarizer must be adjusted so that its polarizing effect is added to (not neutralized by) the polarizing effect of reflection through a single prism. The optimum point is that at which the reddish cast of the darkened field changes abruptly to greenish. At that point the field is at maximum darkness. This effect may be completely obviated by placing the analyzer just above the objectives and below the inclined monocular or binocular body prism system. In this case rotation of the plane of polarized light and lightening and darkening of the field are accomplished by placing the polarizer in the rotating substage mount.

To center a rotating mechanical stage, place on the stage the centering slide provided for that purpose, a stage micrometer, or any other section. With the eye select some conspicuous detail near the center of the field and commence rotating the stage. If the selected object describes an arc, manipulate the stage centering screws so as to bring the apparent center of rotation to near the middle of the field. Then select some object on the edge of the field and rotate the stage. The selected object should follow around the edge of the field. Make the necessary slight adjustment with the stage centering screws until it does.

When using polarized light it is necessary to employ appropriate preliminary technical procedures for the preservation of the material that one desires to study. Fats and lipids must be studied in material that has not at any time been subjected to the action of fat solvents. The usual fat stain preparations from frozen sections are usable, though it may sometimes be desirable to have an unstained frozen section as well. For myelin, frozen sections are also necessary, while for striated muscle and crystals such as silica, either paraffin or frozen sections will serve. It is to be noted that a common doubly refractile material in paraffin sections is the so-called formaldehyde pigment, acid formaldehyde hematin, which is formed from hemoglobin by acid formaldehyde during fixation (see pp. 390–393). The birefringence of collagen, well discerned in such mounting media as cellulose caprate and the resins, may be completely lost in preparations mounted in glycerol gelatin.

After treatment with acetic Zenker and certain other acid aqueous fixatives, red corpuscles may become doubly refractile, lightening and darkening like crystals on rotation of the stage.

Skeletal muscle, when correctly oriented to the plane of polarized light, gives sharply contrasting light and dark bands. At a 45° rotation these bands may be quite inconspicuous; hence rotation is necessary. Either stained or unstained, frozen or paraffin sections may be utilized. Cardiac muscle often gives only a barely discernible diffuse glow without distinct bright and dark bands, and no appreciable change is noted on rotation. Sometimes, however, distinct dark and light bands, brightening and darkening on rotation, are discernible; and on occasion it appears that insufficient illumination is the cause of the failure to show bright and dark bands. Use of azure eosin stained sections of skeletal or cardiac muscle gives bright bands which are nearly white or bluish white and deep pink in alternating quadrants of rotation. Lint or cellulose fibers accidentally included in the mounting medium often glow brilliantly, but above the section plane.

Smooth muscle, especially when sections are mounted in a medium of low refractive index, such as xylene cellulose caprate, often exhibits a distinct birefringence, more diffuse than that of striated or cardiac muscle, and generally less brilliant than that of the collagen fibers in the same section.

This property of collagen and of hair can be very valuable in finding the focal plane of unstained sections with inconspicuous or sparsely distributed colored histochemical reactions. It has further enabled the decision as to whether a given histochemical procedure blocked the staining reactivity of collagen or solubilized and destroyed it.

FLUORESCENCE MICROSCOPY

This procedure is employed for the demonstration of substances which of themselves possess the property of emitting light of longer wavelength (in the visible range) when excited by light of a shorter wavelength. Also, objects stained with certain fluorescent dyes may be demonstrated by this means. The latter demonstration in its application to the auramine staining of tubercle bacilli is the commonest use of the procedure (pp. 121, 579).

Usually ultraviolet light of 350–400 mμ wavelength is employed as the exciting light. For this purpose we have used a G.E. Mazda 100 watt A4H mercury vapor lamp with the G.E. autotransformer for 4H lamps. This gives an initial voltage of 245 to establish the arc and then drops automatically to a lower voltage. This lamp should be shielded with an adequately ventilated lamp housing and a wooden screen so placed that the light of the lamp falls only on the substage mirror of the microscope. Stray light can be very disconcerting, both in photographic work and in occasioning cutaneous or corneal burns. Lempert (*Lancet* **247**:818, 1944) used the Mercra lamp of the British supplier, Thomson Houston, Ltd., Crown House, Aldwych, London. The glass bulb of this lamp is made of a dark glass which cuts off most of the visible light—only dark red is seen—and 95% of the light is of the 364 mμ band of the mercury arc. With the G.E. lamp that we have used, it is necessary to interpose filters between the lamp and the condenser to screen out most of the visible light. Most of these filters also pass a certain amount of far red and infrared light. Their transmission bands in the ultraviolet vary in width, position and total transmittancy. The width and position of the band are more important when a carbon arc lamp is used as a light source than with the mercury vapor lamp. The latter emits a bright line at 365 mμ, with no other bright lines in the nearby portion of the spectrum.

Suitable filters are Corning's red purple corex A 9863, maximum 81% transmittance at about 320–350 mμ, but transmitting over 10% between 264 and 402; red purple ultra 5970, 86% at about 360–370 mμ, over 10% from 318–407; HR red purple ultra 5874, 66% at about 362–368 mμ, over 10% from 322–398; red ultra 5840, 56% at about 356–363, over 10% from 320–386; and violet ultra 5860, 28% at about 360, over 10% from 340–379. The last is preferred for selectivity but is of rather low intensity. The HR red purple ultra 5874 is probably the best among the higher intensity group, or perhaps the red ultra 5840.

Most of these filters transmit a considerable amount of light at the far red end of the visible spectrum. Insertion of a thin glass water cell containing 5–10% acidulated copper sulfate solution is recommended to cut off this red light.

These mercury vapor lamps, both the British and the American, require perhaps a minute to warm up after they are turned on, and when the current is turned off, one must let them cool perhaps 10 minutes before they can be turned on again. The lamp is brought as close to the substage mirror as possible—Lempert specified 4½ in. (114 mm)—and no converging lens system is used. The glass lenses of such lens systems would take out too much light. However, if a converging light is desired to obtain greater intensity or more critical illumination, a Florence flask or a double watchglass lens filled with distilled water could be used, or a concave mirror placed behind the lamp.

A condenser is necessary for adequate illumination; but for light in the 350–380 mμ spectral region it need not be of quartz, though greater intensity may thus be obtained. Similarly, quartz slides transmit more ultraviolet light at this wavelength than do glass slides. Popper has used quartz slides and a glass condenser; Endicott conversely used a quartz condenser and glass slides. The latter procedure allows greater transmission of ultraviolet light because of the shorter light path through glass. If one has a quartz condenser available, it is much more convenient to be able to use ordinary glass slides. Lempert used both glass slides and glass condenser. Metcalf and Patton (*Stain Techn.* **19**:11, 1944) found glass slides and condensers satisfactory. Note also that the Abbé type is satisfactory: the aplanatic is better because of the better spherical correction and greater concentration of light; the achromatic type occasions too much light loss. A removable dark field disk about 166 mm in diameter should be inserted in the substage below the condenser. This gives a luminous object in a perfectly dark field. The cardioid condenser was not so satisfactory. Of the filters mentioned, only the violet ultra 5860 gave a black background without the dark field disk.

The ordinary glass objectives and eyepieces are used, and a yellow filter is employed over the eyepiece to screen out ultraviolet light and avoid ocular damage. Such a filter should absorb as fully as possible the 340–420 mμ region of the spectrum. For photography it is necessary to absorb also the red end of the spectrum, which most of the ultraviolet passing filters also transmit in addition to the 365–366 mμ mercury line. Or one may use a film which is insensitive to red light.

As a yellow filter Lempert first used tartrazine stained gelatin filters, and later obtained "suitable" glass filters which did not fluoresce in ultraviolet light. Corning's Noviol O 3060 is the nearest to colorless of the ultraviolet cutoff filters that we have used, and is the best for judging the color of fluorescences. However, it transmits some far-violet light below 400 mμ and can give headaches on continued use. The same company's Noviol A 3389 is a quite pale yellow which transmits very little light below 425 mμ; and the next, Noviol B 368, gives little below 450, but is a deeper yellow.

All these filters give some diffuse fluorescence which occasions no difficulty visually but is quite disturbing for photographic purposes, producing a diffuse fogging of films.

Paraffin, balsam and cedar oil fluoresce of themselves; the first must be removed from sections, and the other 2 must be avoided as mounting media. According to Metcalf and Patton (*loc. cit.*) a xylene or toluene solution of isobutyl methacrylate is a satisfactory mounting medium, at least for temporary mounts. Preparations can be mounted in liquid petrolatum or in glycerol. Popper found an objectionable fluorescence in glycerol in his vitamin A studies. The low fluorescence modified mineral oils used as immersion fluids possess a higher index of refraction than unmodified heavy mineral oil (nΔ 1.515 *vs.* 1.483) and like it do not fade the sensitive Romanovsky stains. These oils and glycerol can also be used as immersion fluids for smears, though Lempert preferred to examine auramine stained smears with dry lenses.

In the fixation of tissue which is to be studied by fluorescence microscopy, formalin, alcoholic and acetic formalins and an acetic variant of
Regaud's fluid have been used; but Metcalf and Patton warn against
fluids containing heavy metals (except zinc), chlorides, bromides, iodides
or nitro compounds. Picric acid is the only one of the last group commonly used in fixing fluids.

Native Fluorescence. A number of substances possess natural fluorescence, including carotenes and vitamin A, chlorophyll, porphyrins, ceroid,
riboflavin, atabrine and a number of alkaloids. These possess each its
own fluorescence colors and spectra. The latter may be observed with
Amici prisms or with the Jelley microspectroscope.

According to Popper (*Arch. Path.* **31**:766, 1941) vitamin A yields a
green fluorescence which fades fairly promptly: small quantities perhaps
in 10 seconds; normal amounts in the liver in about 45 seconds. Glycerol
gave a disturbing fluorescence of its own, so sections were studied in
water (oil dissolves vitamin A). Malaria pigment, hemosiderin and bile
pigment did not fluoresce. Hepatic lipofuscin gave a brown fluorescence
which was stable under continued ultraviolet irradiation. After alcohol
extraction the lipofuscin fluorescence changed to red, while the extract
gave the green labile vitamin A fluorescence. Similar brown red fluorescence was given by adrenal lipofuscin. Brown fluorescence is given by a
brown acetone soluble pigment in the testicular Leydig cells; and there
was an alcohol insoluble lipofuscin with brown red fluorescence in the
testicular germinal epithelium; as well as brown fluorescing lipid droplets,
and, in involuting testes, granules of ultraviolet stable, bright yellow,
fluorescent material. Lutein cells yield a faint brown fluorescence after
the green vitamin A fluorescence has faded. Heart-muscle lipofuscin gives
red fluorescence. Yellow fluorescent granules are seen in the epithelium
of sweat glands and of the prostate. Amyloid gives a dim blue fluorescence. Ceroid, according to Endicott and to Popper, yields golden brown
fluorescence in paraffin sections, in frozen sections greenish yellow slowly
changing to yellowish white. This is given by both paraffin sections and
frozen sections in water, dry or in paraffin; but not in xylene or xylene
Clarite (*Am. J. Path.* **20**:149; 1944; *Arch. Path.* **37**:161, 1944). Riboflavin
(vitamin B_2) gives a green fluorescence like that of vitamin A, but is
quickly reduced and rendered nonfluorescent by saturated aqueous
sodium hydrosulfite ($Na_2S_2O_4 \cdot 2H_2O$) solutions. Thiochrome, the oxidation product of thiamine (vitamin B_1), has a bluish fluorescence.
Chlorophyll, used sometimes as a fat stain, gives a fiery red, quickly
fading fluorescence. Atabrine gives an intense green fluorescence; pron-
tosil, a red; penicillin, a green; sodium salicylate, a blue.

Heating of preparations to 170–200°C for 3–5 minutes alters the natural
blue and green fluorescences of muscle and of certain drugs to give contrasting colors (Helander, *Nature* **155**:109, 1945). Thus, heating to 170°C

for 5 minutes gives yellow sulfathiazole and blue muscle fluorescence. Heating of sulfanilamide, sulfapyridine, papaverine or inulin to 200°C for 3 minutes gives yellow drug and blue muscle fluorescence.

Enterochromaffin cells exhibit a golden yellow fluorescence in formaldehyde fixed tissues (Erös, *Zbl. allg. Path.* **54**:385, 1932). This property has been urged in support of the identification of the enterochromaffin substance with 5-hydroxytryptamine, whose formaldehyde condensation product gives a similar fluorescence. (See Lillie, *J. Histochem.* **9**:44, 1961, for tabulation of fluorescence and other reactions of certain phenols and phenylamines in formaldehyde fixed serum models.)

According to du Buy and Showacre (*Science* **133**:196, 1961), tetracycline added to tissue cultures at 10–20 γ/cc induces intense yellow fluorescence sharply localized in mitochondria. Injection of mice with 100 γ/gm body weight induced similar localization in liver, spleen and brain mitochondria in sucrose centrifugates and in fresh frozen sections. The treatment of fresh frozen sections or cell suspensions with tetracycline in Ringer's or Locke's solution at 1–2 mg/100 cc might be a useful procedure for demonstration of mitochondria.

Tetracycline given *in vivo* may also be used to localize newly deposited calcium salts in bone and cartilage (Milch, Tobie and Robinson, *J. Histochem.* **9**:261, 1961).

ABSORPTION SPECTROSCOPY OF TISSUES

Two rather dissimilar technics have been applied. In the one, undispersed light is passed through the condenser, object and objective-ocular magnifying system, and then through a dispersing prism or grating system so located as to receive the light from only a small portion of the microscope field. The resulting band spectra are photographed and compared with similar spectra taken from unoccupied areas in the object plane. Of necessity this method lacks precise cytologic localization, but it gives a general view of the total spectrum of the tissue component studied.

In the second technic, the light source is a monochromatic beam proceeding from a monochromator through the usual quartz or glass optics of the microscope. The results may be registered qualitatively by photomicrographs taken at selected wavelengths; or quantitatively by means of electrophotometric cells placed in the projection plane to receive light only from the area under study. Since the actual size of the sensitive surface of the photoelectric cell is constant in any given apparatus, variation in object area is achieved through changes in the lens system and the bellows extension. Again it is necessary to compare the light intensity received through the structure under study with that received (preferably simultaneously) through unoccupied areas of the object field.

And again only the average absorption received over the total sensitive surface of the photometric cell can be recorded.

For spectroscopic studies with ultraviolet light between 200 and about 350 mμ, quartz condensers, objectives and oculars are required. Objectives may be corrected for a wavelength between 500 and 550 mμ (green) as well as for the ultraviolet range desired, so that the microscope may be focused visually, and the monochromator then shifted to the desired wavelength. Or fluorescent screens may be employed for focusing, and materials selected which emit fluorescence in the visible spectrum when excited by the required ultraviolet bands.

A considerable amount of attention has been paid in the last decade to the photometric estimation of the deoxyribonucleic acid content of individual nuclei, usually after application of a carefully standardized Feulgen procedure. The subject is discussed *in extenso* by P. M. B. Walker and B. M. Richards in Chapter 4 of Brachet and Mirsky: *The Cell*, Academic Press, Inc., New York, 1959, pp. 91–138, and by C. Leuchten-berger, Cytochemistry of Nucleic Acids, in P. M. B. Walker's *New Approaches to Cell Biology*, Academic Press, Inc., New York, 1960. Pollister and Ornstein's Chapter 1 in Mellors's *Analytical Cytology*, McGraw-Hill Book Company, New York, 1955, is classic in this field and is brought up to date in the second edition of Mellors's *Analytical Cytology*, McGraw-Hill Book Company, New York, 1959. Birge reports a new photometer assembly which may be of interest; see *J. Histochem.* 7:395, 1959. Papers by Kasten, *ibid.* 4:462, 1956, and 5:398, 1957; Barka, *ibid.* 6:197, 1958; Di Stefano *et al.*, *ibid.* 7:83, 1959, and *Endocrinology* 67:458, 1955; and Goldstein, *J. Histochem.* 2:274, 1954, may be consulted for details and further references.

The reflecting microscope used by Mellors (*Science* 111:627, 1950) would appear to lend itself not only to the studies in the ultraviolet range for which he used it, but also for work in the infrared and visible ranges. Since it is without the chromatic aberrations inherent in refracting systems, objects are in focus at the same objective plane throughout the utilizable spectrum.

Mellors used Kodak 103-0 UV spectroscopic plates for high sensitivity and speed in photography of living tissue cultures, and Kodak 1372 (35 mm film) for high resolution with diminished speed and sensitivity. Corning Vycor No. 791 ultraviolet transmitting coverglasses were used. The tissue culture fragment was enclosed in an aqueous film between 2 such coverglasses. Mellors washed the nutrient medium off the hanging drop culture with a suitable Locke type of saline solution before enclosing it with the second coverglass for photography. Focusing was done with the green mercury line and exposure to the 253.7, 265.2, 275.3, 280.4, 312.6 and 334.1 lines kept to the minimum required for photographic exposure.

PHASE MICROSCOPY

The refractive index, "n∆," is a constant, characteristic of each transparent substance, and represents the ratio of the velocity of (sodium) light in a vacuum to the velocity of light in the substance in question. It is the ratio of the sine of the angle of incidence to the sine of the angle of refraction in the medium.

It follows that when 2 transparent substances of the same or nearly the same refractive index abut on each other there is no refraction at the interface, or very little; and the 2 substances are not visually distinguishable in the unstained state.

In the case of the relation of the refractive indices of mounting or examination media to the index of the included tissues, it is possible to vary greatly the refractive index of the including medium by suitable selection of its constituents. This problem is considered in more detail in Chapter 5, pp. 92–98, 100–103.

In the case of interfaces between the various transparent substances within tissues, small differences in refractive index may be exaggerated by advancing or retarding by ¼ wavelength, the phase of the diffracted rays relative to that of the direct rays passing through an object and forming an image at the rear focal plane of the objective. This phase change is accomplished by depositing under high vacuum thermal evaporation on a phase plate or directly on an objective lens, usually in an annular pattern, a film of glass of sufficient thickness to alter the phase of green light by ¼ wavelength.

In order to compensate for the greater intensity of the undiffracted light, a metal absorbing film is deposited in the area of the phase plate annulus to equalize the intensity of the diffracted and undiffracted light.

An annular aperture diaphragm is placed in the front or lower focal plane of the substage condenser, and is illuminated by the Köhler method (p. 6) to form a secondary source of light. In accord with the principle of Köhler illumination, the lighted circle of the annular aperture forms in the rear focal plane of the objective an image which should coincide accurately with the phase altering annulus. Thus the oblique light which passes directly through the object without diffraction passes also through the altering annulus of the phase plate while the diffracted light which has been deviated from its direct path by encountering interfaces of differing refractive indices passes through the remaining area of the objective phase plate without the advancement or retardation of ¼ wavelength produced by the phase plate annulus. When these diffracted rays are brought to focus along with the undiffracted light passing through the same object area, they differ in phase by ¼ wavelength and consequently interfere. The positive phase plate accelerates the undiffracted light, and the interference produces dark areas in a bright background; the negative phase plate retards the undiffracted light, and the interference pattern gives brighter spots on a darker background.

Specially designed objectives covering the usual range of magnifications are available for positive and negative phase contrast, and annular aperture substage diaphragms are provided for each objective.

A telescope ocular is provided for insertion in place of the usual observation oculars for use during accurate centering of the image of the substage annulus on the objective or phase plate annulus.

The method of phase microscopy appears to offer its greatest advantages in the observation of surviving cells in warm stage preparations, tissue cultures and the like.

MICROMETRY

In order to measure the absolute size of microscopic objects, one uses either projection or an eyepiece micrometer. The projection method is convenient when many measurements are to be made in the same field. This is accomplished by first projecting the image of the stage micrometer ruling on the ground glass screen of a bellows camera, and then adjusting the magnification by varying the bellows length so that a simple magnification factor is reached. The rulings of the usual stage micrometer are at 10 μ intervals and cover a total space of 1 mm. The image on the ground glass is readily measured with a millimeter rule. If the total 1 mm ruling covers a space of 10 cm on the screen, it is evident that one has a magnification of 100 diameters.

After the projection system has thus been set up at an appropriate magnification, the desired field is then substituted for the stage micrometer and photographed or measured directly on the ground glass screen with a millimeter rule. Division of the measurements in millimeters by the magnification factor yields the true measurements.

More often the virtual image of a tiny scale engraved on a clear glass disk is used as a standard of comparison. This disk is inserted into the desired eyepiece by unscrewing its top lens, inserting the disk on the shelf within the eyepiece so that the engraved figures are erect and not reversed, and replacing the top lens of the eyepiece. The scale on this disk is brought directly over or beside the object to be measured, and the number of divisions on the scale is noted.

The value of each single division of the eyepiece micrometer scale, as well as that of the whole 100 or 200 such divisions comprised in the total ruling, in terms of absolute measurement, should be determined in advance by direct comparison of the eyepiece micrometer scale with that of the stage micrometer. It is necessary to record these values for each objective that is used with the microscope, and if the micrometer disk is used with different eyepieces, for each eyepiece as well.

Each worker should possess one of these eyepiece micrometer disks and should have a card beside his microscope carrying the value of the eye-piece micrometer divisions in micra for each lens combination that he uses. One stage micrometer should suffice for a group, as this is used only occasionally. If no stage micrometer is available, the rulings of a good hemocytometer may be used instead. The small squares in the central area are $\frac{1}{400}$ sq mm, and hence measure $\frac{1}{20}$ mm or 50 μ each way. The group of 25 small squares measures 250 μ each way, as do the 16 subdivisions of the outer 8 squares of 1 sq mm each.

MECHANICAL STAGES

Although it is quite possible to explore a section adequately by freehand movement of the slide on a plain stage, one can never be sure that every area has been seen by this method, especially when higher magnifications are being used. For systematic search of a preparation, the mechanical stage is invaluable. Generally the types which form an integral part of the microscope stage are superior to the detachable accessory type, since the former are less apt to present lost motion and do not give the distressing variation in vernier readings which is contingent on removing and re-placing a stage of the detachable accessory type.

Periodically the mechanical stage should be thoroughly cleaned with xylene or benzene or other appropriate solvent, and then regreased with petrolatum. This facilitates free movement and reduces wear.

Verniers are usually placed on mechanical stages and serve to permit the reading of tenths of a millimeter. The small vernier scale presents 10 divisions covering a space of 9 mm. When the 0 on the vernier scale is directly opposite one of the markings on the stage scale, read the whole number of millimeters indicated. When the 0 on the vernier scale lies between 2 markings on the stage scale, read the whole number of milli-meters next less than the point opposite the 0 on the vernier, and then count the number of vernier divisions to the point where one of these is directly opposite one of the divisions on the stage scale. The number of vernier divisions thus counted is the number of tenths of a millimeter to be added to the whole number of millimeters just below the zero point on the vernier.

Chapter 2

Equipment

MICROTOME KNIVES

These should be of the type recommended by the manufacturer for freezing, paraffin and celloidin microtomes, respectively. Commonly these knives are provided with detachable backs for use during sharpening. The purpose of these backs is to insure the correct bevel in the edge of the knife. Handles are also generally provided which can be screwed into the base of the knife.

The process of sharpening can be divided into three stages: the removal of gross nicks in the edge on a fine Carborundum stone or on a glass plate with emery powder; the honing proper on a fine water hone or on a glass plate with diamantine powder; and the stropping on a leather strop mounted on a board or on a glass plate with rouge powder. When these procedures are done by hand, in the first two the edge of the knife is moved forward, and the blade is drawn toward the operator in a diagonal stroke. In the stropping step the back of the knife is drawn forward and toward the operator, with the edge following.

When several technicians can be served it is a true economy to purchase a machine operated knife sharpener, even though the price appears to be high. Sharpening by hand takes an average of more than an hour daily for a histologic technician, and even 2 or 3 hundred dollars can soon be saved in technicians' time. Further, the machine sharpening is more uniform and will grind the full length of the knife evenly rather than produce the familiar concave edge of the hand sharpened knife.

Devices for holding safety razor blades are quite valuable for paraffin and frozen sections, since these blades are readily replaced when they become dull, and they cut nearly as good sections on most material as microtome knives. Mallory recommended them particularly for partially calcified material. Many workers find them unsatisfactory when section thicknesses less than 10 μ are required.

PARAFFIN OVEN

An incubator of bacteriological pattern that can be regulated to 55–60°C is quite satisfactory. Incubators with water jackets maintain a more even temperature. Sufficient space should be available for paraffin to be filtered within the oven. Beakers holding between 30 and 50 cc are useful containers for the paraffin infiltration of individual specimens, and a 2-liter beaker forms a good reservoir for the stock of melted paraffin. A vacuum chamber installed within the oven or a specially built vacuum oven is useful for quick infiltration of tissues, particularly of lungs. Such a vacuum chamber can be improvised from a domestic pressure cooker of appropriate size. The services of a plumber are required to make the necessary connections.

I have made an even simpler model by fitting a porcelain electric light socket to the inside of the lid of the pressure cooker, and setting the cooker itself in a wooden box packed around the cooker with sawdust covered with plaster of paris. The temperature was regulated by changing the wattages of the electric bulbs until one was found which kept the temperature at 55–60°C.

The small paraffin units on the Technicon tissue changer are also quite satisfactory. They expedite infiltration by a continuous gentle rotation which brings fresh paraffin continually to the surface of the tissue and removes the solvent as it diffuses out.

For field use I have improvised a paraffin oven by using a flat tin for a paraffin container, a larger tall tin with a hole cut in the side at the bottom so that the paraffin container could be inserted for part of its length, and an electric light bulb set in the lid of the tall tin as a heat source. The position of the paraffin container, partly under the light, should be so adjusted that paraffin remains unmelted at its outer end. Tissues for infiltration are placed in the melted paraffin immediately adjacent to the remaining unmelted paraffin.

For work where the preservation of undenatured proteins (such as enzymes) is important, the vacuum type unit is highly recommended.

MECHANICAL TISSUE CHANGERS

Electrically operated devices are now available which will transfer tissues from one fluid to another at prescribed intervals. Tissues may thus be carried through a succession of fixing, washing, dehydrating and clearing baths, and even through paraffin infiltration if desired. One such device not only transfers tissues from one fluid to another by the clock, but also continually agitates the fluid by rotation of the specimen carrier in it, so that diffusion and fluid interchange are materially accelerated. Such machines can be set for a schedule of 24 hours or of 48 hours or longer by cutting clock disks appropriately. By substitution of a shorter period clock and a slide carrier, the device can be altered to a routine slide stainer, carrying slides through deparaffinization, hydration, staining, washing, counterstaining, dehydration and clearing. At present there is a limit of 12 steps, but the usual routine technics can be adapted readily to such a schedule.

To remove paraffin from metal imbedding molds, Technicon tissue carriers, etc. (including the nylon-plastic carriers furnished by the Technicon Company), boil them for 5–10 minutes completely immersed in a tall metal vessel containing about 10–12 gm (a level tablespoonful or 16 cc) of powdered Oakite, Calgonite or other technical sodium phosphate detergent in about a liter of water. Then cool until the paraffin can be removed as a solid cake; rinse and dry. The greasy film left by xylene cleaning is absent with this method, and the danger of working with an inflammable solvent is eliminated (Peers, *Am. J. Clin. Path.* **21**:794, 1951).

OTHER INCUBATORS

Besides the paraffin oven, which is kept regulated to a temperature 2–5°C above the melting point of the paraffin used, it is often necessary to maintain other temperatures over fairly long periods. Small thermostatically controlled incubators that can be regulated at 37°C and at 45–50°C are valuable for enzyme digestions, chemical extractions, metallic impregnations, enzyme localization technics and other methods.

At least 1 such incubator should be available, preferably 2, if such incubation technics are in frequent use.

WATER BATH

Of even greater value than incubators for maintenance of temperature during various staining and incubation procedures is a thermostatically regulated serologic water bath. The contents of Coplin jars quite promptly reach a temperature, within 1–2°C of the surrounding bath; and temperature maintenance seems to be more steady than in incubators. It is valuable to have a well fitting but easily removable cover to aid in maintaining temperatures above 60°C and to retard evaporation of the bath.

EXTRACTION WITH HOT SOLVENTS

A reflux extraction apparatus for treatment of slides with boiling acetone, ether, xylene, and the like is readily improvised by selecting a beaker large enough to contain a metal or glass slide rack, and a Florence flask of such diameter that it will fit the top of the beaker quite closely, but will not quite go down into it. The Florence flask is fitted with a 2 hole rubber stopper, and a current of cold water is run through the Florence flask while the contents of the subjacent beaker are kept gently boiling on an electric hot plate. I have boiled acetone in such an apparatus for several hours without having to replenish it.

MICRO REACTION CHAMBER FOR VISUAL OBSERVATION

A simple reaction chamber for on-slide histochemical tests may be improvised by applying thin 22 × 22 coverglasses to the slide toward each end from the observation area, fastening them down with petrolatum jelly or, for a more permanent chamber, with xylene cellulose caprate. The section, smear or suspension material is deposited on the slide between the two coverslips with a drop of water or other suitable aqueous fluid. Then a long coverslip is applied, resting on the two small coverslips and fastened down by capillary attraction or with petrolatum jelly.

As usual for such observations, fluid is sucked out from one side by filter paper and reagent is fed in on the other with a small medicine dropper while the significant features of the preparation are under continued microscopic observation.

With No. 1 coverslips the depth of the chamber is about 0.15 mm, the width is that of the superimposed coverslip, and the length is the distance between the edges of the small coverslips. The reaction volume is thus readily computed.

The contents of the chamber may be recovered for microchemical assay after completion of visual observation.

CRYOSTAT

Cryostats have undergone a considerable number of modifications since Linderström-Lang's first model was introduced in 1938, and a fair number of differing models have been marketed commercially. Many of these are quite satisfactory and permit the preparation of coherent frozen sections of fresh unfixed tissues at temperatures ranging from −2 to around −20°C. Most of the models have enclosed sectioning chambers which are observed through glass windows and which require insertion of the operator's hands into heavy fur lined gloves to manipulate microtome, sections and slides.

Chang (*Am. J. Clin. Path.* 35:14, 1961, and *J. Histochem.* 9:208, 1961; 8:310, 1960) has described two models, now commercially available, in which the axle of the microtome wheel passes through the wall and is turned by a wheel crank on the outside. The top is open, permitting ready access to and viewing of the interior without frosting. With this ready access to the interior, manual control of sections with the traditional camel's hair brush of paraffin technics becomes possible, and the mechanical anti-rolling devices, which so often become clogged, are unnecessary and have been eliminated.

In the 1961 model the expansion valve is inside the cold chamber. Thermostatic control of cold chamber temperature has been introduced, and cooling coils are included in the four lateral walls. The hand wheel readily disengages, permitting easy removal of the microtome for cleaning and oiling. For oiling, Berg (*J. Histochem.* 8:310, 1960) suggests Dow Corning No. 510 silicone lubricant as satisfactory down to −50°C. The whole assembly weighs less than 100 kg (200 lb) and should be readily moved from one laboratory to another.

INSTRUMENTS

Instruments should include surgeon's knives, scissors, thumb forceps, scissors type forceps (both with and without mouse tooth tips), a hacksaw with spare blades for cutting bone specimens, section lifters of flat metal for celloidin sections, dissecting needles for handling frozen sections, thin double edged brain knives, safety razor blades, and some glass syringes for injecting. A slab of paraffin affords a convenient surface on which to cut tissue blocks for later imbedding. Its surface is readily cleaned and smoothed from time to time by flaming or by melting and recasting.

STAINING DISHES AND CARRIERS

For unattached "loose" or "free floating" frozen sections small flat covered glass dishes are desirable. In these a few cubic centimeters of stain or enzymatic substrate will suffice. Loose celloidin sections can be similarly handled.

For paraffin sections and attached cryostat, frozen, Carbowax, gelatin or celloidin sections slotted containers or carriers are used. Glass Coplin jars with 5–15 slots are valuable, particularly for corrosive solutions and reagents. The 5 slot Coplin jar is also available with a screw cap which is fairly gas tight. These are used for treatments with hot solutions of volatile reagents. The ordinary Coplin jar is quite valuable for staining methods in which it is desired to use a relatively small (30–40 cc) quantity of stain or reagent. See Table 2-1 for fluid requirements for a small Coplin jar with 1, 5 or 9 slides in it.

In using 5 slot vertical Coplin jars for staining it is essential to see that the two slides occupying the end slots face toward the center of the jar. The construction of these jars is such that the end slides may be so closely applied to the glass ends that little or no stain or reagent is present into the slide-jar interval.

Recently there have been developed 12 dish assemblies of oblong plastic vessels accommodating plastic staining racks carrying 25 or 50 slides.[1] I have used the 25 slide size with much satisfaction. A 12 dish assembly occupies 66 × 11.4 cm (26 × 4.5 in.) of table space and stands

---

[1] Available from Scientific Products, Dallas, Texas.

108 mm (4.25 in.) high. Three dish units are also available, which we use for xylene for deparaffinization and for clearing. They are readily moved to the mounting area for application of resin and coverslips.

The plastic slide carrying racks carry slides standing on end, with clear space beyond each end slide sufficient to supply an adequate volume of stain or reagent to the outer surfaces of the end slides. With fully loaded slide racks the staining dishes require about 200 cc of fluid. A space of 58.4 mm (3.2 in.) is allowed for the 25 slides, or with the end wells 63.5 mm (3.4 in.), over 2 mm (0.1 in.) per slide.

It is sometimes important to know in advance what volume of an unstable or expensive reagent will be required to immerse the sections on slides. Table 2-1 gives a rough indication of requirements for a Coplin jar with 1, 5 or 9 fairly thin slides.

TABLE 2-1. VOLUME OF FLUID AND HEIGHT
OF FLUID LEVEL RELATED TO NUMBER
OF SLIDES IN AVERAGE
5-SLOT COPLIN JAR

Volume of fluid, cc	Height of fluid, mm		
	1 slide	5 slides	9 slides
15	15	20	25
17	20	25	32
20	25	33	40
25	33	42	50
30	42	50	65
35	50	62	75

For many procedures slides are stained face up with small amounts of reagent. For this purpose parallel glass rods joined together at one end at about a 5 cm (2 in.) interval are convenient. These should rest over a trough or large bowl or sink to catch spilled and discarded reagents. For this purpose we have used for years large copper trays with a drain at one corner to empty into a small sink, a bucket, or other convenient receptacle. These trays measure $25 \times 50 \times 5$ cm ($10 \times 20 \times 2$ in.). Fastened in each, near one corner, is a smaller and deeper container— say 15×10 cm and 10 cm deep ($6 \times 4 \times 4$ in.)—in which running water is received. This serves for washing slides in running water. On one edge is cut a shallow V-shaped depression to allow overflow of water. It is convenient to place this V on the side opposite the drain so that the overflowing water will traverse most of the area of the large pan before reaching the outlet.

Very convenient for dispensing small quantities of stain and reagents on individual slides are dropping bottles which possess glass stoppers with slots on each side to match slots cut on the inside of the bottle neck. A 90° turn closes the bottle tightly, and the stopper is equipped with an overhanging point opposite one of the slots, from which the drops fall.

Serologic pipets of 1 cc, 5 cc, and 10 cc capacities are invaluable for dispensing measured quantities of stains and reagents on individual slides. Rubber bulb pipets or medicine droppers of 1–2 cc capacity with straight or curved tips can also be very useful for application of small amounts of reagents or stains. A hemocytometer can be used as a reaction chamber; the sections are mounted on an ordinary coverglass or even a slide which is then inverted over the fluid containing area of the chamber. Reagents are then introduced from one side with a medicine dropper, syringe or pipet, filling the space 0.1 mm deep by capillarity. Fluid may simultaneously be drawn off from the other side with blotting paper or a pipet or dropper tip inserted in one of the moat areas on one side while fluid is introduced in the other moat area on the other side of the slide.

Graduated cylinders, both stoppered and open, with capacities of 10, 25, 50 and 100 cc should be available, as well as a few larger open cylinders, with capacities of say 250, 500 and 1000 cc.

A balance of perhaps 1–2 mg sensitivity and 100 gm capacity serves well for most stains and reagents in the histologic laboratory. It is well to have access also to quantitative analytic balances and to scales of larger capacity.

A pair of 50 cc burets with buret stand may sometimes be useful.

In **heating equipment,** Bunsen burners, a 1 burner gas plate for heating large amounts of water, an electric hot plate with covered elements for heating flammable fluids, thermostatically controllable warm plates which may be set at 35–40°C for spreading paraffin sections, or at 70–80°C for heating to steaming during staining, are accessories which will prove their value.

However, I have done very well with a long copper plate which can be heated at one end with an alcohol lamp.

CLEANING OF SLIDES AND COVERSLIPS

New slides and coverslips may often be satisfactorily cleaned by simply immersing them in alcohol and carefully polishing them with a soft cloth. Usually we have found it preferable to wash them in warm soapy water first and rinse them in several changes of warm water before putting them in alcohol for polishing. In this procedure, if a 1% aqueous solution of acetic acid is substituted for the alcohol, slides take a brilliant polish. Some writers recommend acid alcohol from which to polish slides.

In cleaning used slides on which blood films or unstained paraffin sections remain, slides should first be boiled in an aqueous solution of sodium carbonate or trisodium phosphate or a commercial detergent powder of similar nature. Remnants of sections are then readily wiped off, as is glass marking ink. The usual soapy water, water, alcohol or acetic acid sequence follows.

LABELING

Labeling of slides before staining is a necessity in a pathology laboratory. The traditional diamond pencil can be used, but slides so marked are quite prone to breakage during and after staining. For several years now I have used a black glass marking ink which resists all ordinary reagents and even serves in place of paper labels when the slides are filed after examination. Such inks are removed by alkali, especially when fresh.

Paraffin blocks are readily labeled by affixing with a hot iron on one side a small paper label inscribed with India ink.

Specimen bottles can be conveniently labeled by inserting within the bottle a label first written with India ink on paper and then immersed briefly in smoking hot paraffin. The paper should promptly lose all its contained air and water as bubbles and should have a translucent appearance. Opaque looking paper labels are not adequately waterproofed and tend to go to pieces. Similar labels may often profitably be prepared and affixed with a hot iron to the outside of reagent bottles, especially those containing reagents which tend to destroy ordinary gummed labels.

SPECIMEN BOTTLES

Specimen bottles, both for storage of specimens and for their collection, fixation, dehydration and clearing, should be procured in a variety of sizes ranging from perhaps 25 cc or 1 oz up to brain jars containing some 4 liters for the fixation of whole human brains. They should be wide mouthed and furnished with covers. In the case of storage bottles the covers should fit closely to prevent evaporation. We have found that 25 cc bottles are most often required for storage, 50 and 100 cc bottles for fixation and dehydration procedures. The bottles used commercially for mayonnaise are quite convenient. They have a paraffined paper inside seal and a screw cap which may be removed by a quarter turn. These are available in quart, pint, half pint and quarter pint sizes, or about 960, 480, 240 and 120 cc.

REAGENTS

Reagents should be purchased from reputable manufacturers under appropriate specifications for the purpose for which they are to be used. There is no point in paying for reagent grades when ordinary technical grades are perfectly satisfactory.

TABLE 2-2. PHYSICAL CHARACTERISTICS OF SOLVENTS

Solvent	M.P.[1]	B.P.[1]	nΔ	Pounds av. per liter	Kilograms per liter
Acetone................	−95	56.5	1.3591	1.747	0.793
Alcohol 100%..........	−112	78.4	1.3610	1.748	0.789
Alcohol 95%..........	....	78.1	....	1.796	0.8115
Amylbenzene sec........	....	187/189	1.4894[2]	1.897	0.860[2]
Aniline................	−6.2	184.4	1.5683	2.252	1.022
Benzene..............	5.5	80.1	1.5017	1.938	0.879
Benzyl benzoate........	21	323/324	1.5685	2.473	1.122
n-Butyl alcohol........	−79.9	117	1.3991	1.786	0.810
sec-Butyl alcohol.......	−114.7	99.5	1.3968	1.781	0.808
iso-Butyl alcohol.......	−108.0	108.1	1.3924	1.768	0.802
tert-Butyl alcohol......	25.6	82.6	1.3878	1.717	0.779
Carbon bisulfide........	−108.6	46.3	1.6276	2.786	1.263
Carbon tetrachloride....	−22.6	76.8	1.4630	3.515	1.595
Cedar oil, thin.........	....	168/237	1.5030[2]	2.043	0.927
Chloroform............	−63.5	61.2	1.4457	3.283	1.489
p-Cymene.............	−73.5	176/177	1.4866[2]	1.890	0.857
Diethylbenzene[4]........	−32/−84	181/184	1.4957[2]	1.876	0.851[2]
Diethylene glycol.......	−10.5	244.8	1.4475	2.467	1.118
1,4-Dioxane...........	9.5/10.5	101	1.4221	2.278	1.033
Ether USP solvent......	−116	34.6	1.3497	1.576	0.708
Gasoline 100 octane.....	−107.4	99.2	1.4040[5]	1.584	0.718[2]
Glycerol 95%..........	17.9	290	1.4660[2]	2.762	1.252
Glycol................	−15.6	197.4	1.4318	2.455	1.113
Methyl alcohol, synth...	−97.8	64.7	1.3288	1.746	0.792
Methyl benzoate........	−12.5	198/199	1.5144	2.397	1.087
Methyl salicylate.......	−8.3	222.2	1.5377	2.606	1.182
Paraffin 56°...........	56.5	324[3]	1.4262[6]	1.714	0.777[2]
Petroleum ether 20–40..	−130/−160	22/38	1.3554[7]	1.367	0.620[2]
Petroleum ether 30–65..	ca. −120	30/65	1.3754[8]	1.394	0.632[2]
Petroleum ether 30–80..	....	30/80	1.3876[9]	1.480	0.670[2]
n-Propyl alcohol........	−127	97.8	1.3854	1.772	0.804
iso-Propyl alcohol......	−85.8	82.5	1.3776	1.738	0.789
Toluene..............	−95	110.8	1.4955	1.921	0.866
Trichloroethylene.......	−73	87.2	1.4777	3.232	1.466
Trimethylbenzene[4]......	−25/−45	165/176	1.4931[2]	1.898	0.861[2]
Water................	0.0	100.0	1.3330	2.205	0.9982
Xylene[4]..............	13/−47	138/144	1.4966[2]	1.903	0.863[2]

[1] Slant bar indicates melting and boiling range of compounds in the commercial mixtures. To judge by its melting point, the paraffin seems to be chiefly pentacosane.

[2] Melting and boiling points, densities and refractive indices determined by Greco, Pathology Laboratory, National Institutes of Health. (Other melting points, etc., are from Lange.)

[3] Boiling point of tetracosane.

[4] These are technical grades and are homolog mixtures. Melting and boiling ranges are given.

[5] Approximate nΔ of octanes of the same density.

[6] Refractive index of pentacosane at 80°.

[7] nΔ for mixture of pentane and isopentane.

[8] nΔ of hexane.

[9] nΔ of heptane.

To find cost per liter, multiply the price per pint by 2.113; or the price per gallon by 0.264; or the price per pound by the pounds-per-liter factor given above; or the price per kilogram by the density in kilograms per liter.

Dyes are unstable organic chemicals and should be bought in such quantities as are likely to be used up within 2 or 3 years. It is good practice to stamp the date of receipt on each bottle of dye purchased. Unless one is prepared to test his own dyes for quality he should require certification by the Biological Stain Commission (pp. 108–109).

Inorganic chemicals of stable nature may be bought in larger quantities, especially if considerable amounts are apt to be required suddenly.

Solvents are often interchangeable one with another as far as results are concerned, and cost may be a material item in the selection of a dehydrating agent or a paraffin solvent. Here prices per unit weight are deceiving, since these solvents are used by volume. Carbon tetrachloride, for example, is nearly twice as heavy per unit volume as toluene, and at 17 cents a pound is actually the same price as the latter at 30 cents a pound. For convenience a table of conversion factors for common solvents is appended. The relative prices per liter, given in previous editions, have been omitted. These prices are readily calculated from the factors given.

Chapter 3

Fixation

The greatest handicap to the pathologic histologist is improper preservation of material. Several factors enter into this, among which are delay in fixation, postmortem decomposition, drying of tissues, inadequate quantity of fixing fluid, poor penetration of fixing fluid, fixing fluids improper for the material, prolongation of fixation beyond the proper interval, improper storage fluids for prolonged storage, and poor dehydration, imbedding and sectioning technics.

Tissues should be fixed as promptly as possible after cessation of circulation. Autopsies should be made as soon after death as possible; and when this is not immediately possible, prompt refrigeration is of material advantage. Surgical specimens should preferably be fixed as soon as removed. The practice of keeping tissues unfixed until an operation is concluded often results in a distorting dehydration of surface layers, and the practice of keeping them in physiologic saline solution at operating room temperatures permits autolysis to progress often to a confusing extent. Animal autopsies are preferably made on animals killed or dying immediately before dissection. Complete evisceration by a trained attendant and fixation of the entire visceral mass is a procedure preferable to storage on ice, as far as histologic detail is concerned; but when bacteriologic investigation is an essential part of the autopsy, prompt refrigeration should be the rule when immediate autopsy is not possible.

Slow freezing of unfixed tissue at temperatures near the freezing point of water is to be scrupulously avoided; relatively enormous ice crystal artifacts are produced. Repeated freezing and thawing disrupts cell organelles, releases enzymes and produces diffusion of solubilizable constituents.

The practice of immediately embalming human bodies before autopsy does avoid autolytic changes and give more uniform histologic preservation. It prevents, however, the use of a number of special fixing procedures such as the chromaffin reaction, the application of fat solvent fixatives to remove lipids completely, etc. Some fixations can be satisfactorily applied after embalming, others cannot. These considerations are entirely aside from the distortion of gross pictures and prevention of microbiological investigation. Many enzymes are inactivated; some resist brief formalin fixation quite well.

Tissue blocks should be cut of such thickness that the fixing fluid readily penetrates throughout in a reasonably short period of time. This time varies with the fixative, and inversely with the fixation temperature. While low temperatures retard fixation, they also stop autolytic changes; so that the best fixation with many fixatives may be attained by prolonged fixation at temperatures approaching the freezing point of the mixture. With mixed fixatives, it must be recalled that the rates of penetration may vary for the different constituents. For example, mixtures of acetic acid and mercuric chloride, such as sublimate acetic, susa, Zenker, and the like, may show practically pure acetic acid effect in the deeper parts of the block, with dissolution of albuminous granules, and the like, while in the outer zone these structures are preserved.

The volume of fixing fluid employed should be 15 or 20 times that of the tissue to be fixed. The length and breadth of blocks to be fixed should be such that they are not bent or folded by the container in which tissue is fixed. It is well to open hollow viscera or fill them with fixing fluid. Lungs of small animals may be conveniently fixed by filling them by intratracheal injection, taking care to allow the fluid to escape freely around the injecting needle so as to avoid overdistension. This procedure may also be applied to small areas of human or large animal lungs.

Fixation by intravascular perfusion must be preceded by washing out blood with an indifferent fluid such as Ringer's or Locke's solution or 0.85% saline (p. 104). Here it is important so to regulate the injection pressure that it does not exceed the blood pressure. Otherwise, fixation artifacts are produced. This method has the disadvantage that the blood content of the vessels is lost. Further, the method is not possible when postmortem clotting of the blood in the vessels has occurred.

From the point of view of the histologist, the practice of hardening an entire human brain without perfusion, by immersion in dilute formaldehyde solution or other fixative before dissection, can only be condemned. It seems preferable, when topographic study is contemplated and perfusion cannot be done, to divide the brain stem first by a single transverse section just anterior to the oculomotor roots and the anterior margins of the anterior colliculi, thus separating the cerebrum from the mid- and hindbrain. Then make a series of transverse sections through the brain stem and attached cerebellum at 5–10 mm intervals, leaving part of the meninges unsevered so as to keep the slices in sequence. Then separate the 2 cerebral hemispheres by a sagittal section, perhaps better slightly to one side of the median plane, or through the third ventricle. Then on the sagittal surface identify dorsal and ventral points through which sections should pass so that the brain sections will agree in plane with one of the standard cross or frontal section atlases. Make the first section through these points perpendicular to the sagittal surface. Then section the rest of the brain at perhaps 10 mm intervals, cutting parallel to the first plane. This greatly facilitates identification of various areas for the anatomist or pathologist to whom the human brain is an occasional object of study.

For these sections a long thin bladed knife is essential. We find a 2 gal (8 liter) brain jar suitable for thus fixing a human brain.

In general, solid viscera should be cut in slices perpendicular to the surface, in such wise as to expose their anatomic structure to best advantage. For instance, kidney sections should show cortex, medulla, pelvis and pyramid. Adrenal sections should show cortex and medulla. Sections of tumors should show adjoining tissue sufficient to identify the blocks anatomically and to give the relation of the expanding tumor margin to preexistent tissue. Abscess walls should also show adjacent, relatively uninvolved tissue. The margin as well as the center of a pneumonic focus is often instructive. Digits and other skin covered objects should be opened so as to admit fixative to the significant areas; skin is almost waterproof. Small bones should be largely stripped free of muscle if their marrow is of interest.

Friedenwald (*The Pathology of the Eye*, The Macmillan Company, New York, 1929) condemned the practice of freezing the eye and bisecting it before fixation because of the damage resulting from the formation of ice crystals and because of immediate collapse of the tissues and wrinkling when they are placed in fixative after freezing; yet I have had excellent results from the very rapid freezing obtained by immersion in petroleum ether with solid carbon dioxide, followed by immediate axial or paralenticular anteroposterior section and immersion in fixatives while still frozen. Even with Carnoy's fluid the rods and cones remain fully expanded and clearly delineated, and the retina generally remains in contact with the choroid. A sharp razor blade must be used, and care must be taken not to fracture the frozen tissues.

FIXING FLUIDS

Formaldehyde

The most widely used fixing agent for pathologic histology is formaldehyde. Not only is it used as the sole or principal active agent in fixing fluids, but it also enters into many fixing mixtures. Formaldehyde is ordinarily available commercially as an approximately saturated solution of the gas in water. Such solutions contain from 37 to 40% by weight of formaldehyde gas and are commonly called **"formol," "formalin"** or, better, **"strong formalin."** The word "formal," sometimes erroneously used as a synonym, refers properly to quite another substance, $CH_3O—CH_2—OCH_3$, dimethoxymethane.

In designating the strength of aqueous formaldehyde solutions it is common practice to denote a dilution of 1 volume of 40% formaldehyde solution with 4 or 9 volumes of water as 20% or 10% formalin. Others designate the same solutions as 8% or 4% formaldehyde, or perhaps when the formaldehyde concentration of the stock solution is lower than 40%, as 7.4% or 3.7%, for example. Actually this last practice is erroneous. Concentrated formaldehyde solution of 40% designated strength and specific gravity of 1.124 contains approximately 45 gm in 100 cc; and 37% solutions, with specific gravity of 1.111, contain 41 gm. Hence 20% and 10% dilutions contain actually 8.2–9% and 4.1–4.5% formaldehyde, respectively.

TABLE 3-1. FORMALDEHYDE CONTENT OF SOLUTIONS

% by weight	Specific gravity	Grams per 100 cc	Molarity
40	1.124	44.96	14.97
39	1.120	43.67	14.54
38	1.116	42.39	14.12
37	1.111	41.12	13.69
36	1.107	39.86	13.27
35	1.103	38.605	12.86

Solutions of formaldehyde diluted with distilled water are commonly acid, owing to the presence of small amounts of formic acid either as an impurity remaining during manufacture or as a result of oxidation of part of the formaldehyde. For certain silver impregnation technics this natural acidity may be desirable, but for azure eosin methods and for study of possibly iron containing pigments, it is essential to correct it. A common practice is to shake the diluted formaldehyde solution with calcium carbonate and store it over a layer of this salt. This gives only approximate neutrality; Romeis cites pH levels of 6.3–6.5. Others have used magnesium carbonate, attaining pH levels of about 7.5. With either of these methods, formaldehyde solution drawn from the storage reservoir and used for fixation very promptly becomes more acid as the tissue is fixed. Levels of pH 5.7–6 are not uncommon after calcium carbonate treatment.

This shift in pH is avoided by using a soluble buffer in the dilute formaldehyde solution used for fixation. Addition of 4 gm monohydrated acid sodium phosphate (or of the anhydrous acid potassium phosphate) and 6.5 gm anhydrous disodium phosphate per liter gives approximately pH 7 and a total salt content of the 2 sodium salts of about 1%, dry weight.

Substitution of this fluid for fixation in certain toxicologic studies resulted in a definite increase in frequency of demonstrability of ferric iron in blood pigments, and it almost entirely prevents formation of the so-called formalin pigment.

Fixation in formaldehyde is influenced by the concentration of the reagent and by temperature, just as are other chemical reactions. A 4.1–4.5% formaldehyde solution (10% formalin) fixes *adequately* in 48 hours at 20–25°C (68–77°F), in 24 hours at 35°C (95°F), and an 8–9% formaldehyde solution (20% formalin) hardens in 3 hours at 55°C. However, autolysis is also hastened by higher temperatures, so that better fixation is attained with longer exposures at lower temperatures; some writers have recommended fixation at 0–5°C. The use of higher formaldehyde concentrations also tends to overharden outer tissue layers and to affect staining adversely, especially with azure eosinates. With alcoholic formaldehyde fixations the above times may be reduced by 50%.

The use of temperatures above 60°C involves the factors of heat coagulation and of loss of formaldehyde through volatilization. Small pieces of tissue up to 5 mm thick may be hardened throughout by 2 minutes' boiling in 0.85% sodium chloride solution alone, and an egg may be boiled hard in 10 minutes.

Substitution of alcohol as the diluent of formaldehyde solution results in faster fixation, greater hardening, loss of fats and lipids, better preservation of glycogen, poorer preservation of iron bearing pigments, and sometimes partial lysis of red corpuscles.

The foregoing fixation times are traditional. In recent work, where it was desired to minimize the harman condensation of tryptophan, or to preserve dopa oxidase activity, I have used times of 1–2 hours in calcium acetate formalin (p. 38, formula 5) with very satisfactory results. The enzyme reaction is carried out immediately after fixation and washing of very thin slices; for the indole reactions, hardening in alcohol is prolonged to 1 or 2 days to give better cutting consistency.

Addition of 0.085% sodium chloride to 4% formaldehyde solutions is strongly recommended by some writers. On most material little difference is discerned.

Ramón y Cajal's ammonium bromide formalin, "formol ammonium bromide," is often prescribed for central nervous tissues, especially for silver impregnation technics. It is a strongly acid mixture containing free hydrobromic acid and methenamine as well as NH_4 and Br ions and at least 4.2% unreacted formaldehyde. On mixing the formaldehyde (pH 4–7, Ramón y Cajal prescribed "neutral") with the ammonium bromide (pH 5–5.2) the pH of the mixture promptly falls below 2.0, and readings of 1.4 have been obtained on unused stock mixture. During fixation the pH rises slightly (1.7 after 3 weeks). The fluid is not recommended for histochemical studies. Red corpuscles are lysed, nuclei become directly Schiff positive from a Feulgen hydrolysis during fixation and it is probable that hemosiderin iron is at least partly extracted.

Baker's (1%) $CaCl_2$ (10%) formalin and his (1%) $CaCl_2$, (1%) $CdCl_2$, (10%) formalin (*Quart. J. Micr. Sci.* **85**:1, 1944) were recommended especially for the fixation and preservation of phospholipids in tissues (p. 484). Pearse (1960) recommends a variant containing 1.1% $CaCl_2$ and 15% formalin (2 M HCHO). To combine the effect of the calcium ion and of buffering I have substituted 2% calcium acetate (monohydrate) for the calcium chloride of Baker's formula, attaining an approximate pH 7 and about equal resistance with the phosphate formula to pH displacement by deliberate addition of formic acid.

In regard to these calcium formalin solutions, Baker's $CaCl_2$ formula is 90.2 mM with respect to Ca^{++}, and Lillie's acetate formula is 113.5 mM. Baker's requires adjustment to neutrality by shaking with $CaCO_3$ or by adjustment with NaOH; in the acetate formula the calcium salt itself acts as an automatic buffer with a similar capacity for formic acid to the phosphate-buffered formalin (see Formulae, p. 38).

Formaldehyde alone is a rather soft fixative and often does not harden certain cytoplasmic structures adequately for paraffin imbedding. Brush borders of renal epithelium are often frayed, and radial striation is partially obscured in paraffin sections, while at least the latter feature is plainly discernible in frozen sections of the same material. Also, cross striations of heart muscle are better defined in frozen than in paraffin sections of material fixed with formaldehyde. Pyramidal cells in the cerebral cortex often are surrounded by clear spaces because of shrinkage in paraffin sections.

To remedy this soft fixation one may substitute for or add to formaldehyde various other reagents such as mercuric salts, chromic acid and its salts, osmium tetroxide, picric acid, alcohol or various other less commonly used reagents. Likewise, treatment with chromate, picric acid and mercuric chloride solutions may be used after a previous formalin fixation (p. 86).

Formulae for Formaldehyde Solutions

1. 10% formalin

Concentrated formaldehyde solution (37–40%)	100	cc
Tap water	900	cc

2. Formol saline

37–40% formaldehyde solution	100	cc
Sodium chloride	8.5	gm
Tap or distilled water	900	cc

3. Neutral 10% formalin

37–40% formaldehyde solution	100	cc
Water	900	cc
Calcium or magnesium carbonate to excess		

4. **Neutral buffered formaldehyde solution (pH 7.0)**

37–40% formaldehyde solution	100	cc
Water	900	cc
Acid sodium phosphate, monohydrate	4	gm
Anhydrous disodium phosphate	6.5	gm

5. **Calcium acetate formalin**

37–40% formaldehyde solution	100	cc
Distilled water	900	cc
Calcium acetate (monohydrate)	20	gm

6. **Sucrose formalin.** In an effort to avoid intrafixation diffusion or disruption of cell organelles, sucrose solutions have been recommended. I have used (*J. Histochem.* 8:182, 1960) ice cold 30% (0.88 *M*) sucrose for 30 minutes followed by fixation in formalin 10 cc, calcium acetate monohydrate 2 gm, sucrose 30 gm, distilled water to make 100 cc for 18 hours at 2–5°C. Material is then washed 4 hours in running water at 20–30°C to remove sucrose, and dehydrated over a 48 hour period in 70%, 80%, 95% and 100% alcohols, infiltrated 18 hours in 1% collodion (Parlodion, celloidin) in ether alcohol, cleared and hardened in 2 changes of chloroform (30 minutes each) and infiltrated for 2 hours in hard paraffin (57°C) under reduced pressure (15 mm mercury). This procedure permitted the preparation of serial sections of rodent intestine at 4 μ.

It is essential that the sucrose be thoroughly washed out before dehydration. Cutting consistency is seriously impaired if sucrose is not removed.

7. **Baker's Formol Calcium for Lipids**

	Formol calcium	Calcium cadmium formol	Pearse's variant	
CaCl₂ (anhydrous)	1 gm	1 gm	1.3%	85 cc
CdCl₂ (anhydrous)		1 gm		
40% formaldehyde	10 cc	10 cc		15 cc
Distilled water	90 cc	90 cc		

8. **Ramón y Cajal's formol ammonium bromide, FAB**

	Ramón y Cajal	Davenport	Conn and Darrow
37–40% formaldehyde solution	140 cc	120 cc	150 cc
Ammonium bromide	20 gm	20 gm	20 gm
Distilled water	1000 cc	1000 cc	850 cc

9. Alcoholic formalin

37–40% formaldehyde solution   100   cc
95% alcohol   900   cc

If desired, one may add 0.5 gm calcium acetate to this formula, to insure neutrality.

10. Tellyesniczky's acetic alcohol formalin

	Tellyes-niczky[1]	Fekete[2]	Opie & Lillie's Lavin[3]	AAF[4]	Bodian[5]
37–40% formaldehyde	5 cc	10 cc	5 cc	10 cc	5 cc
Glacial acetic acid	5 cc	5 cc	5 cc	5 cc	5 cc
Alcohol { concentration	70%	70%	80%	95–100%	50%
Alcohol { amount	100 cc	100 cc	90 cc	85 cc	100 cc

Alcoholic formalin and acetic alcohol formalin are excellent for glycogen preservation and are good cytoplasmic fixatives when ribonucleic acid digestion tests are to be performed. In the latter case it is well to fix at 0–5°C or lower for 24 hours only. Tellyesniczky recommended a similar fluid to the last, containing 50 cc each of formalin and acetic acid and 1000 cc of alcohol. This fluid is to be distinguished from the same author's acetic bichromate formula. Both are often referred to as Tellyesniczky's fluid. Mallory, Langeron and Romeis noted only the acetic bichromate fluid, Cowdry gave only the acetic alcohol formalin and Lee gave both.

Traditionally, material fixed in aqueous formalin solutions is stored indefinitely in the same fluid. For this purpose the buffered solution is superior to the unbuffered, even if solid calcium carbonate is included in the storage bottle. On storage in formalin, gradual decrease in basophilia of cytoplasm and nuclei occurs, as well as a progressive loss in reactivity of myelin to Weigert's iron hematoxylin method. Lipids undergo not too well understood alterations (p. 474).

Buffered formalin retards the loss of basophilia, but storage in 70% alcohol or in 10–20% diethylene glycol in water appears to be better. Ethylene glycol and triethylene glycol probably can be used in the same way, but have not been tested so exhaustively.

After alcoholic formalin fixation, storage in 70% alcohol would appear to be superior to leaving the tissue in the formalin solution.

Acrolein, Glutaraldehyde, Hydroxyadipaldehyde

Acrolein, $CH_2=CH—CHO$, and **glutaraldehyde**, $OCH—CH_2CH_2CH_2-CHO$, were reported by Sabatini, Bensch and Barrnett (*J. Cell Biol.* 17: 19, 1963) as good fixatives when electronmicroscopy was to follow, and

[1] *Arch. mikr. Anat.* **52**:202, 1898.   [2] *Am. J. Path.* **14**:557, 1938.   [3] *J. Exp. Med.* **84**:107, 1946.   [4] *Anat. Rec.* **103**:611, 1949.   [5] *Stain Techn.* **33**:47, 1958.

Tice and Barrnett (*J. Histochem.* 10:754, 1962) reported similar good morphologic fixation with **hydroxyadipaldehyde**, $C_4H_7OH—(CHO)_2$.

Acrolein (B.P. 52.5°C) is lachrymatory and toxic and should be handled in a chemical fume hood. It is freely soluble in water (40%) and melts at —87.7°C. Aqueous 10% solutions have been used, with added 1% $CaCl_2$ for lipids, adjusted to neutrality with $CaCO_3$ or buffered with 0.1 M phosphates or cacodylate to pH 7.4.

Enzyme electronmicrographers add 5.3–10.7% sucrose (0.2–0.4 M). Glutaraldehyde is used at 4–5.6% in pH 7.4 phosphate or cacodylate as above. Wachstein and Besen (*J. Histochem.* 11:447, 1963) fixed kidney at 4°C for electronmicroscopic localization of adenosine triphosphatase in 0.5% glutaraldehyde at pH 7.2 (tris maleate buffer). After the phosphatase reactions had been performed on 40 μ frozen sections, the sections were postfixed in buffered osmic acid as usual.

Tice and Barrnett (*J. Histochem.* 10:754, 1962) used tissue blocks fixed with hydroxyadipaldehyde, $C_4H_7(OH)(CHO)_2$ at 12.5% in 50 mM tris maleate buffer of unstated pH, containing 0.4 M (10.7%) sucrose, for 1–2 hours at 4°C, using blocks of about 5 cu mm volume. This fixation is followed by several hours' washing in tris maleate sucrose solution. The fixation is said not to inhibit glucose 6-phosphatase completely. Such material was subjected as frozen sections or as very small blocks to the enzyme reaction and was then postfixed in buffered osmic acid for electronmicroscopy.

All these fixatives are said to give good morphologic fixation, to be usable for at least some enzyme histochemistry, to be adaptable to buffered osmic acid postfixation for electronmicrography. Hydroxyadipaldehyde has been used for electronmicroscopic studies of glucose 6-phosphatase.

Van Duijn (*J. Histochem.* 9:234, 1961) described a widespread positive Schiff reaction of tissues after 5% acrolein 95% alcohol treatment (15 minutes) of formalin or Carnoy fixed material in paraffin sections. This is ascribed to ethylene condensation with SH, NH_2 and imidazole groups, and to phospholipids. Apparently guanidyl, hydroxyl and peptide bond groups are unreactive. The reactivity of indoles and phenols remains in doubt. These condensations leave the aldehyde group of acrolein free to react with Schiff and other aldehyde reagents.

Norton, Gelfand and Brotz (*J. Histochem.* 10:575, 1962) used a 10% solution of freshly distilled acrolein in 1% aqueous $CaCl_2$ to which 0.05% hydroquinone was added before using. The pH varied from 6.4 to 6.8. The solution was best prepared fresh but could be kept 3–4 days at 4°C.

This fixative produced, even in a few hours, a definite and rather large decrease in extractable brain lipids (20–30% in 24–48 hours). Decreases in extractable lipid with Baker's Ca-Cd formalin were much less (*ca.* 10% at 24 hours). Like formaldehyde, acrolein destroyed reactivity of plasmalogen. Norton *et al.* have noted the widespread positive Schiff reaction of tissue proteins and the binding of acrolein to lipids to produce an artifactual lipid aldehyde.

When these reports are considered it seems evident that acrolein, at least, should not be used as a general histologic or histochemical fixative, especially when any aldehyde localization technics, such as the Feulgen or the periodic acid Schiff method or ammoniacal silver methods, are involved.

Since the 3 fixatives are all aldehydes, it is to be expected that all would bind with protein amino and phenol groups, indoles, catecholamines, etc., in much the same way as formaldehyde.

In introducing dialdehyde and acrolein fixations, the expectation was that they would serve to fix proteins more firmly by establishing cross linkages in which the 2 aldehyde groupings, or the aldehyde and ethylene groups of acrolein, would both be utilized to combine with available amino groups in neighboring protein chains. This cross linkage undoubtedly occurs in the tanning of leather. But here a relatively large amount of protein is present to react with a carefully regulated dosage of the aldehyde reagent; whereas in tissue fixation, especially on the electronmicrography scale, relatively minute amounts of tissue are exposed to relatively huge amounts of acrolein or dialdehyde, and the expectation would be that the reactive tissue sites would be combined with a reagent molecule whose second reactive group would be left free because of preoccupation of all available tissue sites. The general aldehyde reactivity of tissue reported by Van Duijn after reaction with acrolein supports this view.

Aldehyde attachment of acrolein, with the known reactivity of osmium tetroxide for ethylenic double bonds, should give rise to some interesting osmium artifacts. And with the dialdehydes, aldehyde reactivity should be demonstrable wherever a molecule of dialdehyde is attached in a Schiff's base union or substituted methylene bridge.

Nevertheless these fixatives do have real value for the specific purposes for which they have been recommended.

Alcohol Fixatives

Alone, **alcohol** has only limited application as a fixing fluid. Absolute alcohol is often used for preservation of glycogen, for fixation of pigments and for fixation of blood and tissue films and smears. For the last purpose methyl alcohol is usually preferred and is effective in 80–100% concentration. Lower percentages hemolyze red cells and inadequately preserve leucocytes. Preservation of hemosiderin is less adequate with ethyl acohol fixation than with buffered formaldehyde solutions. In 60–80% concentration at low temperature (-20 to $-25°C$) alcohol is a useful fixative for preserving certain proteins and enzymes in relatively undernatured state. Such tissue should be rapidly frozen with liquid nitrogen or solid carbon dioxide mixtures, to avoid ice crystal artifacts.

In fixation of tissue, absolute or 100% alcohol alone penetrates rather slowly. In combination with formalin at a 9:1 ratio it fixes adequately in 18–24 hours or less. In the Carnoy mixtures fixation may be completed in 1–2 hours. Thin (3–5 mm) slices of tissue should be used. With Carnoy's mixture (No. 2, below), fix for 1–2 hours. This mixture is the one usually referred to as *Carnoy* in pathologic usage, and is the only fluid given under Carnoy's name alone by Langeron, Romeis, Schmorl, Mallory and Cowdry. Fixation at about 0°C for 18–24 hours is sometimes advantageous. Wash in 2 changes of 100% alcohol of 30–60 minutes each, and store in thin cedar oil. For prolonged storage one may transfer the slices into liquid petrolatum or imbed them in paraffin.

Or if immediate imbedding is desired, carry the slices from the second 100% alcohol into a mixture of equal volumes of 100% alcohol and benzene for 20 minutes, and thence through two 30 minute changes of benzene into paraffin.

Carnoy fixatives hemolyze, occasion a considerable shrinkage and dissolve acid soluble cell granules and pigments. They do not decalcify appreciably in the 2–3 hours required for fixation. They give excellent nuclear fixation. Nissl granules are well preserved, and many cytoplasmic structures are adequately fixed. Myelin is lost. Glycogen is apparently better preserved than with 100% alcohol, and I prefer Carnoy for this purpose. Alcoholic 10% formalin, with or without 5% of glacial acetic acid, is perhaps superior to Carnoy for glycogen. Fix 12–24 hours or longer.

Newcomer's (*Science* 118:161, 1953) fluid is recommended as a substitute for Carnoy's fluid for the fixation of chromosomes. It is said to preserve Feulgen stainability of chromatin better than chloroform containing fluids.

Formulae

1. Carnoy A

100% alcohol	75 cc
Glacial acetic acid	25 cc

2. Carnoy

100% alcohol	60 cc
Chloroform	30 cc
Glacial acetic acid	10 cc

This fluid is the one commonly referred to as Carnoy's fluid in pathologic practice. It is sometimes called Carnoy II.

For both the foregoing, fix thin slices (3–5 mm) 4–5 hours at 25°C or, perhaps better, 18–24 hours at 3–5°C.

3. **Newcomer's Carnoy substitute** (*Science* 118:161, 1953)

Isopropanol	60 cc
Propionic acid	30 cc
Acetone	10 cc
Dioxane	10 cc

Fix 12–24 hours at 25°C and store at 3°C in a fresh portion of the same fluid. Wash and dehydrate with isopropanol.

4. **Methanol + chloroform.** When it is desired to test the lipid nature of some tissue component, fix in a 2:1 mixture, changing to 1:1 on the second change, preferably at 60°C, in screw capped bottles (paraffin oven) for 12–48 or more hours, changing fluid daily. Clear in 2 changes of chloroform and imbed in paraffin.

We now routinely use this fixation schedule: until 5 or 6 P.M. in 2:1 methanol chloroform at 60°C; a second bath of the same mixture overnight at 20–25°C; 1:1 mixture for 9–11 hours at 60°C; overnight in 1:2 methanol chloroform at 20–25°C; from 8 A.M. to 3 P.M. at 60°C in the 1:2 mixture; then two 1 hour changes of absolute alcohol + ether (1:1) at 20–25°C; and 1–3 days in 1% celloidin in alcohol ether. Clear in 2 changes of chloroform, thus hardening the celloidin, and imbed in paraffin as usual. We have cut serial sections of human cerebellum at 2 μ by this procedure.

Acetone

Acetone was long used as a rapid fixative for brain tissue in rabies diagnosis and for a time was the fixative of choice for preservation of phosphatases and lipases. In these latter technics 24 hours' fixation at 0–5°C was prescribed. Latterly the use of fresh frozen sections, freeze dry technics, freeze substitution methods and ice cold "formol calcium" has been preferred for these purposes.

Acetone has recently come into favor as a solvent for certain metallic salts for use at low temperatures in freeze substitution technics for tissue blocks.

Chang and Hori (*J. Histochem.* 9:292, 1961) in their **Section freeze substitution technic** prepare cryostat sections by quick freezing in liquid nitrogen, section at about −15°C in their open cryostat (p. 25) and gently further flatten the sections with a camel's hair brush. The still frozen sections are then transferred to prechilled anhydrous acetone and fixed and dehydrated in a closed vial buried in solid carbon dioxide for 12 hours or more, up to 4 weeks. The dehydrated sections are then mounted by floating them in chilled acetone over Dry Ice and picking them up on a chemically clean coverglass which has been predipped in acetone; a needle is used to guide the sections. The coverglasses with adherent sections are then immersed in cold (−70°C) 1% collodion in

30:30:40 ether:alcohol:acetone. After a few seconds, drain and dry at 25°C and keep at room temperature until stained. Storage at +25°C for 7 days or at −10°C for 2 months was reported as giving no loss of enzyme activity. This procedure was recommended especially for the study of water diffusible enzymes.

For mounting without collodionization, the acetone containing the sections is allowed to warm gradually in an empty Dewar flask or in the freezing area of the refrigerator, and then to room temperature. Sections are then transferred to 95% alcohol for 2 minutes, floated onto coverslips, flattened and carried into the staining procedure. This variant is recommended for nonenzymatic stains and reactions.

At 3°C acetone dissolves out fats at once; at −70°C much fat may remain demonstrable by Sudan stains after acetone freeze substitution (Hitzeman, *J. Histochem.* **11**:62, 1963).

Lead

Sylvén (*Exp. Cell Res.* **1**:582, 1950), Bunting (*A.M.A. Arch. Path.* **49**:590, 1950) and others have used simple 4% aqueous solutions of basic lead acetate for fixation of the connective tissue mucins. Sylvén prescribed 1 day in the lead solution followed by 1 day in 5% formaldehyde.

Basic lead acetate exists in 3 forms: $CH_3COOPbOH$ and combinations of lead acetate with 1 and 2 mols of lead hydroxide. All these forms are quite soluble in water. However, neutral and basic lead acetates readily take up carbon dioxide and form insoluble lead carbonate. The solution should be filtered. Alternatively, cautious addition of acetic acid to the 4% solution lowers the pH to about 4.1 and completely dissolves the residue. First add 0.5 cc glacial acetic acid if solution is quite turbid; then drop by drop until just clear. Lead nitrate solutions give about the same pH levels and the salt is regularly freely soluble (38.8% at 0°C; 66% at 30°C, Lange), but solubility in strong alcohol is distinctly limited (less than 1% in 95% alcohol); 8% lead nitrate will tolerate about 75% alcohol. Dissolve 8 gm lead nitrate in 15–20 cc distilled water and add 95–100% alcohol gradually until turbidity appears; clear with a little more water and then more alcohol, proceeding thus until a total volume of 100 cc is reached. Formalin, if desired, is included as part of the water.

Lillie's alcoholic lead nitrate formalin

Lead nitrate	8 gm
40% formaldehyde	10 cc
Water $\Big\}$ see text above	11 cc
95% alcohol	79 cc

Fix 24 hours at 25–30°C, or longer at 0–5°C (2–3 days). At −75°C 10–14 days may be needed, and probably only about 1% lead nitrate can be used.

Similar solutions in water are more easily prepared and are also quite effective, and good fixation is obtained with the alcoholic solution from which the formalin is replaced by water.

The pH of 4% lead subacetate is 3.8–4.2; that of 8% lead nitrate solutions lies between 3.6 and 4. Formaldehyde has little effect on the pH level. With the addition of 2% sodium acetate ($NaCO_2CH_3 \cdot 3H_2O$) the pH of 8% aqueous $Pb(NO_3)_2$ rises to 5.15.

Mercuric Salts

Usually the chloride $HgCl_2$ is used, and this most often in saturated (5–7%) solution in water. Mercuric chloride rapidly hardens the outer layers of tissues into a quite hard, white mass. It penetrates poorly after the first 3 or 4 mm; consequently, tissue should be cut in thin slices, not more than 5 mm in thickness. It hardens cytoplasm well, preserves its affinity for acid dyes better than formaldehyde and increases the affinity of cellular, bacterial and rickettsial chromatin for basic aniline dyes less than formalin. Nuclear chromatin tends to apppear in finer particles with mercuric chloride than with formaldehyde. Because of the relatively increased affinity of cytoplasm for acid dyes, the differences in basophilia and oxyphilia of regenerating, mature and necrosing cells are less well shown than with formaldehyde. Cytoplasmic structure of renal epithelium, fibrin, connective tissue, cross striae of muscle and other features may be better shown.

Because of its poor penetration and the shrinkage of tissues produced by it, mercuric chloride is seldom used alone. It is combined with acetic and other acids, with chromates, with formaldehyde, with alcohol and with various mixtures.

Except for the susa mixtures, material fixed in mercuric chloride fixatives generally requires treatment with iodine to remove granular black precipitates which are distributed throughout the tissues. This may be done by soaking blocks of unimbedded tissue in 70% alcohol containing enough tincture of iodine to color it a fairly deep reddish brown or port wine color (about 0.5% iodine). It is necessary to inspect daily and add a few more drops of tincture of iodine to restore the color, until the alcohol is no longer decolorized.

However, in pathologic practice (particularly when conservation of time is important) it is customary to imbed and section without iodizing and to remove the precipitates from the deparaffinized sections before staining. Sections are treated 5–10 minutes in 0.3–0.5% iodine in 70–80% alcohol (a 1:15 or 1:20 dilution of the U.S.P. Tincture of Iodine), rinsed in water, decolorized 1–5 minutes in 5% sodium thiosulfate, and washed 5–10 minutes in running water before staining.

Lee preferred the practice of iodization before imbedding, and stated that serious artifacts were produced during imbedding if the mercury was not first removed. Mallory condemned this process, preferring to iodize after sectioning, and stated that prolonged iodization of blocks impaired the staining quality of cells. I have used both methods and can see little important difference. Generally I prefer to iodize after sectioning, because of the time factor.

After mercuric chloride fixation the excess fixative should be washed out, preferably with 70–80% alcohol, except when combined with chromates. In the latter case washing overnight in running water is recommended. Storage in 70% alcohol is usually recommended.

On long storage in alcohol the material becomes quite hard and brittle. Hence it seems better to complete the dehydration of material not wanted at once and either clear and imbed it in paraffin or store it in thin cedar oil. This fluid keeps the tissue reasonably soft and seems to improve its quality for sectioning.

Formulae

1. **Saturated aqueous mercuric chloride.** The usual formulae are based on the late nineteenth century German laboratory temperature of about 15°C, at which temperature solubility is about 5.6%. The solubility curve is almost a straight line from 10 to 40°C, actual values at 20°C and 30°C being only 0.1% less than thus calculated.

TABLE 3-2. MERCURIC CHLORIDE CONTENT OF SATURATED SOLUTIONS[1]

0°C	5°C	10°C	15°C	20°C	25°C	30°C	35°C	40°C
3.6	4.2	4.8	5.6	6.5	7.4	8.3	9.3	10.2

[1] Italicized figures are interpolated.

This solution is quite acid (pH 3). Spuler (Ehrlich's *Encyklopädie*) recommended addition of 0.5 to 0.75% sodium chloride, thereby increasing the solubility of $HgCl_2$ to about 9%. Aqueous **mercuric acetate** (5%) is also acid (pH 3.2).

2. **Acetic sublimate.** Lee added 1% acetic acid to saturated mercuric chloride solution; I have used 2% acetic acid, which gives pH 2.3, and 5% acetic acid in 5% $HgCl_2$. Losses of acetic acid soluble proteins are somewhat increased, and sharpness of chromatin staining is improved.

3. **Buffered sublimate (B-4).** On occasion I have used a formaldehyde free variant of the B-5 fixative, containing 6 gm mercuric chloride and 1.25 gm anhydrous sodium acetate per 100 cc. The pH is about 6, and the fluid serves for fixation of Paneth, pancreatic and other zymogen granules, when for histochemical reasons it is desired to avoid formaldehyde. Enterochromaffin does not appear to be preserved, but the fluid has been shown to oxidize enterochromaffin in formaldehyde fixed sections to a quinonoid form, from which it can be reduced by

$Na_2S_2O_4$. Mercurial precipitate is sparse or absent, and iodination can be omitted (p. 45).

4. **Saturated alcoholic mercuric chloride** (33% at 25°C in 99% alcohol, Lange). This solution fixed tissues very rapidly. Much weaker solutions are used currently in freeze substitution technics; Feder and Sidman used a 1% solution at −75°C for blocks not over 3 mm thick which were first frozen in 3:1 propane:isopentane at −170°C (using liquid nitrogen as the cooling agent). Fixation took a week, longer for thicker blocks, when done in a Dry Ice chest. On completion of the fixation exposure, the fluid is allowed to warm to room temperature and dehydration and imbedding are completed as usual.

A similar solution in acetone can probably be used, but it must be freshly prepared and promptly chilled to −75°C; at 25°C mercuric chloride and acetone react in a few hours to produce a copious black precipitate.

5. **Schaudinn's mercuric chloride alcohol** ("sublimate alcohol"), cited from Giemsa (*Deutsche med. Wschr.* 35:1751, 1909):

Saturated aqueous mercuric chloride	2 parts
Alcohol (absolute)	1 part

Fix 24 hours, replace fixative with fresh solution and continue fixation another 24 hours. Then transfer to 70% alcohol.

I consider the cytoplasmic fixation achieved with this fluid inferior to that achieved with Zenker's fluid. Giemsa recommended it for wet smear fixation, and the fixative has often been attributed to him.

5a. **Huber's fluid**

Mercuric chloride	5 gm
Trichloroacetic acid	15 gm
95% alcohol	100 cc

is said to give no mercurial precipitate, and is recommended by Peters (*Stain Techn.* 33:47, 1958) for nerve material destined for his protein-silver nerve impregnation method. The customary iodine treatment is omitted for this purpose.

6. **Ohlmacher's fluid** (Ehrlich's *Encyklopädie*) (a), **Fluid of Carnoy and Lebrun** (Cowdry, McClung, Lee) (b).

100% alcohol	(a)	32 cc	(b)	15 cc	may be kept
Chloroform	(a)	6 cc	(b)	15 cc	as stock solution
Glacial acetic acid	(a)	2 cc	(b)	15 cc	tion

Before using, add 8 gm mercuric chloride to the above 40 cc mixture of Ohlmacher's fluid. Lebrun's is saturated with mercuric chloride. Add 4 gm, which is an excess. These mixtures fix very rapidly. Ohlmacher's fluid penetrates about 1 mm in the first 10–15 minutes, 2.5 mm in 2–3 hours. Blocks should be cut quite thin before fixation. Handle while in the fluid with instruments previously dipped in hot paraffin to avoid contact of the mercurial solution with metal. Wash in 2 changes of 100% alcohol, about 1 hour each; clear in cedar oil and store surplus tissue in this fluid. Ohlmacher's fluid gives comparatively little mercurial precipitate, and there is little difference in appearance between material fixed 30 minutes and that fixed 150 minutes. It preserves glycogen poorly in comparison with Carnoy.

Formaldehyde Sublimate Formulae

7. **Heidenhain's susa fluid** (4th ed. Z. *wiss. Mikr.* **33**:232, 1916, Romeis) consisted of 4.5 gm mercuric chloride, 0.5 gm sodium chloride, 20 cc 40% formaldehyde, 80 cc distilled water, 4 cc glacial acetic acid, 2 gm trichloroacetic acid. A 12 hour fixation is followed by washing in 95% alcohol. Mercurial precipitates are said not to be formed. Glycogen was not preserved in the few trials I made of this fluid.

8. **Acetic mercuric chloride formalin** (pH 1.9–2)

Mercuric chloride	6 gm
Glacial acetic acid	5 cc
40% formaldehyde solution	10 cc
Distilled water	85 cc

   Add the acetic acid and formalin to the mercuric chloride solution at time of using.

9. **Sodium acetate mercuric chloride formalin** ("B–5") (pH 5.8–6)

Distilled water	90 cc
Mercuric chloride	6 gm
Sodium acetate (anhydrous)	1.25 gm
At time of using add 40% formaldehyde	10 cc

If the salt available is the trihydrate $NaCO_2CH_3 \cdot 3H_2O$ use 2.074 gm. Calcium acetate as monohydrate, 2 gm, has been substituted; but it may be necessary to filter to remove the slight turbidity resulting probably from the presence of a small amount of calcium hydroxide in the salt.

Fixation with these mercuric chloride formalin mixtures appears to be adequate in 12–24 hours, but even rodent livers are not overhardened in 6–7 days. Tissues should be transferred directly to and stored in 70% or 80% alcohol.

Spuler (Ehrlich's *Encyklopädie*) recommended for blood a strong mercuric chloride solution to which he added 1% acetic acid and 10% formalin. W. H. Cox (*Anat. Hefte* **10**:99, 1898) employed for nerve cell (Nissl) granules a mixture of 30 cc saturated aqueous mercuric chloride solution, 10 cc formalin and 5 cc glacial acetic acid. Stowell (*Arch. Path.*

46:164, 1948) recommended **Stieve's fluid** in studies of liver regeneration. This consists of 76 cc saturated aqueous mercuric chloride solution, 20 cc formalin and 4 cc glacial acetic acid. **Dawson** and **Friedgood** (*Stain Techn.* 13:17, 1938) in studies of the anterior lobe of the hypophysis used a mixture of 90 cc physiological saline solution saturated with mercuric chloride (10% or more?) and 10 cc formalin. I have used mixtures of 10 cc formalin, 5 cc glacial acetic acid, 6 gm mercuric chloride and 85 cc water and of 10 cc formalin, 2 gm calcium or sodium acetate, 6 gm mercuric chloride and 90 cc water. G. Brecher in my laboratory found the last mixture (B–5) excellent for differentiation of pancreatic islet cells.

Unbuffered mercuric chloride formalin mixtures are quite acid (*ca.* pH 2.9); the acetate formulae are much less so (pH 5.9–6, 5.85 for sodium and calcium formulae); but the acetic formula is slightly more acid (pH 1.9). The stock solutions appear to be quite stable, but the formaldehyde mixtures are unstable and should be freshly prepared. Formaldehyde reduces mercuric chloride to calomel and metallic mercury, evident as a white to gray or black-flecked precipitate.

Mann (*Z. wiss. Mikr.* 11:479, 1894) gives 2 mercuric chloride formulae which are still sometimes used. His *osmic-sublimate* is composed of equal volumes of 1% aqueous osmium tetroxide and of 0.75% aqueous sodium chloride solution saturated with mercuric chloride. In his *tannin-picro-sublimate* he adds 1 gm each of picric acid and of tannin to 100 cc of Heidenhain's 0.75% aqueous sodium chloride solution saturated with mercuric chloride. These fluids were originally used for the study of nerve cells. Lee as early as 1896 changed the solvent to physiological salt solution, and Cowdry prescribes 0.85% sodium chloride.

Sublimate Bichromate Fluids

Both the original **Acetic sublimate bichromate** fluid of **K. Zenker** (1894) and the formalin variants introduced by Spuler (Ehrlich's *Encyklopädie*, 1903) and Helly (*Z. wiss. Mikr.* 20:413, 1904) have enjoyed a wide popularity and have undergone many, usually minor, modifications. The original Zenker's fluid was made by saturating Müller's fluid (p. 55) with mercuric chloride and then adding, just before use, 5% glacial acetic acid. This precaution was necessary in 1894 because acetic acid was then recovered from the pyroligneous acid obtained from the destructive distillation of wood, which was composed of nearly equal amounts of methanol, acetone and acetic acid. Each of the major constituents, as prepared in commercially pure form, was often considerably contaminated with the other two. Zenker's fluid made with modern reagent grade acetic acid is quite stable over prolonged periods, even at elevated temperatures (3 months at 60°C). At 100°C acetic acid reduces potassium bichromate slowly.

TABLE 3-3. COMPOSITION OF ZENKER AND ZENKER FORMOL FLUIDS

	Zenker (Gray)	Zenker (Enzyk)	Zenker (AFIP)	Zenker (Lillie)	Spuler (Enzyk)	Helly	Bencosme	Guthrie (Lee ix)	Zenker base
Distilled water................	960	1000	1000	950	1000	1000	800	1000	1000
Potassium bichromate..........	20	25	25	25	25	25	20	25	25
Sodium sulfate................	10	10	10	...	10	10	8	10	10
Mercuric chloride.............	49.2	50	50	50	50	50	40	50	50
Glacial acetic acid............	.....	...	...	50					
Add at time of use:									
Glacial acetic acid............	50	50	52	...	...	...	...		
Formic acid..................	...	...	...	...	...	...	...	50	
40% (w/v) formaldehyde.......	...	...	...	...	100	50	200		

The formaldehyde and formic acid mixtures start to darken in some hours and become quite dark brown and turbid in a day or two. Hence it is necessary with all these mixtures to defer addition of formalin and of formic acid to the moment of using.

The most common variant from the above formulae is the omission of sodium sulfate. With higher laboratory temperatures than the traditional German 15°C, some workers have added 60 or even 70 gm $HgCl_2$. It is questionable that the additional sublimate is necessary or even valuable. It probably only adds to the cost of the fluid. In view of the quite adequate mercurial fixation achieved with fluids containing only 1–3% $HgCl_2$, even 5% is probably more than necessary.

Fixation times vary from 4 to 24 hours; longer periods are said to produce overhardening and are not generally recommended. However, I have seen rodent livers fixed 6–7 days in Spuler's formalin variant which cut well and gave quite satisfactory histologic staining. If very thin (2–3 mm) blocks are cut, 2–3 hours may well suffice. The premixed acetic Zenker's fluid can be placed on the Technicon and used repeatedly, being changed perhaps weekly to avoid excessive dilution and contamination by blood and serum.

In all cases blocks should be thin; hollow organs should be opened. All Zenker fluids penetrate solid tissue slowly, and the acidic and formaldehyde components penetrate faster than the metallic salts, so that in overthick blocks one soon reaches a zone, 5–10 mm deep and below, where the fixation effect appears to be predominantly that of acetic acid or formalin.

Acidity. The acetic Zenker fluids are generally quite acid (pH 2.3), and this acidity is not affected by the presence of Na_2SO_4. The formalin variants are a little more acid (pH 3.4) than corresponding fluids without $HgCl_2$ (pH 3.8–3.95), but they are less acid than unbuffered sublimate without bichromate (pH 3).

The formic acid variant, attributed to Mary J. Guthrie in the ninth edition of Lee's *Microtomists' Vade Mecum* (1928), is an active decalcifying agent and was redevised for that purpose (1943) in our laboratory. Otherwise, fixation effects are similar to those of Zenker's fluid. Formic acid reduces $HgCl_2$ to $HgCl$, so that calomel precipitation starts in about 3 hours. Potassium bichromate solution without $HgCl_2$ changes color from orange to dark red brown in about 48 hours, but without precipitation.

Bencosme (*Arch. Path.* 33:87, 1952) prescribed 24 hours or *more* washing in running water. Embryonic and very young animal tissues were then dehydrated in successive 2 hour changes of 40%, 50%, 60%, 70% alcohol; 3 hours in 90% alcohol; and 10 hours in 95% alcohol; the last 2 containing 0.25% iodine. Dehydration was completed with 3 and 5 hour changes of 100% alcohol. Tissues from older animals were transferred directly from the wash water to 0.25% iodine in 95% alcohol for 24 hours, followed by 4 changes of 100% alcohol, the first 2 of which were used, the last 2 fresh.

Embryonic tissues were cleared through 1:1 and 3:1 toluene:100% alcohol mixtures (2 hours each), and 4 changes of toluene (3, 10, 2 and 4 hours); adult tissues directly from 100% alcohol in 4 changes of toluene (8, 16, 8, 16 hours). Used toluene was employed for the first 2 changes, fresh toluene was used for the last 2 changes in both cases.

Bencosme infiltrated with a mixture of 9 parts 50–52°C paraffin and 1 part yellow beeswax. Embryonic tissues were infiltrated 2 hours at room temperature in equal parts of toluene and paraffin and were then transferred to the melted beeswax paraffin at 55°C. With adult tissues this step was omitted, and the tissues were infiltrated directly in beeswax paraffin. Three ovens were required, and tissues were kept in them for 8 hours, 16 hours and 1–5 days respectively. It is claimed that the toluene is not adequately eliminated unless 3 separate ovens are employed.

I cite this schedule as an example of the elaborateness which cytologists can achieve. Because of the high concentration of formalin in this mixture, I would advise very thin blocks. Otherwise considerable differences of fixation of surface and inner zones are apt to be observed. The solvent toluene can be eliminated from the tissue far more expeditiously, and probably more effectively, by infiltration *in vacuo* (10 mm mercury) for 30–60 minutes. The process can be hastened still more by substituting a low boiling petroleum ether for the toluene. The latter is also less toxic than toluene.

For all these Zenker variants, wash overnight in running water, or in 2–3 changes of water, 1–2 hours each on the Technicon, then store in 70% alcohol, or proceed at once with dehydration, clearing and imbedding.

For washing of tissue blocks, which is required for the foregoing chromate mercury fixations as well as for the following dichromate methods, the use of a siphon washer (Fig. 3-1) has proved quite convenient. Operating on the same principle as commercial pipet washers, the siphon washer probably removes excess chromate from tissues more rapidly and more surely than the traditional continuous flow washing, especially when the water inlet tube is not taken all the way to the bottom of the washing jar. I have seen a stratum of deep yellow bichromate solution in the bottom of a bottle, surrounding the tissue blocks, after overnight washing.

Chromates and Chromic Acid

The most commonly used primary chromate fixations are Orth's and Möller's (Regaud's) mixtures. I have used Orth's extensively for routine work. It is equal to formaldehyde for the study of early degenerative processes and necrosis. It is perhaps superior to formaldehyde for demonstrating rickettsiae and bacteria. Chromaffin takes its characteristic brown tone and its basophilia is well brought out with Orth's fluid. Myelin is better preserved, and the pericellular shrinkage seen about the pyramidal cells after the use of formalin is avoided. Hemosiderin is less well preserved with Orth's fluid than with buffered neutral formalin.

The **fixation period** for Orth's fluid should be between 36 and 72 hours. Human tissues are usually given 48 hours; brain is perhaps better with 72 hours, though 48 hours is adequate. Mouse tissues appear to be over-hardened in 48 hours, and 24 hours is often adequate. Rat and guinea pig tissues should be fixed longer, perhaps 36–48 hours. After fixation, tissues are washed overnight in running water. The traditional storage fluid is 70% alcohol; but tissues may be kept at least a year in 10% formalin, so that material for fat stains can continue to be available. Glycogen is well shown by the Bauer method after Orth fixation.

Romeis's acetic variant of Orth's fluid gives similar pictures, except that partial hemolysis occurs, more iron pigment is lost and nuclear chromatin is more sharply defined. This variant was used routinely by Ophüls for many years. He commonly fixed in it for 3–4 days. Tellyesniczky used an acetic bichromate mixture without formalin. This mixture appears to be stable.

I have employed Kose's variant of Orth's fluid, which contains 3 gm potassium bichromate in place of 2.5 gm/100 cc, and find that it gives greater hardening in the same period of time, without appreciable change in the overall picture. This fluid, like Zenker's, renders ribonucleic acid relatively highly resistant to specific enzyme digestion. This effect is less

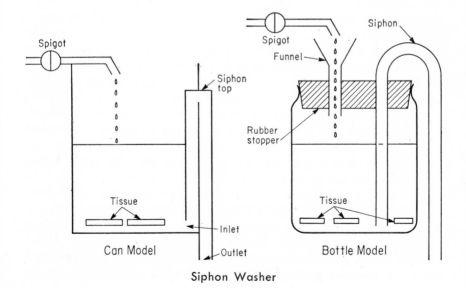

Siphon Washer

evident when 2% calcium or sodium acetate is added to Kose's fluid or to Spuler's formalin Zenker mixture.

Möller's or Regaud's fluid is similar in general effect to Orth's but hardens more rapidly and to a harder final consistency. With this 20% formalin bichromate mixture, as with aqueous 20% formalin and with Bouin fluids containing 20–25% formalin, an outer zone of hyperoxyphilia of tissues is produced. In this zone nuclear staining is apt to be poor, and

TABLE 3-4. BUFFERED BICHROMATE SOLUTIONS

1N HCl, cc	0.2M KH$_2$PO$_4$, cc	0.2M Na$_2$HPO$_4$, cc	0.2M Acetic, cc	0.2M NaAcet, cc	6% K$_2$Cr$_2$O$_7$, cc	pH
26	24	....	....	....	50	1.46
15	35	....	....	....	50	2.01
7	43	....	....	....	50	2.52
2.6	47.4	....	....	....	50	3.00
			46.5	3.5	50	3.51
			40	10	50	4.00
			31	19	50	4.50
			13	37	50	5.00
	45.5	4.5	....	....	50	5.01
				50	50	5.52
	37.0	13.0	....	....	50	5.50
	28.0	22.0	....	....	50	5.98
	50	....	....	....	50	6.27

cytoplasm will stain more strongly with acid dyes there than in the center of the block.

Sometimes it is desirable to modify the naturally quite acid pH level (3.8–3.95) of potassium bichromate solutions. For example, iron containing pigments are better preserved at higher pH levels. Lower pH levels seem necessary to elicit the chromaffin reaction of the enterochromaffin cells. Addition of 5% of acetic acid to a 3% potassium bichromate solution lowers the pH to 2.9. This solution is stable for months, but the further addition of formaldehyde quite promptly causes the usual reduction changes: first darkening to dark brown, then to brownish green. Hence formalin should not be added to acidified bichromate mixtures until the time of using. Formulae for the buffering of bichromate solutions appear in Table 3-4. Adding 10 parts of 40% formaldehyde to 90 parts 3% bichromate produces little change of pH level: perhaps a rise of 0.05 below pH 4; none above. The upper pH levels do not darken on addition of formaldehyde; but at pH 6.3 some dark green precipitate is formed in 18–24 hours, the solution remaining clear chromate yellow and smelling strongly of formaldehyde. The more acid pH 5.5 acetate solution shows no precipitation.

Formulae

1. **Müller's fluid** (Ehrlich's *Encyklopädie*). Dissolve 2.5 gm potassium bichromate and 1 gm sodium sulfate in 100 cc distilled water.
2. **Orth's fluid** (*Berlin. klin. Wschr.* 33:273, 1896). To 100 cc Müller's fluid add 10 cc 37–40% formaldehyde solution at the time of using. I regularly use 2.5% potassium bichromate in place of Müller's fluid; Mallory used 2–2.5%. Romeis and Schmorl reduced the Müller's fluid to 90 cc. Fix 1–4 days, usually 2. Wash overnight in running water.
3. **Romeis's and Ophüls's variants.** Romeis used 85 cc 3% potassium bichromate, 10 cc formalin and 5 cc glacial acetic acid. Ophüls used 100 cc Müller's fluid; I use 100 cc 2.5% potassium bichromate in place of Romeis's 85 cc 3%. The acid and formalin were added immediately before using. The mixture darkens rapidly. Fix 6–24 hours according to Romeis, 2–4 days according to Ophüls. Wash overnight in running water.
4. **Ciaccio's fluid.** This appears to have been a somewhat variable mixture of potassium bichromate solution, formalin and a little formic acid or acetic acid, with or without mercuric chloride. Ciaccio changed it according to need from time to time, and it is sometimes uncertain which mixture he used in any given study.

Reference	$K_2Cr_2O_7$, gm	40% HCHO, cc	Acetic acid	Formic acid, gtt	Water, cc
Anat. Anz. **23**:401, 1903	5	10		3–4[1]	100
Ibid.	3	10		3–4	100
Zieglers Beitr. **50**:317, 1909	4	20		10–15	80
Ibid.	4	20	10–15[2]gtt		80
Huber, *Mikroskopie* **12**: 91, 1957	5	20	1cc		80

[1] 0.15–0.22cc
[2] 0.25–0.4cc

Ciaccio (and Huber) usually fixed for 3 days and postchromed in 3–5% $K_2Cr_2O_7$ for a further 3–7 days. I have usually employed Kose's fluid without added acid and postchromed in 3–5% $K_2Cr_2O_7$ for intervals of 4–10 days, according to the material being studied and the time available. The stronger solution required the shorter time.

Huber (*loc. cit.*) also cites **Sanfelice's fluid** as composed of 64 cc 1% CrO_3 to which are added at time of using 4 cc glacial acetic acid and 32 cc 40% formaldehyde. He fixed 24 hours at (European) room temperature and washed 1–2 days in running water.

5. **Kose's fluid** (Ehrlich's *Encyklopädie; Sitzb. Deutsche naturwiss. Vereins "Lotos," Prag,* 46(N.F. 18):224, 1898). To 90 cc 3% potassium bichromate add 10 cc 37–40% formaldehyde solution at time of using (pH 3.6–3.9). Fix 1–3 days. Wash 16 hours in running water.

6. **Buffered Orth.** Dissolve 25 or 30 gm potassium bichromate and 16.2 gm sodium acetate crystals in 1000 cc water. To 90 cc of this fluid add 10 cc 40% formaldehyde solution at time of using (pH 5.5). Fix 1–3 days. Wash 16 hours in running water.

7. **Tellyesniczky's acetic bichromate** (*Arch. mikr. Anat.* 52:202, 1898). To 100 cc 3% potassium bichromate add 5 cc glacial acetic acid at time of using. (The mixture keeps well for months after mixing.) Fix 1–2 days. If simultaneous decalcification is desired, substitute 5 cc 90% formic acid for the acetic. This latter mixture must be fresh; it darkens in some hours.

8. **Möller's or Regaud's fluid.** To 80 cc 3% potassium bichromate add 20 cc 40% formaldehyde solution at time of using. Fix 1–2 days. Möller (*Z. wiss. Zool.,* 66:69, 1899) prescribed 1 day fixation, followed by 3–4 days in 3% potassium bichromate. Regaud (*Arch. anat. micr.,* 11:291, 1910) recommended 4 days, and followed it with 8 days' further chromation in 3% potassium bichromate for mitochondria. This seems excessive for general purposes. In my experience the prolonged chromation interferes with nuclear staining. However, certain methods for Golgi substance and for mitochondria call for the long chromate treatment. Ehrlich's *Encyklopädie* (1903) and Regaud cite this fluid as Möller's; Mallory, Langeron, Romeis, Conn and Darrow, Lee and Cowdry all call it Regaud's.

9. **Kolmer's fluid.** For fixation of eyes, Walls (*Stain Techn.* 13:69, 1938) recommends Kolmer's fluid. Mix just before using.

5% aqueous potassium bichromate solution	20 cc
10% formalin	20 cc
Glacial acetic acid	5 cc
50% trichloroacetic acid	5 cc
Saturated aqueous (10%) uranyl acetate	5 cc

Fix 24 hours, wash 6 hours in water or 25% alcohol, followed by 6 hour baths in ascending alcohols: 35%, 50%, 70%, 95%, 100%.

10. **Held's fluid.** To 100 cc 3% potassium bichromate solution add 4 cc 40% formaldehyde and 5 cc glacial acetic acid and allow to ripen for some weeks until the solution is green in color. In this fluid the formaldehyde is partly oxidized to formic acid; the chromic acid is partly reduced to chromic salts; and the pH rises from an initial level of about 3 to about 3.8 (Romeis).

Osmium Tetroxide

Osmium tetroxide ("osmic acid") mixtures are little used in general pathology because of their high cost, poor penetration, and interference with various staining methods. Since the development of modern frozen section methods for fat and degenerating myelin, they have less general value than formerly. Osmium tetroxide is especially valuable for fixation of cytoplasmic structures; but nuclei are poorly stainable, and when its action is prolonged, unsaturated fats reduce it to form black masses.

The vapor of 1–2% aqueous solution may be used for the fixation of blood and tissue films. This requires 30–60 seconds or more according to the thickness of the film. Slides are placed face down over a small flat dish containing a thin layer of the solution.

1. **Flemming's strong solution** (Ehrlich's *Encyklopädie* and all modern texts) contained 20 cc 2% osmium tetroxide, 75 cc 1% chromic acid and 5 cc glacial acetic acid. Fix 1–3 days; wash 6–24 hours in running water; store in 80% alcohol.

2. **Hermann's fluid** (Ehrlich's *Encyklopädie*) substituted 75 cc 1% platinum chloride for the chromic acid in Flemming's, with the same 20 cc 2% osmium tetroxide and 5 cc glacial acetic acid. It was used in the same manner.

3. **Marchi's fluid** consists of 1 part 1% osmium tetroxide and 2 parts Müller's fluid (p. 55). This composition is that given in all modern texts. Its main use is for demonstration of degenerating myelin.

4. **Mann's fluid.** See p. 49.

5. **Buffered osmic acid** is generally recommended for preparation of material for electronmicroscopy. Palade (*J. Exp. Med.* **95**:285, 1952) introduced this fluid, fixing 1–4 hours in 1% OsO_4 in pH 7.4 Veronal acetate buffer. Rhodin (*Exp. Cell Res.* **8**:572, 1955) made this fluid isotonic in order to prevent artifactual cell swelling.

   Barrnett and Palade (*J. Histochem.* **6**:1, 1958) were using 1% OsO_4 in pH 7.6 Veronal acetate buffer containing enough sucrose to raise the osmolar concentration to 0.44 M.

   Rhodin (*Int. Rev. Cytol.* **7**:485, 1958) suggested also 1% OsO_4 in Veronal acetate with 3% dextran. McGill and Geer at this school are using 1% osmic acid in pH 7.4 Veronal acetate buffer containing 4.5% sucrose.

6. **Feder and Sidman** (*J. Histochem.* **6**:401, 1958) used 1% **osmic acid** made up in **acetone** prechilled to −75°C in their freeze substitution technic. Thin blocks, 3 mm or less, are fixed 6–7 days at −75°C and washed in 2–3 changes of acetone at the same temperature. Although prefreezing in propane-isopentane at −170°C was prescribed, the usual isopentane at −150°C can probably be used, and even material

frozen in solid carbon dioxide acetone mixture would probably be quite satisfactory, except for electronmicroscopy.

Osmic acid is rapidly reduced by acetone at room temperatures.

Picric Acid

Picric acid gives a quite hard fixation which is excellent for many purposes. Aniline blue methods of the Mallory type, with its Heidenhain and Masson variants, do well after this fixation. Unless very thorough washing of sections is done, it interferes with azure eosin stains. It penetrates well and fixes small objects rapidly.

Feder and Sidman (*J. Histochem.* 6:401, 1958) recommended 5% picric acid in alcohol in their freeze substitution method (p. 57). Fix 3 mm blocks 7 days at −75°C; wash in alcohol at +25°C and imbed in paraffin as usual.

The most popular picric acid fixative is Bouin's fluid. Lee recommended not more than 18 hours' fixation; Masson, up to 3 days; Cowdry, 24 hours; and I have found 1–2 days satisfactory.

This fluid contains 75 cc 1.2% (saturated) aqueous picric acid solution, 25 cc formalin (40% formaldehyde) and 5 cc glacial acetic acid (Ehrlich's *Encyklopädie*).

It is quite common practice to add an excess of picric acid crystals to the stock bottle of Bouin's fluid. The resultant fluid should be somewhat more acid. Allen's B-15 modification contains in addition 2 gm urea and 1.5 gm chromic acid, while in his PFA3 modification the formalin is reduced to 15 cc, the acetic acid increased to 10 cc, and 1 gm urea is added (Lee). I have found that the superficial hyperoxyphilia seen in Bouin fixed tissues when 20–25% formalin is included may be obviated by decreasing the formalin content to 10%. On substitution of 90–95% formic acid for the glacial acetic acid the fluid will decalcify small bones during 24 hours fixation. This PFF fluid (*J. Tech. Methods* 24:35, 1944) contains 85 cc 1.2% picric acid, 10 cc 40% formaldehyde, and 5 cc. 90–95% formic acid.

Bouin fixatives generally lake red cells and remove the demonstrable ferric iron from blood pigments. They render ribonucleic acid relatively resistant to ribonuclease digestion.

Lee recommends extraction with 50% and 70% alcohol until most of the yellow color is removed. Masson (*J. Tech. Methods* 12:75, 1929) transferred tissues from the fixative to water, using enough to cover them and leaving them in it until ready to imbed them. I find that alcohol extraction of blocks may take many days with daily changes of alcohol, and prefer to imbed and section after no more than 2–3 days in 70–80% alcohol. It is far easier to wash the excess picric acid out of the sections after removal of paraffin. Surplus tissue is to be stored in 70% alcohol.

Two alcoholic picric acid fluids which have enjoyed some popularity as glycogen fixatives are Rossman's and Gendre's fluids.

Rossman's fluid (*Am. J. Anat.* **66**:342, 1940) consists of 90 volumes of 100% alcohol saturated (about 9%) with picric acid and 10 volumes of neutralized commercial formalin. Fix for 12–24 hours and wash for several days in 95% alcohol.

Gendre's fluid (*Bull. histol. appliq. physiol.* **14**:262, 1937) is composed of 80 volumes of 90% (by weight, equals 95% by volume) alcohol saturated with picric acid, 15 volumes of 40% formaldehyde solution and 5 volumes of glacial acetic acid. Fix 1–4 hours in this mixture and wash in several changes of 80% alcohol. I find that 4 hours at 25°C gives excellent fixation of glycogen in liver tissue. Two changes each of 80%, 95% and 100% alcohol give adequate washing and dehydration.

Vom Rath's (*Anat. Anz.* **11**:286, 1895) picrosublimate acetic fluid is sometimes attributed to Tellyesniczky (*Arch. mikr. Anat.* **52**:202, 1898). This was a mixture of equal volumes of mercuric chloride saturated in warm sodium chloride solution and of filtered cold saturated picric acid solution. Vom Rath added either 0.5% or 1% glacial acetic acid to the mixture. Tellyesniczky used the latter proportion and condemned the mixture both for resting nuclei and for cytoplasm.

The **Bouin-Hollande fluid** is recommended by Hartz (*Am. J. Clin. Path.* **17**:750, 1947) for fixation and gross demonstration of calcification. Bone, calcified necrotic tissue and calcified fat necrosis appear dark green on a pale yellowish green background.

Formula. In 100 cc distilled water dissolve successively without heating 2.5 gm copper acetate, 4 gm picric acid, 10 cc 40% formaldehyde, and 1.5 cc glacial acetic acid. The fluid keeps well and will decalcify small bones in a week or less.

Heat

I have occasionally fixed small objects, up to 5–10 mm in thickness, by boiling them in physiologic (0.85–0.90%) sodium chloride solution for 2–3 minutes. This method may be of value where it is desired to avoid the introduction of alien chemical substances. Some shrinkage is produced. The method has the further advantage of speed. Frozen sections may be completed in a matter of minutes after removal of tissue from the body.

It is possible that formaldehyde solutions employed in this way have some additional insolubilizing effect on tissue proteins. Boiling in saline solution is worthy of further trial in the study of basic proteins and terminal amine groups by histochemical methods.

It is well known that boiling water dissolves starch and glycogen (*Bull. Int. A. Med. Museums* **27**:23–61, 1947, especially p. 34). Fixation in boiling distilled water destroys red corpuscles, but, if brief, leaves a good deal of glycogen in liver cells, and preserves nuclear and cytoplasmic detail quite well. Collagen is not greatly altered.

UNFIXED TISSUES

This was of course the original type of material studied by the first histologists and histochemists. With the advent of fixation and sectioning procedures this material was little studied for a long period except for the observation of motility of cells and cell organs, of the progress of the mitotic process, of phagocytosis and pinocytosis and other phenomena requiring the observation of living or surviving cells.

With the rise in interest in the last two decades in the precise localization in tissues of various enzymes, preparation methods have developed in which denaturation, extraction and diffusion of enzymes are minimized.

In some instances simple air desiccation of impression smears and of fresh frozen sections gives just enough protein denaturation to prevent diffusion and extraction without seriously impairing activity. The *in vacuo* desiccation of the Altmann-Gersh freeze dry procedure seems to have a similar effect. Freezing itself is deleterious in some instances; in these cases the enzyme demonstration reaction has been done by perfusion of intact tissue and by immersion of thin unfrozen slices, and fixation follows the reaction.

Several manufacturers now furnish effective equipment for vacuum desiccation of tissues previously frozen in isopentane or butane with liquid nitrogen. These devices usually operate at 10^{-5} or 10^{-6} mm mercury pressure, and their effectiveness appears to depend on the shortness of the path from the object to a condensing surface kept at a considerably lower temperature to remove water vapor from the system. The object is usually maintained at -30 to $-70°C$, desiccation being faster at the higher temperature, at which also ice crystal growth is more likely to occur. Ice crystal size seems to have its greatest importance in electron microscopy.

When fully desiccated, tissues may be directly infiltrated with paraffin or Carbowax without breaking the vacuum. The imbedding wax should be defoamed before being used by melting *in vacuo*.

About 1954, I attempted to utilize the same principle as in organic distillations, of circulating inert gas through the desiccation chamber and a condensing chamber under lower temperature, using only partial vacuum. Mechanical difficulties prevented our success with this process. I believe it has been successfully used by others since.

Kulenkampff (*Z. wiss. Mikr.* **62**:427, 1955) prefers propane chilled with liquid nitrogen as the freezing agent, claiming temperatures of about $-190°C$ and hence finer ice crystal size.

Much work on unfixed tissue is now done by direct sectioning by a cold knife procedure, such as the Adamstone-Taylor and cryostat methods (see also under individual enzyme methods).

Chapter 4

Sectioning

FREEHAND SECTIONING

Freehand sectioning with a sharp razor is sometimes employed in making sections, either of unfixed or of fixed tissue, thin enough to be translucent. This method was employed by Terry (*J. Tech. Methods* **12**:127, 1929) for his rapid diagnosis method. Following the preparation of the thin sections they are placed upon a glass slide, and a drop of dilute stain is carefully placed on one surface and rinsed off after a few seconds. With practice it is readily possible to regulate this staining interval so that only 1 or 2 surface layers of cells are stained. For this purpose Terry recommended a neutralized polychrome methylene blue made by boiling with alkali for variable periods and then neutralizing. This solution is commercially available from at least one American manufacturer, but 1% solutions of thionin, azure A or toluidine blue will serve. After rinsing, cover with a coverglass and examine at once. Preparations are temporary.

Aside from this procedure, almost all sectioning is done with microtomes. With these instruments sections may be prepared which are much thinner and more uniform than those prepared by freehand methods. Microtomy requires a firmer consistency than is present in raw or fixed tissue. This consistency is attained by freezing or by infiltration with imbedding masses in a fluid state, followed by solidification of the imbedding medium. The commonly used imbedding media are paraffin and other waxes, soaps, gelatin, agar, Carbowaxes and polyethylene glycols, polyvinyl alcohol, celloidin and other nitrocelluloses, and for electron microscopy, methyl and butyl methacrylate resins which are polymerized after infiltration.

FROZEN SECTIONS

The freezing microtome is used for preparation of sections for rapid diagnosis, for the study of fatty and lipid substances which would be lost if paraffin or nitrocellulose methods were employed, and for many metallic impregnation methods.

Place a few drops of water on the object holder of the freezing microtome, lay a 3–5 mm slice of tissue in this water, freeze rapidly until the surface of the tissue appears dry, wait a few seconds, and then try cutting a section at a time at short intervals until satisfactory coherent sections at 10–15 μ are obtained. The sections as cut remain on the edge of the microtome knife. They are conveniently transferred to small dishes of water by first moistening the outer side of the left little finger with water, and then wiping the sections off the knife edge with the moistened area and dipping the finger with sections into the dish of water. The sections float off, first as shreds, when the block is too hard; then as coherent sections which fold freely in the water as they float. When this point is reached, quickly cut a dozen or more sections, removing 3 or 4 at a time to the water. Store sections from each case in an individual small covered dish with a small slip of paper bearing the case number in the water with the sections. The number can be written in pencil; but if prolonged storage is contemplated, write labels with India ink and then dip them in smoking hot paraffin. For prolonged storage use 10% diethylene glycol by preference; otherwise 5–10% formalin. Vials holding 10–15 cc are convenient for this purpose. The India ink label is put inside with the sections.

In selecting sections for staining, complete sections which fold and unfold freely in water are to be chosen. Sections which float rigidly are too thick. For rapid diagnosis such frozen sections may be stained in toluidine blue, thionin, or azure A. Mallory recommended 0.5% thionin or toluidine blue in 20% alcohol for 30–60 seconds. For fixed tissue the addition of 0.5–1% of glacial acetic acid sharpens the stain and makes it more selective for nuclei. Sections may be stained thus by immersion in a small amount of stain in a watchglass, then fished out with a needle after the required time, rinsed in a large container of water and floated onto a slide. Bring the edge of the section on the slanted slide carefully to just above the surface of the water. Tease the remainder of the section half floating in the water into a reasonably flat position, and gradually raise the slide out of the water. If any portion of the section is not flat, dip that side again under the water so as to float it smooth, and again withdraw. Blot dry with hard, smooth filter paper; dehydrate with a few drops of acetone; clear with acetone and xylene, then with xylene; and mount in synthetic resin.

Some prefer first to float sections onto slides as above, then blot them down firmly with hard filter paper, immerse them briefly in 0.5–2% collodion solution in ether and 100% alcohol, drain for 30–60 seconds, and harden in chloroform, 80% alcohol or water before staining. This method is to be preferred if sections are to be heated or treated with alkaline solutions. Such sections may then be handled as are paraffin or attached nitrocellulose or celloidin sections (pp. 76, 79).

Sections stained for demonstration of fats with oil soluble dyes (pp. 454–461) are to be floated out on slides and blotted flat as above, but all dehydrating agents or fat solvents are to be avoided. Instead, mount directly in a gum arabic, gelatin glycerol, syrup or other aqueous mounting medium; or temporarily in pure glycerol, water or other indifferent fluid (pp. 99–106). Gelatin media require melting before use and may be very tenacious of air bubbles. They may be degassed by placing the bottle in a vacuum paraffin oven and turning on vacuum to about 350–400 mm mercury (15 in.). Care must be taken not to boil the gelatin solution. Water boils at about 124 mm at 55°C, 149 at 60°C. These pressures correspond to 636 mm = 25.2 in. and 611 mm = 23.9 in. on the usual vacuum gauge. Gum arabic (acacia) media are fluid at room temperatures of 25–15°C and most of them dry hard. Fructose syrup will dry hard if the humidity is not too high, but, like Arlex gelatin, will remain sticky for some time in hot, humid weather. Such syrup mounts may be sealed by painting the edges of the coverglasses with a polystyrene or other resin solution; cellulose caprate is excellent.

Adamstone-Taylor Cold Knife Technic for Frozen Sections

In this procedure (*Stain Tech.* 23:109, 1948) fresh tissue is quickly frozen in slices of 2 mm thickness or less, either on the freezing block of the microtome, or by immersion in liquid nitrogen or in isopentane chilled with liquid nitrogen or in petroleum ether containing chunks of solid carbon dioxide. By using one of the latter procedures a number of blocks may be quickly frozen and then stored in Dry Ice at −75°C or in a deep freeze compartment at −25°C until sectioning becomes convenient. Since the essence of the technic is the avoidance of thawing until sections are finally attached to slides, it is necessary to chill the knife of the microtome by fastening to it on each side of the cutting area blocks of solid carbon dioxide. Use Scotch tape or thin strips of sheet metal cut from scrap copper or tin plate.

When the knife is chilled, the tissue blocks are placed on the freezing head and frozen to the block. As the sections are cut, a small camel's hair brush is used to hold them flat as they come onto the knife blade. Then Adamstone and Taylor used a small, hollow scoop containing dry ice chips to transfer the flat sections to slides, and pressed them down. As the sections soften, but before complete melting, they must be immersed in the chosen fixative. If the objective is microincineration for demonstration of soluble salts, quick heating to coagulate tissue protein would seem preferable to exposure to the solvent action of any liquid fixative.

The authors warn that the procedure is much more difficult in a warm or humid atmosphere. The whole process might be much easier (though less comfortable to the operator) if it could be carried out in a refrigerator room at a temperature somewhat below 0°C.

For this purpose the use of a cryostat (p. 25) is suggested. In this type of apparatus the sections can be kept for a time in the frozen state, without the necessity of immediate processing required by the open air cold knife method

Use of the cold knife procedure on formalin fixed tissue may permit preparation of thinner and more coherent sections of such tissues as heart muscle.

IMBEDDING METHODS

The other commonly used sectioning methods require infiltration with imbedding masses. Of these the polyvinyl alcohol, Carbowax, gelatin, agar and soap masses are soluble in water, and tissue may be infiltrated directly. Nitrocellulose is soluble in a mixture of 100% alcohol and ether, paraffin in various fat solvents; and tissues must first be freed of water (dehydration) and brought into the appropriate solvent before infiltration.

Feder's Polyvinyl Alcohol Imbedding (*J. Histochem.* 7:292, 1959; **10:** 341, 1962), **as modified by Wachstein.** Dissolve 200 gm polyvinyl alcohol in 600 cc water, add 200 gm glycerol and boil 30 minutes. Fix tissue in suitable aqueous fixative, block, wash well in water and transfer directly to the polyvinyl alcohol mixture. Infiltrate at 25°C using 3 graded water mixtures of, say, 1:2, 2:1 and undiluted, of 24 hours each. Imbed in small waxed paper containers and harden at icebox temperature (0–5°C) for enzyme studies (about 3–5 weeks), at room temperature for other purposes. Perhaps a week will be required at 25°C; at 37°C 3 days might suffice. Shrinkage is considerable in Feder's original method, in which free evaporation was permitted. This should be minimized in Wachstein's 5°C variant.

Enzymes and lipids, including birefringent lipids, are said to be well preserved.

At 25°C and 0–30% humidity (use desiccator with P_2O_5 if necessary) the mass dries to a firm, tough, transparent block which is cemented to wooden or metal block carriers and sectioned on a rotary microtome at 1–100 μ.

Feder prescribes Gelvatol-130, procurable from the Shawinigan Corp., Springfield, Massachusetts. I have had completely unsuccessful results with another brand.

Carbowax. Polyethylene Glycols. These water soluble waxes conserve many lipids well. Mellors (*J. Nat. Cancer Inst.* **10:**1331, 1950) stated that glycols and polyethylene glycols did not dissolve neutral fats but that they did have considerable solvent activity on aromatic compounds such as steroids, especially those of the adrenal cortex. Pearse (1960, p. 65), however, states that cholesterol and cholesterol esters are insoluble

---

[1] *Imbed, embed:* The latter term is a hybrid Franco-Saxon word and is not used in this text.

both in aqueous solutions and in melted polyethylene glycols. While Carbowax imbedding has been considerably used in the study of tissue lipids, specific statements as to the amount of birefringent lipid in Carbowax sections and in control sections are scarce. Wade (*Stain Techn.* **27**:71, 1952) specifically notes good preservation of the acid fast material in lepra bacilli. Infiltration can be done directly from water or, more rapidly, on frozen dried material (Hack, Blank, *J. Nat. Cancer Inst.* **12**: 225, 1951). Sections can be cut on the usual paraffin microtome and are said to ribbon better at humidities below 60% and temperatures under 20°C (Pearse, 1960, p. 774), but Zugibe *et al.* (*J. Histochem.* **6**:133, 1958) put the limits at 75% and 27°C, and reported satisfactory ribboning at 6 μ routinely and as low as 2 μ. Cutting consistency is improved by preheating Carbowax 4000 to 175°C for about 30 seconds (Firminger, *J. Nat. Cancer Inst.* **10**:1350, 1950).

The practice of first infiltrating with a low molecular weight, relatively low melting Carbowax, followed by a second infiltration with the final imbedding medium seems as futile to me as the practice of infiltrating first with a low melting "soft" paraffin, and then with the final higher melting harder paraffin for sectioning. Blank's suggestion of infiltrating at a lower temperature in an aqueous solution, followed by *in vacuo* desiccation, to avoid thermal destruction of enzymes seems eminently sensible.

Most writers infiltrate tissues directly from water in the polyethylene glycol. Blank and McCarthy (*J. Lab. Clin. Med.* **36**:776, 1950) used 9:1 Carbowax 4000: Carbowax 1500 at 55–60°C, allowing 80 minutes for blocks 2 mm thick, and longer in proportion for thicker blocks. Even 4 days' exposure was said to produce little distortion. Firminger (*loc. cit.*) preferred pure Carbowax 4000 for Washington, D.C., summer use (30–36°C). McLane (*Stain Techn.* **26**:63, 1951) infiltrated at about 52°C in Carbowax 4000 (M.P. 50°C) and claimed preservation of tetrazolium dehydrogenase activity in plant tissue. However, we have reported inactivation or extraction of M-Nadi oxidase and verdoperoxidase by glycols and melted Carbowax (*J. Histochem.* **1**:8, 1953). Pearse (*loc. cit.*) records considerable diffusion of alkaline phosphatases, less of acid phosphatase and peroxidase. Wade used a 15:85 mixture of Carbowaxes 1540 and 4000 and infiltrated 6 hours, using 2 changes. Hack's practice of freeze drying followed by Carbowax infiltration has been adopted by Zugibe *et al.* (1958) for fresh frozen material. He also dehydrated formalin fixed tissue in graded Carbowax 1000 solutions (30%, 50%, 70%, 95% and pure Carbowax) at 1 hour each, ending with 2 hours in 100% Carbowax at 47°C. Pearse's directions are similar: place 3–4 mm blocks of formalin fixed tissue in 70% polyethylene glycol 1000, M.P. *ca.* 40°C (?), for 30 minutes, in 90% for 45 minutes and in 100% for 1 hour, stirring at intervals. Imbed in wax paper cups, chilling to 4°C. Cut on rotary microtome at 4–6 μ, float sections on 40% diethylene glycol, 10% formalin and 50% water mixture, pick up on gelatin coated slides and dry at 37°C for 10 minutes. Room temperatures are presumed to be 15–20°C. For laboratory temperatures of 20–25°C a harder wax would be preferred, say a mixture of Carbowax 1000 and 1500; at 25–30°C mix Carbowax 1500 and 4000; above 30°C use Carbowax 4000.

Since Carbowax sections dissolve instantly in water with violent diffusion currents, various other flotation liquids have been proposed. Metallic mercury is not suitable because of the scum of oxide particles, Carbowax and probably albumen which forms on the mercury. Also, particles of metallic mercury adhere to the sections (Firminger, personal communication). Wade (*loc. cit.*) used 5 mg/100 cc Turgitol 7 in distilled water; Blank and McCarthy (*J. Lab. Clin. Med.* **36**:776, 1950) used 0.02% each of gelatin and potassium bichromate, boiled together in daylight for 5 minutes.

Zugibe *et al.* (*J. Histochem.* **7**:101, 1959) make a stock gelatin dichromate mixture at 0.2% each, boil, cool and filter. For use take 10 cc stock mixture, 4 cc glycerol, 4 cc formalin, 1 gm cetyltrimethylammonium bromide and distilled water to make 100 cc. This solution is cleared by heating to 30°C. Sections are floated on this, picked up on slides and dried at 42°C.

Giovacchini (*Stain Techn.* **33**:248, 1958) similarly smears slides with a gelatin glycerol adhesive, places dry Carbowax sections on them and exposes them in a horizontal position to a temperature of 58–60°C for 15 minutes. The mounted sections are then dried at 58–60°C for 24 hours and are said to adhere well in routine oil red O hemalum stains. This gelatin solution is made by dissolving 15 gm gelatin in 55 cc warm water, then adding 50 cc glycerol and 0.5 gm phenol.

Gelatin. Zwemer (*Anat. Rec.* **57**:41, 1933) recommends washing tissues 4 hours or more in water, followed by 24 hours' infiltration at 37°C in 5% gelatin and 12–16 hours further in 10% gelatin. The tissues are then oriented and imbedded in 10% gelatin which is allowed to harden by cooling at 0–5°C.

Blocks may then be sectioned by the freezing method and mounted before staining. The gelatin may be removed with warm water. This avoids gelatin staining artifacts which can be disturbing, especially with connective tissue stains. We have found this method useful for the sectioning of atheromatous small arteries, such as coronaries. I am indebted to Mrs. Margaret Giglioni for notes on this procedure. She infiltrates directly in 10% gelatin, sections in the cryostat at 5–7 μ, collects sections directly on slides and dries them for some hours at 20–25°C so that the sections will adhere well. Then gelatin is rinsed off with warm water (35–40°C) and slides are dried at 52°C before staining.

Usually it is preferable to harden the gelatin first by a day or more of fixation in 10% formalin. Zwemer prescribed several hours. Blocks may be sectioned on the freezing microtome or may be dehydrated and imbedded in paraffin.

The advantage of the method lies in making coherent sections of friable or fragmented tissues. Such material as uterine curettings may thus be handled as a single block. The disadvantage is that the gelatin stains rather strongly with basic aniline dyes and the stained mass may be confusing. I have found the method helpful, on occasion, in outlining individual cells in masses that were otherwise apparently syncytial in nature.

Baker (*Quart. J. Micr. Sci.* **85**:1, 1944) infiltrated in 25% gelatin at 37°C for 20–24 hours. Ordinarily he then cooled, blocked and hardened the sections in his calcium cadmium formalin (p. 38). If thin sections were required, he infiltrated instead for 30 hours in an open container over anhydrous calcium chloride in a vacuum desiccator at 37°C. Concentration was stopped best just before the gelatin sol set to a gel. The solution was then cooled, blocked and hardened as before.

In both instances sections were cut on the freezing microtome. With the vacuum concentration technic, 5 μ sections were prepared by this author.

Nicolas (*Bibliogr. Anat.*, Paris, 1896, p. 274) practically perfected the gelatin infiltration method for preparing frozen sections of eyes. Oakley (*J. Path. Bact.* **44**:365, 1937) fixed first for 4 days in 10% formalin saline (p. 37). He recommended postchroming in Müller's fluid (p. 54) for 6 weeks in the incubator (37°C), or in Perdrau's fluid ($K_2Cr_2O_7$ 5, CrF_3 2.5, water 100), or in Perdrau's fluid half strength for 4 days at room temperature. Large eyes are then windowed before being washed for 24 hours. After washing them, cut the eyes in half and infiltrate them at 37°C overnight in 12.5% gelatin and in 25% gelatin for 24 hours. Use gelatin not more than twice, and add 1% phenol to prevent mold growth. Imbed cut surface down in 25% gelatin, and harden by cooling to not below 0°C. Trim the blocks and harden them 2–3 days in 10% formalin. Wash them for 15 minutes in water before sectioning. Sections of 5–10 μ are claimed for this method. Since the gelatin tolerates dehydration poorly, sections should be mounted in glycerol gelatin.

Agar. I have occasionally infiltrated tissues from water in melted 2% agar at 55–60°C for 2–4 hours. This mass becomes quite stiff on cooling and may be cut on the freezing microtome. Its value is for holding exudates and friable tissues in place. I have used it for the study of fat content of loose pulmonary alveolar exudates. It does not stain appreciably with the usual dyes. The method is not suitable when specific carbohydrate stains are to be used.

Friedland (*Am. J. Clin. Path.* **21**:797, 1951) accelerates this procedure by transferring tissues previously fixed briefly in boiling formalin to melted agar, and boiling gently for 1 minute. The agar infiltrated tissue is then sectioned on the freezing microtome. This variant is recommended for friable and partially necrotic tissues, to improve coherence.

Paraffin. In order to infiltrate tissues with paraffin it is necessary to displace from them the aqueous or alcoholic fixing fluids, or the water or alcohol used to wash these out, and to replace with a fluid miscible with paraffin. This is usually accomplished by diffusion of the contained fluid out of the tissue block into a surrounding bath of another fluid, which in turn diffuses into and replaces the original fluid content.

Since most water miscible fluids are not paraffin solvents, it is usually necessary to dehydrate first with a water miscible fluid, and then to replace the dehydrating agent with a paraffin solvent which is at the same time miscible with the dehydrating agent used.

One fluid—1,4-diethylene dioxide or dioxane—is freely miscible with water on the one hand and with melted paraffin on the other. Lee (10th ed.) warns against the cumulative toxicity of this compound and speaks of a lack of warning odor. Actually there is a distinctive odor, but this is no longer noticed after a short time. This text recommends the interposition of a bath of equal volumes of dioxane and paraffin at 56°C after dehydration. Mallory recommended the schedule of Graupner and Weisberger, which included successively 3 changes of dioxane and 3 of melted paraffin.

The greatest disadvantage of dioxane is the very low tolerance of its mixtures with paraffin solvents or with paraffin for small amounts of water (Table 4-1). A slight excess of water carried into the dioxane-paraffin bath will occasion stratification with a lower dioxane-water layer and an upper dioxane-paraffin layer. To combat this water intolerance Tannenberg (*Am. J. Clin. Path.* 19:1061, 1949) adopted an automatic siphonage chamber into which dioxane drips at a fairly rapid rate (3.75 liters/hour) and which drains down to a level just above the specimens by means of a siphon as often as the fluid level rises to the top of the siphon tube, 2–3 cm above the tissue. Adequate dehydration of blocks 2 mm thick in 2 hours is claimed, and of curettings in 1 hour. The used dioxane is again dehydrated with anhydrous $CaCl_2$ or CaO for 18–22 hours before it is used again. The reuse of the dioxane is required because of its high initial cost (currently about 3–4 times that of tax free 100% alcohol) and the large volume used in this procedure.

Tannenberg then transferred tissues directly to melted paraffin (2 changes of 30–60 minutes each). He suggested further shortening of the total time required by use of vacuum infiltration (pp. 72–74). The boiling point of 1,4-dioxane is 101.1°C, and its volatilization at reduced pressure would be much slower than that of some of the more volatile solvents.

The traditional dehydrating agent is ethyl alcohol. It is usual to transfer tissues from water into 70% alcohol, thence to 80% or 85%, then to 95% and to 100% (absolute) alcohol. Two changes daily may be made, ending with at least 2 or 3 changes covering 2–4 hours in 100% alcohol. Some workers omit the first step and start directly with 80% alcohol.

For cytologic work and for dehydration of embryos, eyes and other large or delicate objects, longer intervals in each grade of alcohol and a greater number of gradations are used, and it is advisable to start with alcohol as low as 50% or 60%.

By use of continued mechanical agitation and multiple changes of each grade of alcohol, and by cutting thin blocks for imbedding, the intervals may be cut down to 2 or 3 hours in each grade of alcohol.

TABLE 4-1. PERCENTAGE OF ADDED WATER REQUIRED TO RENDER TURBID EQUAL-VOLUME MIXTURES OF DEHYDRATING AND CLEARING AGENTS

Dehydrant	Ben-zene	Xylene	Chloro-form	Carbon tetra-chloride	Petro-leum ether B	100-octane gasoline	Methyl sali-cylate
Methanol, absolute...	6.5–7	3–3.5	17.5–18	4.5–5	1	immisc.	6.25
Ethanol, absolute.....	12–14	7–8	13–14	10–11	4.5	3.5–4	13.25
Isopropanol, 99%.....	9.5–10	10	7–7.5	7.5–8.5	11–11.5	8.5–9	17
Acetone, technical....	1.75–3	1.5–2	2–2.2	1.5–1.6	0.5–1	1.5–1.6	4.75
1,4-Dioxane, pure.....	1.5–2	1–1.5	1.5–2	1–1.5	1.5	1–1.5	3.75

Isopropyl alcohol, 99%, is probably the best all-round substitute for ethyl alcohol, and is now procurable at a modest price ($3.70 per gallon, 1965) even when compared with tax free ethyl alcohol. The tolerance of its mixtures with various paraffin solvents for small amounts of water at least equals on the average that of corresponding ethyl alcohol mixtures (Table 4-1). As seen in the same table the tolerance of corresponding acetone and dioxane mixtures for water is low, that of methanol mixtures is intermediate.

According to Hauser (*Mikroskopie* 7:208, 1952), tissues may be infiltrated in paraffin directly from isopropanol or from a warm (50°C) mixture of paraffin and isopropanol.

Nevertheless, in spite of its avidity for atmospheric water vapor and the low tolerance of its fat solvent mixtures for water, acetone is often a very effective dehydrating agent when rapidity of action is desirable. It can be obtained for $1.76 per gallon (1965) in technical grade. No fewer than 4 changes of acetone of 40 minutes each should be used as a matter of routine. Of these only the fourth need be fresh acetone. For the third change use the acetone which has previously been used once for the last change, for the second use that previously used twice, and for the first that used for 3 previous changes. The acetone used 4 times can be saved for cleaning paint brushes or for redistillation, or it may be discarded.

Even this process may be expedited by using 4 changes of fresh acetone for 20 minutes each.

Following dehydration with alcohol or acetone, blocks should be transferred to a paraffin solvent which is miscible with the dehydrating agent. An intermediate bath composed of equal parts of the dehydrating agent and of the paraffin solvent or even 2 such baths, the first of a 2:1, the second of a 1:2 mixture, are to be recommended, particularly when working in very humid atmospheres.

Paraffin Solvents. The best paraffin solvents are benzene, toluene, xylene, petroleum ether, carbon bisulfide, chloroform, carbon tetrachloride and cedar oil. All these agents are miscible with paraffin at 56°C. The disagreeable odor and the toxicity of the fumes of carbon bisulfide usually operate to exclude it as a paraffin solvent, although it is said to give excellent results (Lee).

As far as I can determine on direct comparison of blocks of the same tissues, chloroform (B.P. 61°C, vapor pressure 160–248 mm at 20–30°C) has no definite superiority over the far cheaper and probably less toxic carbon tetrachloride (B.P. 77°C, vapor pressure 91–143 mm at 20–30°C). (The lethal dose of carbon tetrachloride is perhaps double that of chloroform in mice.)

Benzene, although its fumes are more toxic, seems at least as good as its more expensive and less volatile homologs toluene and xylene, on the same basis of direct comparison.

For many years I used with great satisfaction a high test gasoline, designated *white gas* or *aviation gasoline, lead free,* which is essentially a petroleum ether. (Caution: lead tetraethyl is dangerously toxic.)

From the data in Table 4-1, methyl salicylate would seem to have very interesting possibilities as a clearing agent with a relatively high tolerance for water. Its odor is powerful, but it should be useful when anhydrous alcohol is unavailable.

Of the fluids cited, cedar oil, gasoline and petroleum ethers occasion the least hardening of tissues. Overnight immersion in gasoline and petroleum ether does not render tissues brittle. Chloroform and xylene appear to make tissues more brittle, but this does not interfere especially with sectioning. Thin cedar oil is an excellent dealcoholization or clearing agent and is highly recommended for such objects as human skin, uterus, thick masses of smooth muscle and tendon and the like, since it appears to improve their consistency for cutting. It requires multiple changes of paraffin to remove it from the tissue. I usually prefer to interpose 2 or 3 baths of 20–40 minutes each in gasoline, xylene or benzene. Tissues may be left in cedar oil for months without harm. After use for clearing for some time, cedar oil may be restored by filtering and then heating to 60°C *in vacuo* for 30–60 minutes to remove alcohol, acetone and water.

Occasionally, after use for clearing of material fixed in acetic alcohol fixatives, cedar oil may crystallize into a firm mass melting at around 35°C. A small quantity of this altered oil will cause a whole bottleful to crystallize. Heating to 200°C restores the normal behavior of the oil.

Popham (*Stain Techn.* **25**:112, 1950) recommends, instead of heating, the addition of a little (1:80) xylene to reliquefy the altered cedar oil.

Except for cedar oil, I recommend at least 2 changes of the paraffin solvent between the dehydration and the paraffin infiltration.

The use of saturated solutions of paraffin in the solvent has been recommended as an intermediate step between clearing and paraffin infiltration. It is unnecessary for routine work, and I have not used it for years. It may be necessary, however, for such difficult objects as parasitic worms, fleas and ticks, on account of their chitinous exoskeletons.

Paraffin Infiltration. This is done in an oven regulated to a temperature a few degrees above the melting point of the paraffin used. Ordinarily paraffin is quite satisfactory as obtained from the refiners. It may be obtained in approximately 5 kg blocks directly from the refiners in lots of 8 blocks at a materially lower cost than when bought in pound blocks from biological supply houses.

Ribboning consistency is sometimes improved by addition of 10% or 20% beeswax or by addition of 3–5% Halowax. Soft, or 52°C, paraffin will dissolve 15% by weight (but not 20%) of this Halowax (M.P. 115–125°C) with a resultant *fall* of the congelation point to about 50.5°C, and quite pronounced hardening of the paraffin. Paraffins of even lower melting point (40–42°C) are available, and may be similarly hardened. Beeswax makes the mixture more sticky than pure paraffin so that sections stick together better.

Paraffins recommended for sectioning range in melting point from 45 to over 60°C. For our laboratory conditions I find 45°C and 50°C paraffin too soft. Some workers recommend a mixture of 50°C and 55°C paraffin, and some prescribe infiltration first by a soft, then by a hard paraffin. To my mind this practice simply prolongs the heating period unnecessarily. For ordinary work I found a paraffin of 55–56°C melting point satisfactory with laboratory temperature ranging from about 22°C in winter to 30–35°C in summer.

The usual practice is to use 3 or 4 changes of melted paraffin of 30–60 minutes each, in order to infiltrate tissue thoroughly and rid it of traces of the solvent which might unduly soften the paraffin within the tissue.

Such prolonged heating inevitably shrinks tissues to a considerable ex-

TABLE 4-2. SCHEDULES[1] FOR DEHYDRATION, CLEARING AND PARAFFIN INFILTRATION

I	II	III	IV	V	VI	VII
Water	Water	Water	Water	Water	Water	Water
70% alcohol 16 hr		Acetone (used 3x) 40 min	Acetone (fresh) 20 min	Acetone (used) 40 min	Alcohols or acetones as before	Dioxane 1 hr
85% alcohol 8 hr	80% alcohol 16–24 hr	Acetone (used 2x) 40 min	Acetone (fresh) 20 min	Acetone (used) 40 min		Dioxane 1 hr
95% alcohol 16 hr	95% alcohol 16–24 hr	Acetone (used 1x) 40 min	Acetone (fresh) 20 min	Acetone (used) 40 min		Dioxane 1 hr
100% alcohol 2 hr	100% alcohol 1 hr	Acetone (fresh) 40 min	Acetone (fresh) 20 min	Acetone (fresh) 40 min		
	100% alcohol 1 hr					
100% alcohol + benzene[2] āā, 1 hr		Acetone + benzene āā 40 min		Acetone + benzene āā 40 min	Cedar oil 16 hr	
Benzene 30 min	Benzene 30 min	Benzene 40 min	Benzene 20 min	Benzene 30 min	Benzene 30 min	
Benzene 30 min	Benzene 30 min	Benzene 40 min	Benzene 20 min	Benzene 30 min	Benzene 30 min	
				Benzene 30 min		
				Benzene 30 min		

Paraffin (55°) 30 min OR	Paraffin (55°C) in vacuo at 25 mm mercury 15 min	Dioxane + paraffin āā, 1 hr
Paraffin 30 min		Paraffin 15 min
Paraffin 30 min		Paraffin 45 min
Paraffin 30 min		Paraffin 2 hr

———————————————— IMBED ————————————————

[1] Schedules I and III are routine alcohol and acetone schedules; II and IV are accelerated schedules; V is a special schedule for very fatty tissues; VI is a cedar oil schedule for skin, muscle, uterus and other difficult objects; and VII is a dioxane schedule.

Labels written on paper with India ink and dipped in smoking hot paraffin should be carried through the solvents with the tissue and finally attached to the paraffin block.

[2] Other paraffin solvents, such as carbon tetrachloride, gasoline, petroleum ether, chloroform, toluene and the like may be substituted for benzene.

tent. For some 15 years I used a vacuum chamber within the oven for infiltration *in vacuo*. With the use of a volatile solvent, 10–30 minutes' infiltration at an absolute pressure of 25 mm mercury is adequate, and pressures as high as 175–200 mm can be used (= −585 to −560 mm or 23–22 in. of vacuum). Vacuum infiltration furthermore removes air and gases from cavities within the tissues, notably the pulmonary alveoli, and permits their filling with paraffin.

Dr. Peers used a 3-day Technicon schedule for whole human brain stems (Table 4-3, p. 74, schedule H); also for cerebellum, large blocks of cerebral cortex, whole hemispheres of dog, cat and monkey brains and the like. Blocks are cut transversely about 6 mm thick after fixation in 10% formalin for some days or even weeks. They are then hardened for 3 days in 2.5% aqueous potassium bichromate solution and washed 6 hours in running water. On the Technicon they then pass through twelve 6-hour baths for dehydration, clearing and paraffin infiltration. Sections are floated out on 70% alcohol warmed to 40–45°C, dipped out on large slides, immediately blotted down with hard, smooth filter paper and then dried 1–18 hours at 40–45°C.

I have included also in Table 4-3 Technicon schedules for fresh and formalin fixed surgical tissues (A, B, C, D) and for autopsy tissues (E, F, G). Schedules E, F and G are designed to use the same time disk and solutions. Tissues fixed in chromate fixatives (including Zenker variants) are started at step 1 on the schedule; mercuric chloride tissues, which are normally transferred directly to 70% or 80% alcohol, start at step 3; and tissues fixed in acetic alcohol fluids, such as Carnoy, acetic alcohol formalin, etc., start at step 5. The calcium carbonate in the 95% alcohol of step 5 is intended to neutralize acetic acid which is carried over from the fixing fluid.

Latterly I have preferred to complete the dehydration, clearing and paraffin infiltration by hand when fixation has been done in either of the Carnoy fluids or in methanol chloroform mixtures. From the Carnoy fluid pass thin tissue blocks into equal volumes of ethanol and chloroform for 30–60 minutes and thence to two 30–60 minute changes of chloroform. Tissues from the second (1:1) methanol chloroform are cleared directly in the 2 changes of chloroform.

In working with Zenker variants it is necessary to use plastic capsules for tissue and to have the metal parts completely protected by first coating them with smoking hot paraffin. It is probably best to put tissues into the Technicon only after the fixation period is completed.

Incomplete dehydration is a common cause of the shrinkage and hardening of tissues within paraffin blocks after they have been cut from and put away. It is to be avoided by the use of sufficient changes of pure dehydrating agent to dehydrate the tissues completely before clearing and paraffin infiltration.

TABLE 4-3. TECHNICON SCHEDULES FOR FIXATION, DEHYDRATION AND PARAFFIN INFILTRATION

	Surgical schedules				Autopsy tissue schedules			Peers's brain schedule: formalin 4 days, chromate 3 days, wash 6 hr
Fast schedule	Fresh tissues			Prefixed tissues	48 hr formalin chromate fixatives	24 hr sublimate formalin fixatives	24 hr alcohol acetic fixatives	
	Alcoholic formalin	Zenker's fluid						
A	B	C	D	E	F	G	H
1. Alcoholic formalin 15 min	Alcoholic formalin 6 hr	Zenker's fluid 8 hr	80 % alc. 2 hr	Water 2 hr			80 % alc. 6 hr
2. 95 % alc. 15 min	95 % alc. 1 hr	Water 2 hr	80 % alc. 1 hr	Water 2 hr			80 % alc. 6 hr
3. 99 % alc. 15 min	95 % alc. 1 hr	Water 2 hr	95 % alc. 1 hr	80 % alc. 2 hr	80 % alc. 2 hr		95 % alc. 6 hr
4. Acetone 15 min	95 % alc. 1 hr	80 % alc. 0.5 % I_2 1 hr	95 % alc. 1 hr	80 % alc. 16 hr	80 % alc. 16 hr		95 % alc. 6 hr
5. Acetone 15 min	95 % alc. 1 hr	95 % alc. 0.5 % I_2 1 hr	100 % alc. 1 hr	95 % alc. $CaCO_3$ 1 hr	95 % alc. $CaCO_3$ 1 hr	95 % alc. $CaCO_3$ 1 hr	100 % alc. 6 hr
6. Acetone 15 min	95 % alc. 1 hr	91 % alc. 1 hr	100 % alc. 1 hr	95 % alc. 1 hr	95 % alc. 1 hr	95 % alc. 1 hr	100 % alc. 6 hr
7. Chloroform 15 min	95 % alc. 1 hr	91 % alc. 1 hr	Acetone + xylene $\overline{aa}$ 1 hr	95 % alc. 2 hr	95 % alc. 2 hr	95 % alc. 2 hr	Acetone + xylene $\overline{aa}$ 6 hr
8. Chloroform 15 min	99 % alc. + xylene $\overline{aa}$ 1 hr	Methyl salicylate 1 hr	Xylene 2 hr	100 % alc. 2 hr	100 % alc. 2 hr	100 % alc. 2 hr	Xylene 6 hr
9. Paraffin 15 min	Xylene 1 hr	Xylene 1 hr	Cedar oil 2 hr	100 % alc. 2 hr	100 % alc. 2 hr	100 % alc. 2 hr	Cedar oil 6 hr
10. Paraffin 15 min	Xylene 1 hr	Xylene 1 hr	Xylene 2 hr	Cedar oil 16 hr	Cedar oil 16 hr	Cedar oil 16 hr	Xylene 6 hr
11. Paraffin 15 min	Paraffin 1½ hr	Paraffin 1½ hr	Paraffin 2 hr	Gasoline 1 hr	Gasoline 1 hr	Gasoline 1 hr	Paraffin 6 hr
12. Paraffin 15 min	Paraffin 1½ hr	Paraffin 1½ hr	Paraffin 2 hr	Gasoline 1 hr	Gasoline 1 hr	Gasoline 1 hr	Paraffin 6 hr
Time 3 hr IMBED	Time 18 hr IMBED	22 hr IMBED	18 hr IMBED	48 hr	44 hr	26 hr	72 br IMBED
				PARAFFIN *IN VACUO* 15–30 MIN			
				IMBED	IMBED	IMBED	

Imbedding. During the process of imbedding, the tissue blocks must be oriented so that sections will be cut in the desired plane. Generally it is convenient to place the surface of the block from which sections are desired next to and parallel to the bottom of the imbedding container.

A convenient imbedding container may be made from a 5 x 7.5 cm (2 x 3 in.) oblong of fairly heavy (2–3 mm thick) sheet metal and two L shaped cross sections of angle iron about 2–3 cm high. Angle iron may be obtained in various sizes from 3 to 5 or more cm arm length, and cut with a hacksaw into desired lengths. The 2 L shaped pieces are laid on the metal plate so as to enclose a rectangular or square space. This is then partly filled with paraffin, and the tissue is placed in it in the desired position and pressed firmly against the bottom. The container is then filled with melted paraffin and allowed to cool until a coherent film forms on the surface. It should then be chilled rapidly in cold or preferably ice water. Rapid cooling gives smaller crystal size to the imbedding mass and improves cutting consistency, as well as decreasing permeability to water and air. The metal blocks are removed by dropping them sharply on the table, when the three metal pieces and the paraffin block usually separate cleanly.

Trimming of Blocks and Preparation for Sectioning. The upper curved surface which is to form the back of the block is then trimmed off flat with a fairly stout knife. The 4 sides are then cut down square to within 1 or 2 mm of the edge of the tissue block on the cutting surface and sloping outwardly toward the back, so as to form a truncated pyramid. When ribbons are to be cut it is convenient to cut narrow triangular wedges from the 4 corners of the block, so that in the ribbon formed by the coherent sections V shaped notches are present on both sides between the individual sections. When the block is trimmed the number should be affixed to one side with a hot spatula.

Special blocking and trimming procedure for cross sections of multiple small tubular structures. When it is desired to prepare cross sections of a number of small tubular structures in a definite arrangement in the final section, the following special procedure may be of value. It can be used to arrange in proper sequence several levels of small animal intestine or several small arteries and veins.

On collecting the material, place each block successively in the desired order on an ordinary straight pin. For example, with guinea pig intestine we first place on the pin 2 levels of duodenum, starting from the pyloric end, then 2 or 3 levels of jejunum and 2 or 3 of ileum so spaced as to represent the whole extent of the small intestine. We have often placed 7-8 segments of intestine 1-2 cm in length on a single pin. The pin is left in place throughout the dehydration, clearing and paraffin or celloidin paraffin infiltration procedures. When the imbedding stage is reached lay the combined block flat in the bottom of a metal plate L-block assembly which has been partly filled with paraffin. So place the row of intestinal segments so that the end from which the first sections are to be cut abuts against one end of the imbedding mold and the head of the pin which still holds them together abuts against one of the sides. Press down firmly and chill the block.

When trimming, the original bottom of the block forms the face which will first strike the microtome knife and the end against which the extremities of the intestinal segments abut is the surface from which sections are to be cut. On trimming the two sides the head of the pin is uncovered and the pin pulled out with a slight twisting motion, using forceps if necessary. The original upper surface of the poured block is the side away from the knife in cutting and is trimmed to come fairly close to the intestines at the cutting surface and sloped away to form a broad base at the other extremity of the block which is to be attached as usual to a metal block carrier.

If animals are starved or fed on soft cooked food, free of cellulose and lignin, for 24 hours before killing, the material should section readily. Calcified small blood vessels should be decalcified.

For attachment to the microtome it is necessary to fasten the paraffin blocks to wooden or fiber blocks or to metal object holders. The last are the most convenient, as they may simply be heated to above the melting point of paraffin and then pressed firmly against the back of the paraffin block. The block and object holder are then immersed in cold water. The object holder should be hot enough to melt its way 1–2 mm into the back of the block, but not further.

For attachment to wooden or fiber blocks, melt the back surface of the block with a hot metal spatula, press it immediately against the wood or fiber and immerse at once in cold water.

Sectioning. The wooden or fiber block or metal object holder is then inserted into the object carrier of the microtome and clamped firmly in place. The object carrier is then oriented so that the surface of the block is parallel to the knife edge. While adjusting the microtome, its motion should be locked to avoid accidental cuts either to the specimen or to the hands of the operator.

One then cuts off paraffin in rather thick sections by operating the microtome in the usual manner, until the tissue is reached. It may be necessary to readjust the orientation of the block at this point, so as to obtain complete sections in the desired plane.

Sections may then be removed individually by a small dampened scalpel; or by holding the end section with the same implement at a slight tension, a number of sections may be cut in series so as to form a ribbon. This is necessary when serial sections are required. Convenient lengths of ribbon are transferred to a smooth board or cardboard surface and cut into segments of the desired number of sections with a sharp knife. They adhere to the cardboard along the line of cut and are loosened from it by passing the edge of the knife obliquely along the line of adhesion. Sections are then lifted singly or in strips onto the surface of a pan of water heated to about 38°C, or onto water on a 25 × 75 mm glass slide which is then warmed on a metal plate. In preparation of serial sections, a number of rows of sections may thus be arranged in proper order on a single slide. The warming causes the wrinkles in the section to flatten out, and the whole section or ribbon segment elongates during the process. Persistent wrinkles or rolls may be flattened out by stretching the section with a pair of small knives or needles. From the pan the sections are then floated onto clean glass slides and removed from the water; one edge of the section is held in place with a needle or knife. If the sections are floated on slides, the excess water is drained off to one side, the section being held in place as before. When preparing serial sections of several rows to a slide, it is well to place a length of blank paraffin ribbon at each margin, so that sections will not lie under the edge of the coverglass when stained.

It is preferable to use fresh distilled water for floating out sections. If rapid drying is required one may use 30% or even 95% ethyl alcohol instead.

Many workers prefer to spread a minimal quantity of Mayer's albumen glycerol fixative on the surface of the slide before floating the section onto it. A very small drop is placed on one end of the slide, the previously thoroughly cleansed ball of the little finger is used to spread it over the whole surface of the slide, and any excess is then wiped off on the hypothenar portion (little finger side) of the palm of the hand.

Traditionally (Ehrlich's *Encyklopädie*) Mayer's albumen glycerol is made by thoroughly mixing 1 volume of the whites of perfectly fresh eggs with an equal volume of pure glycerol. The mixture is then filtered through absorbent cotton or relatively coarse filter paper at 55–58°C (paraffin oven temperature). A small lump of thymol or camphor is added to prevent growth of molds.

We (*Stain Techn.* **20**:99, 1945) have successfully substituted a 5% solution of dried egg white made by shaking gently at intervals for 1 day in 0.5% sodium chloride solution. Avoid frothing when shaking, and filter on a Buchner funnel with vacuum. At least 90–95% of the solution should be recovered as a clear filtrate. To 50 cc of this filtrate add 50 cc glycerol and 0.5 cc 1:10,000 Merthiolate (sodium ethylmercurithiosalicylate).

Since 2 or 3 cc distilled water is used to float out a section on a slide thinly coated with this fixative, and the constituents of the fixative are readily soluble in water, it is difficult to imagine that any of the "fixative" remains on the slide to fasten a section to it. It seems probable instead that it functions as a surface tension depressant, and thereby secures closer capillary adhesion of the section to the slide.

Priman (*Stain Techn.* **29**:105, 1954) recommends diluted mammalian blood serum (15 cc + 5 cc distilled water + 6 cc 5% formalin; filter through filter paper) and states that the material spreads well, does not stain and is superior to egg albumen fixatives in adhesiveness. Although blood plasma in vessels often colors red with periodic acid Schiff technics, it is probable that a thin film of a diluted serum would have too low a density to occasion an appreciable staining artifact.

Ordinarily such paraffin sections are dried overnight before deparaffinizing and staining. With the aid of gentle heat and an air current they may often be dried sufficiently for staining in an hour or so. By using dilute alcohol for floating the sections onto the slides, and heat for drying, I have stained sections without undue losses in 30 minutes.

Some workers routinely dry at paraffin oven temperature or even at 65°C in the open. Smith (*Stain Techn.* **37**:339, 1962) warns against this procedure, noting considerable interstitial shrinkage of cells as a result of it, as well as diminished staining with specific connective tissue stains. I consider it probable that drying at 5–10°C above the melting point of the paraffin tends to permeate all structures thoroughly with melted paraffin, thereby rendering it more difficult to remove, enhancing the frequency of Nedzel's paraffin artifacts (p. 84) and preventing the use of procedures employing undeparaffinized sections for staining. The practice of floating on 30–80% alcohol for spreading and smoothing of sections also accelerates drying and can be carried out successfully at room temperatures of 20–30°C.

Hard paraffin is more apt to curl when sections are cut than soft; but soft paraffin permits more lateral compression of tissues along the path of the knife. Paraffin blocks may be made harder for cutting by preliminary immersion in ice water, and it may be advisable to chill the microtome knife as well. An electric light bulb near the object carrier of the microtome tends to make the blocks softer.

Sometimes during ribbon sectioning the ribbon acquires a charge of static electricity which causes it to move about violently and to adhere to various adjacent objects. Breathing on the ribbon and block surface may remedy this difficulty.

Tissues containing much blood or yolk (and certain other substances, including bone and cartilage) are apt to be brittle and to shatter under the microtome knife instead of yielding coherent sections. Painting the surface of the block before cutting each section with a 0.5% solution of collodion in absolute alcohol and ether or acetone will prevent their crumbling. The sections smooth out better if floated on 80% alcohol, but if the collodion film is thin enough this is often not necessary.

Lendrum (*Stain Tech.* **19**:143, 1944) recommends that when tough and hard tissues fail to give satisfactory paraffin sections, the paraffin block be soaked face down in a mixture of 9 parts glycerol and 1 part aniline for 1–3 days. This probably serves best with incompletely dehydrated tissues, as it seems to make little difference when care has been taken to dehydrate completely before paraffin infiltration.

After sectioning from a paraffin block I have found it good practice to dip the cut surface briefly into rather hot (70–80°C) paraffin before putting it away. This helps to prevent drying out and shrinkage of perhaps imperfectly dehydrated tissues. With adequate dehydration this practice should not be necessary, but it takes little time and also helps protect tissue from roaches. I have seen unprotected tissue completely eaten out of the paraffin blocks.

Paraffin blocks should be stored in a reasonably cool place. I have found small pasteboard boxes containing the blocks of one or more consecutive cases convenient. These are packed consecutively, standing on end, in drawers of slightly greater depth than the greatest diameter of the boxes, with the exposed end bearing the case number. The drawer bears the first and last case numbers on its exposed end.

Ester Wax. Steedman's ester wax (*Quart. J. Micr. Sci.* 88:123, 1947) has been considerably modified to improve flattening and adherence of sections (*Quart. J. Micr. Sci.* 101:459, 1960); a variant that permits sectioning at room temperatures up to 37°C is called *tropical ester wax* (*ibid.* 101:463, 1960). These are formulated as follows:

	Ester wax 1960, gm	Tropical ester wax, gm
Diethylene glycol distearate	60	60
Glyceryl monostearate	30	30
300-Polyethylene glycol distearate	10	
Triethylene glycol monostearate		10
Total	100	100

Both preparations are obtainable from British Drug Houses, Poole, Dorset, England.

Ester wax, 1960, melts at about 48°C. About 4 hours is required for infiltration; this time may be reduced by stirring. Sections are cut at 17–27°C. The knife bevel angle should be about 25°. Sections are flattened on water, either on the slide or in a pan at 45–50°C.

Infiltration may be done from 2-ethoxyethanol (cellosolve), *n*-butanol, ethanol or xylene, but dewaxing of sections is done with xylene.

With tropical ester wax infiltration is done at about 50°C, and sectioning may be performed at room temperatures of 17–37°C. If blocks and microtome are prechilled, sectioning can be done at even higher temperatures.

Both waxes tend to flocculate when kept liquid for some days at 48–50°C, but they may be cleared by heating to 70–80°C. After this reheating they may again be kept at normal infiltration temperatures for similar periods.

Celloidin and Low Viscosity Nitrocellulose Imbedding. The lower viscosity of low viscosity nitrocellulose permits more rapid infiltration with solutions of higher concentration. Consequently, harder blocks may be obtained in less time and thinner sections can be cut.

In pathology this method is utilized principally for eyes and for the study of bones and their surrounding tissues *in situ*, and when it is essential to avoid shrinkage and the creation of artificial spaces. For such tissues a rather slow dehydration and a gradual infiltration are required.

The following schedule can be recommended for eyes.

1. After 10% formalin fixation for at least 48 hours.
2. Dehydrate the eye with successive 24 hour baths of 35%, 50%, 65%, 80% alcohol.
3. Open the eye by cutting off the upper and lower portions of the posterior chamber with 2 cuts passing horizontally respectively through the upper and lower margin of the anterior chamber, and including the nerve head and the fovea centralis between them.
4. Return it to 80% alcohol for 3–4 hours.
5. Then give it a 24 hour bath in 95% alcohol.
6. Then 24 hours in 2 changes of 100% alcohol.
7. A 6 hour bath in equal volumes of 100% alcohol and ether.
8. Infiltrate 5–7 days in 10% nitrocellulose in 100% alcohol and ether, and a similar period in 20% nitrocellulose, in a tightly stoppered container.
9. Imbed in a fairly deep, cylindrical glass dish in which the 20% nitrocellulose, sufficient to cover the eye, reaches about halfway up the side. Place under a bell jar and examine daily.
10. When the surface is solid and the deeper portion still somewhat soft, flood with chloroform and let stand 16–24 hours.
11. Pour off the chloroform and let dry until the solid nitrocellulose block can easily be dislodged from the dish. Trim the block into octagonal form, leaving 1–2 mm of nitrocellulose on all sides. Dip the back surface of the block into 20% nitrocellulose and mount it on a fiber or wooden block with a scored or incised surface. Fasten an identifying number to the side of the block with a little 20% nitrocellulose.
12. Let dry a few minutes and return the mounted block to chloroform for several hours.
13. Transfer through successive 24 hour baths of 3:1 and 1:1 chloroform and cedar oil mixtures to pure cedar oil. Keep in cedar oil at least 1 day before cutting.
14. Drain, and fasten the fiber or wooden block in the object clamp of the celloidin microtome. Cut sections and store them in 80% alcohol.

The technic for decalcified bone is similar. Sections have been cut as thin as 5 μ by this technic. Ordinarily 10 μ sections will serve.

After susa fixation for 12 hours, transfer eyes directly to 95% alcohol. Treat with iodine until the alcohol is no longer decolorized by adding tincture drop by drop with constant agitation. Let the brown solution stand 30 minutes. Wash out the excess iodine with 3 or 4 changes of 95% alcohol. Let stand overnight in 95% alcohol. Open the eye as described above. Complete dehydration, infiltration and imbedding are as above.

When sectioning is completed, cut the nitrocellulose or celloidin blocks off the fiber or wooden block and store them in cedar oil or mineral oil. The latter is cheaper and does not dry or evaporate.

Chesterman and Leach (*Quart. J. Micr. Sci.* **90**:431, 1949) used 3 baths of low viscosity nitrocellulose, at 5%, 10% and 20% in ether alcohol mixture, allowing 3–5, 1–2 and 1–5 days respectively. They then imbedded in a solution of 140 gm "industrial nitrocellulose damped with 7:3 butyl alcohol. HX.30/50," in 210 cc 100% alcohol and 250 cc ether, adding 5 cc tricresyl phosphate as a plasticizer to prevent cracking and separation from the tissue blocks. This solution is designated "20%." Apparently the nitrocellulose contains 98 gm (or 70%) of the principal ingredient; and the 20% is by weight of the final mixture. Blocks are allowed to set in a loosely closed space for 1–3 days until a moderately stiff but still flexible gel is formed. They are then hardened for 1–3 days in 2 or more changes of 70% alcohol. Such blocks become hard and may be cut dry on a celloidin or paraffin microtome. Sections of 15 μ from half a cat brain, or 5–7 μ from blocks 5 mm square are reported.

Rapid Nitrocellulose Imbedding. Koneff and Lyons (*Stain Techn.* **12**:57, 1937) recommend the following rapid schedule for low viscosity nitrocellulose imbedding. I have not tried this method.

1. Fix 1 hour at 56°C or 2–5 hours at 37°C in neutral 10% formaldehyde (formalin?), Bouin, susa or Carnoy II (which last is a chloroform formula, probably formula 2, p. 42, but not here more colsely defined). Use screw capped bottles.
2. Wash in several 1-hour changes of distilled water, except Carnoy material, which is extracted 2 hours at 56°C in 3–5 changes of 100% alcohol, and then transferred directly to step 4.
3. Dehydrate in two 30-minute changes each of 70%, 80%, 95% and 100% alcohol at 56°C. Use iodized 70% alcohol for the first step if fixation was in susa.
4. 100% alcohol and ether 1 hour at 56°C.
5. Infiltrate 1 hour at 56°C in 10 gm low viscosity nitrocellulose dissolved in 50 cc 100% alcohol and 50 cc ether.
6. Infiltrate overnight in 25 gm nitrocellulose in 45 cc 100% alcohol and 55 cc ether.
7. Infiltrate 2–3 hours at 56°C in 50 gm low viscosity nitrocellulose in 40 cc 100% alcohol and 60 cc ether.
8. Imbed on a fiber block in 50% nitrocellulose as usual.
9. Harden the blocks 1 hour in 2 changes of chloroform.
10. Transfer to 80% alcohol, 3 changes, 20 minutes each.
11. Section the blocks while wet with 80% alcohol, and store blocks and sections in the same.

I suggest the cedar oil procedure (given on p. 80) from "Imbed" on as an alternative, since this method appears to give thinner sections than sectioning from alcohol.

For squirrel and lizard eyes, Wall (*Stain Techn.* **13**:69, 1938) recommends fixation by immersion in Kolmer's fluid for 24 hours, followed by successive 6 to 18 hour baths in water, 35%, 50%, 70% and 95% alcohols and infiltration by a hot nitrocellulose process (p. 81). For demonstration of the ellipsoids particularly, Heidenhain's iron hematoxylin and phloxine are recommended.

For thinner sections of retina, Wall recommends removal of the lens before imbedding. In any case it is necessary to cut a window through the sclera with a sharp razor blade before nitrocellulose infiltration.

Nitrocellulose and Paraffin Imbedding. For difficult and fragile objects a combined celloidin or low viscosity nitrocellulose infiltration and paraffin infiltration and imbedding process has been recommended. One infiltrates with the nitrocellulose as usual, clears with chloroform and cedar oil as above, and carries the blocks thence through 2 changes of benzene or chloroform into paraffin as usual.

I have used this process with a variable degree of success. The sections do not flatten well when floated on water, and are likely to curl and separate from the slides. They flatten better if floated on clean slides with 95% alcohol. This softens but does not dissolve the nitrocellulose. If sections still curl, it may be necessary to soften them with ether vapor, blot down with filter paper and soak in 0.5–1% collodion before deparaffinizing. In any case deparaffinize the section and simultaneously harden the nitrocellulose in chloroform, transferring thence directly to 95% alcohol.

For sectioning bones without decalcification, Arnold (*Science* 114:178, 1951) dehydrates in acetone and infiltrates in a mixture of 55 gm air dried $\frac{1}{2}$ sec nitrocellulose, 45 gm diamyl or dibutyl phthalate and 65 to 100 gm anhydrous acetone for several days. The acetone dehydrated tissues are placed in a separatory funnel and the air is evacuated down to 10 mm mercury with a vacuum pump attached to the upper end of the funnel. The lower end is then immersed in the nitrocellulose solution and the stopcock is opened slowly to allow the nitrocellulose to enter and cover the specimens. When 5 or 10 times the volume of the tissue has entered, the vacuum line is opened and the pressure is allowed to rise to atmospheric pressure. Tissues are then transferred to closed containers and infiltration is continued at 58°C under 3 atmospheres pressure. (Acetone boils at 56.5°C; infiltration in an ordinary screw capped bottle in the paraffin oven should be adequate to prevent evaporation.) Imbedding is then completed by filling a paper container to 4 or 5 cm height with the nitrocellulose-plastic solution, orienting the specimen in the bottom and allowing evaporation at 20°C to a height of about 1 cm to produce a puttylike consistency. Then cut out the specimen, reorient it and cement it to a regular fiber block with the same solution. Let it dry for a week at 25°C until quite hard. Cut the hard tissues at 5–8 μ, wetting the block and sections in a 1% aqueous Aerosol solution. Use a heavy sliding microtome and a specially hardened knife blade.

Lillie and Henson's Sucrose Formalin and Formalin, Celloidin, Paraffin Procedure (*J. Histochem.* 8:182, 1960). For the preparation of thin serial sections of rodent intestine for the differential study of enterochromaffin and Paneth cell granules I have successfully utilized the following procedures:

1. Fix either directly in calcium acetate formalin or in a similar formula containing 30% sucrose after a prior 30 minute soaking in 30% sucrose at 3°C. Fixation in either formalin solution is done at 3°C for 18–24 hours.
2. Wash 4 hours in running water to remove sucrose.
3. Dehydrate over a 48 hour period in 70%, 80%, 95% and 100% alcohol.
4. Infiltrate 16–20 hours in 1% celloidin in equal volumes of absolute alcohol and ether. This step may be prolonged to several days if expedient.
5. Drain briefly on a paper towel or blotter and harden in 2 changes of chloroform, 2 hours each.
6. Infiltrate in paraffin containing 5% beeswax for 2 hours at 60°C and 15 mm mercury pressure.
7. Imbed and section serially at 4 μ.

In this study sections were stained by azure A+ eosin B, ferric ferricyanide, fast garnet GBC salt, the postcoupled benzylidene procedure and a sequence combining the 2 last methods.

Excellent cell structure was shown by this procedure.

Chapter 5

General Staining and Mounting Procedures

DEWAXING AND HYDRATION BEFORE STAINING

After sectioning, the prepared sections must be brought into appropriate solvents for the staining procedure to be used; and when the staining procedure has been completed the sections must then be brought without loss of the desired stain into media suitable for examination and temporary or permanent preservation.

The technics employed for these purposes vary with the method of sectioning and with staining and mounting methods.

Paraffin sections are generally first warmed to just above the melting point of paraffin and then immersed in xylene to dissolve out the paraffin. If immersion in xylene is prolonged for some minutes, heating is unnecessary. A second change of xylene is necessary to prevent carrying paraffin into succeeding reagents. The xylene is then removed from the sections in 2 successive changes of 100% alcohol. They turn white at this point. Two changes each of 95% and 80% alcohol follow. These reagents should be changed at intervals; the second change of each may be moved over so as to form the first change, and fresh reagents then replace the second changes.

Paraffin Artifacts. Nedzel's observations (*Quart. J. Micr. Sci.* **92**:343, 1951) indicate that the usual practice of immersing unheated sections in cold xylene may be inadequate to remove paraffin from sections. Birefringent crystals with the same melting point as the paraffin employed may often be found in cell nuclei. These may be stained with oil red O heated to above the melting point of the paraffin. These birefringent crystals are more apt to persist after brief acetone dehydration than after alcohol xylene sequences. The use of hot xylene at either the deparaffinization or the clearing stage, or the practice of melting the paraffin before immersion in xylene, will tend to eliminate these artifacts; and heating of sections mounted in resins to 60 or 65°C will cause most of them to disappear permanently.

Collodionization. *Torn or ragged sections,* or those which tend to become detached from the slides during staining or metallic impregnation procedures, may be attached more securely to the slides by immersion in

0.5–1% ether alcohol solution of collodion for 5 or more minutes. This step is inserted immediately after the 100% alcohol step. After soaking them in collodion, drain the sections for about 1 minute and then harden for 5 minutes or as much longer as is convenient in 80% alcohol. When it is also necessary to iodize the sections for removal of mercury precipitates, it is advantageous to combine the hardening of the collodion with the iodine treatment by using a 0.5% solution of iodine in 80% (or 70%) alcohol for both purposes. It may be necessary to prolong staining intervals to as much as double the time usual in technics not devised for collodionized paraffin or attached celloidin and nitrocellulose sections. This procedure, like celloidin imbedding, tends to diminish shrinkage and creation of artificial spaces during staining. Before acetylation or benzoylation procedures which employ pyridine as the solvent, or methylation in absolute methanol mixtures, collodionization is futile. Pyridine and methanol both dissolve collodion. If later portions of the procedure require collodionization, wash the sections with 100% alcohol after the pyridine or methanol and then collodionize as usual.

Collodion films prevent the access of enzymes to their substrates in the sections. Therefore, if the procedure is necessary for later parts of the technic, dehydrate and collodionize after the completion of digestion.

Undeparaffinized Sections. Goetsch, Reynolds and Bunting (*Proc. Soc. Exp. Biol. Med.* **80**:71, 1952) report successful staining of undeparaffinized paraffin sections by direct 18 hour immersions in aqueous or alcoholic 3% eosin solutions, Van Gieson's stain, 2% aniline blue, 0.25% light green, 0.05% toluidine blue, 2% methylene blue, 0.5% methyl green or Bullard's hematoxylin.

Less cytologic distortion than in deparaffinized sections is claimed for this method. After staining, the sections are washed in water or alcohol to remove the excess; they are then dried, deparaffinized and mounted. The paraffin, unlike collodion, does not prevent access of amylases to glycogen. (But see p. 497.)

In using undeparaffinized sections for staining, avoid heating to near or above the melting point of the paraffin. Even momentary melting forms a virtually impenetrable film. Ordinary staining procedures may require 6–12 times as long as in deparaffinized sections; enzyme digestions, 30–60 times as long.

Iodizing and Hydration. When material fixed with mercury or lead salts is being handled, substitute a 5 minute bath in 0.5% iodine in 80% alcohol for the usual second 80% alcohol step. The usual prescription calls for 0.3–0.5% in 70–95% alcohol. Mallory used 0.5% in 95% alcohol. After the iodine, rinse the material in water and immerse it for a few seconds in 5% sodium thiosulfate ($Na_2S_2O_3 \cdot 5H_2O$). Mallory used a 5 minute bath in 0.5% solution. Then wash 5 minutes in running water.

However, when the following technic contains an iodine step, as in the Gram and Gram-Weigert methods, preliminary iodization may be omitted on mercury fixed material.

With material fixed in nonmercurial fixatives the foregoing steps are omitted and the sections are transferred either directly to the staining solution (if this is in a hydroalcoholic solvent) or to water. However, if both types of fixations—mercurial and nonmercurial—are included in the material being stained, the iodine thiosulfate procedure seems to be harmless to the latter in most instances.

Postmordanting. Often one desires to use some special staining method for which the author has prescribed a fixation method other than that used on the tissue in question. Although in many instances the methods will work quite as well after other fixations than that prescribed, it is still often desirable to have the prescribed fixation or to be able to modify the tissues by some pretreatment in lieu of the prescribed fixation.

In lieu of Bouin or Zenker fixations for Masson trichrome methods, I have found that mordanting for 2 minutes in a saturated (6–8%) alcoholic picric acid solution in place of Bouin's fluid (cf. pp. 391–392, 544), or with saturated aqueous mercuric chloride solution for 5 minutes in place of Zenker's fluid, will serve (Stain Techn. **15**:17, 1940).

Peers (Arch. Path. **32**:446, 1941) reported that 3 hours' mordanting in saturated aqueous mercuric chloride solution at 58°C was required for formalin fixed material in place of the primary Zenker fixation prescribed by Mallory for his phosphotungstic acid hematoxylin stain. Earle, however, was able to stain successfully after fixation in buffered neutral formalin (personal communication).

I have long used a 48 hour mordanting of brain tissue in 2.5% potassium bichromate after primary formalin fixation, before dehydration and imbedding, in lieu of a primary Orth fixation, to prevent pericellular shrinkage during imbedding. This procedure does not preserve the characteristic staining of chromaffin in the adrenal.

In place of primary fixation in Ramón y Cajal's formalin ammonium-bromide for metallic impregnation methods on brain tissue, Globus (Arch. Neurol. Psychiat. **18**:263, 1927) prescribes soaking frozen sections of old formalin fixed material in a 1:10 dilution of 28% ammonia water for 24 hours. Then rinse rapidly in 2 changes of distilled water and immerse for 2–4 hours in a 1:10 dilution of 40% hydrobromic acid. Then rinse in 2 changes of 1:2000 dilution (Conn and Darrow) of 28% ammonia water and proceed.

Arcadi (Stain Techn. **23**:77, 1948) modifies the foregoing procedure by placing the sections in concentrated (28%) ammonia water and then washing slowly with a 1 mm stream of water for 24 hours, repeating this procedure for a second 24 hour period and ending the ammonia treatment with a 7 minute bath in concentrated ammonia water. From this, the sections are transferred directly to a $\frac{1}{20}$ dilution of 40% hydrobromic acid and incubated at 38°C for 1 hour. This is followed by 4 washes of 4 minutes each in distilled water. Arcadi used this method for preparation of old formalin material of monkey brains for a modified Del Río Hortega-Penfield method for oligodendroglia.

DEHYDRATION

After staining, paraffin sections are usually dehydrated with 2 changes of 95% alcohol followed by 2 of 100% alcohol. Then follows a mixture of equal volumes of 100% alcohol and xylene, followed by 2 changes of xylene. In place of alcohol 2–3 changes of acetone or of 99% isopropyl alcohol may be used, and these are followed by an equal volume mixture of the dehydrating agent and xylene, and then 2 changes of xylene as before. Some workers have used toluene in place of xylene as a clearing agent; but there is more hazard of drying, with more evaporation from the clearing jars; and it is at least no better.

The choice of a dehydrating agent depends on several factors. Alcohol extracts methylene blue and other thiazin dyes from the sections; acetone does not. Isopropyl and, even better, *tert*-butyl alcohol also fail to extract thiazins appreciably. Acetone dissolves collodion films from sections; isopropyl alcohol does not; and ethyl alcohol does partly. Ethyl alcohol aids in the differentiation of certain stains.

MOUNTING

Paraffin Sections Stained with Oil Soluble Dyes. For the demonstration of certain lipid substances which are not lost in the dehydration, clearing, imbedding, deparaffinization and hydration procedures, these sections must be mounted in media which are not fat (and dye) solvents. For this purpose it is sufficient to drain off the excess water and mount in gum syrup, glychrogel, glycerol gelatin or the like.

Mounting in Resinous Media. After sections stained by ordinary methods have been cleared in xylene, they are mounted preferably in some resinous medium. Formerly xylene and chloroform solutions of Canada balsam or gum dammar, thickened cedar oil, euparal and the like were preferred as mounting media. Canada balsam is useful for hematoxylin eosin stains. For aniline blue and acid fuchsin connective tissue stains Curtis (*Arch. Méd. Exp. Anat. Path.* **17**:603, 1905) first prescribed acidifying with salicylic acid. A quantity of xylene balsam of thin syrupy consistency is saturated with salicylic acid crystals, filtered through filter paper and mixed with an equal quantity of xylene balsam. The use of the fully saturated solution as a mounting medium is apt to produce visible crystals in the preparations. All the above resins are unsatisfactory for

Romanovsky stains, causing progressive fading of the blue component. The best medium for preservation of these stains is heavy mineral oil, but preparations must be sealed with a gelatin or pyroxylin cement and they inevitably leak. However, preparations so mounted, though messy, were readily cleaned, and showed good stain preservation after 20 years. Langeron suggests Apáthy's gum syrup as a cement.

Actual *mounting* of resin and gum syrup mounts is accomplished in this wise. Select coverglasses of appropriate size to cover the section. We use 22×22, 22×32 and 22×44 mm sizes. Deposit in the center of a square cover a moderate sized drop of thin syrupy xylene resin or gum syrup; with long covers, 2 drops. The coverglasses lie flat on a paper towel or blotter on the table. As many as 6 coverglasses may be thus laid out at one time for xylene resin mounts; but with gum syrup mounts of frozen sections, 1 at a time is better. The stained section is taken from xylene or water, as the case may be, drained and placed face down with one long edge of the slide in contact with the blotter adjacent to the edge of the selected coverglass, and with the other edge perhaps 1 cm up from the table. The slide is then gradually rotated downward with the edge in contact with the blotter as an axis until the section comes in contact with the drop of xylene resin or gum syrup. The drop spreads to the edges of the coverglass, picking it up from the table surface. If air bubbles chance to be included under the coverglass, they may be coaxed out by gentle pressure on the coverglass with a needle point, or by slightly raising one edge of the coverglass. Sometimes it is necessary to add more mounting medium. One then blots the 2 lateral edges of the coverglass, holding the slide face down at an angle of about $30°$ to the table top, to remove excess mounting medium. Slides are then laid flat on trays in a warm place to dry.

Do not wipe the edges of the coverglass with a xylene wet pledget of gauze. This often dissolves a little resin and spreads it over the previously clean upper surface of the coverglass. When this dries, it forms an optically uneven, streaky surface, which seriously interferes with microscopy and is difficult to remove.

When cellulose tricaprate dries, any excess is extruded at the edges of the coverglass as small firm beads which can readily be cut off with a small knife or with the thumbnail.

In mounting large sections for topographic study of whole human breasts, cerebral hemispheres, bones, embryos and the like, air spaces are apt to form between the base and covering glasses after mounting has been accomplished with apparent success. The use of thicker resin solutions, warmed to lower the viscosity, is suggested to avoid aspiration of air after mounting. The polystyrenes are unsuitable for this purpose because of their very high viscosity at relatively low solution concentrations. Natural balsam, the relatively neutral ester gums and some of the cycloparaffin and terpene resins are suggested; if warmed somewhat, they can be used at 60–80% concentration in xylene.

Opaque or cloudy areas in mounted stained sections are often due to incomplete dehydration. Microscopic examination reveals numerous fine droplets of water in and above the section. Such areas tend to show severe fading of stains. The remedy is simple. Remove the coverslip, wash off the synthetic resin or balsam with xylene and again dehydrate with the appropriate agent (100% alcohol, acetone or isopropyl alcohol); again clear through the appropriate xylene mixture and 2 or 3 changes of fresh xylene, and remount.

Restaining. If fading has already occurred, it may be necessary to restain. In this case, after soaking off the coverglass in xylene (and it may take several hours to loosen it), pass the section through 100% alcohol and succeeding reagents just as with a fresh section.

The same technic may be employed when only a stained section is available and some other staining procedure is desired than that originally employed. In this case one may need to decolorize the previous stain with acid alcohol; then wash thoroughly with water and proceed with the new technic. Ordinarily sections previously stained with iron hematoxylin are not suitable for the iron reaction with potassium ferrocyanide, since the iron lake reacts.

Where there were 2 sections of the same block on a slide, I have sometimes restained one of them by another method, leaving the other covered by a coverglass during the new staining procedure.

CELLOIDIN SECTIONS

Nitrocellulose sections may be affixed to slides either before or after staining. They are floated out in a vessel of appropriate size onto the surface of clean slides and manipulated on the slanted, partly immersed slide until they lie smooth. They are then blotted firmly with filter paper.

If the section is not already stained, one should tilt an open bottle of ether so that the heavy vapors can be seen descending from the mouth of the bottle onto the surface of the slide. This softens the nitrocellulose so that it adheres firmly to the slide. Or one may dip the slide into 0.5% nitrocellulose in ether alcohol mixture for a few seconds, drain, wipe the back of the slide clean and harden the film by immersing the slide in chloroform for 5–10 minutes. Sections are then carried into successive baths of 95% alcohol, 80% alcohol (0.5% iodine in 70% alcohol 10–15 minutes, 5% sodium thiosulfate 5–10 minutes for mercury fixations only) and water; or directly into stain if this is in a hydroalcoholic solution. After staining, wash free of excess stain as prescribed in the method used.

Loose Nitrocellulose Sections. Some prefer to stain celloidin and nitrocellulose sections before attaching them to slides. This is particularly convenient when large numbers of sections from the same block are to be prepared for class use.

In this case sections are transferred on the slightly curved spatulas known as section lifters, perhaps with the aid of a needle, from the 80% alcohol in which they are stored, through 70% and 50% alcohols and water, or through 0.5% iodine in 70% alcohol if it is necessary to remove mercury precipitates; and thence to sodium thiosulfate solution and to water, or directly into alcoholic staining solutions.

Dehydration and Clearing of Nitrocellulose Sections. After staining, loose sections are dehydrated and cleared by transfer through dishes of the same successive reagents used for attached nitrocellulose sections. Attached sections are handled much as are paraffin sections, and the same technics apply to collodionized paraffin sections.

The more resistant stains may be dehydrated with 95% alcohol, cleared in Weigert's (Ehrlich's *Encyklopädie*) "carbol-xylene" which is a mixture of 1 volume of melted phenol crystals with 3 volumes of xylene, washed in 2 to 4 changes of xylene and mounted as described for paraffin sections in Depex, Permount, balsam or other suitable resin.

Destaining of Nitrocellulose. If the staining of the nitrocellulose with basic aniline dyes is objectionable, it may be removed in 2% alcoholic rosin solution, and dehydration and clearing may be completed as above or by one of the following methods.

Clearing of Sections Stained by Easily Extracted Dyes. For basic aniline dyes which are extracted by his carbol-xylene, Weigert (Ehrlich's *Encyklopädie*) suggested clearing by repeated application of xylene and blotting with filter paper between applications.

Many writers have used various essential oils for clearing, among which the best seems to have been the Cretan origanum oil. Sections stained with basic aniline dyes, especially with azure eosinates, may be dehydrated with 2 or 3 changes of 99% isopropyl or *tert*-butyl alcohol, which do not dissolve nitrocellulose and do not extract the azure either from the section or from the surrounding nitrocellulose; and then passed through a mixture of equal parts of the alcohol and xylene and 2–3 changes of xylene. Or they may be differentiated with a 2% solution of colophonium (pine rosin) in 95% alcohol until the nitrocellulose is colorless, and then dehydrated and cleared by the isopropyl alcohol xylene sequence just described. Or after the rosin alcohol one may blot and flood with xylene alternately for 2 or 3 times until the sections are clear.

FROZEN SECTIONS

Fat Stains. Frozen sections stained for fats are floated out smooth on clean slides. One brings one edge of a section in contact with the partially immersed, obliquely held slide, raises the slide gradually so that the section settles smoothly on the surface of the glass, smoothing out folds by varying the angle of immersion so that the folded portion is floated loose while the rest remains above water on the slide. Needle manipulation may occasionally be necessary, especially with irregular or torn sections. When the section is satisfactorily smoothed out, drain and blot it with smooth, hard filter paper by running the tip of one finger along the slide on top of the paper while one end of the paper and slide are firmly held down with the other thumb. Then mount as described above (p. 87) in a suitable aqueous medium. Glycerol may be used for temporary mounts. These may be sealed by carefully drying the border zone of the slide and coverglass and painting with xylene or toluene balsam or with a pyroxylin cement. With a small drop of glycerol which does not quite reach the edge of the coverglass, edging with polystyrene, as below, should afford a fairly permanent mount.

Polystyrene Edging. To seal sticky glycerol gelatin or Arlex gelatin mounts, I often dip a glass rod in 20% polystyrene in xylene and run it along each edge of the coverglass. It dries to nonstickiness in an hour and can be packed away in direct contact with other slides on the next morning, without fear of the slides sticking together. Xylene–cellulose caprate serves well.

Lanolin rosin was recommended by Romeis as the best of the sealing media for aqueous mounts. Dry 20 gm anhydrous lanolin in a hot porcelain evaporating dish, stirring it for 15 or 20 minutes. Then add, bit by bit, 80 gm rosin, stirring the while until a clear, light brown fluid results. It is best to heat it on a closed electric hot plate to avoid the chance of fire. Pour it out into small molds and let it harden. To use, heat a glass rod or metal spatula quite hot, melt off a few drops from a block of the lanolin rosin and fix the corners of the coverglass in place. Then apply more hot, melted rosin to complete the sealing.

For permanent mounts, media containing gum arabic or gelatin are usually employed. The first dry hard after a time; the second have to be melted for use and they set on cooling. Formulae for several usually successful media are described on p. 101 and tabulated in Table 5–2, p. 103.

RESINOUS MOUNTING MEDIA

These are composed in general of a solid natural or synthetic resin dissolved in a suitable solvent to lower the viscosity to a point where the solution will readily enter tissue interstices, flow between slide and coverglass to fill the space completely and quickly release entrapped air bubbles. The solvent (either that in which a natural resin is dissolved as it comes from its source or a suitable added solvent, usually an aromatic hydrocarbon; but sometimes an alcohol or a chlorinated hydrocarbon) must be sufficiently volatile to allow fairly prompt drying of the resin to a hard state, and at the same time not so volatile as to dry prematurely during mounting.

It has been observed that highly volatile solvents, such as benzene and to a less extent toluene, are likely to produce air spaces under cover-glasses because of their excessive evaporation. This fault may be assigned also to low concentration of resin in the solvent. However, higher boiling solvents, such as xylene (B.P. 138–144°C), trimethylbenzene (B.P. 165–176°C) and diethylbenzene (B.P. 181–184°C) are less likely to give rise to air bubbles. Indeed, trimethylbenzene solution mounts remain liquid internally for a long time.

The rate of drying and the tendency of some mounting media to aspirate air into the mounting space have importance in relation to the conditions of study. Prompt drying to nonstickiness and to nondisplace-ability of coverglasses is of great importance to the surgical pathologist; the late aspiration of air bubbles poses problems only if it is necessary to refer back to the same section. On the other hand, with 50–100 μ sections and with mounts of membranes, eggs and small embryos, time is of less consequence, and it becomes highly important that air should not enter the preparations.

The refractive indices of mounting media have been much discussed by microscopists, some of whom strongly advocate media with low indices, whereas others insist on high. Without going into theoretical optics, the practical effect seems to be that in media of refractive indices ranging from 1.44 to 1.50 much detail is apparent microscopically, even in un-stained and uncolored objects, by reason of the difference in average refractive index of tissues (1.530–1.540) from that of these mounting media. As the index of refraction of the mounting medium approaches that of the tissue, the latter becomes more and more transparent, and unstained objects may be extremely difficult or quite impossible to discern. I have seen partly faded Nissl preparations in which one had great difficulty in even finding the section, either grossly or microscopically. When the critical range (about 1.535) is passed, unstained objects again become evident by reason of their now lower refractive index, and media with refractive indices above 1.60 may be quite useful.

Much stress has been laid by some writers, notably Groat, on the refractive index of the dry resin as opposed to that of the solution used for mounting. Groat agrees with me (personal correspondence, 1950) that both indices are important. Obviously the refractive index of a resin solution will lie between that of the solvent and that of the dry resin; and as the solvent evaporates, the refractive index of the medium surrounding the specimen gradually approaches that of the dry resin.

It appears from the foregoing discussion that no single mounting medium will serve all purposes equally well. For this reason data regarding refractive indices of mounting solutions and of dry resins are presented in Table 5–1 (p. 98).

Natural Resins

Balsams are deep amber or yellow resins composed to a considerable extent of terpenes and their carboxylic acids such as abietic acid (pine rosin) and levopimaric acid (French fir), both of which are said to contain 2 carbon double bonds (Karrer).

Canada balsam is derived from the liquid rosin of the Canadian fir *Abies balsamea*. Its acid number ranges from 88–106; its saponification number, from 105–116 (Lange). When prepared by heating with water until the evolution of steam ceases, it solidifies to a clear yellow, hard, brittle resin which is freely soluble in xylene, toluene, benzene, chloroform, etc. Xylene solutions of 60–65% by weight of the hard resin correspond in consistency to the syrupy solutions commonly recommended. The resin sets slowly and takes many months to dry hard enough so that slides will not stick together if warmed to summer room temperatures.

Hematoxylin and eosin stains are well preserved in Canada balsam, though there is a gradual differentiation of the eosin so that after a year or two muscle, connective tissue fibers, cytoplasms and oxyphil inclusion bodies present a considerably greater difference in intensity of staining than was evident when the preparations were fresh. I have found renal intranuclear inclusion bodies much more conspicuous in such aged preparations than by most other methods. Canada balsam is superior to many of the synthetic media for preservation of the cobalt sulfide deposits in alkaline phosphatase preparations. Basic aniline dyes are poorly preserved, and Prussian blue fades fairly soon. Acid fuchsin in Van Gieson stains fades, but this fading may be retarded by half saturating the balsam with salicylic acid (p. 87). This procedure I have modified from Curtis (*Arch. Méd. Exp. Anat. Path.* **17**:603, 1905). Its rationale is obscure.

Natural syrupy Oregon fir balsam possesses a refractive index of 1.5271. On being heated to 200°C it does not boil, but with an air stream it loses about 18% of its weight and solidifies on cooling. Its refractive index then reads 1.5407.

This resin sets slowly and takes months to dry hard. It fades basic aniline dyes, bleaches Prussian blue promptly and conserves cobalt sulfide well. Thus its properties are closely similar to those of the usual xylene solutions of Canada balsam.

Dammar is a common resin used in the varnish and lacquer industries, derived from various East Indian trees of the genus *Shorea*. It softens at 75°C and melts at 100°C. Its acid and saponification numbers are 35 and 39 respectively (Lange), and it contains unsaturated compounds (iodine number 64–112). It dissolves in aromatic hydrocarbons, chloroform, ether and the like. It is commonly used as a xylene solution of about 60–75% resin content by weight.

Since dammar is often dirty, and its 60–75% solutions are practically impossible to filter because of their viscosity, the usual practice is to dissolve it in a much larger volume of benzene or xylene, filter and then evaporate down to the required viscosity or to the predetermined weight of solution. Evaporation of xylene is greatly expedited by passing a fairly rapid air stream over the surface of the solution while heating it on a closed electric hot plate under a chemical hood. The xylene may be recovered by use of a condenser.

Rosin or **colophony,** obtained from various pines, is composed largely of abietic acid. It is a dark brown, brittle resin with a melting point of 120–135°C. Its acid number is 155–175; saponification number, 167–194; iodine number, 80–220. This rosin is sometimes used as a 1% alcoholic solution for acid differentiation of azure stains, occasionally as the xylene solution for mounting, but most often as a constituent of varnishes and cements.

Cedar oil when used as a mounting medium is usually concentrated to the point where its refractive index has risen from the initial 1.503 to about 1.5150. On being heated in an oil bath, the native solvent boils off at 168–187°C, and the oil loses about 52% of its initial weight as the thin cedar oil for clearing. The refractive index of the residual resin is 1.5262, and the resin is solid at room temperatures.

Cedar oil mounts set slowly and take months to dry hard. Basic aniline dyes fade gradually. Wolbach used this action to differentiate his Giemsa stain for rickettsiae (p. 583). Prussian blue fades completely in this medium, but cobalt sulfide is well preserved.

Semisynthetic Mixtures

Euparal is composed of gum sandarac dissolved in a mixture of eucalyptol and paraldehyde with a liquid mixture of camphor and phenyl salicylate of unstated proportions and a refractive index of 1.53576, according to Gilson (*Cellule* 23:425, 1906). Gum sandarac contains 85% sandaracolic acid and 10% callitrolic acid. Its acid number is 140–154; saponification number, 142–174; iodine number, 66–160 (Lange). These characteristics of acidity and unsaturation place this mixture in the same general group as the natural resins. The carbonyl group of the paraldehyde offers a possible additional reducing agent.

The refractive index of Euparal is usually given as 1.483. At 20°C we got 1.4776. On concentration in partial vacuum at 60°C it rose to 1.5174, and the resin solidified on cooling. Romeis states that the solid resin has a refractive index of 1.535.

Euparal sometimes causes discoloration and fading of hematoxylin stains (Lee). The green or *vert* variant contains a small amount of a copper salt to prevent this action. Basic aniline dyes and Romanovsky stains are fairly well preserved, though not so well as in some synthetic resins. Prussian blue is reduced and bleaches. Cobalt sulfide is well preserved.

Diaphane is composed of a juniper gum base with certain natural and synthetic phenols, according to its manufacturers, the Will Corporation. No formula has been published. The refractive index of Diaphane and of green Diaphane is quoted as 1.483; at 20°C we found 1.4777 and 1.4792. On concentration *in vacuo* at 60°C, Diaphane lost 59.6% of its original weight and solidified on cooling. Its refractive index was 1.5486.

Like Euparal vert, green Diaphane contains a little copper to intensify and conserve hematoxylin stains. Basic aniline dyes and Romanovsky stains are fairly well preserved, Prussian blue is decolorized, and cobalt sulfide is excellently conserved. Some fading of fuchsin and of acid fuchsin is observed, which I am inclined to attribute to reduction to leuco dyes rather than to acid action.

Ester Gums

Attempts at neutralizing the acid of the natural balsams with small amounts of sodium or calcium carbonate in the cold have been largely futile, since the resins themselves consist largely of carboxylic acids.

Esterification of abietic acid from pine rosin with glycols or glycerol has resulted in the formation of essentially neutral esters, called generally *ester gums* and used widely in the varnish industry. The class of these which has proved most useful in microscopy is the neutral or low acid class, with acid numbers below 8. Clear, amber to light brown resins result, soluble in aromatic hydrocarbons to 70% or 80% by weight at syrupy viscosity.

After mounting in 75% ester gum in xylene, coverglasses become fairly immovable in an hour or 2; but the resin remains rather soft, and slides will stick together if packed back to face, unless dried for some weeks.

Stains with basic aniline dyes and Romanovsky stains are well preserved. Prussian blue is reduced and decolorized. Cobalt sulfide is well preserved. Fuchsin and acid fuchsin tend to decolorize.

Synthetic Resins

Those now in use include styrene polymers (Monsanto's Lustron L 2020 and Lustrex L-15, Zirkle's L-15, Gurr's Depex, Distrene and others); Groat's styrene + isobutyl methacrylate copolymer; synthetic terpene resins, especially β-pinene polymers (Harleco synthetic resin HSR, Fisher's Permount, and the Will Corporation's Bioloid); a coumarone + indene copolymer (Technicon resin), a coumarone mixture with other resins (Gurr's medium), a maleic polymer with plasticizer (Gurr's Xam), the naphthalene or cycloparaffin polymers (Clarite and Clarite X introduced by Groat and now unavailable, and the old Fisher Permount, now replaced by a new β-pinene polymer sold under the same name); and some entirely secret proprietary preparations such as Rhenohistol of the Rheinpreussen Chemical Works, Homberg-Niederrhein, Germany; and Mahady's Micromount. According to the Farbenfabriken Bayer, Leverkusen-Bayerwerk, Germany (letters, 1951) Caedax is a mixture of a chlorinated aromatic hydrocarbon and a cyclohexanone dissolved in xylene. Usual solvents and concentrations by weight, nature of synthetic resins and refractive indices are presented in Table 5-1, p. 98.

Diatom Media. Brief mention is made also of a few media of very high refractive index, such as Hyrax, n∆ 1.82248 (Hanna, *J. Roy. Micr. Soc.* **50**:424, 1930); Flemming's Naphrax, n∆ 1.76 to 1.80 (*J. Roy. Micr. Soc.* **63**:34, 1943); and 2 media of the George T. Gurr Co.; Clearax, a diphenyl resin of 66°C M.P. and n∆ 1.666 (for the solid resin) furnished as a chloroform solution of n∆ 1.602; and Refrax, a naphthalene formaldehyde polymer, similar to Naphrax, of 60°C M.P. and n∆ 1.78 (as solid resin) furnished as a xylene solution containing plasticizer (Flemming used dibutylphthalate in Naphrax, n∆ of solution 1.598. These media are employed particularly by students of diatoms.

General Properties. In general these synthetic resins are quite neutral, and basic aniline dyes are well preserved in them. The chlorinated aromatic hydrocarbon of the usually neutral Caedax may occasionally (in contact with water?) break down and become highly acid, and Mahady's Micromount appears to be acid from the start. Otherwise the resins differ importantly in refractive index (see p. 92 for discussion), in rate of setting and drying to a nonadhesive state and in degree of residual unsaturation. The more unsaturated resins, and the ketonic resins including the natural resins and ester gums, the terpenes and β-pinene resins, the coumarones and coumarone-indene resins, though often quite satisfactory for stains where oxidation-reduction potential is not involved, appear to reduce Prussian blue to the greenish white ferrous ferrocyanide, but they preserve cobalt sulfide preparations relatively well. Conversely, the more oxidized or saturated resins preserve Prussian blue well but allow fading of cobalt sulfide preparations. There are also important differences in solubility in solvents, in viscosity of solutions, in rate of drying and in tendency to form air bubbles in mounts. Plasticizers are added to combat this last tendency, but they tend to retard drying to nonstickiness.

Some fading of the acid fuchsin component of Van Gieson stains is observed with the Bioloid resin, Euparal, Diaphane, and Canada balsam and to a less extent with the Micromount, Xam and the ester gums. There is moderate fading of the azure component of azure eosin stains with Diaphane and Xam; severe fading with Micromount, which bleaches even alum hematoxylin. The eosin component of this stain fades somewhat in Euparal and Bioloid, and occasionally in polystyrenes.

Polystyrene media are usually employed in aromatic hydrocarbon solvents. Their viscosity is too great to permit much over 20–25% concentration of resin. Consequently, they set rapidly but tend to form large air spaces under coverglasses. This tendency is combated either by use of a higher boiling solvent, such as diethylbenzene, trimethylbenzene, p-cymene or a mixture of equal volumes of amyl benzene and xylene; or by addition of orthocresyl phosphate or dibutylphthalate as plasticizers. Excessive amounts of plasticizer must be avoided, as they retard setting and hardening. Addition of 5 cc dibutylphthalate to 70 cc xylene and 25 gm polystyrene seems adequate to prevent air aspiration, and does not greatly retard setting; 10 cc dibutylphthalate and 65 cc xylene did considerably delay setting of the mount.

I strongly recommend 20–25% solutions of Monsanto's Lustron L-2020 in diethylbenzene,[1] trimethylbenzene[1] or a mixture of secondary amylbenzene and xylene in equal volumes. Some workers find the odor of the amylbenzene disagreeable. These fluids are easy to mount in: the coverglasses are immovable in an hour, and the slides may be packed tight together without sticking by the following morning.

Gurr's Depex resin is quite satisfactory. Kirkpatrick and Lendrum's DPX contained 20 gm polystyrene, 15 cc tricresylphosphate and 80 cc xylene. I have had excellent results also with solutions of 5 or 10 cc dibutylphthalate, 70 or 65 cc xylene and 25 gm polystyrene. The lower quantity of plasticizer permits faster setting and is usually adequate to prevent bubbles in thin sections. For thick sections Zirkle uses 20 gm Lustrex 15, 20 cc dimethoxytetraethylene glycol and 60 cc xylene. The medium sets slowly but forms no bubbles even with 50–100 μ sections. Ollet (*J. Path. Bact.* **63**:166, 1951) also recommends Lustron L-2020, of which he dissolves 100 gm in 50 cc dibutylphthalate and 300 cc monochlorobenzene. Xylene is omitted because it "leads to fading of the Gram's stain."

Polystyrenes contain virtually no titratable acid and little or no residual unsaturated material. Consequently they are excellent for conservation of stains with basic aniline dyes, hematoxylin, Van Gieson's stain and Mallory aniline blue variants. The Prussian blue and Turnbull's blue of the Perls, the Tirmann-Schmelzer and the ferric ferricyanide reduction reactions are well preserved. Cobalt sulfide gradually disappears, presumably by oxidation, but may be restored by demounting and reimmersion in ammonium sulfide.

Cellulose caprate, tricaprate, tridecanoate, introduced as a mounting medium in 1955 (*Stain Techn.* **30**:133) is a pale yellow resin of low refractive index (1.4743 when dry), which yields solutions of satisfactory viscosity for mounting at 50 gm resin: 50 gm xylene ($n\Delta$ 1.4860). Adhesion to glass in excellent, coverslips become immovable in an hour and preparations are nonsticky in less than a day. Excess droplets of resin

[1] Obtainable from the Eastman Chemical Company, Rochester, N.Y.

TABLE 5-1. REFRACTIVE INDICES OF RESINOUS MOUNTING MEDIA IN SOLUTION AND DRY

Resin	Class	Solvent and % resin	Refractive index Solution	Refractive index Solid
Canada balsam......	Dried natural resin	Xylene, 60%	1.5232	1.5447 c
Oregon fir balsam....	Liquid natural resin	Turpentines, *ca.* 82%	1.5251	1.5407 o
Gum dammar.......	Dried natural resin	Xylene, 60%	1.5317	1.5589 c
Cedar oil...........	Liquid natural resin	Turpentines, *ca.* 48%	1.5030 1.5151[1]	1.5262 o
Euparal............	Semisynthetic resin mixture	(see text)	1.4776	1.5174 o 1.535 R
Diaphane..........	Semisynthetic resin mixture	(see text)	1.4777 1.4792	1.5486 o g
Ester gum (5 samples)	Glycol resin acid esters	Xylene, 75%	{1.5352 1.5379	1.5516 c 1.5552 c
Harleco HSR........	β-Pinene polymer	Xylene, 60%	1.5202	1.5390 c
Fisher Permount.....	β-Pinene polymer	Toluene, 60%	1.5144	1.5286 c
Willco Bioloid.......	β-Pinene polymer	Xylene, 60%	1.5272	1.5505 c
Technicon Resin.....	Coumarone indene polymer	Benzene + xylene, 60%	1.5649	1.6205 c
Gurr's Medium......	Coumarone resin mixture	Cineol, *ca.* 77%	1.5310	1.5574 o
Gurr's Pale Medium..	....	Cineol, *ca.* 77%	1.5082	1.5296 o
Cellulose caprate.....	Cellulose tricaprate neutral ester	Xylene, 50%	1.4860	1.4734 LH
Gurr's Xam........	Maleic polymer plasticized	Xylene, *ca.* 77%	1.5219	1.5401 o
Clarite.............	Cycloparaffin polymer	Toluene or xylene, 60%	......	1.544 G
Clarite X...........	Cycloparaffin polymer	Xylene, 60%	1.5352	1.5647 c
Fisher's old Permount	Cycloparaffin polymer	Toluene, 62.5% Xylene, 60%	1.5172 1.5170	1.5376 c
Caedax............	Cyclohexanone and chlorinated diphenyl resin	Xylene, 82%	1.6306	1.6724 c
Rhenohistol.........	Ketone + HCHO condensation	Xylene, 60%	1.520	1.533 c
Hyrax..............	Naphthalene resin (secret)	Aromatic hydrocarbon	......	1.8225 H
Naphrax............	Naphthalene HCHO polymer	Xylene + dibutyl phthalate	......	1.76– 1.80 F
Gurr's Clearax.......	Diphenyl resin	Chloroform	1.602	1.666 a
Gurr's Refrax........	Naphthalene HCHO polymer	Xylene + plasticizer	1.598	1.780 a
Gurr's Depex........	Polystyrene	Xylene + plasticizer	1.5228	1.6 a
Mahadey's Micromount	....	Xylene (?), *ca.* 43%	1.4918	1.4839 c
Groat's Copolymer...	Styrene + *iso*butyl methacrylate	Toluene, 45%	1.5193	1.5500 c
Lillie's polystyrene (Monsanto L–2020)	Styrene polymer	Diethylbenzene, 20%	1.5150	1.6193 c

Note: *c*, calculated from solution data; *o*, observed after concentration of commercial solution; *a*, as advertised by manufacturer; *R*, according to Romeis; *H*, according to Hanna (see text); *F*, according to Flemming (see text); *G*, according to Groat (*Anat. Rec.* **74**:1, 1939); [1] immersion oil; *g*, determined by Greco; *LH*, Lillie & Henson, *Stain Techn.* **30**:133, 1955.

which form at edges of coverslips are readily cut off with a knife or thumbnail. Unstained sections remain readily visible, nuclei, cell granules, muscle striations and the like are readily perceived. Azure eosin and routine hematoxylin stains are well preserved. Prussian blue is well preserved; cobalt sulfide bleaches somewhat in a month and completely in 15 weeks. Many histochemical reactions are well preserved.

Chemically it is a neutral ester of a straight chain saturated fatty acid, capric or decanoic acid $C_9H_{19}COOH$, 3 mols per repeating hexose unit of cellulose, and possesses no reducing capacity. I now use this medium for all histochemical work where dehydration and clearing in nonpolar solvents are permissible.

Polyvinyl acetate[1] 20% in 80% alcohol, has been recommended by Burstone (*J. Histochem.* **5**:196, 1957) as a mounting medium in esterase and phosphatase technics where azo dyes are formed by liberated α- and AS-naphthols in the presence of stable diazonium salts. Stains with Schiff reagent, celestine blue, alum and chrome alum hematoxylins and aldehyde fuchsin are well preserved, and cobalt sulfide does not fade. The initial refractive index of the alcoholic solution is very low (1.3865) but is said to rise as the solvents evaporate. Drying to immovability of coverslips occurs in an hour, and preparations are nonsticky in 3–4 hours.

Mineral Oil

This medium is unexcelled for preservation of azure eosin, Van Gieson, and similar stains. I used it for several years before the introduction of Clarite, for mounting azure eosin stains; and sections 20 years old still showed excellent preservation of color. The oil does not dry, however, and preparations sealed with nitrocellulose cements often leaked badly. Nevertheless, stains are well preserved and preparations may be remounted after brief soaking in acetone to dissolve the cement. Refractive indices are low—1.460–1.483—the heavier, more viscous oils possessing the higher indices. Modified mineral oils, sold for immersion oil, may be obtained which possess refractive indices about 1.518–1.520, or nearly that of crown glass. I have used such oils only for temporary mounts; but it is to be noted that Giemsa stained blood films, put away without cleaning after use of such immersion oils, do not exhibit the fading in oil wet areas that is usually seen in films where cedar oil has dried after use.

AQUEOUS MOUNTING MEDIA

Permanent mounting media of this type fall perhaps into 4 general classes: simple syrups, gum arabic media, glycerol gelatins and acid media of the lactophenol type. Of these the last type is used principally in botany and insect histology. They do not in general conserve stains

---

[1] Shawinigan Corp., Springfield, Mass.

well, especially nuclear stains. Abopon,[1] recommended by Lieb (*Am. J. Clin. Path.* **17**:413, 1947) for mounting crystal violet stains of amyloid, is excellent for *this* purpose, and for acetic orcein stains, which are conserved for years (Hrushovetz and Harder, *Stain. Techn.* **37**:307, 1962), who also found it useful for Giemsa stains). However, it promptly bleaches alum hematoxylin stains. Gum arabic and glycerol gelatin media often cause diffusion of basic aniline dyes into the medium ("bleeding"). This bleeding occurs both in acid gum arabic media and in the neutral glycerol gelatins. It is not prevented by addition of small quantities of potassium acetate that suffice to raise the pH to 6.5 or higher. It is prevented by high salt concentrations, even though the medium remains acid. It does not occur in strong sucrose, fructose or D-sorbitol syrups, though the pH of fructose may be as low as 4. Addition of large amounts of these sugars to glycerol gelatin, gelatin or gum arabic media prevents bleeding.

About 20% by weight of potassium acetate or about 60% of one of the sugars suffices to prevent bleeding of crystal violet stains for amyloid.

Refractive indices of permanent aqueous mounting media are generally low (1.41–1.43). The highest levels, 1.49–1.50, are attained with media containing large proportions of sugars, notably fructose and D-sorbitol.

Gum arabic media are generally acid (pH 3.5–4.2). The amount of potassium acetate needed to raise the pH to 6.5 or 7 is more than $\frac{1}{10}$ and less than $\frac{1}{2}$ the weight of gum arabic. Glycerol or sugar, sometimes both, is added to aqueous gum arabic solutions to raise the refractive index or to retard overdrying.

Amann's Viscol was apparently a mixture of phenol, gum arabic and glycerol, according to Dahl (*Stain Techn.* **26**:97, 1951), who gave a substitute formula for Amann's secret preparation. Formulae for gum arabic media are given below.

The commercial prepared media Clearcol[2] and Viscol[3] are quite acid (pH 1.5 and 2.9, respectively), and their refractive indices are low (1.4039 and 1.4167). They set promptly after mounting and are not sticky. Fat stains are well preserved, but crystal violet stains of amyloid bleed badly. The Paragon[4] mountant is less strongly acid (pH 5.6) but affects stains similarly. Its refractive index is 1.4241. Alum hematoxylin counterstains faded in 1 month in Viscol but were fairly well preserved in the other 2 media.

Syrups often serve well as temporary mounting media, but they remain wet, sticky and more or less fluid in moist climates, and they furnish excellent nourishment for molds. Sucrose, glucose, invert sugar, Karo and

[1] Valnor Corp., Brooklyn, N.Y.
[2] H. W. Clark Co., Melrose, Mass.
[3] Drogueries Réunies, Lausanne, Switzerland.
[4] Paragon C. & C. Co., New York, N.Y.

maltose syrups crystallize around and under coverglasses after a time. A fructose syrup available around 1900 (Ehrlich's *Encyklopädie*) did not crystallize and had a refractive index of 1.500. These properties are nearly duplicated by the modern crude sorbitol syrup Arlex. The commercial corn syrup Karo has had some vogue as a temporary mounting medium.

Addition of 10% gelatin to syrups is enough to render them solid at 20–25°C. I have used an Arlex gelatin thus prepared with some success, but it tends to be sticky in hot weather and is probably unsuitable for tropical use.

The glycerol gelatin media (formulae below) require melting for use, but they set firmly in a few days. Their refractive indices are low (1.41–1.42). They are tenacious of air bubbles but can be degassed by exposure to 350–400 mm vacuum while melted in a few minutes.

Formulae

Farrants's Glycerol Gum Arabic. Dissolve 50 gm gum arabic (acacia) in 50 cc warm distilled water. Add 1 gm arsenic trioxide and 50 cc glycerol. The viscosity is rather high. The index of refraction is 1.43600 at 20°C. Addition of 1 gm potassium acetate is recommended if a relatively neutral medium is desired. The As_2O_3 can be replaced by 15 mg merthiolate or 0.1 cc cresol.

Gum Syrup, modified from Apáthy by Lillie and Ashburn (*Arch. Path.* **36**:432, 1943). Dissolve 50 gm acacia (gum arabic) and 50 gm cane sugar in 100 cc distilled water by frequent shaking at 55–60°C. Restore volume with distilled water. Add 15 mg merthiolate (sodium ethylmercurithiosalicylate) or 100 mg thymol as a preservative. Place in vacuum chamber for a few minutes while warm to remove air bubbles. Highman (*Arch. Path.* **41**:559, 1946) adds 50 gm potassium acetate or 10 gm sodium chloride to this formula, to prevent bleeding of crystal violet stains for amyloid.

Dahl's Formula to replace Amann's Viscol (*Stain Techn.* **26**:97, 1951). Dissolve 80 gm gum arabic in 40 gm (32 cc) glycerol and 90 gm water; then add 20 gm phenol.

Various sugars may be added in varying amounts to gum arabic media. Their effect is to raise the refractive index and to diminish the setting quality of the mountant.

Kaiser's Glycerol Gelatin as Modified by Mallory. Soak 40 gm gelatin 2 hours in 210 cc distilled water. Add 250 cc glycerol and 5 cc melted phenol. Heat gently, stirring constantly for 10–15 minutes until the mixture is smooth. Store in refrigerator at 0–5°C and melt as needed. Mallory notes a deleterious effect of the phenol on alum hematoxylin stains. The substitution of 50 mg merthiolate (sodium ethylmercurithiosalicylate) for the phenol is suggested.

Glychrogel (Zwemer, *Anat. Rec.* **57**:41, 1933). Dissolve 0.2 gm chrome alum ($KCr(SO_4)_2 \cdot 12H_2O$) in 30 cc distilled water by heating. Dissolve 3 gm granulated gelatin in 50 cc distilled water by heating. Add 20 cc glycerol to the still warm gelatin solution and mix thoroughly; then add the warm chrome alum solution, mix thoroughly and filter in a 37° incubator. Add a crystal of thymol or camphor as a preservative, or 10 mg merthiolate (sodium ethylmercurithiosalicylate). According to Wotton and Zwemer (*Stain Techn.* **10**:21, 1935), this medium possesses quite a high index of refraction (1.75) after drying a week. This compares with 1.46 for glycerol, 1.47 for glycerin jelly and 1.54 for Canada balsam. On occasion we have had great difficulty with the filtration of this medium, and see no great advantage in it.

Fructose (Levulose) Syrup. This sugar formerly occurred in commerce only as a syrup of about 1.500 refractive index (Ehrlich's *Encyklopädie*), which fact probably accounts for its introduction as a mounting medium. Mallory directs: Dissolve 30 gm fructose (levulose) in 20 cc distilled water by gentle heat.

In my experience this concentration is too low. A 70–75% solution has a more suitable viscosity and a higher refractive index (60% fructose 1.43892, 70% 1.46011, 75% 1.4762, 80% 1.4906 at 20°C).

Fructose syrups do not crystallize in the mounts and when sealed (p. 91) can well serve as permanent mounting media. In dry climates sealing may be unnecessary, since the preparations become quite hard. Fructose is much higher in cost.

Most sugars crystallize badly after a time, spoiling the mounts. A 70% sucrose syrup has suitable viscosity for mounting and a refractive index of 1.46468. It serves well for a temporary mountant but crystallizes in a month or so. The refractive index of 70% glucose is 1.4614; of 80% maltose, 1.4512; of 75% fructose, 1.4762; of white Karo, 1.4799; and of commercial Arlex D-sorbitol syrup, 1.4860. Glucose, invert sugar and maltose syrups crystallize in a month after mounting. Karo is somewhat acid (pH 5.8) and crystallizes after a time with or without addition of 1% potassium acetate. The Karo and maltose syrups set hard, but both crystallize. Arlex D-sorbitol syrup did not crystallize and had the highest refractive index, and it was found that addition of 10% gelatin produced a medium which set well and preserved fat and amyloid stains well.

Arlex Gelatin of Lillie and Greco. Heat 89 gm Arlex D-sorbitol syrup in a boiling water bath, add 10 gm gelatin and stir until dissolved. Add 1 gm potassium acetate and 10 mg merthiolate. The pH is 6.0 or higher, the refractive index is 1.4936. Preparations set promptly but remain sticky for some time (see p. 91), especially in moist climates.

Much of the foregoing material is derived from the reports of the Committee on Mounting Media of the Biological Stain Commission (*Stain Techn.* **25**:1,11, 1950; **28**:57, 1953).

TABLE 5-2. COMPOSITION AND PROPERTIES OF WATER MISCIBLE MOUNTING MEDIA

	Gum arabic, gm	Gelatin, gm	Glycerol, gm	Sugar or syrup, gm	Potassium acetate, gm	Merthiolate, mg	Other ingredients, gm	Water, gm	Refractive index	pH	Bleeding methyl violet
Apáthy gum syrup (LA)	50	...	...	Sucrose 50	...	15	...	100	1.4170	4.1	+
Apáthy gum syrup (H-a)	50	...	...	Sucrose 50	50	15	...	100	1.4266	6.8	-
Apáthy gum syrup (H-b)	50	...	...	Sucrose 50	...	15	NaCl 10	100	1.4252	4.0	-
Apáthy gum syrup (L-fr)	50	...	...	Fructose 50	50	15	...	100	1.4228	6.7	+
Glycerol gum syrup (L)	20	...	20	Sucrose 20	20	5	...	20	1.4600	7.1	-
Farrants glycerol gum arabic	50	...	50	...	...	...	As_2O_3 1	50	1.4360	4.4	+++
Farrants (KAc)	50	...	50	...	50	15	...	50	1.4404	7.2	-
Viscol (Dahl)	40	...	20	...	...	...	Phenol 10	45	1.4167	2.9	+++
Kaiser glycerol gelatin (M)	...	8	50	...	...	...	Phenol 1	42	1.4164	6.9	+++
Kaiser glycerol gelatin (F)	...	8	50	...	10	...	Phenol 1	42	1.4197	6.7	+++
Kaiser glycerol gelatin (L)	...	8	50	...	...	10	...	42	1.4130	7.0	+++
Kaiser sucrose glycerol gelatin	...	8	8	Sucrose 50	1	10	...	33	1.4519	6.6	-
Arlex gelatin	...	10	...	Arlex 89	1	...	...	1[1]	1.4936	6.0	-
Zwemer glychrogel	...	3	20	...	...	...	Chrome alum 0.2	80	1.75 Z	6.0	-

Note: LA, Lillie and Ashburn; H-a and H-b, Highman; L, Lillie; KAc, potassium acetate; M, Mallory; F, Friedenwald; [1] water included in the Arlex sorbitol syrup; Z, according to Zwemer.

TABLE 5-3. FORMULAE OF INDIFFERENT DILUTING FLUIDS

1. **Physiologic saline solution**
   Sodium chloride   8.5 gm, usually 9.0
   Distilled water   1000 cc
   Sterilize in autoclave.

2. **Ringer's solution and Locke variant**

Sodium chloride	8.5 gm	8.5 gm
Potassium chloride	250 mg	420 mg
Calcium chloride	300 mg	250 mg
Sodium bicarbonate	(200 mg)[1]	200 mg
Distilled water	1000 cc	1000 cc

   Sterilize by filtration with Berkefeld.
   Add calcium chloride last. Make
   fresh.

3. **Locke-Lewis solution**

Sodium chloride	8.5 gm
Potassium chloride	420 mg
Sodium bicarbonate[1]	200 mg
Glucose	100–250 mg
Calcium chloride	250 mg
Distilled water	1000 cc

   Add calcium chloride last.
   Sterilize by Berkefeld filtration.
   Make fresh as needed.

4. **Tyrode solution**   pH 7.5–7.8

Sodium chloride	8.0 gm
Potassium chloride	200 mg
Calcium chloride	200 mg
Magnesium chloride	100 mg
Sodium acid phosphate	50 mg
Sodium bicarbonate	1 gm
Glucose	1 gm
Distilled water	1000 cc.

   Add salts to water in order given.
   Sterilize by Berkefeld filtration.

5. **Pannett and Compton's buffered
   saline[2] solution**   pH 7.5

Sodium chloride	6.4 gm
Potassium chloride	366 mg
Calcium chloride	160 mg
Distilled water	960 cc

   Boil or autoclave, cool and add 40 cc of
   the following:
   Monosodium phosphate monohydrate
   12.5 mg
   Disodium phosphate, anhydrous 67.6
   mg
   Distilled water 40 cc which has been
   similarly sterilized
   The last is approximately 5.7 cc of
   stock 0.1 *M* phosphate buffer, pH
   7.5, diluted with 34.3 cc water
   (p. 664).

[1] Sodium bicarbonate is often omitted from Ringer's solution. It may be added to the Ringer-Locke solution and to the Locke-Lewis solution after the remaining constituents have been boiled to sterilize. The bicarbonate decomposes at 80°C in solution; hence it should not be added until solutions are below that temperature.

[2] In the Pannett-Compton solution, the chlorides and phosphates must be autoclaved separately and mixed after cooling.

The formulae are quoted as follows: No. 1, traditional at National Institute of Health (most authors give 0.9%); No. 2, both formulae are as in Lee, Romeis and Cowdry; No. 3, as in Romeis and Cowdry; No. 4, as in Cowdry, Lee, Mallory and Romeis; No. 5, emended from Lee.

Fernando's Dextrin Sucrose Sodium Chloride. This solution is recommended for amyloid stains with crystal violet.

Dissolve 16.7 gm sucrose, 16.7 gm dextrin and 10 gm sodium chloride in 100 cc distilled water, heating and stirring until clear. Add 10 mg sodium merthiolate (ethylmercurithiosalicylate). Store in tightly closed bottle. It is acid (pH 3.75) and has a high refractive index, nD 1.54 (*J. Inst. Sci. Techn.* 7:No. 2, 1961).

Substitution of 2.33 gm sodium acetate ($NaCO_2CH_3 \cdot 3H_2O$) for 1 gm of the sodium chloride should raise the pH of the mixture to near 7, without altering the molar salt concentration.

Abopon[1] is now available as a thick viscous mass or as crystals. It should be diluted with 0.2 M phosphate buffer, pH 7, to a manageable consistency but should still be saturated, with a few crystals in the bottom when cool. Hrushovetz and Harder (*Stain. Techn.* 37:307, 1962) direct as follows (I have supplied amounts):

Heat 60 cc Abopon (gum or crystals) on water bath to 60–70°C in a beaker. Add gradually about 20 cc 0.2 M phosphate buffer, pH 7 (8 cc 0.2 M NaH_2PO_4 + 17 cc 0.2 M Na_2HPO_4 should be about right), rotating slowly to mix, avoiding entrapment of air bubbles, until all crystals have dissolved. Store in about 40 cc amounts in small dropper bottles. A few crystals should form in the bottom; if they do not, add a few from the stock supply. If, as occasionally happens, microscopic debris is seen in the mounting medium, heat to 80°C on water bath and filter while hot through Whatman No. 1 paper.

Polyvinyl alcohol has been used also by Burstone where it was necessary to avoid strong alcohol (verbal communication). It would seem possible to use for mounting sections the glycerol water solution of the type used by Feder (p. 164) as an imbedding medium, perhaps as recently modified by Masek and Birns (*J. Histochem.* 9:634, 1961): 20 gm polyvinyl alcohol, 3 gm glycerol and 45 cc distilled water. The solution solidifies after a time but may be reliquefied by melting in a water bath; it then remains liquid again for a period. See Feder (*J. Histochem.* 10: 341, 1962).

MEDIA FOR SURVIVING CELLS

Many procedures exist for the examination of tissues, blood or their constituent cells or products in the fresh state or in aqueous media. For the study of surviving cells, protozoa and bacteria, a drop of tissue— perhaps diluted in serum or some indifferent fluid (see p. 104 for formulae) such as physiologic ("normal") saline solution, Ringer's fluid or Locke's fluid—is placed on a clean slide and at once covered with a coverglass. The edges of the coverglass may then be covered with petrolatum to prevent evaporation. Various reagents may be introduced by placing a few drops on the slide at one margin of the coverglass and drawing it into the observed space by applying filter paper to the opposite side of the coverglass.

[1] Valnor Corp., Brooklyn, N.Y.

Some procedures for the observation of living cells demand the use of a warm stage. Warm stages may be procured in various designs from the instrument makers. W. R. Earle found the most practical procedure was to enclose his microscope within a box with hand holes and holes for the eyepieces, and to keep the whole chamber warmed by using the heat of the microscope lamp or other heat source to maintain the desired temperature, which he controlled with a thermometer. For extended investigations and prolonged observation, thermostatic control is necessary.

Chapter 6

Stains and Fluorochromes

The examination of unstained material often has considerable value. However, it is usually restricted to the study of surviving cells and tissues, examinations with polarized light, fluorescence microscopy, phase microscopy, ultraviolet photography, microincineration procedures and the study of pigments. In a sense, histochemical blocking and control procedures also often yield essentially unstained preparations.

The purpose of staining is to make more evident various tissue and cell constituents and extrinsic materials. Some stains are strictly solution phenomena, such as the staining of neutral fats with oil soluble dyes; others are strictly chemical, such as the formation of Prussian blue by hemosiderin in the presence of acid and ferrocyanide; others depend on the presence of mordants, as hematoxylin depends on the presence of ferric or aluminum or other metallic salts; in others a so-called adsorption phenomenon may be responsible.

Generally, sequences or combinations of stains are employed, to render 2 or more tissue elements conspicuous in contrasting colors. No process has been devised which will show all tissue elements to the best advantage; but procedures exist which will stain differentially as many as 4 elements, such as the elastin-collagen procedures which show cell nuclei and cytoplasmic structures as well as elastic and collagen fibers. Some procedures are best adapted to the general study of cell nuclei and cytoplasms, and these are often employed as general oversight stains for primary examination of tissues.

Certain stain solutions are employed in a variety of procedures. To prevent duplication it seems well to describe these solutions first. Others, used only in certain single or related procedures, are best described in connection with the special methods in question. Simple solutions of dyes in single solvents need no special description and will be referred to as such in the procedures concerned, though they may be used in a variety of procedures.

The dyes used in staining may be classed in various ways: according to origin as natural and synthetic; according to chemical class, as azo, triphenylmethane, fluorane, quinoneimid and others; or according to their chief use in microscopy.

Origin is of little significance, and certain dyes, such as the indigos and orcein, may be derived either naturally or synthetically. Each of the chemical classes contains dyes used for diverse purposes, and chemically dissimilar dyes may be used for the same purpose. For example, the disazo dye Sudan IV and the anthraquinone dye coccinel red impart nearly identical colors to neutral fats; hematoxylin and certain oxazine dyes are good iron mordant nuclear stains. Two of the best collagen stains are the triphenylmethane dye methyl blue and the disazo dye amido black 10B.

For practical purposes a classification based on use seems best and will be followed in this work.

Dyes are generally complex organic chemicals whose behavior depends to a variable extent on their precise chemical constitution. They may often be mixtures of homologs varying by differences of one or more methyl, ethyl or phenyl groups, by the number of sulfonic acid or carboxylic acid radicals included or by the degree of oxidation or reduction. Many are quite stable in the dry state and in solution; others alter spontaneously in solution or even in the dry state. These alterations are generally accelerated by heat and light, and it is well to store dyestuffs in a cool dark place.

On purchasing dyes—particularly unusual ones or those whose names closely resemble those of other perhaps dissimilar dyes—it is well to specify the "Colour Index" Number (abbreviated C.I. No.) of the dye in question; or if it has no C.I. No., its chemical constitution or the precise designation given by the manufacturer, *including the manufacturer's name.*

The second edition of the *Colour Index,* issued in 4 volumes in 1957–1958, jointly by The Society of Dyers and Colourists, Bradford, Yorkshire, and by the American Association of Textile Chemists and Colorists, Lowell, Massachusetts, lists over 3500 synthetic and natural dyestuffs and pigments, and a supplement has recently been issued (1963). It gives many physical characteristics, solubility data, chemical constitution, often the method of manufacture and a list of the various synonyms applied to each dye.

In regard to nomenclature of dyes, I have generally followed that adopted in the Biological Stain Commission's publication, *"Biological Stains,"* 7th ed., 1961 (H. J. Conn *et al.,* editors), though in some instances I have preferred the original names from the *Colour Index.*

The Biological Stain Commission is a nonprofit corporation whose trustees are for the most part representatives of the various American scientific societies in those fields which use stains. The function of the Commission is to test stains and to supply and disseminate information regarding their constitution, behavior and uses.

Because of the variability of performance of various lots of dyestuffs, it is well to purchase only dyestuffs which have been tested for the purpose for which they are to be used. In this country such testing is done on many common dyes employed in biological staining procedures by the Biological Stain Commission in accord with the tests given in the latest edition of *Biological Stains;* and dyes bearing the Commission's certificate are generally reliable for the purposes specified by the Commission, provided they have not decomposed since the date of certification. Dates of certification may be determined approximately by consulting the periodic lists of certifications published by the Stain Commission, in *Stain Technology.* It is good practice to write the date of receipt on each bottle of dye purchased, using a nonfading ink.

Statements regarding the identity and chemistry of dyestuffs are derived generally from Conn's *Biological Stains*, from the *Colour Index*, from the literature and from our own files; and generally are made without specific reference. For further details the first 2 references above are recommended.

NUCLEAR STAINS

The general procedures for staining of cell nuclei fall into 2 main classes: (1) those done with basic ("cationic") dyes and depending on the presence of deoxyribonucleic and ribonucleic acids to form dye salt type unions; (2) those done with sequence or combination procedures using a di- or trivalent metal ion mordant and a dyestuff, usually *o*-diphenolic in nature, capable of forming a chelate complex with the metal ion, which in turn is bound to tissue groups which are not necessarily acid in nature. The latter group often functions quite well for nuclear demonstration in material from which the nucleic acids have been removed by acid extraction, as in decalcified tissue. Hence these mordant stains, particularly the aluminum "lakes" (chelate complexes) of hematoxylin, are more widely useful in general pathology than the more precise and specific basic aniline dyes.

The term *basophilic* is properly applied to those tissue substances of acid nature which color readily with basic aniline dyes, such as the nucleic acids, the sulfated polysaccharides, the sialic and uronic acid polysaccharides and proteins containing an excess of carboxylic acid over amino groups. Although the metal mordant dyes often color many of the same morphologic elements, they also color under some circumstances substances lacking acidic groups, such as neutral mucopolysaccharides, and under others lipids such as myelins and even basic (*oxyphil, acidophil* or *eosinophil*) substances such as pituitary alpha cells and eosinophil leucocyte granules. Hence it is better not to use the term *basophil* to indicate stainability with alum hematoxylin. The old term *siderophilia* to indicate stainability with iron hematoxylin was at least logical, and a term *metallophilia* would probably be more generally significant of the tissue characteristics inducing staining with these metal mordant complexes. The term *sudanophilia* is similarly used to denote stainability with oil soluble dyes such as Sudan III and IV, Sudan black *et al.*

Mordant Dyes. This group includes hematoxylin, brazilin, carmine and carminic acid, alizarin, purpurin, anthracene blue SWR, gallocyanine, gallamine blue and celestine blue B. All these dyes possess one or more *o*-diphenol groups; carminic acid also presents an *o*-hydroxybenzoic acid grouping, which should also serve for a metal chelation site.

TABLE 6-1. MORDANT DYES USED AS STAINS[1]

Colour Index no.		Class color no., Colour Index, 2d ed., Part I	HT3 stain class	Common name	Nuclear stains			Textile mordant colors	Calcified tissue
1st ed.	2d ed.				Al^{+++}	Cr^{+++}	Fe^{+++}		
1027	58000	MR-11	M	Alizarin	R	...	...	Al, Cr, Sn, Fe:R	R
1037	58205	....	M	Purpurin	R	...	...	....	R
1239	75490	Nat R-4	M	Carmine, carminic acid	R	...	...	Zn, Hg, Al, Sn:R; Cr: P; Ba:V; U:G; Pb,Cu:FR	
1243	75280	Nat R-24	M	Brazilin	R	CR	GN	Al, Sn:R; Cu:RF; Fe: BG– RF	
1246	75290	Nat N-1	M	Hematoxylin	B	CB	BN	Cu; BG; Sn:PR	
883	51030	MB-10	M	Gallocyanine	...	B	BN		
894	51045	MB-45	M	Gallamine blue	...	B	BN		
900	51050	MB-14	M	Celestine blue B	...	B	BN		
1062	58605	MB-32	M	Anthracene blue SWR, BN	...	...	...	Cr, VN	

Color abbreviations: *P*, Tyrian purple; *R*, red; *O*, orange; *Y*, yellow; *G*, green; *B*, blue; *V*, spectral violet; *F*, brown (fuscus); *C*, Gray (canus); *N*, black (niger). Combination of 2 symbols indicates an intermediate color, the second somewhat stronger.

[1] No proper names included among the above dye names and no capitalization is required. The country Brazil was named after the dyestuff, which was known to Chaucer.

TABLE 6-2. OTHER MORDANT DYES POSSIBLY USABLE AS STAINS[1]

Colour Index no.		Class color no., Colour Index 2d ed., Part I	HT3 stain class	Common name	Textile mordant colors	COONa SO₃Na group
1st ed.	2d ed.					
1063	58610	MB-23	M	Alizarin cyanine BBS	Cr:PN	
1064	58615	.....	M	Alizarin cyanine R	Cr, Al:V, P	
1065	58620	.....	M	Alizarin cyanine black G	Cr:BN	
1066	67410	.....	M	Alizarin blue	Cr:BV	
1067	67415	MB-27	M	Alizarin blue S	Cr:BV	
1068	67405	.....	M	Alizarin green S	Cr:G	
1069	67425	.....	M	Alizarin black P	Cr:N	
1070	67430	.....	M	Alizarin black S	Cr:N	
1040	58255	MR-2	M	Anthrapurpurin	Cr, Al:R	
	58260	MR-2	M	Acid anthrapurpurin	Cr, Al:R	SO₃Na
1045	58500	MV-26	M	Quinalizarin	Cr:V	
722	43820	MB-3	M	(Chrome) Cyanine R	Cr:VB	COONa 2
720	43830	MB-1	M	Pure blue B	Cr, Ba:B; Al, Be:B	COONa 2

Note: Color abbreviations are the same as in Table 6-1.

[1] No proper names are included among the above dye names and no capitalization is required.

According to Conn alizarin and purpurin form scarlet lakes with aluminum and have occasionally been used as nuclear stains. Their principal use, along with alizarin red S (the monosulfonate of alizarin), is as histochemical reagents for calcium (p. 436).

Carmine, or, more properly, carminic acid, and hematoxylin have been widely used as aluminum lakes for the staining of nuclei, neutral and acid mucins (p. 509) and, in the case of carmine, glycogen as well (p. 499). Hematoxylin has also been widely used with Fe⁺⁺⁺ in sequence mordant methods, in regressive differentiation lake methods and in progressive mordant stains (pp. 165–171). Brazilin has been used similarly to hematoxylin but much less extensively. Phosphotungstic (p. 537), phosmolybdic and molybdic acids have also been employed in combined solutions with hematoxylin. The three oxazin dyes celestine blue B, gallamine blue and gallocyanine have been used as iron lakes for nuclear staining in place of hematoxylin (p. 178). Gallocyanine with chrome alum in acid solution is an excellent nuclear and tigroid stain (p. 178), and anthracene blue SWR has been used as an aluminum lake in place of hematoxylin (p. 177).

Although it is usually stated that hematoxylin, brazilin and carmine do not function as stains without metal mordants, it has been shown, first by Clara (*Z. Zellforsch.* **22**:318, 1935) for enterochromaffin, that hematoxylin and several other dyes with catechol groups slowly react, in the absence of mordants, to form deeply colored complexes. This reaction has been extended to trichohyalin, keratohyalin, eosinophil leucocyte granules and some elastic membranes (*J. Histochem.* **4**:318, 1956). See also pp. 244–245.

Two acid dyes of the triphenylmethane group are classed in the *Colour Index* as mordant blues (Nos. 1 and 3). C.I. No. 43830 chromoxane pure blue B, usually called Pure Blue B "with various trade name prefixes, was used by Pearse (*Acta histochem.* **4**:95, 1957) as a reagent for the demonstration of Be^{++} and Al^{+++}, under the trade name Solochrome Azurine BS. Pearse used Mordant Blue No. 3, C.I. No. 43820, chromoxane cyanine R, commonly called "Cyanine R" or "Chrome Cyanine R with various trade prefixes, as a stain for nuclei (blue) and various cytoplasmic structures (red) under the trade name of Solochrome Cyanine R (p. 178).

Cyanine R, C.I. 43820
C.I. Mordant Blue No. 3

Pure Blue B, C.I. 43830
C.I. Mordant Blue No. 1

Closely allied to those mordant dyes is a group of reagents also yielding strong color reactions with metallic ions by the formation of chelate complexes. The principal use of these reagents, however, is in the demonstration of metallic ions in the tissues. Some of them are included in the *Colour Index* as mordant dyes.

Resorcin green (C.I. No. 10000, 2,4-dinitrosoresorcinol) has been used for the demonstration of iron in hemosiderin (p. 405). A dye designated as naphthochrome green B (Clayton Aniline Co.) has been used by Denz (p. 435) for the demonstration of beryllium. This dye seems to correspond most closely to C.I. No. 44530, Mordant Green 31, naphthochrome green G.

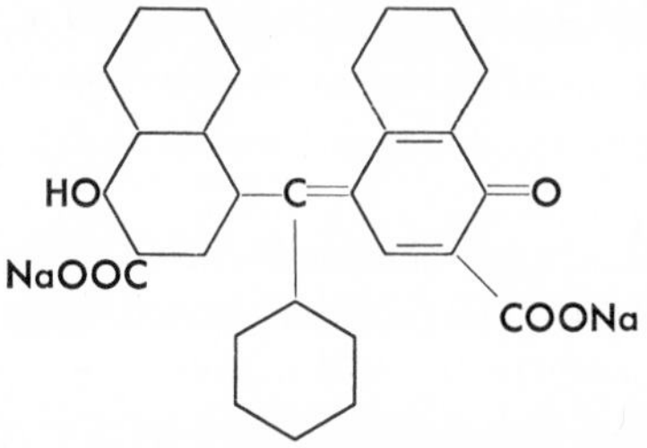

C.I. No. 44530
Naphthochrome
green G

Dithizone (diphenylthiocarbazone: Eastman 3092, M.W. 256.34) is used to produce a red color with zinc in tissue (p. 450). Purpurin (C.I. No. 58205), alizarin red S (C.I. No. 58005), anthrapurpurin or alizarin SX or A (C.I. No. 58255) and calcium red (Kernechtrot, nuclear fast red, an aminoanthroquinone sodium sulfonate, no C.I. No.) are similarly used for demonstration of calcium carbonate and phosphate deposits, but they do not show the oxalate (p. 439). Dipotassium rhodizonate (Eastman 2942) or the sodium salt is used for the demonstration of strontium and barium

TABLE 6-3. CHELATE REAGENTS FOR METAL IONS[1]

Colour Index No.		Colour Index, 2d ed., Part I, Class color no.	HT3 stain class	Name	Color(s)	Metallic ions	SO₃Na residues
1st ed.	2d ed.						
1	10000	.....	M	Resorcin green	G	Fe	
	44530	MG-31	M	Naphthochrome green G	G	Be	
			M	Dithizone	R	Zn	
1057	58205	.....	M	Purpurin	RP	Ca	
1034	58005	MR-3	M	Alizarin red S	R	Ca	1
1040	58255	MR-2	M	Anthrapurpurin	RP	Ca	
			M	Calcium red	R	Ca	
			M	Rhodizonate (K or Na)	R, R, F	Sr, Ba, Pb	
	43810	.....	M	Chrome violet CG	R+	Al	
			M	Rubeanic acid	GN, BN, YF	Cu, Ni, Co	
			M	Diethyldithiocarbamate	YF, F	Cu, Mn	
2	10005	MG-4	M	Naphthol green Y	R, GN, FG, F	Co, Fe, Ce, Cu	
1027	58000	MR-11	M	Alizarin	R	Ca	
720	43830	MB-1	M	Pure blue B	B	Be, Al	

Abbreviations: *M*, mordant; *R*, red; *Y*, yellow; *F*, brown; *G*, green; *B*, blue; *P*, purple; *N*, black; *R+*, dark red.

[1] No proper names are included among the above dye names and no capitalization is required.

(p. 435), to which it gives red colors, and of lead, which it colors brown (p. 445). Aurine tricarboxylic acid (C.I. No. 43810, chrome violet CG) colors aluminum salts dark red (p. 433) and yields violet with chromic acetate in textile dyeing.

In the foregoing group Kernechtrot, nuclear fast red needs some special discussion because of the confusion which has arisen from the application of these two names not only to the sulfonated aminoanthroquinone dye supplied as calcium red but also to a totally unrelated basic azin dye related to neutral red and also to the stable diazonium salt fast red B "Kernechtrotsalz B," C.I. No. 37125. Neither of the first two is entered in the *Colour Index* or its 1963 *Supplement* or in Conn's 7th edition of *Biological Stains.*

Dithiooxamide or rubeanic acid (Eastman 4394) gives a greenish black with Cu^{++}, blue violet with Ni^{++} and yellowish brown with Co^{++} (pp. 442, 443). Sodium diethyldithiocarbamate (Eastman 2635) also reacts with Cu^{++} to yield a yellow brown color (p. 123).

Naphthol green Y (C.I. No. 10005, 1-nitroso-2-naphthol) reacts with cobalt (red), iron (green to black), chromium (olive) and copper (brown).

Basic Aniline Dyes

The **basic azo dyes** Janus green B (C.I. No. 11050) and the Bismarck browns (C.I. Nos. 21000, 21010) are valuable nuclear stains in contrast staining for fats, as they possess the valuable property of relative permanence and lack of diffusion in aqueous syrup media. Janus green B seems also to excel methylene blue as a nuclear counterstain for the acid fast method for tubercle bacilli in tissues; but for permanence alum hematoxylin is to be preferred for this purpose. The Bismarck browns possess a metachromasia in yellower tone, and stain mucus and cartilage well. Janus green B, Janus black I (a mixture of Janus green B and some brown dye) and the related Janus blue are widely used in the vital staining of mitochondria.

Basic azo dyes are tabulated also in Table 6-4 following the thiazins. It will be noted that two Janus greens are listed, one made by coupling diazotized phenosafranin into dimethylaniline, the other using diethylsafranin (C.I. No. 50205) (50206?). The latter (C.I. No. 11050) appears to be the true composition of Janus green B, rather than the former (C.I. No. 11045), which was that in the first edition of the *Colour Index.*

Similarly, tolusafranin (C.I. No. 50240) and diethyltolusafranin diazotized and coupled into β-naphthol yield C.I. No. 12210, basic blue 16, indazole blue R, indoine blue R or 3B, a textile dye, and Janus blue B, respectively. The constitution of C.I. No. 135 in the first edition of the *Colour Index* was apparently incorrect for Janus blue.

Janus green and Janus blue have been used principally for supravital staining of mitochondria, a process which now seems to be related to the oxidative enzymes localized in these bodies (p. 286). They are also useful as basic dyes for counterstains (p. 578).

The **safranins**, safranin T, A or O (C.I. No. 50240), phenosafranin (C.I. No. 50200, safranin B extra) and its N-N-dimethyl and -tetraethyl derivatives, methylene violet RRA(C.I. No. 50205) and heliotrope B, 2B or amethyst violet (C.I. No. 50225) have all been used as nuclear stains. The first (C.I. No. 50240) has been preferred for this purpose and as a counterstain for Gram negative organisms and tissue cells in the Gram stain (p. 567). After ferro- and particularly ferricyanide technics, safranin O produces dark red crystalline precipitates which are difficult to prevent or remove. Hence the fuchsins are preferred in this case (p. 406). Safranin O exhibits a strong yellow orange metachromasia which apparently demonstrates more of the mucins than does azure A or thionin.

Safranin O and rarely methylene violet RRA have been used as diazotizable amines to produce fresh diazonium salts (p. 224) which demonstrate enterochromaffin in blue black or very dark violet on a red to red purple background stain of protein aromatic amino acid residues. This stain is useful both for enterochromaffin and for protein studies. Safranin O has been the chief dye used for this purpose. I have also used methylene violet RRA, and phenosafranin should be usable, but heliotrope B (C.I. No. 50225) has both its amine groups fully ethylated and would not be diazotizable. Molecular weights are 322.807 for phenosafranin, 350.861 for safranin O and methylene violet RRA and 435.023 for heliotrope B. Diethylphenosafranin is used chemically as the diazonium base in the synthesis of Janus green and Janus black.

The principal use of the azin dye neutral red (C.I. No. 50040) is in vital staining, in tigroid staining and in such neutral stains as Twort's light green neutral red.

Three weakly basic red dyes of the xanthene group are the pyronins Y and B (C.I. Nos. 45005, and 45010) and rhodamine B (C.I. No. 45170). I have occasionally used these as red nuclear stains but find other dyes better, notably the fuchsins and the safranins.

All three have been used as basic stains for cytoplasm, basophil granules and bacteria in contrast to a nuclear stain with methyl green. The pyronins are used for this purpose in the Unna-Pappenheim-Saathof methods (p. 152) and are also employed as counterstains in the α-naphthol oxidase methods (p. 371). Rhodamine B has also been employed in the supravital staining of mitochondria (p. 286), and as a fat stain in aqueous solution for fluorescence microscopy.

The **oxazin dyes** brilliant cresyl blue (C.I. No. 51010) and cresyl fast violet, or *Cresylechtviolett*, are used, the one chiefly for supravital staining, the other for Nissl staining and for its metachromatic properties. Gallamine blue, gallocyanine and celestine blue have been discussed under "Mordant Dyes" (p. 110). The remaining commonly used member of this group is Nile blue (C.I. No. 51180). This dye has been used both as an ordinary basic dye and as a special reagent for the staining of fatty acids (blue) and neutral fats (red). This use is discussed at length on p. 281.

The **thiazins**, thionin (C.I. No. 52000) and its mono-, di-, tri- and tetramethyl derivatives azure C, azure A, azure B (C.I. No. 52010) and methylene blue (C.I. No. 52015); its relatives toluidine blue (C.I. No. 52040) and new methylene blue (C.I. No. 52030) are valuable nuclear stains and exhibit in varying measure the property of metachromasia, or of staining cartilage matrix, mucin and the granules of mast cells in a more violet or redder tone than they do nuclei. Of these, new methylene blue is the reddest, then thionin, azure C, azure A, toluidine blue, azure B and methylene blue in order. The middle three members of the series afford perhaps the greatest color contrast between nuclei and cytoplasm on the one hand and cartilage and mucus on the other.

They are much used as bacterial stains and (in combination with dyes of the eosin group) as general tissue stains, especially for blood and blood forming tissues.

The higher homologs, methylene blue and azure B, readily undergo oxidation with loss of methyl groups and evolution of formaldehyde, and give rise to lower homologs and to certain deaminized oxidation products which are relatively insoluble in water and have been thought to contribute to the polychromasia of blood stains. The substance Bernthsen's methylene violet appears to be a mixture of these. This oxidation of methylene blue to azures and methylene violets is known as polychroming, and mixtures of methylene blue with these products are called polychrome methylene blue.

This process of polychroming occurs freely in alkaline solutions without added oxidants, and is expedited by rise in pH level above 8 and by heat. It is inhibited in acid solution. It may be induced by deliberate oxidation in acid solution by addition of chromic acid, but in this instance only azures appear to be formed, and the amount of alteration is strictly proportional to the amount of available oxygen furnished. Thus, use of 250 mg potassium bichromate per gm 88% methylene blue produces a product which is spectroscopically and tinctorially chiefly azure B, while double that amount produces chiefly azure A. The reactions are thus: $K_2Cr_2O_7$ furnishes $3O$, Cr_2O_3 and K_2O, the metallic oxides being promptly converted into salts by the excess of acid present. One mol of methylene blue $C_{16}H_{18}N_3SCl + 1\ O$ yields 1 mol azure B $C_{15}H_{16}N_3SCl + 1$ mol formaldehyde HCHO.

A similar decomposition of methylene blue and the higher azures appears to go on even in the dry dyes, and occurs readily also in methyl alcohol solutions of their eosinates and more slowly in glycerol methanol solutions. Also in these solutions the change is accelerated by higher temperatures and by presence of alkali and is retarded by acid. Particularly annoying is its occurrence during the drying of eosinate precipitates. Here thorough washing with distilled water, rigid adherence to temperatures below 40°C for drying and the use of alcohol or vacuum to accelerate drying are of help.

The **triphenylmethane basic dyes** pararosaniline (C.I. No. 42500) as chloride, or the more soluble acetate, fuchsin or rosaniline (C.I. No. 42510) and new fuchsin (C.I. No. 42520) are widely used for demonstration of acid fast bacteria in sputum, exudates and tissue sections (p. 576), as a component of the Weigert iron resorcin fuchsin (p. 553) and the Fullmer iron orcinol new fuchsin (p. 556) elastic tissue stains, as a red nuclear stain for use in Prussian and Turnbull blue reactions and in variants of the Gram stain for bacteria (p. 567), in its sulfite leuco form in the Schiff reagent for aldehydes (p. 270) as used in the Feulgen nucleal (p. 149) and plasmal (p. 468) reactions and in the Bauer and McManus polysaccharide methods (p. 195).

Crystal violet (C.I. No. 42555, N-hexamethylpararosaniline) and methyl violet (C.I. No. 42535, the related mixture of somewhat redder lower homologs) are used extensively in the Gram stain for bacteria in exudates and tissues (p. 565) and the Gram-Weigert fibrin stain (p. 262), as stains for amyloid, which exhibits an alcohol labile red metachromasia to these dyes, and as the basic component of certain neutral stains (p. 295). Iodine green (C.I. No. 42556) is also sometimes used for amyloid.

Methyl green (C.I. No. 42585) and ethyl green (C.I. No. 42590), methyl and ethyl addition products to crystal violet, are used for nuclear chromatin (deoxyribonucleic acid) in the methyl green pyronin and related procedures (p. 152). C.I. No. 42590 was originally named methyl green and is the dye furnished by at least some manufacturers.

Spirit blue (C.I. No. 42775), or alcohol soluble aniline blue, is used in alcoholic solutions as a stain for nuclei, cartilage and other acidic substances; it has also been used in hydroalcoholic solutions as a fat stain.

Among these dyes pararosaniline (C.I. No. 42500) has also been used as a base for diazotization, and the resultant diazonium salt, hexazoniumpararosaniline, has been used for the capture of naphthol in enzyme localization work (p. 314).

The Alcian dyes of Imperial Chemical Industries (ICI) and a group of similar dyes produced by Farbenfabriken Bayer A.G., (FBy) are basic dyes in which the chromogen is the phthalocyanine nucleus and the basic side chain is partially identified (Alcian Blue 8GX, C.I. No. 74240; Phthalogen Brillant Blue 1F3G, C.I. No. 74160) or quite unrevealed (Alcian Blues 2GX, 5GX, 7GX; Alcian Greens 2GX and 3BX, Alcian Yellow GX, Phthalogen Blue 1B, Phthalogen Brilliant Blue 1F3GM, Phthalogen Blue Black IVM and Phthalogen Brilliant Green 1FFB). The

Alcian Blue 8GX
C.I. No. 74240

X = an immonium base, *e.g.*, $-CH_2-S-C$

Astracyanine B
C.I. No. 42705

reader is referred to the second edition of the *Colour Index* and to its supplements for further information regarding constitution of these dyes. Mowry has noted (p. 510) that Imperial Chemical Industries has changed the composition of Alcian blue 8GX at least once, to render it more soluble.

Of these dyes, one, Alcian blue 8GX, has been widely used as a stain for mucopolysaccharides, and some workers have claimed histochemical specificity for it. Such claims appear to rest on about the same kind of ground as the pine splinter test for indole, since the constitution of the reagent is unrevealed and is subject to change at its manufacturer's convenience.

TABLE 6-4. BASIC ANILINE DYES[1]

Colour Index no.		Colour Index, 2d ed., Part I, class color no.	Name	Color		Mol. wt.	Amine groups			Solubility, gm/100 cc	
1st ed.	2d ed.			Ortho-chromatic	Meta-chromatic		prim NH2	sec NHR	tert NR2	Water	Alcohol
Azins											
840	50200	......	Phenosafranin	R	...	322.807	2	...	...	Sol.	Sol.
843	50205	BV-5	Methylene violet RR	PR	...	350.861	1	...	1	Sol.	Very sol.
	50206	......	Diethylphenosafranin	P	...	378.915	1	...	1	Sol.	Sol.
847	50225	......	Heliotrope B, 2B	V	...	435.023	...	...	2	Sol.	Sol.
841	50240	BR-2	Safranin T, A, O	R	YO	350.861	2	...	...	5.45	3.41
825	50040	BR-5	Neutral red	R	...	288.790	1	...	1	Sol.	Sol.
Pyronins											
740	45000	......	Acridine red 3B	R	...	274.478	...	2	...	Sol	Sol.
739	45005	......	Pyronin G, Y	R	...	302.812	...	...	2	8.96	0.6
741	45010	......	Pyronin B	PR	...	358.920	...	...	2	Sol.	Sol.
Oxazins											
(877)	51010	......	Brilliant cresyl blue	B	PR	332.844	2	...	1	Sol.	
			Cresyl fast violet	V	R	339.834	1	...	1	0.38	0.25
913	51180	BB-12	Nile blue (sulfate)	B	...	732.874	1	...	1	Sol.	Sol.
Thiazins											
920	52000	......	Thionin	V	R	263.759	2	...	...	0.25	0.25
			Azure C	BV	R	277.786	1	1	...	Sol.	Sol.
	(52005)	......	Azure A	VB	PR	291.813	1	...	1	Sol.	Sol.
	52010	......	Azure B	B	V?	305.840	...	1	1	Sol.	Sol.
922	52015	BB-9	Methylene blue	GB	...	319.867	...	...	2	3.5	1.5
924	52020	BG-5	Methylene green	G	BV	364.867	...	...	2	1.5	0.1
927	52030	BB-24	New methylene blue N	B	PR	347.921	...	2	...	13.3	1.6
			Methylene violet Bernthsen	V	...	256.332	...	...	1	Insol.	Sol.
925	52040	BB-17	Toluidine blue	B	PR	305.840	1	...	1	3.8	0.5
Basic Azo Dyes											
133	11045	......	Janus green	G	...	454.975	1	...	1	Sol.	Sol.
	11050	......	Janus green B	G	...	511.083	...	...	2	Sol.	Sol.
135	12210	BB-16	Indazole blue	B	...	506.019	1	...	...	Sol.	Sol.
	12211	......	Janus blue B	B	...	562.127	...	...	1	Sol.	Sol.
331	21000	......	Bismarck brown Y	YF	Y	419.336	4	...	...	1.3	1.1
332	21010	......	Bismarck brown R	RF	...	461.417	4	...	...	1.1	1.0

The Astra blue of the Germans appears to be used similarly to Alcian blue 8GX and to have similar "specificity" for acid mucopolysaccharides. The new supplement to the *Colour Index*, though it does not formulate the dye in Part II, reveals in Part I that Astra blue 4R is a triarylmethane dye, not improbably similar to the known dark blue Astracyanine B, C.I.

TABLE 6-4. BASIC ANILINE DYES(*Continued*)

Colour Index no.		Colour Index, 2d ed., Part I, class color no.	Name	Color		Mol. wt.	Amine groups			Solubility, gm/100 cc	
1st ed.	2d ed.			Ortho-chromatic	Meta-chromatic		prim NH$_2$	sec NHR	tert NR$_2$	Water	Alcohol
Triphenyl- and Diphenylnaphthylmethanes											
657	42000	BG-4	Malachite green	G	...	364.926	...	...	2	Sol.	Very sol.
676	42500	BR-9	Pararosaniline chloride	R	...	323.834	3	...	...	0.26	5.98
	42500	......	Pararosaniline acetate	R	...	347.423	...	...	...	4.15	13.63
677	42510	BV-14	Rosaniline, fuchsin (anhyd.)	R	...	337.861	3	...	...	0.39	8.16
	42510	BV-14	Rosaniline, fuchsin (cryst 4 H$_2$O)	R	...	409.920					
678	42520	BV-2	New fuchsin	R	...	365.915	3	...	...	1.13	3.20
680	42535	BV-1	Methyl violet	P	R	380,394 & 408	1, 0	1, 0	2	2.93	15.21
681	42555	BV-3	Crystal violet	V	PR	407.996	...	...	3	1.68	13.87
684	42585	BB-20	Methyl green	G	...	458.488	...	...	2²	Sol.	insol.
685	42590	......	Ethyl green	G	...	516.974	...	...	2²	Sol.	
686	42556	......	Iodine green	G	R	472.515	...	...	2²	Sol.	
689	42775	SB-3	Spirit blue	B	...	Variable mixture	1, 0	2, 3	..	Insol.	1.1
690	42563	BB-8	Victoria blue 4R	B	...	520.127	...	...	3	3.23	20.49
728	44040	BB-11	Victoria blue R	B	...	458.056	...	1	2	Sol. hot	Very sol.
729	44045	BB-26	Victoria blue B	B	...	506.300	...	1	2	Sol.	Sol.
731	44085	BB-15	Night blue	B	...	576.235	...	1	2	Sol.	Readily sol.
Phthalocyanines (composition not yet completely revealed)											
	74240	Ingram B1	Alcian Blue 8 GX	...	...	....	...	...	4(?)		
		SB-37	Luxol Fast Blue AR								
		SB-34	Luxol Fast Blue G								
		SB-38	Luxol Fast Blue MBSN								
808	.....	......	Pinacyanole	R	...	480.401	...	...	2 ring	Sol.	Sol.

[1] Among the above dye names the words Nile, Bernthsen, Janus, Bismarck and Victoria are proper names and require capitalization. The Luxol dyes and Alcian Blue 8GX bear trade names and are of partly or entirely secret composition. Their names are capitalized as above.

[2] 1—$\overset{+}{N}R_3$ group present.

Note: *B*, blue; *G*, green; *P*, Tyrian purple; *R*, red; *V*, spectral violet; *Y*, yellow.

No. 42705, which is a triaminoditolylphenylmethane basic dye that could well prove equally useful.

Fluorochrome Stains. These stains comprise a number of acid and basic dyestuffs, mostly yellow or orange in color, which fluoresce more or less intensely in near ultraviolet (and violet) light. Most of them function as ordinary acids and bases to color oxyphil and basophil (basic and acid) tissue elements in the same manner as the acid and basic dyes used with visible light. Three, fluorescein, rhodamine B and sulforhodamine B, have been used more or less extensively to condense with free protein amino groups, thereby "tagging" them so that these proteins may be localized by their green or red fluorescence. Fluorescein and rhodamine B have been used as isocyanates or, preferably, as the more stable and commercially available isothiocyanates. With sulforhodamine B, a sulfamido condensation (Chadwick *et al., Lancet* 1:412, 1958) has been used. This dye has usually been referred to by one of its trade names, often without noting the manufacturer's name: Lissamine Rhodamine B200, Imperial Chemical Industries Ltd., and Acid Rhodamine B, National Aniline Division, Allied Chemical and Dye Corporation.

A few basic (amino) dyes and two acid dyes have been used as fat stains, by reason of their relatively higher oil solubility. Since they do contain amino or acid groups, their specificity for fat staining is open to question. Acetyl or benzoyl esters might be prepared, as has been done with oil red O, Sudan IV and Sudan black B (*J. Histochem.* 1:8, 1953).

Of the basic acridine fluorochromes, one, acridine orange, C.I. No. 46005, has received special attention. It was said for a time to permit discrimination between living and dead cells; now it is found that with an appropriate technic it gives a green fluorescence to deoxyribonucleic acid and a red fluorescence to ribonucleic acid. The free base, C.I. No. 46005B, is said to be selectively very soluble in stearic acid (C.I. Part I, Solvent Orange 15).

In regard to magdala red, the *Colour Index* relates that Basic Red No. 6, C.I. No. 50375, contains as first product of synthesis about 92–94% rhodindine (*a*), a monoamino trinaphthosafranin, from which 6–8% of true magdala red (*b*), the diamino homolog, is extracted with boiling water. It is believed that this latter fraction is meant by the term *Magdalarot echt*. I do not know whether rhodindine has ever been used intentionally as a stain, and it would appear to be relatively insoluble in water.

Thiazol yellow G, C.I. No. 19540, has been supplied as a biological stain also under the synonyms "titan yellow" and "Clayton yellow."

The alkaloid berberine and the yellow drugs rivanol and quinacrine (atabrine) are included with the dyes in Table 6-5.

Kasten (*Nature* 184:1797, 1959) has used a number of fluorescent basic primary amine dyes to form Schiff reagents, chiefly for use in the Feulgen reaction. These include auramine O (C.I. 41000), acridine yellow G (C.I. 46025), acriflavine (C.I. 46000), coriphosphine O (C.I. 46020), phosphine (C.I. 46045), flavophosphine N or benzoflavine (C.I. 46065), neutral red (C.I. 50040), phenosafranin (C.I. 50200), safranin O (C.I. 50240) and rhodamine 3G (C.I. 45310).

The antibiotic tetracycline apparently functions as a mordant dye to demonstrate newly deposited calcium *in vivo*, after the traditional manner of madder (p. 636).

TABLE 6-5. FLUOROCHROME DYES AND DRUGS USED IN HISTOCHEMISTRY AND HISTOLOGY[1]

Colour Index no. 1st ed.	2d ed.	Colour Index, 2d ed., Part I, class color no.	HT3 stain class	Preferred name	Mol. wt.	$-SO_3Na$ $(-CO_2Na)$	NH_2	NHR	NR_2	Color Ortho-Chromatic	Color Ultra-violet fluoro-chrome	Solubility Water	Solubility Alcohol
655	41000	BY-2	BF	Auramine O	303.842		1	…	2	Y	Y	Very sol. hot; sol.	Sol.
749	45170	BV-10	BF, OSF[1]	Rhodamine B	479.029	1 CO_2H	…	…	2	R	YO, R	Sol.	Sol.
753	45210	BR-3	BF	Rhodamine 3G	436.948		1	…	1	R	R	Sol.	Sol.
790	46000		BF	Acriflavine	259.747		2			Y	Y	Very sol.	Sol.
788	46005	BO-14	BF	Acridine orange	301.828		1	…	2	OR, G	OR, G	Sol.	Sol.
787	46020	BY-7	BF	Coriphosphine	287.801		1	…	1	Y	Y	Sol.	Sol.
785	46025		BF	Acridine yellow	273.714		2			Y	G	Sol.	Sol.
793	46045	BO-15	BF, OSF	Phosphine	362.396		2			YO	Y	Sol.	Sol.
791	46065		BF	Benzoflavine	349.872		2		1 ring 1	Y	YG	Sol.	Sol.
815	49005	BY-1	BF	Thioflavine TCN	318.878				1	GY	YG	Sol.	Sol.
	50375a	BR-6	BF	Rhodindine	457.971		1		…	R	O	Very slightly sol.	Sol.
857	50375b	BR-6	BF, OSF	Magdala red (echt)[3]	472.987		2		1 ring	R	O	Sol. hot	Sol.
			BF,	Berberine sulfate	433.446					·	Y	1.0	Slightly sol.
			BF	Quinacrine-2HCl-2H_2O	508.936			1	1	Y	GY	2.9	
			BF	Rivanol	253.309		2	1		Y	GY	6.5	
			MF[2]	Tetracycline	440.418		1 amide		1	·····	Y	Sol.	
225	14780	DR-45	AF, OSF	Thiazine red R	599.588	2				R	V	Very sol.	Sol.
813	19540	DY-9	AF, OSF	Thiazole yellow G	695.746	2		1		Y	B	Sol.	Sol.
370	22120	DR-28	A, AF	Congo red	696.690	2	2			FR	R	Sol.	Sol.
692	42685	AV-19	AC, AF	Acid fuchsin	585.550	3	3			R	R	45.0	3.0
748	45100	AR-52	AF	Sulforhodamine B	580.665	2			2	R	R		
766	45350	AY-73	AF	Fluorescein diNa	376.282	1 CO_2Na				Y	G	50.0	7.0
768	45380	AR-87	A, AF	Eosin Y diNa	691.914	1 CO_2Na				Y	Y	44.0	2.0
812	49000	DY-59	AF	Primuline	475.556	+	1			Y±	B, BV	0.25	0.03
816	49010	DY-7	AF	Thioflavine S	uncertain	+	1			Y	G, BG	Very sol.	Sol.

Abbreviations: BF, basic fluorochrome; AF, acid fluorochrome; Y, yellow; G, green; O, orange; R, red; B, blue; V, violet; F, brown (fuscus).

[1] OSF oil soluble fluorochrome [2] MF mordant fluorochrome

[3] Although Magdala would seem to have been a proper name, Conn (7 ed, 1961) writes it in lower case. The other dye names are all uncapitalized.

122

PLASMA STAINS

For the most part these are sulfonic and carboxylic acids which combine more or less firmly with tissue bases, mainly proteins containing an excess of the basic amino acids arginine, lysine, hydroxylysine and histidine over acidic amino acids. A few nitro and nitroso dyes react similarly. These are tabulated in Table 6-6.

A few among these merit special mention. The nitro dye picric acid, formulated as 2,4,6-trinitrophenol and as its yellower tautomer,

serves both as an acid and as a yellow contrast stain in collagen methods of the Van Gieson type (pp. 539–543). It is used also as a simple plasma stain in contrast to hematoxylin and to various basic dyes. In the latter usage, either the acid or its ammonium salt may be used; ammonium picrate is ineffective in Van Gieson and similar stains. If ammonium picrate is not available, it may be made by adding ammonium hydroxide solution gradually to boiling water containing 10–15% picric acid, until the steam a minute after the last addition is alkaline to moist litmus or nitrazine paper. Then continue boiling until the steam is no longer alkaline.

Most of the simple plasma stains included in Table 6-6 need no special discussion at this point. Merits of certain dyes as "specific protein stains" will be discussed in Chapter 8.

A few acid dyes which exhibit strong fluorescence in violet and near ultraviolet light have been presented as fluorochrome dyes (p. 122, Table 6-5), with the usage symbol AF.

Since Conn (7th ed., p. 179) has seen fit to condemn eosin B as a too weakly acid dye to perform satisfactorily in a Romanovsky type "neutral" stain, I feel that it should be pointed out that nitrocarboxylic acids generally present somewhat lower pK values than the homologous chloro, bromo and iodo derivatives, just as these in turn show lower pK levels than corresponding unsubstituted carboxylic acids.

In Nocht type Romanovsky stains, eosin B performs equally well with eosin Y and gives more brilliant red colors. For azure eosin and Giemsa substitute staining on most pathologic material I have long abandoned eosin Y in favor of eosin B. It is likewise my experience that for tissue staining the extempore mixtures of the aqueous solutions of the azures

TABLE 6-6. ACID DYES USED PRINCIPALLY AS PLASMA STAINS[1]

Colour Index no.		*Colour Index*, 2d ed., Part I, class color no.	HT 3d ed. stain class	Name	Mol. wt.	Color	SO_3Na	CO_2Na and other acids	Amino groups			Solubility, gm/100 cc	
1st ed.	2d ed.								NH_2	NHR	NR_2	Water	Alcohol
7	10305	......	A	Picric acid	229.114	Y	.....	1 NO_2H	...	...	....	1.18	8.96
10	10316	AY-1	A	Naphthol yellow S +3 H_2O	358.206 412.254	Y	1	......	...	...	(2 NO_2)	8	Slight
Monoazo Dyes													
27	16230	AO-10	A	Orange G	452.386	O	2	......	...	...	....	10.86	0.22
29	16570	AR-29	A	Chromotrope 2R	468.386	R	2	......	...	...	....	19.30	0.17
79	16150	AR-26	A	Ponceau 2R	480.440	R	2	......	...	...	....	Sol.	Very slight
88	16180	AR-17	A	Bordeaux R	502.446	R	2	......	...	...	....	Sol.	Slight
138	13065	AY-36	A	Metanil yellow	375.391	Y	1	......	...	1	....	5.36	1.45
153	16540	AR-21	A	Azofuchsin G	468.386	R	2	......	...	...	....	Sol.	Very slight
154	16535	......	A	Azofuchsin GN, S	438.402	R	1	......	...	...	....	Sol.	Sol.
225	14780	DR-45	A	Thiazine red R	599.588	R	2	......	...	...	Thiazole ring	Very sol.	Sol.
640	19140	AY-23	A	Tartrazine	534.385	Y	2	1	...	...	1 pyrazole ring	Very sol.	Slight
Disazo and Polyazo Dyes													
252	27290	AR-73	A	Brilliant crocein	556.500	R	2	......	...	...	....	5.04	0.06
280	26905	AR-66	A	Biebrich scarlet	556.500	R	2	......	...	...	....	Sol.	Slight
370	22120	DR-28	A, AF	Congo red	696.690	R	2	......	2	...	....	Sol.	Sol.

No.	C.I. No.	Abbrev.	Class	Name	Color	Mol. wt.						
375	22145	DR-10	A	Congo Corinth G	R	697.674	2	1	....	....	Sol.	Slight
454	23510	DR-15	A	Brilliant purpurin R	F	826.793	3	2	....	....	Sol.	Mod.
520	24400	DB-15	A	Benzo pure blue	B	992.842	4	2	....	....	6	0.5
581	30235	DN-38	A	Chlorazol black E	N	781.760	2	3	....	....	Sol.	Mod.

Triphenylmethane Acid Dyes

No.	C.I. No.	Abbrev.	Class	Name	Color	Mol. wt.						
696	42571	AB-13	A	Fast acid violet 10 B	V	643.771	2	....	....	3	Very sol.	Slight
698	42650	AV-17	A	Formyl violet S4B	PV	749.959	2	....	....	3	Very sol.	Very sol.
699	42576	AB-34	A	Eriocyanine A	VB	706.850	2	....	....	3	Sol.	Sol.
712	42051	AB-3	Redox A	Patent blue V · ½Ca^{+}	B	579.733	2	....	....	2	Very sol.	Slightly sol.
715	43535	......	Redox A	Cyanol FF	B	554.630	2	....	....	2	Sol.	Very sol.
716	43530	......	Redox A	Ketone blue 4BN, "Cyanol"	B	602.674	2	....	....	2	Sol.	Sol.

Quinolines

No.	C.I. No.	Abbrev.	Class	Name	Color	Mol. wt.						
801	47005	AY-3	A	Quinoline yellow	Y	Uncertain	+(2?)	1	....	....	Sol.	Sol.
802	47010	AY-2	A	Quinoline yellow	Y	Uncertain	+	1	....	....	Sol.	

Fluorane-Xanthene Dyes

No.	C.I. No.	Abbrev.	Class	Name	Color	Mol. wt.						
768	45380	AR-87	A	Eosin Y	OR	691.914	....	1	....	....	44.2	2.18
771	45400	AR-91	A	Eosin B	R	624.098	....	1	....	....	39.11	0.75
773	45430	AR-51	A	Erythrosin B	R	879.890	....	1	....	....	11.1	1.87
778	45410	AR-92	A	Phloxine B	PR	829.710	....	1	....	....	Sol.	Sol.
779	45440	AR-94	A	Rose Bengal	PR	1017.686	....	1	....	....	36.25	7.53

125

[1] Conn, 6th ed.

Abbreviation: *A*, acid dye; *AC*, acid dye; collagen stain colors: *R*, red; *O*, orange; *Y*, yellow; *G*, green; *B*, blue; *V*, violet; *F*, brown; *P*, red purple; *N*, black.

TABLE 6-6. ACID DYES USED PRINCIPALLY AS PLASMA STAINS (*Continued*)

Colour Index no.		Colour Index, 2d ed., Part I, class color no.	HT 3d ed. stain class	Name	Mol. wt.	Color	SO₃Na	CO₂Na and other acids	Amino groups			Solubility, gm/100 cc	
1st ed.	2d ed.								NH₂	NHR	NR₂	Water	Alcohol
				Azins									
828	50085	AR-101	A	Azocarmine G	579.599	R	2	…	…	1	…	Sl. sol.	Sol.
829	50090	AR-103	A	Azocarmine B	681.648	R	3	…	…	1	…	Very sol.	
				ACID DYES USED BOTH AS PLASMA STAINS AND AS COLLAGEN FIBER STAINS									
246	20470	AN-1	AC	Amido black 10B (naphthol blue black)	616.516	BN	2	…	1	…	…	Sol.	Sol.
282	27195	AR-112	AC	Ponceau S	760.598	R	4	…	…	…	…	20.35	0.82
670	42095	AG-5	AC	Light green SF	792.874	G	3	…	…	…	2	16.04	0.35
	42053	FG-3	AC	Fast green FCF	808.875	G	3	…	…	…	2	Very sol.	Insol.
692	42685	AV-19	AC	Acid fuchsin	585.550	R	3	…	3	…	…	Very sol.	
706	42780	AB-93	AC	Methyl blue	799.827	B	3	…	…	3	…	Very sol.	
707	42780	mixture	AC	Aniline blue	mixture	B	…	…	…	…	…	Sol.	
707	42755	AB-22	AC	"Water blue I"	737.756	B	3	…	1	2	…	Sol.	Slight
737	44090	AG-50	AC	Wool green S	576.636	G	2	…	…	…	2	Sol.	Sol.
758	45190	AV-9	AC	Violamine R	612.647	PR	1	1	…	2	…	Sol.	Sol.
1180	73015	AB-74	AC	Indigocarmine	466.370	B	2	…	…	2i	…	1.68	0.01
				"Ponceau S"									
282	……	……	AC	Ponceau S¹ (disazo) (silk scarlet N, 2R, S)	468.476	R	1	…	…	…	…	Sol.	Sol. hot
196	15635	AR-9	A(C?)	Ponceau S (monoazo)	400.397	R	1	…	…	…	…	Sol. hot	Slight
	14700	FR-1	A(C?)	Ponceau SX (monoazo)	480.440	R	2	…	…	…	…	Sol.	Slight
64	16140	AR-24	A(C?)	Excelsior lake ponceau JN (Ponceau scarlet)	466.413	R	2	…	…	…	…	Sol.	
282	27195	AR-112	AC	Ponceau S (disazo)	760.598	B	4	…	…	…	…	Sol.	

¹ Among the above dye names the words Biebrich, Congo, Corinth and Bengal are proper names and require capitalization. ² i = indole N.

and the two eosins, B and Y, are to be preferred to the prepared eosinates in methanol or methanol glycerol stock solutions. The erythrosins and phloxines have not given satisfactory results in neutral staining, probably because of relative insolubility of their azure salts, but they do better in sequence procedures such as Mallory's phloxine methylene blue and alum hematoxylin eosin technics.

Collagen Stains. A considerable group of dyes, included in Table 6-6, can be used both as simple plasma stains and for the specific purpose of staining collagen fibers which appear to be only weakly basic, in technics involving concomitant or sequential use of phosphomolybdic, phosphotungstic, picric and other acids. These uses are taken up in Chapter 15, and the dual usage of these dyes as acid dyes (A) and collagen fiber stains is noted in the table by the symbol AC.

Among this group ponceau S requires some special discussion. This dye was used by Curtis (*Anat. path.* (Paris) 17:603, 1905), who called it "ponceau S extra." In 1945 (*J. Tech. Meth.* 25:1) I identified this dye as C.I. No. 282, formulated in *Biological Stains*, sixth edition, as a monosulfonated disazo dye.

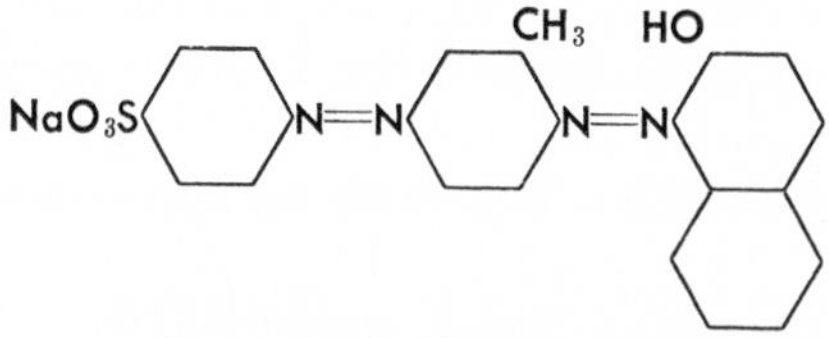

Conn, 6 ed. C.I. No. 282

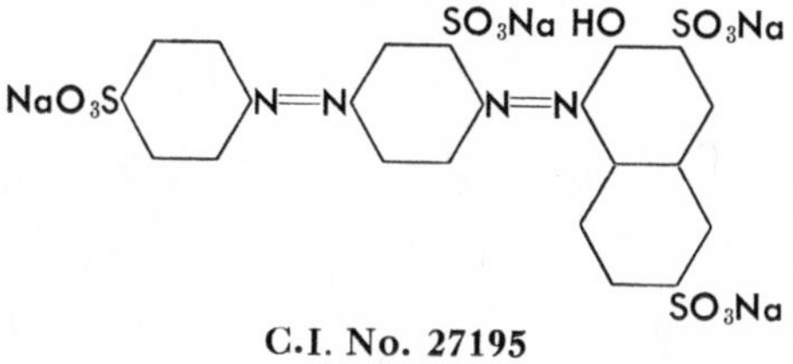

C.I. No. 27195

But the second edition of the *Colour Index* identifies C.I. No. 282 with C.I. No. 27195, which is a tetrasulfonic derivative of a similar azo dyestuff. C.I. No. 27195 is apparently obsolete as a textile dye. The term "ponceau S" is now applied to C.I. No. 15635 (silk scarlet, N, 2R, S); "Ponceau SX," to C.I. No. 14700; and "ponceau scarlet," to C.I. No. 16140, which are both mono- and disulfonated monoazo dyes. From Curtis's statement that highly sulfonated dyes were superior, I suspect that the second edition of the *Colour Index* may have correctly formulated the dye which Curtis used.

C.I. No. 14700   C.I. No. 16140

C.I. No. 15635

Aniline blue, used in these methods, was, according to Conn, a somewhat variable mixture of methyl blue, C.I. No. 42780, and water blue I, C.I. No. 42755. The latter has not been used specifically as such, although it would probably function in the same way as the mixture. Methyl blue is now being furnished under the designation "aniline blue" by one manufacturer. I have interchanged the 2 dyes successfully in Mallory, Curtis and Mann technics and have no doubt that methyl blue can be used in place of aniline blue W.S. with no appreciable difference in results.

Another dye in the above group, naphthol blue black, also deserves

TABLE 6-7. ACID AMINO DYES USED AS SUPRAVITAL STAINS[1]

Colour Index no.		Colour Index, 2d ed., Part I, class color no.	HT 3d ed. stain class	Name	mol. wt.	Color	SO₃Na	CO₂Na and other acid	Amino groups			Solubility in 100 parts	
1st ed.	2d ed.								NH₂	NHR	NR₂	Water	Alcohol
438	22850	(DR)	SVA	Trypan red	1002.857	R	5	...	2	...	...	3.5	0
456	23570	DR-34	SVA	Vital red	826.793	R	3	...	2	...	...	3.75	0.17
	23860	DB-53	SVA	Evans blue	960.842	B	4	...	2	...	...	7	0.7
465	23690	DB-25	SVA	Dianil blue 2R	844.761	B	3	...	...	...	...	5	0.01
477	23850	DB-14	SVA	Trypan blue	960.842	B	4	...	2	...	...	1	0.02
			SVA	Vital new red (Conn, 6th ed.)	782.777	R	2	...	...	4	...	Sol.	
			SVA	Vital new red (E. Gurr)	986.885	R	4	...	...	4	...	1.3	0
	25375	DR-49	SVA?	Benzo light eosin BL	986.885	R	4	...	...	4	...	Sol.	Slight

Abbreviations: *SVA*, supravital acid; colors: *R*, red; *B*, blue.
[1] Among the above dye names only the word Evans is a proper name and must always be capitalized.

special mention. Under its original German name, *Amidoschwarz 10B,* it has had considerable use in Europe and among chemical chromatographers as a "specific protein stain." This usage is discussed later (p. 251). However, the name "amido black 10B" has been adopted in this edition.

A small group of sulfonated triphenylmethane dyes, acid fuchsin, patent blue V and cyanol FF, produce leuco dyes on reduction with zinc and acid; these leucos are used for the demonstration of hemoglobin (p. 365) and are included in Table 6–6 as "redox" dyes. Methyl blue behaves similarly in the hemoglobin peroxidase technic.

Members of a further group of acid disazo dyes have been used as **supravital** stains for phagocytic and pinocytic activity. The biologists who have used them have retained the traditional names dianil blue RR or 2R, trypan red and trypan blue for these three dyes, but have renamed some of the others. Vital red was "diamine purpurin 3B." Trypan blue is itself more commonly referred to as "blue 3B" or "direct blue 3B," with or without various brand prefixes.

Vital new red is formulated by Conn (6th ed.) as the disulfonic derivative of the same base as C.I. No. 25375, which is a tetrasulfonate and agrees almost exactly, except for the position of the 2 naphthyl sulfonic groups, with E. Gurr's formulation of vital new red. It is probable that C.I. No. 25375, benzo eosin LB or benzo light eosin LB would serve. Evans blue is identified with direct pure blue BF (Fran), which is C.I. No. 23860.

Orcein, formed from orcinol, 3,5-dihydroxytoluene, by air oxidation in the presence of ammonia, forms purple alkali salts and is to be considered an acid dye or dye mixture of red orcein $C_{28}H_{24}N_2O_7$, a yellow compound $C_{21}H_{29}NO_5$ and an amorphous product similar to litmus. It is sold in both natural and synthetic forms. Chromosome cytologists often insist on the natural product for acetic orcein technics (p. 158); the synthetic product appears to be effective in elastin stains (p. 552).

FAT STAINS

The oldest member of this group, osmium tetroxide, is not a dye at all but an unstable oxide which is reduced to a black substance by unsaturated fats and fatty acids, by eleidin and by other substances. Osmium tetroxide, commonly called osmic acid, is now finding increasing use in histology as a fixative for electron microscopy, in addition to its histochemical usage in the demonstration of unsaturated fats and other reducing substances such as eleidin, melanin, catecholamines, etc. For demonstration of degenerating myelin I now prefer frozen section methods which permit combination of normal myelin methods with fat stains of contrasting color.

The commonly used oil soluble dyes fall into 2 main groups: (1)

Table 6-8. Oil Soluble Dyes Used as Fat Stains[1]

Colour Index no. 1st ed.	Colour Index no. 2d ed.	Colour Index, 2d ed., Part I, class color no.	HT 3d ed. stain class	Name	Mol. wt.	NH_2	NHR	NR_2	OH	Water	Alcohol	Glycol	Xylene	Color
				Monoazo Dyes										
73	12140	SO-7	OS	Sudan II	276.342	—	—	—	1β	Insol.	0.28	1.25	3.0	Y
81	12020	SF-5	OS	Sudan brown	298.348	—	—	—	1α	Insol.	Sol.	...	Sol.	F
113	12150	SR-1	OS	Sudan R, Sudan red B	278.315	—	—	—	1β	Insol.	Sol.	...	Sol.	R
	12085	PR-4	OS	Permanent red R	327.737	—	—	—	1β	Insol.	Sol.	...	Sol.	R
		SF-9	OS	Oil brown D	......	...	...	...	...	Insol.	Sol.	...	Sol.	F
		SR-40	OS	Sudan Corinth 3B	......	...	...	...	...	Insol.	Sol.	...	Sol.	R
	12155	SR-17	OS	Sudan red (E. Gurr)	292.332	—	—	—	1β	Insol.	1	1.25	1.25	R
				Disazo Dyes										
248	26100	SR-23	OS	Sudan III	352.402	—	—	—	1β	Insol.	0.25	3.15	2.25	OR
258	26105	.....	OS	Sudan IV	380.456	—	—	—	1β	Insol.	0.5	2.5	3.5	R
	Similar	.....	OS	Sudan red 4BA	......	—	—	—	1β	Insol.	Sol.	...	Sol.	R
	26120	SR-26	OS	Oil red 4B, EGN	394.483	—	—	—	1β	Insol.	Sol.	...	Sol.	R
	26125	.....	OS	Oil red O	408.510	—	—	—	1β	Insol.	0.5	2.5	3.5	R
	26050	SR-19	OS	Sudan red VII B	379.472	—	1β	—	—	Insol.	4.25	4	10.45	R
	26150	SN-3	OS	Sudan black B	456.559	—	2(4,5)	—	—	Insol.	0.25	1.0	2.5	BN / GN
				Acylated Dyes										
	26105 (Ac)	.....	OS	Acetyl Sudan IV	422.494	—	—	—	Ester	Insol.	Sol.	...	Sol.	R
	26150 (Ac)	.....	OS	Acetyl Sudan black	540.635	—	Amide	—	—	Insol.	Sol.	...	Sol.	BN / GN
	26125 (Bz)	.....	OS	Benzoyl oil red O	512.619	—	—	—	Ester	Insol.	Sol.	...	Sol.	R

TABLE 6-8. OIL SOLUBLE DYES USED AS FAT STAINS (*Continued*)

Colour Index no. 1st ed.	Colour Index no. 2d ed.	Colour Index, 2d ed., Part I, class color no.	HT 3d ed. stain class	Name	Mol. wt.	NH₂	NHR	NR₂	OH	Water	Alcohol	Glycol	Xylene	Color
				Triphenylmethane Dyes										
689	42775	SB-3	OS B	Spirit blue	490.057 { mixture 552.128	1 —	{ 2 3 }	—	—	Insol.	1.5	4.0	...	B
				Aminoanthroquinone Dyes										
	61100	V-1 Disp	OS	Sudan violet	238.250	$2^{(1,4)}$	—	—	—	Insol.	3.2	4.0	5.0	V
			OS	Sudan blue	294.358		$2^{(1,4)}$	—	—	Insol.	4.0	3.75	5.0	B
	62545	Sol.	OS	Sudan green	434.500		$2^{(1,4)}$	—	—	Insol.	3.2	4.85	1.6	G
	61555	SB-14	OS	Oil blue N	376.504		$2^{(1,4)}$	—	—	Insol.	Sol.	...	Sol.	B
			OS	Carcinel red	291.353		$1^{(1)}$	—	—	Insol.	Sol.	...	Sol.	R
			OS	Coccinel red	376.504		$2^{(1,5)}$	—	—	Insol.	Sol.	...	Sol.	R
				Fluorochrome Dyes										
			OSF	3,4-Benzpyrene	252.316	—	—	—	—	Very slight	Sol.?	...	Sol.	fBW

Abbreviations: *OS*, oil soluble dye; *OSF*, oil soluble fluorochrome; *B*, basic dye. Colors: *R*, red; *O*, orange; *Y*, yellow; *F*, brown; *G*, green; *B*, blue; *N*, black; *fBW*, blue white fluorescence. Sudan red 4BA is "similar" to Sudan IV, C.I. No. 26105. The — sign indicates "none."

[1] Among the above dye names only the words Sudan and Corinth are proper names and must be capitalized.

131

basic arylamines with very low water solubility, such as Sudan black B and Sudan red VII B, also called Fettrot VII B, among the azo dyes, the basic triphenylmethane dye spirit blue and the 6 aminoanthraquinone dyes included in Table 6-8; and (2) β-naphthols such as the original disazo dyes, Sudans III and IV and their close relatives oil red O and oil red 4B or EGN and Sudan IV BA (which may well be a synonym of oil red 4B) and a small group of monoazo dyes, Sudan II, Sudan brown, Sudan R, Sudan red and a few others. I have included with them in the table permanent red R, which has the interesting trade names Blazing Red, Flaming Red and Fire Red, and has been used occasionally as a fat stain (Putt, *Lab. Invest.* **5**:377, 1956).

Of the 3 acylated dyes tested, which do not form stable unextractable pigments with neutrophil leucocyte granules, as their parent dyes do, one, acetyl Sudan black, is commercially available from National Aniline Division, which also prepared for me a benzoylated oil red O. Oil red 4B or EGN (*Stain Techn.* **19**:55, 1944) was identified for me by the National Aniline Division as *p*-xylylazo-*o*-tolylazo-β-naphthol, C.I. No. 26120; and oil red O, as *p*-xylylazo-*p*-xylylazo-β-naphthol, which is now included under C.I. No. 26125.

Oil red 4B   Oil red O

Several other excellent dyes for fat staining by our supersaturated iso-propanol technic (p. 457) were mentioned in the same report: oil brown D (NAC), Sudan brown 5B (G), Sudan red 4B (G) and Sudan Corinth B (G). Sudan red 4BA (G) is stated to be similar to C.I. No. 26105, Sudan IV; Sudan Corinth 3B (G) is identified as Solvent red 40, an azo dye of unstated composition, and oil brown D (W) is solvent brown 7, an unidentified monoazo dye.

In fluorescence microscopy several acid and basic dyes have been used in simple aqueous solution as fat stains. Of these phosphine, a basic acridine dyestuff, seems to be one of the best (p. 459). Also used are methylene blue, rhodamine B, magdala red (echt), all basic dyes, and the acid dyes titan yellow or thiazol yellow G (C.I. No. 19540) and thiazine red R (C.I. No. 14780) (see Table 6-5, p. 122).

STABILIZED DIAZONIUM SALTS

I have included most of the commercially available stabilized diazonium salts in Table 6-9, which gives the second edition *Colour Index* num-

TABLE 6-9. STABILIZED DIAZONIUM SALTS USED IN HISTOLOGIC STAINING PROCEDURES[1]

Colour Index no., 2d ed.	Colour Index Azoic Diazo no.	Preferred name	Colors developed			Usual stabilizers	Mol. wt. of amine	Coupling rate				Synonyms
			β-Naphthol AS naphthol	α-Naphthol	Entero-chromaffin			ICI	N	B	L	
37245	....	Fast black B	N	...	RF-N	$ZnCl_2$	199.3	...	...	...	f	Black B, BS
37190	38	Fast black K	BN	...	N	$ZnCl_2$, also Zn free	302.3	...	...	...	f	Black K, NK
37235	48	Fast blue B	B+	FN	FP	$ZnCl_2$	244.3	s	f	s	m	Blue B, BNS, diazo blue B
37175	20	Fast blue BB	VB-VN	...	OR	$ZnCl_2$	300.4	s	...	...	m	Diazo blue BB, blue 2B, DB
37155	24	Fast blue RR	PR-VB+	N	R±	$ZnCl_2$	272.3	s	...	...	s	Blue RR
37255	35	Fast blue VB	VB+	...	O	$\bar{C}l$	263.3	...	...	s	s	Variamine blue B, BA, BD, BN blue V, fast blue BM, MB
37135	1	Fast Bordeaux GP	PR	P	O+	$ZnCl_2$	168.2	f	...	...	s	Bordeaux GP
37020	....	Fast brown RR	F	...	...	$ZnCl_2$	177.0	f	...	f	...	Brown RR
37200	21	Fast brown V	F	...	...	Not stated	320.7	...	s	f	...	Fast brown VA
37160	43	Fast Corinth LB	PR	...	...	$ZnCl_2$	276.7	...	...	f	...	Corinth LB, diazo Corinth LB
37220	39	Fast Corinth V	PR-FR	...	...	$ZnCl_2$	300.3	...	...	...	...	Corinth V
37195	51	Fast dark blue R	VBN	...	BN	$ZnCl_2$	371.2	s	...	f	f	Navy blue RN
37210	4	Fast garnet GBC	R	RF	OR+	SO_4H	225.3	f	m	...	f	Garnet GBC
37215	27	Fast garnet GC	FR	...	...	$\bar{C}l$	225.3	f	f	...	...	Fast Garnet AC, diazo garnet GC, Garnet GC, AC, GCD
37025	6	Fast orange GR	RO	...	OR	$ZnCl_2$	138.1	f	f	...	...	Diazo red AL, Red AL, ALS
37275	36	Fast red AL	R	...	F	$ZnCl_2$	223.2	f	f	...	...	1-Aminoanthraquinone diazo
37125	5	Fast red B	R+	...	OR+	Disulfonaphthalene	168.2	f	...	...	f	Red B, red V, Fast red 5NA, BN

TABLE 6-9. STABILIZED DIAZONIUM SALTS USED IN HISTOLOGIC STAINING PROCEDURES (*Continued*)

Colour Index no., 2d ed.	Colour Index Azoic Diazo no.	Preferred name	Colors developed			Usual stabilizers	Mol. wt. of amine	Coupling rate				Synonyms
			β-Naphthol AS naphthol	α-Naphthol	Entero-chromaffin			ICI	N	B	L	
37035	37	Fast red GG	R	...	OR+	BF₃, SŌ₄H, etc.	138.1	f	...	...	f	Nitrazol CF, nitrosamine red / Para red, red 2G, GG, 2J
37110	8	Fast red GL	R+	...	PR	Disulfonaphthalene	152.2	f	...	f	...	Diazo red G, red G
37040	9	Fast red 3GL	R	...	FR-OR+	ZnCl₂	172.6	f	...	f	...	Red 3GK, 3GL, 3G / Diazo red or fast red 3GL
37150	42	Fast red ITR	R	...	...	ZnCl₂	258.3	mf	...	...	...	Red ITR
37120	10	Fast red RC	R	RF	...	ZnCl₂	157.6	f	...	...	...	Diazo red RC, red RC / Fast red 4GA
37100	14, 34	Fast red RL	PR	...	R+	BF₃	152.2	f	f	...	f	Red RL, fast red NRL
37085	11	Fast red TR	R+	F	...	Disulfonaphthalene	HCl 178.1	f	...	...	...	Fast red 5CT, TRN / Red TR, TA, TRS
		Fast red violet LB	PR	...	...	Cl	260.7	f	...	f	...	Red violet LB
37010	3	Fast scarlet GG	OR	...	OR+	ZnCl₂	162.0	f	f	...	...	Scarlet 2G, GG / Fast scarlet GGS, GGN
37130	13	Fast scarlet R	R	RF	...	ZnCl₂	168.2	f	...	f	...	Diazo scarlet R, / Scarlet R, fast scarlet 4NA
37165	41	Fast violet B	BV	...	OF	ZnCl₂	256.3	s	...	...	...	
37265	...	α-Naphthylamine	R	R	R	Disulfonaphthalene	143.2	...	...	...	...	
37260	45	Fast black G	N, FN	...	FN		...	...	...	...	s	

Abbreviations: Colors—R, red; Y, yellow; O, orange; G, green; B, blue; V, violet; P, purple (redder than violet); F, brown; N, black. Coupling rates: s, slow; m, medium; f, fast. N, Nachlas; B, Burstone; L, Lillie; ICI, *Imperial Chemical Industries Manual.* β-Naphthol and naphthol colors are from the *Colour Index*; enterochromaffin, mostly from Lillie; α-naphthol colors, from various sources.

[1] Among the "preferred names" only the words Bordeaux and Corinth are proper names and require capitalization. The synonyms are further subject to the usual rules covering trade mark names.

bers and the Azoic Diazo numbers, the molecular weights of the un-diazotized bases, the colors given with naphthols and with entero-chromaffin, the nature of the usual stabilizer or anion, available data as to coupling rates and the commoner synonyms.

The names used under "Preferred name" are those specified by the *Journal of Histochemistry and Cytochemistry* (7:281, 1959), with 1 or 2 additions.

A few fresh diazonium salts are employed; directions for their preparation are included under Phenols, in Chapter 8, pp. 222–224.

Amine contents of these stabilized salts vary from 18% to a stated 100%, and they vary also among manurfacturers for the same salt; 20% is a common level. Some data on amine content are included in *Biological Stains*, 7th ed., The Williams & Wilkins Company, Baltimore, 1961. Ordinarily, when knowledge of this subject is important, it may be obtained from the manufacturers.

It is necessary to take care that the base is not furnished under the same name. When ordering, always specify which is required, the base or the salt. In using the "base" it is necessary to diazotize with nitrous acid according to the usual chemical procedure for the specific diazonium salt in question; the "salt" is ready for immediate use.

THE TETRAZOLES

These are colorless, fairly readily water soluble compounds of the general structure given below, which yield insoluble, usually highly colored pigments on reduction and are used in histochemistry as hydrogen acceptors to localize results of various enzymatic oxidations.

The tetrazoles are divided into mono- and ditetrazoles; in the latter two tetrazole rings share a biphenylene group as one of the substituents.

Formulae II and III are of course identical. The three formulae are presented to illustrate the confusion which exists in naming and numbering these compounds. Purely for the sake of uniformity I have formulated all ditetrazoles with the biphenylene group at 2,2'.

Nitro blue tetrazolium is written by Nachlas, Tsou *et al.* as (III) 2,2'-dinitrophenyl-5,5'-diphenyl-3,3'-(3,3'-dimethoxy-4,4'-biphenylene)tetrazolium chloride but is drawn with the methoxy groups ortho to the diphenylene bond. I follow Conn and Pearse in the position of the methoxy groups, and have formulated the diphenyl at 2,2' to agree with neotetrazolium and blue tetrazolium, recognizing that the 2,2' and 3,3' diphenylene formulations are tautomeric to each other.

Nitro NT is accordingly 2,2'-biphenylene-3,3'-di-*p*-nitrophenyl-5,5'-diphenylditetrazolium chloride. Note that Nitro NT is distinguished from NNT.

Tetranitro NT is 2,2'-biphenylene-3,3',5,5'-tetra-*p*-nitrophenyl-ditetra-

TABLE 6-10. MONO- AND DITETRAZOLES WITH SHORT NAME AND COMMON[1] ABBREVIATION

Usual abbreviation	Short name	Chemical description
TTC, TPT	Triphenyl tetrazolium	2,3,5-Triphenyltetrazolium chloride
NT	Neotetrazolium	2,2'-Biphenylene-3,3',5,5'-tetraphenyl-ditetrazolium chloride
	M and B 1767	2,5-Biphenyl-3-*p*-styrylphenyltetra-zolium chloride
INT	Iodonitrotetrazolium	2-*p*-Iodophenyl-3-*p*-nitrophenyl-5-phenyltetrazolium chloride
BT	Blue tetrazolium	2,2'-Di-*o*-anisylene-3,3',5,5'-tetra-phenylditetiazolium chloride
Nitro-BT	Nitro blue tetrazolium	2,2'-Di-*o*-anisylene-3,3'-di-*p*-nitro-phenyl-5,5'-diphenylditetrazolium chloride
Nitro NT	Nitroneotetrazolium	2,2'-Biphenylene-3,3'-*p*-nitrophenyl-5,5'-diphenylditetrazolium chloride
Tetranitro NT	Tetranitroneotetrazolium	2,2'-Biphenylene-3,3',5,5'-tetra-*p*-nitro-phenylditetrazolium chloride
Tetranitro BT	Tetranitro blue tetrazolium	2,2'-Di-*o*-anisylene-3,3',5,5'-tetra-*p*-ni-trophenylditetrazolium chloride
MTT	. . . .	3-(4,5-Dimethylthiazolyl-2)-2,5-di-phenyltetrazolium chloride
TV	Tetrazolium violet	2,5-Diphenyl-3-(2,4-dinitrophenyl)-tetrazolium chloride
NNT	*m*-Nitroneotetrazolium	2,2'-Biphenylene-3,3'-diphenyl-5,5'-*m*-nitrophenylditetrazolium chloride

[1] This list of names of tetrazoles contains no proper names, and no capitals are required. The abbreviations are capitalized as given.

zolium chloride, and tetranitro BT is the corresponding 2,2'-di-*o*-anisylene compound.

MTT is 3-(4,5-dimethylthiazolyl-2)-2,5-diphenyl tetrazolium chloride. Pearse's considerations as to formation of two 5 membered chelate rings require that the charged N be at 3 rather than 2. He does not account for the second valency bond of the Co ion (*J. Histochem.* 5:515, 1957).

Tetrazolium violet, TV, is 2,5-diphenyl-3-α-naphthyl-tetrazolium chloride (Glenner *et al.*, *J. Histochem.* 5:591, 1957; Pearson, *ibid.* 6:112, 1958). Pearson highly recommends *m*-nitroneotetrazolium, NNT, 2,2'-diphenyl-5,5'-di-*m*-nitrophenyl-3,3'-*p*-*p*-diphenylene, which I write as the tautomer to agree with the other ditetrazole formulae. The formazan is very finely crystalline and insoluble in alcohol. An 80% alcohol extraction is recommended to remove fat and prevent later crystal growth in the aqueous mounts.

At this writing, 3 ditetrazoles seem about equal for fineness of crystal

Formulation of tetrazoles

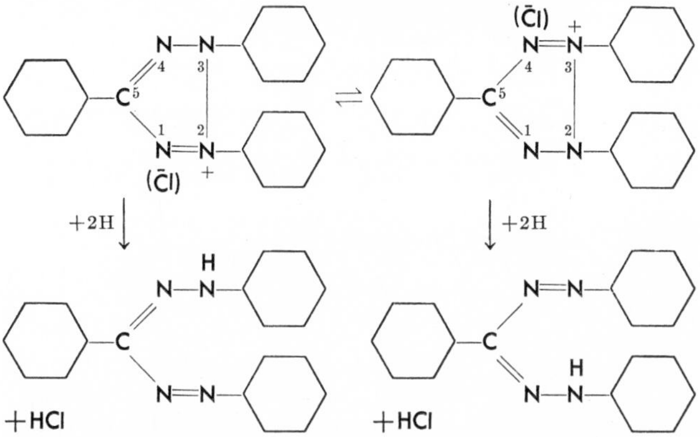

Tetrazole
M.W. 334.818.

Formazans

Usual form   Tautomeric form

Triphenyltetrazolium chloride and tautomer, with respective formazans

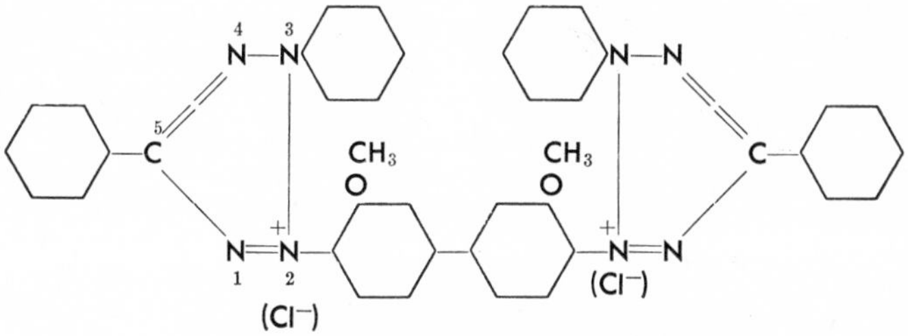

Blue tetrazolium
M.W. 692.674

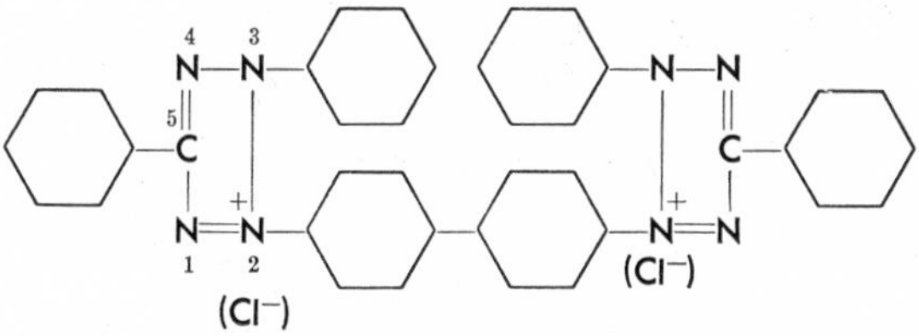

Neotetrazolium
M.W. 632.620

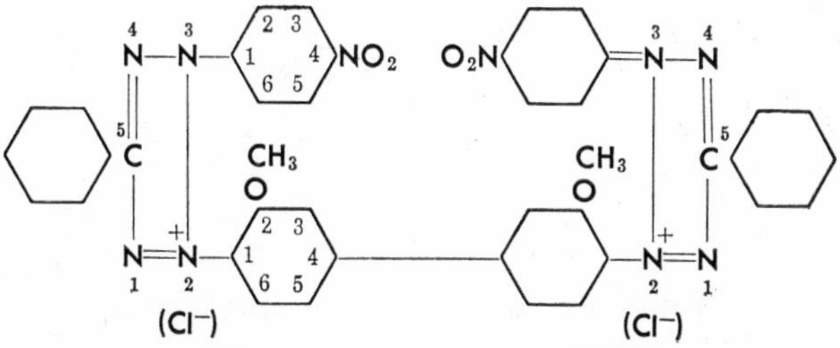

I. Nitro blue tetrazolium (NBT)
M.W. 817.674

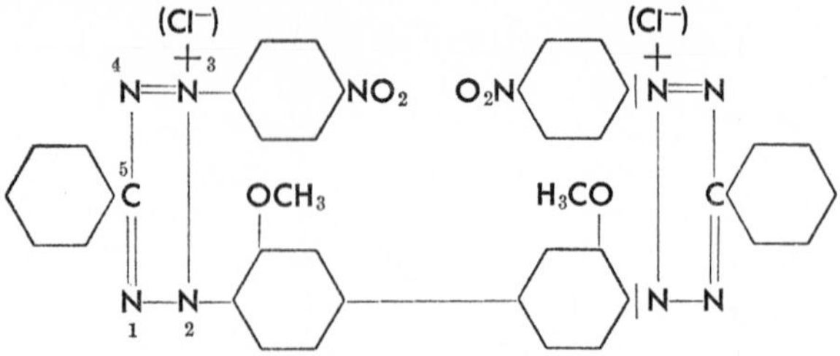

II. Tautomeric ditetrazole (NBT)

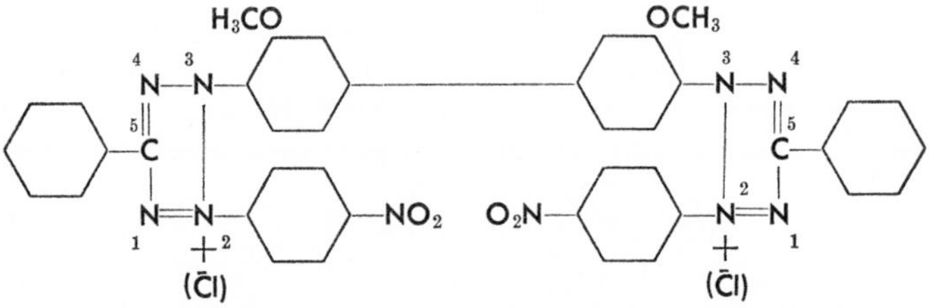

III. Nitro blue tetrazolium tautomer, renumbered

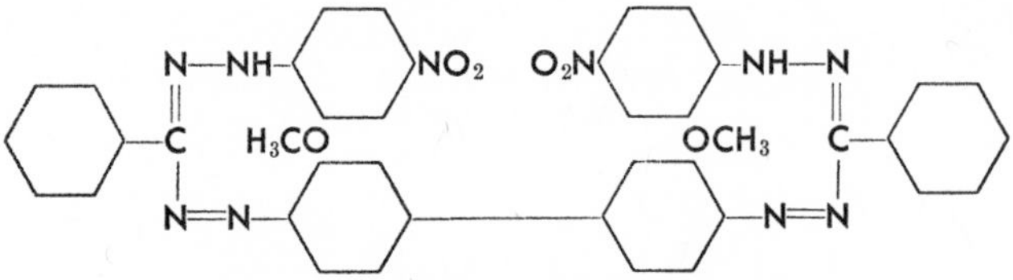

IV. Nitro blue tetrazolium formazan

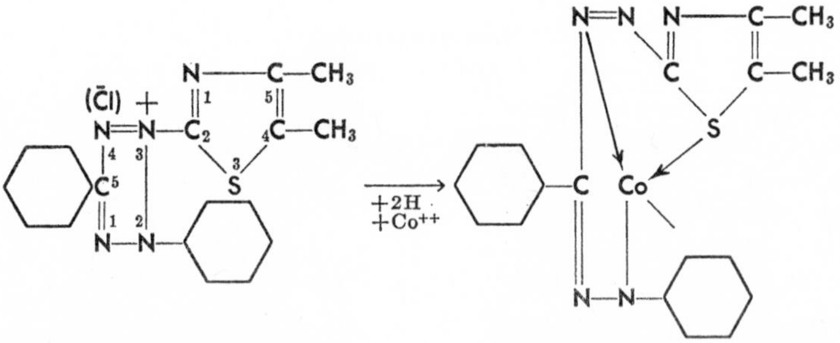

MTT, 3-(4,5-dimethyl-
thiazolyl-2)-2,5-diphenyl
tetrazolium

Cobalt chelated formazan

Tautomeric form, to agree with other formulae

Pearson's NNT, m-Nitroneotetrazolium chloride (5-m-NNT)
M.W. 757.620

Tetranitro blue tetrazolium (TNBT)[1]
(Rosa and Tsou, *Nature* **192**:990, 1961)
M.W. 907.674
Formazan, reddish brown, not fat soluble (Nachlas *et al. J. Histochem.* **5**:420, 1957)

Iodonitrotetrazolium chloride (INT)
M.W. 505.720

Tetrazolium violet (TV)
M.W. 384.878

[1] Available from Nutritional Biochemicals Corp., Cleveland 28, Ohio.

Tetranitroneotetrazolium (TNNT)
M.W. 847.620
Formazan, brown, not oil soluble (Nachlas *et al.; J. Histochem.* **5**:420, 1957)

Nitroneotetrazolium (3P-NNT) of Nachlas *et al.*
M.W. 757.620
Formazan, red to purple, partly fat soluble (*J. Histochem.* **5**:420, 1957)

size, rapidity of reaction and insolubility in fats: Nitro-BT, Tetranitro BT and Pearson's 5,5′-*m*-nitroneotetrazolium (NNT). This last is to be distinguished from the nitro NT of Nachlas *et al.*, which is a 3,3′-di-*p*-nitrophenyl neotetrazolium, is partly fat soluble and forms mixed fine and coarse crystals. Seligman's group preferred the blue color of the nitro BT to the red brown of the otherwise equal tetranitro BT. Of the 3, the first 2 have been made commercially available.

The thiazolyl monotetrazole MTT is preferred for electronmicrography because of its metal chelation capability, but it is difficult to obtain, even in England.

Iodonitrotetrazolium (INT) seems to be preferred for microchemical assay of extracts by colorimetry at 494 mμ.

IODINE

Probably the oldest of all stains,[1] used by Raspail (*Ann. Sci. Nat.* **6:** 224, 384, 1825) and Caventou (*Ann. chim.* **31**:358, 1826) in the study of the structure of the starch granule, the element iodine is still widely used in a variety of tests, which are detailed in the appropriate sections. It gives reactions with amyloid, cellulose, chitin, starch, carotenes and glycogen. It is used as a reagent to alter crystal and methyl violet so that they are retained by certain bacteria and fibrin. It may serve as an oxidiz-

[1] Although Robert Hooke (*Micrographia*, Royal Society, London, 1665) notes the use of tinctures of "Logwood and Cocheneel" in tinging liquors (p. 13), in his observation of dyed hairs with the microscope he does not identify the dyes used.

TABLE 6-11. COMPOSITION OF LUGOL'S IODINE SOLUTION

Formula[1]	Iodine	Potassium iodide	Distilled water
Lugol's "rubefacient solution," 1830..........	1	2	12
U.S.P. 1870 to XIV, A.M.A. editors, *Army Technicians' Manual*.........................	5	10	100
Lee, 1890–1937; Cowdry, 1943, 1948...........	4	6	100
Mosse in Ehrlich's *Encyklopädie;* Schmorl, 1907, 1929; Roulet, 1948; Lillie, 1948; Langeron's "double," 1934, 1949[2].....................	1	2	100
Langeron, 1934, 1949.........................	1	2	200
Romeis, 1932–1948; Roulet, 1948; Gomori (see p. 240)[3].................................	1	2	300

[1] For all these formulae, I recommend that the potassium iodide be first dissolved in 1–2 times its weight of water. The iodine then dissolves easily in this concentrated solution. When solution is complete, add the rest of the prescribed volume of water.

[2] Commonly called Weigert's or Gram-Weigert's iodine.

[3] Commonly called Gram's iodine.

ing agent. It is widely used for the removal of mercurial fixation artifacts.

It is used in the form of dilute alcoholic solutions and in various modifications of Lugol's solution. The term *Lugol's solution* has been quite variously used by different writers, as shown in Table 6-11. Many writers simply refer to it by name, without hint as to which formula was used.

Chapter 7

Nuclei, Nucleic Acids, General
Oversight Stains

Nuclear chromatin, which is the substance demonstrated when nuclei are stained in histologic sections, is composed of the 2 nucleoproteins. Deoxyribonucleoprotein, which occurs only in cell nuclei, is the major component of the chromosomes, replicates itself during the intermitotic-mitotic cycle and also serves in the synthesis of ribonucleoprotein, found in chromosomes, nucleoli and cytoplasmic granules. This second nucleoprotein is present in considerable amount wherever active synthesis of other proteins is being carried out.

Deoxyribonucleic acid is composed of units of 2-deoxyribose condensed in successive units with the purines adenine and guanine and the pyrimidines thymine and cytosine. These units are linked with 3-5 ester linkages by moles of phosphoric acid, whose third acid group serves to bind the nucleic acid to a basic protein. Ribonucleic acid is similarly constituted, except that the sugar is D-ribose and the pyrimidine uracil replaces the thymine of the deoxyribonucleic acid. In actively growing or protein synthesizing cells at least, there is fairly rapid turnover of purines, pyrimidines, phosphorus and sugars. This turnover has been utilized for selective radioautographic labeling of deoxyribonucleic acid with tritium tagged thymine, or of ribonucleic acid with H^3-uracil. C^{14} labeled adenine, P^{35} phosphate and other labeled compounds have also been used.

Deoxyribose, when hydrolyzed from its purine (and pyrimidine) linkages, is promptly Schiff positive, like other 2-deoxyaldoses. Ribose does not react promptly with Schiff reagent, nor do glucose, mannose and other ordinary aldoses. This reactivity forms the basis of the Feulgen reaction, which is regarded as highly specific for deoxyribonucleic acid (abbreviated DNA or PNA in English; ADN in French; DNS in German, etc.

The phosphoric acid residues which are ordinarily bound to nuclear histones by salt linkages, are apparently readily available for the binding of basic (cationic) aniline dyes, and since phosphoric acid is a fairly strong acid, nuclei stain with azure A, methylene blue, safranin and the

Formulae

Segment of double helix of deoxyribonucleic acid. Dotted lines indicate interchain purine-pyrimidine hydrogen bonding. H^+ indicates phosphoric acid residues for bonding to basic proteins or cationic dyes.

Adenine   Guanine   Cytosine   Uracil

Thymine   Deoxyribose   D-Ribose

like, even from quite weak solutions, at pH levels as low as 2, and with stronger solutions down to pH 1. Only sulfate esters of mucopolysaccharides and oxidatively created cysteic acid residues stain at lower pH levels. It is characteristic of salt linkage basic dye staining that stained preparations are again readily decolorized by exposure to dilute mineral acids in aqueous or alcoholic solution, and by certain salt solutions.

Certain basic dyes with free NH_2 groups, notably rosaniline and pararosaniline are capable of irreversibly staining nuclei from warm (60°C) alcoholic (70%) hydrochloric acid (0.1–0.2 N). The mechanism of this staining has not been conclusively worked out, but it is believed to result from hydrolysis of the purine (and pyrimidine) bonds with the aldoses and condensation of the liberated aldehydes with the dye amino groups to form Schiff's bases of the secondary amine or "diphenamine" type (*J. Histochem.* **10**:303, 1962). This coloration is acid fast and probably is the type occurring in those acid fast stains for tubercle bacilli which result in failure of nuclear decolorization. Since this diphenamine condensation with aldehyde and the hydrolytic liberation of aldehyde itself both occur more rapidly in acid than in neutral solutions, it follows that for differential staining of acid fast organisms and lipids, strongly acid dye solutions probably should be avoided.

Mordant dyeing with alum hematoxylin, posthydrolytic staining with pure dilute hematoxylin and azo coupling of nuclei (Pearse) persist after salt type basic dye staining and the Feulgen reaction have been abolished by a 1 hour or more hydrolysis at 60°C in 1 N hydrochloric acid; hence these stainings are to be assigned to the basic proteins or histone fraction of the nucleus. Staining of nuclei by acid ("anionic") dyes, with or without prior methylation to esterify the free phosphoric acid residues, also depends on histone, and specific arginine reactions can be similarly employed to demonstrate the histone.

In practice it is often desirable, for morphologic detail, to combine a nuclear stain with a second stain designed to demonstrate some other tissue element or elements, such as basic proteins, connective tissue fibers, mucopolysaccharides or other elements, and technics are given below exemplifying this practice. In addition nuclear stains are often added when the primary objective is the demonstration of other tissue constituents. Such technics appear in other chapters.

NUCLEIC ACIDS

The Caspersson school have used extensively the ultraviolet absorption of the nucleic acids at 260 mμ as a means of localizing these substances. Caspersson (*J. Roy. Micr. Soc.* **60**:8, 1940) uses a rather complicated apparatus for photometric estimation of ultraviolet absorption in quite small field areas. The estimates obtained by photography are quantitatively cruder, though qualitatively more accurate. In its applicability to living cells the method has certain special values. Mellors (*Science* 111: 627, 1950) found that living tissue cultures would tolerate as many as 30 photographic exposures at 260 mμ before being killed. The apparatus is expensive, whether for ultraviolet photography alone or for photometry as well, and seems adapted to highly specialized studies. For most purposes the histochemical procedures for the identification of nucleic acids are easier, more flexible and more differential.

Enzymatic Digestion and Acid Extraction Procedures for Selective Removal of the Nucleic Acids

Deoxyribonuclease Digestion. Kurnick (*Stain Techn.* 27:233, 1952) used a preparation DNase (obtained from the Worthington Laboratories, Freehold, N.J.) at a concentration of 2 mg/100 cc, in 0.01 M tris buffer, pH 7.6 (Gomori's, p. 667, diluted 1:5 with distilled water). On material fixed in 80% alcohol or Carnoy's fluid, digestion periods of 2 hours at 37°C or 24 hours at 21°C were recommended. Controls treated with buffer alone for the same period and unextracted controls should be used. Kurnick used his variant of the methyl green pyronin technic as the demonstration method (p. 152); but see the method of Love and Rabotti (p. 147).

The definitive test for the histochemical identification of ribonucleic acid is its digestion by the enzyme ribonuclease. This is ordinarily prepared from pancreas. Brachet used a boiled acid extract of pancreas. Ribonuclease is thermostable in acid. Most workers have preferred the crystalline substance isolated by the method of M. Kunitz (*J. Gen. Physiol.* 24:15, 1941) and now available commercially. The commercial enzyme has proved active in my hands at a 1:100,000,000 dilution. It functions well in 0.8% saline solution buffered with phosphates to pH 6. I prefer this pH level to the 6.75–7 levels of other workers because of the decreased section losses at the more acid level. I have found that commercial barley malt diastase also contains a thermostable ribonuclease, which I have explored extensively.

This digestion, at least in the case of the malt diastase ribonuclease, is largely inhibited by fixation in Kose's, Orth's and Möller's bichromate formalin fluids; less so by Zenker's fluid fixation. With formalin fixation the digestibility is influenced both by the duration of fixation and by the diluent. Longer aqueous formalin fixations make tigroid and ribonucleic acids generally more resistant. Brief alcoholic formalin fixations facilitate this ribonuclease activity of the diastase. Still better is Carnoy's fluid. Bouin's fluid fixation almost entirely prevents barley malt ribonuclease digestion of ribonucleic acids, but Gendre's alcoholic picroformalin acetic fixation allows fairly prompt digestion. Pancreatic ribonuclease does not appear to affect the basophilia of cartilage matrix or nucleus pulposus, in contrast to the crude barley malt diastase (pp. 496, 515).

Technic of Ribonuclease Digestion of Tigroid and Cytoplasmic Ribonucleic Acid.

1. Fix in Carnoy's fluid at 0°C or in acetic alcohol formalin (p. 39) for 18–24 hours. Wash in 95% alcohol over calcium carbonate. Complete the dehydration, dealcoholization and paraffin infiltration as usual.
2. Bring paraffin sections through xylene and alcohols to water. Do *not* collodionize. Collodion films prevent enzyme action almost completely.
3. Immerse for 1 hour or more at 37°C (or 50°C for more drastic action. The enzyme is destroyed at 60°C) in a buffered solution. Use simultaneous digestion controls in the solvent without enzyme.

   The solvent contains 8 gm sodium chloride, 0.28 gm anhydrous disodium phosphate and 1.97 gm sodium acid phosphate monohydrate per liter to give pH 6. This pH level has less detergent effect on sections than pH 7, and allows effective enzyme action. Commercial ribonuclease, obtained from Armour in 100 mg lots, is quite effective on cytoplasmic ribonucleic acid and on tigroid at 1:1,000,000; but is ineffective on glycogen at 1:5000. A concentration of 1:100,000 seems appropriate for testing purposes. The ribonuclease activity of malt diastase is evident to about 1:3000 dilution; its glycogenolytic action, to about 1:100,000. Hence a 1:1000 dilution is used for both purposes as a matter of routine.
4. Rinse in water and counterstain by azure eosin, by thionin, or by the other procedures which effectively demonstrate the tissue elements under consideration in undigested controls.

For precise work, after determination of the fact of digestibility under the conditions of the test, it is desirable to determine the minimum enzyme concentration which is effective in a set period, such as 1 hour at 37°C. This figure may be used for rough comparison with other sets of conditions or other objects.

Some enzyme preparations may contain also small amounts of a deoxyribonuclease (or protease?), whose action is manifest after 8–16 hour digestion periods. This activity (as well as amylase activity) may be selectively destroyed by adding 0.57 cc glacial acetic acid per 100 cc solution in distilled water (0.1 M) and boiling for 5 minutes. Then cool and neutralize with 1 N sodium hydroxide to about pH 6.2, using 1 to 2 drops of 1% aurin (rosolic acid) or nitrazine as an indicator, or adjusting with the pH meter. Since the solution now contains approximately 0.1 M sodium acetate (0.82%), addition of sodium chloride is unnecessary and has been found deleterious under some circumstances.

Leuchtenberger and Lund (*Exp. Cell Res.* 2:150, 1951) record that the keratohyalin granules of the dog epidermis are Feulgen negative and lose their basophilia to toluidine blue or azure A on digestion with ribonuclease.

TABLE 7-1. SOLUTION FORMULAE FOR NUCLEASES ACCORDING TO LOVE
AND RABOTTI

Deoxyribonuclease (crystallized)....	0.4 mg	......	1 mg	
Ribonuclease (2× or 5× crystallized)............................	......	4 mg	....	10 mg
0.2 M Magnesium chloride (4.066% $MgCl_2 \cdot 6H_2O$)..................	9 cc	9 cc	22.5 cc	22.5 cc
0.2 M Calcium chloride (2.22% $CaCl_2$)	1 cc	1 cc	2.5 cc	2.5 cc
0.1 M Tris buffer pH 7.3 (p. 667)....	8 cc	8 cc	20 cc	20 cc
Distilled water....................	22 cc	22 cc	55 cc	55 cc
Total volume....................	40 cc	40 cc	100 cc	100 cc

As noted on p. 496, human saliva also exhibits ribonuclease activity. Its action on tigroid was noted by Szent-Györgyi in 1931 (*Nature* **128:**761), who interpreted the action as indicating a polysaccharide nature of the tigroid.

For nuclease digestions Love and Rabotti (*J. Histochem.* **11:**603, 1963) used crystallized deoxyribonuclease (Worthington) at 1 mg/100 cc and ribonuclease (Worthington, 2× or 5× crystallized) at 10 mg/100 cc, both in 0.02 M tris buffer adjusted to pH 7.3 with 1 N HCl, containing 45 mM $MgCl_2$ and 5 mM $CaCl_2$. Digestions were for 2 hours at 37°C. For the differential effects of digestion in much weaker solutions, 0.6– 6 γ/100 cc of deoxyribonuclease and 6 γ/100 cc of ribonuclease, see the original paper.

The above concentration was the same as I recommended for Armour ribonuclease in the 1954 edition of this book, noting that it was still effective at 100 γ/100 cc but not noting the effect of a further decimal dilution to 10 γ/100 cc. In 1953 the effects recorded in 1963 by Love and Rabotti would have been regarded simply as incomplete digestion, so it appears that the additional crystallizations have operated to purify the effect, but not especially to increase the potency of the enzyme.

PERCHLORIC ACID EXTRACTION

It has long been known that the acids used in decalcification tend to destroy cytoplasmic basophilia and to impair nuclear staining. A number of workers have used perchloric acid solution for the differential extraction of ribonucleic acid: Ogur and Rosen (*Fed. Proc.* **8:**234, 1949), Seshachar (*Science* **110:**659, 1949), Sulkin and Kuntz (*Proc. Soc. Exp. Biol. Med.* **73:**413, 1950), Di Stefano (*Science* **115:**316, 1952).

Koenig and Stahlecker (*J. Nat. Cancer Inst.* **12:**237, 1951) report differential removal of ribonucleic acid from nerve cells by 10% aqueous perchloric acid in 15 minutes at 37°C, 2 hours at 25°C, 6 hours at 23°C,

12 hours at 20°C, and failure to extract in 4 days at 4°C. Liver cell ribonucleic acid was easier to remove, requiring 18 hours at 4°C and only 1 hour at 23°C. As with ribonuclease, prolonged formalin fixation greatly retards solution of ribonucleic acid in perchloric acid.

Extraction in hot perchloric acid (90°C) also removes deoxyribonucleic acid. Most other proteins are dissolved only to a minor extent; so the method is fairly differential.

It may be noted that after brief alcohol fixation, cytoplasmic basophilia of blood lymphocytes (in smears) may be removed by extraction for 1 hour at 58°C in distilled water or in 0.9% sodium chloride solution, and is impaired by even 10 minutes' extraction at this temperature.

Although the specificity of the extraction has not been determined, it is noted that brief treatment with alcoholic potassium hydroxide (1% in 80% alcohol, 20 minutes) differentially destroys cytoplasmic basophilia of formaldehyde fixed tissue, leaving nuclear staining unimpaired.

As noted before, other acids share this property of removing ribonucleic acid. Fisher (*Stain Techn.* **28**:9, 1953) showed that 2 *M* dilutions of nitric, hydrochloric or sulfuric acid at 0–5°C would differentially remove cytoplasmic basophilia of pancreas, various epithelia, gastric chief cells and Nissl substance of nerve cells in 16–24 hours. Extraction with stronger acid at the same temperature, or with the same concentrations at 25°C or 37°C was less differential; a good deal of nuclear basophilia was extracted as well.

These extractions induce sufficient hydrolysis of deoxyribonucleic acid to yield a Feulgen reaction with sufurous acid leucofuchsin but under the recommended conditions do not appreciably impair nuclear staining with azure A, even when the extraction at 0–5°C is prolonged to 32 hours.

The metachromasia of mast cells and of pyloric gland mucin, as well as the periodic acid Schiff reaction, were unimpaired by these extractions.

Atkinson (*Science* **116**:303, 1952) showed the parallelism in action between normal perchloric and hydrochloric acids, and pointed out that both reagents also extracted mucus, even at 5°C. Only toluidine blue stains were mentioned. The basophilia of mast cells and of cartilage was almost as resistant to these extractions as was that of cell nuclei.

SPECIFIC STAINING METHODS

Deoxyribonucleic (Thymonucleic) Acid

The Feulgen reaction is now generally considered specific for deoxyribonucleic acid. It depends on acid hydrolysis of the nucleic acid, which by liberating first the purines (and then the pyrimidines) from the deoxyribose phosphoric acid complexes leaves a reactive aldehyde group free on the latter. Although a similar liberation undoubtedly also occurs with ribonucleic acid, it is an observed fact that normal aldoses such as glucose, ribose, xylose, lyxose and the like do not form the deep red purple color complex with Schiff's sulfite leucofuchsin reagent, except perhaps very slowly; and that 2-deoxy aldoses, as well as other aldose sugars in which carbon 2 does not present a hydroxyl group, react promptly. Ketone also reacts, but more weakly and slowly. Hence it would appear that the application of Schiff reagent to sections should not be unduly prolonged. (See pp. 418–419).

Hydrochloric acid hydrolysis of nucleic acids is not instantaneous. It is observed that longer hydrolysis may give a more intense reaction, and that further prolongation of the treatment beyond the optimum weakens and finally completely destroys it. This last is sometimes observed when bone is treated with mineral acids for an unduly long period. For routine tissues hydrolysis with normal hydrochloric acid for 10 minutes gives a more intense reaction than it does in 5 minutes at 60°C. Usually, preceding and following 1 minute baths in normal hydrochloric acid at room temperature are prescribed. I fail to discern any advantage in these steps and have omitted them for some time as a matter of routine.

The optimum hydrolysis time for a maximal Feulgen reaction varies considerably with the object under study and the method of fixation employed. For the best results the time should be determined experimentally for each object studied.

The reaction of the hydrolyzed nuclear material with the Schiff reagent occurs quite promptly and appears to be as strong in 2 minutes as it is with the traditional 2 hour treatment. Use of the shorter period would appear to lessen the chance of confusing the slower reactions of ketones and normal aldoses.

The precise fuchsin content and method of manufacture of the Schiff reagent appear to have little influence. The same Schiff reagent as used for other purposes seems quite satisfactory for the Feulgen test.

The Feulgen Reaction. This reaction (modified from our 1948 text) for formalin fixed material is as follows:

1. Bring paraffin sections through xylene and alcohols to water as usual, (with the usual iodine thiosulfate sequence for removal of mercurial precipitates if required).
2. Place in normal hydrochloric acid (preheated) at 60°C for 10–15 minutes.
3. Immerse in Schiff reagent (p. 270) for 10 minutes.
4. Wash 1, 2 and 2 minutes in 3 successive baths of 0.05 M sodium bisulfite (0.52% $NaHSO_3$; 0.475% $Na_2S_2O_5$; 0.55% $K_2S_2O_5$).
   The sulfite baths should be discarded daily.
5. Wash 5 minutes in running water.

6. Counterstain a few seconds in 0.01% fast green FCF in 95% alcohol. The stain does not wash out in alcohol, but if it is too intense it may be removed promptly in water. Many workers prefer to omit this step.
7. Complete the dehydration with 100% alcohol; clear through 1 change of alcohol and xylene (50:50) and 2 of xylene. Mount in polystyrene, ester gum, Permount, HSR or other synthetic resin or in balsam.

Results: Nuclear chromatin is a deep red purple. The chromatin of plasmodia, sarcosporidia, toxoplasmata, histoplasmata and some yeasts is Feulgen positive, though often paler red than that of host cells. Feulgen positive globules are seen in *Cryptococcus neoformans* in some specimens and not in others. Similarly, small red bodies are seen in endosporulating coccidioides. No definite Feulgen positive material was found in vegetative forms of this fungus or of *Haplosporangium parvum*. Mold mycelia and Gram positive and Gram negative bacteria generally fail to stain. Typhus rickettsiae in yolk sac material are Feulgen negative; and *Pasteurella tularensis* and psittacosis rickettsiae usually are Feulgen negative, though I have seen occasional clusters of each stain red. Trophonuclei of *Trypanosoma cruzi* in its leishmania forms in heart muscle stain as deep purplish red rings. In some clusters blepharoplasts are unstained; in others they appear as deeper red purple rods. In vegetative trypanosomes in the blood (*T. brucei, T. equiperdum*) trophonuclei may stain with difficulty, and blepharoplasts may fail to stain. In encephalitozoa, chromatin varies from vague, poorly stained pink granules to fairly definite, oval and round, small red pink vesicles. Many coccidia (*Eimeria*) lack Feulgen positive material, but some young intraepithelial forms present more or less numerous small red rings apparently outlining the refractile granules seen in these organisms. Tigroid, mast cell granules, cartilage matrix, mucus are Feulgen negative (*J. Lab. Clin. Med.* **32**:76, 1947).

Although elastic fibers in arteries and elastic ligaments and laminae of some species are often Schiff positive after the Feulgen hydrochloric acid hydrolysis (especially in rodents), the same fibers tend to be more strongly Schiff positive when the acid treatment is omitted; and the reaction of elastica in Feulgen stains may be prevented by interposing a 30 minute bath in 5% phenylhydrazine before the acid hydrolysis step.

Kasten (*Nature* **184**:1797, 1959) recommends 15 minute 60°C hydrolysis in 1 N HCl for formalin fixed tissues, using his fluorochrome Schiff reagents (p. 272), but he often prefers room temperature hydrolysis, 6 minutes in 6N HCL.

Spicer (*Stain Techn.* **36**:337, 1961) utilizes the fact that Bouin fixation renders ribonucleic acid insoluble and at the same time hydrolyzes deoxyribonucleic acid to the aldehyde state to give a 2 color differentiation of the 2 nucleic acids.

Spicer's Feulgen Azure A Sequence Stain for Nucleic Acids.

1. Fix fresh tissues 18–24 hours in Bouin's fluid at 25°C.
2. Dehydrate, clear, infiltrate and imbed in paraffin as usual. Section shortly before staining; cut sections deteriorate on storage in the exposed state, perhaps because of air oxidation or hydration of aldehyde residues.
3. Deparaffinize and hydrate as usual, wash 5 minutes in running water to remove remaining free picric acid.
4. Schiff reagent (2 gm fuchsin per 100 cc, p. 270), 10 minutes.
5. 0.5% $Na_2S_2O_5$, 3 changes 1, 2 and 2 minutes, wash 10 minutes in running water.
6. Stain 30 minutes in 0.02% azure A or methylene blue in pH 3 or 3.5 McIlvaine citric acid disodium phosphate (p. 662). It is presumed that other appropriate buffers may be substituted.

Take 0.8 cc 1% azure A, 0.35 cc 0.2 M Na_2HPO_4, 1.65 cc 0.1 M citric acid and distilled water to make 40 cc for the pH 3 mixture, 0.6 and 1.4 for the pH 3.5 mixture. The lower pH level gives less dense thiazin staining.

7. Dehydrate in acetones or *tert*-butyl alcohol, clear and mount in synthetic resin.

Results: Nuclear deoxyribonucleic acid, purplish red; ribonucleic acid, blue. Metachromatic staining is more with azure A than with methylene blue. Carboxylic acids may be blocked from methylene blue staining by 1 hour 60°C methylation in 0.1 N HCl methanol, but most mucins do not stain with methylene blue after Bouin fixation. At least at pH levels below 4.5 acidic protein basophilia is not a complicating factor.

Turchini (*Trav. Mem. Soc. Chim. Biol.* **25**:1329, 1943) reported a method for the two nucleic acids which depends on specific colors produced by deoxyribose and ribose with 9-methyl- or -phenyl-2,3,7-trihydroxy-6-fluorone. Deoxyribose gives a blue violet color, ribose gives a yellowish rose in spot tests; purines, pyrimidines and phosphoric acid give no significant color. Backlar and Alexander (*Stain Techn.* **27**:147, 1952) reported a workable modification. At that time I had difficulty in obtaining a satisfactory sample of the reagent and there appears to have been little subsequent use of the method. For details the reader is referred to the second edition of this work and to the references cited above.

Basic Aniline Dyes. Staining 5–30 minutes in 0.1–1% solutions of safranin O (C.I. No. 50240), Janus green B (C.I. No. 11050), thionin (C.I. No. 52000), toluidine blue O (C.I. No. 52040), azure A, methyl or ethyl green (C.I. Nos. 42585, 42590) in 0.5–1% acetic acid solution in water or, even better, in 0.01 N HCl, will give quite selective chromatin staining even without much further differentiation.

Many prefer the practice of staining in solutions of similar strength in distilled water (or 20% alcohol to prevent growth of molds) for 5–20 minutes, followed by 1 minute differentiation in 5% to 5 minutes in 1% acetic acid. Mitotic nuclei are rendered more conspicuous when these differentiations are carried to a point where resting nuclei remain only rather lightly stained. This corresponds to a point where the sections appear only lightly colored on gross inspection, and when the differentiating fluid ceases to extract color clouds.

Many writers use far stronger solutions for nuclear staining than the 0.1–1% aqueous solutions noted above, alleging superior results. Saturated alcoholic and aqueous solutions and mixtures of them are recommended in the case of safranin; and one widely used formula, that of Babes (*Z. wiss. Mikr.* 4:470, 1887), recommended saturating 2% aniline water with (5–6%) safranin O (C.I. No. 50240) by heating to 60–80°C. This solution keeps only 1–2 months. It stains instantaneously. Differentiation in alcohol gives good staining of both resting and dividing nuclei; and use of 0.1–0.5% hydrochloric acid alcohol decolorizes resting nuclei more rapidly than chromosomes.

Material fixed with osmium tetroxide methods or subjected to prolonged chromation is more difficult to stain, and more prolonged exposures, higher pH levels and stronger dye solutions are necessary.

Methyl Green Pyronin

This method has had a revival of popularity in recent years. When correctly used on properly fixed material it differentiates specifically between deoxyribonucleic acid (green) and ribonucleic acid (red).

Its behavior is much influenced by prior fixation procedure. Best results have been obtained after neutral and acid alcoholic fixatives, especially Carnoy fluids (including alcohol formalin and acetic alcohol formalin; pp. 39, 42), and after the aqueous bichromate formaldehyde fixatives. Aqueous formalin and Zenker's fluid give inferior results: sections stain either all red or all blue.

The proportions of methyl green (C.I. No. 42585) or ethyl green (C.I. No. 42590) and pyronin Y (C.I. No. 45005) or pyronin B (C.I. No. 45010) vary greatly in various formulae.

The amount of phenol in the mixture should be small. More than 3% seems definitely deleterious. Some seems to be beneficial, though I have had good results without any.

The presence of glycerol is probably chiefly valuable in retarding evaporation when slides are stained flat with small volumes of solution. Alcohol seems unnecessary.

With fresh samples of methyl green and pyronin, it may be necessary

TABLE 7-2. CONSTITUTION OF METHYL GREEN PYRONIN FORMULA CALCULATED TO APPROXIMATELY 100 CC VOLUME

Formula	Methyl green, mg	Pyronin, mg	Alcohol, cc	Glycerol, cc	Phenol, cc	Water	"Carbolwater" %	"Carbolwater" cc	Total
Saathoff, 1905[1,2]	150	500	5	20	1.5	73.5	2	75	100
Saathoff–Conn[3,4]	800	200	4	16	1.6	78.4	2	80	100
Unna[1,2,5,6]	150	250	2.5	20	0.39	77.11	0.5	77.5	100
Ramón y Cajal[7]	150	250	2.5	20	0.5	78	....	....	101
Weill[5]	300	700	....	....	....	100	....	....	100
Masson[8]	2000	2000	....	....	5	100	....	....	105
Slides and Downey[9]	500	500	2.5	20	0.5	99.5	0.5	100	122.5
Slides and Downey reduced to 100[9]	408	408	2.04	16.3	0.41	81.3	0.5	81.7	100
Lillie[10]	700	300	....	20	0–2	80–78	....	....	100
Trevan and Sharrock[11]	36	157.6	....	....	....	100	....	....	100+ 65 mg orange G

Pappenheim's original prescription was inexact (Romeis, Unna in Ehrlich's *Encyklopädie*, 1903) and is omitted.

[1] Saathoff: "Die Methylgrün-Pryonin-Methode für elektive Färbung der Bakterien im Schnitt," *Deut. med. Wschr.* **32**:2047, 1905.
[2] Mallory: *Pathological Technique*, Philadelphia, W. B. Saunders Company, 1938.
[3] Conn, H. J.: *Biological Stains*, 4th ed., Geneva, N.Y., Biotech Publications, 1940.
[4] Conn, H. J., and Darrow, Mary: *Staining Procedures*, Geneva, N.Y., Biotech Publications, 1947.
[5] Romeis, B.: *Taschenbuch der mikroskopischen Technik*, 13th ed., Oldenbourg, Munich and Berlin, 1932.
[6] Schmorl, G.: *Die pathologisch-histologischen Untersuchungsmethoden*, 15th ed., Vogel, Leipzig, 1928.
[7] Ramón y Cajal, S.: *Histology*, translated by Fernán-Núñez, William Wood & Company, Baltimore, 1933.
[8] Langeron, M.: *Précis de microscopie*, 5th ed., Gauthier-Villars, Paris, 1936.
[9] Cowdry, E. V.: *Laboratory Technique in Biology and Medicine* Williams & Wilkins Company, Baltimore, 1948.
[10] Lillie, *Histopathologic Technic and Practical Histochemistry*, 2d ed., McGraw-Hill Book Company, New York, 1954.
[11] Trevan, D. J. and Sharrock A.: *J. Path. Bact.* **63**:326, 1951.

to vary the proportions. Make 2% aqueous solutions of each dye, mix in the desired proportions and add an equal volume of a mixture of 4 gm phenol, 56 cc water and 40 cc glycerol. The phenol is 2% in the final mixture and may be reduced to 2 gm or 1 gm if it is desired to try a 1% or 0.5% level.

The technic is simple.

1. Deparaffinize and hydrate paraffin sections as usual.
2. Stain 20 minutes in methyl green pyronin.
3. Wash in cold, recently boiled distilled water.
4. Dehydrate with acetone; clear through acetone + xylene (50:50) and 2 changes of xylene; mount in synthetic resin.
4a. Or: blot dry; differentiate a few seconds in equal volumes of triethyl phosphate and xylene; clear in xylene; mount in synthetic resin (Rosa, *Stain Techn.* 25:165, 1950).

Results: Nuclei, blue green; bacteria and basophil cytoplasm, red.

Rosa's procedure is said to preserve the methyl green better than the usual alcohol dehydration. I have used acetone for the same reason.

Some workers—notably Kurnick, and Trevan and Sharrock, among others—insist on the purification of methyl green by extraction of the aqueous solution with chloroform until no more methyl violets appear in the chloroform solution. Trevan and Sharrock use 2% aqueous methyl green, extracting it in a separatory funnel with chloroform, and state that the extracted solution remains free of further extractable violet for 6 months.

Kurnick noted that pyronin was considerably extracted from cytoplasm by dehydration and by the differentiating agents used for the removal of methyl green from background structures. Therefore he converted the method into a sequence procedure and used the pyronin as a saturated or one-tenth saturated acetone solution after dehydration and differentiation of the methyl green, thus avoiding irregular extraction of the pyronin by the acetone.

Kurnick's (*Stain Techn.* 27:233, 1952) **Methyl Green Pyronin Variant.**

1. Fix in Carnoy, cold 80% alcohol, cold acetone, neutral formalin; imbed and section in paraffin as usual; or use frozen dried material imbedded in paraffin directly.
2. Deparaffinize and hydrate as usual.
3. Stain 6 minutes in repurified 0.2% methyl green in water or in pH 4.2 0.01 *M* acetate buffer. (The solution should be extracted in a separatory funnel by shaking with successive changes of chloroform until no more color is extracted.)

4. Blot dry and dehydrate with 2 changes of *n*-butyl (or *tert*-butyl) alcohol.
5. Stain 30–90 seconds in acetone freshly saturated with pyronin B. For more delicate staining dilute 1 part of the saturated solution with 9 parts acetone and prolong the time somewhat.
6. Clear directly in cedar oil, wash in xylene and mount in terpene resin (Bioloid, Permount, HSR).

Results: Blue green chromatin, red nucleoli, pink to red cytoplasm, green cartilage, purplish pink bone, brown erythrocytes.

For formalin fixed tissue Trevan and Sharrock used a weaker formula than most others (Table 7-2) and added orange G as an acid cytoplasmic stain, selecting a slightly bluish pyronin which did not precipitate with orange G. Two stock solutions were kept: one of 72 mg chloroform extracted methyl green and 315 mg pyronin in 100 cc distilled water; the other of 130 mg orange G in 100 cc 0.2 M acetate buffer of pH 4.8. Working mixtures of equal volumes of the 2 stock solutions keep for about 2 weeks. They direct: Deparaffinize paraffin sections of 3–5 μ, hydrate; stain 10 minutes to 24 hours; wash about 7 seconds in flowing distilled water; blot; dehydrate with acetone; clear through acetone xylene and 2 changes of xylene; and mount in polystyrene. Nuclei and mucin, green to blue green; tigroid and basophil cytoplasms, magenta; nucleoli, pink; oxyphil cytoplasmic components, orange; mast cell granules, usually dark red brown.

I have no great faith in the specificity of this method, especially on formalin fixed tissue. It is often capricious and difficult to control. Such methods as the acid iron hematoxylin safranin sequence stain (p. 507) seem to yield a similar differentiation with far greater certainty and less limitation as to fixing methods.

For assaying the effect of ribonuclease digestions, I find the azure A eosin B technic superior. The pink of the basic protein left after removal of ribonucleic acid contrasts much better with the blue than does the remaining pink of pyronin staining with the red of undigested preparations.

Acridine Orange. Von Bertalanffy and Bickis (*J. Histochem.* 4:481, 1956)[1] used acridine orange 0.1% in distilled water, further diluted with buffered Ringer's solution, on impression smears and cold knife fresh frozen sections of liver at 15 μ. Carnoy's acetic alcohol fixation was used for the colored pictures, and exposures of 10–15 minutes in 1/5000 or 1/10,000 acridine orange in pH 6 Ringer's solution were employed. Cytoplasmic ribonucleic acid and mast cell granules colored with red fluorescence, nuclei colored with bright green. Green nuclear fluoro-

[1] See 67 papers in bibliography.

chrome staining and red mast cell coloration still occurred at 1/100,000 dilution; at 1/1000 overstaining in red dominated even with 1 minute exposure. Carnoy's alcohol chloroform acetic and absolute alcohol gave similar preparations to acetic alcohol.

Formalin fixation largely prevented and Bouin fixation completely prevented differential staining of ribonucleic and deoxyribonucleic acid sites, giving only green fluorescence with weak solutions and red with strong.

Cytophotometry of Ribonucleic Acid. For this purpose Ritter, Di Stefano and Farah (*J. Histochem.* **9**:97, 1961) used 10 μ paraffin sections of tissues fixed in neutral 10% formalin. Sections were deparaffinized and hydrated as usual and stained 2 hours at 45°C in 0.1% cresyl violet which was adjusted to pH 4.2 with 0.1 N hydrochloric acid. To remove nonspecific staining, sections were then extracted from 30 minutes to 16 hours in absolute ethanol. After 16 hours no further dye extraction occurred up to 24 hours and the bound dye showed strict proportionality to section thickness when measured photometrically at 585 mμ. This absorption peak did not shift with changes in dye concentration as it does with toluidine blue, azure A and gallocyanine. Digestion with ribonuclease (5 mg/100 cc, 20 minutes, 40°C, pH 6) completely prevented cytoplasmic cresyl violet staining. Nuclei are also stained by cresyl violet. Preparations mounted in Permount have not appreciably faded or lost in photometric density in 14 months.

Since the cresyl violet also stains nuclear deoxyribonucleic acid, photometric studies require the use of adjacent serial sections, the one digested with ribonuclease and the other not.

Tigroid, or the **Nissl substance,** occurs as angular and elongate particles of varying size in the cytoplasm of nerve cells. It stains deeply with thionin, azure A, methylene blue, toluidine blue and the like; less conspicuously with safranin, fuchsin or neutral red; more differentially from acid solutions or with acid differentiation; poorly or not at all with hematoxylin.

Generally, alcohol fixation is prescribed, formalin serves well, and quite good pictures may be obtained with the azure eosinate method on fresh material fixed in Orth's fluid, or in formalin followed by chromate treatment before imbedding.

Gersh and Bodian (*Biol. Symp.* **10**:161, 1943) stained nerve cells overnight in filtered 1% toluidine blue, differentiated in alcohol and mounted in balsam. I have found a 30 second stain in 0.1% aqueous thionin (buffered to pH 4 with acetates) followed by the acetone, xylene, resin sequence quite effective for most of the tissues noted above, but generally prefer the azure A + eosin B technic (p. 162) because of the more definitive color change from blue to pink when the digestion tests are performed.

Windle's Thionin. Windle (Conn and Darrow) uses thionin in buffered solution for a so-called "end point" method of staining. He prescribes Carnoy or other alcoholic fixative or 10% formalin.

Paraffin or nitrocellulose sections are brought to water as usual. The water should be distilled and freshly boiled to expel carbon dioxide. Stain 20 minutes in 1 cc 1% aqueous thionin solution in 40 cc dilute acetate buffer of pH 3–4. Rinse in distilled water. Wash in 2 changes of 70% alcohol until no more color comes out (about 5 minutes). Dehydrate, clear and mount. This yields blue violet tigroid, blue chromatin, blue glia cytoplasm and a clear to faint blue background.

Windle also suggests a variant in which sections are stained at pH 4–5 and differentiated 2–5 minutes until no more color comes out in 0.2% aqueous acetic acid solution. This largely decolorizes glia cytoplasm as well.

Laskey's Thionin Method for Frozen Sections. Use old or freshly fixed formalin material. Cut frozen sections at 10–15 μ. Wash in distilled water, immerse 5 minutes in 70% alcohol, and wash in distilled water. Stain 10 *seconds* in 0.1% thionin in 4 cc 0.2 M acetic acid, 1 cc 0.2 M sodium acetate and 95 cc distilled water. Wash in distilled water, dehydrate in 95% and 100% alcohol or 2 changes of acetone and clear in 1:4 carbol xylene for a few seconds. Float onto slides, blot and mount in HSR or polystyrene.

Results: Nissl bodies and glia nuclei, dark blue; background, nearly colorless.

Dempsey (*Anat. Rec.* 98:417, 1947) used the dye uptake at various pH levels for the characterization of the basophilic substances in tissues. He stained 24 hours at 25°C in 0.5 mM methylene blue (0.1595% of the pure dye, or 0.18% at 87.5% dye content; 0.2% should do about the same). He measured the dye uptake photometrically, obtaining quite characteristic "pH signatures" for each substance.

It should be pointed out, however, that these pH signatures, just as the isoelectric points which govern acidophilia and basophilia toward azure eosin stains (p. 163), are considerably altered by the fixative employed. With brief formaldehyde or Orth fixation, nuclei and tigroid still take up thionin at pH 1.5 and melanin as low as pH 0.8; after long storage in 10% formalin there is no staining of nuclei at pH 2 and only feeble blue coloration at pH 3. At the latter level melanin colors green; at pH 2 it remains almost pure brown.

The following data are based on material fixed 48 hours only in buffered 10% formalin or Orth's fluid. Dempsey used Zenker fixation of unstated duration.

Staining for 1–30 minutes in 0.05% thionin in 0.01 M acetate buffer of pH 3.5, or even in 0.01 M acetic acid (pH about 3.4) gives good staining of nuclei, tigroid and strongly basophil cytoplasm; and metachromatic staining of mast cells and cartilage. Oxyphil material, muscle and connective tissue remain unstained; and red corpuscles appear in light yellow. In a similar buffer of pH 4.11, muscle and connective tissues appear faintly greenish, and at pH 5.1 they take a fair grade of light blue green. Phosphate buffers from pH 5 to pH 1.5 precipitate thionin almost quantitatively, but do not throw down azure A or toluidine blue.

At higher pH levels (6–7.5) and at higher dilutions (10 mg/liter = 27.5 μM of 88% dye-content methylene blue, or similar concentrations of azure A, thionin, and toluidine blue) and overnight staining, connective tissue, keratin, muscle and oxyphil materials in general assume a rather diffuse and light green; red corpuscles—a darker, somewhat olive green; basophil cytoplasms—blue violet; nuclei—fairly deep blue, greenish blue or lighter bluish green; and cartilage matrix and mast cell granules (at least with azure A, thionin, and toluidine blue)—a brilliant purplish red. Epithelial mucins may fail to stain.

Azure Eosinate. I have found that azure eosinate stains of formalin or Orth material done at pH 4 show nuclei and tigroid well, with the advantage of a pink stained background (pp. 160–164).

Acetic Orcein. A very precise chromatin stain used on crush preparations is the acetic orcein method. This was shown me by A. J. Dalton of the National Cancer Institute.

1. Tissue either fresh or stored at 5°C is simultaneously fixed and stained by immersion for 48 hours in acetic orcein. Dissolve 1 gm natural orcein in 45 cc hot glacial acetic acid; cool, and add 55 cc distilled water. The synthetic orcein is less satisfactory.
2. After staining take a small fragment and gently crush it between a slide and a coverglass to about a single cell layer. Slides should first be coated with Mayer's glycerol albumen.
3. Fix the preparations as they are (with coverglass and slide in place) by standing them on end for 48 hours in a closed vessel containing in its bottom absorbent cotton saturated with 95% alcohol.
4. Then immerse in 95% alcohol and take off the coverglass. The tissue may adhere to either the slide or the coverglass.
5. The film is then counterstained for a few seconds in 60 cc 100% alcohol containing about 1 cc 1% fast green FCF. The tissue should appear faintly greenish at this stage.
6. Mount directly from absolute alcohol in Diaphane or Euparal. Or if this clouds, rinse in 2 changes of 100% alcohol, 1 of equal volumes of 100% alcohol and xylene and 2 of xylene. Then mount in xylene balsam.

This is a very precise red chromatin stain. Chromosomes are very conspicuous. Cytoplasm is pale green, without appreciable difference in tone between apparently surviving and definitely necrotic cells. Herein the method seems to me inferior to the azure eosin methods, but for chromosome identification studies it is unexcelled.

Hrushovetz and Harder (*Stain Techn.* 37:307, 1962) make permanent preparations from coverglass tissue cultures. Fix 10 minutes in Carnoy A (p. 42), let dry thoroughly in air, stain 15 minutes in moist chamber (45% acetic acid vapor) at 37°C in filtered (natural) orcein 2% in 45% acetic acid, floating each coverglass face down on a drop of stain on a clean glass plate or slide. Wash in 45% acetic acid to remove excess stain, and in several changes of distilled water. Mount in Abopon (p. 105).

Stains thus mounted have remained unimpaired as long as 7 years.

In vivo Staining of Nuclei. DeBruyn and coworkers (*Exp. Cell Res.* 4:174, 1953) report that nuclei of living cells may be stained with fluorescent diaminoacridine dyes. The affinity appears to be specific for intranuclear nucleic acids. Proflavine hydrochloride is administered intravenously to mice in dosages of 25 mg/kg. Fresh frozen sections are observed under long wave ultraviolet for fluorescence (pp. 13–16).

On fixed material these dyes show only the same specificity as other basic dyes.

Humason-Lushbaugh Pinacyanole for Frozen Sections.

1. Mount fresh or fixed frozen section on slide and drain (I suggest blotting down firmly with hard filter paper; cryostat sections should be melted and allowed to dry briefly to insure adhesion).
2. Flood with 0.5% pinacyanole in 70% alcohol 6–10 seconds.
3. Here authors float and wash in water; I suggest draining, blotting firmly and washing in distilled water.
4. Remount, blot off excess water, cover with glycerol, glycerol gelatin or Abopon. Mounts are temporary, and leaching of dyes occurs. Alcohol removes most of the stain. Highman Apáthy gum syrup might be suitable for longer conservation.

Results: Chromatin, blue to violet; muscle, violet to purple; connective tissue, pink; elastin, dark violet; hemosiderin, orange; plasma cell granuloplasm, red; amyloid, carmine red; red cells and leucocyte granules, unstained; neutral fat, unstained to faint blue; lipids, violet to purple.

AZURE EOSIN METHODS

Excellent as the hematoxylin eosin stains are for permanence, I prefer for routine use procedures of the azure eosin type. The latter give definitely good staining of bacteria and rickettsiae in tissues, and they demonstrate tissue mast cells, which are not evident with hematoxylin.

They act as sensitive indicators of early necrobiotic changes in cells, in that the normal light blue staining of cytoplasm is replaced abruptly by a brilliant pink. Regenerating liver cells are blue, in contrast with the normal, more or less violet tone. With the buffer procedure now in use it is possible to stain as many as 100 slides at a time by a routine technic without the troublesome individual differentiation formerly required, and to attain a great uniformity of results even on miscellaneous formalin material sent in by mail from various places.

These azure eosin procedures comprise sequence stains such as Mallory's eosin or phloxine "methylene blue," and neutral stains employing azures and eosin in extempore mixtures or in preformed azure eosinates in glycerol and methanol stock solutions. In the neutral stain group, such methods as Maximow's and Wolbach's were carried out at approximate neutrality and the excess of azure subsequently differentiated out by means of alcohol, dilute acid, "colophonium alcohol" or sunlight. I have preferred to regulate the red blue balance of the final stain by variation of the pH of the stain mixture by means of buffers. This last procedure gives very constant results on material fixed in formalin, chromate and mercury fixatives, with some adjustment of pH for the fixative employed. It is less suitable for picric acid and absolute alcohol acetic fixations. With this method, more acid pH levels give sharper and more selective chromatin staining, denser eosin staining of muscle and red cells and less cytoplasmic basophilia. Less acid, higher pH levels give denser nuclei, pink to blue gray muscle, orange erythrocytes and increased cytoplasmic basophilia. Results are more or less similar for the following methods and are given in detail only on p. 164 to avoid duplication.

For **Mallory's eosin** or **phloxine methylene blue** method, Zenker fixation was prescribed. Sections were deparaffinized and hydrated in the usual manner, treated with 0.5% iodine in alcohol for 5–10 minutes and with 0.5% sodium thiosulfate for 5 minutes (5% removes iodine at once) and washed in water.

1. Stain 1 hour or longer at 52–55°C in 2.5% eosin Y or, preferably, phloxine B (C.I. No. 45410).
2. Cool, decant and rinse carefully in water.
3. Stain 5–20 minutes in a mixture of equal volumes of 1% azure II in distilled water and of 1% methylene blue in 1% borax solution. This is filtered just before use and poured onto and off the slides several times to insure even staining.
4. Then place slides in the water and decolorize individually in 0.2–0.5% colophonium alcohol. Mallory recommended adding 2–5 cc of a stock 10% solution in absolute to 100 cc of 95% alcohol. With formalin fixed material 3–10% colophonium alcohol is recommended for differentiation. (Mallory's "colophonium" is apparently commercial dry pine

rosin, which is largely abietic acid.) Slides are kept in constant motion during differentiation. When the general background becomes pink and nuclei are still blue (microscopic control).

5. Dehydrate in 3 changes of 100% alcohol.
6. Pass through 1 change of equal parts 100% alcohol and xylene and 2 changes of xylene. Mount in synthetic resin. (Mallory, of course, used balsam.)

Mallory preferred phloxine B (C.I. No. 45410) to eosin Y (C.I. No. 45380) in this technic because of the deeper reds achieved. Borax methylene blue is essentially an alkaline methylene blue which gradually alters to azures and methylene violets, changing faster when kept warm than when cold. Azure II was a mixture of equal parts of methylene blue and of azure I, which was originally azure B or trimethylthionin. However, the usual azure furnished in the United States from 1925 to 1940 was azure A or asymmetrical dimethylthionin, a more violet dye than azure B and it seems probable that this dye was meant by Mallory. The borax methylene blue varies in composition with age, and may contain all three azures—A, B and C—as well as methylene blue and methylene violets.

Maximow's Hematoxylin Azure II Eosin (Z. wiss. Mikr., 26:177, 1909; Mallory). Fixation in Spuler's (Maximow's) variant of Zenker formalin (p. 49) was prescribed. Originally Maximow removed mercury precipitates with iodine alcohol before imbedding and insisted on celloidin (nitrocellulose) imbedding. He attached the sections to slides with ether vapor before staining. I have successfully used paraffin sections and the usual iodine and thiosulfate treatment after sectioning, and have found that the method works quite well on Orth and formalin fixed material.

1. Stain sections with alum hematoxylin as usual. I have used a 5 minute stain in an acid, iodate ripened solution of full (0.5%) strength. Mallory recommended 24 hours in very dilute Delafield's hematoxylin (1 or 2 drops per 100 cc water). Wash in water.
2. Stain 18–24 hours in azure II eosin: Dilute 5 cc 1:1000 eosin Y with 40 cc distilled water and add 5 cc 1:1000 azure II. Mallory recommended water buffered to pH 6.8–7 with Sörensen's phosphate mixture, but see under Lillie's methods (pp. 162–164).
3. Differentiate sections individually in 95% alcohol until gross blue clouds cease to come out into the alcohol, and red cells and collagen are pink.
4. Two changes of 100% aliohol, 100% alcohol and xylene, 2 changes of xylene, mount in synthetic resin (Maximow used dammar).

Nuclei stain blue; basophil leucocyte and mast cell granules, purple to violet; cartilage, purple; red corpuscles, pink; cytoplasm, blue to pink; secretion granules and eosinophil granules, pink. (See also pp. 164–165.)

Giemsa Stain. In place of the extempore mixture of azure II and eosin, a 1:50 dilution of *Giemsa's blood stain* (p. 585) may be used with identical results. *Wolbach* (personal communications; Mallory) recommended addition of 2–4 drops (0.1–0.25 cc) of 0.5% sodium bicarbonate to a 1:40 dilution of Giemsa's stain. After staining he differentiated in weak colophonium alcohol, dehydrated in 100% alcohol, cleared in xylene and mounted in cedar oil. Exposure to diffuse daylight or even sunlight after mounting produced a further differentiation which was valuable for rickettsiae. Wolbach prescribed fixation in Möller's (Regaud's) fluid rather than Zenker's.

The azure eosinate method of Lillie and Pasternack was derived from a staining accident with the Maximow method, in which the use of acid distilled water obviated the necessity for the usual differentiation. Any commercial azure eosinate may be used, or eosinates may be prepared with the yellowish eosin Y or the deeper red eosin B (C.I. No. 45400) from methylene blue, azure B, toluidine blue, azure A, azure C, thionin, or new methylene blue. Nuclei vary in color from pure blue at the methylene blue end of the series to purple at the new methylene blue end; mast cell granules, mucin and cartilage matrix, from blue violet to purplish red (the *metachromatic* colors). Contrast is greatest between the normal and metachromatic colors in the middle of the series; hence I usually prefer azure A or the often nearly identical azure C. It makes little difference which is used. Commercial samples labeled with either name usually contain more or less of the other, so that on spectroscopic examination some samples of azure A have been found to be more nearly azure C than some other samples labeled azure C, and *vice versa*. Other zinc free thiazin dyes may be substituted in the same amounts, and the zinc double salts may be used as well, if appropriate allowance is made for their lower dye content. The phloxines, rose Bengal and the erythrosins do not yield satisfactory thiazin salts for use in this technic. The eosinates are made up as 1% stock solutions in equal volumes of glycerol and C.P. methyl or 100% ethyl alcohol.

For the last 20 years I have preferred to use, in place of the prepared eosinates, aqueous solutions of the eosin and the thiazin dye preferred, mixed at time of using (*J. Tech. Methods* 24:43, 1944). The same dyes may be used. The following technic may be carried out in Coplin jars or in the Technicon staining racks.

Lillie's Azure A Eosin B:

1. Bring paraffin sections to water as usual, using the 0.5% iodine, 5% sodium thiosulfate sequence for material fixed with mercuric chloride.
2. Stain 1 hour in:

	Coplin jar	*Technicon*
Azure A	4 cc 0.1%	6 cc 1%
Eosin B	4 cc 0.1%	6 cc 1%
0.2 M acetic acid	1.7 cc	34 cc
0.2 M sodium acetate	0.3 cc	6 cc
C.P. acetone	5 cc	90 cc
Distilled water	25 cc	580 cc

The larger quantities prescribed for the Technicon schedule are allowed to stand 1 hour after mixing, and are then filtered. The mixture is used repeatedly, being discarded at the end of each week. The smaller, Coplin jar quantities are used at once and discarded after use, although we have, on occasion, successfully stained a second group of slides just after the first.

3. Dehydrate in 2–3 changes of acetone, clear in a 50:50 acetone xylene mixture and 2 changes of xylene. Mount in synthetic resin. Depex, Permount, HSR, polystyrene, cellulose tricaprate, Groat's copolymer, and ester gum are satisfactory.

Because of the poor keeping quality of aqueous citric acid solution I have replaced the McIlvaine buffer with the Walpole series. For pH 4, use 1.7 cc 0.2 M acetic acid and 0.3 cc 0.2 M sodium acetate; for pH 4.5, use 1.25 and 0.75; and for pH 5, use 0.7 and 1.3 cc, respectively. Further variations may be made from the buffer tables. Use the phosphate series below pH 3 and Sörensen's phosphates from pH 6–8. With surgical material and fresh animal tissue fixed in formalin, pH 4 is about optimal; autopsy tissues may stain better at 4.5. Zenker fixations require pH 4.5; Bouin and Carnoy fixations require pH 5 or 5.5; heavily chromated tissue may require pH 6 or 7.

The optimal pH for staining with azure A eosin B after fixation with buffered mercuric chloride (B-4 p. 46, B-5 p. 48) is at about 5–5.5. Omission of the customary iodine thiosulfate sequence before staining raises this level by about 0.5 pH. After formalin fixation, iodination has a less marked effect and perhaps acts to depress the optimal staining pH slightly. The effect of omission of the iodine thiosulfate sequence on pure acid dye staining is greater and rather irregular, so that it seems that the excess acid dye uptake may be due to absorbed Hg^{++} rather than to protein iodination. In the mixture one may substitute 0.5 cc 1% azure eosinate in glycerol and methanol for the separate aqueous solutions of azure and eosin (10 cc for the Technicon schedule). With Giemsa stain use 0.6 and 12 cc, respectively.

Phthalate Buffer. Substitution of 10 cc 0.2 M sodium (3.76%) or potassium (4.16%) hydrogen phthalate for the other buffer and part of the water in the above mixture gives a final buffer concentration of 0.05 M

and pH 4, which is quite satisfactory for formalin fixed surgical and experimental tissues.

Nitrocellulose sections and collodionized sections require 2–2½ hours staining, or 2–3 times as much dye. If it is necessary to preserve the collodion coat, substitute isopropanol for acetone in the dehydration and clearing schedule.

Results with Azure Eosin Methods

The following results apply generally to the foregoing azure eosin technics (pp. 161–164): Blue nuclei, bacteria, rickettsiae, tigroid and ribonucleoprotein generally; blue violet mast cell and basophil leucocyte granules; reddish violet cartilage matrix; dark blue calcium deposits; light blue to violet or lavender cytoplasm of surviving cells; bright pink cytoplasm of necrosing and necrotic cells and muscle fibers (Zenker's degeneration or necrosis); pink to red secretion granules in pancreatic and salivary gland acini and Paneth cells; pink cytoplasm of gastric gland parietal cells, and blue cytoplasm of chief cells; yellowish green to green chromaffin after chromate fixation only; pink to red eosinophil and pseudoeosinophil granules; pink keratin, amyloid, fibrin, muscle cytoplasm, thyroid colloid, nuclear and cytoplasmic oxyphil inclusion bodies and bone matrix; orange red erythrocytes and hemoglobin. Various hyaline degeneration products in liver cells, in Hassall corpuscles of the thymus, in the follicles of the spleen, and elsewhere also stain pink. The mucins vary in color from unstained through pale greenish blues to fairly deep blue violet. Variation of buffer level toward the acid side increases precision of nuclear staining and decreases diffuse basophilia. Conversely, variation to the alkaline side increases the amount of blue in various elements. At about pH 5 Orth and formalin fixed material will present pale gray blue smooth muscle; and at higher pH levels perhaps only eosinophil granules and erythrocytes remain red. Conversely, mast cell granules, cartilage matrix and lymphoid cell cytoplasm retain their blue or violet staining at lower pH levels than do most other elements. After certain alcoholic fixations the ellipsoids of retinal rods stain brilliantly in red.

The azure eosin methods are also widely useful in the identification of the cells of inflammatory exudates in the tissues. Lymphocytes and plasma cells present the characteristic basophilic (blue) cytoplasm (broader and eccentric in the latter) and the round nucleus with relatively coarse, deeply stained chromatin granules, perhaps radially placed. The cytoplasm of monocytes, histiocytes or macrophages is broader and less basophilic, and may enclose phagocytosed material. The nucleus of this cell type is characteristically larger than that of the lymphocyte, is round, oval or indented in form, and is relatively pale in appearance (*leptochromatic*), with quite finely divided chromatin. The nucleus of *Endamoeba histolytica* is much smaller, vesicular, as pale as that of the macrophage group or paler, and contains a small nucleolus. Its cytoplasm is similar to that of the macrophage group, and may contain phagocytosed erythrocytes. The granules of the polymorphonuclear leucocyte are less well shown in section material than in Giemsa stained smears. They are much more conspicuous in some species, notably rabbits and guinea pigs, than in others.

Leishmania and the leishmania forms of *Trypanosoma cruzi* in heart muscle, skeletal muscle, and skin are well shown, with deep blue, rod shaped blepharoplasts and lighter blue rounded trophonuclei in relatively lightly basophilic cytoplasm. Sarcosporidia, encephalitozoa and toxoplasmata all appear as fairly conspicuous bodies with blue chromatin in the pink backgrounds of striated muscle and central nervous tissues. *Bartonella bacilliformis* in human liver is well shown by azure eosin methods, notably Wolbach's Giemsa variant. I have not had opportunity to use the buffered azure eosin technics with this material. Plasmodia present deep blue chromatin and lighter blue cytoplasm. In human spleen they may sometimes be more easily discerned with an iron hematoxylin technic (pp. 168–169).

MORDANT STAINS FOR NUCLEI AND OTHER STRUCTURES

These include stains with hematoxylin, brazilin, carmine, the oxazine dyes gallocyanine, gallamine blue and celestine blue, anthracene blue and other catecholic substances combined with or in sequence after treatments with salts of iron, chromium, copper, aluminum, tin and other chelate forming metals and with phosphotungstic, phosphomolybdic and molybdic acids.

Iron Hematoxylins

These fall into overstaining and regressive differentiation methods, divided into sequence methods and combined solution methods, and into progressive methods with acid or an excess of iron salt to prevent overstaining.

The sequence methods depend on a preliminary mordanting with an aqueous solution of a ferric salt, staining with an aqueous solution of hematoxylin until black and then differentiating with an acid or a ferric salt solution until the desired grade of differentiation is evident on microscopic examination. These methods are widely used by cytologists and protozoologists for the study of chromatin, chromosomes, spindles, centrosomes, mitochondria and other cytologic details. They are too cumbersome for routine use in pathology because of the excessive amount of time required for each slide.

Hematoxylin solutions for these technics are variously prescribed as fresh or ripened. Ripening is usually accomplished by allowing the solution to stand at 15–25°C for weeks or months. Some of the proposed ripening technics arouse skepticism, such as the proposal to ripen by bubbling air through the solution for a few hours (Rawlins and Takahashi, *Stain Techn.* **22**:99, 1947). Although it is possible that bubbling air through an alkaline aqueous solution would serve to oxidize catechol residues of hematoxylin, the authors do not say whether an aqueous or an alcoholic solution was used. Acid solutions are more resistant to oxidation.

Recent experience indicates that air bubbling requires some 3–4 weeks to ripen alum hematoxylin, and that even pure oxygen takes some days (Palmer, current studies[1]). Moreover hematoxylin as it comes from the manufacturer contains a variable proportion of hematein, sometimes containing as much as 100% (*Colour Index*). Also, some technics encourage the carryover of a little iron alum solution into the hematoxylin bath. In this case the Fe^{+++} ion itself serves as an effective oxidant.

Short exposures to mordant and to hematoxylin, and fresh hematoxylin solutions tend to yield blue black stains; longer exposures and aged hematoxylins yield black or even brownish black stains.

Benda's method, two of M. Heidenhain's, a Masson-Regaud variant and an iron chloride method of Mallory's are included in Table 7-3.

The myelin methods, which generally require alkaline differentiation, are discussed under lipids in Chapter 13.

Regressive iron hematoxylin methods are still much used for the identification of intestinal *Endamoebae* in smear preparations. For this purpose a preliminary 15 minutes' fixation of fresh, still moist films in Schaudinn's mercuric chloride alcohol (p. 47) is prescribed. Then treat with 0.5% iodine in 70% alcohol for 3 minutes; and decolorize with 95% alcohol, or for 1–2 minutes in 5% sodium thiosulfate. Wash in water and stain as usual with Mallory's, Heidenhain's or other technic (p. 167).

I see no especially good reason why one of the premixed "neutral" or acid iron hematoxylins should not be used for this purpose. I have often used Weigert's acid iron chloride hematoxylin with picrofuchsin (p. 540) in the study and identification of *Trypanosoma cruzi* in heart muscle. The blepharoplasts appear as intensely black, rod shaped structures; the trophonuclei, as rounded, gray bodies. *Endamoeba histolytica* is also well shown in sections by this method, and plasmodia and sarcosporidia are readily identified. However, such parasites are often more easily found when azure eosin methods (pp. 160–164) are employed.

Some elaborate schedules for staining *E. histolytica* in tissue have been prepared. I cited one of these, Goldman's (*Am. J. Clin. Path.* **21**:198, 1951), in the second edition of this book. However, I have found the usual Weigert iron chloride hematoxylin, Van Gieson picrofuchsin se-

[1] Palmer and Lillie, *Histochemie*, 1965, in press.

TABLE 7-3. COMPARATIVE SCHEDULES FOR SEQUENCE IRON HEMATOXYLIN STAINING

	Benda	Heidenhain	Heidenhain	Masson's Regaud variant	Mallory
Mordant solution	Liq. Fer. Sulph. Oxid. P.G. in 50–33% dilution	1.5–4% iron alum in water	2.5% iron alum	5% iron alum	5% ferric chloride
Time and temperature	15–20°C, 24 hr	15–20°C, ½–3 hr	15–20°C, 3–12 hr	45–50°C, 5–10 min	25°C, 1 hr or more
Washing	Dist., then tap water	Water	Water	Thorough, water	3 changes water
Hematoxylin	1% aq.	0.5% aq.	0.5% aq.	1%	0.5% aq.
Ripened?	No	No	Yes, 4–6 weeks	No	No, fresh
Staining time and temperature	15–20°C, until black	15–20°C, 30 min	15–20°C, 24–36 hr	45–50°C, 5–10 min	25°C, 1 hr or more
Differentiating agent	5–30% acetic, or weaker acetic, or 1:30 Liq. Fer. Sulph. Oxid. P.G.	1.5–4% iron alum	2.5% iron alum	⅔ saturated (6%) alcoholic picric acid	0.25% ferric chloride
	Note	Note	Note		

Note: Liquor Ferri Sulphurici Oxidati P.G. consisted of 80 gm iron sulfate, 40 gm water, 15 gm sulfuric acid and 18 gm nitric acid, and contained 10% metallic iron by weight. Iron alum is $Fe_2(SO_4)_3 \cdot (NH_4)_2SO_4 \cdot 24H_2O$. 15–20°C is taken as average German laboratory temperature, 25°C as American. Saturated alcoholic picric acid solution is approximately 9% according to Conn's *Biological Stains*, 7th ed. Heidenhain directs periodic transfer to water for microscopic examination during differentiation.

Benda's formula and the second formula of Heidenhain above are cited from Ehrlich's *Encyklopädie*; the first formula of Heidenhain is from Lee; the Regaud formula is from Masson (*J. Tech. Methods* **12:**75, 1929); and Mallory's is from his 1938 text.

167

quence (p. 540) quite satisfactory for demonstration of *Endamoeba* in tissues, and far less time consuming.

More generally useful in pathology are the premixed ferric salt hematoxylins. These fall into 2 groups: those mixed with an optimal amount of iron for dense staining and used for regressive staining (principally in the myelin and related methods) and those made more or less selective for nuclei by addition of acid or by an excess of ferric salt.

About 0.5 gm metallic iron in the ferric state is required for each gram of hematoxylin for maximal staining (Lillie and Earle). This corresponds to 3.9 cc of the official solution of iron chloride, to 2.419 gm $FeCl_3 \cdot 6H_2O$, or to 4.32 gm iron alum. Doubling the quantity of ferric iron in the mixed solution prevents overstaining.

The 2 commonest mixed iron hematoxylins used for regressive staining are Weigert's and Weil's. Both prescribed the mixture of an equal volume of an aged and "ripened" 1% alcoholic hematoxylin with an aqueous solution of a ferric salt. Weigert used 4 cc of the official (P.G.) iron chloride solution and 96 cc of water. A 2.5% (w/v) solution of ferric chloride crystals may be substituted for the dilute official solution. (4 cc U.S.P. or P.G. solution of iron chloride = 2.481 gm $FeCl_3 \cdot 6H_2O$). Weil used 4% iron alum. With Weil's hematoxylin I find that a hematoxylin solution only 1–5 days old is superior to the solution several months old prescribed by Weil, and also is readily available at all times. Inasmuch as ferric salts oxidize hematoxylin promptly, it is difficult to see the necessity for previously oxidized hematoxylin. For further details on the methods, see pp. 489–491.

Satisfactory formulae for progressive staining of nuclei without overstaining are those of Janssens and of Weigert. Both stain nuclei in 3–5 minutes and do not overstain in 10–30 minutes, and color effects are the same.

Janssens (*Cellule* 14:203, 1898) dissolved 2 gm hematoxylin in 60 cc methanol, and 20 gm iron alum in 200 cc water, mixed the 2 solutions and added 60 cc glycerol. The solution becomes blue black at once, then purplish, and in about an hour brownish black. It remains usable perhaps 4–5 weeks.

Weigert's (*Z. wiss. Mikr.* 21:1, 1904) solution is less stable, lasting only 2–3 weeks, and if large numbers of sections are being stained, it may have to be made fresh twice weekly. It is the easiest to prepare, requiring only one weighing and no glycerol. Mix 100 cc fresh 1% hematoxylin in 95% alcohol with 95 cc distilled water, 1 cc concentrated hydrochloric acid and 4 cc of the official (U.S.P. XI = P.G.) solution of iron chloride (2.48 gm $FeCl_3 \cdot 6H_2O$ may be substituted.) This hematoxylin undergoes the same color changes as Janssens' formula, but even more rapidly.

Since the official iron chloride solution has disappeared from the U.S. Pharmacopeia it has become relatively difficult to obtain, and it now seems indicated to replace it with a simple aqueous solution of reagent

TABLE 7-4. EQUIVALENCE OF IRON MORDANT SALTS AND SOLUTIONS

Salts usually prescribed	m mol Fe	Metallic iron, mg	FeCl$_3$· 6H$_2$O, mg	Fe$_2$(SO$_4$)$_3$ 9H$_2$O, mg	Iron alum, mg	Official solution iron chloride	
						cu mm	mg
Fe, 1 m mol............	1.0	55.85	270.32	281.02	482.21	390.55	558.5
Iron alum, 4 gm[1]......	8.3	463.3	2242.5	2337	4000	3240	4633
Sol. iron chloride, 4 cc[2].	9.2	512.6	2481	2579	4941	4000	5126
Sol. iron chloride, 4 gm	7.2	400	1936	2013	3544	2747	4000
Iron alum, 1 gm........	2.1	115.8	560.6	583	1000	809.5	1158
Sol. iron chloride, 1 cc..	2.3	128.15	620	645	1235	1000	1281.5
Sol. iron chloride, 1 gm.	1.8	100	484	503	863.4	699.3	1000

[1] Iron alum is (NH$_4$)$_2$SO$_4$·Fe$_2$(SO$_4$)$_3$·24 H$_2$O.
[2] Sol. iron chloride = Liquor Ferri Chloridi P.G. and U.S.P. I–IX.

grade ferric chloride. The pharmacopeial solution contained 10% by weight of metallic iron and had a specific gravity of 1.230–1.283. Thus it was 2.29 M ferric chloride, or 37.2% (w/v). However, the Weigert aqueous solution can be further simplified by using 1.5 gm anhydrous FeCl$_3$ (= 2.5 gm FeCl$_3$·6H$_2$O), 1 cc concentrated HCl (37.5%) and 99 cc distilled water (92.5 mM). An 0.1 M FeCl$_3$ solution in 0.1 N HCl would probably serve.

Doubling the HCl content of the iron solution and reducing the amount of hematoxylin render the Weigert formula more selective for nuclei, and addition of ferrous sulfate stabilizes it so that with occasional to moderate use the solution remains active for several weeks.

Stabilized Iron Chloride Hematoxylin (Weigert-Lillie).

Distilled water	298 cc
Concentrated hydrochloric acid (37.5%)	2 cc
Ferric chloride crystals FeCl$_3$·6H$_2$O	2.5 gm
Ferrous sulfate crystals FeSO$_4$·7H$_2$O	4.5 gm

When the salts are dissolved then add a

Fresh 1% alcoholic solution of hematoxylin	100 cc

The solution turns blue black at once and is usable within a few minutes. Over some weeks the color slowly shifts toward brown. If the solution is much used it may be necessary to replace it sooner because of depletion of dye.

Iron "Toning" of Alum Hematoxylin Stains. When a preparation stained in alum hematoxylin is rinsed in distilled water and then immersed in 1.5% $FeCl_3$ (2.5% $FeCl_3 \cdot 6H_2O$) for 30 seconds, nuclear staining is changed from blue to black. Use of alum hematoxylin with picric acid plasma stains, or with picric acid mixtures of the Van Gieson type, yields a deep red brown nuclear stain. Introduction of a 30 second 1.5% ferric chloride bath after the hematoxylin step changes the nuclear coloration to black. See also the Kattine phosphotungstic phosphomolybdic postmordanting (p. 540).

Hansen's iron hematoxylin is occasionally called for: Dissolve 10 gm iron alum and 1.4 gm ammonium sulfate in 150 cc distilled water and pour into a solution of 1.6 gm hematoxylin in 75 cc distilled water. Heat and boil not more than 30–60 seconds. Cool, and keep in a nearly full bottle. Stain 1–10 minutes and differentiate in 2–3% sulfuric or 0.5–1% acetic acid; or for pure nuclear staining add ⅓ to ½ volume of 1% sulfuric acid to 1 volume of stain (cited from Romeis).

The official solution of ferric sulfate, used by Benda in his sequence iron hematoxylin method, also contained 10% iron by weight, according to both the 1884 German Pharmacopoeia and the present U.S. Dispensatory. Its specific gravity of 1.43 indicates a content of 14.3 gm iron or 71.9 gm ferric sulfate crystals, $Fe_2(SO_4)_3 \cdot 9H_2O$ per 100 cc.

The common iron alum $(NH_4)_2SO_4 \cdot Fe_2(SO_4)_3 \cdot 24H_2O$ used in histolgy contains 11.58% metallic iron.

Since the active agent in each of these three preparations is ferric iron, they are readily interchangeable in equivalent quantities. The Weigert 2.5% $FeCl_3 \cdot 6H_2O$ should be suitable.

Hematoxylin Substitutes: Other dyestuffs can replace hematoxylin in forming iron and aluminum mordant stains. Besides the closely related carmine and brazilin (C.I. No. 75280), there are gallamine blue (C.I. No. 51045, p. 178), gallocyanine (C.I. No. 51030, pp. 110, 178), celestine blue B (C.I. No. 51050), and anthracene blue SWR (C.I. No. 58605). All these dyestuffs possess o-diphenolic groupings or quinonoid oxidation products thereof. It is worthy of note that good gray to black nuclear stains may be obtained by immersing sections in fresh mixtures of ferric chloride solution with aqueous solutions of catechol, pyrogallol or hydroxyhydroquinone (1,2-, 1,2,3- and 1,2,4-hydroxybenzene, respectively); but not with phenol, resorcinol, hydroquinone or phloroglucinol, which do not possess ortho-dihydroxy groupings. The iron o-diphenol mixtures darken quite rapidly and are probably unstable.

Metal Uptake Reactions with Dilute Hematoxylin Demonstration. Dilute hematoxylin may be used to demonstrate uptake of various metals by tissue elements. Controls with hematoxylin alone should always be compared, and further controls exposed to solvent alone at the same pH as that determined for the metal solution under test are required.

I have used 1–10 μM solutions of various metal salts in this way, incubating sections 1 hour at 40°C, washing thoroughly in double distilled water and then reacting for 1 and 6 hours in 0.01% hematoxylin in 0.01 M pH 7 phosphate buffer (p. 664).

$FeCl_3$, CrF_3, $CuSO_4$ and $ZnCl_2$ give marked enhancement of the 1 hour staining of keratohyalin and trichohyalin, with blue black colors for Fe^{+++} and Zn^{++}, greener tones with Cr^{+++} and Cu^{++}. Decrease in the metal concentration decreases the effect; the metals may be removed by extraction with 1 N HCl and then replaced by reexposure, indicating that it is probably a true tissue chelation of the metal. Cell nuclei require higher metal concentration, at least 1 mM, and their staining is enchanced by prolongation of the time in hematoxylin to 6 hours.

Substitution of pyrogallol for hematoxylin in the above technic resulted in brown colors of keratohyalin and trichohyalin only, best with Fe^{++} and Cr^{+++}. Dopa and catechol gave, respectively, feeble and negative results.

Wigglesworth reports some interesting results regarding iron uptake by fixed tissue sections, with particular reference to iron which apparently goes into a masked state and becomes nonreactive to ferrocyanide. This iron is unmasked by ammonium sulfide. It has been shown that nucleic acid solutions precipitate from saturated urea solution when a little ferric chloride is added, and that the iron thus precipitated is nonreactive to thiocyanate. He attributes iron uptake to mono- and diesters of phosphoric acid, which form firm, nonionized unions, or to free carboxyl groups. The stability of the complexes formed is attributed to chelation. I cite his technics.

Wigglesworth's Iron Sulfide Technic (*Quart. J. Micr. Sci.* 93:105, 1952).

1. Fix in Carnoy, Bouin, susa, Zenker or Helly. Prepare paraffin sections, deparaffinize and hydrate as usual.
2. Immerse 1 minute in saturated iron alum solution.
3. Wash well in running water.
4. Immerse 15 to 20 seconds or more in dilute ammonium sulfide.
5. Rinse, dehydrate and mount in balsam.

Results: Nuclei, blue black; chromosomes, intense blue black; cytoplasm, gray or brown; fibrous tissue, pale chocolate; basal layer of epidermis, blue; erythrocytes, pale blue gray.

Staining may be intensified by transferring after step 4 to potassium ferricyanide solution, which forms Turnbull's blue. Then sections may be again put through steps 2, 3 and 4. They acquire additional iron sulfide in the process without removal of the ferrous ferricyanide, and thus the intensity of the reaction is deepened.

Wigglesworth interprets the reaction as demonstrating free carboxyl and phosphoric acid groups. He finds that iron uptake is greatly reduced by 2 or 3 days of methylation in 0.1 N HCl in methanol (cf. p. 282).

Maximum uptake of iron by nucleic acids occurs at pH 1.5; by proteins, at pH 4 or higher.

For further interesting details the original should be consulted.

Alum Hematoxylin

Aluminum salt complexes of hematoxylin are usually made with ammonium aluminum sulfate or ammonia alum and are commonly referred to as alum hematoxylins. Occasionally the potassium or sodium alum is substituted with essentially equivalent results. Since the oxidation product of hematoxylin, hematein, is required for staining and the aluminum salts, unlike ferric salts, are not oxidants in themselves, it is necessary to oxidize or "ripen" alum hematoxylin for use. Hematein is formed gradually by bubbling air through hematoxylin solutions (3–4 weeks may be needed for adequate staining) and by some weeks of exposure of solutions in open containers, and also by exposure of the solid dye in opened bottles in moist climates. Certain chemical oxidants such as peroxides, iodates, permanganates, perchlorates, mercuric oxide and ferric salts ripen hematoxylin at once, though some of these agents require heat as well.

The selectivity of alum hematoxylin for nuclei is increased by the presence of an excess of aluminum salts or, better, by the presence of acids in the solution. Many workers prefer to overstain with an unacidified alum hematoxylin and then differentiate with acid or acid alcohol or other differentiating agents.

Hematoxylin in aqueous 10% ammonium alum gives pH readings about 2.95; inclusion of 2% acetic acid in the solution brings it to pH 2.34; inclusion of 4% acetic acid, to pH 2.22.

As recorded in the *Colour Index*, the amount of hematein present in various batches of hematoxylin as manufactured is variable, the product sometimes being nearly all hematein. I have seen individual lots of alum hematoxylin ripened by the "natural process" which performed adequately in as little as 8–10 days; 8–10 weeks is, of course, more usual, though Schmorl recorded an 8–10 day ripening period for Boehmer's hematoxylin. Occasional lots of hematoxylin are encountered which are severely overoxidized by the standard amount of sodium iodate. I call to mind one such instance in which 1 gm $NaIO_3$ was used to 6 gm hematoxylin. This is below Mayer's proportion, though more than I have been recommending in recent years.

Adequately ripened alum hematoxylin solutions, diluted in distilled water to an equivalence of about 10 mg hematoxylin per liter, present an absorption spectrum characterized by a rather broad peak with maximum at 554–560 mμ and a secondary low shoulder at 430 mμ. The optical density at 560 is generally 3–4 times that at 430. On overoxidation, whether by age and long exposure to air or by overdose of a chemical oxidant, the solution changes its color from purple through red to orange or even yellow brown, and the 430 peak now becomes the dominant absorption maximum spectroscopically. The 560 peak may become quite inapparent.

On the basis of these recent studies of Palmer and Lillie (*Histochemie*, **5**:44, 1965) in my laboratory, I would recommend with iodate ripening that one try about 40 mg $NaIO_3$ for each gram of hematoxylin used, and forthwith test the batch for staining, allowing graded intervals of, say, 2, 6, 20 and 60 minutes. If satisfactory staining is attained only with the longest interval, add another 10 mg $NaIO_3$ per gm hematoxylin and test again. In this way overoxidation can be avoided and a hematoxylin can be prepared which stains adequately in 2–6 minutes and which will improve for a time with use. Such hematoxylins are apt to have a longer useful life than those in which maximum ripening or perhaps slight over-ripening is attained at once.

It is hoped that definite spectrophotometric density standards for adequate ripening can be developed. The indications are good that such will be the case, but a considerable period of comparison of spectrophotometric and practical staining data on various batches of dye will be necessary first.

Other Oxidants

Though the traditional amounts, 177 mg potassium permanganate, 200 mg sodium iodate and 500 mg mercuric oxide per gram hematoxylin work well in practice, recent work indicates that considerably smaller quantities of some of these oxidants may be used with good immediate ripening and probably a longer useful life of the solution. Quantities recommended per gram hematoxylin are sodium iodate, $NaIO_3$, 40–100 mg; potassium permanganate, $KMnO_4$, 175 mg; potassium periodate, KIO_4, 50 mg; mercuric oxide, HgO, 100 mg. Of these the first 3 are used cold, the fourth is boiled. $KMnO_4$ and KIO_4 dosages need restudy.

Considering these properties, it makes little difference how the hematein is formed. Solutions vary in vigor of staining according to the amount of dye used in their preparation, and to their stage in oxidation or over-oxidation, and in selectivity on progressive staining according to their acidity. The function of alcohol seems to be principally preservative against molds; that of glycerol to stabilize the solution against over-oxidation. In fact, I have seen deliberately overoxidized 30% glycerol solutions regain their staining capacity to a considerable extent on standing.

Table 7-5 gives a number of the more usual formulae on a per liter

TABLE 7-5. FORMULAE FOR 1 LITER OF ALUM HEMATOXYLIN[1]

Ingredients	Mayer hemalum	Mallory aqueous	Harris	Boehmer-Schmorl	Apáthy	Lillie-Mayer	Delafield	Ehrlich acid	Bullard
Hematoxylin	1	2.5	5	5	3.3	5	6.4	6.4	8
Ammonium alum	50	50	100	100	30	50	60	40+	60
Ethyl alcohol	....	....	....	60	233	....	200[2]	322	333
Glycerol	....	....	....	....	333	300	160	322	330
Water	1000	1000	1000	1000	423	700	640	322	334
Chemical ripening agent	$0.2NaIO_3$[3]	None	2.5HgO	None	None	$0.2{-}0.4\ NaIO_3$[3]	None	None	8HgO
Time and temperature	15°C, inst.	25°C, 10 days	100°C, few min	15°C, 8 days	15°C, 6 wk	25°C, inst.	25°C, 6-8 wk	15°C, 6-8 wk	100°C, few min
Alternate ripening	....	$0.44KMnO_4$	....	Air bubbling	....	....	....	$0.64NaIO_3$	
Time and temperature	....	25°C, inst.	....	2-6 wk, 23°C	....	....	....	15°C, inst.	
Added Acid:									
Normal	None	None	None	None	Acetic 10	Acetic 20	None	Acetic 32	Acetic 34
Variant	1 citric or 20 acetic	....	40 acetic						
Stated life	2-3 mo	2-3 mo	Months to years	Months to years		Months to years	Years	Years	Indef.
Preservative	50 chloral hydrate	2.5 thymol	....	....	0.33 acid salicylic				

[1] In general it is prescribed that glycerol and acid be added after ripening is well along. In case of iodate ripening the sequence of combination of ingredients appears to make no difference. 25°C is adopted as average American room temperature, 15°C as German. Quantities are in grams for solids, in cubic centimeters for liquids. "inst." = instantaneous.

[2] Originally 40 cc ethyl and 160 cc methyl alcohol.

[3] See text on iodate ripening, p. 173.

basis. Some methods prescribe dissolving the hematoxylin first in alcohol or water and oxidizing either by exposure to air or by addition of an oxidizing agent. On trial it seems to make no difference whether the alum, glycerol, water, acetic acid and other constituents are added to the hematoxylin solution before or after oxidation, and the method of oxidation is similarly unimportant. Alcohol and glycerol may themselves consume chemical oxidants.

Delafield's formula is cited from Mayer in Ehrlich's *Encyklopädie*. I have set the amount of alum at 60 gm, which is a slight excess over the amount demanded by the 1:11 solution described as saturated by Mayer. Mallory called for a 15% alum solution and used ethyl alcohol throughout. The latter recommendation seems logical.

Both Mallory's and Schmorl's formulae are essentially modifications of the vague original Boehmer formula (*Encyklopädie*) and are cited from the texts of the 2 authors.

Mayer's formula (*Z. wiss. Mikr.* **20**:409, 1904) is cited in essentially the form given by nearly all texts subsequent to the *Encyklopädie*. My modification (*Stain Techn.* **16**:1, 1941, **17**:89, 1942) resembles Mayer's glycerol hemalum in its solvent, but contains 0.5% hematoxylin in place of the 0.4% hematein of that mixture (Ehrlich's *Encyklopädie*). Langeron cites a similar, weaker formula with 0.1% hematoxylin, 0.02% sodium iodate, 20% glycerol and 5% alum, which was devised by Carazzi (*Z. wiss. Mikr.* **28**:273, 1911).

Apáthy's formula is cited from Lee in modified form. The (1%) hematoxylin was first ripened in 70% alcohol, and this was then mixed with equal volumes of glycerol and 3% acetic, 9% alum solution.

Harris's formula and Ehrlich's mixture I have cited from the *Encyklopädie*. I have set the amount of alum in the latter at 4%, which is more than sufficient for saturation at 30°C. Iodate ripening of Ehrlich's formula was suggested by Mallory, and I have used it successfully.

Bullard's hematoxylin is the most concentrated formula that I have encountered. Dr. Bullard told me (April, 1949) that the formula was devised for the relatively crude, dark colored American hematoxylin available in 1915–1918. It was originally published by MacCallum in *Laboratory Methods of the U.S. Army*, 2d ed. Lea & Febiger, Philadelphia, 1919, p. 69. Bullard directs: Dissolve 8 gm hematoxylin in 144 cc 50% alcohol, add 16 cc glacial acetic acid and a (heated) solution of 20 gm ammonia alum in 250 cc water. Heat to boiling and add slowly (to avoid frothing) 8 gm red mercuric oxide. Cool quickly, filter and add 275 cc 95% alcohol, 330 cc glycerol, 18 cc glacial acetic acid and 40 gm ammonia alum.

If spontaneous ripening of hematoxylin solutions is preferred to one of the chemical means, it is necessary to anticipate one's needs by several months, and keep a supply ahead in various stages of ripening.

I prefer the solutions containing glycerol because of their greater stability and those containing 0.5% or higher of hematoxylin because of their greater vigor of staining and capacity for staining larger numbers of sections before exhaustion. Acidified hematoxylins are preferable for routine nuclear staining, but the nonacidified ones have valuable properties as well. Alum percentages generally approach saturation and are lower in the partly alcoholic and glycerol solutions than in the aqueous. The alum prescribed is always ammonium aluminum sulfate, $(NH_4)_2SO_4 \cdot Al_2(SO_4)_3 \cdot 24H_2O$. Since this is a salt of strong acid with relatively weak bases, alum hematoxylin solutions present pH levels about 2.6–2.8 even without added acid. (See also p. 172.)

STAINING TECHNICS

Alum Hematoxylin and Eosin Y

For permanency with reasonable differentiation of nuclei and cytoplasm the preferred method is still hematoxylin and eosin. Many variants have been proposed. Some workers use acid hematoxylins, others differentiate with acid after staining with an unacidified or partly neutralized hematoxylin. Some use strong eosin solutions before the hematoxylin; some mix the hematoxylin and eosin solutions; others use aqueous or alcoholic solutions of eosin after the hematoxylin; and some insist on the color acid of eosin Y (C.I. No. 45380) dissolved in alcohol. Others prefer other dyes to eosin Y, such as eosin B (C.I. No. 45400), erythrosin B (C.I. No. 45430), or phloxine B (C.I. No. 45410). Eosin B is a slightly bluish pink, erythrosin B is quite similar, phloxine B is a deeper red, while eosin Y is a yellowish pink. The technic follows.

I. The Acid Hematoxylin Variant.

1. Bring sections to water.
2. Stain 2–5 or more minutes in an acid alum hematoxylin (p. 174). Zenker material may need as much as an hour. Sections do not overstain.
3. Wash thoroughly in tap water until sections are blue. Some workers add a few drops of ammonium hydroxide to 500 cc water. Some use a weak (1%) sodium acetate, or sodium bicarbonate or disodium phosphate solution.
4. Stain 1 minute in 0.5% aqueous eosin Y.
5. Rinse in water.
6. Dehydrate in 2 changes each of 95% and 100% alcohol.
7. Pass through 100% alcohol + xylene (50:50) mixture into 2 changes

of xylene. Mount in a synthetic resin (or balsam). Nuclei are blue; cartilage and calcium deposits, dark blue; cytoplasm, muscle and other structures, varying shades of pink; mucin, often light blue; kerato-hyalin, often dark blue.

II. The Unacidified Hematoxylin Variant.

1. Brings sections to water.
2. Stain sections 5 minutes or more in an unacidified alum hematoxylin (p. 174). The sections are overstained.
3. Differentiate in acid alcohol until red. (Concentrated hydrochloric acid 1 cc, 70% alcohol 99 cc).
4. Wash thoroughly in tap water or 1% sodium acetate or bicarbonate or disodium phosphate until blue.
5. Counterstain 1 minute in 0.5% eosin Y.
6. Rinse in water.
7. Dehydrate with 2 changes each of 95% and 100% alcohol.
8. 100% alcohol + xylene, then 2 changes of xylene.
9. Mount in Permount or balsam.

Results differ only slightly from the preceding method. Myelin and similar substances may retain some blue if hematoxylin staining has been prolonged and formalin or a chromate fixation has been used.

Substitution of certain acid azo dyes for the eosins may give pleasing effects. Orange G (C.I. No. 16230) gives orange to yellow tones; chromotrope 2R (C.I. No. 16570), pink and orange red tones; Bordeaux red (C.I. No. 16180), somewhat redder tone; Biebrich scarlet (C.I. No. 26905), varying pink to scarlet tones. Lee recommended this last in 1% solution as the best plasma stain he had tried.

Other Mordant Dyes

Neumeyer (*Zbl. allg. Path.* 84:109, 1948) recommends as a substitute for alum hematoxylin a 0.1% solution of Anthracene Blue WR extra of Badische Anilin (C.I. No. 58605, 1,2,4,5,6,8-hexahydroxyanthraqui-none) in 5% aqueous aluminum sulfate solution. Boil the fresh solution 8 minutes, filter while hot and add 1 cc 40% formaldehyde per liter. The solution is quite stable.

Neumeyer's Anthacene Blue SWR and Eosin Technic.

1. Hydrate paraffin sections (10 μ) of formalin fixed tissue as usual.
2. Stain 10–30 minutes in the anthracene blue SWR solution.

3. Differentiate 30 seconds to 2 minutes in 2% concentrated HCl in alcohol. Nuclei resist longer differentiation quite well.
4. Wash 15 minutes in running water.
5. Counterstain in 0.5% eosin ½–2 minutes; or other suitable method.
6. Alcohols, xylene alcohol, xylenes, synthetic resin.

Results: Nuclei, blue black; muscle, violet; connective tissue, bright red; cytoplasm of glycogen laden cells, blue violet.

Pearse's (*Acta Histochem.* 4:95, 1957) **Phosphoric Acid Cyanine R Method for Nuclei and Various Cytoplasmic Bodies.** Chromoxane cyanine R, C.I. No. 43820, usually called cyanine R or chrome cyanine R, with various brand name prefixes, is soluble in hot and cold water and in alcohol. Pearse's staining method is simple.

Deparaffinize and hydrate as usual. Stain 5–20 minutes in 0.2% cyanine R in 1% phosphoric acid at 18–25°C. Wash briefly in hot water (3–5 minutes) until color of section changes from orange through red and begins to turn bluish. Dehydrate rapidly in graded alcohols (70%, 85%, 95%, absolute), clear in xylene and mount in suitable synthetic medium.

Results: Nuclei, blue; collagen and reticulum, unstained or faint pink; eosinophil granules, Russell bodies, enterochromaffin cell granules, keratin, muscle, fibrin, fibrinoid, erythrocytes, myelin, nucleoli, spermatozoon heads, hypophyseal alpha cell granules, red; Paneth granules, pink. Reactions of other zymogen granules were not recorded by Pearse. $Al(OH)_3$ is figured as stained rose red.

Iron lakes of the oxazin dyes are recommended by Proescher and Arkush (*Stain Techn.* 3:28, 1929) as selective nuclear stains. The lakes are prepared by boiling for 3–5 minutes 0.5% solutions of celestine blue B (C.I. No. 51050), gallamine blue (C.I. No. 51045) and gallocyanine (C.I. No. 51030) in 5% ferric ammonium alum. The first of the 3 dyes was preferred. Nuclei stain blue black in 3–5 minutes, leaving cytoplasm unstained. Van Gieson counterstains change the nuclear color to green. I have not tried these stains.

A gallocyanine chrome alum method has been highly recommended by Einarson (*Am. J. Path.* 8:295, 1932) for the staining of Nissl granules, and is widely used for this purpose, especially by Scandinavian workers.

Einarson's Method. Dissolve 10 gm chrome alum $KCr(SO_4)_2 \cdot 12\ H_2O$ in 200 cc distilled water, add 300 mg gallocyanine, and heat slowly to boiling. Boil with frequent shaking for 15–25 minutes, cool slowly, and filter. This solution has a pH of about 1.84. Sections of material fixed in alcohol, 20% formalin, 10% alcoholic formalin, sublimate alcohol, or in a solution of 10 cc formalin, 40 cc 95% alcohol and 50 cc 6% aqueous mercuric chloride solution, stain well in 24 hours; but acetic Zenker material requires longer. Either paraffin or nitrocellulose sections may be used. These are brought to water in the usual way before staining, stained 24–

48 hours, dehydrated as usual with alcohols, cleared with xylene and mounted in balsam (or synthetic resin). This stain is not extracted by alcohol.

Carmine (C.I. No. 75470)

Formerly the most important dyestuff in the histologist's armamentarium, carmine is less and less used today. I have used it as a nuclear stain in such procedures as Weigert's fibrin stain, and occasionally in other methods; but now no longer use it in any procedure except the Best carmine stain for glycogen, Mayer's mucicarmine and for coloring injection masses red. Formulae for these will be given under the special methods.

Orth's formula (Mayer in Ehrlich's *Encyklopädie*) called for 2.5–5 gm carmine, dissolved by boiling 15 minutes in 100 cc saturated aqueous lithium carbonate solution. After cooling, 1 gm thymol was added as a preservative. Sections were stained 2–5 minutes and differentiated in a 1:100 dilution of concentrated hydrochloric acid in 70% alcohol.

In Grenacher's formula Mayer (Ehrlich's *Encyklopädie*) recommended 2 gm carmine dissolved by boiling for 1 hour in 100 cc 5% ammonium alum, restoring water to maintain volume. After cooling Mallory added 1 gm thymol. Grenacher originally used 0.5–1% carmine and 1–5% alum.

Mayer's (Ehrlich's *Encyklopädie*) alcoholic carmine ("paracarmine") may be used when it is desired to avoid aqueous solutions. Dissolve 1 gm carminic acid, 0.5 gm aluminum chloride and 4 gm calcium chloride (crystals?) in 100 cc 70% alcohol. Filter before using. Stain sections 15–30 minutes and wash with 70% alcohol, adding 2.5% glacial acetic acid if a more purely nuclear stain is desired.

Mayer's Carmalum (Mallory). Carminic acid 1 gm, ammonium (or potassium) alum 10 gm; dissolve in 200 cc distilled water, warming if necessary; cool and add 0.2 gm salicylic acid or other suitable preservative, such as merthiolate.

Chapter 8

Chemical End Groups

ETHYLENES

Ethylenic linkages exist principally in histochemistry in relation to the unsaturated fatty acids and in certain long chain aliphatic alcohols which are found in cutaneous fats such as hair oil or sebaceous secretions.

There are three principal histochemical methods for the demonstration of ethylenic double bonds: the oldest empirically discovered reaction with osmium tetroxide; the demonstration of aldehyde residues with Schiff reagent or other reagent after oxidation with peracetic or performic acid; and the new bromination silver technics depending on the introduction of bromine into double bonds and its subsequent removal by silver nitrate to form insoluble, photosensitive silver bromide which is then reduced to metallic silver *in situ*.

With most lipids osmium tetroxide adds quantitatively to double bonds in the proportion of 1 molecule OsO_4 to each C=C residue (Kahn, Riemersma and Booij, *J. Histochem.* 9:560, 1961) for oleic acid and simple oleates, 2 moles of OsO_4 to 1 glycerol trioleate, but the reaction is modified in choline and ethanolamine (colamine) phosphatides (lecithins and cephalins). Generally the first reaction product is an osmic

ester which then hydrolyzes to a glycol and a lower hydroxy acid of osmium (Criegee, *Liebigs Ann. Chem.* 522:75, 1936; 550:99, 1942).

Osmium tetroxide also blackens other substances: enterochromaffin, melanin, adrenaline and noradrenaline, probably also dopamine, eleidin, tannin and other strongly reducing substances. When osmic acid treatment is preceded by treatment with more selective oxidants, such as bichromates, the blackening is restricted to substances, such as triolein, which resist oxidation by the $K_2Cr_2O_7$ bath. This is the basis of the

Marchi procedure for degenerating myelin. During the earlier part of this century, following the introduction of the Sudan dyes, osmium tetroxide passed into almost total disuse in the study of fats, except for some very special purposes, such as the demonstration of the Golgi lipids. With its introduction as a nearly ideal morphologic fixative for electron microscopy it has received renewed attention, not only for fixation but also for histochemical study.

Osmium Tetroxide Method. Cut frozen, gelatin or polyvinyl alcohol sections of formalin fixed material.

1. Soak part of the sections in 2.5% potassium bichromate for 2 days, then a day or 2 further in a mixture of 6 cc 2.5% potassium bichromate and 3 cc 1% osmium tetroxide. Wash in water and mount in gum syrup. Degenerating myelin and neutral fats are blackened.
2. Treat another group overnight in 0.25% OsO_4, wash in distilled water
2a. Mount in glycerol gelatin or aqueous polyvinyl alcohol glycerol
   or
2b. Dehydrate and mount in balsam or synthetic resin.
   In critical studies, multiple sections and graded time intervals should be used, and appropriate controls should be applied. Also, preparations may be mounted in osmic acid with a coverglass sealed with petrolatum (vaseline) and observed repeatedly during the reaction period.
3. Treat a third group of sections 24 hours in 1% osmium tetroxide, wash in water 6–12 hours, soak several hours in absolute alcohol to obtain the secondary staining of fats. Wash in water and mount in gum syrup. This procedure is supposed to demonstrate saturated neutral fats as well as unsaturated, but probably it actually demonstrates those lipids which are easily oxidized by potassium bichromate and are dissolved in the neutral fats. The alcohol undoubtedly removes unaltered alcohol soluble lipid and may serve to reduce further the osmic ester or lower acid.

Material treated in the block with osmium tetroxide, alone or with chromates, can be imbedded in paraffin or nitrocellulose. For paraffin imbedding, clearing with cedar oil or briefly with chloroform is preferred, and chloroform balsam is said to be better for mounting.

The Marchi Method. A method formerly widely used for degenerating myelin was slightly modified from Schmorl:

1. Fix 2 days in Orth or 10% formalin.
2. Mordant 7 days in 2.5% potassium bichromate, changing on the third and fifth days.
3. Osmicate 14 days in the dark in 2 changes of 7 days each of a mixture

of 2 volumes 2.5% potassium bichromate and 1 volume 1% osmium tetroxide.

4. Wash 24 hours in running water.
5. Dehydrate with 4 changes of acetone, 30–45 minutes each.
6. Clear in petroleum ether, 2 changes of 30 minutes each.
7. Infiltrate with paraffin, 3 changes, 30 minutes each, or one change of 30 minutes *in vacuo.*
8. Imbed and section.
9. Deparaffinize with chloroform and mount in chloroform balsam.

Results: Degenerating myelin, black; background, brownish yellow. It is probable that polyene fats are oxidized by chromation and that chiefly olein remains for the osmium reaction.

Recently I have preferred a frozen section method with a modified Weigert myelin stain combined with Sudan II (C.I. No. 21401) for the degenerating myelin (p. 460).

Peracetic and Performic Acid Schiff Procedures. Certain oxidants, such as performic and peracetic acids, potassium permanganate and perhaps chromic acid attack ethylenes to form epoxides, glycols, peroxides and aldehydes. Chemical studies have shown about 92% recovery of glycolic fatty acids from peracetic oxidation of unsaturated fatty acid (Findley *et al., J. Am. Chem. Soc.* **67**:412, 1945; and Swern *et al., ibid.* **67**:1786, 1945). Experiments in our own laboratory gave on oxidation of 0.1 mol allyl alcohol with an excess of peracetic acid and distillation of the reaction mixture, a recovery of about 8 m-mol formaldehyde, as determined by iodine titration of the bisulfite compound; this agrees perfectly with the works of Swern, Findley and Scanlan.

These oxidation technics, reported by Pearse (*Quart. J. Micr. Sci.* **92**: 393, 1951) and Lillie (*Stain Techn.* **27**:37, 1952) essentially simultaneously,[1] depend on the production of aldehyde by performic or peracetic acid and the demonstration of that production by Schiff's sulfite leucofuchsin reagent according to the reactions

$$CH_3-(CH_2)_x-CH\!=\!CH-(CH_2)_y-COOH + 2CH_3CO_3H \rightarrow$$

$$CH_3-(CH_2)_x-\underset{\underset{O-O}{|\quad\;|}}{CH-CH}-(CH_2)_y COOH \rightarrow CH_3-(CH_2)_x CHO$$

$$+ OCH-(CH_2)_y-COOH \text{ by cleavage of the peroxide}$$

Permanganate, by virtue of its ability to also cleave the α-glycols formed by oxidation of the ethylene bond, with the formation of aldehyde, also gives a positive Schiff reaction which might well be more intense by virtue of the possibility of essentially total conversion of the double bond to aldehyde residues, but it also oxidizes aldehyde to carboxylic and

---

[1] *Quart. J. Micr. Sci.* 92/4 actually appeared about 2 weeks later than *Stain Techn.* 27/1.

carbonic acid residues. Prior bromination (1 hour at 25°C in 1 cc bromine to 39 cc carbon tetrachloride) completely blocks the reaction, whereas acetylation does not. After the oxidation step, interposition of blockades with sulfite, aniline, phenylhydrazine or semicarbazide prevents the lipids from coloring with Schiff reagent when the usual 10 minute exposure is used. Long exposures (2–3 hours) may overcome sulfite blockades and brief (30 minutes) phenylhydrazine blockades; and the aldehydes react with the usual red purple color. Prolonged phenylhydrazine and aniline hydrochloride blockades (4–72 hours) appear to be permanently effective.

The action of performic acid and of peracetic acid is quite comparable, and both reagents are readily prepared. According to Greenspan (*J. Am. Chem. Soc.* **68**:907, 1946) performic acid is formed in adequate concentration in 30–60 minutes, but deteriorates practically to inactivity by the next day. Peracetic acid takes 2–3 days to reach maximum concentration; it may be kept several weeks. I have used the same jar repeatedly. Hence the performic acid is preferable for an occasional test and the peracetic is better for frequent routine use. The following directions for manufacture of the reagents are derived from Greenspan.

Performic Acid Reagent. To 8 cc of 90% formic acid add 31 cc of 30% hydrogen peroxide and 0.22 cc concentrated sulfuric acid. Keep at or below 25°C. About 4.7% performic acid (HCO_3H) is formed within 2 hours, and the solution deteriorates after a few more hours. Make fresh daily.

Peracetic Acid Reagent. To 95.6 cc glacial acetic acid add 259 cc 30% hydrogen peroxide and 2.2 cc concentrated sulfuric acid. Let stand 1–3 days. Add 40 mg disodium phosphate as stabilizer. Store in the refrigerator at 0–5°C. I have kept such solutions for months. A single Coplin jar of this reagent may be used for 8–10 groups of 9 slides before it is discarded; but a positive control should be included, at least in the later groups.

Using the foregoing formulae, a maximum concentration of about 4.7% performic acid is reached in 2 hours, and a maximum of 8.6% peracetic acid in 80–96 hours. If 90% hydrogen peroxide is used, concentrations of peracetic acid around 45% are reached. Since there are indications that this high a concentration of peracetic acid may destroy aldehyde (Findlay's letter, 1954), its routine use is not recommended.

Lillie's Peracetic or Performic Acid Schiff Reaction.

1. Fix and section in accordance with the solubility requirements of the lipid under study. For ceroid, any fixation and paraffin or frozen sections; for lipofuscin pigments, routine formalin and paraffin sections; for retina and myelin, aqueous formaldehyde or, better, formaldehyde bichromate sequence fixations and paraffin sections.

2. Bring sections to water as usual.
3. Oxidize 2 hours in peracetic acid reagent or 90 minutes in performic acid reagent.
4. Wash 10 minutes in running water.
5. Immerse in Schiff reagent for 10 minutes.
6. Wash in 3 changes of 0.5% sodium bisulfite or metabisulfite, 2, 2, and 2 minutes.
7. Wash 10 minutes in running water.
8. If desired, counterstain 1–2 minutes in Weigert's acid iron hematoxylin (p. 168), wash 4 minutes in running water and stain 1 minute in saturated aqueous picric acid solution. Or use other suitable counterstain.
9. Dehydrate, clear and mount by the alcohol, alcohol + xylene, xylene, polystyrene sequence. Or, if required because of the solubility of the lipids concerned, wash in water and mount in glycerol gelatin or polyvinyl alcohol.

Results: Ceroid, retinal rod acromere lipid, many lipofuscin pigments react with a red purple color. Myelin sometimes reacts quite well, especially in frozen sections or in well chromated paraffin material.

If no counterstain is employed, nuclei are also colored red by the concurrent Feulgen reaction. The latter may be induced by corresponding mixtures of formic or acetic acid with a little sulfuric acid and distilled water replacing the hydrogen peroxide solution. The red color of nuclei is almost completely suppressed by iron or alum hematoxylin counterstains.

Hair cortex also colors red-purple, a reaction which Pearse (*Quart. J. Micr. Sci.* **92**:393, 1951) attributed to cystine, although he was not able to repeat the reaction with cystine *in vitro.* Like that of ceroid, this reaction is prevented by prior bromination and is not reversed by even prolonged extraction in fat solvents, hot or cold. Like ceroid, hair cortex is also acid fast by Ziehl-Neelsen technics; but unlike ceroid, it is not sudanophilic in paraffin sections. The Schiff reaction is best prevented by sulfite blockade.

Pearse makes peracetic acid by mixing 5 cc 30% hydrogen peroxide with 20 cc acetic anhydride and notes that it is less active than his performic acid mixture. Apparently he used it immediately, without allowing the 24–48 hour interval which Greenspan recommends for reaction to form peracetic acid. His performic acid reagent is made by adding 4 cc 30% hydrogen peroxide to 40 cc 98% formic acid and letting the mixture react for 1 hour before using it.

Greenspan used about 1.57 mols of H_2O_2 per mol of acetic acid, a proportion designed to give a maximum yield of peracid. Pearse's prescription calls for only 0.20 mol of H_2O_2 per mol of acetic anhydride.

Thus the latter contains much less water and much more acetic acid in proportion than does Greenspan's mixture.

With performic acid, Greenspan's directions call for about 1.55 mols of peroxide per mol of formic acid; Pearse's, for only 0.038 mol; again providing less water and a far greater excess of formic over performic acid.

This reaction is controlled by omission of the hydrogen peroxide from the performic or peracetic acid reagent, substituting the same amount of water.

Bromination Blockades and the Bromine Silver Procedures. Prior chlorination or bromination, but not iodination, prevents the foregoing reaction. Iodine chloride and bromide should also serve but have not been used histochemically. For insoluble lipids, bromine in carbon tetrachloride 2.5% by volume is usually employed; for substances soluble in CCl_4 the preferred mixture now seems to be a solution in aqueous KBr (Norton et al., J. Histochem. 10:83, 1962), rather than bromine water or gaseous bromine. Chlorine and bromine and strong halogen acids react with ethylene groups to form halogen substituted saturated compounds. $RCH{=}CH{-}R'{-}COOH + Br_2 \rightarrow RCHBr{-}CHBr{-}R'COOH$, and $RCH{=}CH{-}R'COOH + HI \rightarrow RCHI{-}CH_2R'{-}COOH$.

It must be noted that with prolonged exposures such polysaccharides as starch and glycogen are also brominated or chlorinated (3–6 hours in 2.5% bromine in CCl_4).

Since prolonged exposure of aliphatic halogen compounds to silver nitrate results in the formation of silver halides, bromination has been made the basis of 2 bromine silver methods for localization of ethylenic residues, that of Mukherji et al. (J. Histochem. 8:189, 1960), which used bromine vapor and preferred an ammoniacal to a neutral silver nitrate solution, and that of Norton et al. (loc. cit.), which brominated in a weak KBr bromine solution and silvered with strongly acid silver nitrate to avoid nonspecific silver reduction. Norton and coworkers did not specifically note the negative silver reactions of melanin and enterochromaffin, but it is known that the argentaffin reactions of these substances are prevented by adequate prior oxidation and by bromination and iodination specifically (J. Histochem. 5:325, 1957, for melanin; ibid. 9:184, 1961, for enterochromaffin). Whether the 1 minute bromination of this technic is adequate for this purpose remains undetermined. Mukherji and coworkers have noted a positive reaction of sterols.

The reactions involved are as follows:

$$RCHBr{-}CHBr{-}R'{-}COOH + 2AgNO_3 \rightarrow RCH(NO_3){-}CH(NO_3){-}R'{-}COOH + 2AgBr$$

$$AgBr + H \rightarrow Ag + HBr \text{ (light or photographic developer)}$$

Bromination Silver Technic of Norton et al. for Unsaturated Fats. Fix 18 hours or more in Baker's calcium cadmium formol saturated with calcium carbonate. Wash blocks 3–5 hours in running water. Cut 10 μ frozen sections and collect in distilled water.

1. Immerse 1 minute in 0.1 N bromine in 2% potassium bromide (add 1 cc bromine to 388 cc 2% KBr) and rinse in distilled water.
2. Immerse 1 minute in 1% sodium bisulfite.
3. Wash in 7 changes distilled water.
4. Treat 18–22 hours in 1% silver nitrate in 1 N nitric acid.
5. Wash in 7 changes distilled water.
6. Develop in Eastman Dektol diluted one-half in distilled water, 10 minutes.
7. Wash well in water, mount in glycerol gelatin or glycerol polyvinyl alcohol. Reactive sites, brown to black. Suitable counterstains can be tried if desired.

The reaction is controlled as follows:

1. By omission of free bromine from the 2% KBr of step 1
2. By 1–2 hour oxidation in performic acid (p. 183) before step 1. Wash in 7 changes distilled water.
3. By removal of silver bromide by immersion in 5% sodium thiosulfate for 5 minutes at step 5. To accomplish the removal of AgBr in this way steps 4, 5 and the thiosulfate extraction must be done in the photographic darkroom (Pizzolato, *J. Histochem.* **10**:102, 1962). A 1% KCN extraction in the presence of air will, as usual, remove the silver, either before or after development. About 20 minutes should serve.

The reacting lipids may also be removed by extraction with appropriate solvents. In this case it must be remembered that Baker's calcium cadmium formol was designed to insolubilize phospholipids and that after formalin fixation many such lipids remain demonstrable in paraffin sections with Sudan and hematoxylin procedures.

The bromine solution is stable for some weeks at least.

PEROXIDES

Peroxides are formed in the course of air oxidation of unsaturated fats and give rise to aldehyde cleavage. The same process apparently occurs to some extent in the course of performic and peracetic acid oxidation of olefines, although in this case the principal products are epoxides and glycol groups.

Sehrt (*München. med. Wschr.* **74**:139, 1927) and Lison (*Bull. Soc. Chim. Biol.* **18**:185, 1936) showed that the Winkler-Schultze or "M-Nadi" indophenol blue synthesis from α-naphthol and p-amino-N,N-dimethylaniline could be mediated nonenzymatically by partially oxidized un-saturated fats. I have found that part of the lipofuscin pigment of the human ovary and rat liver ceroid in choline deficiency cirrhosis give this reaction under relatively anaerobic conditions, and the reaction is en-hanced or engendered anew by prior peracetic acid oxidation, thus sup-porting the view that the aldehyde produced by this oxidant from ethylenes goes through a peroxide stage. The following directions are from Lillie and Burtner (*J. Histochem.* **1**:8, 1953).

The Winkler Schultze Reaction Applied to Fatty Acid Peroxides.

1. Paraffin or frozen sections are brought to distilled water as usual. Dissolve 576 mg (4.02 m-mol) α-naphthol in 6 cc 1 N sodium hy-droxide and dilute to 50 cc with distilled water. Dissolve 691 mg (4.00 m-mol) p-amino-N,N-dimethylaniline (*as* p-dimethylphenylenedi-amine) in 50 cc distilled water. Mix, filter and use at once.
2. Immerse sections in mixture for 3 minutes, or flood them with it.
3. Decant, rinse in distilled water.
4. Immerse 3 minutes in dilute Lugol's solution (0.2% iodine, 0.4% KI). Wash 20 minutes in lithium carbonate 5 mg/100 cc distilled water. Mount in glycerol gelatin. Faint to moderate blue or green coloration indicates presence of peroxides. The browner pigments give a greener color.

Granados and Dam (*Acta Path. Microbiol. Scand.* **27**:591, 1950) noted that the earlier, lighter yellow stages of vitamin E deficiency pigment gave the leucodichloroindophenol reaction for peroxides, and Glavind *et al.* (*Experientia* **5**:34, 1949) reported the following method devised by that group for the histochemical localization.

The Hemin Catalyzed Leucodichloroindophenol Peroxide Reaction of Glavind *et al. Solution A.*

1. Prepare the stable **stock solution of hemin** (obtained from Hoffman, LaRoche) by dissolving 40 mg in 10 cc pyridine and 20 cc glacial acetic acid. This keeps for a long time.
2. Prepare leuco 2,4-dichlorophenolindophenol (identified by Gibbs as 3,5-dichloro-4,4'-dihydroxydiphenylamine) by the method of Gibbs, Cohen and Cannan (*Pub. Health Rep.* **40**:699, 1925) or by reducing a solution of 2,6-dichlorophenolindophenol in 50% alcohol with the stoichiometric amount of ascorbic acid. Precipitate as sodium salt with NaCl. Purify by redissolving in alcohol and reprecipitating with water, repeating several times to eliminate traces of ascorbic acid.

Gibbs and coworkers made the indophenol by condensing 2,6-dichloro-quinonechloroimid[1] with phenol in alkaline solution and salting out with NaCl, purifying by repeated aqueous re-solution and salting out, and then reduced the product with K_2S and recrystallized from an acid solution containing H_2S to prevent reoxidation (*ibid.* 39:381, 1924).

Solution B. Dissolve 25 mg leuco 2,4-dichlorophenolindophenol (3,5-dichloro-4,4'-dihydroxyphenylamine) in 3.5 cc absolute alcohol. Mix with 5 cc distilled water. Use at once.

Float frozen sections onto slides, blot dry. Add 0.74 cc solution A to solution B, mix and pour onto slides. Let stand 3–5 minutes, wash thoroughly with distilled water, mount in glycerin gelatin or Farrants's gum arabic (p. 101).

Peroxide sites are shown in red. Since the retention of the red dye locally depends on its oil solubility in the fats, preparations are not dehydrated. The blotting before staining is important, since an excess of water will precipitate the hemin and prevent the reaction.

ALCOHOLS

As Lison aptly states, this grouping has had little histochemical interest. Undoubtedly alcohol groups are among those rendered strongly metachromatically basophil by sulfation and phosphorylation, but these reactions do not permit their distinction from α-glycols and perhaps phenols as well. Hence detailed comparison of results of these procedures with those of procedures demonstrating α-glycols and phenols more specifically would be necessary to localize alcohol sites which do not fall into the other categories.

Actually the class of compounds which should be considered as nonglycolic aliphatic alcohols is considerably larger and more important than Lison seemed to consider, if one includes in it, as seems proper, the nonperiodate reactive acetylaminopolysaccharides which are not already sulfated. I hesitate to include the Landing-Hall (*J. Histochem.* 4:41, 1956) phosphorylation reaction, since it now appears that phosphorylation of tissues engenders, besides basophilia, a positive Schiff reaction in many structures such as elastin, collagen, pituitary chromophils, gastric parietal cells, Paneth cells, erythrocytes, muscle and glycogen. Moreover these authors considered that phosphoryl chloride reacted not only on OH groups but also on SH and primary and secondary amines (Haust and Landing, *J. Histochem.* 9:548, 1961). The Schiff reaction was tentatively attributed to $\equiv$PO or $=$POCl groups. The former seems improbable, since $\equiv$PO appears in normal phosphates, which are not Schiff positive.

Hence the sulfation technic appears to be the method of choice for

[1] Available from K and K Laboratories, Jamaica, N.Y.

creation of sulfate ester residues on alcohol sites. Mowry's technic (*J. Histochem.* **6**:82, 1958; McManus and Mowry, p. 142) appears to be convenient for this purpose.

Mowry's Ether Sulfuric Sulfation Method.

1. Pack cracked ice around a Coplin jar containing 25 cc anhydrous ethyl ether.
2. Add gradually 25 cc concentrated sulfuric acid. The reaction is exothermic. When the mixture is again cold, cover the Coplin jar with a cover that has its edges coated with Vaseline (Petrolatum U.S.P.).
3. Deparaffinize sections with xylene, wash in absolute alcohol and in ether.
4. Sulfate in the ether sulfuric acid mixture for 5 minutes (or more, if required).
5. Wash in alcohol and water.
6. Stain one pair of sulfated and unsulfated control sections in 0.01% toluidine blue in 3% acetic acid (pH about 2.5) for 5–30 minutes. Dehydrate in acetone, melted *tert*-butanol or ethanol, clear in xylene, mount in Permount or cellulose caprate.
7. Stain another pair of sulfated and unsulfated control sections by the periodic acid Schiff method (p. 198).

Structures which are metachromatically stained by toluidine blue in sulfated tissue but not in unsulfated controls and which are negative to the periodic acid Schiff reaction without sulfation are to be considered as probably containing alcohol and to be periodate negative polysaccharides. The adequacy of the sulfation may be appraised by the completeness of prevention of the periodic acid Schiff reaction. Mowry, as well as others, recorded strong orthochromatic blue staining of collagen with the sulfation toluidine blue sequence, and metachromatic staining of glycogen, mucins, reticulum, basement membranes, smooth muscle stroma and, using alcoholic toluidine blue, also dextran. But apparently collagen fibers in mucin or cartilage do not stain. Alcian blue staining after sulfation was largely limited to collagen. Mowry has speculated that the positive orthochromatic reaction of collagen might be due to its hydroxyproline content.

Recently (*J. Histochem.* **12**:821, 1964) it was found in a study of sulfuric acid catalysis of acetic anhydride 1:3 acetic acid acetylation that in histochemical usage such reagents resulted in cessation of the acylation reaction in the sulfation stage, even with very minute amounts of sulfuric acid (1:12,500: v/v). Reduction of the acetic anhydride to 5% by volume was tolerated; 2.5% was marginal when 1:400 dilutions of sulfuric acid were used. Low pH azure A staining was induced at 1:62,500; blocking of Van Gieson collagen staining occurred at 1:2500.

Since such mixtures appear to sulfate rapidly and as fully as the older mixtures containing much larger amounts of sulfuric acid, and since they engender inappreciable amounts of heat on mixing, their use seems practical, at least for inducing azure A staining at sulfation sites and for blocking the periodic acid Schiff reaction more completely than the pyridine acetylation mixtures; it appears that they may be useful for these and some other purposes. As with sulfation with the Mowry and Spicer (*J. Histochem.* 8:18, 1960) mixtures, the sulfation effect is readily abolished by methanolysis in methanol HCl or H_2SO_4 mixtures, and is relatively resistant to alkali saponification.

Spicer's Mixture. A mixture of 10 cc concentrated sulfuric acid + 30 cc glacial acetic acid gives quite adequate sulfation of gastrointestinal mucins, basement membranes, reticulum and collagen with a 3 minute immersion, as demonstrated by a following 20 minute stain with 0.05% azure A in 0.01 N HCl. Smooth muscle, cytoplasm and other normally eosinophilic structures are not stained.

Weaker similar sulfation mixtures, containing 7.5 and 2.5% sulfuric acid by volume, are also effective but require longer sulfation intervals, *i.e.*, 15–30 minutes for the 7.5% and 1 hour for the 2.5%.

The glacial acetic, acetic anhydride, sulfuric acid mixtures very promptly confer an intense basophilia toward azure A at pH 1 (0.125 N HCl), not only on mucins, starch, glycogen, basement membranes, reticulum and collagen, but also on smooth muscle and cytoplasms as well. The periodic acid Schiff reaction is blocked, as is staining with acid dyes and with both components of the fast green Van Gieson connective tissue stain. The blockade is broken effectively by 1–2 hour methylation at 60°C (p. 283), and in the case of the Van Gieson variant also partially by alcoholic ammonia (p. 197) or 1% KOH in 70% alcohol (20 minutes).

It appears to be indicated that this reagent sulfates NH_2 groups as well as OH groups, but further studies are needed on this point.

Blockade of Hydroxyl and Amine Groups

Benzoylation and acetylation are used to render NH_2 and OH groups nonreactive by esterifying them. In general in unfixed proteins esterification of amines is accomplished more quickly and at lower temperatures. Starch, glycogen and cellulose are the most difficult objects to render nonreactive to the periodic acid Schiff reaction. With the 3 hexose polysaccharides, individual particles may remain strongly reactive after fairly prolonged treatment while most of the same material demonstrable in controls has disappeared. Cartilage matrix and thyroid colloid are also strongly resistant to acetylation and benzoylation. In cartilage the pericellular areas are more resistant than the intercellular. Thyroid colloid, in benzoylation, presents strongly reactive areas adjacent to negative areas.

Cartilage matrix is almost completely acetylated after 18–24 hours at 25°C in 40% acetic anhydride + pyridine mixture; but 6 hours at 58°C in 2.5% benzoyl chloride + pyridine was not quite adequate. Although most of the glycogen is acetylated in similar periods, a few granules may remain. Benzoylation for 6 hours at 58°C completely abolished the reactivity of glycogen. Two hours was nearly sufficient, but 24 hours at 25°C was not quite adequate. Epithelial mucins are moderately resistant to acetylation, 6 hours at 25°C being adequate for most of them, but are quite readily benzoylated, practically completely so in 2 hours at 25°C in 10% benzoyl chloride + pyridine. Connective tissues, mast cell granules, cuticular borders, retinal rod acromere lipid, ocular membranes, amyloid, hyaline droplets, plasma, fibrin and the like are acetylated and benzoylated quite promptly. Benzoylation for 20 hours in 10% benzoyl chloride + pyridine mixture is used by Danielli to prevent the reaction of histidine, tryptophan and tyrosine with diazonium salts.

Stronger mixtures of benzoyl chloride with pyridine give rise to considerable amounts of crystalline precipitate, which redissolves when sections are brought into alcohol. These precipitates are suspected of causing localized areas of reaction failure. Weaker mixtures—2.5% or 5% benzoyl chloride by volume in anhydrous pyridine—seem about as effective in blocking the periodic acid Schiff reaction as stronger, crystal producing mixtures.

Benzoylation at 58°C for 6 hours appears to destroy the capacity of nuclei to stain with iron hematoxylin. Hence, either a lower temperature (37°C or 25°C) for a longer period should be employed, or exposure to 58°C should be limited to 2 or 3 hours. Similarly, acetylation in 40% acetic anhydride in pyridine for 6 hours at 58°C is about as effective as a 24-hour treatment at 25°C. Neither can be relied upon to acetylate consistently all the glycogen, starch and cellulose; but cartilage matrix appears to acetylate almost completely in 6 hours at 58°C or in 18–24 hours at 25°C.

Technics used in our laboratory are as follows: Bring sections to 100% alcohol as usual. Dip in pyridine and transfer to the reagent solution.

Acetylation. 16 cc acetic anhydride + 24 cc anhydrous pyridine. Incubate 1–24 hours at 25°C in accordance with desired effect; or ½–6 hours at 58°C. The longer intervals are necessary to approach complete acetylation of glycogen, starch, cellulose and cartilage.

Benzoylation. 2 cc benzoyl chloride + 38 cc anhydrous pyridine. Incubate 1–24 hours at 25°C or ½–6 hours at 58°C. Glycogen, starch, cellulose, thyroid colloid and cartilage require the most drastic treatments. After either treatment wash with 2 changes each of 100%, 95% and 80% alcohol.

Results: A 2 hour acetylation blocks the periodic acid Schiff reaction of collagen, basement membranes, reticulum, adrenal lipofuscin, colonic "melanin" and renal brush borders; but not that of glycogen, starch, cellulose, cornea, vitreous, lens capsule, Descemet's membrane, gastrointestinal mucins, cartilage nor (usually) adrenal chromaffin. With 6 hours of acetylation, starch, cellulose, glycogen, gastric mucin, cartilage and sometimes chromaffin remain reactive. With 16 hours, cartilage matrix remains faintly reactive; but this is lost at 18–20 hours.

According to Shackleford (letter, December 13, 1961), phthalic anhydride condenses with polysaccharide sites in the same manner as acetic anhydride and thereby induces intense reactivity to toluidine blue as well as enhanced reactivity to colloidal iron and alcian blue. It did not, under the conditions employed, apparently impair reactivity to the periodic acid Schiff reaction. This would appear to be another example of the superior efficiency of positively chromogenic reactions over those of related nature which tend to prevent another chromogenic reaction.

Shackleford's Phthalic Anhydride Toluidine Blue Method.

1. Deparaffinize and hydrate sections as usual.
2. Immerse sections 15–20 minutes in saturated phthalic anhydride pyridine heated to 58°C in a water bath in the chemical hood, heating controls similarly in pure pyridine.
3. Wash in graded alcohols to water.
4. Stain 30 minutes in 0.01% toluidine blue in 0.2 *M* acetate buffer pH 2.6 or 3.6.
5. Rinse in buffer and dehydrate quickly in *tert*-butanol or acetone, clear in xylene and mount in synthetic resin.

Neutral and acid polysaccharides are largely or completely unstained in controls and exhibit strong orthochromatic basophilia after the acylation. As with sulfation, the presence of vicinal glycol or amino alcohol groups would not seem to be required.

| Phthalic anhydride | Saccharide hydroxyl | Phthalyl saccharide ester with free carboxyl |

Hence, saccharides with 1–3 glycosidic linkages, 2 acetylamino-3-hydroxy groups and the like should react as well as glycols. It seems not improbable that phenols would also react, but the observations reported do not especially suggest reaction of protein amino groups.

Tosylation. In 1961 (*J. Histochem.* **9**:184) I reported that tosylation prevented azo coupling, Clara hematoxylin, ferric ferricyanide reduction and ferrous ion uptake reactions of enterochromaffin. Further studies, not pertinent to that report, indicated that tosyl chloride (*p*-toluenesulfonyl chloride) in dry pyridine and in 87.5% pyridine saturated with borax was ineffective, but usable results were obtained with the 50% acetone borax solution suggested in Noller's text. Studies with the periodic acid Schiff reaction showed that the greatest blocking effect was obtained with an 8 hour interval, the blockade being less effective both at 2–4 hours and at 16–32 hours. Since the previously reported azo coupling and hematoxylin reactions of enterochromaffin disappear at 2–4 hours' tosylation and reappear when the tosylation time is prolonged to 32 hours, it is thought that the alkaline solution hydrolyzes the sulfonyl esters formed earlier in the process. Similarly, the incomplete blocking of eosin staining seems greatest at 4 hours, diminishing again thereafter. The dilute hematoxylin staining of rat arterial elastic tissue and proventricular keratohyalin was unimpaired by any of the tosylation intervals tried (2, 4, 8, 16, 32 hours).

Tosylation Technic. Reagent. Dissolve 1 gm *p*-toluenesulfonyl chloride in 20 cc acetone. Dissolve 1 gm borax ($Na_2B_4O_7 \cdot 10H_2O$) in 20 cc warm distilled water. Mix and use at once. Replacement with fresh solution at 4 hour intervals is suggested for longer tosylation intervals.

Deparaffinize sections with xylenes, wash in 2 changes of acetone and immerse in tosylation reagent for the desired interval. A 4–8 hour interval seems indicated, shorter for phenols, longer for amines and glycols. Wash in water and carry through the demonstration procedure. Controls are exposed to 2.5% borax in 50% acetone for the same period.

Saponification was employed histochemically by McManus and Cason to reliberate glycols for reaction with periodic acid after acetylation. It was believed that only acetyl esters would be thus hydrolyzed, and not the amides formed by acetylation of amine groups (McManus and Mowry, 1960, p. 105). McManus's original saponification procedure, a 45 minute exposure to 0.1 *N* potassium hydroxide in water, although chemically effective, often also totally removed the sections from the slides. In 1951, I introduced a 20% dilution of concentrated ammonia water (28% NH_3) with absolute alcohol as an effective deacetylating reagent (*Stain Techn.* **26**:123, 1951), which, however, required 24 hour exposures to unblock acetylated glycols effectively. A 0.1 *N* NaOH in 85% alcohol had effectively removed sections from slides in 1 hour.

Later I tried much shorter intervals in alcoholic potassium hydroxide and found that 15–30 minute intervals in 1% KOH in 70% or 80% alcohol were usually chemically adequate and should not be exceeded if section losses are to be avoided. The 70% alcohol solution is perhaps a little more effective, and 20 minutes is usually enough.

However, a 20–30 minute extraction with 1% KOH in 70–80% alcohol, with or without prior periodic acid oxidation or acetylation, more or less completely and promptly destroys the cytoplasmic basophilia of gastric chief cells, pancreatic acinar cells, Lieberkühn crypt cells and the like, so that in azure eosin stains the nuclei now appear deep blue on a pale purple to pink background. This would appear to be another procedure for the selective extraction of ribonucleic acid. For periodic acid Schiff, azo coupling and other reactions the alcoholic KOH deacetylation procedure has been generally satisfactory. Although pancreas fixed in aqueous formaldehyde or in acetic alcohol formalin loses its cytoplasmic basophilia on 10–20 minute extraction by 1% potassium hydroxide in 70% alcohol, the same tissue remains strongly basophil after a 24 hour treatment with 5.6% ammonia in 80% alcohol (1 volume 28% ammonia + 4 volumes absolute alcohol). Hence, when preservation of ribonucleic acid is important this slower saponification procedure may be employed.

This 1% KOH, 70% alcohol saponification procedure has successfully restored the capacity of acetylated carbohydrates to react to the periodic acid Schiff reaction, of phenols to azo couple, of catechols such as reduced melanin to reduce acid silver nitrate, of basic proteins to stain with acid dyes and, after methylation, the capacity of sulfonic, phosphoric and carboxylic acid residues to stain with basic dyes.

With the ammonia alcohol procedure deacetylation for shorter periods (4–6 hours, 37°C) after the periodic acid reaction, reveals as Schiff positive or partly so such tissues as ocular lens capsule and Descemet's membrane, cornea, vitreous humor, glycogen, gastric and intestinal mucins, cartilage and chromaffin. Longer treatment intensifies these reactions. Overnight treatments are required to deacetylate most collagen, vascular basement membranes, cuticular and brush borders of epithelial cells and some pigments.

The acromere substance of the retinal rods is one of the easiest to acetylate (40 minutes in acetic anhydride + pyridine mixture) and probably the most difficult to deacetylate, requiring the full 24 hours in the 60% alcohol, 20% ammonia, water mixture. Even 48 hours in 80% alcohol 20% ammonia may be inadequate to deacetylate this material.

GLYCOLS

Polysaccharides, Mucopolysaccharides, Glycolic Fatty Acids. In histochemistry the most widely used reaction for these substances is the periodic acid, Schiff sulfite leucofuchsin reaction, usually abbreviated PAS (French, APS; German, PSS or PJS from *Perjodsäure* Schiff). It is based on the Malaprade reaction, in which 1,2-glycols undergo oxidative cleavage to form aldehyde. In the Nicolet-Shinn reaction one of the hydroxyls may be replaced by a primary or secondary amino group, but apparently not by an amide group, since saccharides bearing an acetyl-amino group adjacent to the other available ring hydroxyl are unreactive to periodic acid. The isolated amino acids serine and threonine are attacked by periodic acid, but when the α-amino group is used in a peptide bond, as is usually the case with amino acids when protein bound, what is essentially an amide group is now adjacent to the hydroxyl and the grouping is unavailable for periodic acid oxidation.

It must not be assumed that this is the only oxidative action of which periodic acid is capable, but in other cases demonstrable aldehyde is not known to be produced, and a histochemically demonstrable aldehyde reaction which has resulted from relatively brief periodic acid oxidation at 15–35°C may generally be assumed to denote the presence of 1,2-glycol or aminoalcohol groupings. If demonstrable sudanophilia is absent at the site of aldehyde reaction, the reaction is generally to be assigned to the presence of a polysaccharide. If the reaction is accompanied by sudanophilia, the presence of partially oxidized unsaturated fats or of glycolipids is to be considered.

Other oxidants have been used besides periodic acid. Lead tetraacetate and sodium bismuthate apparently attack much the same groupings as periodic acid. Chromic acid and potassium permanganate also produce aldehyde from polysaccharides, but they further attack and destroy aldehydes, probably converting them first to carboxyl groups and then to carbon dioxide. Further, these two oxidants probably (for $KMnO_4$, assuredly) attack ethylenic double bonds. This is discussed further under that topic.

The first glycol to aldehyde oxidative reaction used in histochemistry was the Bauer reaction (*Z. mikr. anat. Forsch.* **33**:143, 1933), which produced a positive Schiff aldehyde reaction in glycogen, starch, cellulose and various mucopolysaccharides. Because of the further oxidation of aldehyde by chromic acid, less density of aldehyde reaction is achieved and structures with fewer glycol groups are not demonstrated, such as basement membranes and collagenous and reticular fibrils. Prolonged exposure to CrO_3 or $KMnO_4$ completely destroys aldehydes, both those which they themselves have produced and those previously formed by other agencies; native aldehyde or that produced by less drastic oxidants or hydrolysants (Lillie, *Stain Techn.* **26**:123, 1951). The $KMnO_4$ glycol to aldehyde reaction in histochemistry was reported independently by Rossman (*Carnegie Contr. Embryol.* **30**:97, 1942), Casella (*Anat. Anz.* **93**:289, 1942) and Lillie (*Bull. Int. A. Med. Mus.* **27**:23, 1947), the existence of the war conditions at the time preventing mutual access to the publications.

The most used of the reactions, the periodic acid Schiff, was discovered independently by Hotchkiss in 1945, though his report was delayed 3 years (*Arch. Biochem.* **16**:131, 1948), by McManus a year later (*Nature* **158**:202, 1946) and perhaps slightly later by Lillie (*J. Lab. Clin. Med.* **32**:910, 1947; *Bull. Int. A. Med. Mus.* **27**:23, 1947), who did not report his findings promptly.

McManus was attempting to demonstrate serine, threonine and hydroxylysine residues in tissue, not realizing at that time, as most of us did not, that the amide nitrogen of the peptide bond did not constitute one of the groupings susceptible to the Nicolet-Shinn reaction. His first report called attention particularly to the reaction of mucins. My own first reports dealt chiefly with reticulum and glycogen, respectively, and came about in the course of an exploration of the mechanism of the Bauer glycogen stain as a result of a verbal suggestion by C. S. Hudson (Jackson and Hudson, *J. Am. Chem. Soc.* **59**:2049, 1937) that I try periodate.

Early technics used the alkaline sodium salt Na_3IO_5 and the potassium salt KIO_4 as well as the acid H_5IO_6, depending on commercial availability at the time. My first attempt to demonstrate glycogen with Na_3IO_5 failed because I had not then learned to acidify the solution. But addition of 0.5% nitric acid to the 1% Na_3IO_5 brought the pH down to 1.6, and the reaction succeeded.

I have tabulated the solutions used in Table 8-1 giving reagent used, concentration in grams per 100 cc and in molarity, pH of solution, presence of buffer or alcohol and recommended exposure time.

It has been reported by Dempsey, Singer and Wislocki (*Stain Techn.* **25**:73, 1950) that a 1 hour oxidation at 37°C of Zenker fixed, paraffin imbedded tissue in 1% aqueous periodic acid (H_5IO_6) induced very pronounced basophilia in sites containing high cystine concentrations. They

TABLE 8-1. PERIODIC ACID OXIDIZING BATHS

Author and date	Source HIO_4	Gm/100 cc	M	Solvent	pH	Time, min	Temperature, °C	Reducing bath
McManus, 1946, 1960..	H_5IO_6	0.5	0.022	Distilled water	2.1	5	Room	No
Lillie, 1947............	Na_3IO_5	1.0	0.036	0.5 % HNO_3 aq.	1.6	10	22–32	No
Hotchkiss, 1948 (A)....	H_5IO_6	0.8	0.035	Aq. 0.02 M NaAcet	2.5	5	Room	Yes
Hotchkiss, 1948 (B)....	H_5IO_6	0.8	0.035	70 % alcohol 0.02 M NaAc	2.4	5	Room	Yes
Lillie, 1950............	KIO_4	0.69	0.030	0.3 % HNO_3 aq.	1.9	10	24	No
Mowry, 1952..........	H_5IO_6	1.0	0.044	90 % alcohol	1.5	120	24	No
Lillie, 1953–1961.......	H_5IO_6	1.0	0.044	Distilled water	1.95 1.81	10	25	No
Pearse, 1960, p. 831....	H_5IO_6	1.0	0.044	0.02 M NaAc		5	18–22	Yes
Pearse, 1960, p. 832....	H_5IO_6	0.5	0.022	Distilled water	2.1	2–5	18–22	No
0.05 M..............	H_5IO_6	1.14	0.05	Distilled water	1.9	10	24	No

attributed the reaction to cysteic acid. In our hands oxidation of skin for 2 hours at 60°C in 1% periodic acid gave only a very moderate basophilia of distal hair cortex, as compared with the intense reaction obtained by 10 minute oxidation with peracetic acid. An 18 hour fixation at 24°C in 1% periodic acid 10% formalin, although the usual structures were rendered Schiff positive, did not induce basophilia of keratin or other structures.

Hence it would appear that the cystine → cysteic acid oxidation by periodic acid probably does not occur to any appreciable extent at temperatures of 25°C and below, but that their reaction must be considered when temperatures above 35°C are used in the periodic acid oxidation step.

When Staple's (*J. Histochem.* **5:**472, 1957) rather equivocal results on the prevention of lead tetraacetate oxidation of *cis*-hydroxyls by competitive boric acid complexing appeared, we made some abortive experiments with periodic acid but were unable to discern consistent differences between borated and unborated tissues. Staple's own photomicrographs of mouse tissue were not too impressive in demonstrating differences either in the room temperature or in the 50°C glacial acetic lead tetraacetate reaction.

Periodic acid solutions apparently may be used for quite large numbers of sections and over several weeks without becoming exhausted. Nevertheless it is good practice to check a standard test section for adequacy of staining from time to time; for example, the completeness of staining of the fine reticular or sarcolemmal structure in human smooth muscle. Since 0.02 M periodic acid for 10 minutes appears adequate, it is evident that there is a large margin of safety in the usual solutions.

Hotchkiss's recommendation of an alcoholic solution was based on the then current belief that glycogen in fixed tissues was readily soluble in water. Since a 16 hour exposure to boiled aqueous diastase solution does not appreciably diminish the amount of demonstrable glycogen in liver tissue (*Anat. Rec.* **103:**635, 1949), this precaution seems unnecessary for this purpose.

Hotchkiss's reducing rinse (KI 1 gm, $Na_2S_2O_3 \cdot 5H_2O$ 1 gm, water 20 cc, alcohol 30 cc, 2 N HCl 0.5 cc), in McManus's experience as well as mine, appears to block partially the coloration of collagen and reticulum, much as does a deliberately interposed bisulfite blockade step, and is not recommended as a routine procedure.

The usual method of demonstrating the aldehyde produced by the various oxidants is with Schiff's reagent (p. 269). I have used usually the "cold Schiff" solution (p. 270) with 1 gm rosaniline or pararosaniline per 100 cc. I have tried also both hot traditional (p. 270) and "cold Schiff" variants containing 0.5 gm fuchsin per 100 cc and find the staining less intense and less complete in the usual 10 minutes' staining interval than with the stronger variant. Longer staining intervals enhance the staining with the 0.5% fuchsin variant, but there is a tendency also to overcome sulfite blockades with the longer stains.

In the use of the periodic acid Schiff procedure care should be taken that the Schiff reagent has not gradually lost in potency. A good test object is the tunica muscularis of a human appendix. The fine red mesh-work of sarcolemma between individual smooth muscle fibers, especially in cross section, should be demonstrated. Prolonging the exposure compensates for the deterioration to some extent, but it is better to make small batches frequently, using the "cold Schiff" procedure.

Traditionally the Schiff reaction is followed by several rinses in dilute sulfurous acid to remove excess reagent and prevent adventitious pigmentation from air oxidation of adsorbed leucofuchsin. Leuchtenberger (Danielli's *General Cytochemical Methods,* vol. 1, 1958), Lison, Davenport, Gomori, McManus, Mowry and I have adhered to this practice; Pearse now uses simple water washing, as does the *Gridley Manual.*[1] With copiously chlorinated water supplies, I regard this practice as hazardous.

Since there is always a slight carryover of leucofuchsin into the sulfite rinses, and since even considerably diluted leucofuchsin can produce appreciable staining on recoloration, it is necessary to discard these rinses at frequent intervals. I find it good practice to make up fresh dilutions from a stock of 10% $Na_2S_2O_5$ solution daily, and to discard at least the first rinse more often, moving the second and third rinses up one, and supplying fresh bisulfite for the last rinse if many slides are being stained. The times allotted are entirely arbitrary.

The solution has usually been prescribed as 0.05 M $NaHSO_3$, or simply as sulfurous acid (McManus) or as 0.4% potassium metabisulfite ($K_2S_2O_5$) in a 1% dilution of concentrated hydrochloric acid (Hotchkiss). Apparently 0.5% sodium metabisulfite ($Na_2S_2O_5$), which is slightly stronger than 0.05 M $NaHSO_3$, is quite satisfactory.

The Periodic Acid, Schiff Sulfite Leucofuchsin Reaction (PAS)

1. Deparaffinize and hydrate through xylene, alcohols and distilled water as usual.
2. Oxidize 10 minutes in 1% (0.044 M) H_5IO_6
3. Wash 5 minutes in running water.
4. Immerse for 10 minutes in Schiff reagent (p. 270).
5. Transfer quickly and directly to 3 successive baths: 2, 2 and 2 minutes in 0.5% sodium metabisulfite ($Na_2S_2O_5$). Replace sulfite rinses daily or more often.
6. Wash 5 minutes in running water.

[1] *Manual of Histologic and Special Staining Technics,* Armed Forces Institute of Pathology, Washington, D.C. 1957, *in memoriam* Mary Frances Gridley.

7. Counterstain nuclei and cytoplasm as desired: *e.g.*, stain 2 minutes in a 2% acetic hemalum solution of about 0.1% hematoxylin content (Mayer's or a one-fifth dilution of Lillie's, p. 174). Wash in water, and blue with 1 or 2 drops of 20% Na₂CO₃ in 200 cc water. *For critical histochemical work omit all counterstains.*

8. Dehydrate (and differentiate) in 2 changes each of 95% and 100% alcohol. Clear in 1 change of alcohol xylene mixture (1:1) and 2 changes of xylene. Mount in suitable resin, such as polystyrene, HSR, Permount, ester gum, cellulose caprate, Depex, or the like.

Results appear on pp. 199–202. It is to be noted that alum hematoxylin and freshly mixed Weigert's iron hematoxylin may stain nonnuclear structures excessively, sometimes partly converting the red purple of Schiff reactions to gray purple or violet. This may be overcome by keeping the staining period short and by allowing the Weigert mixture to age an hour or so before using it. Acid differentiation is useful, and this is one of the functions of the picric acid counterstain. A 20 second dilute Pal's bleach (p. 491) renders the iron hematoxylin stain almost purely nuclear.

When diastase or other enzymatic digestion tests are employed, the sections are likely to become detached during the oxidation or aldehyde demonstration procedures. Hence it is recommended that collodionization be interposed immediately *after* the enzymatic digestion. Collodion films almost totally inhibit enzyme penetration; therefore the collodionization should not be inserted before enzyme digestion. Since anhydrous methyl alcohol dissolves nitrocellulose, of necessity collodionization if practiced at all must follow a methylation or methanol extraction procedure. Similarly, since pyridine dissolves both paraffin and collodion, collodionization must follow pyridine extractions and pyridine acetylation technics.

On the other hand saponification procedures (p. 193) and various other chemical blockade procedures which also tend to detach sections may more conveniently follow collodionization.

For the Bauer reaction, substitute at step 2 a 1 hour bath in 5% chromic anhydride (CrO₃); and for the Casella reaction, a 20 minute immersion in 1% potassium permanganate. These are the usual directions, though I have reduced the chromic acid treatment to 20 or 30 minutes at the same concentration, and the permanganate treatment to 0.5% for 10 minutes with essentially similar results, and fewer section losses.

One may combine such procedures as the ammine silver reticulum methods or the ferric mannitol or dialyzed iron or alcian blue mucin methods with the periodic acid Schiff by interposing them before the periodic acid oxidation, before step 9 (pp. 510, 512, 536, 549).

Results: Oxidation Schiff reactions have been recorded as positive from a quite extensive list of substances (Lillie, *Stain Techn.* **26**:123, 1951).

The substances reacting more strongly with the periodic acid method usually give positive Bauer and Casella reactions as well. These include the polysaccharides glycogen, starch, cellulose and the rather slowly digestible polysaccharide of *Sarcocystis*. Similar Bauer positive polysaccharides are present in *Eimeria stiedae*, in *Klossiella muris*, in the egg cytoplasm of *Capillaria hepatica*, and in *Toxoplasma sp.*, for which the periodic and permanganate reactions have not been recorded. Among the epithelial mucins those of the gastric surface epithelium, peptic gland neck cells, cardial and pyloric glands, uterine cervical glands, and rodent vaginal epithelium give all 3 reactions, as do also the prostatic gland secretion and corpora amylacea, the seminal vesicle contents and renal hyaline casts. The ocular lens capsule and the membrane of Descemet and the colloids of the thyroid and anterior hypophysis also give strong periodic acid and positive Bauer and Casella reactions. Rossman noted the latter 2 reactions for ovarian pigment; it often reacts strongly to periodic acid.

With a second group of substances the Casella reaction is generally weak or negative; the Bauer, moderately strong; and the periodic Schiff, positive to strongly positive. This group includes the mucins of the salivary glands, of the conjunctiva, of the oropharyngeal glands of most of the species studied, of Brunner's duodenal glands, of intestinal goblet cells, of tracheobronchial glands and goblet cells and of ovarian follicles and cysts. The cuticular borders of the epithelium of the villi of the small intestine and of the renal convoluted tubules react similarly, as does the zona pellucida of rodent ova. The Casella reaction of cartilage matrix is weak or negative; the Bauer and periodic acid Schiff reactions are positive, with or without antecedent diastase digestion. Agar used as an imbedding matrix behaves similarly. Hypophyseal cyanophil or beta cells react similarly, as do cerebral corpora amylacea. Amyloid gives a rather light red coloration with the periodic acid Schiff, and weakly positive Bauer and Casella reactions. Positive Bauer and HIO_4 Schiff reactions, with negative Casella reaction, are given by the cell walls of various yeasts and molds, by the filamentous material in the granules of actinomycosis and botryomycosis, and by certain diphtheroid organisms. The coagulum in the vitreous humor and corneal collagen usually stain well with the HIO_4 Schiff method and weakly with the Bauer and Casella methods.

With a third group of substances the periodic acid Schiff reaction is positive and the Bauer and Casella reactions vary from weakly positive to negative. This category includes the acromere lipid of the retinal rods, the ceroid pigment of the choline deficiency cirrhosis of rats, the pharyngeal gland mucin of the rabbit, the mucins in the bases of the colonic glands, chordoma mucin, Russell bodies and the kerasin of Gaucher's disease.

Collagens from areolar connective tissue and sclera give positive HIO_4 Schiff reactions, negative Bauer, and weak or negative Casella tests. Megakaryocyte granules color pink with the HIO_4 Schiff, and vary according to species with Bauer and Casella reactions. Chromaffin in chromate fixed adrenal gives a gray red after HIO_4 only.

Vascular and certain epithelial basement membranes, and reticulum give good positive HIO_4 Schiff reactions, a negative Bauer and a dubious or negative Casella reaction. The colonic melanosis pigment of man; a similar pigment in the guinea pig intestine; adrenal lipofuscin pigment of man, guinea pigs and mice; fibrin; often plasma and serum; salivary zymogen granules of man and various rodents; pancreatic zymogen granules of man, rabbits and some mice, but not rats or guinea pigs; Paneth cell granules of rats, guinea pigs and rabbits, but not regularly those of men and mice; granules of many mast cells in man, few in mice, none in rats; and the bacterial cell walls of some organisms (including anthrax, streptococcus and various intestinal bacteria) give fairly good positive HIO_4 Schiff reactions and negative Bauer and Casella tests.

A relatively weak periodic acid Schiff reaction and negative Bauer and Casella reactions are recorded for bone matrix; myxoma mucin, the mucinous coagula in the lymphatic spaces of the umbilical cord matrix; nucleus pulposus mucin; *collacin,* or collagen in the state of "basophil degeneration;" and the lipofuscin of heart muscle.

Finally, positive HIO_4 Schiff reactions (without information as to Bauer and Casella tests) are recorded for eosinophil leucocytes in the monkey but not in man (see p. 591); for the vitamin E deficiency ceroid pigment of the rat uterus; for the ceroid pigment of the mouse testis and adrenal; for Kurloff bodies in guinea pigs; for goblet cells in the pancreatic ducts; for certain nuclear inclusion bodies in the human vas deferens; for acrosomes and head caps of intratesticular spermatozoa; for egg albumen and gelatin; for cytoplasmic granules in the rat lacrimal gland; and for a nonlipid component of the Golgi apparatus. Bauer and periodic Schiff positive materials have been recorded in schistosome egg shells and in opercula of the eggs of *Capillaria (Hepaticola) hepatica.*

The reactions of blood cells are presented on p. 591.

Keratin and keratohyalin,—of pharynx and esophagus generally, of the proventriculus of muridae, and of epidermis and hair cortex—are not stained; but, curiously, hair cortex reacts strongly to the periodic acid Schiff procedure after bromination.

The positive reactions of arterial elastica and of elastic laminae and ligaments which are seen after periodic oxidation, especially in rodents, occur also when the oxidation step is omitted. They may be prevented by interposing a 30 minute bath in 5% aqueous phenylhydrazine hydrochloride before the periodic acid step. Wash 5–10 minutes in running water after the phenylhydrazine. Lignin of plant tissues, often seen in intestinal contents, is also directly Schiff positive, without prior oxidative treatment (Jensen, *Botanical Histochemistry*, W. H. Freeman and Company, San Francisco, 1962).

Crippa (*Boll. Soc. Ital. Biol. Sper.* **27**:599, 1951) reports on the use of lead tetraacetate as an oxidant in place of chromic or periodic acid in a procedure utilizing the oxidation induced aldehyde reaction for the demonstration of mucin and mucoid substances.

The reagent, which is stable for an indefinite period, is a 1% solution of recrystallized lead tetraacetate in glacial acetic acid. The solution is clear and colorless. The technic follows.

Crippa's Lead Tetraacetate Method for Mucins and Mucoids.

1. Fix as usual. Imbed in paraffin, section and deparaffinize in xylene.
2. Wash in 50:50 xylene: glacial acetic acid and in glacial acetic acid.
3. Immerse for 30–60 minutes at room temperature in 1% lead tetraacetate in glacial acetic acid.
4. Wash in 3 changes of glacial acetic acid to remove lead acetates.
5. Pass through xylene: glacial acetic acid 50:50 mixture, xylene and descending alcohols to water.
6. Immerse in Schiff reagent 15–20 minutes.
7. Wash in 3 changes of 0.5% sodium bisulfite, 1, 2 and 2 minutes.
8. Wash in running water 10 minutes.
9. Counterstain if desired, as with the periodic acid Schiff method; or dehydrate, clear and mount directly in balsam or synthetic resin.

Results: Aldehyde deposits engendered by lead tetraacetate oxidation show in red purple.

If desired, steps 7–13 of Gomori's methenamine silver method for glycogen and mucins (p. 500) may be substituted for steps 6–9 above. The mucins then appear in black.

McManus (February, 1952) wrote me that lead tetraacetate renders Schiff positive essentially the same structures as does periodic acid. Jordan and McManus use a fresh mixture of 1 part of a strong to saturated solution of lead tetraacetate in glacial acetic acid with 3 parts of a mixture of 20 gm anhydrous sodium acetate, 25 cc glacial acetic acid and 50 cc water. They use a shorter oxidation time, 30–120 seconds. Lhotka (*Stain Techn.* **27**:213, 1952) uses 5 gm potassium acetate dissolved in 100 cc glacial acetic acid saturated with lead tetraacetate, and the same short oxidation times as McManus. Leblond and coworkers (*Stain Techn.* **27**:277, 1952) observed that glycogen was not stained by room temperature oxidation but did react vigorously at higher temperatures. Our experience with the Lhotka reagent indicated prompt reaction of glycogen.

Shimizu and Kumamoto (*Stain Techn.* 27:97, 1952) use a solution similar to McManus's:

1. Deparaffinize and hydrate as usual.
2. Molar sodium acetate solution 5 minutes (13.6% $NaCO_2CH_3 \cdot 3H_2O$).
3. Oxidize 10 minutes in lead tetraacetate 1 gm dissolved in 30 cc glacial acetic acid + 70 cc 46.5% (saturated) sodium acetate solution.
4. Wash 5 minutes in molar sodium acetate solution.
5. Wash 10 minutes in running water.
6. Schiff reagent 15 minutes.
7. Wash in 3 changes of sulfite solution, 2 minutes each.
8. Wash 10 minutes in running water.
9. Counterstain, dehydrate, clear and mount as in periodic acid Schiff methods (p. 198).

Results: Vic-glycols in red purple.

Although the authors prescribe the original Schiff reagent and sulfite rinse of Feulgen and Rossenbeck, undoubtedly the more recent variants will give fully satisfactory results.

It is to be noted that lead tetraacetate, in *warm* acetic acid solution, also reacts with olefines to form glycol diacetates and unsaturated acetoxy compounds (Hickinbottom, *Reactions of Organic Compounds*, Longmans, Green & Co., Inc., New York, 1948, p. 32).

Staple (*Nature* 176:1/25, 1955) records that inclusion of 0.01 M boric acid (61.8 mg/100 cc) in a 1% lead tetraacetate solution in glacial acetic acid would prevent the subsequent Schiff reaction of *cis*-glycols but not that of adjacent trans hydroxyls in model experiments with galactogen and glycogen. The reaction period in lead tetraacetate was 4 hours at 23°C. The reaction of intestinal goblet cell and laryngeal mucous gland mucins was inhibited in the presence of boric acid.

Lhotka (*Stain Techn.* 27:259, 1952) recommends the use of sodium bismuthate in aqueous phosphoric acid solution as another reagent for the cleavage of vic-glycols and α-hydroxycarboxylic acids to carbonyl. Organic solvents can also be used. Overoxidation is said not to occur. The bismuthate solution in phosphoric acid is unstable and must be used at once.

Lhotka's Sodium Bismuthate Schiff Procedure for Vic-glycols and α-Hydroxycarboxylic Acids.

1. Section formalin fixed tissue in paraffin, deparaffinize and hydrate sections as usual.
2. Suspend 1 gm sodium bismuthate in 100 cc 20% phosphoric acid

solution. The suspension is bright orange yellow and soon turns brown by precipitation of bismuth pentoxide.

Oxidize sections 3 minutes in the fresh suspension.

3. Wash in running water for 1 minute.
4. Rinse 15 seconds in normal hydrochloric acid to remove Bi_2O_5 from sections.
5. Rinse in distilled water.
6. Schiff reagent 10 minutes.
7. 0.5% $Na_2S_2O_5$ or SO_2 water, 3 changes, 2 minutes each.
8. Wash in running water 5 minutes. (I prefer 10 minutes.)
9. Counterstain with alum hematoxylin or as desired.
10. Dehydrate, clear and mount by alcohol, xylene, synthetic resin sequence.

Results: Pictures are similar to those obtained with periodic acid or lead tetraacetate. Sites of vic-glycols and α-hydroxycarboxylic acids in red purple.

Iron Methods

The mucins, as well as collagen, reticulum and various other tissue components, have the property of taking up in more or less selective fashion ferric ions from colloidal solutions of ferric salts. These combined ferric ions may then be demonstrated by the usual ferrocyanide reaction (p. 407) as Prussian blue. Alternatively, they may be subjected to a silvering procedure, such as the Gomori-Burtner methenamine silver method (p. 240), and the sites of iron uptake will be shown in black. A 10 minute bath in 1% aqueous ferric chloride is adequate for this purpose.

The number of reacting tissue elements is profoundly influenced by the pH of the iron solution. With alkaline solutions of the Lillie-Mowry type, practically only gastric mucins react.

The Ferric Mannitol Technics of Lillie and Mowry (Bull. Int. A. Med. Mus. **30**:91, 1949). Fix tissues preferably in cold 70% alcohol for 3–4 days, imbed in paraffin and section at 5 μ. Prepare ferric mannitol solutions as follows:

For *pH 5 ferric manitol* dilute 2.18 cc of U.S.P. Solution of Iron Chloride to 50 cc with distilled water to make 0.1 *M* ferric chloride. Add 50 cc 0.1 *N* acetic acid (p. 673) and 5 gm mannitol, and shake to dissolve. Then add 145 cc 0.1 *N* sodium hydroxide with continuous agitation. Check pH. Cautiously add more 0.1 *N* NaOH, checking pH frequently, until pH 5 is reached. Avoid precipitation of ferric hydroxide. A total of about 220 cc 0.1 *N* NaOH is required. Then add distilled water to make a total of 500 cc. Store in refrigerator at 0–5°C.

For *pH 8 ferric mannitol* reagent dissolve 5 gm mannitol in 50 cc of 0.1 *M* ferric chloride solution (2.18 cc U.S.P. XI Solution of Iron Chloride + 47.82 cc distilled water), add 125 cc 0.1 *N* NaOH, shake thoroughly and then add more 0.1 *N* NaOH, 1–2 cc at a time, until solution is almost clear. Then adjust with 1% acetic acid to pH 8. Store in the refrigerator at 0–5°C.

Technic.

1. Deparaffinize and hydrate sections as usual. Wash in 4 changes of distilled water.
2. Incubate 30 minutes at 25°C in ferric mannitol solution.
3. Wash in 4 changes of distilled water.
4. Mix 20 cc 5% acetic acid and 20 cc fresh 2% aqueous potassium ferrocyanide solution, preheat to 45° or 50°C, put sections in and incubate 30 minutes in paraffin oven at 58°C.
5. Wash in 1% acetic acid.
6. Counterstain 2 minutes in 0.1% safranin O in 1% acetic acid.
7. Wash in 1% acetic acid, dehydrate with alcohols, clear with 100% alcohol + xylene and 2 changes of xylene, mount in polystyrene or other saturated synthetic resin.

Results: With the pH 8 ferric mannitol, gastric epithelial mucin and the mucigen granules of the necks of the peptic glands color blue. Esophageal keratohyalin is blue. The argentaffin cells of the rabbit gastric mucosa exhibit a fine blue cytoplasmic granulation after various alcoholic fixations only. Parietal and chief cells stain pink to faint gray blue; collagen and reticulum remain unstained; intestinal gland and goblet cell mucins stain metachromatically orange with the safranin; and nuclei stain red.

With the pH 5 ferric mannitol, all the gastric and intestinal epithelial, goblet cell and gland mucins color an intense blue; the cuticular border of the villi is blue; reticulum, collagen and connective tissue mucin color a moderately deep blue; cartilage matrix stains partly deep blue, partly bright orange. Nuclei and the cytoplasm of pancreatic acini and chief cells are deep red; smooth muscle, parietal cells and cytoplasms generally color pale blue green.

With pH 3 ferric mannitol mucins are less intensely colored; collagen and reticulum are less conspicuous; cytoplasms and muscle are moderately gray blue; and altogether contrasts are decreased.

The alkaline ferric mannitol technic does not demonstrate the enterochromaffin substance. In alcohol fixed material in which this method succeeds, the methenamine silver and ferric ferricyanide technics fail, and in aqueous formalin fixed material, in which the 2 latter methods demonstrate numerous enterochromaffin cells, the alkaline ferric mannitol method fails completely.

Hale (*Nature* **157**:802, 1946) reported a procedure for the use of a colloidal iron solution which impregnated acid mucopolysaccharides more or less selectively and then demonstrated the sites of Fe^{+++} uptake by the application of the Prussian blue reaction. A number of modifications have been proposed, chiefly in the method of preparation of the working colloidal iron solution. When commercial colloidal iron of satisfactory quality became difficult to obtain, various recipes were proposed, mostly entailing the use of prolonged dialysis. The following Müller-Mowry variant is one of the easiest to prepare and seems satisfactory in practice.

The Müller-Mowry Variant of the Hale Dialyzed Iron Procedure (McManus and Mowry, p. 135, emended). Preparation of the reagent: Weigh out 1 m-mol of ferric chloride (162 mg anhydrous = 270.3 mg $FeCl_3 \cdot 6H_2O$) and dissolve the salt in 4–5 cc distilled water, or take approximately 4.354 cc official Solution of Iron Chloride. Bring 250 cc distilled water to active boiling and gradually add from a 5 cc pipet the strong iron solution, stirring as the iron is added. Continue boiling. When the solution has turned a clear dark red remove from heat and let cool. This is the stock colloidal iron solution. If adjusted to a final volume of 250 cc it is approximately 4 *mM* in ferric chloride. The solution is stable for months.

For use dilute 20 cc stock solution with 15 cc distilled water and 5 cc glacial acetic acid. Use once and discard.

Technic.

1. Deparaffinize and hydrate as usual, removing mercury deposits by the iodine thiosulfate sequence (p. 85) if necessary.
2. Rinse in 12.5% acetic acid.
3. Immerse in the diluted iron solution for 1 hour.
4. Wash in 4 changes 12.5% acetic acid, 3 minutes each.
5. Immerse exposed section and untreated control section in a freshly prepared mixture of 0.25 *N* HCl and 2% potassium ferrocyanide, 20 cc each, for 20 minutes at 25°C (40 minutes at 15°C, 30 minutes at 20°C).
6. Wash 5 minutes in running water.
7. Counterstain if desired with a red or other contrasting nuclear stain. An alum hematoxylin van Gieson sequence gives brownish red nuclei, yellow erythrocytes and muscle and red collagen; the Feulgen sequence gives pure purplish red nuclei.
8. Dehydrate, clear and mount in a synthetic resin such as Depex, polystyrene, cellulose caprate or the like. Reducing resins tend to convert Prussian blue to greenish white ferrous ferrocyanide after a time.

At step 7 the periodic acid Schiff procedure may be substituted, giving essentially the Ritter-Oleson effect (*Am. J. Path.* **26**:639, 1950). The van Gieson combination suggested gives the Rinehart-Abul-Haj effect (*Arch. Path.* **52**:189, 1951).

See also pp. 510, 512 for Mowry's later combinations and modifications. It is to be noted that none of the Hale variants covers the alkaline range of the ferric mannitol method.

SULFUR AMINO ACIDS

The methods for demonstration of the sulfur amino acids cystine, cysteine and methionine in protein combination, probably all depend on the initial presence of or the formation of the sulfhydryl radicle in the course of the demonstration reaction. Methods purporting to distinguish protein bound disulfide (—SS—) and sulfhydryl (—SH) are to be accepted with great caution. Air oxidation of paraffin sections while they are still undeparaffinized, and even of unsectioned tissue within a previously sectioned paraffin block, can in some days or weeks render negative the previously demonstrable sensitive ferric ferricyanide reaction of the first sections cut from the same block. On the other hand, alkaline demonstration reagents tend to reduce disulfide to sulfhydryl. This occurs in alkaline cyanide solutions without obvious reducing groups (KCN in the presence of atmospheric oxygen converts the reduced metallic silver back to the relatively oxidized double cyanide), as well as in alkaline tetrazolium solutions where the tetrazole itself is a reducing agent. The old sodium plumbite reagent contains no obvious reducing group, yet it reacts readily with distal hair cortex to form lead sulfide. Perhaps some such reaction goes on in strong alkali as $RSSR + 2H_2O \rightarrow 2RSH + H_2O_2$, and the peroxide in turn acts as a reducing agent, as it does with ferric ferricyanide, releasing 2H and liberating molecular oxygen (O_2).

From these considerations it would appear that when it is desired to distinguish SH from SS groupings, every precaution should be taken to protect the sensitive SH groups from oxidant fixatives, from exposure to air and from mercaptide forming heavy metal fixatives. Here, if the solubilities of the proteins under study permit, such fixatives as the Carnoy acetic alcohol (1:3) and acetic chloroform alcohol (1:3:6) are to be recommended. They should be used cold, or even by a freeze substitution process, in tightly closed containers.

Paraffin infiltration is perhaps preferably done *in vacuo* to reduce the heating interval to a minimum. I have compared the chloroform Carnoy at 5°C with the often recommended 5–10% trichloroacetic acid in 80% alcohol on keratinization of hair in skin of newborn animals and found demonstration of SH by ferric ferricyanide after Carnoy fixation at least equal if not better, than after trichloroacetic acid and general morphologic preservation seems distinctly better. For such proteins as are dissolved in acetic alcohol fixatives, chloroform methanol may be tried, or freeze drying.

Formaldehyde fixation is distinctly inimical to satisfactory —SH demonstration. The acid and neutral reagents would seem preferable to alkaline. I would suggest ferric ferricyanide with appropriate blockade controls, and the mercaptide reagents as more specific though perhaps less sensitive reagents. Barrnett and Seligman's (*J. Nat. Cancer Inst.* **13**:215, 1952; **14**:769, 1953) dihydroxydinaphthyl disulfide (commonly called DDD) and Pearse's (*J. Histochem.* **1**:460, 1953) tetrazolium method both employ alkaline solutions and are apt to show some alkali cleavage of SS in their application, thereby giving misleading results (Findlay, *J. Histochem.* **3**:331, 1955). Hyde (*ibid.* **9**:640, 1961) notes that trichloroacetic acid fixed material may prove relatively resistant to thioglycolate reduction, thus decreasing the amount of demonstrable SS.

When total protein sulfur demonstration is desired these latter methods, following an appropriate reduction, give excellent results. The presence of reducing agents during or after the Barrnett-Seligman reaction is to be avoided; the SS bond on whose formation the reaction depends is itself susceptible to cleavage.

The Ferric Ferricyanide Reduction Test

This test was introduced into histochemistry by Golodetz and Unna (*Monatsh. prakt. Derm.* **48**:149, 1909), for the demonstration of reduction sites in tissue. At first it was attributed to tyrosine, but all of Unna's later papers refer simply to "Reduktionsorte." Ferric ions are reduced to ferrous and in the presence of ferricyanides in the solution yield insoluble Turnbull's blue.

The method was cited by Schmorl for the identification of lipofuscin pigments. I have found it applicable to the pigment in phagocytes and parenchyma cells of the adrenal cortex, to a granular pigment found in phagocytes in the ovary adjacent to involuting corpora lutea, to the so-called melanosis pigment of the human appendix and colon and to a homologous pigment in the intestine of the guinea pig (*Anat. Rec.* **108**: 239, 1950).

The method also demonstrates chromaffin of the adrenal medulla in material appropriately fixed in bichromate fixatives (Lillie, *loc. cit.*).

Gomori (*Arch. Path.* **45**:48, 1948) and I independently discovered that the enterochromaffin or argentaffin substance of the basal granular cells of the gastrointestinal mucosa gives this reaction. Laskey and Greco (*Arch. Path.* **46**:83, 1948) compared it with the Masson silver method and found it nearly as efficient and much briefer.

Chèvremont and Frederic (*Arch. Biol.* **54**:589, 1943), apparently unaware of the previous use of this reaction for lipofuscins, utilized it for the demonstration of fixed sulfhydryl groups. They recognized, however, that other unidentified substances might react, and required the use of specific sulfhydryl blocking reagents for confirmation of the identification. They used mercuric chloride—Yao (*Quart. J. Micr. Sci.* **90**:1401, 1949) prescribed 1 hour in 6% aqueous solution—or 1% alcoholic chloropicrin solution or 4% aqueous monoiodoacetic acid.

Fisher and I have noted that thyroid colloid colors quite deep blue by this method.

Mast cells of rats and mice often conspicuously reduce ferric ferricyanide, coloring bright blue diffusely, with small rounded clear areas representing the granules.

Cutaneous keratin, as noted by Golodetz and Unna (*loc. cit.*), and keratohyalin granules, as noted by Chèvremont and Frederic (*loc. cit.*), and the corresponding structures in the stratified epithelium of the forestomach of rats and mice color deep blue by this reaction. Mercurial fixations do not inhibit the reaction in the rodent forestomach, and incubation at 37°C for 16 hours in 5% mercuric chloride does not stop it in skin sections. Chèvremont and Frederic disagree with us and with Golodetz and Unna and deny the reaction of cutaneous keratin. A 20 minute treatment with 2% CrO_3 destroys the reactivity, but 18 hour treatments with $K_2Cr_2O_7$ (0.1 M) and HIO_4 (0.03 M) do not.

In vitro Tests with Ferric Ferricyanide. The histochemical reaction mixture is promptly reduced by ascorbic, oxalic and uric acids, by phenols (phenol, resorcinol, hydroquinone, pyrogallol, *o*-cresol, α-naphthol, β-naphthol, adrenaline, L-tyrosine, tyramine, thyroxine); by indoles (indole, skatole, tryptophan, tryptamine, nitrosoindole, nitrosotryptophan); by aryl amines (aniline, α-naphthylamine, benzidine, diphenylamine); by thiols (ethyl mercaptan, mercaptoethanol, thiophenol, thio-2-naphthol, rubeanic acid, glutathione, cysteine, DL-methionine); by hydrazines (phenylhydrazine, semicarbazide, aminoguanidine); by stannous chloride, nascent hydrogen, carbon disulfide; by inorganic sulfides, sulfite, dithionite and thiosulfate; by glyoxal, benzaldehyde and benzyl alcohol; by nitrous acid; by hydrogen peroxide, lecithin, cod liver oil and linseed oil.

Pyrocatechol gives a green black precipitate with $FeCl_3$; *p*-dimethylaminoaniline and salicylic acid, a deep purple; the aminophenols (*o*-, 2,4-diaminophenol), red to brown; nitrosoresorcinol and 1-nitroso-2-naphthol, brown; *p*-phenylenediamine, dark brown; Na_2S, NaSH, $(NH_4)_2S$ and H_2S, greenish black; but premixed with potassium ferricyanide and allowed to stand for a minute or so, they all yield prompt blue or green colors with ferric chloride.

Other substances tested took an hour or more, more often overnight, to produce blue or green colors, and probably need not be considered as demonstrable by the histochemical reaction when the reaction time is restricted to 10 minutes. These included isopropanol, formaldehyde, acetaldehyde, acrylic acid, tartaric acid, citric acid, cholesterol and fructose, which gave blue or green colors in an hour but no precipitate; piperidine and pyridine, which gave brown precipitates with ferric chloride and whose premixed ferricyanide solutions which had stood for 1 hour or more gave Prussian blue reactions with ferric chloride; and a larger group giving no reaction at 1 hour: DL-serine, DL-lysine, histidine, histamine, DL-valine, L-glutamic acid, L-arginine, DL-aspartic acid, DL-threonine, L-proline, L-cystine, DL-alanine, DL-phenylalanine, methanol, ethanol, *n*-butanol, glycol, diethylene glycol, glycerol, 1,4-dioxane, allyl alcohol, acetone, formic acid, glucose, urea, guanine, caffeine, uracil, thiouracil, inositol, chloral hydrate, $HgCl_2$, HCl and distilled water.

Fixation of Material. For demonstration of the melanins, neuromelanin, melanosis and lipofuscin pigments routine formalin fixation is satisfactory. I have had good results on the adrenal pigment after alcoholic formalin, acetic alcohol formalin, Carnoy, aqueous and alcoholic lead nitrate and mercuric chloride formalin mixtures, and a variety of other non-chromate containing fixatives. Potassium bichromate fixations generally weaken or abolish the reactivity of these pigments.

For the argentaffin or enterochromaffin substance, routine fixations of 1–15 days in aqueous 10% formalin are satisfactory. Acetic formalin fixation is unsatisfactory. Alcoholic fixations of all sorts remove the argentaffin substance. It is preserved poorly or not at all with aqueous fixatives lacking formaldehyde. Bichromate formaldehyde fixations weaken the reaction and give a green color in place of clear blue. Formalin storage of 8 months to years prevents the reaction.

For chromaffin, fixation in potassium bichromate formaldehye mixtures without added acid is preferred. The Möller and Kose mixtures (p. 56) give good results.

For sulfhydryl Chèvremont and Frederic prescribe a 4–18 hour fixation in saline formalin or Bouin's fluid, and avoid prolonged treatment with melted paraffin, or use frozen sections. They state that longer than 48 hour exposure to formaldehyde will reduce or abolish the reactivity of sulfhydryl groups.

Although sulfhydryls form stable nonreactive mercaptals on reaction with aldehydes, strong HCl or $ZnCl_2$ is required as catalyst. Only thiol acids react directly without catalysts. Hence formalin fixation can be tolerated if not unduly prolonged.

I find Carnoy's acetic chloroform alcohol mixture (p. 42) and a mixture of 5 gm trichloroacetic acid, 75 cc alcohol and 20 cc water—both at 5°C—superior to formalin for preservation of sulfhydryl in the basal layers of the epidermis and the hair follicle cells. Use of sublimate formalin with sodium acetate (p. 48) inhibits the reaction of these structures, but not that of keratin. I use a 30 minute vacuum infiltration in paraffin for skin. It appears to be necessary to work up this material promptly after preparation. Paraffin sections which have been saved for some weeks after cutting have utterly failed to give the reaction at sulfhydryl sites, though those which were reacted at once from the same blocks gave good results.

For thyroid colloid the use of alcoholic fixatives seems preferable to that of aqueous formalin. The use of dichromate fixatives appears to be contraindicated, both because they tend to oxidize reducing groups and because they appear to engender a more or less diffuse, moderate blue green coloration of collagen, epithelia and the like.

The Reagent. Golodetz and Unna, Staemmler, Schmorl, Laskey and Greco and I (1950) all prescribed a 5 minute bath in a freshly prepared mixture of equal volumes of 1% ferric chloride and freshly prepared 1% potassium ferricyanide. The mixture should remain clear and greenish brown in color. Chèvremont and Frederic prescribed a mixture of 1 volume of fresh 0.1% potassium ferricyanide solution and 3 volumes of 1% ferric sulfate solution; they noted that the mixture was acid (pH 2.4) and that it was stable for about 2 hours in daylight and longer in the dark. A 20–25 minute immersion in this solution was required for paraffin sections.

I have found this highly disproportionate mixture—about 50 mols of ferric salt to 1 of ferricyanide—advantageous in giving a much clearer background than the Golodetz-Unna mixture, which gives only 2 mols of ferric salt to 1 of ferricyanide, but the concentration of ferricyanide is so low that prolonged exposures are necessary; and even then the demonstration of enterochromaffin cells is uncertain, and the reactivity of some of the pigments is dubious.

After considerable experimentation we have settled on 30 cc of 1% ferric chloride, 4 cc fresh 1% potassium ferricyanide ($K_3Fe(CN)_6$) and 6 cc distilled water. The final mixture thus contains 0.75% $FeCl_3$ and 0.1% potassium ferricyanide, a molar proportion of about 15:1. A 10 minute bath in this solution appears adequate.

Ferric Ferricyanide Reduction Technic (1951).

1. Fix material in accord with requirements on p. 210, imbed in paraffin, section at 5 to 10 μ and deparaffinize.
2. At the appropriate point in the hydration schedule, interpose blockade tests as indicated.
3. Wash in water and immerse in ferric ferricyanide reagent: 4 cc fresh 1% potassium ferricyanide solution, 30 cc 1% ferric chloride solution and 6 cc distilled water, freshly prepared (see above) for 10 minutes at 20–30°C.

4. Wash in 1% aqueous acetic acid solution.
5. Counterstain 10 minutes in 1:5000 new fuchsin (C.I. No. 42520) or fuchsin in 1% acetic acid. Omit if bromination or peracetic oxidation was done at step 2.
6. Rinse in 1% acetic acid.
7. Dehydrate, clear and mount through 95% and 100% alcohol, alcohol + xylene, xylenes, synthetic resin, polystyrene, or mineral oil. Mount uncounterstained sections in cellulose caprate.

Results: Sites or reducing substances (p. 208) should be blue; background, pale pink or faint green; nuclei, pink to red, or refractile and pale greenish yellow if not counterstained.

Since the ferricyanide in the Golodetz-Unna mixture would react directly with ferrous salts in the sections to produce Turnbull's blue, a series of controls should be used, substituting 2% potassium ferricyanide for the ferrocyanide in the Perls method (p. 407), to demonstrate ferrous salts as such.

For demonstration of disulfides in hair keratin, insert at step 2 a 10 minute bath at 25°C in a 10% solution of sodium thioglycolate, adjusted with sodium hydroxide to pH 9.5, and wash thoroughly with distilled water.

Perhaps better for this purpose is the peracetic acid azure A method on p. 219.

The Nitroprusside Reaction. Glick cited only the nitroprusside technics, which so far are applicable only to frozen sections of fresh unfixed tissue. The technic was cited by Giroud and Bulliard (*Protoplasma* 19: 381, 1933) and modified by Glick. It is no longer used in histochemistry because of poor localization, and is therefore omitted from this edition.

Mercury Orange. Bennett's method (*Anat. Rec.* 110:231, 1951) uses a red, mercury containing azo dye, p-chloromercuriphenyl-azo-β-naphthol, to form insoluble mercaptide linkages with sulfhydryl groups in tissue. The reaction appears to be specific. It does not occur with the corresponding mercury free azo dyestuff. It is prevented by agents which oxidize: 25.3 mg/100 cc iodine in propanol (1 mM), molar hydrogen peroxide + ferric chloride mixture in isopropanol or 1 mM in water; or alkylate sulfhydryl: 1.85% iodoacetamide or 1.86% iodoacetic acid (0.1 M) in n-propanol. It is prevented also by organic mercurials which form mercaptides with sulfhydryl: 1 mM n-propanol solutions of phenylmercuric chloride (31.3 mg/100 cc), tolyl mercuric chloride (32.7 mg/100 cc) or methyl mercuric iodide (34.5 mg/100 cc). Tissues and sections are brought through appropriate solvents to pure n-propanol, then immersed for several hours in the propanol solutions of the blocking reagents, washed in several changes of propanol and then transferred, along with control, unblocked, positive material of the same general character (*i.e.,* sections with sections, smears with smears, teased tissue with teased tissue), to the sulfhydryl reagent.

Mescon and Flesch (*J. Invest. Derm.* **18**:261, 1952) have further adapted Bennett's method for frozen sections of unfixed and paraffin sections of formalin fixed material.

Unfixed material is sectioned by the Adamstone-Taylor procedure or in the cryostat, mounted on slides, and at once immersed in the sulfhydryl reagent.

Routine paraffin sections of formalin fixed tissue are deparaffinized and brought to 80% alcohol as usual. Then stain, dehydrate, clear and mount as for the frozen sections.

Bennett fixed muscle tissue in 5% trichloroacetic acid, washed in distilled water, dehydrated in graded alcohols and transferred to propanol or butanol. Alternatively, the tissue was quickly frozen in isopentane cooled with liquid nitrogen, and dehydrated while still frozen by several changes of *n*-propanol or *n*-butanol at −20 to −25°C for 10–12 days. Muscle tissue was then teased out to isolate single fibers and small groups, which were stained whole. He also used paraffin and nitrocellulose sections, which were brought to *n*-propanol or *n*-butanol for reaction.

The reagent is *p*-chloromercuriphenyl-azo-β-naphthol. This is dissolved according to Bennett at 12.5 μM (6 mg/liter) in butanol or at 5.6 μM (3 mg/liter) in *n*-propanol; or according to Mescon and Flesch by dissolving 3 mg in 100 cc 100% ethyl alcohol at room temperature, and then adding 25 cc distilled water to reduce the alcohol concentration to 80%. Mescon's reagent is stored at 4°C and keeps fairly well.

Bennett's *p*-Chloromercuriphenyl-azo-β-naphthol Method for Sulfhydryl, with Modifications from Mescon and Flesch.

1. Deparaffinize paraffin sections and bring to 80% alcohol. Transfer Adamstone-Taylor frozen sections and nitrocellulose sections directly, and ordinary frozen sections after blotting on slides to
2. The Mescon-Flesch reagent for 1–3 hours.
3. Dehydrate, clear and mount through 95% and 100% alcohol, alcohol + xylene, 2 changes of xylene in a synthetic resin.
1a. Bring teased muscle preparations, tissue fragments to *n*-propanol; or nitrocellulose sections to isopropanol, which does not dissolve the nitrocellulose.
2a. Immerse several hours or overnight, according to size and thickness of material, in Bennett's propanol reagent solution.
3a. Wash 2 or 3 hours in *n*-propanol.
4a. Clear through propanol + xylene in 2 changes of xylene and mount in synthetic resin.

Results: Sites of sulfhydryl are colored red. If phenyl-azo-β-naphthol is used instead of its mercury derivative there should be no reaction.

Interpose blockade reactions after step 1. The reagents are described on p. 212. It is suggested that 1 of the mercaptide reagents be used as well as an alkylating or an oxidizing reagent; or better, 1 of each of the 3 types. The blockade reagent should be used for 4–18 hours and should be followed by a 2–6 hour bath in the same solvent to remove excess blocking agent. Then transfer to 80% alcohol or to *n*-propanol and proceed with step 2 or 2a.

The color is not extracted by toluene, benzene, 70% alcohol, 50% propanol, 0.1 *N* NaOH, 0.1 *N* CaCl$_2$ (about 0.55%), 0.1 *N* NH$_4$OH (about 0.68% dilution of 28% ammonia water) or 1 *M* NaCl (5.85%) on overnight exposure. The color is extracted by overnight immersion in 1 *mM* propanol solutions of mercaptans: β-mercaptoethanol, cysteine, 2,3-dimercaptopropanol (BAL), glutathione and thioglycolic acid (M.W. = 78, 121, 124, 307 and 92 respectively).

Hence if extraction tests are required, interpose after step 2 or 2a, hydrating as usual for the use of aqueous reagents, washing first with propanol for use of the propanol reagents and dehydrating for use of toluene, benzene or other similar solvent. After the prescribed exposure, wash out the extracting agent with the same solvent, dehydrate if necessary, clear and mount as usual.

After our 1957 introduction of a glacial acetic acid azo coupling step to intensify the color of the *p*-dimethylaminobenzaldehyde reaction with indoles, especially protein tryptophan, it seemed desirable to demonstrate that other *p*-N,N-dimethylaminophenyl compounds with tissue would also undergo an ortho azo coupling reaction in glacial acetic acid. To this end Dr. Glenner synthesized *p*-N,N-dimethylaminophenylmercuriacetate according to Whitmore (*Organic Compounds of Mercury,* Am. Chem. Soc. Monogr., New York, 1921).

Dark red azo coupling with diazotized safranin was demonstrated at SH sites, and was completely decolorized by 2,3-dimercaptopropanol in propanol. The procedure has since proved useful from time to time, and repetition of the synthesis has posed no important difficulties on several batches. Hence I include the method here.

Mercaptide Method of Lillie and Glenner for Sulfhydryl. The reagent *p*-N,N-dimethylaminophenylmercuric acetate is not presently available commercially: Dissolve 32 gm mercuric acetate in 100 cc distilled water [the calculated amounts are 31.87 gm Hg(CO$_2$CH$_3$)$_2$ and 12.18 gm = 12.74 cc dimethylaniline]. A slight excess of the Hg salt is used deliberately, and the excess is maintained throughout the process to prevent formation of the diaryl compound. Since addition of alcohol alone to warm or room temperature (24°C) 32% HgAc$_2$ gives rise to a copious yellow precipitate, cool to 3°C and add 12.5 cc N,N-dimethylaniline in 100 cc absolute alcohol also prechilled to 3°C. As the cold alcoholic dimethylaniline solution is poured into the aqueous mercuric acetate a yellow color and a little precipitate appear, but the latter redissolves on shaking. When about half the alcoholic solution has been added a white precipitate starts to form, and as the addition is completed it fills the entire fluid and sets into a firm mass with just a little yellow fluid remaining. The flask is then stoppered with a clean rubber stopper and shaken violently. This soon breaks up the clot into a fairly thick suspension of white precipitate in a colorless fluid. This is allowed to stand overnight at 3°C and then filtered out on paper and washed with distilled water until no more reaction is given with sulfides. The moist precipitate is then transferred to a vacuum desiccator and dried for 3–6 days at 25°C. Yield: calculated, 37.32 gm; actual, 30.7 gm.

Histologic Technic of Mercaptide Azo Coupling Reaction for Sulfhydryl.

1. Bring 5 μ paraffin sections, preferably of Carnoy fixed material, through xylenes and absolute alcohol to isopropanol.
2. Treat 18–24 hours in 0.7% N,N-p-dimethylaminophenylmercuriacetate in 99% isopropanol at 20–25°C. This solution is nearly saturated at 25°C.
3. Wash in 3 changes of isopropanol and 1 change of glacial acetic acid.
4. To 38 cc of glacial acetic acid at about 18°C add 2 cc 0.1 M diazosafranin which has been freshly diazotized for 20–30 minutes (p. 224). Immerse sections 5 minutes.
5. Wash in 3 changes of glacial acetic acid, 5 minutes each, or alternatively in 0.1 N hydrochloric acid 3 changes for 5 minutes each.
6. From glacial acetic acid wash in alcohol, alcohol xylene and xylenes. From hydrochloric acid wash in running water 5–10 minutes.
7. Dehydrate and clear in xylene.
8. Mount in cellulose caprate, Permount, balsam or other resin.

Results: Sulfhydryl sites appear in dark red, other tissues are unstained. With the HCl alternative in step 5, preparations may be counterstained with alum hematoxylin after step 6. The acetic variant in step 5 is less apt to occasion section losses.

Prior blockade with iodoacetic acid (p. 212) prevents the staining, and exposure for 24 hours to 1 mM 2,3-dimercaptopropanol or β-mercaptoethanol in isopropanol after completion of step 7 will remove this stain.

The reactivity of the method is essentially the same as that of Bennett's mercury orange. It does offer a deeper red color. The acetic acid azo coupling step creates no background staining, so that control preparations put through the technic omitting step 2 are as colorless as those destained by β-mercaptoethanol or 2,3-dimercaptopropanol.

Barrnett and Seligman utilize 2,2'-dihydroxy-6,6'-dinaphthyl disulfide as a reagent for both —SH and —SS— groups. Dr. Barrnett communicated this method to me after its presentation at the Histochemical Society in 1952.

Barrnett and Seligman's Dihydroxydinaphthyl Disulfide Method for Sulfhydryl and Disulfide (*J. Nat. Cancer Inst.* 13:215, 1952; 14:769, 1953).

1. Fix 24 hours in 80% alcohol containing 1% trichloroacetic acid.
2. Dehydrate, imbed in paraffin and section at 5–10 μ. Use minimal amount of albumen fixative, or preferably none.
3. Deparaffinize, collodionize with 0.5% collodion and hydrate through alcohols as usual.
4. To demonstrate —SS— groups as well as —SH groups, insert here a 2–4 hour bath at 50°C in 0.2–0.5 M thioglycolic acid (1.8 to 4.6%), adjusted with sodium hydroxide to pH 8.0.
5. Dissolve 25 mg 2,2'-dihydroxy-6,6'-dinaphthyl disulfide in 15 cc 100% alcohol and add 35 cc Michaelis's pH 8.5 Veronal sodium HCl buffer (p. 670). Stain up to 9 slides in a Coplin jar at 50°C for 1 hour.
6. Remove the Coplin jar from the water bath and cool for 10 minutes at room temperature.
7. Rinse briefly in distilled water.
8. Wash 10 minutes in 0.01% acetic acid (pH 4–4.5).
9. Dehydrate with graded alcohols, pass through 100% alcohol + ether 50:50, and extract with ether for 5 minutes to remove excess reagent and reaction byproducts.
10. Rehydrate through graded alcohols to distilled water.
11. Stain 2 minutes in a fresh solution of 50 mg fast blue B in 50 cc 0.1 M Sörensen's phosphate buffer of pH 7.4 (p. 664).
12. Wash 2 minutes in running water.
13. Mount in glycerol gelatin or dehydrate with acetone, clear in xylene and mount in synthetic resin (Permount, HSR, polystyrene, etc.).

Results: Reaction sites show pink, red and blue red to blue with increasing intensity of the reaction.

Barrnett wrote me that interposition of an iodine treatment after step 3 completely blocks the sulfhydryl reaction, thus: Immerse for 4 hours at 25°C in 1.5 mM iodine (378 mg/liter) containing a trace of KI at pH 3.2.

Blocking is also accomplished by a 4-hour bath at 37°C in 0.1 M ethyl maleimide (1.25%), buffered with Sörensen's phosphates to pH 7.4; or by a 20 hour bath at 37°C in 0.1 M (Na) iodoacetate (*ca.* 2%) at pH 8.0.

Incubation in 0.03 M glutathione (0.92%) at pH 8.5 for 3 hours at 50°C between step 10 and step 11 completely prevents the development of color.

Barrnett (*loc. cit.*) formerly used at step 4 a 1½ hour bath at 50°C in 10% ammonium sulfide. Step 4 as given above represents his 1953 procedure (personal communication). I have found ammonium sulfide ineffective in rendering distal hair cortex reactive to the ferric ferricyanide test, and have had similar failures with sodium dithionite, sulfite and thiosulfate. Stannous chloride not only failed to render hair cortex reactive but occasioned a diffuse deposit of Turnbull's blue over most other structures in the sections.

Pearse notes that for opening disulfide groups, relatively brief treatments with alkaline potassium cyanide are preferable because of the destruction of sulfhydryl by alkali. I have had rather irregular and generally unsatisfactory results with KCN and prefer 10% sodium thioglycolate adjusted with NaOH to pH 9.5. This reagent appears to render hair cortex strongly reactive to the ferric ferricyanide method on a 10 minute exposure at room temperature (25°C). Longer exposures at higher temperatures appear simply to increase section losses without any appreciable gain in reactivity. This reagent works well after Carnoy, hot methanol chloroform, formalin and the like. After Spuler's Zenker formol, apparently only sulfhydryl groups become demonstrable, and prolonged chromate fixations decrease or abolish reactivity. This last finding suggests that the mercurial binding of sulfhydryl groups may operate to protect them against bichromate oxidation.

Unalkalinized 10% sodium thioglycolate solution (pH 5.5) may also be effective in opening disulfide bonds, but it apparently requires heat (60°C) and longer exposures. Its use may be desirable when it is necessary to avoid alkali.

Foraker and Wingo (letter, August 31, 1954) use a solution containing 5 gm sodium sulfite (Na_2SO_3) and 10 gm sodium acetate per 100 cc, treating sections for 1 hour at 22–30°C. This is said to reduce —SS— groups to —SH without unblocking —SH groups previously alkylated by iodoacetate. In my hands, using the ferric ferricyanide method, this has failed to demonstrate —SS— in distal hair cortex.

Kekule and Linnemann used iodine to convert mercaptans to disulfides in 1862 (Hickinbottom, p. 131); hence this method of blocking —SH groups prior to trying to localize —SS— groups would seem inappropriate, as the iodine created —SS— groups might be difficult to distinguish from those occurring naturally.

Recent experience indicates that sodium thioglycolate may deteriorate in dry form, so that this reagent may also fail to open —SS —bonds. Also 5% potassium cyanide (pH 10.8), 10 minutes, 25°C may fail to convert hair cystine to sulfhydryl. Good results have been attained with a 10 minute exposure at 25°C to 5% sodium sulfide (Na_2S). This solution is strongly alkaline (pH 11), and longer exposures engender undue section losses. It appears, however, that this reagent may overcome iodoacetate blockade.

Barrnett and Seligman (*Science* **116**:323, 1952) noted in rat tissues strong reactions in hair cortex at the zone of keratinization, in pancreatic acinar cells, in intestinal smooth muscle, in Hassall's corpuscles of the thymus, in lens and in Purkinje cells of the cerebellum; moderate reactions of hair cortex near the root, of epithelia of epidermis, hair sheaths, sebaceous glands and intestinal villi, of Paneth cells and stroma cells of villi and of striated and smooth muscle of the skin. Intense staining of vascular elastica occurred, but this was not prevented by iodine and hence is not a sulfhydryl reaction.

The sodium plumbite reation for reactive sulfur in hair dates back to 1893 (Salkowski's *Physiologisches Praktikum*, p. 94). Unna (*Biochemie der Haut*, Fischer, Jena, 1913) directs: Dissolve 0.5 gm lead acetate in 10 cc water and add 10% NaOH until the lead hydroxide at first precipitated is redissolved as Na_2PbO_2. Treat celloidin sections of alcohol fixed skin (plantar) with this reagent until the keratin is well blackened. This method demonstrates hard and soft keratin and sites chemically containing cystine, as well as the more easily reactive cysteine and glutathione.

Methenamine silver impregnation at 60°C, carried to the point of blackening collagen, demonstrates the keratinization zone of hair cortex quite well, leaving hair bulb cytoplasm pink and distal hair cortex brown to yellow. When the blackening of collagen is prevented by prior acetylation, keratinizing hair cortex still blackens, and when deacetylation with 1% KOH in 80% alcohol (20 minutes) is practiced, distal hair cortex also blackens, indicating cleavage of SS groups. That the reaction in hair cortex is due to SH groups appears highly probable.

Cysteic Acid Methods. Another group of methods for cystine is based on the fact that peracetic and performic acids convert cystine quantitatively to cysteic acid. Bromine in carbon tetrachloride solution (1 cc:39 cc, 1 hour) and aqueous potassium permanganate solution (0.5%, 30 minutes followed by 5 minutes in 1% oxalic acid or bisulfite) are somewhat less effective; and periodic acid, which was recommended by Dempsey, Singer and Wislocki (*Stain Techn.* **25**:73, 1950), has been ineffective in our hands when elevated temperatures are not employed. In accordance with the strongly acid character of cysteic acid, keratin thus oxidized takes up thionin even from a solution in 0.1 N hydrochloric acid. In unoxidized skin sections only the mast cells stained with this solution.

The Peracetic Acid Azure Eosin Method for Hair Keratin.

1. Paraffin sections of skin fixed in the usual fixatives are deparaffinized and hydrated through xylene and descending alcohols as usual.
2. Oxidize for 10–120 minutes in peracetic acid mixture prepared 1–10 days previously (p. 183).
3. Wash 5 minutes in running water.
4. Stain 1 hour in azure A eosin B according to technic on p. 162; or for 30 minutes to overnight in thionin, azure A, or methylene blue in 0.125 N HCl (pH 1.0) or in 0.1 M sodium citrate HCl buffer of pH 2, 3 or 4. The dye concentration should be 0.05% for $\frac{1}{2}$ hour staining and may be as low as 10 mg/liter for overnight.
5. Dehydrate with acetone, clear in acetone + xylene and 2 changes of xylene. Mount in synthetic resin.

Results: Hair cortex and cuticle, dark violet to black in dermal and free portions, grading to greenish blue toward the root in hypodermal portion; stratum corneum, moderate violet; melanin granules, dark green to dark violet; nuclei, blue violet; keratohyalin, red to purple; muscle, pink; connective tissue fibers, pale pink; cartilage matrix, violet to purple; mast cell granules, dark purple or dark violet.

Methylation (p. 283) in 0.1 N HCl methanol at 60°C for 24 hours, done after the peracetic acid step, abolishes all basophilia except that of the keratins and melanin. The basophilia of hair cortex, engendered by peracetic acid, is destroyed by methylation at 60°C for about 3–6 days. Even 7 day methylation at 60°C is without effect on the basophilia of hair cortex when applied before the peracetic acid oxidation. Since methylation acts to destroy basophilia by esterifying open acid groups, and no cysteic acid is present until after oxidation of the disulfide, this behavior is to be expected.

Demethylation in 1% KOH/70% alcohol, 20–30 minutes, restores basophilia at pH 1, both in hair cortex cysteic acid and in melanin, but not in mast cells or cartilage.

Adams and Sloper (*J. Endocr.* **13**:221, 1956) use a cysteic acid method for the demonstration of cystine in the neurosecretory substance of the hypothalamus and hypophyseal stalk. This method depends on the highly acid character of cysteic acid as produced by performic (or peracetic) acid oxidation. They used Pearse's formula for preparation of performic acid (p. 184) and 1% Alcian Blue 8GS in 2 N sulfuric acid.

Performic Acid Alcian Blue Method of Adams and Sloper for Disulfides.

1. Fix in 4% formaldehyde, imbed in paraffin as usual, section at 15 μ or 7 μ, deparaffinize and hydrate as usual.

2. Oxidize 5 minutes in Pearse's performic acid (make fresh daily) and wash 5 minutes in distilled water.

If section is loosening from slide at this point, heat at 60°C until just dry, to secure readherence.

3. Stain 1 hour in 1% Alcian Blue 8GS in 2 N H_2SO_4 (pH 0.2) (5.4 cc 98% H_2SO_4 + H_2O to make 100 cc).

4. Wash 5 minutes in running water, dehydrate in alcohols, clear in xylene and mount in balsam or Depex.

Results: Neurosecretory substance and hair keratin, bright blue; stratum corneum, unstained. Staining of ground substance in collagen and cerebral corpora amylacea was reported also without performic acid oxidation. Nuclei stain faintly or not at all after performic acid.

The more stable peracetic acid (p. 183) serves as well, and other strongly basic dyes can be substituted for alcian blue (p. 218) with equal or superior results.

PHENOLS

The Azo Coupling Reaction. Aside from special phenolic complexes of limited histologic distribution, such as enterochromaffin, the reaction of proteins generally to the azo coupling reaction is assignable to the aromatic amino acid residues, tyrosine, histidine and tryptophan. Pauly (*Hoppe Seyler Z. physiol. Chem.* 42:508, 1904) and Gomori (p. 121) stated that tryptophan did not azo couple; Danielli (*Cold Spring Harbor Symp.* 14:32, 1950) stated that it did. I have found tryptamine more reactive at pH 4 than tyramine or histamine and about equally so at pH 8.5, using fast red GG. Only yellow colors were produced in the acid range; orange to brown precipitates appeared at pH 8.5. The amines were used, rather than amino acids, because of their greater water solubility.

The colors produced by tissue proteins with the older azo coupling reagents were weak, chiefly yellows, or even inappreciable. Hence attempts have been made to enhance the color by using tetrazonium salts and then exposing afterward to a naphthol solution to couple this to the second, hitherto unused diazonium group. This procedure was introduced by Clara and Canal (*Z. Zellforsch.* 15:301, 1932), who first used monodiazotized benzidine to couple with enterochromaffin, then repeated the nitrous acid step and coupled in alkali with resorcinol, salicylic acid or β-naphthol. They also used tetrazotized benzidine, and the latter practice was adopted by Danielli and used by later workers.

Postcoupled Tetrazonium Method. As currently practiced (Pearse, 1960, pp. 795–796), the reaction includes a 15 minute primary azo coupling in freshly tetrazotized benzidine or a 2% fast blue B salt at pH

9.2, washing in pH 9.2 buffer and a second enhancement coupling with 2% H acid (1,8-aminonaphthol-3,6-disulfonic acid) at pH 9.2 for 15 minutes, followed by washing in water, dehydration in alcohols, clearing and mounting.

Since diazonium salts are bases, salt combinations with tissue carboxylic, sulfuric and phosphoric acid residues are to be expected at pH 9.2 as well as azo bonding, and the second naphthol coupling should produce azo dyes bound to acid sites as well as to sites of simple adsorption or even impregnation of dense fibers such as cellulose by the diazonium salt. Cotton fabrics are often dyed by being first soaked ("padded") with a naphthol and then exposed to a suitable diazonium salt, which precipitates an azo dye within the fiber. Burstone (*J. Histochem.* 3:32, 1955) noted histochemical staining of cellulose by this method.

Fortunately diazonium salts are now available which yield sufficiently deep coloration at presumed tyrosine and histidine sites in tissue on direct alkaline and even "acid" azo coupling to render enhancement by Clara's procedure unnecessary. Diazosafranin and fast black K both yielded red "background" colors which became quite dark in such materials as keratin, some zymogen granules, melanosis pigment, erythrocytes and muscle. These colors resist prolonged extraction in 0.1 N hydrochloric acid in water or alcohol, whereas safranin staining is promptly extracted. The color is promptly bleached by sodium dithionite

TABLE 8-2. SOME CHARACTERISTICS OF COMMON DIAZONIUM SALTS

Name	Colour Index No.	Amine Mol. wt.	Color			
			Enterochromaffin	β-Naphthol	Naphthol AS	Protein
Safranin	50240	350.8	Blue black	Blue	Dark blue	Red
Fast red GG, p-Nitroaniline	37035	138.1	Red	Red	Red	Yellow
Fast red B, p-Nitro-o-anisidine	37125	168.2	Red	Red	Red	Pale yellow
Sulfanilic acid	.....	173.2	Red	Red	Red	Pale yellow
Fast garnet GBC o-aminoazotoluene	37210	225.3	Red	Red	Red	Pale yellow
Fast blue B, di-o-anisidine	37235	244.3	Red brown	Blue	Blue	Pale yellow
Benzidine	.....	184.2	Red brown	Blue	Blue	Pale yellow
Fast black K salt (base not available)	37190	302.3	Blue black	Blue black	Blue black	Red orange

($Na_2S_2O_4$), which cleaves the azo bond. It is believed that the following technics will give a truer picture of the azo coupling reaction of tissue proteins than the postcoupled tetrazonium method.

Normal Method for Preparation of Freshly Diazotized Amines. *Reactions.*

$$O_2N \cdot C_6H_4 - NH_2 + NaNO_2 + 3HCl \rightarrow O_2NC_6H_4\overset{+}{N} \equiv N \cdot \overset{-}{Cl} + NaCl + H_2O + HCl$$

$$O_2N \cdot C_6H_4 - \overset{+}{N} \equiv N \cdot \overset{-}{Cl} + HCl + 2NaOH \rightarrow O_2NC_6H_4N = N\overset{-}{OH} + 2NaCl + H_2O$$

Dissolve or suspend 1 m-mol of the amine in 3 cc 1 N hydrochloric acid and 6 cc distilled water. (The diazonium salts are generally more soluble than the bases.) Chill to 2–3°C in freezing compartment of refrigerator or by placing container in ice bath. Add 1 cc 1 N sodium nitrite (= 1 m-mol or 69 mg) and return to refrigerator or ice bath. Diazotize 20–30 minutes.

This technic allows 1 m-mol HCl to neutralize the amine, 1 m-mol to convert the $NaNO_2$ to HNO_2 and 1 m-mol to furnish the necessary acidity for the reaction. Hence in transferring the fresh diazotate to an alkaline buffer it is regarded as existing in 0.2 N HCl, and corresponding allowance is made in the mixing of Veronal or tris buffers. Electrometric measurement of the final solutions has confirmed the validity of this assumption. The 10 cc of fresh diazotate is 100 mM in concentration, and dilutions to the desired concentration are made accordingly.

Azo Coupling Reaction. Fresh Diazotates. For 5 mM solution take 2 cc of fresh diazotate + 2 cc distilled water + enough additional 0.1 N HCl to make the prescribed quantity in the Michaelis table plus the required amount of Veronal sodium for the pH level desired. For pH 8.5, use 2.1 cc (6.1 − 4.0) 0.1 N HCl + 33.9 cc 0.1 M Veronal sodium. The buffer solutions are precooled to 3°C. For pH 8, the values would be 6.3 (10.3 − 4.0) cc 0.1 N HCl + 29.7 cc 0.1 M Veronal sodium.

For stable diazotates, weigh out the calculated quantity to furnish the desired molarity. For example, with a sample of fast red GG containing the equivalent of 20% of the primary amine, M.W. 138, 138 mg would be adequate for 200 cc of 1 mM solution, so for 40 cc one would use 27.6 mg; for 2 mM, 55.2 mg; and for 5 mM, 138 mg in 40 cc (see Table 8-4).

For fast black K I find 1 mM (60 mg/40 cc) and 1–5 minutes often quite adequate at pH 8 or 8.5, but for some special purposes use 2mM for 2 minutes (p. 223). The same values hold for freshly diazotized safranin.

For acid azo coupling at pH 3 or 4, a higher concentration, 5 mM seems adequate, and longer times are needed—30 minutes to 2 hours. This requires 300 mg/40 cc for fast black K and 2 cc/40 cc for freshly diazotized 0.1 M safranin; 0.1 M acetate buffers are used as the diluent for the stable diazotates; the HCl citrate series at 0.1 M can be used for

TABLE 8-3. REAGENTS FOR AZO COUPLING AT pH 3, 4, 8 AND 8.5

Reagents	Fast black K salt 20% amine				Freshly diazotized safranin			
	pH levels				pH levels			
	3	4	8	8.5	3	4	8	8.5
0.1 N HCl, cc.........	29.4	26.4	11.4	6.1	25.4	22.4	10.6	5.3
0.1 M Na citrate.......	10.6	13.6	......	......	10.6	13.6		
0.1 M Na Veronal, cc...	......	.....	28.6	33.9	.....	.....	28.6	33.9
Stable diazo, mg.......	300	300	60	60				
Fresh diazo 0.1 M, cc...	......	.....	......	....	2	2	0.4	0.4
Distilled water, cc......	......	.....	......	....	2	2	0.4	0.4
Time at 3°C...........	1–2 hr	1 hr	2–5 min	2–5 min	1–2 hr	1 hr	2–5 min	2–5 min

For stable diazonium salts the appropriate acetate, borate or tris buffers may be substituted, if desired. The Sörenson phosphate series is useful at pH 5–7.

the fresh diazo, with the equivalent of the amount of diazotate deducted from the prescribed amount of 0.1 N HCl and with the fresh diazotate considered as 0.2 N HCl.

Technic. Use thin paraffin sections, preferably 3–5 μ.

1. Xylene, 2 changes; 100%, 95% and 80% alcohols, 2 changes each; distilled water.
2. Chill buffers to 3°C in refrigerator or with ice bath. Chill Coplin jar.

In using stable diazotates, compute the amount to be employed on the manufacturer's stated percentage of primary amine represented by the preparation used. Usually this is around 20%. Molarities are computed on this basis. Some supposedly pure diazonium chlorides are supplied. In this instance molarities are computed on the formula weight of the diazonium chloride, not on that of the undiazotized base.

Thus on the basis of 20% amine, a 5 mM solution requires the equivalent of the molecular weight of the base (amine) in milligrams of the stable salt to 40 cc of buffered solvent (20% of 1 m-mol in $\frac{1}{25}$ liter).

TABLE 8-4. MOLARITY OF SOLUTIONS OF SOME COMMON STABLE DIAZOTATES

Diazo	MW amine	Stated % base	mg/40 cc	
			1 mM	5 mM
Fast garnet GBC.........	225.3	18	49.5	247.5
Fast red GG.............	138.4	20	27.6	138.4
Fast red B..............	108.2	20	37.6	168.2
Fast blue B.............	249.3	20	48.8	244.3

Care should be taken that the stable diazo employed in enzyme demonstration reactions does not contain metal salts inhibitory to the enzyme. Stable diazotates are often zinc chloride double salts; boron trifluoride is also often used. Aluminum salts are often present.

Standard Fresh Diazo Method with *p*-nitroaniline, 5 *mM*, pH 8

Preparation of Fresh Diazotate. Dissolve 138 mg *p*-nitroaniline (1 m-mol) in 3 cc 1 *N* HCl + 6 cc distilled water, warming if necessary. Cool to 3°C and add 1 cc 1 *M* sodium nitrite (1 m-mol = 69 mg). Let stand 20 minutes at 3°C to diazotize.

Meanwhile bring paraffin sections through xylene and alcohols to distilled water as usual.

Mix and chill Michaelis buffer (to make pH 8 finally) 0.1 *M* Veronal sodium, 28.6 cc; 0.1 *N* HCl, 7.4 cc; distilled water, 2 cc. Then add 2 cc fresh diazotate and pour over slides in prechilled Coplin jar. Let stand 2 minutes at 0–5°C. Wash in 3 changes 0.1 *N* HCl 5 minutes, 5 minutes, 5 minutes; distilled water, 2 changes, 1 minute, 1 minute; and counterstain in azure A for 15 minutes (1% azure A, 2 cc; 0.1 *N* HCl, 4 cc; distilled water, 34 cc; pH 2). Rinse in distilled water, acetone 3 times, acetone + xylene, xylenes, cellulose caprate.

If preliminary procedures are to be applied to the sections, start the diazotization when the sections are due to be removed from the last step of the preliminary procedure. Sections can be held 10–15 minutes in distilled water, or for some hours in 80% alcohol, unless contraindications are specifically noted.

Diazosafranin. For the *p*-nitroaniline in the above technic, substitute 1 m-mol of safranin 0, C.I. No. 50240, 351 mg, diethylsafranin, C.I. No. 50206, 378 mg, or dimethylsafranin, C.I. No. 50205, 351 mg, with appropriate allowances for dye content. These solutions in 3 cc 1 *N* HCl + 6 cc water are reasonably stable and may be made up in larger quantities, if desired. For use mix 9 cc with 1 cc 1 *N* NaNO₂. If kept cold the nitrite solution is also stable for a week or more. With the diazosafranins omit the counterstain.

The acid diazo mixture is not very stable and should be used within 2 hours of mixing for best results. It is probable that internal acid coupling occurs on longer standing, since only 1 of the 2 amino groups of the safranin can be diazotized in acid aqueous solution, and therefore the dye residue remains capable of acid (amine) coupling with diazonium groups. On overnight storage at 3°C the acid diazo mixture changes from blue to dark red in color and gives only feeble coloration of argentaffin cells on alkalinization. Addition of 1 cc of acid diazo mixture to 40 cc 0.1 *M* di-sodium phosphate solution brings the reaction to pH 7.7, which is sufficiently alkaline for phenol coupling, and not alkaline enough to remove the sections from the slides.

In vitro, alkaline azo coupling reactions occasion no noteworthy color changes with catechol, anisole, phloroglucinol, *o*-aminophenol, amidol, uracil, guanine, phenylalanine or cysteine. Dark brown precipitates are produced with phenol, *o*-cresol and *p*-cresol; a very dark red brown precipitate occurs with resorcinol; red purple to dark red purple or purple precipitates occur with hydroquinone, pyrogallol and tyrosine; and dark blue violet precipitates, with α- and β-naphthols.

Model experiments on formalin fixed, phenol impregnated, gelatin-paper strips gave coupling colors with diazosafranin as follows: Pink to colorless with the blank gelatin control, with phenol, catechol, hydroquinone, pyrogallol, phloroglucinol, *o*-aminophenol, 2,4-diaminophenol, tyrosine, tyramine, 3,4-dihydroxyphenylalanine, adrenaline, noradrenaline, indole, tryptophan, tryptamine, cysteine, guanine, *m*- and *p*-aminophenol. Pink to purple colors were obtained with *o*- and *p*-cresols and 5-hydroxytryptamine; Gomori has reported blue with the last, but I have obtained definite blues only with resorcinol and with α- and β-naphthols.

For testing the reactions of various phenolic substances in comparison with argentaffin granules, Gomori followed the suggestion of Coujard and used the following technic.

Substances to be tested are dissolved 0.25–1 at 1% in a mixture of equal parts of serum and 5% gelatin. Marks are written with a clean steel pen dipped in a slightly warmed solution on a slide; more than 25 different substances can be tested on one slide. The slides are dried and subsequently exposed to formaldehyde fumes in a closed jar for several hours; the excess formaldehyde is driven off in the paraffin oven. The dry slides can be stored for weeks. For the test the slides are run through xylene and alcohols to distilled water and stained just as tissue sections would be. It should be noted that substances susceptible to air oxidation will probably be in the oxidized state. Quinones do not azo couple.

I have occasionally used the Gibbs reaction with 2,6-dichloro- or dibromoquinonechloroimid (*Am. J. Path.* **36**:623, 1960), but have found it rather temperamental and unreliable. The reagent condenses with phenols with an open *para* (or *ortho* ?) position to yield indophenol dyes.

Gibbs's Indophenol Reaction for Phenols (from Pearse, 1953, p. 478).

1. Deparaffinize and hydrate thin (5 μ) paraffin sections of formalin fixed material.

2. Immerse 15 minutes in 0.1% Gibbs's reagent in pH 9.2 Veronal buffer (p. 670).
3. Wash 5 minutes in running water, counterstain in 0.5% safranin or 1% neutral red, differentiate and dehydrate in 70% and absolute alcohol, clear in xylene and mount in synthetic resin.

When successful, the method demonstrates enterochromaffin granules in dark gray blue.

Acylation Blockade

The azo coupling reaction may be blocked by acylation and restored by saponification procedures. For prevention of the azo coupling reaction of phenols the alcohol acetic anhydride method proves to be superior to pyridine solutions of either benzoyl chloride or acetic anhydride (*J. Histochem.* **12**:522, 1964).

Alcoholic Acetylation for Blocking the Azo Coupling Reaction of Phenols.

1. Bring thin paraffin sections through xylenes to absolute alcohol.
2. Acetylate 1 hour in equal volumes of acetic anhydride and absolute alcohol.
3. Wash in 80% alcohol and 10 minutes in running water.
4. Azo couple acetylated and unacetylated control sections in fast black K, diazosafranin or diazotized *p*-nitroaniline as usual, wash in 0.1 *N* HCl and in water, dehydrate and mount.

Tyrosine

The Millon Reaction. Cowdry, Romeis and Glick all recommend the method of Bensley and Gersh for protein containing tyrosine.

Millon Reagent. Saturate 500 cc of 4% aqueous nitric acid with mercuric nitrate crystals. Filter, and to 40 cc filtrate add 0.2 cc 70% nitric acid and 140 mg sodium nitrite.

Prepare paraffin sections of frozen dried material, or material fixed in an anhydrous fixative. Mount on slides by floating on 95% alcohol, or without flotation. Deparaffinize, dip briefly in 100% alcohol, blot and immerse directly in Millon reagent. Remove sections at intervals, inspecting for the presence of rose or red color. The action reaches its maximum in about 3 hours. Rinse in 1% nitric acid, dehydrate with 100% alcohol (dropper bottle or several changes), clear in xylene and mount in balsam.

Results: Tyrosine, rose red. Glick regards the reaction as specific.

Serra (*Stain Techn.* **21**:5, 1946, emended) recommends the following modification of Millon's reaction as essentially specific for tyrosine.

Stock Reagent. Dissolve 7.5 gm mercuric sulfate, 5.5 gm mercuric chloride and 7 gm anhydrous sodium sulfate in 85 cc distilled water. Add 12.5 gm (6.8 cc) concentrated sulfuric acid (sp. gr. 1.836) and when cool dilute to 100 cc.

Procedure. Sections—loose, on coverglasses or on slides—are immersed in stock reagent for 30 minutes at 60°C in covered vessel. Then cool to room temperature by immersion of container in cold water and let stand 10 minutes. Add an equal volume of distilled water and a few drops of molar (6.9%) sodium nitrite solution. A red color develops, reaching a maximum in 3 minutes. Mount in glycerol and seal with lanolin rosin (p. 91) or polystyrene.

The Protein Diazotization Coupling Reaction for the Demonstration of Tyrosine (Lillie, *J. Histochem.* **5**:528, 1957; Glenner and Lillie, *ibid:* **7**:416, 1959). That tyrosine bearing proteins develop a yellow color on treatment with nitrous acid has been known since 1888 (Richard, *Bull. Soc. Chim. Ind.* Mulhouse, p. 75), and it was noted at the same time that the yellow color of wool and silk turned brown on exposure to light. The procedure was developed by Morel and Sisley to yield various azoic colors on coupling in the dark with various phenols and naphthols (*Bull. Soc. Chim.* **41**:1217, 1927). The reaction is formulated thus.

Our own experiments confirmed the necessity for cold and strict darkness, determined the optimal dizaotization time at about 16 hours at 3°C and selected S acid (8-amino-1-naphthol-5-sulfonic acid) and H acid (8-amino-1-naphthol-3,6-disulfonic acid) as the most appropriate coupling agents. Urea is added to the coupling reagent to decompose excess HNO_2. A dark chamber is improvised by inverting over the Coplin jar containing the slides an empty tin can of sufficient height (10 cm) and breadth to cover it completely.

The fixation method must be such as to conserve the protein under particular study. Neutral aqueous formalin has proved suitable for most objects. The technic follows.

1. Prepare paraffin or frozen sections and attach to slides as usual. Bring to distilled water.

2. Diazotize 16 hours at $3°C$ in strict darkness with 1 N sodium nitrite in 1 N acetic acid: Dissolve 2 gm $NaNO_2$ in 28 cc distilled water and add 1.7 cc glacial acetic acid. (Do not mix the dry salt with the glacial acetic acid; this produces an immediate evolution of brown gaseous oxides of nitrogen.)

3. To 50 cc 70% alcohol add successively 500 mg S acid, 500 mg potassium hydroxide and 1 gm urea or 500 mg ammonium sulfamate. Dissolve and chill to $3°C$.

   Wash sections in 4 changes of distilled water at $3°C$, 5 seconds each, and introduce into the cold alkaline coupling reagent for 1 hour. This I usually do also in the dark, though Glenner noted that diazotized tyrosine was much less photosensitive in alkali.

4. Wash in 3 changes 0.1 N HCl, 5 minutes each, and 10 minutes in running water.

5. Counterstain, if desired, with alum hematoxylin. I usually omit this step.

6. Dehydrate in alcohols, clear in xylene, mount in xylene cellulose caprate or other resin.

Results: Tyrosine sites, red purple to pink. Hair cortex, soft keratin, elastic laminae, the inner sheath cells and medulla of the root zone of hairs show the strongest reactions; moderate reactions are seen in zymogen granules of salivary and gastric glands, pancreas and Paneth cells, smooth and striated muscle, some nuclei and cytoplasms, thyroid and hypophyseal colloid. Eosinophil leucocytes, enterochromaffin cells and mast cells are not identified.

In step 3 Glenner substituted 500 mg ammonium sulfamate, which consumes 2 mols HNO_2 per mol, equalling the 2 mols consumed by urea. Urea (M.W. 60) is thus nearly twice as effective as ammonium sulfamate (M.W. 114) on a weight for weight basis and currently costs about half as much. I have adhered to the use of urea in this step. The quantity can probably be safely reduced to 250 mg, since the carryover of HNO_2 in the washed sections must be infinitesimal.

Geyer (*Acta Histochem.* **13:**355, 1962) notes that the Morel-Sisley reaction can be accelerated and intensified by a 1–6 hour pretreatment with 10% iodine in alcohol. The sections are then washed in alcohols and water and nitrosated at 3–5°C for 1 hour only, using 1 N $NaNO_2$/1 N acetic acid, strictly in the dark.

Pretreatment with tetranitromethane 0.1 cc in 10 cc pyridine and 20 cc 0.1 N HCl 6 hours at East German laboratory temperature, and washing in alcohol or acetone (2 times, 5 minutes each) and water (10 minutes) will completely prevent the Morel-Sisley and Millon reactions for tyrosine and moderately impair the xanthydrol and Adams reactions for tryptophan (Geyer, *Acta Histochem.* **13:**357, 1962).

Histamine

Lagunoff, Phillips and Benditt (*J. Histochem.* 9:534, 1961) direct as follows for the demonstration of histamine in mast cells.

1. Freeze in isopentane chilled with liquid nitrogen, desiccate at -30 to $-40°C$ *in vacuo* over P_2O_5.
2. When dry transfer to desiccator containing paraformaldehyde and calcium chloride, seal on lid with petrolatum, partially evacuate and heat in paraffin oven at 55–60°C for 4–96 hours.
3. Imbed in paraffin, section at 5–10 μ.

Paraffin sections are subjected to azo coupling in 2.5% Na_2CO_3, with freshly diazotized *p*-bromoaniline: 3 cc 5% in 1 N HCl $+$ 3 cc 5% $NaNO_2$ for 1 minute; add 30 cc ice cold 2.5% Na_2CO_3; expose sections to the alkaline solution 10–15 minutes at 0°C.

Fast garnet GBC and fast black K were also used in 0.5% solution in pH 7.8 borate buffer, but they gave weaker reactions. It may be pointed out that their fresh diazotate contains a large (2.46 times) excess of nitrite, the unused part of which is carried over into the coupling stage.

The mast cells also give the ferric ferricyanide reduction test (p. 211), reduce hot methenamine silver (p. 240) and present a yellow green fluorescence in near ultraviolet. A negative tryptophan reaction by the Adams method, a negative chromaffin reaction and a positive diazotization coupling tyrosine reaction (p. 227) were also observed.

I have seen azo coupling and ferric ferricyanide reactions in gastric mast cells of mice after routine calcium acetate formalin fixation, but have not applied the critical test of first demonstrating the cells by metachromatic staining at low pH and then decolorizing and redemonstrating the same cells in the same locations in the same section to prove identity. Neither did Lagunoff *et al.*

Lagunoff *et al.* speculate on the possible concurrent presence of tyramine, dopa or dopamine to account for the positive tyrosine test, but they did not include this test in their model experiments.

Lagunoff *et al.* quoted Frankel and Zellmer (*Biochem. Z.* 110:234, 1920) concerning the condensation of formaldehyde with histamine to form imidazoleisopiperidine, which I formulate below for both histamine tautomers.

$$N\text{---}C\quad CH_2 \quad + H_2C\text{=}O \quad N\text{---}C\quad CH_2$$

In the presence of a positive tyrosine (or tyramine) reaction at the same site I do not believe that this application of the Pauly reaction can be assigned surely to the presence of histamine, though the idea is naturally attractive.

Tryptophan

The Romieu reaction for proteins (according to Glick, Lison and Cowdry) indicates the presence of tryptophan. Fix in alcohol, Bouin or formalin. Prepare rather thick paraffin or nitrocellulose sections. Deparaffinize and hydrate as usual. Blot. Cover with a few drops syrupy phosphoric acid and heat for a few minutes at 56°C (use a paraffin oven). Remove, apply coverglass and examine at once. A red to violet color indicates the presence of tryptophan.

The Voisenet-Fürth Reaction. This is recommended by Serra (*Stain Techn.* **21**:5, 1946).

1. Fix in a formaldehyde fixative, or mordant hydrated paraffin sections in 10% formalin for 1–5 hours.
2. Immerse in 12% sodium silicate solution (sp. gr. 1.10) for 3–5 seconds. If material is well hardened this step may be omitted. Drain on filter paper and
3. Transfer directly to fresh Voisenet reagent for 10–15 minutes. *Voisenet reagent:* to 10 cc concentrated hydrochloric acid add 1 drop 2% aqueous formol and 1 drop 0.5% sodium nitrite (fresh aqueous solution). Mix well. Prepare fresh daily.
4. Mount directly in glycerol and examine at once (the color fades).

Results: Violet color indicates presence of tryptophan. The reaction is given by indolic compounds, and in proteins is specific for tryptophan.

The p-dimethylaminobenzaldehyde methods are less destructive and yield stronger colors and sharper localizations.

Postcoupled Benzylidene Reaction for Indoles (Glenner and Lillie, *J. Histochem.* **5**:279, 1957). Fix briefly in buffered (pH 7) 10% formalin. Generally, results have been satisfactory with 3 hour fixation; both poor and good results have been obtained with material fixed 24–72 hours. Prolonged formalin and oxidative fixations have been unsatisfactory. Alcohol hardening overnight or longer, after the brief formalin, is helpful for paraffin sections, and the thin celloidin paraffin technic seems excellent.

Dehydrate, clear, imbed in paraffin and section at 5 μ.

1. Xylene, 100% alcohol, dry briefly and immerse in
2. 1 gm *p*-dimethylaminobenzaldehyde in 10 cc concentrated hydrochloric and 30 cc glacial acetic acid, 5 minutes, 25°C.
3. Glacial acetic acid, 3 washes, 30 seconds, 60 seconds, 60 seconds.
4. Add 1 cc freshly diazotized S acid or safranin to 40 cc cold (15–20°C) glacial acetic acid, mix and pour into cold Coplin jar over the sections. Let react 5 minutes.
5. Wash in 2 changes glacial acetic acid.
6. If desired, counterstain 5 minutes in 0.05% new fuchsin in glacial acetic acid and wash in 2 changes glacial acetic acid, 1 minute each.
7. Acetic acid + xylene, 3–4 changes of xylene, cellulose caprate.

Results: Reaction sites, blue. Stomach: peptic gland zymogen granules, moderately reactive; eosinophil leucocyte granules, strongly reactive; keratin, unreactive. Pancreas: zymogen granules, deep blue; cytoplasm of acini, unstained; duct contents, blue; alpha cells, light blue; beta cells, unstained. Small intestine: Paneth cell granules and mucosal eosinophils, blue; cytoplasm of epithelium of villi, pale gray blue. Artery: elastica, negative. Salivary gland, parotid type, zymogen granules, blue; secretory duct type, rat, deep blue secretory granules.

To demonstrate Paneth granules (deep blue) use an animal which has been starved overnight. If such a preparation is subjected to a following fast garnet GBC azo coupling at pH 8.5, the enterochromaffin cells are also demonstrated in a contrasting deep red.

The Rosindole Reaction for Tryptophan and Other Indoles. Adams (*J. Clin. Path.* **10**:56, 1957) and Glenner (*J. Histochem.* **5**:297, 1957) almost simultaneously rediscovered the rosindole reaction of E. Fischer (*Ber. Deutsch. chem. Ges.* **19**:2988, 1886) which Mikosch used histochemically in Reichl's variant (*Mschr. Chem.* **11**:155, 1890), reporting his otherwise unpublished results privately to Reichl. This reaction depends on the same benzylidene condensation with indoles as in the previous method. The blue color is developed, however, not by azo coupling after the condensation in step 2 but by immersion in a 5 cc concentrated HCl, 35 cc glacial acetic acid mixture which is poured onto 500 mg sodium nitrite in a Coplin jar; slides are transferred from acetic acid (step 3) immediately into this bubbling mixture for about 1 minute at 25°C. They are then washed in 2 changes of glacial acid, acetic acid + xylene, 3–4 changes of xylene and mounted in xylene cellulose caprate.

Results are essentially similar to those of the preceding method but are somewhat less precise, and, particularly with the Adams variant, not cited here, there is more damage to tissue structure from the strong acid employed.

Xanthydrol condenses with indoles to form purple to violet complexes. In glacial acetic acid the condensation occurs only at position 3, which is, of course, occupied and unavailable in tryptophan. However, in the presence of hydrochloric acid in the glacial acetic acid, an oxonium salt of xanthydrol is formed and this condenses readily with indoles at positions 1, 2 and 3 to form colored complexes. Accordingly we tried xanthydrol in a 3:1 mixture of acetic and hydrochloric acids, and obtained strong coloration in violet of pancreatic zymogen granules (*J. Histochem.* **5**:188, 1957).

Paraffin sections of formalin fixed tissue are deparaffinized in xylene, rinsed in glacial acetic acid and reacted 5 minutes in a fresh solution of 1 gm xanthydrol in 36 cc glacial acetic acid with which 4 cc concentrated hydrochloric acid is mixed just before using. The preparations are then washed in glacial acetic acid, acetic + xylene and 4 changes of xylene and mounted in cellulose caprate.

Preparations are good for 2–3 months after mounting but may fade completely in 6 months.

Hršel's (*Acta Histochem.* **4**:47, 1957) chromic acid followed by phosphomolybdic acid and sequence staining with eosin and light green is said to give specific red coloration of tryptophan containing proteins, but the author admits some important exceptions in his protein model staining, and he does not make any topochemical comparisons with the *p*-dimethylbenzaldehyde procedures as published by Lison or with my 1956 method. The method does not seem to have been used to any great extent since. Further exploration of it might be of interest.

Chromaffin

Wildi (*Science* **113**:188, 1951) records reduction (*in vitro*) of neutral silver nitrate by various *o*- and *p*-dihydroxyaryl compounds: pomiferin, isopomiferin, dihydroisopomiferin, 3′,4′,7,8-tetrahydroxyflavanone, eriodictol, catechol, hydroquinone, tetrabromocatechol and pyrogallol. Phenol, meta-dihydroxyaryl compounds, and compounds which formed insoluble silver salts failed to react. Wildi's reactions were performed in about 91% alcohol, with about 0.5% $AgNO_3$. Most reactive substances reacted in 15 minutes at 20–25°C. Some required heating to 60°C for 1 minute.

Chromaffin cells share the property of reducing diammine silver salts exhibited by argentaffin cells, and Masson considered the latter as belonging to the chromaffin system.

The Ogata-Ogata Silver Method (*Beitr. path. Anat.* **71**:376, 1923). This method depends directly on this property.

1. Treat fresh tissue for 1–2 hours in the dark in a 1% dilution of 28% ammonia water (1 cc and 99 cc water).

2. Place blocks in the Bielschowski-Maresch diammine silver solution (p. 527), diluted with an equal volume of distilled water, for 3–5 hours in the dark.
3. Transfer to several changes of 1:100 dilution of ammonia water, during 30 minutes, in the dark.
4. Fix 1 hour in 3% sodium thiosulfate in the dark.
5. Wash 1 hour in running water.
6. Fix 1–2 days in 10% formalin. Cut frozen sections, float onto slides, dehydrate, clear and mount in balsam or a synthetic resin as usual.

Ogata and Ogata note also the reduction of osmium tetroxide by adrenal medulla cells, but this is overshadowed by the greater blackening of the cortical lipids.

The chromaffin reaction, first reported by Gregor Joesten (*Arch. Heilk.* **5**:97, 1864) and by Henle (*Z. rat. Med.* **24**:143, 1865), is a brown coloration of the cytoplasm of adrenal medulla cells and of the chromaffin cells of various paraganglia in the abdomen. It is shown also in varying measure by the enterochromaffin cells of the stomach (R. Heidenhain, *Arch. mikr. Anat.* **6**: 368, 1870) and intestine (J. E. Schmidt, *Arch. mikr. Anat.* **66**:12, 1905) and in "Dopamine" cells of ruminant duodena and capsules of lung and liver (Falck, Hillarp and Torp, *J. Histochem.* **7**:323, 1959).

In the adrenal the reaction is assigned to oxidation products of adrenaline and noradrenaline. Lison formulates the reactions thus:

Adrenaline   Adrenochrome Oxoadrenochrome

Melanoid Pigment

Noradrenaline undergoes similar reactions

Iodate oxidation, at first thought to be equivalent to chromate oxidation, is now believed to demonstrate noradrenaline specifically. Hillarp and Hökfelt (*J. Histochem.* 3:1, 1955) prescribed immersion of very thin (0.5 mm) slices of adrenal medulla in 10% KIO_3 for 48 hours, followed by fixation for 24 hours in 10% formalin and sectioning at 10–20 μ on a freezing microtome. The oxidation product does not resist paraffin imbedding procedures, but the authors prescribe a red nuclear counterstain and mounting in *Canada balsam.* But Carbowax may be used, or 15–30 minutes' paraffin infiltration (*J. Histochem.* 7:149, 1959).

During this fixation process adrenaline is converted to sparingly soluble, increasingly red 2-iodoadrenochrome. Hence adrenal medulla cells lacking noradrenaline (guinea pig, rabbit) remain uncolored. The two catecholamines appear in separate cells (rat, hamster). Noradrenaline cells are very conveniently located in the latter species in the periphery of the medulla. Eränkö (*J. Histochem.* 4:11, 1956) used the same procedure and compared the iodate reactive areas with fluorescent areas in the contralateral formalin fixed hamster adrenal sections (cryostat sections postfixed in Baker's formol calcium).

Owing to the substitution of the terminal amine group of adrenaline it does not condense so readily with formaldehyde to form the fluorescent tetrahydroisoquinoline derivative, although formalin fixed serum models of both catecholamines are fluorescent, adrenaline somewhat less than noradrenaline (Lillie, *J. Histochem.* 9:44, 1961). Falck *et al.* (*ibid.* **10:** 348, 1962) found much smaller amounts of noradrenaline and dopamine detectable by this method.

There appears to be no good reason for using the potassium salt instead of the commoner sodium iodate, unless one wishes to conduct the reactions at 0–5°C. The solubility advantage of KlO_3 is present only at low temperatures, disappearing at about 15°C.

Eränkö (*J. Histochem.* 5:408, 1957) also demonstrated the binding of I^{131} from radioactive potassium iodate by noradrenaline cells of the hamster adrenal radioautographically. Iodate formalin mixtures, on the other hand, did not give specific noradrenaline localization, but rather presented a general medullary radioactivity and also a strong cortical reaction.

TABLE 8-5. SOLUBILITY OF $NaIO_3$ AND KIO_3 AT 0–100°C (LANGE) IN GRAMS PER 100 CC WATER

	Temperature, °C							
	0	10	20	30	40	60	80	100
$NaIO_3$.....	2.50	5.8[1]	9.0	12.0[1]	15.0	21.0	27.0	34.0
KIO_3......	4.73	6.4[1]	8.13	11.2	12.8	18.5	21.8	32.2

[1] Interpolated.

The **chromaffin reaction proper,** with potassium bichromate, is most often done with formalin bichromate mixtures, though the earlier workers, before the introduction of formaldehyde into histologic technic in the 1890s, used it alone or with sodium sulfate or other salts. I have repeated Heidenhain's experiment with 5% $K_2Cr_2O_7$ and found the chromaffin reaction of rabbit gastric argentaffin cells excellent, but a good deal of cell separation was present and nuclear staining left much to be desired.

Some evidence exists that the pH of the dichromate solution may be quite important in the production or nonproduction of a satisfactory chromaffin reaction. Hillarp and Hökfelt (*J. Histochem.* 3:1, 1955) found the adrenal chromaffin reaction most intense when a pH level of 5–6 was maintained (100 cc 5% $K_2Cr_2O_7$ + 10 cc 5% K_2CrO_4). They preferred to defer formalin fixation until after chromation, as with the iodate method.

The formaldehyde condensation noted above occurs fairly rapidly and prevents the subsequent performance of a satisfactory chromaffin reaction.

Even as little as 1 hour of preliminary treatment with formalin may prevent the chromaffin reaction, though the tissues are fixed thereafter for the usual length of time in Orth's fluid. The presence of acid in the bichromate fixatives may also prevent chromaffin from staining. Ophüls's acetic variant of Orth's fluid and Tellyesniczky's acetic bichromate fluid (p. 54) and the acetic Zenker fluid may fail to demonstrate chromaffin in the same material as gave good chromaffin staining after primary Orth fixation. The Spuler-Maximow variant of Zenker's fluid (p. 50) demonstrates chromaffin better than the original acetic Zenker, but not so well as Orth's fluid.

After Orth, Kose or Möller (Regaud) fixation, chromaffin is manifest, even in frozen sections stained with fat stains and in paraffin sections stained with alum hematoxylin, as a diffuse brown coloration of the cytoplasm of the chromaffin cells. This material is tinged orange by safranin O and green by toluidine blue O, thionin and azure A. The azure A eosin B technic (p. 162) stains chromaffin yellowish green to bluish green. Schmorl used a 24 hour Giemsa stain in formalin bichromate fixations. Wiesel's method (from Schmorl) required sequence staining in 1% toluidine blue or aniline blue and by safranin O. The 2 stains were used for 20 minutes each, with 5 minutes of washing between. Sections were differentiated in 95% alcohol until the blue color reappeared, then cleared in carbol xylene and xylene and mounted in balsam. Chromaffin stained green; other cytoplasms, blue; nuclei, red.

The **Vulpian reaction,** according to Cowdry, indicates the presence of adrenaline. Immersion of fresh adrenal tissue in a dilute solution of ferric chloride produces a green coloration of the chromaffin cells of the medulla. According to Karrer, ferric chloride gives a green color with solutions of catechol. Since adrenaline is a catechol derivative, this may be the explanation of the Vulpian reaction.

Ciaccio (*Anat. Anz.* **23**:401, 1903) adapted the Vulpian reaction for histologic use. He fixed very thin slices in a 5% solution of ferric chloride in 100% alcohol for about 10 minutes, transferred them to a mixture of 1 part ammonia with 10 parts 100% alcohol and followed this treatment by hardening in 100% alcohol. Penetration was poor, only to about 100 μ. The medulla cells and medullary veins contain granules of violet to brown material.

Fixation in aqueous formaldehyde ferric chloride mixtures does not give the Vulpian reaction nor preserve chromaffin.

It would appear that Ciaccio's procedure could well be applied to paraffin sections of frozen dried material.

Aniline Blue + Orange G. Gomori (*Am. J. Clin. Path., Tech. Sect.* **10**: 115, 1946) reported on the use of the Mallory, Heidenhain technic (p. 545) for demonstration of the chromaffin cells of the adrenal medulla. Aqueous formalin, Bouin's fluid and M. Heidenhain's mercuric chloride formalin are the recommended fixatives. Bichromate fixatives were considered inferior, and alcoholic fixatives were unsuitable.

The azocarmine G of step 2 is reduced to 0.05%, and staining is altered to 60–90 minutes at 55–60°C only. The aniline alcohol differentiation is done under microscopic control until chromaffin cells stand out in deep pink with pale cortex cells. The phosphotungstic acid bath is reduced to 2% or 3% and to 20 minutes. Mallory's aniline blue, orange G mixture is used undiluted for 15–40 minutes only. Quinoline yellow (C.I. No. 47005?) and tartrazine (C.I. No. 19140) are recommended as substitutes for orange G in Mallory's mixture; they yield a greenish yellow cortex cell stain in place of the dull orange of the original mixture, contrasting better with the purplish red granules of the chromaffin cells.

Three quinoline yellows appear in the *Colour Index.* Nos. 47000, 47005 and 47010. The first is insoluble in water; the other 2 are sulfonic acids. Probably C.I. No. 47005 is meant.

Alpha cells of pancreatic islets, some cells of the anterior pituitary, neutrophil leucocytes and myelocytes and enterochromaffin cells also possess granules staining deep purplish red to violet by this technic; hence it appears that this technic demonstrates other cell granules of chromaffin cells, not chromaffin itself.

Perhaps the best methods of demonstrating chromaffin substance in paraffin sections after chromate fixations are the ferric ferricyanide reduction test (p. 211), which colors chromaffin a deep greenish blue; and the periodic acid Schiff reaction (p. 198), which colors medulla cells a dark grayish red to gray pink. Both tests should be employed in critical cases.

It has been shown in test tube experiments that the potassium bi-

II   III

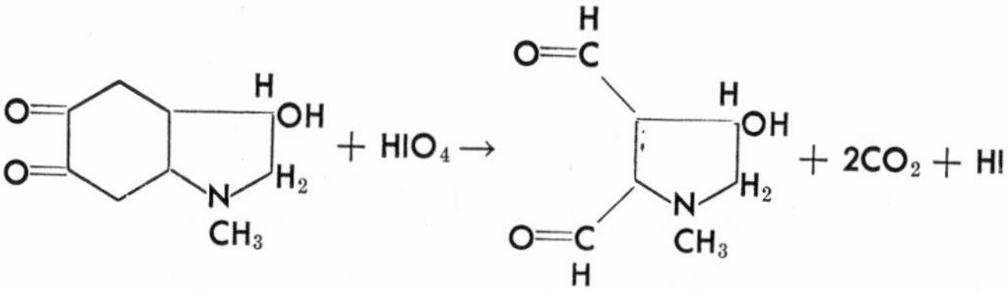

The Hudson suggestion of the periodate oxidation of adrenochrome

I   II

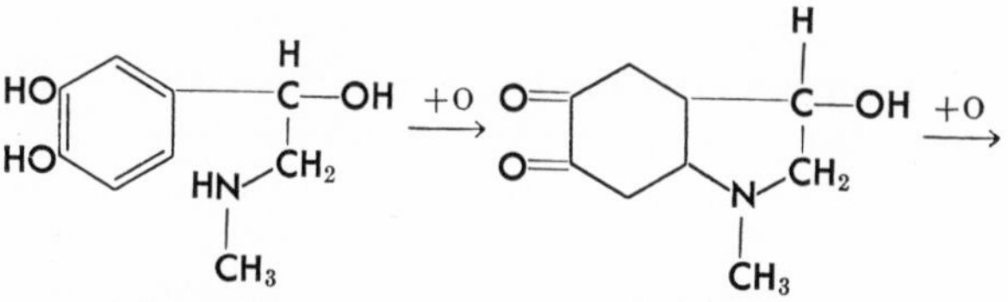

Adrenaline   Adrenochrome

III

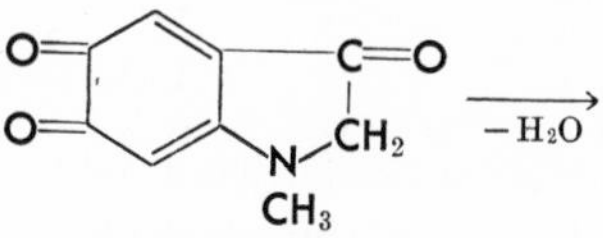

Oxoadrenochrome

IV

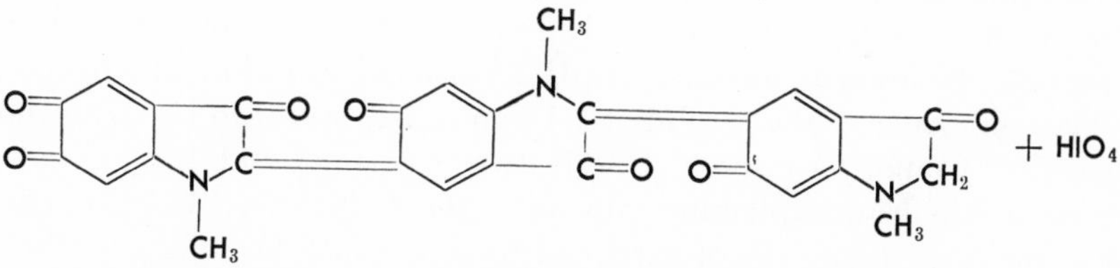

CH₃

Trimer of Lison's "Melanine" type (Lison, 1960, p. 249)

V

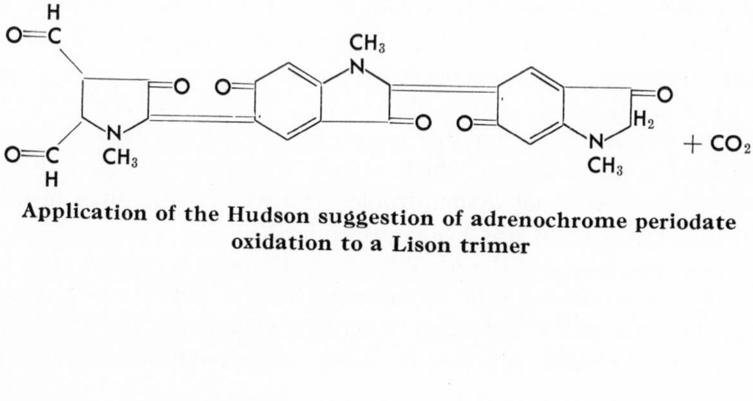

Application of the Hudson suggestion of adrenochrome periodate
oxidation to a Lison trimer

chromate precipitation products formed with catechol, adrenaline, dopa and the like promptly reduce ferric ferricyanide mixtures.

Since these reactions occur also in the guinea pig adrenal, which lacks noradrenaline, and are limited to chromate fixed material, it would appear that they must be reactions of adrenochrome, 3-keto-adrenochrome or the dimer of the last postulated by Lison. We have shown *in vitro* that when an excess of catechol is reacted with periodic acid, no demonstrable aldehyde is produced. But the condition of the histochemical reaction is that of a large excess of periodic acid reacting on adrenochrome or an oxidation polymer thereof. With polymers of the type postulated by Lison, the suggestion made to me by the late Prof. C. S. Hudson when we first encountered the reaction with periodic acid seems much more pertinent than with adrenaline or adrenochrome, because of the increased probability that the reaction product would remain insoluble. Dr. Hudson proposed that the quinone carbons of adrenochrome would be further oxidized to carbon dioxide and be eliminated and that carbons 4 and 7 would form aldehyde.

Enterochromaffin or Argentaffin Cells

These cells occur in varying numbers in the epithelia of surface and glands of the stomach and intestines, characteristically appearing adjacent to the basement membrane between the basal portions of the adjacent epithelial or gland cells. They are characterized by the presence of a chromaffin substance which yields a yellowish brown color on fixation in formalin bichromate mixtures of pH 2.5–5.5 and, after formalin fixation, reduces ammoniacal silver solutions. Lison considered it to be a catechol derivative; Gomori, a resorcinol derivative; Erspamer and, recently, also Pearse, a 5-hydroxytryptamine. Masson (*Am. J. Path.* 4:181, 1928) considers these the type cells of carcinoid tumors, which he calls argentaffin cell tumors.

These hypotheses I have considered in detail elsewhere (*J. Histochem.* 9:184, 1961), concluding that a catechol structure was probable, but that a para configuration was not excluded; that this diphenol was reversibly oxidizable to a quinone status in which azo coupling was prevented but could be restored by dithionite reduction; that the resorcinol hypothesis was untenable for that reason and because of lack of demonstrable keto tautomerization which occurs in *m*-diphenols; and that an indolic structure was not demonstrable even when tryptophan in other loci in the same section was brilliantly stained.

The reactions used for the identification of enterochromaffin cells and of the phenol producing cells of carcinoid tumors fall into two general classes: (1) the metal reduction reactions, comprising the chromaffin reaction, the argentaffin reaction, the ferric ferricyanide reaction and the seldom used osmic acid reaction; and (2) the specific phenol reactions, including the azo coupling reaction, the Gibbs indophenol condensation, probably Clara's catechol dye condensation reaction and a few other infrequently used procedures.

The chromaffin reaction has been mentioned above and was described in more detail under "Adrenal Medulla" (p. 233).

The Argentaffin Reaction; Argyrophilia. The term *argentaffin* is of Latin origin: *argentum*, silver; *affinis*, neighboring, related by marriage. Argyrophilia is of Greek derivation: *argyros*, silver; *philos*, a friend, or *philein*, to love. Despite their etymologic similarity in meaning, the terms have by convention acquired distinctly different significance. *Argentaffin* means possessing the capacity to reduce silver salts in the dark, without the aid of any added or following reducing agent. Lison's term *argento-reductrice* was more definite but has the same meaning; it never gained general acceptance. *Argyrophil*, on the other hand, indicates that the tissue element so described can be impregnated with silver, but that light or a reducing agent is required to produce the black deposit of metallic silver. The hybrid term *argentophil* was in wide use for a considerable period, with the same meaning. Clara (*Acta Neuroveg.* **16:**294, 1957) suggested that it be discarded and replaced by the purely Greek equivalent *argyrophil;* this practice seems logical and has been generally adopted.

Masson reported a block method for demonstration of argentaffin cells, which was cited in the first edition of this book. I have abandoned it completely in favor of section methods which allow the comparison of a variety of other procedures on adjacent sections. I cite first Masson's section method.

Masson's Section Method. Frozen, paraffin and celloidin sections of formalin fixed material can be used. It is advisable to collodionize paraffin sections as for other alkaline silver methods (p. 85). Bring sections to distilled water.

1. Treat with diammine silver hydroxide (p. 240) for 12–48 hours in the dark in a covered vessel. Overexposure decreases specificity. Imbedded sections require longer than frozen sections.
2. Wash in distilled water.
3. Tone in 2 cc 1% gold chloride, 3 gm ammonium thiocyanate, 3 gm sodium thiosulfate, 98 cc distilled water for 5 minutes. This is our modification of Ramón y Cajal's toner. Note modifications below.
4. Wash in distilled water.
5. In any case fix 1 minute in 5% sodium thiosulfate.
6. Wash 2–3 minutes in running water.
7. Counterstain 1 minute in 0.1% safranin, 2–3 minutes in distilled water.
8. Rinse and differentiate briefly in 1% acetic acid.

9. Wash briefly in water, dehydrate and clear and mount with the usual alcohol, xylene, synthetic resin sequence.

This method is modified by us from Masson (*loc. cit.*). Lison used a simple 0.1% gold chloride toner for 4–6 minutes; Jacobson omitted the gold.

Lillie's Diammine Silver Method. I now prefer a simple diammine silver reaction similar to that of Hamperl, done without gold toning or counterstaining. The same diammine silver solution and the same basic technic are used also for studies of melanin and lipofuscin pigments. Exposure times vary according to the object under study, and in the characterization of an unfamiliar substance, graded exposure times are used.

Diammine Silver. To 2 cc 28% ammonia (sp. gr. 0.900) add about 35–40 cc 5% silver nitrate, fairly rapidly at first, swirling between each addition to dissolve the brown silver oxide. As the clearing interval starts to lengthen, add smaller amounts each time; stop when a faint but definite permanent turbidity is achieved.

Glassware. Beakers and Coplin jars should be chemically clean. Remove previous silver deposits by gently flowing a small amount of concentrated nitric acid over the entire inner surface. Then wash with several changes of distilled water.

Technic. Deparaffinize and hydrate thin paraffin sections as usual.

1. Wash in distilled water.
2. Expose to diammine silver solution in covered Coplin jar in the dark 1–10 minutes for melanins, 15 minutes for neuromelanin, 8–24 hours at 25°C for enterochromaffin, lipofuscins, melanosis coli pigment, hematoidin and bile pigment.
3. Wash in distilled water, "fix" in 0.2 M (5%) sodium thiosulfate.
4. Wash 10 minutes in running water, dehydrate in alcohols, clear in xylene and mount in xylene cellulose caprate.

Gomori (*Arch. Path.* **45**:48, 1948) detailed a modification of his methenamine silver method (p. 500) for enterochromaffin, which required 12–48 hours. Burtner and I have devised a much more rapid variant of this procedure which seems adequately selective in practice.

The Gomori-Burtner Methenamine Silver Method for Argentaffin Cells (*Stain Techn.* **24**:225, 1949). *Solutions.* Stock methenamine silver solution: Dissolve 3 gm methenamine (hexamethylene tetramine) in 100 cc distilled water. Add 5 cc 5% aqueous silver nitrate. This solution can be stored in a cool, dark place for months.

Working solution: To 30 cc stock methenamine silver solution add 8 cc Holmes's pH 7.8 borate buffer (p. 670).

Glassware. The Coplin jars should be chemically clean. Previous silver mirror deposits should be removed with concentrated nitric acid.

Technic.

1. Treat deparaffinized sections with Weigert's iodine solution (p. 141), 10 minutes.
2. Bleach with 5% sodium thiosulfate ($Na_2S_2O_3 \cdot 5H_2O$), 2 minutes.
3. Wash in running water, 10 minutes.
4. Rinse in 2 changes of distilled water.
5. Place sections in Coplin jars containing preheated buffered methenamine silver solution and put in a 60°C (paraffin) oven for 2–3 hours. Preheating to 60°C reduces impregnation time by ½–1 hours and is now our regular practice.
6. Rinse in distilled water.
7. Tone in 0.1% gold chloride ($HAuCl_4$), 10 minutes.
8. Rinse in distilled water.
9. Fix in 5% aqueous sodium thiosulfate, 2 minutes.
10. Wash in running water, 5 minutes.
11. Counterstain with 0.1% safranin O in 0.1% acetic acid, 5 minutes.
12. Dehydrate with acetone, clear in xylene and mount as usual.

Results: At 2–3 hours impregnation is optimal. Argentaffin cells are well blackened and appear in numbers as great as with longer impregnations. Coarse connective tissue of the submucosa sometimes shows a variable amount of blackening at this time. In 2 hours' incubation, partial blackening of argentaffin cells in reduced numbers is seen. At 1½ hours, only lignin is black. At longer intervals than 3 hours, besides the connective tissue, the granules of eosinophil leucocytes, nuclei, smooth muscle and surface epithelium become blackened. By 4 hours a silver mirror begins to appear on the sides of the slides and Coplin jars.

Human mast cell granules remain unblackened and brilliantly red with the safranin counterstain after nuclei and reticulum are blackened. Rat mast cells may blacken selectively even before enterochromaffin, or along with it, when preparations are silvered 2½ hours at 60°C.

Gomori (*loc. cit.*) used Gram's iodine in step 1 (personal communication). In step 2 he used either a bisulfite or a thiosulfate solution of unspecified strength. His borate buffer was slightly different: To 100 cc 0.2 *M* boric acid add 8 or 12 cc 0.2 *M* borax for pH 7.8 or 8.2 respectively. (0.2 *M* borax tends to crystallize out at 20–25°C.) His methenamine silver working solution contained 25 cc of the above stock solution, 25 cc distilled water and 5 cc borate buffer. He silvered at 37–45°C for 12–24 or even 48 hours.

If preparations appeared oversilvered at step 6, Gomori differentiated in 0.5% sulfuric acid containing 0.1–0.2% iron alum until the background was almost clear. He then washed in 0.5–1% hydrochloric acid in 70% alcohol, and resumed the above procedure with step 9.

Gomori's regressive differentiation of oversilvered preparations with weak acidified iron alum solution did not give particularly satisfactory results with our variant. With the shorter incubation periods used in this new technic, it is more practical to repeat the procedure with a briefer silvering time on duplicate sections.

If a 10-minute bath in 1% ferric chloride or a 1-hour bath in 5% chromic acid is introduced at step 3, the silvering of enterochromaffin cells is inhibited and the method is converted to a more or less selective demonstration technic for collagen and mucin. The time in the methenamine silver is reduced to 2 or 2½ hours for this purpose.

Neither treatment prevents the silvering of the enterosiderin pigment of guinea pigs. Ferric chloride prevents the silvering of adrenal lipofuscin, but chromic acid does not.

Effective blackening of collagen, much reticulum and the mucins of the colonic, pyloric and duodenal glands and of intestinal goblet cells was obtained by both methods. Ferric chloride afforded partial blackening of gastric surface epithelial mucin; chromic acid, a more complete silvering. The reaction of cellulose and lignin is enhanced and accelerated by both variants.

The chromic acid variant is of course essentially the Gomori silver method for mucin and glycogen (p. 500).

The ferric ferricyanide reaction, which is probably the most sensitive as well as the easiest reaction for enterochromaffin, has been presented on pp. 208–211. Its value is similar to that of the diammine silver reactions. It was first observed for enterochromaffin about 1947 in Gomori's laboratory (*Arch. Path.* **45:**48, 1948) and in mine (Laskey and Greco, *ibid.* **46:**83, 1948).

Argyrophil cells are found in the gastrointestinal mucosa in much the same localization as argentaffin cells, but in larger numbers and in certain locations where argentaffin cells are not demonstrable, *e.g.*, in normal human and rat stomach mucosa (Hamperl, *Virchow Arch. path. Anat.* **371:**482, 1952; Dawson, *Anat. Rec.* **100:**319, 1945) and at earlier stages in embryonic development. Argyrophil cells are also reported in pancreatic islets.

The identity of at least part of the argyrophil cells of the intestine with argentaffin cells was shown in comparison microscope studies on adjacent serial sections stained respectively with the Masson-Hamperl method and with a Gros-Bielschowsky variant similar to the following, in parallel studies by Hamperl (*loc. cit.*) and by Hellwig (*Z. Zellforsch.* **36:** 546, 1952).

It may well be that the principal difference between the intestinal argentaffin cell, which is also argyrophil, and the argyrophil cell, which is nonargentaffin, lies in the relatively minute quantity of the phenolic reducing substance present in the latter. In the reserpine induced discharge of the enterochromaffin substance ferric ferricyanide, azo coupling, Clara hematoxylin and methenamine silver reactions disappear completely during the peak period of discharge, serotonin assays fall dramatically, but counts of cells demonstrable by Hamperl's Bodian procedure for argyrophil cells remain essentially unaltered (Lillie *et al.,* J. *Histochem.* 7:23, 1959). The traces remaining in the discharged cells are adequate for argyrophil staining.

Feyrter's "genormtes Gros-Bielschowsky Verfahren." I am indebted to F. Feyrter for the directions for his standardized Gros-Bielschowsky procedure for *argyrophil granulation.*

1. Material should be fixed at least 4 weeks in formalin. Either frozen or paraffin sections are used. Bring to distilled water as usual and soak 5–10 minutes.
2. Fasten frozen sections to slides. Smear slides twice with albumen glycerol, dry over Bunsen flame, float on sections and press down firmly with filter paper. Fix with 1–2 drops of 40% formaldehyde which has previously been run through a Berkefeld filter, while holding the filter pressed down firmly. After 15–20 minutes the filter can be removed without detaching the section (Roulet).
3. Postfix 3–4 weeks in unneutralized 40% formaldehyde.
4. Wash in 5% formaldehyde. Blot off with several folds of filter paper. Do not wash in distilled water.
5. 20% $AgNO_3$ in the dark for 1 hour at 25–30°C (on top of paraffin oven). Blot off with several layers of filter paper.
6. Ammoniacal silver, 5 minutes. (Add 28% ammonia, drop by drop, to 20% $AgNO_3$ until precipitate is dissolved. Let stand 1–2 hours. Just before using add 0.6 cc more 28% ammonia for each 10 cc.)
7. Take out sections and lay to one side. To each 10 cc of the ammoniacal silver add 0.02–0.05 cc 20% formaldehyde which contains 1 cc 85% formic acid per 100 cc.
8. Replace sections in the ammoniacal silver formaldehyde mixture, stirring about to start impregnation, which takes some minutes and requires microscopic control. For observation, sections are taken out and washed in the ammonia of step 9, wiped dry on the bottom. After observation, return sections to the formalin silver for further development.
9. When impregnation is adequate, remove, blot and transfer to a 20% dilution of 28% ammonia for 1–2 minutes, to stop the impregnation.
10. Blot and transfer to 1% acid solution to neutralize, 1 minute.
11. Blot or rinse in distilled water.
12. Tone in gold chloride, 0.5 cc 2% solution to 100 cc distilled water, until sections are an even gray, perhaps 15 minutes.
13. Blot or rinse in distilled water.

14. 2.5% sodium thiosulfate, 1 minute.
15. Wash 20 minutes in several changes of tap water.
16. Counterstain 1 minute in alum carmine or Ehrlich's hematoxylin.
17. Alcohol, terpineol, xylene (brief), Canada balsam.

Gomori further recorded (*Arch. Path.* **45**:48, 1948) the pale green staining of argentaffin cells by very dilute ferric chloride solution; the production of dark yellowish shades by nitric acid, bromine water and iodates; a brilliant ruby to purplish or bluish red coloration with the Mallory-Heidenhain stain (p. 545); and the application of Gibb's reaction with 2,6-dichloroquinonechloroimid to produce blue indophenol dyes in the presence of phenols as giving a distinct reaction with argentaffin granules.

Azo Coupling Reaction. This is one of the more specific identification reactions for the enterochromaffin substance. Its use dates back to Cordier and Lison (*Bull. Histol. Appl.* **7**:140, 1930). Its sensitivity is generally less than that of the ferric ferricyanide reaction, as determined by cell counts on adjacent serial sections. Freshly diazotized *p*-nitroaniline (fast red GG) is about as sensitive with brief coupling periods as ferric ferricyanide. Freshly diazotized safranin (p. 224) gives black enterochromaffin cells on a red protein background and has been quite useful. Among the stable diazotates fast black K gives similar contrasts, but the background is more orange. Red enterochromaffin cells with pale yellow backgrounds are given by the stable diazos fast red B and fast garnet GBC. For further diazonium salts and their results see Lillie, Henson and Cason, *J. Histochem.* **9**:11, 1961. Technics are presented on pp. 223–224.

The 1 *mM* Hematoxylin Stain for Enterochromaffin, Keratohyalin and Eosinophil Leucocytes (modified from Clara, *Z. Zellforsch.* **22**:318, 1935); **Used on Carcinoid Tumors** (Lillie and Glenner, *Am. J. Path.* **36**: 623, 1960).

Staining Solution. 35.6 mg hematoxylin dissolved in the following solvent:

0.1 *M* KH$_2$PO$_4$	5.2 cc
0.1 *M* Na$_2$HPO$_4$	4.8 cc
Distilled water	90.0 cc

Paraffin sections 5 μ to xylene, descending alcohols, distilled water. Stain in the above 1 *mM* hematoxylin 24–48 hours at 22–25°C. Rinse in distilled water, alcohols, xylenes, cellulose caprate. I have also used extensively 0.01% hematoxylin (1 cc 1% aqueous or alcoholic hematoxylin, freshly prepared, included in above solvent).

Results: Soft keratin, blue gray; cutaneous eleidin, keratohyalin of skin and gastrointestinal tract, dark blue; trichohyalin may stain also in alcohol fixed material but may fail to stain after formalin fixation. Enterochromaffin cells, basal cells in some carcinoid tumors and eosinophil leucocytes show blue to black granules. Elastic laminae of rodent arteries often color dark blue. Hair cortex may sometimes take a light pink color. Hemosiderin and enterosiderin color black; this last coloration is prevented by acid or dithionite desiderization. Copper gives a blue green color.

Carotid Body Tumors. Barroso-Moguel and Costero (*Am. J. Path.* **41:** 389, 1962) report a variant of Del Río Hortega's method for pigments and pigment precursors which they used in a study of silver reactive cells in carotid body tumors. This method is claimed to give more reliable results, showing more numerous "argentaffin cells" with more copious granulation than other methods.

1. Fix in aqueous 10% formalin and Cut frozen sections. Wash in distilled water.
2. Impregnate in 2% silver nitrate until yellowish.
3. Rinse in distilled water.
4. Impregnate in Del Río Hortega's ammoniacal silver carbonate (p. 525), to which add 3 drops of pyridine for each 10 cc, and heat to 60°C, until sections are light tobacco color.
5. Rinse in distilled water.
6. Tone in 0.2% gold chloride at 60°C for several minutes.
7. Fix in 5% sodium thiosulfate (0.2 M).
8. Wash 10 minutes in several changes of distilled water, dehydrate in alcohol, clear in xylene and mount in balsam or Permount.

Results: Silver positive granules, black; other structures, pale purplish.

In my judgment this is not a histochemical technic for true argentaffin substances. The second silver reagent is used hot and contains pyridine, both of which factors increase "sensitivity" and decrease "specificity." It is possible that methenamine silver when used hot also shares this decreased specificity and enhanced reactivity, but at least some time limits have been placed on that method, and it is recognized that in 5–6 hours everything is black.

These same cells have, however, been shown to react to a rigidly applied Masson-Hamperl technic (p. 240) (Glenner, *Proc. 59th Ann. Meet. Am. A. Path. Bact.* May 2–4, 1962, pp. 18–19). Glenner identified the argentaffin substance as noradrenaline. Chromaffin and iodate reactions are applicable.

AMINES

The Ninhydrin Test

Serra (*Stain Techn.* **21**:5, 1946) directs as follows: Deparaffinize and hydrate as usual, or use frozen sections. Flood sections with a mixture of equal volumes of pH 6.98 phosphate buffer (p. 664) and of a freshly prepared 0.4% aqueous solution of ninhydrin (triketo-hydrindene-hydrate). Place sections on a rack over boiling water and steam for 1–2 minutes. A blue or violet color develops. Drain, mount in pure glycerol and cement with lanolin rosin cement (p. 91) or polystyrene. Observe at once, since the color fades in a day or so.

Serra states that the reaction is given in adequate intensity by the amino acids except proline and hydroxyproline, and by peptides and proteins. Langeron notes ready diffusion of color.

The Alloxan Reaction

Langeron cites this for amino acids and proteins generally. Alloxan reacts with amine groups to form murexide, or purpurate of ammonium.

Flood sections with 1% alcoholic alloxan solution. Proteins color in red or rose. Serra (*loc. cit.*) recommends use of a neutral (pH 7) phosphate buffer as solvent and accelerates the reaction by heating over a boiling water bath. On fixed tissues the reaction is weak. The color is diffusible and is given also by nonprotein NH_2 groups and perhaps by SH groups.

The Ninhydrin and Alloxan Schiff Reactions

According to Yasuma and Ichikawa (*J. Lab. Clin. Med.* **41**:296, 1953), the ninhydrin reaction with α-amino acids may be used for the demonstration of protein with Schiff reagent. Briefly, ninhydrin decomposes amino acid residues to carbon dioxide, ammonia and the next lower aldehyde, suffering reduction of one of its own hydroxyl groups in the process. This reduced ninhydrin then conjugates with a mol of ammonia and a mol of ninhydrin to form a blue violet compound. This compound is quite diffusible, and its use for protein identification has been unsatisfactory.

However, the aldehyde formed on the oxidized amino acid residues may be quite well demonstrated with Schiff reagent. Thus Dr. Longley in my laboratory obtained quite good reactions with muscle protein, collagen and thyroid colloid. It may be noted that deamination (p. 253) prevents their reaction.

Fixations with 10% formalin, with Zenker variants or with absolute alcohol are recommended. Paraffin sections at 5–10 μ are deparaffinized and brought to 100% alcohol as usual. Then incubate at 5–24 hours in 0.5% ninhydrin (or 1% alloxan) in 100% alcohol at 37°C. Wash for a few minutes in running water, immerse for 30 minutes in Schiff reagent (p. 270), wash 1, 2 and 2 minutes in 3 changes of 0.5% $Na_2S_2O_5$, wash 10 minutes in running water, dehydrate and clear and mount through an alcohol, xylene, synthetic resin series. Counterstains have not been successful in our hands so far.

This chemical explanation given by the original authors is, of course, the reaction of ninhydrin or alloxan with a free uncombined amino acid and is manifestly inapplicable to amino acids which are incorporated by peptide bonds in protein chains. The precise nature of the reaction is still controversial. Puchtler and Sweat (*J. Histochem.* **10:**365, 1962) attacked the validity of the reaction on much the same grounds, pointing out the ready solubility of aldehydes formed from loosely included amino acids and those hydrolyzed from protein by ninhydrin. Although gelatin is Schiff positive, non-pretreated collagen is not, and glycine, proline and hydroxyproline do not yield aldehyde on treatment with ninhydrin.

Kasten (*J. Histochem.* **10:**769, 1962) defends the value of the reaction, admitting the obscurity of the chemical mechanism. He apparently postulates an amino acid with free carboxyl and α-amino groups, bound to protein at its other end. He offered no speculation as to which amino acids might be so attached.

Glenner (*J. Histochem.* **11:**285, 1963) points out that oxidative deamination to aldehyde is not limited to α-amino acids, occurring with many other primary aliphatic amines. Hence the ε-amino groups of the lysines and the α-amino groups of γ-glutamyl and β-aspartyl peptides should be available and reactive. This last suggestion accords well with the known blocking of ninhydrin and alloxan Schiff reactions by nitrous acid deamination.

The probable reaction is hence a simple oxidative deamination:

The Xanthoproteic and Murexide Reactions

Serra (*Stain Techn.* **21**:5, 1946) prefers "strong" fixations but uses fresh material as well. Cover sections with concentrated nitric acid for several minutes until they become intensely yellow. Wash in distilled water. Expose to ammonia fumes or immerse in dilute ammonia solution. The color changes to orange. Mount in glycerol after rinsing in water.

The reaction is produced by tyrosine, phenylalanine or tryptophan, as well as by phenols. Langeron (*op. cit.*, 7th ed., p. 1264) notes in addition that purine bases give a violet to purple color by this method, the **murexide reaction.** Uric acid is distinguished from guanine by its relative solubility in piperazine hydrate and its relative insolubility in iron alum and mineral acids. A negative test means nothing.

Fullmer's Hematoxylin Method for Basic Nuclear Protein

Fullmer (*J. Histochem.* **10**:502, 1962) has modified Clara's hematoxylin reaction to use it as a quite specific stain for basic nuclear protein. The reaction is prevented by deamination, acetylation or prolongation of acid hydrolysis beyond 18 hours. It was first noted by me in the course of an investigation of the catecholic reactions of keratohyalin and trichohyalin (*J. Histochem.* **4**:818, 1956). The technic follows:

1. Fix 24 hours in neutral formalin, prepare paraffin sections, deparaffinize, collodionize and hydrate as usual.
2. Hydrolyze 1 hour at 60°C in preheated 1 N hydrochloric acid.
3. Rinse in distilled water.
4. Stain 1 hour at 37°C in preheated 0.1% hematoxylin in pH 8.14 tris buffer (p. 667).
5. Wash in distilled water, dehydrate, clear and mount in synthetic resin.

Results: Nuclei, dark blue; background, unstained.

It is to be noted that azure A staining and the Feulgen reaction have disappeared with 20–45 minute hydrolysis, and that this reaction is maximal at 1–2 hours, and still moderately strong at 6 hours. The hematoxylin reaction of keratohyalin, eosinophils and enterochromaffin may resist prior acid hydrolysis for some time, but these tissue elements are readily distinguished.

The method of Weiss, Tsou and Seligman (*J. Histochem.* **2**:29, 1954) is said to demonstrate only primary amino groups (II) utilizing the azomethine condensation (III) of 2,3-hydroxynaphthaldehyde (I), followed by alkaline azo coupling with fast blue B (IV). It is doubtful whether the second azo group of the di-*o*-anisidine tetrazonium salt is utilized in formation of the final colored reaction product (V or probably Va), since the initial coupling probably uses up all the available tissue naphthol sites.

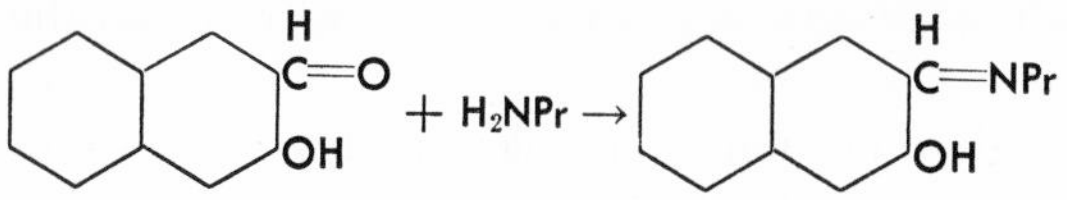

$$\text{I} \qquad \text{II} \qquad \text{III}$$

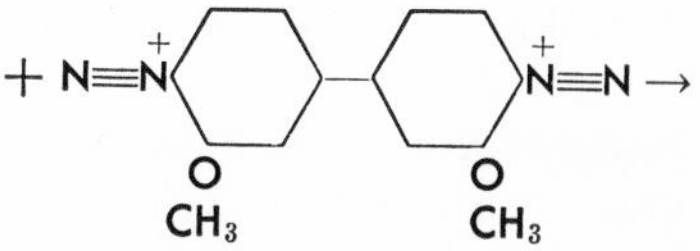

IV

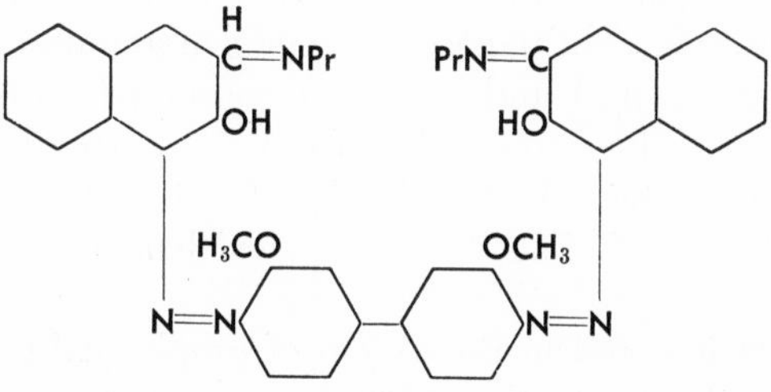

V

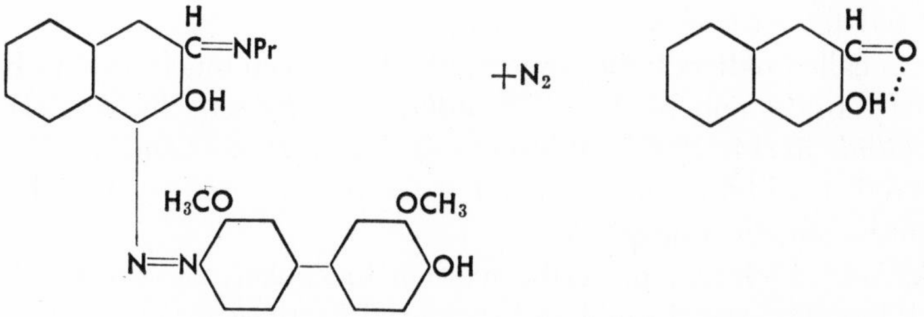

$$+ N_2$$

Va   VI (in acid)

In this, I dissent from the formulation in the original paper and in the paper of Hopman (*Mikroskopie* 12:1, 1957). Unlike the arylamine condensation with tissue aldehydes, this reaction is said to proceed better in alkaline solution. The lack of reactivity in the acid media is assigned to ring formation by hydrogen bonding (VI).

Weiss, Tsou, Seligman Hydroxynaphthaldehyde Method for Tissue Amines

1. Bring paraffin sections through xylene and alcohols to distilled water.
2. Immerse for 1 hour at 24°C in 2,3-hydroxynaphthaldehyde[1] 20 mg in 20 cc acetone + 30 cc Veronal HCl buffer pH 8.5 (p. 670).
3. Wash in distilled water, 3 changes, total 15 minutes.
4. Azo couple 3–5 minutes in 25 mg fast blue B in 50 cc 0.1 M Veronal

[1] Available from Borden-Dajac, Philadelphia, and from K and K, Jamaica, N.Y.

HCl buffer pH 7.4 at 25°C. The dry diazonium salt is stirred into the buffer at the time of using.
5. Wash 5 minutes in running water, dehydrate, clear and mount in synthetic resin through the usual acohol xylene sequence.

Reaction sites are red to blue.

Formalin fixed tissue is only faintly reactive. Best results for nuclear proteins are attained with acetic Zenker fixation; for cytoplasmic structures, with 80% alcohol. Paneth, keratohyalin and trichohyalin granules are not mentioned in the descriptions. Ribonucleo- and deoxyribonucleoprotein sites stain strongly, smooth and striated muscle react strongly.

It is noted, however, that pancreatic zymogen granules reacted strongly in formalin fixed material and were not conserved with the other fixations. Erythrocytes color brown after formalin, purple brown after alcohol; they remain unstained after Zenker fixation. Eosinophil leucocyte granules do not stain. Collagen stains paler than muscle, and elastin is unstained.

Strong staining is noted in the mucin of esophageal glands and in the lumen of the esophagus, in thyroid colloid, in ovarian follicular fluid, in epididymal tubule fluid and in cartilage matrix, but is not specifically mentioned for gastric or intestinal mucins.

The so called **o-diacetylbenzene method** has been much used in Europe since its introduction by Voss (*Z. mikr. anat. Forsch.* **49**:51, 1941) and Dietz (*ibid.* **51**:14, 1942). Wartenberg (*Acta Histochem.* **3**:145, 1956) considered it a highly specific reagent for primary amines, but the exact mechanism remains unexplained.

Barka and Anderson prescribe fixation in Zenker, Gendre or absolute alcohol, but state that formol and mercurial fixatives are unsuitable.

Paraffin sections are brought through xylene and alcohols to water as usual.

1. Immerse in pH 8 Veronal buffer for 1–2 minutes.
2. Mix 20 cc 2% diacetylbenzene in 70% alcohol with 20 cc pH 8 Veronal buffer. Immerse sections in freshly mixed reagent 30–60 minutes.
3. Wash in pH 7 Veronal buffer and thoroughly in distilled water.
4. Dehydrate, clear and mount in balsam or synthetic resin through usual alcohol xylene sequence.

Results: Reaction sites red to purple or violet.

The total alcohol content of the reaction mixture may be increased to around 50–60% to avoid loss of more water soluble proteins and peptides. I have not tried this method.

According to Barka and Anderson the reagent was not commercially available in 1962; I have not seen it listed in recent American catalogs, but the para isomer is available from Eastman.

Structurally the reagent as formulated could be described as a dimethyl phenyl *o*-diketone. It would be interesting to try other aryl methyl ketones.

o-Diacetylbenzene.

Acid dyes

Protein stains with acid dyes have long been used for the demonstration of the more basic proteins. The effect of solution pH control on the results of staining with neutral stains, particularly with reference to blood films, was reported by Pischinger (*Z. Zellforsch.* 3:169, 1926), and we applied this procedure to tissue azure eosin staining in 1932 (*Arch. Path.* 14:515), noting at that time the disappearance or overpowering of eosinophilia of erythrocytes and eosinophils at around pH 5.6 on formalin fixed and Orth fixed human and experimental material. The effect of mercurial and alcoholic fixations in raising the pH optimum for such stains was reported in 1941 (*Stain Techn.* 16:1): Zenker formol, pH 5; methanol, ethanol and Carnoy, 6.5; *vs.* pH 4.2 for neutral formalin or Orth's fluid and 4.5 for acid formalin. The hot chromation of the Elftman procedure (*J. Histochem.* 2:1, 1954) has recently been observed to raise the pH optimum to about pH 7; with buffered $HgCl_2$ (pH 6) the pH optimum was about 6.5.

Mercuric Bromophenol Blue of Mazia, Brewer and Alfert for Proteins (Davenport). Thin sections of fixed material, unfixed smears and cell suspensions are brought into 0.1% bromophenol blue, either in saturated aqueous mercuric chloride solution or preferably in 95% alcohol containing 10% $HgCl_2$. Stain 15 minutes, blue in pH 6.5–7 buffer (0.1 M Na_2HPO_4 should serve), mount and examine in water or dehydrate rapidly, clear and mount.

Although binding of the blue dye to basic protein occurred also in the absence of mercury ions, the authors considered that acid proteins reacted by virtue of COOH, SH and aromatic residues binding the Hg, which in turn took up the dye. Runham (*J. Histochem.* 9:87, 1961) notes that the reaction is completely prevented by deamination, and considers that it demonstrates only protein amino groups. It is not clear why the dye should not react also with guanidino groups of arginine, which resist deamination.

Deitch's (*Lab. Invest.* 4:324, 1955) procedure with naphthol yellow S, disodium flavianate $C_{10}H_4O_8N_2SNa_2 \cdot 3H_2O$, M.W. 412.25, (C.I. No. 10316) was designed for photometric estimation of histone type proteins in material which could be simultaneously reacted by the Feulgen method for deoxyribonucleic acid. The absorption maxima for naphthol yellow S at 435 mμ and for the Feulgen condensation product at 570 mμ are sufficiently far apart to accomplish this end, and the absorption curves are of such shape that no significant overlapping occurs.

Deitch's Standard Naphthol Yellow S Technic. Fix in Carnoy's acetic alcohol (p. 42). Imbed in paraffin, section, deparaffinize and hydrate sections as usual.

1. Stain 15 minutes in 1% naphthol yellow S in 1% acetic acid at 20–25°C.
2. Transfer (as many as 10 slides) to Coplin jars or similar staining jars containing 50 cc 1% acetic acid, and differentiate 15–24 hours. Discard the differentiating fluid when it has been used for 10 slides.
3. Blot and transfer directly to (liquid) tertiary butanol (M.P. 25.6°C), clear in xylene and mount in Shillaber's high refractive index oil (NΔ 1.540).

   The use of xylene cellulose caprate is suggested for preparations which are to be handled extensively, but the high refractive index mountant is required for photometry.

The Biebrich scarlet (C.I. No. 26905) method of Spicer and Lillie (*Stain Techn.* **36**:365, 1961) for basic proteins depends on the same principle of selective dye uptake of certain tissue elements at high pH levels. Certain tissue elements present considerable differences in maximum staining pH between material fixed in formaldehyde and nonformaldehyde containing fixatives, and in the critical pH range formaldehyde treatment of sections of nonformalin material inhibits staining. With other tissue elements pH maxima are the same for formalin and nonformalin fixed material.

Biebrich Scarlet Method of Spicer and Lillie for Basic Protein. For non-formalin fixed material, buffered mercuric chloride (B-4, p. 46) was preferred. The usual iodine thiosulfate sequence (p. 85) was prescribed, and sections were stained 30–90 minutes in 0.01% Biebrich scarlet in appropriate buffer solutions. The Laskey glycine NaOH series was preferred for pH levels above 7.5, the McIlvaine citric acid sodium phosphate series for lower levels (pp. 666, 662). After staining, sections were dehydrated directly in 95–100% alcohol, cleared in xylene and mounted in synthetic resin.

I have generally preferred a somewhat stronger solution and a shorter staining period; *e.g.*, take 1 cc 1% Biebrich scarlet + 49 cc buffer and stain 20 min, dehydrate with alcohol or acetone, clear in xylene and mount, preferably in cellulose caprate, so that unstained tissue elements can be seen.

Results: Tissues that were oxyphil at pH 9.5 after HgCl₂ fixation included seminal vesicle fluid, Kurloff bodies, trichohyalin, keratohyalin
and stratum lucidum, Paneth granules, eosinophil leucocytes, elastic
laminae and spermatozoon heads. With primary formalin fixation only
elastic laminae and eosinophil leucocyte granules still colored strongly.
Posttreatment (6 hours) with formaldehyde gave less reduction of
oxyphilia, spermatozoon heads, trichohyalin and Paneth granules remaining oxyphil.

Deamination and Acylation of Amines

Monné and Slautterback (*Arkiv Zool.* 1:455, 1950) consider that the
acidophil components of nuclei, chromidia and myoglobin, which stain
preferentially with the plasma stain component of procedures of the
Mallory phosphomolybdic acid aniline blue type (pp. 543–547) and resist
procedures which extract the nucleic acids, are probably histones, basic
proteins or protamines. This oxyphilia disappears on application of deamination or milder acetylation procedures.

Application of Van Slyke's (2.17 N) nitrous acid reagent (dissolve
6 gm sodium nitrite in 35 cc distilled water, add 5 cc glacial acetic
acid; 1–12 hours at 20–25°C) completely inhibits azocarmine and
aniline blue staining in the Heidenhain method (p. 545); this indicates
complete destruction of amino groups. Use of 5% chloramine T for 12
hours at 20–25°C has the same effect. Treatment with 0.4% ninhydrin for
12 hours at 80°C inhibited the aniline blue staining of yolk, but not the
azocarmine staining of chromidia. At 4°C exposure to pure acetic anhydride for 1–3 days did not inhibit the azocarmine staining of chromidia,
but did prevent aniline blue staining of yolk, while acetylation for 3 hours
at 80°C prevented both staining reactions. The Van Slyke reagent and
chloramine T treatments do not render the HIO₄ Schiff reaction of yolk
negative; but acetylation does, since it esterifies hydroxyls as well as
amines.

Application of Van Slyke's reagent to blood films promptly destroys the
eosinophilia of erythrocytes, so that these stain yellowish green with
Giemsa's stain after only 10 minutes at 25°C in the nitrous acid reagent.
Eosinophil granules still stain red to pink with Giemsa after an hour in
Van Slyke's reagent, though the intensity of the eosinophilia decreases
with longer exposure so that only a pale pink is seen at 2–6 hours.

Van Slyke's reagent does not impair the periodic acid Schiff reaction of
leucocytes or platelets, nor does it destroy the sudanophilia of neutrophil
leucocytes.

Acetic acid mixtures with sodium nitrite are more rapid in their action
on sections and smears than normal hydrochloric acid + nitrite mixtures,
in spite of the higher pH levels.

I have often found prolonged exposures to nitrous acid necessary to

TABLE 8-6. pH LEVELS OF NITRITE SOLUTIONS

Solution	pH	Solution	pH
Van Slyke's reagent (2.17 N)	3.65	12.5% acetic acid	2.0
1 N NaNO$_2$ in 1 N HCl	0.68	1 N NaNO$_2$ in H$_2$O	6.7
1 N NaNO$_2$ in 1 N acetic	3.7	1 N acetic (6%)	2.2
1 N NaNO$_3$ in 1 N acetic	2.2	1 N NaNO$_3$	5.0

destroy oxyphilia, especially when prolonged formalin fixation has been used. With 48 hour or shorter fixation in neutral formalin, periods of 1–3 hours in 1 N NaNO$_2$, 1 N acetic acid are usually adequate. The oxyphilia of eosinophil leucocytes, which is probably assignable largely to arginine residues, persists up to 18 hours. However, when the technic of graded pH staining with acid dyes is adopted, it is found that the maximum pH at which eosinophil leucocyte granules are stained by the acid dye is depressed from 11 to 7 by 24 hours nitrosation (1 N NaNO$_2$/1 N HAc), which indicates a considerable amount of amine destruction by HNO$_2$. It is known that there is a slow loss of a second N in free arginine after prompt destruction of the α-amino group, and it is possible that this accounts for the shift in protein pK during nitrosation.

Nitrosation at 25°C in 1 N or 2 N NaNO$_2$ acetic acid mixtures does not appreciably impair Van Gieson staining (*J. Histochem.* **6**:352, 1958).

Acylation for 1–2 hours in 0.1 H$_2$SO$_4$:10 acetic anhydride:30 glacial acetic acid weakens or abolishes both muscle and plasma staining with the fast green of the fast green Van Gieson technic, and the deep purple red staining of collagen and reticulum by the acid fuchsin component. A 1–2 hour methylation at 60°C in 0.1 M aged sulfuric acid methanol mixture fully restores both plasma and collagen staining. Saponification overnight in 5.6% ammonia/80% alcohol does not unblock the acylation blockade of the Van Gieson stain. However, a 20 minute saponification in 1% KOH in 70% alcohol does partly, though not fully, restore the fast green Van Gieson staining.

Strong pH 1 azure A staining occurs in smooth muscle and cytoplasms, as well as in the usual mucopolysaccharide sulfation sites, and this also is abolished by methylation but not by saponification as above. Inclusion of 10% propanol, isopropanol or, somewhat less effectively, n-butanol in the above acylation mixture, replacing part of the acetic acid, fairly effectively restricts azure A staining to mucopolysaccharide sites, as with the sulfuric acid glacial acetic acid mixtures with lack acetic anhydride. Ethyl and methyl alcohols did not prevent amine sulfation under the same conditions.

Periodic acid Schiff staining of gastric surface epithelial and pyloric gland mucin and of intestinal striated borders, goblet cells, Brunner's gland and colonic gland mucins is similarly prevented by the same acylation and restored by the same methylation, and the blockade resists ammonia alcohol saponification.

It thus appears that sulfation of amines may be accomplished with acetic acid solutions containing both sulfuric acid and at least 1–2% acetic anhydride, and this effect is prevented if an excess of a suitable alcohol over the sulfuric acid is present.

Sulfation of Amines (Lillie, *J. Histochem.* **12**:821, 1964). Cut thin paraffin sections of material fixed in formalin or otherwise. Deparaffinize as usual in 2–3 changes of xylene and 2 of absolute alcohol.

1. Rinse in glacial acetic acid.
2. Immerse 3–5 minutes in mixture of 10 cc acetic anhydride, 30 cc glacial acetic acid and 0.1 cc concentrated sulfuric acid, thoroughly mixed by being poured back and forth once or twice between a beaker and the Coplin jar.
3. Wash 10 minutes in running water.
4. Stain sulfated sections and unsulfated controls by a suitable acid dye, such as Biebrich scarlet, the fast green Van Gieson technic or other method for basic protein.

Further controls may be methylated after sulfation to restore stainability, using 0.1 N HCl or 0.1 M H_2SO_4 in methanol, 2 hours at 60°C. Saponification by the KOH or ammonia alcohol technics should be ineffective or only partially effective in overcoming the blockade.

Acetylation with acetic anhydride pyridine mixtures or with hot acetic anhydride alone is less effective against simple acid dyes such as eosin Y, eosin B or Biebrich scarlet, but the sulfation induced basophilia is absent and such mixtures as that in the azure A eosin B technic can be used. Attempts to block Van Gieson staining by such procedures are usually unsuccessful. Sulfuric catalysis tends to improve pyridine acetylations and does not appear to induce sulfation basophilia. The oxyphilia to eosin B of smooth and striated muscle, erythrocytes, eosinophils, zymogen granules and the like, when blocked by acetylation, is readily restored by 20 minutes in 1% KOH/70% alcohol.

Deitch (*J. Histochem.* **9**:477, 1961) complained of difficulties in the prevention of her modified Sakaguchi arginine reaction by acetylation. Although her pyridine reagent, 20% acetic anhydride, 1 hour 25°C, and her acetic acid reagent, 5% acetic anhydride, 1 hour at 25°C, would appear to have been inadequate in view of our experience with similar and more concentrated reagents, her 2 hour exposure to pure acetic anhydride at 80°C is only slightly less than that of Monné and Slautterback and should have had more effect. Hydrolysis of the acetyl esters in the strongly alkaline Sakaguchi reagent may, of course, have occurred. Here the foregoing amine sulfation technic could well have been more effective.

Urea

Leschke's Method. Fixation of tissue in a mixture of equal volumes of saturated mercuric nitrate solution and 2% nitric acid is followed by treatment of sections with ammonium sulfide to convert the mercury urea compound to black mercuric sulfide. This method is regarded by both Lison and Glick as highly unspecific.

The Xanthydrol Reaction. This is quite specific; but the reaction is slow, urea is highly diffusible and the localization is therefore poor. Gomori recommends Oliver's method (*J. Exp. Med.* 33:177, 1921): Fix small pieces of tissue in a filtered solution of 6 gm xanthydrol in 35 cc alcohol and 65 cc glacial acetic acid for 6–12 hours. Alcohol dehydration, paraffin imbedding and sectioning follow. The xanthydrol urea crystals are demonstrated under polarized light.

I have used an essentially identical fixing fluid by first freezing tissue in solid carbon dioxide and 100% alcohol mixture and then fixing for 14 days at $-25°C$. At this temperature the alcohol acetic mixture remains liquid, and the tissue melts only as the fixative penetrates. The method needs further study to put it on a good routine basis.

Uric Acid and Urates

Sodium urate is the commonest of the urates occurring in gouty tophi. Its crystals are slightly soluble in cold water, and insoluble in alcohol and ether. Mallory directed fixation in 95% or absolute alcohol. Schmorl recommended Oestreicher's (*Virchow. Arch. path. Anat.* 257:614, 1925) preliminary treatment of 6 hours in 6% xanthydrol (9-hydroxyxanthene) in glacial acetic acid, followed by 48 hours' fixation in 100% alcohol. Mallory preferred celloidin; Schmorl, paraffin imbedding. Stain sections briefly—Schmorl says 2 minutes—in hemalum or other unacidified alum hematoxylin. Wash in water, dehydrate and clear by an alcohol xylene sequence and mount in balsam or Permount. According to Mallory's technic the crystals are colored deep blue; by Oestreicher's xanthydrol method, bright yellowish green.

Schultz (*Virchow Arch. path. Anat.* 280:519, 1931) reported a rather complicated procedure which Mallory recommended. I have not tried it. Fix tissues in 100% alcohol. Pass through 3 changes of acetone of about $1\frac{1}{2}$ hours each. Then place in equal volumes of acetone and benzene for 30 minutes, then 2 changes of benzene, 30 minutes each. Imbed in paraffin, and section.

1. Deparaffinize and bring to 100% alcohol.
2. Stain 5 minutes in carmine, keeping slide in motion. The carmine solu-

tion is essentially similar to Best's and is prepared thus: Boil 1 gm carmine, 2 gm ammonium chloride, 0.5 gm lithium carbonate in 50 cc distilled water. Cool and add 20 cc 28% ammonia water. Mix 6 cc of the filtered stock solution with 3 cc 28% ammonia water and 5 cc methyl alcohol for staining.

3. Wash in several changes of 100% alcohol.
4. Stain 30 seconds, keeping slide in motion, in a half-saturated (about 0.75–0.94%) solution of methylene blue in 100% alcohol.
5. Rinse in 100% alcohol.
6. Stain 15 seconds, keeping slide in motion in sodium sulfate picric acid mixture: 9 cc saturated aqueous picric acid solution, 1 cc saturated aqueous sodium sulfate solution (nearly 50 gm of the anhydrous salt per 100 cc). Filter.
7. Wash in several changes of 100% alcohol.
8. Clear in xylene and mount in balsam.

Results: Nuclei, gray blue; cytoplasm, yellowish; uric acid crystals, deep blue green; sodium urate, brilliant green.

Gerard and Cordier (*Arch. biol.* 43:367, 1932) used Carnoy fixation and observations under polarized light for the demonstration of experimental uric acid deposits.

Uric acid exists in tautomeric trihydroxyl (acid) and (predominant) tricarbonyl (ketonic) forms and is readily oxidizable. It has been found to reduce silver nitrate, on which fact the Gomori and de Galantha methods depended. I have shown that *in vitro* uric acid and sodium urate reduce ferric ferricyanide promptly and hot (60°C) methenamine silver blackens in a few seconds. Ammoniacal silver blackens in a few seconds with the sodium salt, more slowly with the acid. Even neutral silver nitrate solutions turn brown with the acid in 10 minutes, and acid silver nitrate (pH 4, 0.1 *M*) turns brown in a few hours (*J. Histochem.* 5:311, 1957).

Gomori used his methenamine silver solution at pH 9, preheating to 37°C and incubating sections 30–60 minutes to blacken urate crystals. Most other tissue elements remain colorless at this stage. Complete the process as usual (p. 240).

De Galantha's procedure (*Am. J. Clin. Path.* 5:165, 1935) seems unnecessarily complicated, and by its use of a reducing procedure loses in specificity. See the second edition of this book, p. 154, or the original reference.

Arginine

For the demonstration of arginine, Baker (*Quart. J. Micr. Sci.* 88:115, 1947) gives a modification of the Sakaguchi reaction which appears to be specific for substances with the general formula

$$(2)—NH—\underset{\underset{(1)—N}{\|}}{C}—NH—\overset{(3)}{\underset{(5)}{C}}—(4)$$

for example, arginine

$$H_2—\underset{\underset{H—N}{\|}}{C}—NH—(CH_2—)_3—\underset{\underset{NH_2}{|}}{CH}—COOH$$

where (1) and (2) are either hydrogen atoms or methyl groups, and (3), (4) and (5) may be various atoms or radicals. Dicyanamid, mono-, di- and tri-methyl-guanidines, glycocyamine, alacreatine, α-guanidino-*n*-buty- ric acid, galegine, agmatine and arginine are listed as reacting to this test.

Baker recommended 24 hour fixation in Zenker, Bouin, susa, sublimate acetic and formol saline solution; for basic nuclear proteins Deitch found Carnoy's acetic alcohol (formula 1, p. 42) for 1 hour to give stronger colors than 1 or 24 hour fixations in neutral formalin (about 20% and 44% loss, respectively).

For Baker's technic see the second edition of this book, p. 144, or the original reference; the 1961 Deitch method seems about the best so far devised, in our hands.

Deitch's Dichloronaphthol Hypochlorite Method for Arginine (*J. Histochem.* 9:477, 1961). Fix in Carnoy or, for acid or alcohol soluble tissue elements, 1 hour in calcium acetate formalin. Routine pathologic material can be used but gives less intense reactions. Heavy metals at pH levels above 4 are also suggested as probably useful.

Reagents. Dehydrant: *tert*-butanol containing 5% tributylamine. Clear- ing agent: xylene containing 5% tributylamine. Mountants: Shillaber's oil nΔ 1.580 containing 10% tributylamine or xylene cellulose caprate (p. 97) 9 cc + 1 cc tributylamine. In the foregoing reagents dimethylaniline or aniline may be substituted for tributylamine with only slightly less satisfactory results.

Prepare fresh 4% barium hydroxide and filter just before using. Dilute 1 cc commercial 5% sodium hypochlorite (Clorox) with 4 cc distilled water. Dissolve 75 mg 2,4-dichloro-1-naphthol in 5 cc *tert*-butanol (1.5%).

1. Deparaffinize 4 μ paraffin sections and hydrate as usual. Wash in 2 changes distilled water.
2. Mix 25 cc 4% Ba(OH)$_2$, 5 cc 1% hypochlorite and 5 cc 1.5% dichloro- naphthol in butanol and pour over sections in Coplin jars. Let stand 10 minutes at 22–24°C.
3. Move slides one at a time through 3 changes of *tert*-butanol-tributyl-

amine, agitating vigorously for 5 seconds in the first change. Discard first butanol after 2–3 batches of slides, moving up the second and third and adding a fresh jar in position 3.

4. Clear in tributylamine xylene, 2–3 changes, and mount in Shillaber oil or cellulose caprate containing tributylamine. The Shillaber oil was used by Deitch, who found no fading in 14 days. Gilmer, in our laboratory, substituted the cellulose caprate, which sets hard in an hour and seems to preserve the color for 1 or 2 months, but preparations had faded considerably after 6 months.

Results: Arginine sites color red.

The second method, which, in our estimation, still gives acceptable results is the 8-hydroxyquinoline method, introduced by Warren and McManus (*Exp. Cell Res.* **2**:703, 1951), as modified by Carver, Brown and Thomas.

The 8-Hydroxyquinoline Hypochlorite Method for Arginine (*Stain Techn.* **28**:89, 1953; **26**:261, 1951). Fix preferably in Bouin's fluid (p. 58). Fixation in Carnoy's fluid (p. 42) or in 10% formalin also gives successful preparations. Prepare paraffin sections as usual.

1. Take through xylenes and alcohols to 70% alcohol.
2. Immerse 15 minutes at room temperature in a 0.3% solution of 8-hydroxyquinoline (oxine) in 30% alcohol. (Keep a stock 1% solution in 100% alcohol and dilute with water when needed.)
3. Transfer quickly, without draining, to alkaline hypochlorite at room temperature for 60 seconds. (Mix 9.4 cc Clorox of 1.6 N chlorine content with 15 cc 0.1 N potassium or sodium hydroxide and distilled water to make 100 cc.)
4. Transfer quickly, without draining, to alkaline butanol urea, 2 changes, 10 seconds and 2 minutes respectively. (Dissolve 15 gm urea in 15 cc 0.1 N potassium hydroxide, add 70 cc *tert*-butanol and distilled water to make 100 cc.)
5. Dehydrate in 2 changes of *tert*-butanol, 10 seconds and 4 minutes respectively.
6. Clear 3 minutes in aniline, rinse 10 seconds in xylene and mount in Permount containing 0.02% aniline (add 1 cc 0.1% aniline in xylene to 4 cc Permount or see the Deitch method, p. 258).

The reagents in steps 2, 3 and 4 are made fresh daily, and care is taken to keep anhydrous *tert*-butanol in step 5.

Liebman and Thomas used in step 2 a 15 minute bath at 5°C in a fresh 5% aqueous dilution of a 1% solution of α-naphthol in 100% alcohol. In step 3 they used a 90 second bath at 5°C in 0.15 N sodium hypochlorite (11.17 gm/liter) in 0.05 N potassium hydroxide solution (2.8

gm/liter). In step 4 the alkaline butanol urea contained 10 gm urea and 5 cc N KOH per 100 cc of 70% *tert*-butanol, and 2 changes of 5 and 25 seconds at 5°C were used. The butanol dehydration was followed directly by xylene, this was blotted off with hard filter paper and the sections were mounted in heavy white mineral oil. Coverglasses were cemented with lanolin rosin cement (p. 91). Persistence of the orange red color for several months was reported.

Citrulline

Rogers (*J. Histochem.* 11:700, 1963) investigated Fearon's diacetyl monoxime reaction for substituted ureides of the type $RNH-CO-NH_2$ and in particular of citrulline $NH_2-CO-NH=CH_2-CH_2-CH_2-CH$ $\overset{NH_2}{\underset{COOH}{<}}$ and found it too drastic for histochemical use because of the strong acid and high temperature employed. Our own experiences, reducing the temperature to 60°C and using glacial acetic acid as the menstrum for the HCl, were no more successful. However, Rogers obtained quite usable results by condensing with *p*-dimethylaminobenzaldehyde in dilute hydrochloric acid to obtain a yellow color. A high concentration of sodium chloride is used to prevent swelling.

Rogers's Method for Citrulline in Stimulated Hair Follicles of Rat. Denude hair from back by plucking 18 days in advance, so that anagen stage will be reached. Excise skin from preplucked area and fix 48 hours in phosphate buffered formalin (p. 38). Imbed and section in paraffin at 8 μ. Deparaffinize and hydrate as usual.

Make 1% solution of *p*-dimethylaminobenzaldehyde (Ehrlich's reagent) in 4 M sodium chloride 0.5 N hydrochloric acid (Ehrlich's reagent 1 gm, concentrated hydrochloric acid 4 cc, sodium chloride 23.3792 gm, distilled water to make 100 cc).

Place a drop of this reagent on the section, quickly cover with a coverglass and watch under a microscope for the appearance of yellow color in the hair medulla and in the Henle and Huxley layers of the sheath, immediately adjacent to the medullary and lateral areas occupied by the trichohyalin granules. Preparations are not permanent but can be photographed in color.

The trichohyalin granules give a strong red Sakaguchi reaction for arginine and a negative reaction for citrulline. As the hair root is followed toward the keratinization zone, the Sakaguchi reaction for arginine becomes abruptly much weaker and the Rogers reaction for citrulline conversely becomes stronger.

Biochemically no protein breakdown and resynthesis seem to be involved; there is no liberation of arginyl residues nor uptake of citrulline. Instead the guanyl residues of arginine appear to convert directly to ureide residues of citrulline. An interchange with adjacent glutamic acid residues to form γ-glutamide residues is suggested. This would entail no overall change in charge of the protein and would account well for the relatively strong oxyphilia of both areas.

Rogers writes the reaction thus:

$$
\begin{array}{ll}
\overset{|}{NH} & \overset{|}{NH} \\
\overset{|}{CH}-CH_2-CH_2-CH_2-NH-\overset{||}{C}-NH_2 & O=\overset{\diagdown}{C}-CH_2-CH_2-\overset{|}{CH} \\
\overset{|}{CO} \qquad\qquad\qquad\quad NH & HO\diagup \qquad\qquad\quad \overset{|}{CO} \\
\text{Arginyl} & \text{Glutamyl}
\end{array}
$$

$$
\downarrow
$$

$$
\begin{array}{ll}
\overset{|}{NH} & \overset{|}{NH} \\
\overset{|}{CH}-CH_2-CH_2-CH_2-NH-\overset{||}{C}-NH_2 & O=\overset{\diagdown}{C}-CH_2-CH_2-\overset{|}{CH} \\
\overset{|}{CO} \qquad\qquad\qquad\quad O & H_2N\diagup \qquad\qquad\quad \overset{|}{CO} \\
\text{Citrullyl} & \gamma\text{-Glutamide}
\end{array}
$$

PROTEINS

Fibrin

Fibrin is a fibrous protein occurring in various acute inflammatory processes, notably diphtheritic inflammation and lobar pneumonia, and in antemortem and postmortem thrombi.

It is eosinophilic with hematoxylin eosin (p. 176) and azure eosin stains (p. 162). It retains the plasma stains in procedures of the Van Gieson and fast green Van Gieson types (pp. 540, 542) and the Masson-Mallory methods (p. 545). It stains orange in the allochrome method (p. 549), and red to pink in the periodic acid Schiff method (p. 198) changing to orange if a picric acid counterstain is used. It retains the crystal violet iodine complex of the Gram stain when Weigert's aniline xylene differentiation is used (p. 262), but not when alcohol or acetone is the differentiating agent. Mallory's phosphotungstic acid hematoxylin (p. 537) is much favored by some workers.

Stains of the Masson type are more brilliant after Bouin, Zenker or Spuler fixation. With material fixed in formalin, they may be improved by premordanting in saturated alcoholic picric acid for 2 minutes at 25°C or in saturated aqueous mercuric chloride for an hour at 58°C. Bouin fixation, however, interferes with the Weigert fibrin stain. The allochrome method is quite differential and does well on formalin fixed tissue.

According to Glynn and Loewi (*J. Path. Bact.* 64:329, 1952) fibrin is digested in 3 hours at 37°C by 0.1% trypsin in pH 8 phosphate buffer, but fibrinoid and collagen are not.

The Weigert Fibrin Stain

The **Gram-Weigert technic** devised by Weigert in 1887 for fibrin and bacteria differs from the Gram technics in that counterstaining, if any, must be done before the Gram reaction is carried out, and in that the differentiating agent is aniline, alone or weakened by admixture with xylene. Numerous variants have been suggested, chiefly in the counter-stains used. Weigert, writing for the 1903 *Encyklopädie der mikroskop-ischen Technik*, still recommended a carmine prestain. He stated that it was necessary to treat chromate fixed material with oxalic acid before staining for fibrin, and suggested also the pretreatment with 0.33% potas-sium permanganate. This procedure is unnecessary for bacterial staining. On the other hand Weigert also stated that a simple aqueous methyl violet solution was adequate for fibrin staining, while for bacterial stain-ing the aniline methyl or crystal violet solution was to be preferred. In-asmuch as it is often desirable to have both fibrin and bacteria demon-strated in the same preparation, the technic adopted should conform to the above requirements for both.

Gram-Weigert Technic for Fibrin and Bacteria. Paraffin sections to water as usual.

1. Stain 20 minutes in 1% pararosaniline or basic fuchsin in 1% acetic acid (boil, cool and filter).
2. Wash in 3 changes distilled water.
3. Stain 5 minutes in 1% crystal violet in distilled water.
4. Rinse quickly in 1% sodium chloride.
5. Treat 30 seconds in iodine 1:potassium iodide 2, distilled water 100.
6. Blot with filter paper.
7. Decolorize slides lying flat, face up, with 1–2 cc portions of equal vol-umes of aniline and xylene, pouring off several times until no more color comes out into the mixture.
8. Xylene 3 changes.
9. Permount or Canada balsam.

This is nearly the original Weigert method. In step 1 he (Ehrlich's *Encyklopädie*) stained with carmine; for step 3 he used aniline methyl violet (10% alcoholic methyl violet 12 cc, fresh aniline water, filtered, 100 cc). In step 7 when preparing class sets, I have used a succession of 3 Coplin jars of the aniline xylene mixture, allowing sections to stand 2–3 minutes in each, and following with 3 or 4 changes of xylene similarly applied.

Results: Nuclei, red; fibrin, violet; Gram positive organisms, blue black. If a fuchsin nuclear stain has been used and the fixation was Helly or Orth, red corpuscles may remain a deep red, and nuclei are violet to red.

Collagen may retain some violet, but in a lighter shade than fibrin. Kera-tohyalin granules and hair shafts often retain violet, just as they may retain red in Ziehl-Neelsen stains. Young intraepithelial rabbit coccidia (*Eimeria*) contain numerous blue black granules between capsule and nucleus by this technic. In older, free forms these granules are more apt to be Gram negative, and with the acetone technic (p. 568) they are Gram negative in all stages. Mucus also may remain violet with the carbol fuchsin 30 minute prestain at step 1 but is Gram negative with the acetone technic. Sometimes glycogen is demonstrated by Gram-Weigert methods, as noted by Lubarsch (Ehrlich's *Encyklopädie*). Hypophyseal beta granules are violet.

Notes on Modifications of Weigert fibrin stain.

1. Preiodization of mercury fixed tissue may be omitted; step 5 removes mercury deposits.
2. The use of a preliminary $KMnO_4$ oxidation, oxalic acid reduction, sometimes prescribed for material fixed in bichromate fixatives, appears to be quite unnecessary.
3. Elastic stains may be interposed before step 1.
4. A periodic acid Schiff sequence may also be interposed at this point.
5. I have sometimes used Weigert's acid iron chloride hematoxylin for step 1. Violet black effects may appear and confuse the picture.
6. MacCallum's variant seems unnecessarily complicated; see the second edition of this book or *J.A.M.A.* 72:193, 1919.
7. Use of the Feulgen reaction at step 1 gives red purple nuclei, but its effect on bacterial ribonucleoprotein needs further evaluation.
8. Various crystal violet, methyl violet or gentian violet mixtures have been prescribed in step 3. Timing is varied from 1–10 minutes. Aniline and phenol formulae have been urged for bacteria. For these the Hucker-Conn ammonium oxalate formula seems adequate, and aqueous solutions suffice for fibrin.

Both fibrin and fibrinoid give positive indole reactions according to Pearse; Glenner and Lillie (*J. Histochem.* 5:279, 1957) recorded both positive and negative reactions of fibrin in various species. The protein fibrinogen presents 3.3% tryptophan.

Fibrinoid

Fibrinoid is a homogeneous, refractile, oxyphilic substance occurring in degenerating connective tissue, in term placentae, in rheumatoid nodules, in Aschoff bodies and in pulmonary alveoli in some prolonged pneumonitides.

With toluidine blue it is often metachromatic, sometimes not; and in some instances this metachromasia is abolished by predigestion with hyaluronidase, in others not. With phosphomolybdic or phosphotungstic acid aniline blue stains of the Mallory type, it is described sometimes as staining red with the counterstain, sometimes as cyanophil. With phosphotungstic acid hematoxylin (p. 537) it colors partly blue, partly orange to yellow. Altshuler and Angevine record purple staining with crystal violet (p. 262). Its uptake of acid and of basic dyes at various pH levels is similar to that of fibrin. According to Altshuler and Angevine, fibrinoid contains considerable amounts of arginine (p. 258). Pearse records a positive rosindole reaction (tryptophan).

Regarding the Weigert fibrin stain, the literature is vague. Klinge (*Virchow Arch. path. Anat.* **278**:486, 1930) spoke of most of the fibrinoid material as giving a positive fibrin reaction. The fibrin reaction in common use at that time was the Weigert fibrin stain (Schmorl, 1928; Romeis, 1932).

Fibrinoid is conceived of as a precipitation of acid mucopolysaccharide with a basic protein (Altshuler and Angevine, *Am. J. Path.* **25**:1061, 1949).

Like Altshuler and Angevine, Glynn and Loewi (*J. Path. Bact.* **64**:329, 1952) report a strongly positive periodic acid Schiff reaction (p. 198). This reaction is abolished by pectinase digestion and resists tryptic digestion but is weakened by tryptic digestion after denaturation for 18 hours in 36% (6 M) urea.

They also report blackening and demonstration of a fibrillar structure by Gomori's reticulum technic (p. 527). Fibrin did not react by this method. This reaction of fibrinoid was also abolished by pectinase digestion.

For tryptic digestion they used a 0.1% solution of Armour's crystalline trypsin in pH 8 phosphate buffer for 3 hours at 37°C.

In the pectinase digestion a crude preparation from onions was used at 0.4% in pH 4 acetate buffer, for 3 hours at 37°C.

Enzymatic Digestion Tests

Before proceeding to individual tests it seems pertinent to offer the following commentary on this method of identification of tissue components.

1. Since even *purified enzymes* or *crystalline enzymes* are seldom free of all other enzymatic activities, digestion of a given tissue component by a given enzyme preparation does not necessarily identify that tissue component as consisting of the specific substrate of the enzyme employed.

2. When a given enzyme preparation is known to digest a given substrate under specified conditions of fixation and preparation, failure of

that enzyme preparation to digest a tissue component under the same specified conditions may be taken to definitely exclude identification of that tissue component with the stated given substrate.

3. For even presumptive identification of a tissue component by reason of its digestion by a given enzyme, it must be shown that the tissue component in question is not destroyed by the enzyme solvent alone, or by the enzyme after inactivation by physical or chemical means, or in the presence of known specific inhibitors of the enzyme action in question.

Tryptic Digestion

I have used effectively a "1–300" trypsin of the Nutritional Biochemical Company at 0.1% concentration in 0.01 M phosphate buffer of pH 7.6 (p. 664), with or without 0.4% NaCl and 0.1% NaF. This trypsin had also quite a strong glycogenolytic activity. Purer crystalline products are now available. On digestion at 37°C, nuclear and cytoplasmic staining is destroyed in as little as 1 hour in material fixed in 80% alcohol, but it persists much longer in material fixed in aqueous formalin for long periods or in chromate fixatives. Collagen and reticulum are quite resistant; basement membranes are somewhat less so (*Lab. Invest.* **1**:30, 1952). Sarcolemma swells and stains poorly, displaying prominently the fine connective tissue fibrils traversing its outer surface.

Controls of the same buffer solvent without the enzyme should be employed. After alcohol fixation, distilled water removes ribonucleic acid at 60°C.

Peptic Digestion

I have used Difco pepsin at 1:1000 concentration in 0.1 N hydrochloric acid, digesting for varying periods at 37°C. For controls use 0.1 N HCl without enzyme.

Cytoplasmic staining is abolished in 2–4 hours' digestion after cold alcohol fixation, persisting longer in material fixed in aqueous formalin. Periodic acid Schiff positive basement membranes are digested much more rapidly than the collagen or reticulum which is stained blue by the allochrome method (p. 549). Nuclei becomes Schiff positive in 4–6 hours and then swell and vacuolate and lose their sharp definition in 18 hours. Ocular lens capsule and Descemet's membrane are quite resistant to peptic digestion.

Chromation of tissue almost completely inhibits peptic digestion.

Technics for Tryptic and Peptic Digestion.

1. Fix in 80% alcohol, Carnoy or the like. Alcoholic formalin for 18 hours (not more) may be used. Avoid use of prolonged fixation in aqueous

formalin and especially in dichromate mixtures. Imbed and section in paraffin, not celloidin.

2. Sections may be digested without deparaffinizing according to the suggestion of Goetsch, Reynolds and Bunting (*Proc. Soc. Exp. Biol. Med.* 80:71, 1952) regarding amylase digestion. I have not tested this. Generally, deparaffinize and hydrate as usual.

3. Immerse control sections in the same solvent as is used for the enzyme: a 0.01 *M* phosphate buffer of pH 7.6 containing 0.1% sodium fluoride and 0.4% sodium chloride for trypsin, and 0.1 *N* hydrochloric acid for pepsin. Leave controls in until the last test sections are taken out. Use 1:1000 solutions of trypsin and pepsin in the solvents described above. Digest for 30 minutes, 1, 2, 4, 6 or 7 and 16–18 hours, removing test slides at the various times.

4. Wash in water.

5. Counterstain to demonstrate the particular tissue elements under study.

6. Wash and mount in glycerol gelatin; or dehydrate, clear and mount in polystyrene.

Compare digested preparations with each other, with undigested controls and with solvent controls.

We have used 0.1% chymotrypsin and 0.1% papain, both in pH 7.6 phosphate buffer, 1 hour 37°C, in essentially similar procedures (*J. Histochem.* 7:204, 1959).

Antibody Localization

Coons, Leduc and Kaplan (*J. Exp. Med.* 93:173, 1951) in their study of localization of fluorescent antibodies, first cut hard frozen sections (p. 63), then attached them to gelatin coated slides in the cryostat, removed them from the cryostat and melted the section by pressing a finger against the back of the slide under the section. Sections were then dried onto the slides in an air stream at room temperature for an hour and were stored at 4°C overnight. They were then fixed to immobilize the egg albumin and gamma globulin by immersion for 30 minutes at 37°C in preheated 95% alcohol. For bovine serum albumin, acetone was used at room temperature for 15 minutes. After fixation the slides were dried in a vertical position in the 37°C incubator for 30 minutes.

Sections were then reacted with a drop of fluorescein treated antibody for 30 minutes at 37°C washed in buffered saline solution for 10 minutes and mounted in buffered glycerol. They were then examined under the fluorescence microscope. After photographing, the coverglass was floated off and the section was fixed in 10% formalin for 10 minutes, and counterstained with hematoxylin and eosin. The same area was then rephotographed.

Coons had to synthesize not only the isocyanate but also the fluorescein-amine from which it was derived. Moreover the isocyanate was unstable, though it could be kept for limited periods in acetone solution at very low temperatures. Hence, the method is practically restricted to labora-tories with facilities for organic synthesis. Silverstein's (*J. Histochem.* **5:** 94, 1957) technic with rhodamine B isocyanate was subject to the same difficulties, requiring synthesis of a nitrorhodamine B from 4-nitro-phthalic anhydride and *m*-diethylaminophenol, reduction to the amine and conversion to the isocyanate with phosgene.

The introduction of the more stable isothiocyanates, which are said to yield better fluorescent antibodies and other proteins and polysaccharides below, and which have recently been made available commercially, and the introduction of sulforhodamine B, which is readily converted to a sulfonyl chloride to condense with protein amines by sulfamido con-densation, should serve to extend the uses of these procedures.

Production of specific antisera is beyond the scope of the present work. Texts on immunity and original papers should be consulted.

Riggs *et al.* (*Am. J. Path.* **34:**1081, 1958) gave detailed directions for the synthesis of fluorescein isothiocyanate and rhodamine B isothiocya-nate, proceeding from isomer I of Coons's (*J. Exp. Med.* **91:**1, 1950) nitrofluorescein diacetate and from 4-nitrophthalic acid and N,N-diethyl-aminophenol, reducing to amines and converting the amines to isothio-cyanates with thiophosgene. It is probable that other fluorescent amines can be similarly converted to isothiocyanates, but since fluorescein and rhodamine B isothiocyanates are reasonably stable and have been made commercially available, it seems probable that they will replace the unstable isocyanates previously used.

Conjugation Procedure for Isothiocyanates

Riggs *et al.* direct as follows: Mix 10 cc 0.85% sodium chloride, 3 cc 0.5 *M* carbonate bicarbonate buffer adjusted to pH 9 and 2 cc. acetone. Chill the mixture by immersing the Erlenmeyer flask in acetone dry ice mixture until ice crystals form. Then add, with stirring, 10 cc diluted globulin fraction of known protein content. Rechill the mixture to the point of ice crystal formation. Dissolve 0.05 mg fluorescein or rhodamine B isothiocyanate per milligram of protein in 1.5 cc acetone and add gradually, with stirring, to the cold protein solution. Continue stirring for 18 hours in a cold room at 4°C.

Riggs *et al.* then removed excess dye by dialysis (but see Lipp, p. 268), filtered through a millipore filter and shell froze 2 cc quantities in ampules which were stored in the dry-ice chest until used.

The sulfonyl chloride of sulforhodamine B (C.I. No. 45100, Acid Rhodamine B NAC, Lissamine Rhodamine B 200 ICI) has also been used for the tagging of proteins, yielding a brilliant orange fluorescence

(Chadwick *et al., Lancet* 1:412, 1958). The authors direct as follows for preparation of the sulfonyl chloride: Place 1 gm sulforhodamine B and 2 gm phosphorus pentachloride in a mortar and grind together for 5 minutes in the chemical hood. Then add 10 cc anhydrous acetone and stir occasionally for 5 minutes. Then filter the acetone solution of sulforhodamine B sulfonyl chloride. Successful conjugates are obtained up to 18 hours from preparation. Conjugates are prepared at 0–2°C.

To each 1 cc serum or protein solution of similar concentration add 1 cc 0.85% sodium chloride solution and 1 cc 0.5 M carbonate bicarbonate buffer pH 9. Mix and add 1 cc acetone solution of sulforhodamine B sulfonyl chloride drop by drop with constant stirring. Continue stirring in the cold for 12–18 hours. Dialyze against 0.85% NaCl in the cold for 6–8 days, changing fluid at regular intervals, until no more color appears in the dialysate. The final volume of the conjugate is about thrice that of the original mixture; it may be concentrated in an air stream, with or without partial vacuum. The serum conjugates may be stored at 15–20°C and appear to be reasonably stable.

Separation of Labeled Protein from Dye

Lipp (*J. Histochem.* 9:458, 1961) recommends gel filtration for the freeing from uncombined dye of labeled protein. A gel is formed by wetting a special dextran, Sephadex G-25 (Pharmacia, Uppsala, Sweden), with the solvent to be used for elution and packing it to form a column 20 cm high in a UV transmitting glass tube 4–5 cm in inside diameter. The column is then filled with the buffered (0.85%?) saline and drainage is started. The dye and labeled protein mixture are added when the fluid level descends to the top of the column, and when the fluorescent mixture has entirely entered the column more eluent is added. Owing to the restricted pore size of the dextran particles, small molecules enter them and are much retarded in passing, while the tagged protein passes by without entering the particles. As the fluorescent protein descends a nonfluorescent zone appears behind the protein band, separating it from the adsorbed dye. After the fluorescent protein has been collected, the column may be washed free of adsorbed dye with more eluent. Passage of tagged protein through such a column requires 45–60 minutes, in place of the several days of dialysis needed in previous technics.

Reconcentration of Protein Solution

Lipp (*ibid.*) places dry Carbowax 4000 or similar high polymer polyethylene glycol in a dialysis tube, which is then immersed in a slightly wider column containing the protein solution. The lower end of the dialysis tube is sealed, the upper end opens into a funnel. Salts and water diffuse into the dialysis tube and dissolve the Carbowax, forming a solution of high osmotic pressure which cannot diffuse back through the membrane, thereby removing considerable amounts of water from the protein solution.

See also Curtain (*J. Histochem.* 9:484, 1961) for closely similar procedures.

ALDEHYDE AND CARBONYL REACTIONS

Schiff's Sulfurous Acid Leucofuchsin Reagent

This reagent for carbonyl groups, especially aldehydes, has shown itself extremely well adapted to the demonstration of these groups in tissue sections. It is used in Feulgen's nucleal reaction for the aldehyde group of deoxyribose when freed from purine and pyrimidine bases (nucleotide base + sugar + acid) by acid hydrolysis (p. 149), for the aldehyde unmasked in acetal phosphatides by the action of mercuric chloride (the plasmal reaction, p. 408), for aldehydes arising from the peroxidation of unsaturated fats (p. 186), for the demonstration of aldehydes formed by Criegee cleavage reactions of 1,2-glycols and 1,2-aminoalcohols by periodic and chromic acids, potassium permanganate (p. 198), lead tetraacetate and sodium bismuthate (p. 203), for the demonstration of aldehydes resulting from the peracetic and performic acid oxidation of carbon-carbon double bonds (p. 183), in the Oster amine oxidase method (p. 317), the Liang nerve ending technic (p. 621) and other methods (p. 246).

Fuchsin in 0.5–1% solution may be reduced with 6–8% SO_2 water (sulfurous acid), with 0.5–2% sodium bisulfite, metabisulfite or the corresponding potassium salts ($NaHSO_3$, $Na_2S_2O_5$, $KHSO_3$, $K_2S_2O_5$), with 2.25% sodium thiosulfate ($Na_2S_2O_3 \cdot 5H_2O$), with 0.5% sodium dithionite ($Na_2S_2O_4$) (Alexander, McCarty and Alexander-Jackson, *Science* 111:13, 1950) or with 1 cc thionyl chloride ($SOCl_2$) per gm fuchsin (Barger and DeLamater, *Science* 103:121, 1948). The last 3 reducing agents have been little used in histology.

The directions of Feulgen called for dissolving the fuchsin in boiling hot water, filtering while cooling, adding the sulfite and storing in the dark for a day or 2 before use. This practice was followed by nearly all writers up to 1950, when we evolved a satisfactory, abbreviated cold procedure, which will be given here.

Coleman (*Stain Techn.* 13:123, 1938) introduced the procedure of completing the bleaching of the reagent with activated charcoal, which removed a variable amount of residual coloring matter not taken out by the sulfite. Barger and DeLamater state that the charcoal treatment may either precede or follow the sulfite bleaching; Longley (*Stain Techn.* 27: 161, 1952) showed that charcoal treatment before bleaching removed a good deal of fuchsin as well as the so-called yellow component.

Amounts of fuchsin used also vary considerably; the 1 gm in 220 cc cited by Lee (9th ed., 1928) from Feulgen (*loc. cit.*), and others; the 0.25% of Barger and DeLamater (*loc. cit.*); the 1 gm in 120 cc of Bauer (*Z. mikr. anat. Forsch.* 33:143, 1933), C. Bensley (*Stain Techn.* 14:47, 1939), Cowdry and others; the 1 gm/100 cc of our method, presented here; the 2 gm/100 cc which we have occasionally used.

Preparation of Schiff Reagent: Traditional Method.

1. Bring 100 cc distilled water to boiling, remove from the flame and at once dissolve 1 gm basic fuchsin (pararosaniline, rosaniline or new fuchsin). When the solution cools to 60°C:
2. Filter and add to the filtrate 2 gm sodium or potassium bisulfite or metabisulfite ($NaHSO_3$, $KHSO_3$, $Na_2S_2O_5$, $K_2S_2O_5$) and 20 cc 1 N hydrochloric acid (p. 672).
3. Stopper and store solution in the dark at room temperature for 18–24 hours.
4. Add 300 mg activated charcoal, shake vigorously 1 minute and filter.
5. Store at 0–5°C. The solution should be a clear light yellow. Discard it when a pink color develops. We have kept this solution for several weeks.

If thionyl chloride is used in place of sulfite and acid, use 1 cc per gm fuchsin. The pH of the final reagent is about 1.25 with this variant.

Preparation of Reagent by "Cold Schiff" Procedure.

1. Weigh out 1 gm fuchsin and 1.9 gm sodium metabisulfite ($Na_2S_2O_5$). Dissolve in 100 cc 0.15 N hydrochloric acid. For 2 gm fuchsin use 0.25 N HCl and double the $Na_2S_2O_5$.
2. Shake the solution at intervals or on a mechanical shaker for 2 hours. The solution is now clear and yellow to light brown in color.
3. Add 500 mg *fresh* activated charcoal, shake 1–2 minutes.
4. Filter into graduated cylinder, washing the residue with a little distilled water to restore the original 100 cc volume.

The solution should be water white. If it possesses a yellow color a fresh lot of activated charcoal should be obtained and the charcoal decolorization should be repeated. Store at 0–5°C.

Such solutions have been so stored for 2 months, still remaining colorless. Stronger solutions may form a white precipitate on refrigeration. This precipitate is perhaps less apt to form at lower pH levels. It does not dissolve on warming gently. The pH of this fluid is about 2.2. For dilute Schiff reagent, add 1.9% (0.1 M) sodium metabisulfite in 0.15 N hydrochloric acid to desired dilution.

The *dithionite* (*hydrosulfite*) *solution of Alexander et al.* (*loc. cit.*) is prepared by dissolving 1 gm fuchsin in 200 cc boiling hot water, filtering while hot and adding at once 1 gm sodium dithionite ($Na_2S_2O_4$) and 500 mg activated charcoal. Shake thoroughly and filter. The finished product is of light amber color and of unspecified pH. It does not seem to have been used much.

Mowry (*Ann. N.Y. Acad. Sci.* 106:402, 1963) in his combined alcian blue and Hale-periodic acid Schiff technics prescribes a weaker variant of the cold Schiff reagent, which is also apparently less acid than the above:

Basic fuchsin 0.5 gm, sodium sulfite (Na_2SO_3) 5 gm, concentrated hydrochloric acid 3 cc and distilled water to make 200 cc. The amount of fuchsin is 25% that above, the sulfite content is still approximately 0.2 M, but owing to the use of Na_2SO_3, the excess of anions over Na and NH_2 is reduced by about 0.1 N (0.262 *vs.* 0.165 N). Weaker Schiff reagents of this type are quite satisfactory for the demonstration of reactive epithelial mucins by periodic acid methods. For such objects as mucosal reticulum and smooth muscle stroma, the stronger Schiff reagent appears to be necessary. For Feulgen reactions the usual 0.5 gm fuchsin per 100 cc seems adequate and should be adhered to for photometric studies. But I can see no virtue in boiling the water and filtering it hot before adding the sulfite.

Longley's (*Stain Techn.* 27:161, 1952) conclusions that 0.25% fuchsin is often too weak, that 0.5% is usually adequate, that precipitation of the leuco substance is more apt to occur above pH 3 and that a lower pH than the 2.2 achieved in the 1% cold Schiff is of no special value, are in general agreement with the foregoing and with my present position. He further noted that the presence of an excess of SO_2 was not deleterious. Van Duijn (*J. Histochem.* 4:55, 1956) proposed a sulfite leucothionin to give a contrasting color (blue) to Schiff reagent (red) in a combined Feulgen-McManus procedure.

Dissolve 0.5 gm thionin in 250 cc distilled water, boil 5 minutes, cool, restore volume, add 250 cc tertiary butanol (M.P. 25°C), transfer to stoppered bottle without filtration, add 75 cc 1 N HCl and at once 5 gm $Na_2S_2O_5$. Stopper, shake, let stand 24 hours at 25°C and then 48 hours at 4°C. Filter out a portion of the stock solution for use. After using it, return the solution to the stock bottle and keep stored at 4°C. The reagent keeps about 6 weeks from initial mixing and should not be used until aged as specified above, *i.e.*, after 1 day at 25°C and 2 days at 4°C.

Reaction time is longer than with Schiff reagent, the author recommending 15 minutes for routine work and an hour for quantitative work.

The reaction color is deep blue for Feulgen and for McManus reactions. The blue Feulgen color remains stable with a subsequent periodic acid Schiff reaction.

Fluorochrome Schiff reagents have been made by Kasten (*Nature* 184: 1797, 1959) by treatment with gaseous SO_2 or thionyl chloride from acridine yellow G, C.I. No. 46025; acriflavine, C.I. No. 46000; coriphosphine O, C.I. No. 46020; flavophosphine N, C.I. No. 46065; neutral red, C.I. No. 50040; phenosafranin, C.I. No. 50200; safranin O, C.I. No. 50240; rhodamine 3G, C.I. No. 45210; phosphine C.I. No. 46045; and, last and perhaps best, auramine O, C.I. No. 41000.

These dyes, together with the basic and acid fuchsins and thionin, have one chemical structural group in common; all possess at least one primary arylamine group. Feigl, in earlier editions of his *Spot Tests*, spoke of a Schiff reagent made with malachite green which possessed only fully alkylated amino groups. This dye has failed to yield a Schiff reagent in my hands, and one is led to wonder whether Feigl had a partly dealkylated sample. The primary arylamino group appears necessary to form the sulfite complex which serves as a chromogenic aldehyde reagent.

The auramine O Schiff reagent tends to precipitate and is stable for only a few hours, but it gives a very striking intense greenish yellow fluorescence to nuclei in the Feulgen reaction.

Saturate an 0.5% solution of auramine O with sulfur dioxide just before using. Expose hydrolyzed sections (6 N HCl, 6 minutes, 25°C) to the SO_2 auramine O for 45 minutes, wash as usual in 0.1 N bisulfite and 10 minutes in running water.

The other dyes are similarly prepared by treating solutions with SO_2 or thionyl chloride, using 0.5–0.25% dye for Feulgen reagents and 0.1% solutions in periodic acid technics.

Hydrazine Reactions

Albert's plasmalogen reaction with dinitrophenylhydrazine is described on p. 469, and Seligman's method with 2-hydroxy-3-naphthoic acid hydrazide, followed by azo coupling with fast blue B and other stable diazonium salts, has also been used as an aldehyde demonstration reagent after periodic acid oxidation, but it seems to offer no striking advantage over the Schiff reagent. Further, the diazonium salt couples to a variable extent with protein bound aromatic amino acids, usually yielding yellow or orange colors.

This last objection applies also to our new "black periodic" technic (*Stain Techn.* 36:361, 1961), but here the contrast often afforded by black staining of fine reticulum and basement membranes to light red muscle and gland cell cytoplasm enhances the value of the periodic acid method for the study of these structures.

Schiff's Base or Diphenamine Reactions

Arylamines condense readily with tissue aldehydes to form Schiff's bases. Because of the large excess of arylamine present, these are of Eibner's (*Ber. Deutsch. chem. Ges.* **30**:1444, 1897) diphenamine type, as I have recently demonstrated (*J. Histochem.* **10**:303, 1962), thus: $RCHO + 2ArNH_2 \rightarrow RCH(NHAr)_2$. These Schiff's bases, or perhaps better, to avoid confusion with the better known azomethines ($RCH = NAr$), diphenamine bases are quite resistant to acids and indeed are best formed from acid solutions or, even better, glacial acetic acid.

This diphenamine reaction may well be responsible for the success of Arzac's and Kligman's periodic acid, basic fuchsin methods for the demonstration of glycogen, fungi, etc.; it is definitely the reaction in question in our black periodic and black Bauer methods (*Stain Techn.* **36**:361, 1961) and in Spicer's rapid periodic acid diamine procedure for mucopolysaccharides (*J. Histochem.* **9**:368, 1961).

The black periodic procedure is based on the diphenamine Schiff's base condensation of *m*-aminophenol in glacial acetic acid, which at this point prevents the aldehyde Schiff reaction quite completely, followed by alkaline azo coupling with fast black K, C.I. No. 37190. Black and dark brown colors are to be regarded as specific for aldehydes, since this condensation does not occur with ketones. The black reaction of enterochromaffin cells with fast black K is completely prevented, apparently irreversibly, by periodic acid oxidation.

Diphenamines can also be formed with secondary arylamines, at least of the type $ArNHCH_3$ (*J. Histochem.* **10**:303, 1962), so that dyes with primary and secondary amino groups of the type specified may be expected, under appropriate conditions, to form stable compounds with tissue aldehydes. Reference to Tables 6–4 (p. 119) and 6–6 (p. 124) will indicate the commonly used basic and acid dyes which might be thus used.

The Black Periodic Acid Procedure of Lillie, Gilmer and Welsh (*Stain Techn.* **36**:361, 1961). Fix in formalin or other fixative suitable for mucopolysaccharides. Imbed and section in paraffin at 3–6 μ. Deparaffinize and hydrate through xylene and graded alcohols as usual.

1. Oxidize 10 minutes in 1% periodic acid (H_5IO_6).
2. Wash 10 minutes in running water and drain.
3. Dehydrate in 1–2 changes of glacial acetic acid. Drain.
4. React for 90 minutes in 11% (1 M) *m*-aminophenol in glacial acetic acid. (If protected from addition of water or alcohol this solution may be reused for 2–3 weeks or longer. Test sections treated in it periodically for complete blockade of the Schiff reaction.)

5. Wash 10 minutes in running water. Rinse in distilled water.
6. Azo couple 2–4 minutes at 3°C in fast black K (3 mg/1 cc) freshly dissolved in 0.1 M Michaelis Veronal HCl buffer at pH 8 which has been precooled. This solution remains usable for about 2 hours and may be used for 2–3 batches of slides in close succession.
7. Wash directly in 3 changes 0.1 N HCl, 5 minutes each.
8. Wash 10 minutes in running water.
9. Dehydrate in alcohols, clear in xylene and mount in cellulose caprate, Permount or other suitable resin.

Results: Cytoplasms, gray pink to gray red; nuclei, poorly contrasting in somewhat deeper color; glycogen, starch, cellulose and lignin in intestinal contents, black; gastric surface epithelial mucin, intestinal goblet cells, striated border of villi, fungus cell walls, epithelial, glandular and vascular basement membranes, reticulum, rodent elastic tissue, stroma of smooth and striated muscle, black; colonic and some other mucins, black to brown.

Although some measure of success was attained in a diphenamine Schiff's base reaction of rosaniline in 0.2 N HCl alcohol or water and the reaction product was resistant to extraction with the same solvents, the foregoing black periodic procedure seems to fill the same purpose better. However, the Schiff base reaction with acid fuchsin still seems to have some theoretical interest, since ordinary acid-base nuclear staining is avoided by the use of acid dyes with open amino groups. I have used aniline blue with some success, but the best dye which I have tried is acid fuchsin.

Schiff Base Reaction with Acid Fuchsin. After the usual periodic acid oxidation (5–10 minutes in 0.5–1%) wash well in water and immerse in 1% acid fuchsin in 0.01 N HCl for 18–24 hours. (Shorter times may well suffice but have not been tested in detail.) Wash 5 minutes in running water, decolorize 10 minutes (or more) in 1% borax ($Na_2B_4O_7 \cdot 10H_2O$), which leaves control, unoxidized sections pale pink or colorless, except for rodent elastic fibers. Rinse in water, counterstain as desired, *e.g.*, 10 seconds in 0.1% fast green FCF in 95% alcohol, then 100% alcohol, alcohol + xylene, xylene, synthetic resin.

A number of acid dyes with substituted amino groups failed to give this reaction: fast green FCF, wool green S, patent blue V, cyanol. The azo dye Biebrich scarlet also was unsuccessful.

The borax acetone condensation of *m*-aminophenol with periodic acid engendered aldehyde sites is slower and less effective than that in glacial acetic acid. The Schiff reaction of the connective tissue elements, including elastica, disappears promptly (30 minutes), but that of gastrointestinal mucins persists with only slight attenuation for at least 4 hours. Similarly, only the mucins appear in deep purple in the fast black K demonstration procedure with short exposures to the amine aldehyde condensation process. With medium and longer exposures (1, 2, 4 hours) mucins become black, elastica is black and basement membranes, reticulum and collagen fiber attain a final deep gray red at 4 hours' exposure.

These findings support the view that aldehyde concentration is actually lower at the connective tissue sites in that the blocking procedure reduces the Schiff reaction below visibility with relatively brief exposures, and that relatively long exposures are required to build up enough density in the positive azo coupling sequence.

Silver Reactions

Aldehydes reduce silver nitrate rather slowly at pH 6 and scarcely at all at pH 4. Ammoniacal and hot methenamine silver solutions are reduced fairly promptly *in vitro* (*J. Histochem.* **5**:311, 1957). But the situation in sections is less definite. Most periodic acid engendered aldehyde sites, though not all, reduce hot methenamine silver about as well when the periodic acid step is omitted.

Noteworthy exceptions to the above, in which it clearly appears that aldehydes engendered by periodic acid oxidation are actually reducing methenamine silver, are the lens capsule and Descemet's membrane in the eye (but not glycogen, reticulum or cornea), and the surface epithelial mucin of the stomach (but not that of its glands or of the intestine, nor the mucosal or muscular reticulum, nor the cuticular border of the villi) (*J. Histochem.* **2**:130, 1954).

Blockade Methods

Blockade methods are chemical procedures which of themselves fail to give recognizable color reactions in tissue elements but which so alter the latter that they fail to give other color reactions. In this way some quite specific chemical procedures can be made to alter a general color reaction or stain so as to make the failure to react specific evidence of the presence of specific chemical groupings.

Thus deamination (p. 253) prevents certain tissue elements from staining with acid aniline dyes, and thereby gives evidence that the usual staining of those elements was due to the presence of amino groups.

Blockade of Aldehyde Groups

The use of sulfite, semicarbazide and phenylhydrazine to combine with aldehydes and ketones, and thereby prevent color reactions with Schiff reagent or Seligman's carbonyl reagent, aids in the identification of aldehydes and ketones. The reaction of sulfite or sulfurous acid with most aldehydes is quite easily reversed by application of mild oxidants such as 3% hydrogen peroxide; 1% iodine or its equivalent as potassium hypoiodite; 1% sodium iodate or its equivalent in iodic acid; 1% potassium chlorate or its equivalent in chloric acid; or 1% ferric chloride. Intervals of 2–10 minutes in these reagents are sufficient to nullify a 2–4 hour blockade in 0.1 M $NaHSO_3$ and to render the Schiff reaction of HIO_4 generated aldehydes again fully positive. Even 10 minutes washing in tap water from a chlorinated municipal water supply suffices to reverse completely the sulfite blockade of the Schiff reaction. None of these oxidants by itself will produce aldehyde either from 1,2-glycols or from ethylenes.

Though a prolonged treatment with bisulfite after the Feulgen hydrochloric acid hydrolysis, the periodic acid glycol oxidation or the performic or peracetic ethylene oxidation will completely prevent the positive reactions which normally occur in 5–10 minutes in Schiff reagent, a prolonged exposure (2–3 hours) to the Schiff reagent completely overcomes the sulfite blockade; and during this prolonged bath the more strongly reacting tissue elements recover their positive reactions first.

Similarly a 30 minute exposure to 5% phenylhydrazine hydrochloride after periodic or performic acid oxidation completely prevents reaction to a 10-minute bath in Schiff reagent, but is overcome by a 3 hour exposure. However, treatments with phenylhydrazine prolonged for several hours or overnight render some periodic acid generated aldehydes permanently Schiff negative; others are more loosely combined and again become Schiff positive on 3 hour exposure to Schiff reagent, or by interposition of a weak oxidizing agent. But cellulose, mucus and cartilage remain reactive to a 10 minute Schiff bath after 1 hour in phenylhydrazine.

Pearse prescribes 2–3 hours at 60°C in 10% phenylhydrazine in 20% acetic acid. This is undoubtedly effective but necessitates a further control section, heated for the same period in plain 20% acetic acid.

Dimedone I have not used as a blocking agent for carbonyl. It is said to be specific for aldehydes, and some workers recommend it highly. Pearse writes that it is found to block extremely slowly in practice: "It is often difficult to distinguish the reduction in recolorization of leucofuchsin caused by dimedone from that observed in control sections treated with the solvent (acetic-alcohol) only."

Nevertheless, when it does block, the reaction is to be regarded as specific for aldehyde. Failure to block does not exclude aldehyde. The same is true of phenylhydrazine, aniline chloride and hydroxylamine.

Pearse uses a saturated solution of dimedone (5,5-dimethylcyclohexane-1,3-dione) in 5% acetic acid (in alcohol?) for 1–16 hours at 60°C, or for 2–3 days at 22°C.

Pearse preferred hydroxylamine in aqueous sodium acetate solution (10 gm hydroxylamine hydrochloride, 20 gm sodium acetate crystals, 40 cc distilled water) and treats sections 1–3 hours at 22°C. He stated that with this solution "condensation with tissue aldehydes of all varieties is rapid and apparently complete."

I have noted some curious failures to block the Schiff reaction after periodic acid with hydroxylamine, either as a 20% solution in 30% sodium acetate or as a 10% solution in pH 4.5 0.2 M acetate buffer. (The pH optimum for the hydroxylamine aldehyde condensation is said to be 4.7.) The Schiff reaction of gastric surface epithelial mucin and gland mucin, of ocular lens capsule and rod acromeres, of cellulose and lignin, of cartilage and nucleus pulposus, and sometimes of muscle glycogen remained positive with 2 and 24 hours of hydroxylamine blocking after periodic acid in one series of trials in which molar aniline chloride had been completely successful in 24 hours, and largely so in 2 hours. Only gastric gland mucin gave a slight Schiff coloration. Usually exposure to 5% phenylhydrazine hydrochloride for 24 hours completely prevents the Schiff reaction when interposed after periodic, peracetic or hydrochloric acid; and 2 hours is often adequate; but on some objects this agent may also fail to block.

A 1 hour exposure to 5% KCN, adjusted with acetic acid to pH 6.7–7.3, applied after periodic acid oxidation completely prevents the following Schiff reaction of hepatic, muscle and cartilage cell glycogens, of cartilage matrix, tracheal and gastric mucins and liver ceroid. The blockade is broken by a second 10 minute exposure to 1% periodic acid (*J. Histochem.* **4**:479, 1956). A drop of nitrazine solution or of phenolsulfonphthalein as indicator facilitates the pH adjustment. Neutral red, amber at pH 8, is red at pH 7 in KCN solutions.

Aniline, m-aminophenol and p-Toluidine. Arylamines present in excess in the surrounding medium react with tissue aldehydes to form diphenamine Schiff's bases (*J. Histochem.* **10**:303, 1962). For insoluble tissue aldehydes this is conveniently accomplished by immersion of sections in 1 M solutions of the arylamine in glacial acetic acid. At 23–25°C aniline takes 2–3 hours; m-aminophenol, 60–90 minutes; m-toluidine, 2–3 hours; N-methyl-m-toluidine, about 4 hours; and p-toluidine 30–60 minutes to completely block the Schiff reaction of periodic acid oxidized gastric and intestinal mucins.

Of these, all except p-toluidine can be used to direct azo coupling with freshly diazotized saframin (5 mM in glacial acetic acid, 18°C, 10 minutes) in positive demonstration reactions. The use of m-aminophenol for directing alkaline azo coupling is detailed on p. 273.

When lipid aldehydes which are soluble in glacial acetic acid are under study it is necessary to go back to our older technic with aqueous 1 M aniline hydrochloride. It appears probable that the p-toluidine would exhibit similar greater rapidity of action in this solvent also, and that m-aminophenol could be used in a technic similar to the "black periodic" but avoiding fat solvents. However, these alternative procedures have not been tested. m-Aminophenol requires 11% for a 1 M solution, p-toluidine 10.7%, or 14.36% of the commercially available hydrochloride in water. The last has a water solubility, 25%/25°C, high enough for a 1.75 M solution.

For aniline chloride in molar solution dissolve 9.3 gm ($= 9.1$ cc) aniline in 8.1 cc concentrated HCl (0.1 mol each), shaking during addition (the mixture becomes quite hot); dilute to 100 cc with distilled water. This solution effectively renders Schiff negative (with a 10 minute Schiff bath) the aldehyde formed in the Feulgen, peracetic acid and periodic acid reactions. Even a 15 minute aniline chloride bath is adequate to block the Feulgen reaction. A 6 hour exposure to molar aniline chloride or 18 hours in 0.1 M prevents the aldehyde reaction of retinal rod acromeres after peracetic acid oxidation. The periodic acid Schiff reaction of glycogen, retinal acromeres and corneal and scleral collagen is inhibited by 2 hours in 1 M or 18 hours in 0.1 M aniline chloride. That of epithelial mucin requires 4 hours in 1 M or 18 hours in 0.4 M aniline chloride. That of the lens capsule and Descemet's membrane is not blocked by 18 hours in molar aniline chloride; it requires a 2.5 M concentration for the same period.

As prepared above, aniline hydrochloride has a pH of 1.4–1.9. The pH level may be raised to about 4 without obvious decomposition; at about pH 4.5 the solution becomes milky, and at pH 5 it separates into an oily layer and an aqueous phase. The amount of sodium hydroxide required to produce turbidity corresponds to conversion of enough aniline chloride back to aniline to furnish about 1.9% aniline water, just about the usual solubility limit. The advantage of raising the pH level to 4 lies in avoidance of destruction of acid soluble tissue elements. Aldehyde blockade is perhaps more effective with the acid solution and progresses even more rapidly in glacial acetic acid.

Acetylation and Benzoylation of Aldehydes. A 24 hour acetylation at 23–25°C in 40% acetic anhydride/pyridine introduced after periodic acid oxidation of gastrointestinal mucins, glycogen, rodent arterial elastica, etc., more or less completely prevents the following Schiff reaction. The acid azo coupling reaction of aldehydes condensed with m-toluidine is similarly prevented, and the "black periodic" reaction (p. 273) is quite severely impaired. Benzoylation in 5% benzoyl chloride pyridine 4, 8 or 24 hours at 23–25°C is similarly effective. Alcoholic 40% or 25% acetic anhydride is less effective than the pyridine solutions at all time exposures.

Sometimes longer exposures (24 hours) are less completely effective than 4–8 hour exposures. The addition of 0.1 cc sulfuric acid to 10 cc acetic anhydride and 30 cc pyridine appears to increase its effectiveness somewhat and in the presence of the pyridine produces no positive evidence of complicating sulfation of other structures.

The reactions are written: $RCHO + 2 \ (CH_3CO)_2O + H_2O \rightarrow RCH(CH_3COO)_2 + 2 \ CH_3COOH$. The acetyl (or benzoyl) esters may be saponified and the aldehydes again liberated in chemical experiments, though this latter, at this writing has not been tested histochemically. Ketones do not react (Lillie *et al.*, studies on acylation of aldehydes, 1965).

Mixtures of 25 acetic anhydride: 75 glacial acetic acid with 0.2–0.25% by volume of concentrated sulfuric acid added are also quite effective, but it appears at this moment debatable whether the blockade is due to acetylation or to sulfation.

ACID GROUPS

The usual acid groupings demonstrable in tissues are the carboxylic acid residues of fatty acids, of carbohydrate uronic acids and of relatively acid proteins such as pepsinogen; the phosphoric acid residues of the nucleic acids; the sulfuric acid half esters of the aminopolysaccharides such as heparin, chondroitin and mucoitin sulfuric acids; and the sulfonic acid residues such as are produced by oxidative cleavage in the cystine proteins like keratin, and such as not improbably exist in cutaneous and ocular melanins.

Though each of these groups has other identifying reactions, such as the sudanophilia of the fatty acids, the specific amino acid reactions of certain proteins, the immunochemical fluorescence reactions of various globulins, the Feulgen reaction of deoxyribonucleic acid, the Criegee oxidation cleavage reactions of the glycolic polysaccharides, the reducing reactions of the melanins; they have in common the property of staining with basic aniline dyes. This property is known generally as basophilia.

Basophilia is conveniently studied with simple dilute solutions of basic dyes in buffered aqueous solution, and also with balanced mixtures of acid and basic dyes such as the azure A eosin B mixture (p. 162), also in buffered aqueous solutions.

The discriminating factor in both these methods is that sulfuric and sulfonic acid residues take up basic dyes at lower pH levels than do phosphoric acid residues, and that these in turn stain at lower pH levels than do various carboxylic acid groups.

Several factors enter into the estimation of the lowest pH at which a given tissue element stains: (1) The pK of tissue acids, which, especially in proteins, is influenced by the fixation employed. For example, erythrocytes are strongly basophil when stained with azure eosin at pH 8–10. After brief methanol fixation they become amphoteric at about pH 7 and strongly oxyphil at about pH 6.5–6. With 1–3 day formaldehyde fixation this shift occurs at about pH 6–5.5. (2) The concentration of the basic dye employed: Higher concentrations stain the same acidic elements at lower pH levels. (3) The precise dyestuff employed: Azure A at 1 mM concentration stains generally at lower pH levels than methylene blue or thionin, also at 1 mM, and pararosaniline stains at lower levels than crystal violet.

Further it must be recalled that strongly acid solutions hydrolyze nucleic acids to liberate deoxyaldose residues which can in acid solution readily condense with primary and less freely with secondary aryl amines to form stable Schiff's bases of the secondary or tertiary amine diphenamine type. The dye aldehyde compounds thus formed are relatively acid fast, whereas the usual salt union, basic dye + tissue acid reaction product is readily decolorized by acids.

Another factor in the estimation is the time of exposure. It would be expected that 18–24 hour staining ought to yield more intense staining than shorter intervals. This is not regularly the case. On some such trials staining has actually been greater in 30 minutes to 2 hours than in 18–24 hours. The reason for this paradoxical behavior seems related to the probability that in the longer interval hydrolysis occurs and dye base is adsorbed onto the glass container, with consequent lowering of dye concentration in the solution and redecolorization of stained objects in the tissue. This phenomenon is observed only in quite weak solutions (0.1–20 μM).

The pH Signature Technic of Dempsey, Singer and Wislocki (*Endocrinology* **38**:270, 1946; *Anat. Rec.* **102**:175, 1948; *Int. Rev. Cytol.* **1**:211, 1952). This method used dilute solutions of methylene blue, originally on Zenker fixed material, for demonstrating differences in basic dye uptake by various tissue elements. Foraker (*J. Histochem.* **7**:284, 1960) has applied the method to routine formalin fixed surgical material. He used 0.5 mM methylene blue in acetate buffers of pH 3, 4 and 5; phosphate buffers of pH 6 and 7 and Veronal buffers of pH 8 and 9; stained overnight and dehydrated in alcohol, cleared in xylene and mounted in HSR synthetic resin.

Because of the instability of methylene blue, its usual contamination by lower homologs and Bernthsen's methylene violet and of its generally weaker staining power I have usually employed 0.02% azure A (0.685 mM), extended the pH range down to 1 or occasionally to 0.5 and limited the staining time to 30–60 minutes. Because of the partial extraction of thiazin dyes by ethyl alcohol, I have usually dehydrated with acetone. In this we follow the practice reported by Highman from our laboratory in 1946 (*Stain Techn.* **20**:84) for buffered toluidine blue staining, rather than the later modifications of the Harvard group. Formalin fixation is used.

Buffered Azure A Staining. To 49 cc of the selected buffers add 1 cc 1% aqueous or alcoholic azure A. For pH 1 I usually employ 1 cc 37.5% hydrochloric acid in 99 cc distilled water (0.125 N); for pH 2 and 3, the HCl + KH_2PO_4 series; for pH 4 and 5, the acetate series; for pH 6 and 7, Sörensen's phosphates; and for pH 8 and 9, Michaelis's Veronal HCl series.

Acid-base staining with basic dyes should be completely decolorized by a 5 minute exposure to 0.2 N HCl in water or 70% alcohol.

Results: At pH 1 only mast cells, some cartilage, cutaneous and ocular melanins and cysteic acid produced by bromination or performic or peracetic acid oxidation of keratin, etc., should stain. Denser nuclei and mitotic figures appear at about pH 1.5; pancreatic acinar and gastric chief cell cytoplasm, at about pH 2.0. Epithelial mucins, varying according to species and locality, present minimum pH staining levels of 2–4, related probably to their composition, mucoitin sulfates, sialomucins and uronic acid mucins. Fatty acids require pH 3–4, and muscle, collagen and some mucins become basophilic above pH 4.5–5. Erythrocytes acquire basophilia at a somewhat higher level.

Staining with Nile blue constitutes a special case which will be discussed in greater detail under "Fats." When this dye is used in buffered solutions similar to those applied to the thiazin dyes, and sections are then dehydrated in alcohol or acetone, results are essentially similar to those with azure A. But when staining is done in 1% sulfuric acid (v/v, pH 0.85), a dark blue stain is conferred on liquid fatty acids, lipofuscin pigments and peptic gland zymogen granules which can be completely decolorized in a few seconds by acetone in the cases of lipofuscins and pepsinogen, or by glycol in the case of soluble fats with a somewhat longer interval, provided that the decolorization is done directly after the acid staining bath. The coloration is conserved when preparations are mounted in aqueous media. If such stained preparations are washed with water after being stained in the sulfuric acid solution, the fat solvent extractable stain is converted to a salt type of union, and lipofuscin preparations can then be dehydrated and mounted in resinous media. The stain changes, however, to the same relatively light green seen in preparations stained in azure A at pH 4 and similarly dehydrated.

For further details see Lillie, *J. Histochem.* 4:377, 1956; 6:130, 1958.

The Sulfuric Acid Nile Blue Technic for Fatty Acids (*Stain Techn.* 31:151, 1956). Use frozen sections for soluble fats, paraffin sections for lipofuscins, pepsinogen and other protein bound fatty acids. Stain 20 minutes in 0.05% Nile blue in 99 cc distilled water + 1 cc concentrated sulfuric acid. For extraction tests transfer frozen sections to diethylene glycol (HOCH$_2$—CH$_2$)$_2$O for 4 hours; transfer paraffin sections directly to anhydrous acetone, agitating for 1 minute. After acetone, the sections may be cleared in xylene and mounted in cellulose caprate or returned to water and mounted in glycerol gelatin or temporarily in water or glycerol for examination before restaining.

Sections for direct examination after Nile blue and restained sections are washed in several changes of distilled water or in running water of suitable quality and mounted in glycerol gelatin.

It is to be noted that this procedure does not discriminate between free fatty acids and alkaline earth soaps, since the sulfuric acid decomposes the latter to more or less insoluble sulfates and free fatty acids. According to Gomori (p. 205) calcium soaps may be converted to lead soaps by a 10 minute incubation at 55–60°C in 1–2% lead nitrate. The lead soaps are then converted to insoluble brown sulfide by 5–10 minute exposure to dilute ammonium sulfide. Free fatty acids, being insoluble in water and essentially nonionized, do not react. Calcium soaps are distinguished further from simple fatty acids by their insolubility in alcohol and other fat solvents. However, the lipofuscins are at least partly insoluble in boiling methanol chloroform and in hot pyridine, retaining their sudanophilia and Nile blue staining capacity and other reactions.

Lead soaps are often soluble in fat solvents; newly formed lead oleate is readily soluble in alcohol, lead stearate dissolves in hot alcohol, the linoleate is soluble in chloroform (*Merck Index*, 7th ed.).

Alkylation. Usually the Fraenkel-Conrat (*J. Biol. Chem.* **161:**259, 1945) procedure as modified by Fisher and Lillie (*J. Histochem.* **2:**81, 1954) for application in histology has been used. This process uses 0.05–0.1 N hydrochloric acid in methanol at 25°C, 37°C or 58–60°C for varying intervals. The basophilia of nuclei, cartilage, mast cells, mucins, pigments and proteins generally is abolished at intervals which are fairly constant for each constituent at the temperature used, on comparably fixed material. One disadvantage noted has been a swelling, fragmentation and loss of birefringence of collagen fibers which occurs in the hot acid methanol solutions. In about 1960 I tried using sulfuric acid in place of hydrochloric acid, with the purpose of obtaining a more nearly anhydrous methylation reagent and thereby perhaps accelerating methylation and decreasing the collagen destruction which was thought to be hydrolytic in nature. The 0.05 M sulfuric acid solution proved to be at least as effective in methylating as the 0.1 N HCl solution. It was found, moreover, that sulfuric acid methanol solutions of 0.25–0.1 M esterified fairly promptly, so that in 1 or 2 weeks no free sulfuric acid was detectable on testing with barium chloride. Molar solutions, however, remained unesterified or quite incompletely esterified even after several months at 25°C.

It was early observed that the methylation procedure promptly abolished the metachromatic basophilia of mast cells and cartilage and that longer intervals were required for lipofuscins, nucleic acids, etc., with still longer ones needed for cysteic acid produced by oxidation cleavage of cystine and for melanin. In 1957 Kantor and Schubert (*J. Am. Chem. Soc.* **79:**152) reported that the Fraenkel-Conrat reagent desulfated chondroitin sulfates, liberating methyl hydrogen sulfate and leaving unsulfated chondroitins.

In 1958 (*J. Histochem.* **6:**136) I showed that the methylation blockade of the Nile blue staining of peptic gland zymogen granules was broken by saponification in alcoholic KOH, and in 1959 (*J. Histochem.* **7:**123)

Spicer and I showed that while the metachromatic basophilia of peracetic acid oxidized hair cortex was abolished by drastic methylation and restored by saponification, as was the orthochromatic staining of proteins and cartilage above pH 4; the metachromatic staining of mast cells and cartilage occurring at pH 2 and below was not restored by saponification, even though only a quite mild methylation was employed. Spicer (*J. Histochem.* 8:18, 1960) later utilized this mild methylation both in combinations with sulfation and alone, and in contrast with more drastic methylation in studies of the reactivities of rodent mucopolysaccharides to azure A at low and medium pH levels and to alcian blue. This mild methylation apparently attacked only certain strongly acid carboxylic acids.

Methylation Procedures; Fisher-Lillie Technic. For 0.05 N HCl take 0.4 cc, for 0.1 N take 0.8 cc concentrated hydrochloric acid and make up to 100 cc with absolute methanol (reagent grade).

1. Deparaffinize sections in xylene, wash in 2 changes absolute alcohol, drain and immerse in methylation reagent. For methylation at 37°C or 60°C use screw capped Coplin jars, tightly closed, and check at intervals as a precaution against evaporation (methanol boils at 64.7°C).
2. After expiration of the prescribed interval, wash in descending alcohols and water.
3. Stain with azure A eosin B (p. 162), 0.02–0.05% azure A at graded pH levels for 30–60 minutes, with the sulfuric Nile blue technic or other method under study;
4. Dehydrate and clear or wash in water and mount as prescribed for the demonstration technic used.

Spicer's Mild Methylation. Use the 0.1 N HCl mixture above and methylate 1 hour at 60°C or 4 hours at 37°C.

The 0.1 M Methyl Sulfate Technic. Add 2.7 cc concentrated sulfuric acid to about 490 cc absolute methanol, mix thoroughly and add methanol to make 500 cc. Let stand at 25°C for about a week. Then test every day or two, by dropping 0.5 cc into 1 cc 1% barium chloride. When turbidity is no longer produced, the methylation reagent is ready and is stable for some months. Use enough at a time to cover sections in a Coplin jar. Preheat to 60°C or lower temperature if desired. At 60°C use tightly closed screw cap Coplin jars to avoid loss of methanol and increased concentration of dimethyl sulfate (B.P. 188.3–188.6°C).

The methyl sulfate reagent is similar to the Fraenkel-Conrat-Fisher reagent in its effect on basophilia, or, on some trials, it is somewhat slower. It is noteworthy that rat mast cells seem to resist methyl sulfate methylation up to 4 hours at 0.1 M methyl sulfate.

It has been further observed that while the methanol hydrochloric acid reagent completely removes iron from enterosiderin and hemosiderin pigments during a 4–8 hour 60°C methylation exposure, the sulfuric reagent apparently does not attack the iron oxide component of these pigments.

Since the ethyl sulfates of Ba, Sr, Ca and Pb are known to be soluble in water, it remained uncertain whether the active agent in this reagent was dimethyl sulfate or methyl sulfuric acid, CH_3—O—SO_2—OH. On testing this reagent with barium carbonate under microscopic observation, it was found that the $BaCO_3$ crystals become smaller and smaller and finally disappear and that small bubbles of gas are formed.

It is evident that methyl sulfuric acid is at least an important, if not the sole, methylating constituent of the solution.

These methylation technics, particularly the Fisher-Lillie 0.1 N HCl procedure have been used not only to prevent basic dye staining of nucleic acids, protein and polysaccharide carboxyls, and fatty acids as in lipofuscins, but also in a considerable variety of other procedures, such as the staining by elastin stains of elastins and altered collagen Fullmer, J. Histochem. 5:11, 1957; 6:425, 1958), the periodic acid Schiff reaction of glycogen, gastric mucins, thyroid colloid and connective tissues (second edition of this book, p. 163), the prevention of enterochromaffin reactions with diazonium salts and with dilute hematoxylin (Lillie, J. Histochem. 9:184, 1961), the prevention of the deamination of proteins (Terner and Clark, J. Histochem. 8:184, 1960).

Demethylation of carboxylic, phosphoric and sulfonic acid residues is essentially similar chemically to the deacylation of acetylated hydroxyls, except that in this instance it is the acyl radicle which remains immobile and demonstrable in the tissue.

The technic reported in 1958 (J. Histochem. 6:130) for the restoration of Nile blue staining of pepsinogen granules after methylation has proved applicable in several other situations and is essentially identical to the saponification procedure given under "Acetylation," on p. 254; thus:

After methylation treat sections 20–30 minutes in 1% potassium hydroxide in 70% alcohol; wash and stain by the selected demonstration procedures.

It is particularly to be observed here that the staining of ribonucleic acid sites is only partially or perhaps not at all restored. This I have attributed to alkaline alcoholic solution of the ribonucleic acid. It occurs equally on treatment of unmethylated material with alcoholic KOH solutions. It may be avoided by use of the ammonia alcohol saponification reagent recommended in the second edition of this book, thus:

After methylation treat 24 hours in 40 cc absolute alcohol + 10 cc 28% ammonia, wash and proceed with selected demonstration procedures.

Or the ribonucleic acid may be rendered insoluble in alcoholic KOH by postfixing sections 24 hours at 60°C in 8% aqueous formaldehyde or in

5% $K_2Cr_2O_7$ or 5% mercuric chloride. Picric acid and 5% lead nitrate treatments of similar duration were ineffective.

The permanganate demethylation reported by Fisher and Lillie (*loc. cit.*) has been little used and requires further exploration. Similar restoration has occasionally been observed when other oxidants are applied after methylation, *e.g.*, HNO_2, HIO_4, but these occurrences have not been adequately explored. Possibly some such reaction occurs as the following, which parallels the familiar dealkylation of tertiary amines by oxidants seen in the dealkylation of methylene blue.

$$R-CO-OCH_3 + O \rightarrow R-CO-OH + CH_2O$$
$$R-N-(CH_3)_2 + O \rightarrow R-NH-(CH_3) + CH_2O$$

Alkyl halides have occasionally been tried as such in histochemistry for alkylation of primary and secondary amines. Terner and Clark (*loc. cit.*) used ethyl chloride. I have employed methyl iodide and both propyl iodides. The excessive volatility of the first 2 (B.P. 12.3°C, 42.4°C, respectively) is a serious handicap to their histochemical use. Ethyl iodide (B.P. 72.4°C), n-propyl bromide (B.P. 71°C) and isopropyl and n-propyl iodides (89.5°C and 102.5°C) would seem perhaps more convenient.

Chapter 9

Cytoplasmic Granules and Organelles

MITOCHONDRIA

Supravital Technics

These round, oval, rod shaped or filamentous structures are destroyed by such acid fixatives as Zenker's fluid. They may be stained specifically by supravital technics with Janus green B (C.I. No. 11050), diethyl-safranin (C.I. No. 50206), Janus blue (C.I. No. 12211), Janus black I, pinacyanol (1st ed. C.I. No. 808), rhodamine B (C.I. No. 45170), and methylene blue (C.I. No. 52015). Cowdry identifies Janus black I as a mixture of a brown dye and Janus green B, on which latter its action depends. Janus blue or indazole blue is similar in its effectiveness to Janus green B. It is diethylsafranin-azo-β-naphthol (C.I. No. 12210). Pinacyanol is a red basic dye said to be superior to Janus green B. Rhodamine B is a weakly basic red dye.

Supravital Staining of Blood. Cowdry directs: Mix on a clean slide a small drop of blood with a small drop of 1:10,000 Janus green B in 0.85% salt solution (1% aqueous solution 1 cc, distilled water 99 cc, sodium chloride 850 mg, or use 99 cc of a 0.86% sodium chloride solution). Drop on cover-slip and let spread. Ring with petrolatum. In about 5–10 minutes mitochondria are colored deep bluish green. Similarly small fragments of fresh tissue may be crushed in the salt solution to a thin film.

The technics with methylene blue, Janus (indazole) blue, Janus black and rhodamine B are basically similar.

Hetherington (*Stain Techn.* 11:153, 1936) recommended pinacyanol (1st ed. C.I. No. 808)[1] alone or in combination with neutral red. He used a 0.1% solution of pinacyanol in 100% alcohol, diluting 1:40 for use with 100% alcohol, and adding, when desired, between the same and double the amount of neutral red (C.I. No. 50040). Schwind (*Blood* 5:597, 1950) prescribed stock solutions in 100% alcohol: 0.1% pinacyanol and 0.4% neutral red, 9 drops of pinacyanol and 30 drops of neutral red in 5 cc 100% alcohol. I suggest 0.3 cc, 1 cc and 100% alcohol to make 10 cc.

Flame clean slides, flood with one of the dilute dye mixtures, drain in

[1] Obtainable from Eastman Distillation Products Inc., Rochester, N.Y.

a vertical position and let dry, using a gentle, warm air stream in hot humid weather. Place on a clean coverglass a small drop of blood (or marrow diluted with or crushed in a drop of serum), using only enough blood to give a film one cell layer thick and avoid air bubbles. Cover with the stain coated slide and seal edges with petrolatum (petroleum jelly). Schwind recommends application of soft petrolatum with a 5 cc syringe and a short, 23 gauge hypodermic needle, and warns against moving the coverglass during the process, as this tends to rupture cells.

Mitochrondia soon color a deep blue to violet in still living and motile cells. Hetherington's neutral red mixture is reported to give a red color to nuclei, "neutral red granules and vacuoles." Schwind recorded a purplish blue color for nuclei.

Staining occurs more rapidly at 37°C, but preparations do not keep so long. Motility ceases somewhat below this temperature. As the colors are feebler than those in fixed preparations, brilliant illumination and a darkened laboratory are recommended.

As pinacyanol is light sensitive, its solutions must be stored in the dark and stained films must be kept in the dark. Preparations, even when stored in the cold, do not keep more than 2 weeks (Schwind). However, mitochondria remain deeply stained for many hours, contrasting with the fairly prompt fading in Janus green preparations.

Fixed Tissue Methods

Of more general application are methods using fixed tissue. Regaud's method (*Arch. Anat. Micr.* 11:291, 1910) requires fixation with Möller's (Regaud's) fluid (p. 56) for 4 days, followed by 8 days (4 changes of 2 days each according to Mallory) in 3% potassium bichromate. Wash in running water 24 hours. Dehydrate in alcohol, clear in benzene and imbed in paraffin. Cut thin sections (2–5 μ). Deparaffinize, hydrate and mordant 8–10 days in 5–15% iron alum [$NH_4Fe(SO_4)_2 \cdot 12H_2O$] solution. Cowdry reduces this iron alum step to 24 hours in a 5% solution. Wash in water for a few minutes. Stain 24 hours in aqueous 1% hematoxylin containing 10% each of alcohol and glycerol. Regaud specified 6–8 weeks, Cowdry required only 3 weeks' aging. Differentiate in 5% iron alum solution with microscopic control. Wash 30 minutes in running water. Dehydrate by the 95%, 100% alcohol series. Clear in xylene and mount in balsam. Mitochondria are sharply stained black.

Aniline Acid Fuchsin Methyl Green. Cowdry especially recommends the aniline-acid fuchsin-methyl green method of Bensley (*Am. J. Anat.* 12:297, 1911), with the Möller-Regaud fixation in place of Bensley's acetic acid, osmium tetroxide, potassium bichromate fixation:

1. Cowdry fixed thin slices 4 days in Möller's (Regaud's) fluid (p. 56) in a refrigerator at 3°C, changing the fluid daily; and mordanted in

3% potassium bichromate for 8 days, changing every second day. Bensley fixed in 4% osmium tetroxide solution 2 cc, 2.5% potassium bichromate solution 8 cc, and glacial acetic acid 1 drop, for 24 hours. I suggest the following emendation of this formula: 4% osmium tetroxide 2 cc, 4% potassium bichromate 5 cc, 0.5% acetic acid 3 cc. This assumes a value of 0.015 cc for 1 drop of glacial acetic acid.

2. With either fixation, wash several hours to overnight in running water.

3. Dehydrate (Cowdry) with graded alcohols, 70%, 80%, 95%, 100% giving 6–18 hour changes. Then clear through 100% alcohol and benzene, and 2 changes of benzene of 30–60 minutes each. Imbed in paraffin, and

4. Section at 3–5 μ. Deparaffinize and hydrate as usual through xylene and graded alcohols.

5. 1% potassium permanganate 1 minute.

6. Rinse in water.

7. 5% oxalic acid 1 minute.

8. Wash thoroughly in water.

9. Blot water from around the section and heat to steaming in Altmann's aniline acid fuchsin (filtered 5% aniline water 10 cc, acid fuchsin 1.5 gm; shake at intervals for 24 hours before using),[1] let cool and continue staining about 6 minutes (Bensley and Mallory preheated to 60°C and then stained 5 minutes as the solution cooled).

10. Wash 1 minute in distilled water.

11. Dip into 1% methyl green or drop it on the section (1–5 seconds). Bensley sometimes used 1% toluidine blue instead.

12. Wash in 95% alcohol (Cowdry).

13. Dehydrate in 100% alcohol, clear with 1 change of 100% alcohol and xylene (50:50) and 2 changes of xylene. Mount in Permount or neutral balsam.

Results: Mitochondria are crimson; nuclei, green (or blue); zymogen granules, red. If the alcohol takes out too much green, try acetone or *tert*-butanol.

Cain (*Quart. J. Micr. Sci.* 89:229, 1948) at step 10 differentiates in dilute sodium carbonate solution (1/200 saturated: about 0.1%) until cytoplasm is pale pink or colorless. Stop the differentiation and brighten the color of the mitochondria by dipping briefly into 0.125 N hydrochloric acid. Then wash in distilled water and counterstain in 0.5% aqueous methyl blue, rinse in water, dip for 3 seconds in 0.125 N hydrochloric acid, wash with distilled water, dehydrate (at leisure) in alcohols, clear and mount in balsam.

[1] Ehrlich (*Encyklopädie*) and Bensley specified 2 gm acid fuchsin; Conn gives solubility of acid fuchsin at 12–12.5%.

Chang (*Exp. Cell Res.* 11:643, 1956) gives the following modification of the Altmann aniline acid fuchsin method for mitochondria for use on 1 μ paraffin sections of frozen dried material. The aniline acid fuchsin contains only 10 gm acid fuchsin per 100 cc aniline water, is acidulated with 2 drops (*ca.* 0.05 cc) glacial acetic acid and is aged a week or more before using. Filter each time before using.

Chang's Aniline Acid Fuchsin Variant for Mitochondria.

1. Float 1 μ paraffin sections of frozen dried material on 3% formalin 1% $CaCl_2$ on albuminized slides and warm until flattened; drain and dry on slide warmer.
2. Without deparaffinizing, immerse sections 48 hours in 5% $K_2Cr_2O_7$, 1% $CaCl_2$.
3. Wash in running water 90 minutes, dry in air.
4. Deparaffinize and hydrate rapidly through xylene and alcohols.
5. Rinse in distilled water and stain 8–15 minutes in preheated aniline acid fuchsin at 60°C.
6. Rinse in distilled water and differentiate 2–5 minutes in aniline water. Rinse again in distilled water.
7. Counterstain 1 minute in 1% aqueous methyl green.
8. Dehydrate directly in 95% and 100% alcohols, clear with xylene and mount in Permount.

Results: Mitochondria, bright red; erythrocytes, dark red; collagen, red to purplish; nuclei, faintly green; cytoplasm, faint pink.

The exact staining time must be determined for each type of material, and the required differentiation time is determined by unstated criteria.

Material fixed in Baker's formol calcium (p. 38) or alcohol freeze substitution (pp. 41, 43, 313) has been found to give good results.

Phosphotungstic Acid Hematoxylin. Mallory recommended a technic with phosphotungstic acid hematoxylin. Fix 24 hours or more in 10% formalin, mordant 2–5 days in 3–4 changes of 5% aqueous ferric chloride solution, wash briefly in water, harden in 3–4 changes of 80% alcohol for 1–2 days, until the alcohol remains clear. Imbed in paraffin as usual, and bring paraffin sections to water.

1. 0.25% potassium permanganate 5–10 minutes.
2. Rinse.
3. 5% oxalic acid 3–5 minutes.
4. Wash thoroughly in tap water.
5. Stain in Mallory's phosphotungstic acid hematoxylin (p. 537) for 1–2 days.

6. Rinse in tap water.
7. Differentiate in 95% alcohol.
8. Dehydrate with 100% alcohol, clear in xylene and mount in balsam.

Results: Nuclei and mitochondria are stained deep blue; collagen and elastin, reddish; myoglia and neuroglia fibrils, blue.

GOLGI SUBSTANCE

Golgi apparatus was first described as an intricate anastomosing network of cytoplasmic strands and was first demonstrated by Golgi in nerve cells in 1898. It is demonstrable by impregnations with silver, with osmium tetroxide, or both. The technics are fickle and often fail, and considerable experimentation may be necessary to obtain optimal results with any given type of material. For these reasons its study in routine pathologic material would be a matter of considerable difficulty, especially since it requires separate fixation of special tissue blocks.

Ramón y Cajal's Uranium Silver Method. The following technic is recommended by Cowdry for young animals.

1. Fix 8–24 hours in uranyl nitrate 1 gm, formalin 15 cc, distilled water 100 cc.
2. Wash quickly in distilled water.
3. Impregnate 1–2 days in 1.5% silver nitrate.
4. Rinse in distilled water.
5. Reduce 12 hours in a freshly prepared solution of hydroquinone 2 gm, formalin 15 cc, distilled water 100 cc, anhydrous sodium sulfite 150 mg. (*This is Ramón y Cajal's developer.*)
6. Wash in distilled water. Dehydrate, clear and imbed in paraffin, using a short alcohol or acetone schedule.
7. Deparaffinize sections and mount.

Da Fano's Cobalt Silver Method. This method is of more general application. Thus, from Cowdry:

1. Fix in 1 gm cobalt nitrate $[Co(NO_3)_2 \cdot 6H_2O]$, 100 cc distilled water. 6–15 cc formalin for 3–18 hours. Embryonic tissues require the smaller amounts of formalin. With ordinary adult tissues use 15 cc. Cartilage and small organs, such as those of mice, are fixed adequately in 3–4 hours; routine tissues, in 6–8 hours; central nervous tissues, in 8–18 hours.
2. Rinse in distilled water.
3. Impregnate 1–2 days in 1.5% silver nitrate (1% for very small, easily permeable fragments, 2% for fatty and central nervous tissues).

4. Rinse in distilled water.
5. Cut blocks thinner than 2 mm. Reduce in fresh Ramón y Cajal's developer (see above) for 12–24 hours.
6. Wash in distilled water 30 minutes. Dehydrate, clear and imbed in paraffin. For greater permanence, bring sections to water, tone 1–2 hours in 0.1–0.2% gold chloride, wash and counterstain with alum carmine.

Results: Golgi apparatus, black. This technic is essentially that given by Cowdry.

Elftman's Aoyama Silver Method Variant for Golgi Substance. Elftman (*Anat. Rec.* **106**:381, 1950, and letter, May 5, 1950) recommends an Aoyama Golgi body technic for the selective demonstration of Sertoli cells. Fix mouse testis 18–24 hours in neutral 10% formalin (carefully decanted from the excess calcium carbonate) to which is added 1% (43.5 mM) of cadmium chloride ($CdCl_2 \cdot 2\frac{1}{2}H_2O$). Rinse in 2 changes of distilled water. Immerse for 16 hours in 1.5% silver nitrate. Rinse quickly in 2 changes of distilled water. Reduce 5 hours in Ramón y Cajal's developer (p. 290) or in an acid fluid containing instead of 2 gm just 1 gm hydroquinone, 15 cc formalin, 100 cc distilled water and 150 mg sodium bisulfite ($NaHSO_3$). Wash, dehydrate, clear and infiltrate and imbed in paraffin as usual.

If desired, counterstain by the azure eosin method (p. 162) or by some other similar Romanovsky technic.

Sertoli cell cytoplasm blackens, as does Golgi material in the spermatogenic cell series.

Elftman comments that both he and Baker find a 5 hour reduction more than ample in this and the DaFano technic (p. 290). Elftman has had poor success in applying this procedure to paraffin sections. Frozen sections might be tried.

Elftman later (*Stain Techn.* **27**:47, 1952) found prior fixation productive of irregularities, and introduced gold toning to confer greater resistance to subsequent histochemical procedures.

Elftman's Direct Silver Method for Golgi Substance.

1. Place small blocks of fresh tissue in 15% formalin containing 2% silver nitrate (pH 4) for 2 hours. (Adjust with a drop or 2 of acetic acid if necessary, or use pH 4 acetate buffer as the solvent.)
2. Rinse 5 seconds with 15% formalin or distilled water.
3. Immerse in 15% formalin containing 2% hydroquinone for 2 hours.
4. Complete fixation by an additional overnight treatment with 15% formalin.

5. Dehydrate with alcohols, clear and infiltrate and imbed in paraffin and section as usual.
6. Sections may be deparaffinized and mounted at this point for preliminary examination. Otherwise deparaffinize and hydrate as usual.
7. If necessary, reduce density of silver deposit by oxidizing in 0.1% iron alum for a few minutes under microscopic control.
8. Wash in distilled water.
9. Tone in 0.2% acid gold chloride for 10 or 15 minutes.
10. Rinse in distilled water and remove silver chloride in 2% sodium thiosulfate, 2 minutes.
11. Wash 5 minutes in running water.
12. Counterstain as desired: *e.g.*, the periodic acid Schiff procedure (p. 198), the allochrome method (p. 549), a Mallory aniline blue variant, the Van Gieson stain, etc.
13. Dehydrate, clear and mount in synthetic resin (or balsam; a reducing medium seems indicated).

Results: Golgi elements are blackened; but, as Elftman cautions, not all that is black is Golgi material. Omission of the gold toning leaves the silver deposits much more susceptible to oxidative fading, either by subsequently employed histochemical reagents or by the mounting medium.

The Osmium Tetroxide Method. Cowdry recommends especially Ludford's (*J. Roy. Micr. Soc.* **46**:107, 1926) variants of the osmium tetroxide methods. Thus:

1. Fix thin blocks 18 hours in Mann's osmic sublimate fluid (p. 49).
2. Wash 30 minutes in distilled water.
3. Impregnate 3 days at 30°C in 2% osmium tetroxide; or 1 day in 2% osmium tetroxide at 35°C, 1 day in 1% and 1 day in 0.5%.
4. Wash 1 day in water at 30°C or 35°C.
5. Dehydrate, clear and imbed in paraffin.
6. Cut sections at 3–5 μ; deparaffinize and mount.

Results: Golgi apparatus, yolk, and fat are blackened. Other structures remain yellow to brown.

By treatment with turpentine the blackening is gradually removed from yolk and fat, perhaps completely in 10–15 minutes, leaving the Golgi apparatus black (Lee, Baker). If mitochondria are not blackened they may be counterstained (Ludford) with Altmann's aniline acid fuchsin, heating to steaming and letting stand for 30 minutes. Then wash in water and differentiate with 100% alcohol. Or one may counterstain nuclei with safranin, crystal violet or neutral red for a few minutes in dilute (1:1000?) aqueous solutions. Again dehydrate and differentiate with alcohol.

Baker's Sudan Black. Baker (*Quart. J. Micr. Sci.* 90:293, 1949) revised his 1944 method (*ibid.* 85:1, 1944) cited in my first edition, by introducing a chromation after formaldehyde fixation, less vigorous than that of Ciaccio. The method differs from Ciaccio's in that no fat solvent test is applied. Neutral fats are colored in the same way as Golgi bodies; but Baker now states that the latter do not stain with Sudan IV, reversing his previous position. The technic:

1. Fix blocks 2–3 mm in thickness for 1 hour in 10% formalin containing 0.7% sodium chloride and kept over marble chips.
2. Transfer directly to a fresh formalin bichromate mixture containing 88 cc 2.5% $K_2Cr_2O_7$, 7 cc 10% NaCl and 5 cc neutral formalin (kept over marble chips), and let stand for 5 hours.
3. Transfer directly to 5% potassium bichromate for 18 hours at room temperature, and then place in 60°C paraffin oven for 24 hours.
4. Wash 6 hours in running water.
5. Infiltrate at 37°C for 18 hours (or any convenient longer period) in 25% gelatin containing 0.2% sodium *p*-hydroxybenzoate.
6. Cool, block and harden in *formalum,* a solution of 20 cc formalin, 4 gm potassium alum and 80 cc water, for 18 hours, or any convenient longer period.
7. Section at 8–10 μ on freezing microtome.
8. Transfer section to 70% alcohol.
9. Stain 2½ minutes (30 seconds to 4 minutes) in a saturated solution of Sudan black B. (Boil 0.5 gm in 100 cc 70% alcohol under a reflux condenser for 10 minutes, or saturate by shaking at intervals for several days.)
10. Wash 5 seconds in 70% alcohol; and then 1 minute in 50% alcohol.
11. Wash in water, sinking section below surface.
12. Counterstain in Mayer's carmalum (or other alum carmine) for 2–4 minutes.
13. Rinse in *distilled* water and wash in 2 large changes of water.
14. Float onto slide, blot and mount in Farrants's glycerol gum arabic (p. 101). Harden mounts overnight in paraffin oven.

Results: Solid Golgi bodies and outer parts of hollow ones, dark blue; Golgi vacuoles, colorless; cytoplasm, pale gray blue to colorless; chromatin, red or pink; neutral fats (triglycerides), dark blue.

Characteristics of the Golgi Substance. The Smith-Dietrich procedure, as outlined on pp. 482, 487, stains the Golgi substance gray to black if the differentiation procedure is shortened to 8 hours.

The Golgi substance is negative to the Windaus (p. 474) and Schultz cholesterol tests (p. 472). It is removed when fresh tissues are fixed in alcohol or other lipid solvents. After fixation in calcium formalin it withstands boiling water (30 minutes), ether (15 hours), 1 N hydrochloric acid at 57°C (4 hours), boiling 100% alcohol and boiling ether (30 minutes each), or ether alcohol hydrochloric acid at 50°C for 5 hours; but not 30 parts xylene + 70 parts glacial acetic acid at 57°C for 15 hours. (The last was devised as a myelin solvent.) It resists the usual paraffin imbedding technic, thus resembling myelin after formalin fixation.

Elftman reported at the 1953 meeting of the Histochemical Society that the Golgi substance was peracetic acid Schiff positive (p. 183). In the discussion which followed I brought out that the periodic acid Schiff reaction of the Golgi substance reported by Gersh (*Arch. Path.* 47:99, 1949) and attributed by him to glycoprotein, and the peracetic acid Schiff reaction of this substance were probably both due to unsaturated fatty acids and their oxidation products (*J. Histochem.* 1:387, 1953).

After formalin fixation the phosphatides cephalin, sphingomyelin and lecithin likewise resist solution in ether, acetone or 100% alcohol, but may be extracted by pyridine, by a 30:70 xylene acetic mixture, or by a sequence treatment in saturated aqueous sodium oleate or ricinoleate (24 hours) followed by 30 minutes each in boiling 100% alcohol and boiling ether. Cephalin and lecithin are blackened by osmication and withstand decolorization by turpentine; sphingomyelin does not.

Hence the Golgi substance probably consists of cephalin, lecithin or both, at least in the snail spermatocytes investigated by Baker.

Of recent years quite a number of reports of specific enzyme localization in the Golgi area of various cell systems have appeared.

SALIVARY GLAND

The zymogen granules are only moderately oxyphil to neutral stain mixtures. They are dissolved by fixatives containing acetic acid, such as aqueous or alcoholic 5% acetic 10% formalin, Carnoy, Zenker, Tellyesniczky's acetic bichromate, Bouin and Gendre. Their oxyphilia is better shown after fixation with such fluids as Kose's bichromate formalin or Spuler's Zenker formalin than with neutral aqueous formalin. The azure A eosin B technic (p. 162) is suggested for this reaction. The granules resist digestion with 1:1000 malt diastase in pH 6 saline solution, which removes the basophilic ribonucleic acid from the basal cytoplasm.

Parotid zymogen granules give a positive Schiff aldehyde reaction after oxidation with periodic acid (p. 198) but not after potassium permanganate or chromic acid oxidation. The periodic Schiff positive material resists diastase digestion. These reactions have been recorded in man, rabbit, rat and guinea pig. Positive (blue violet) Gram-Weigert staining is sometimes noted in rabbits and rats.

Tryptophan reactions with the xanthydrol (p. 232), the rosindole (p. 231) and the postcoupled benzylidene (p. 230) methods have been recorded for human, monkey and mouse serous parotid acini, for submaxillary demilunes in the monkey and for the eosinophilic granules of mouse submaxillary duct cells (*J. Histochem.* 5:188, 279, 1957). The tyrosine reaction by the diazotization coupling method also appears in the same locations.

Salivary gland mucins are discussed under aminopolysaccharides (pp. 513–514).

PANCREAS

Like those of the serous salivary gland acini, pancreatic zymogen granules are destroyed by aqueous and alcoholic acetic formalins, and by Carnoy's and Bouin's fluids, and they disappear from all but the most superficial acini on fixation with Tellyesniczky's bichromate, Zenker's and Gendre's fluids. They are well preserved by buffered neutral formalin, by Orth's, Kose's, and Möller's bichromate formalin fluids and by formalin Zenker variants. They are also well preserved by buffered neutral mercuric chloride without formaldehyde (see B-4, p. 46). This fixation is useful for the study of amine group reactions.

They stain conspiciously red after neutral formalin and formalin bichromate fixations with azure A eosin B (p. 162) at pH 4–4.5; at pH 5, for Spuler and Helly fixations; and at 5.5–6 after neutral sublimate (B-4). They become especially conspicuous if cytoplasmic ribonucleic acid is first removed by ribonuclease digestion (p. 147) or ice cold mineral acid or alcoholic alkali extraction (p. 194), or if it is rendered unreactive by methylation (p. 282).

In contradistinction to salivary zymogen granules, those of the pancreas may stain or remain unstained by the periodic acid leucofuchsin technic. Both conditions have been seen in man and mice; the negative phase has been seen in rat and guinea pig pancreas; but in rabbits I have seen these granules HIO_4 Schiff positive. They are Bauer and Casella (p. 199) negative, and are usually violet with the Gram-Weigert method (p. 262).

Pancreatic Islets

Bensley's method with neutral stains was designed especially for differentiation of pancreatic islet cells. The neutral stains were made by precipitating aqueous crystal violet with an approximate stoichiometric proportion of acid fuchsin or orange G, or safranin with an acid violet, which last procedure is presented in detail below. Prolonged staining with a 24 hour old 20% alcohol dilution of the stock 100% ethyl alcohol solution of the crystal violet salts was used. In all 3, differentiation is carried out under microscopic control with clove oil and alcohol.

Safranin Acid Violet. Bensley's (*Am. J. Anat.* **12**:297, 1911) safranin acid violet has been used with striking contrasts. This is a true neutral stain made by precipitating saturated aqueous safranin O (C.I. No. 50240) by cautiously adding saturated aqueous acid violet. Bensley did not specify which acid violet, but fast acid violet 10B (C.I. No. 42571) and eriocyanine A (C.I. No. 42576)—two rather blue violets—and a reddish violet formyl violet S4B (C.I. No. 42650) readily form coarse granular precipitates with safranin; and all will probably serve. Eriocyanine A is the bluest of the 3 and resembles the color depicted in Maximow's *Histology*, first ed., p. 692. The eriocyanine A is added until on splashing the mixture up the sides of the flask the color changes, rather abruptly, from red to violet. The precipitate is collected on a filter, dried and dissolved in 100% alcohol as with Bensley's other neutral stains, and the staining technic follows the same general procedure.

Eriocyanine A (Geigy). Two dyes are marketed under this name, Acid Blue 34, C.I. No. 42561, benzyl-pentamethyl-pararosaniline disulfonate, and Acid Blue 75, C.I. No. 42576, dibenzyl-tetramethyl-pararosaniline disfulonate, "Patentblau AE." The second of these was identified as the dye best corresponding to Bensley's acid violet and is prescribed in the safranin eriocyanine A technic of the second edition of this book. In view of the confusion in naming it would perhaps seem wise to abandon the name "eriocyanine A" and revert to the term "patent blue AE," cited as the original name in the *Colour Index*. But patent blue AE is now used by 2 companies to designate C.I. No. 42090, which is a dibenzyl-diethyl-diamino-triphenylmethane trisulfonate (ammonium salt). Hence we adhere to the name previously used and include C.I. No. 42576 in its description.

Bensley specified fixation with his acetic osmic bichromate mixture (p. 288) or with the Spuler-Maximow formalin Zenker fluid (p. 50). Sections should be under 5 μ in thickness. Dilute the stock alcoholic stain with an equal volume of distilled water, let stand 30 minutes, filter and use at once. Stain 5–30 minutes (Bensley), 40–50 minutes (Maurer and Lewis: *J. Exp. Med.* **36**:141, 1922), or as long as 2 hours (Cowdry, McClung). Blot and dehydrate with acetone, clear in xylene or toluene. Maurer and Lewis passed rapidly through 95% alcohol to remove precipitates, dehydrated in 100% alcohol and cleared in benzene. Then differentiate sections individually under microscopic control in a mixture of 3 volumes clove oil and 1 volume of 100% alcohol. Wash thoroughly with xylene (or toluene or benzene) and mount in balsam (in originals).

Nuclei and granules of beta cells of pancreatic islets stain red; granules of alpha cells of pancreatic islets (Bensley) and of hypophysis and erythrocytes stain blue to violet. Hypophyseal chromophobe cells show at most a faint violet stippling.

Maurer and Lewis identified the red staining cells as alpha cells and the blue as beta, and commented on the basophilia of the so-called "acidophil" cells of the hypophysis produced by this method. They further stated that the various types of chromophil cells are impossible to differentiate cytologically, except by the specific granule stains. I find that the same cell areas in which nearly all the cells stain pink with azure eosin, stain predominantly blue in the adjacent section with safranin eriocyanine A.

On trial of the foregoing method it is found that the high alcohol content (50%) of the final staining mixture inhibits staining in covered Coplin jars, just as it does with Wright's blood stain. However, only Maurer and Lewis spoke of staining on the slide as is customary with blood stains.

In order to test out various acid violets to ascertain which was the best for this method, we devised the following method. I cite this because it seems to work well in practice and entails far less trouble than the traditional Bensley method.

Safranin O Eriocyanine A Method.

1. Bring thin paraffin sections through xylenes and alcohols to water as usual, treating mercury fixed material 5 minutes with 0.5% iodine in 70% alcohol and 1 minute in 5% sodium thiosulfate.
2. Stain 30 minutes in

1% safranin O (C.I. No. 50240)	2	cc
1% eriocyanine A (C.I. No. 42576)	2	cc
0.1 M citric acid	1.3	cc
0.2 M disodium phosphate	0.7	cc
Distilled water	34	cc

3. Rinse in water, dehydrate with acetone, clear in acetone and xylene and 2 changes of xylene, mount in polystyrene or other synthetic resin.

Results: Nuclei, beta cells—red; erythrocytes and alpha cells—blue. Staining is already fairly good in 10 minutes, and is perhaps slightly better in an hour than in 30 minutes. A pH 3.8 acetate buffer can probably be used.

If desired the buffer may be omitted and Bensley's 3:1 clove oil + 100% alcohol mixture used for differentiation instead.

I have used this method also on hypophyses fixed in neutral formalin as well as with Orth's and Spuler's fluids, with perhaps even more brilliant contrasts. Negri bodies and necrotic nerve cells appear conspicuous in light blue by this method.

Aniline Blue Orange G. Bensley also recommends a variant of Mallory's aniline blue orange G stain for pancreatic islets, which I requote from Mallory with slight changes: Fix fresh tissue in thin slices with the Spuler-Maximow fluid (p. 50) for 4–24 hours:

1. Presumably after the usual iodine and sodium thiosulfate treatment,
2. Stain 10 minutes in Altmann's aniline acid fuchsin (p. 288).
3. Wash rapidly in previously boiled and cooled distilled water.
4. Mordant 10 minutes in 1% aqueous phosphomolybdic acid solution.
5. Drain and stain 1 hour or less in 0.5 gm aniline blue (C.I. No. 42755), or methyl blue (C.I. No. 42780), 2 gm orange G (C.I. No. 16230), 100 cc distilled water.
6. Drain and differentiate in 95% alcohol until gross color clouds cease coming off.
7. Dehydrate with 100% alcohol, clear in xylene and mount in balsam.

Results: Alpha granules, orange red; beta granules, bluish; acinar cells, bluish violet, sometimes with orange zymogen granules; erythrocytes, red. Bencosme (*Arch. Path.* **53**:87, 1952) recommends a very elaborate schedule using a Masson trichrome procedure, for which the reader is referred to the journal.

Chrome Alum Hematoxylin Phloxine. Bell (*Am. J. Path.* **22**:631, 1946) strongly recommended Gomori's chrome alum hematoxylin phloxine method. Gomori (*Am. J. Path.*, **17**:395, 1941) directed as follows: Bouin's fluid or formalin Zenker fixations are preferred. Cut paraffin sections at 2–4 μ.

1. Run sections through xylene and alcohols to water.
2. Refix in Bouin's fluid for 12–24 hours.
3. Wash sections thoroughly in tap water to remove picric acid.
4. Treat sections for about 1 minute with a solution containing about 0.3% each of potassium permanganate and sulfuric acid.
5. Decolorize with a 2–5% solution of sodium bisulfite. Wash.
6. Stain in the following hematoxylin solution under microscopic control until the beta cells stand out deep blue (about 10–15 minutes): Mix equal parts of 1% aqueous hematoxylin and 3% chrome alum. Add to each 100 cc of the mixture 2 cc 5% potassium bichromate and 2 cc 0.5 N sulfuric acid. The mixture is ripe after 48 hours and can be used as long as a film with a metallic luster will continue to form on its surface after 1 day's standing in a Coplin jar (about 4–8 weeks). Filter before use.
7. Differentiate in 1% (0.125 N) hydrochloric acid alcohol for about 1 minute.
8. Wash under the tap until the section is a clear blue.

9. Counterstain with 0.5% aqueous solution of phloxine (B?) for 5 minutes. Rinse.
10. Immerse in 5% phosphotungstic acid solution for 1 minute.
11. Wash under the tap for 5 minutes. The section should regain its red color.
12. Differentiate in 95% alcohol. If the section is too red and the alpha cells do not stand out clearly enough, rinse the section for about 15–20 seconds in 80% alcohol.
13. Transfer to 100% alcohol, clear in xylene and mount in balsam.

Results: Beta cells are blue; alpha cells, red; delta cells, from pink to red and indistinguishable from alpha cells; acinar zymogen granules, red to unstained in pancreas. In hypophysis, alpha cells are pink; beta cells, gray blue, and not readily distinguished from chromophobes; nuclei, red purple to blue violet; erythrocytes, deep pink; smooth muscle, pink; collagen, unstained; goblet cell mucin, coarsely granular and dark, slightly greenish blue in color.

Bell found that this method permitted ready distinction of alpha and beta granules in the pancreatic islets even on material fixed as much as 12 hours post mortem.

In place of steps 9–12 Bencosme (*Arch. Path.* **53**:87, 1952) substitutes a ponceau acid fuchsin mixture as used for Masson stains (p. 545) and stains 15–45 minutes, rinses in 1% acetic acid, and differentiates in 1% phosphomolybdic acid until alpha and beta cells are clear (5–30 minutes). Rinse in 1% acetic acid. Dehydrate with 100% alcohol.

Mitochondria of islet cells are pale red to orange red, alpha granules are deep red, beta granules are blue gray to black, and cytoplasm of delta cells is pale gray or gray orange.

Ferner (*Virchow Arch. path. Anat.* **319**:390, 1951) used the Gros-Schultze silver method for the specific silvering of islet alpha cells and of certain cells other than the enterochromaffin cells in the gastric mucosa (dog). The beta granules are not blackened, but Heidenhain-Kultschitzky cells do blacken along with Ferner's "silver cells" in the gastric mucosa. Ferner's silver cells do not react by the Masson argentaffin method (but see Bencosme, below), with methenamine silver (p. 240), nor with the ferric ferricyanide reduction test (p. 211), which demonstrates the argentaffin cells of the duct epithelium.

The Gros-Schultze method was originally devised for demonstration of axons and neurofibrils in frozen sections. Material fixed for 10 days to several months in neutral formalin is used. Sections are first impregnated in silver nitrate and then in an ammoniacal silver nitrate solution containing a little excess of ammonia to inhibit silvering of nuclei and connective tissue. Exact prescriptions vary. The original prescription called for formaldehyde treatment between the silver nitrate and the ammoniacal silver steps. Landau's variant for paraffin sections used formaldehyde before the nitrate and after the diammine silver, but not between.

Bencosme (*Arch. Path.* **53**:96, 1952) prescribes fixation in 10% formalin or in the trichloroacetic acid variant of Bouin's fluid (saturated picric 75:40% formaldehyde 25:2% trichloroacetic 5). After paraffin imbedding he employed one of Masson's argentaffin cell stains (p. 239), the Laidlaw reticulum method (p. 528) or Roger's silver method according to Van Campenhout (*Proc. Soc. Exp. Biol. Med.* **30**:617, 1933). It appears probable that all these are argyrophil, not argentaffin, procedures.

Hellweg (*Virchow Arch. path. Anat.* **327**:502, 1955) recommends a variant of the Bodian protargol technic for demonstration of islet alpha cells in formalin fixed material.

1. Float paraffin sections on slides with Ruyter's fluid (8 cc distilled water, 2 cc acetone, 1 drop methyl benzoate) or other *protein free* fluid. Dry as usual.
2. Deparaffinize, hydrate and soak 24 hours in 40% formaldehyde.
3. Wash in distilled water.
4. Incubate 12–24 hours at 48°C in the dark in 1–2% protargol (pH 6.9–7.9), containing 2 gm metallic copper to 50 cc in a Coplin jar.
5. Wash in distilled water.
6. Develop 5 minutes in 1 gm hydroquinone, 5 gm sodium sulfite, distilled water 100 cc.
7. Wash in distilled water.
8. Wash 3 minutes in 2% oxalic acid.
9. Wash in water, dehydrate in alcohols, clear in xylene, mount in balsam.

Results: Pancreatic argyrophil (alpha) cells, brown to black.

Hypophyseal, adrenal medullary and gastrointestinal argyrophil cells generally require a full 24 hours in protargol.

The protargol should be Winthrop's protargol-S or Bayer's "für die Bodian-Methode," and solutions should not be more than a week old. The hydroquinone solution should be made up fresh each time.

Gold toning appeared to be of little value and is omitted. Horse, dog and mouse material gave fair demonstrations of pancreatic alpha cells. The procedure was unsuccessful in rat and rabbit. Human material was apparently not tested.

Bensley's aniline acid fuchsin methyl green method gives green acinar cells with deeper green nuclei; red zymogen granules, basal filaments and mitochondria, deep red alpha granules; green beta granules. For the method see pp. 287–288.

The foregoing methods may be used also for hypophysis, parathyroid and other glands.

HYPOPHYSIS

The alpha or acidophil, beta or "basophil" or cyanophil, and chromophobe cells of the anterior lobe of the hypophysis may be distinguished by use of stains of the hematoxylin eosin type, notably with phloxine according to Mallory, with which the granules of the alpha cells stain pink or red, and those of the beta cells stain blue. Alpha granules stain red by the eosin B azure A technics (p. 162).

Laqueur (personal communication) finds the Gomori aldehyde fuchsin method (p. 556) useful for anterior hypophysis. Using a Mallory-Heidenhain counterstain with fast green FCF instead of aniline blue, the alpha granules are orange red; beta granules, violet to purple; delta granules, green to greenish blue; chief cell cytoplasm, pale gray green; connective tissue, green; elastica, violet; nucleoli and erythrocytes, red.

By the Mallory-Heidenhain and Masson aniline blue (p. 545) technics alpha granules stain red; beta granules, bright blue; delta granules, lighter blue. After mercuric chloride formalin fixation (p. 48) the Masson method gives dark violet alpha granules.

Laqueur considers the periodic acid Schiff method (p. 198) to be one of the most reliable for beta granules and colloid (both red purple). Delta granules are not distinguished from beta granules, though delta cells usually contain less periodic Schiff positive material.

Methyl Blue Eosin. This method, introduced by Mann in 1894 for nervous tissues and extensively used for Negri bodies, has been modified in our laboratory by introduction of buffering of the mixture and staining at 60°C. Water soluble aniline blue, which was formerly a mixture of diphenylrosaniline trisulfonic acid, C.I. No. 42755, and triphenylpararosaniline trisulfonic acid, C.I. No. 42780 (first ed., C.I. No. 707), can be substituted for methyl blue, C.I. No. 42780; the results are essentially identical. This is not surprising since at least one American company now furnishes the same dye, C.I. No. 42780, under both names. The substitution of eosin B (2,8-dinitro-4,6-dibromo-10-(o-carboxyphenyl)-3-hydroxy-7-xanthone, C.I. No. 45400) for Mann's eosin Y (C.I. No. 45380) results in deeper red in erythrocytes, hypophyseal alpha cells, etc. The change in proportion of the two 1% dye solutions from the original equal volume mixture to the 4:1 eosin methyl blue ratio also seems advantageous (Glenner and Lillie, *Stain Techn.* **32**:187, 1957).

Eosin B Methyl Blue Technic. Fix in buffered neutral formalin, buffered sublimate formalin (B-5, p. 48) or Zenker formalin (Spuler or Helly, p. 50). After the usual paraffin imbedding, cut 4–6 μ sections. Attach, deparaffinize and hydrate as usual. Treat mercury fixed tissues 10 minutes in 0.5% iodine 70% alcohol and 2 minutes in 5% thiosulfate; wash 10 minutes in running water.

1. Stain 1 hour, placing slides in solution in Coplin jars at 25°C and transferring at once to 60°C oven, using the following mixture:

1% aqueous eosin B	8 cc
1% aqueous methyl blue or aniline blue	2 cc
McIlvaine citric acid 11:9 disodium phosphate buffer	2 cc
Distilled water	28 cc

A 0.01 M acetate buffer pH 4.5–4.6, 30 cc may be substituted for the McIlvaine buffer and water.

2. Wash 5 minutes in running water, dehydrate through graded (50%, 80%, 100%) acetones, clear with acetone plus xylene (1:1) and two changes of xylene. Mount in Permount or similar resin.

Results: Hypophyseal alpha cell granules, dark red; beta cell granules, dark blue; chromophobes, gray to pink; colloid, red to blue violet; erythrocytes, orange red; collagen fibers, blue.

With staining at pH 3.6 hypophyseal eosinophils, erythrocytes, keratinized epithelium and muscle stain bright pink to red. Hypophyseal chief cells and epithelial and gland cytoplasms stain purplish or grayish pink. Collagen, reticulin and hypophyseal cyanophils stain blue; and some mucins tinge pale bluish. Nuclei stain black with iron hematoxylin, or red without it. Granules of eosinophil leucocytes stain red or blue or perhaps both in the same cell.

McLetchie's method for certain cyanophil granules in the pituitary is perhaps worthy of trial. It depends on pretreatment with iodine and with phosphotungstic acid, and utilizes an acid dye. For this method Lendrum (*J. Path. Bact.* 57:267, 270, 1945) first prepares the "carbacid fuchsin" thus: Mix 1 gm acid fuchsin (C.I. No. 42685) with 0.4 gm melted phenol crystals; cool and dissolve in 10 cc 95% alcohol. Grind 0.5 gm starch fine. Add 0.5 gm dextrin and grind to a fine powder. Suspend in 100 cc water by grinding with gradual addition of the water. Heat to 80°C, cool, filter and add it to the acid fuchsin phenol alcohol mixture to make a total of 100 cc.

For this technic Lendrum prescribes a formalin mercuric chloride fixation and an alcohol, chloroform, paraffin imbedding sequence. For the staining of basement membranes by this technic, Lendrum prescribes exposing the paraffin sections face down over a shallow dish of formalin at 55–60°C for 2 hours, before removal of paraffin. (For cell granule staining this step is not necessary.) Sections are then deparaffinized and brought to water as usual. The usual iodine thiosulfate sequence for treatment of material fixed with mercuric chloride is not mentioned by Lendrum, and would not be required for removal of mercury precipitates, since a treatment with iodine is contained in the technic at a later point. The technic is given by Lendrum as follows:

1. Stain 3–5 minutes with alum hematoxylin.
2. Wash briefly in water.
3. Stain 1–2 minutes in 1% fast green FCF in 0.5% acetic acid, varying the time in accordance with the desired intensity of the green cytoplasmic staining.
4. Rinse in water.
5. Treat for 2 minutes with Lugol's iodine solution (p. 141).
6. Wash off with 95% alcohol.
7. Immerse in 2% alcoholic solution of phosphotungstic acid for 2 minutes.
8. Rinse in water.
9. Stain 2–6 minutes in "carbacid fuchsin." Longer intervals give more staining of collagen and basement membranes. Lendrum prescribes microscopic control but gives no definite criteria at this point.
10. Rinse in water, dehydrate, clear and mount.

The cell granules of apocrine cells and of pituitary beta cells are stained a blackish red. Even without the formalin vapor treatment there is some staining of collagen and basement membranes; but with that treatment they are stained intensely red. The apocrine cell granules are also iron positive with ferrocyanide, and the same cells also contain fat droplets.

Pearse's method (*J. Path. Bact.* **61**:195, 1949) combined a Hotchkiss alcoholic periodic acid Schiff reaction and an alpha granule stain for hypophysis: Fix in Helly, in Zenker, in half-saturated $HgCl_2$ in formalin saline or in formalin saline solution. Paraffin sections.

1. Iodine and thiosulfate sequence to remove Hg precipitates.
2. Bring to 70% alcohol.
3. Treat 5 minutes in 0.8 gm H_5IO_6, 20 cc distilled water, 10 cc 0.2 M sodium acetate solution and 70 cc ethyl alcohol.
4. Rinse in 70% alcohol, wash 1 minute in 1 gm KI, 1 gm $Na_2S_2O_3 \cdot 5H_2O$, 20 cc H_2O, 30 cc ethyl alcohol and 0.5 cc 2 N HCl.
5. Rinse in 70% alcohol and treat 15–45 minutes in fuchsin sulfite solution (Schiff reagent).
6. Wash in running water, 10–30 minutes.
7. Stain 30 seconds in 0.5% celestine blue in 5% iron alum and then 30 seconds or more in Mayer's hemalum (no intervening wash).
8. Differentiate quickly in 2% acid alcohol and blue in water.
9. Optionally stain alpha granules in 2% orange G in 5% phosphotungstic acid for 5–10 seconds (orange II, C.I. No. 15510, gives deeper color).
10. Wash in running water until a yellow tinge is just visible in acidophil areas (or use microscopic control).
11. Alcohols, alcohol + xylene, xylenes, polystyrene (DPX).

Results: Colloid of stalk and vesicles, magenta; cyanophil, "basiphil," (or beta) granules, dark red; acidophil (or alpha) granules, orange; erythrocytes, orange; nuclei, blue black.

Gram Reaction. Pearse also found that the cyanophil cells were Gram positive, and Foster and Wilson (*Quart. J. Micr. Sci.* **93**:142, 1952) use a variant of the Gram stain for differential coloration of cyanophil cells, thus:

Hydrate and stain 2–3 minutes in 1% aqueous crystal violet. Rinse in water and cover with Lugol's (Gram's) iodine for 2–3 minutes. Blot, and differentiate in clove oil. Rinse in xylene and mount in Canada balsam. Beta granules are dark violet.

I find that 30 seconds in Weigert's iodine is quite adequate and presume that the authors meant Gram's solution (p. 141) rather than the strong pharmacopeial Lugol's solution. As usual with oil differentiated Gram stains, collagen tends to remain violet. Differentiation should be carried to the point where cell nuclei are fully decolorized.

Use of the usual aniline xylene mixture for differentiation, as in the routine Gram-Weigert method (p. 262), also gives excellent results. I have used a Feulgen nucleal reaction (p. 149) before a Gram-Weigert stain. The red purple nuclei contrast beautifully with the violet granules of the cyanophil cells.

Iron Hematoxylin. Another method for staining the eosinophil granules of anterior hypophysis cells as well as those of eosinophil leucocytes is a modified Weigert myelin stain, derived from my variant of the Weil method. The success of this procedure indicates the possible presence of a phospholipid component of these granules. Tissue should be fixed in an aqueous fixative containing formaldehyde. Chromation is not essential.

1958 Iron Hematoxylin for Myelin Sheaths, Eosinophils, Hypophyseal Alpha Cells, etc.

A. 2 gm $FeCl_3 \cdot 6H_2O$ + 0.6 gm NH_4Cl + distilled water to make 100 cc. Check pH (should be about 2).
B. 1 gm hematoxylin per 100 cc 95 or 100% alcohol. Mix equal volumes of A and B on same day as used. Formalin fixed, frozen, paraffin or celloidin sections.

1. Stain 1 hour at 60°C. Rinse in distilled water.
2. Differentiate in 0.5 gm borax: 1.25 gm $K_3Fe(CN)_6$:100 cc distilled water until nuclei are decolorized but red corpuscles remain brown to black and myelin sheaths are black. For myelin 10–15 minutes should suffice on formalin fixed material.
3. Wash in distilled water, 3–5 minutes.

4. Counterstain, if desired, 5 minutes in 0.1% safranin in 1% acetic acid.
5. Rinse in distilled water, alcohols or acetone, xylenes, balsam or synthetic resin. (Isopropanol preserves celloidin, acetone dissolves it.)

Coupled Tetrazonium Method of Landing and Hall for Anterior Pituitary Cells (*Stain Techn.* 31:193, 1956). Fix in neutral 10% formalin, dehydrate and imbed in paraffin as usual; sections to water as usual.

1. Rinse in Veronal acetate buffer pH 9.2.
2. Couple in 0.1% fast blue B in Veronal acetate at pH 9.2, 15 minutes, 0°C.
3. Rinse in buffer.
4. Postcouple with 2% H acid in pH 9.2 buffer, 15–30 seconds.
5. Running water, 2 minutes.
6. 1% sodium periodate (Na_3IO_5) in 0.5% HNO_3 (0.8% H_5IO_6 is equivalent), 10 minutes, 20–25°C.
7. Running water, 5 minutes.
8. Van Duijn's sulfite leucothionin (p. 271), 2 hours.
9. Alcohols, xylene, synthetic resin.

Results: Cyanophils, blue; acidophils, brown; chromophobes, unstained.

It appears probable that the blue staining of beta cells in this procedure is simply the periodic acid Schiff reaction which these cells and the colloid are known to give. The brown coloration of the alpha cells seems assignable to tyrosine; Glenner found a strong Morel-Sisley diazotization coupling reaction (p. 227) in the alpha cells (*J. Histochem.* 8:138, 1960). Glenner and Lillie (*J. Histochem.* 5:279, 1957) reported a strong indole (tryptophan) reaction in colloid and beta cells, using the post-coupled benzylidene reaction (p. 230).

Kerenyi and Taylor's (*Stain Techn.* 36:169, 1961) "Niagara Blue 4B," C.I. No. 24400 (first ed., C.I. 520), *Benzoreinblau,* method for differentiating beta cells in bluish purple with a hematoxylin eosin background and in deep blue with Mayer's hemalum alone, seems to have interesting possibilities for routine use. It is applicable to routine autopsy material after formalin fixation, and the benzo pure blue may be applied by restaining routine hematoxylin eosin sections with satisfactory results.

Kerenyi-Taylor Benzo Pure Blue Method for Hypophyseal Beta Cells.

1. Deparaffinize and hydrate 5 μ sections of formalin fixed hypophysis.
2. Stain 2 minutes in 1% aqueous benzo pure blue.
3. Wash in water 1 minute, tap or several changes of distilled.
4. Stain 1 minute in alum hematoxylin (Harris or formula of similar strength).

5. Differentiate in 0.125 N HCl in 70% alcohol, under microscopic control.
6. Blue in 1% Na_2HPO_4 or 1% sodium acetate and rinse in water.
7. Insert eosin counterstain at this point, 10–15 seconds.
8. Rinse, dehydrate, clear and mount in balsam or synthetic resin.

Results: Beta cell granules, deep blue without eosin, bluish purple with it; alpha cell granules, red with eosin, unstained without; chromophobe cytoplasm, pink with eosin, unstained without; nuclei, blue black.

TESTIS AND EPIDIDYMIS

The interstitial cells of the testis contain lipids, pigment, crystalloids and sometimes glycogen. The fats include cholesterol esters at times. The pigment is a lipofuscin and gives a brown fluorescence in ultraviolet light. The crystalloids are rod shaped bodies with rounded or pointed ends. They are singly refractile, dissolve in a pepsin hydrochloric acid mixture, swell in 10% potassium hydroxide and are insoluble in 10% mineral acids and in fat solvents.

Under certain experimental conditions the lipofuscin pigment of the interstitial cells may be greatly increased in amount and may assume the characteristics of the ceroid pigments: acid fastness, staining with oil soluble dyes after paraffin imbedding (p. 480), reactivity to the periodic acid (p. 198) and peracetic acid (p. 184) Schiff methods and to the ferric ferricyanide reduction test (p. 211). See also p. 415.

The spermatozoon head is a favorite cytologic object for the study of the arginine rich protamines (trout) and nucleohistones (p. 258). Methods for nucleic acids, spindles, centrosomes and mitochondria are also considerably used for this organ. The Golgi aggregates of the epithelium of the tubules of the epididymis are readily identified, and this organ has been much used in enzyme distribution studies, especially those concerning the relationship of enzymes to Golgi aggregates.

PEPTIC GLANDS

Peptic gland zymogen granules may be demonstrated in the gastric mucosa of rats and rabbits after fixation with such chromate formalin mixtures as Spuler's, Helly's, Orth's and Kose's fluids by staining in 0.05–0.1% thionin buffered with 0.01 M acetate buffer to pH 4–5 for 1 minute or more. The granules appear as discrete deep blue or greenish blue bodies when stained at pH 5, contrasting with the deep violet blue of the basal cytoplasm. At pH 3 they fail to stain.

The granules are destroyed by acetic acid fixatives and are poorly preserved by neutral formalin. Acid alcoholic fixatives destroy them.

The azure A eosin B technic (p. 162) stains them faintly pink in rats and rabbits, and red in guinea pigs. In guinea pigs the same cells may contain concurrently present retiform periodic acid Schiff positive material, but the granules themselves were recorded as periodic acid Schiff negative in the 3 species mentioned. The eosinophilic granules resist barley malt ribonuclease digestion (p. 145), which destroys the basophilia of the basal cytoplasm.

When paraffin sections of formalin fixed gastric mucosa of various mammals are stained by the sulfuric acid Nile blue procedure for lipofuscins (p. 281), washed in water and mounted in glycerol gelatin, the zymogen (pepsinogen) granules of the chief cells stain selectively dark blue, chief cell basal cytoplasm is a lighter blue and other structures range from blue green to pale greenish yellow. This staining was prevented by immediate acetone extraction after the staining, as with the lipofuscins, and is also prevented by prior methylation in 0.1 N HCl in methanol, 4–6 hours at 60°C, and is restored by demethylation (saponification) of the methyl ester by 1% potassium hydroxide in 70% alcohol, 20 minutes at 25°C. The deacetylation (saponification) reagent recommended in the second edition of this book, 20 cc 28% ammonia + 80 cc absolute alcohol, 24 hours at 25°C, may be substituted, with the advantage that it does not remove cytoplasmic ribonucleic acid, as alcoholic KOH does.

The peptic zymogen granules, however, do not stain with Sudan black, though parietal cell cytoplasm, smooth muscle and erythrocytes stain faintly to moderately.

Peptic zymogen granules color strongly with the tryptophan methods (p. 230) and moderately by the Morel-Sisley tyrosine method (p. 227).

The above findings agree with the published analyses of pepsin; tyrosine, 8.9%; tryptophan, 2.3%; glutamic acid, 21.6%, and aspartic acid, 10.0%; with the basic amino acids—arginine, 1.6, histidine, 1.5, and lysine, 1.3% —comparatively low in amount, accounting for the strong acidity of this protein (the figures are Block's, from p. 294, *Amino Acid Handbook*, Charles C Thomas, Publisher, Springfield, Ill., 1956).

The usual tests for ribonucleic acid (pp. 147–158) are applicable to the basal cytoplasm of the chief cells.

The oxyphilia of the parietal cells does not extend to the high pH levels of the arginine proteins and is strongly affected by nitrosation, suggesting that it is due largely to lysine (and hydroxylysine) residues.

PANETH CELLS

These cells contain conspicuous eosinophilic granules of variable size. The granules may lie in clear vacuolar spaces in the cytoplasm between the nucleus and the gland lumen. Like the zymogen granules of the pancreas and the salivary glands, these eosinophilic granules are destroyed by acetic acid fixatives such as aqueous and alcoholic acetic formalin, and Bouin's, Gendre's and Carnoy's fluids. The acetic bichromate fluids, such as Tellyesniczky's and Zenker's, may preserve them entirely, in part or not at all. They are well preserved by buffered neutral formalin or mercuric chloride formalin (p. 48), by Orth's, Kose's and Möller's bichromate formalin mixtures and by Spuler's formalin Zenker fluid.

They stain red by Lillie's azure A eosin B method (p. 162) at pH 3.75–4.1. They resist malt diastase (ribonuclease) and pancreatic ribonuclease digestions, which render them more conspicuous by destroying the normal basophilia of the cytoplasm. They are sometimes Gram positive by the Gram-Weigert technic (p. 262), especially in man, sometimes in guinea pigs, usually not in rabbits or rats.

They often stain red purple by the periodic acid Schiff procedure (p. 198). Positive reactions have been observed in man, mouse, guinea pig, rat and rabbit, as well as negative reactions in the first three. Application of a picric acid counterstain changes the color of Paneth granules to orange, thereby permitting their ready distinction from the still red purple mucigen granules.

The oxyphilia remains evident up to pH 10.5 with Biebrich scarlet after neutral mercuric chloride fixation, but it disappears at pH 7 or 8 in formalin material (Spicer and Lillie, *Stain Techn.* 36:365, 1961). Nitrous acid and adequate acetylation each decreases the oxyphilia, both after formaldehyde and mercurial fixation (*J. Histochem.* 6:352, 1958). The Barrnett-Seligman DDD technic (p. 216) demonstrates SH and SS groupings in formalin fixed mouse Paneth granules (Selzman and Liebelt, *J. Histochem.* 10:106, 1962). The tryptophan content of the granules is perhaps best demonstrated (in blue) by the postcoupled benzylidene technic (p. 230) on material fixed 2–3 hours only in neutral buffered formalin. Azo coupling with fast garnet GBC or fast red B may be combined with this to demonstrate the enterochromaffin granules in a contrasting (red) color in the same section (*J. Histochem.* 8:182, 1960). The diazotization coupling reaction for tyrosine (p. 227) has been successfully employed after neutral formalin, sublimate formalin (B5, p. 48) and Kose's bichromate formalin fixations (*J. Histochem.* 7:416, 1959). Contrasts are poorer than with the tryptophan reaction, because of the moderate reaction of cytoplasm. I have obtained suggestive reactions with the older α-naphthol and 8-quinolinol hypochlorite arginine technics. The Deitch method (p. 258) should prove more conclusive. Neutral formalin fixation or other fixative which preserves the granules is required. Demonstration in rodents is more successful after the animals have been without food for 8–18 hours.

HAIR, KERATIN AND KERATOHYALIN

Hair cortex is often fully or partly Gram positive, especially when Weigert technics (p. 262) are used. Keratohyalin also retains the violet; keratin retains it less. In Ziehl-Neelsen technics (p. 578) hair cortex is quite strongly acid fast. Hair cortex colors red purple with Schiff reagent on direct exposure of a few hours(p. 186). It becomes Schiff positive with 10 minute exposure after peracetic or performic acid oxidation, but not after periodic acid oxidation. Bromination prevents the peracetic acid Schiff reaction but renders the periodic acid Schiff reaction positive, so that even a 10 minute Schiff reagent bath yields a positive reaction. Keratohyalin and keratin are periodic acid and peracetic acid Schiff negative.

Keratohyalin often colors intensely with progressive alum hematoxylin and iron hematoxylin stains, as well as moderately with basic aniline dyes. With iron hematoxylin myelin procedures such as our "eosinophil myelin" stain (p. 304), differentiated to the point where cell nuclei are decolorized but erythrocytes are still black, keratohyalin varies from black to red; keratin, from light to dark brown; and hair cortex, from black near the root to blue or light blue gray distally.

According to Unna, eleidin may be differentially stained by a picric acid nigrosin sequence technic. Romeis directs as follows: (1) Stain 5 minutes in saturated aqueous picric acid solution. (2) Rinse in water. (3) Stain 1 minute in 1% aqueous nigrosin (C.I. No. 50420). (4) Wash in water, alcohol, oil, balsam. Results: Eleidin, blue black; keratin, bright yellow.

Unlike keratohyalin, trichohyalin does not stain with hematoxylin but stains vividly with acid dyes. The azure A eosin B technic (p. 162) displays these granules in bright red against the lightly to deeply basophilic cytoplasm of the hair follicle.

Near the root zone, hair cortex gives strong sulfhydryl reactions in appropriately fixed material. The ferric ferricyanide reduction test (p. 211) is positive after trichloroacetic alcohol fixation, but negative after mercurial fixations or postmordanting (—SH blockade). Cutaneous keratin and sometimes keratohyalin also color blue with this test, and in these structures the reaction is also positive in our hands after mercurial fixations and blockade treatments.

With the Barrnett-Seligman dihydroxy-dinaphthyl disulfide (DDD) method for sulfhydryl (p. 216), rat hair cortex colors blue at the zone of keratinization, red nearer the root and remains unstained distally. Epithelial cells in root sheaths, hair bulbs and stratum germinativum of the epidermis color red; those of the stratum corneum, pink. The reaction of keratohyalin was not noted.

Sodium plumbite, hot methenamine silver and cystine cysteic acid cleavage methods, as applied to hair cortex, are recorded under cystine reactions (pp. 218–220).

In a reinvestigation of the Meirowsky reaction (*J. Histochem.* **4**:318, 1956) it was found that keratohyalin and the eleidins of the stratum lucidum and in nonformalin fixed tissue the trichohyalin granules color intensely on prolonged exposure to dilute solutions of various catechols, among which were recorded catechol, pyrogallol, dopa, adrenaline, gallocyanine, brazilin and hematoxylin. These reactions occur optimally at about pH 6.5, require some oxygen and can be carried out in double distilled water in the complete absence of chelating metals. Competitive inhibition occurred with $Na_2S_2O_4$ and with cysteine; partial inhibition, with Na_2S, no inhibition, with KCN or NaN_3 (range of inhibition, 1–10 *mM*).

Using hematoxylin this is essentially Clara's hematoxylin method (p. 244). For trichohyalin, use methanol chloroform (50:50 or 60:30) fixation; for keratohyalin, calcium acetate formalin also serves quite well.

The reaction is seen also in stratified squamous epithelia of the pharynx. larynx, esophagus and rodent forestomach.

Hair cortex gives strong reactions to the Millon (p. 226) and Morel-Sisley tyrosine methods (p. 227). Soft keratins of the epidermis and of gastrointestinal stratified squamous epithelia react well by the latter procedure; smooth and striated muscle also colors light red; elastic fibers are a fair red purple; and epithelial cytoplasm takes pink to light pink.

Faint to slight tryptophan reactions have been recorded for hair keratin, outer root sheath and Huxley's layer (Glenner and Lillie, *J. Histochem.* **5**:279, 1957) using the postcoupled benzylidene reaction (p. 230). Smooth and striated muscle react moderately.

Azure A eosin B stains (p. 162) reveal strong basophilia (ribonucleic acid) in active hair follicle cytoplasm, moderate basophilia of the basal and spinocellular layers, very moderate eosinophilia of stratum corneum of the skin, more pronounced eosinophilia in gastrointestinal epithelia, strong eosinophilia of trichohyalin, keratohyalin and stratum lucidum and of part of the hair medulla. Spicer and Lillie (*Stain Techn.* **36**:365, 1961) have shown that the oxyphilia of lucidum, keratohyalin and trichohyalin persists up to pH 10.5 after $HgCl_2$ (B-4, p. 46) fixation though not after formalin, using the dilute Biebrich scarlet technic (p. 252). This oxyphilia has proved relatively resistant to nitrosation (*J. Histochem.* **6**:352, 1958), thus suggesting that it may be due largely to arginine residues, and moderately positive Sakaguchi reactions have been obtained on these structures. Use of the Deitch technic (p. 258) is recommended.

For consideration of melanin, melanogenesis and the dopatyrosinase reactions, see pp. 422–428 and p. 375. For citrulline demonstration, see p. 260.

Large amounts of glycogen may be demonstrated in the large clear cells of the outer sheath of active hair follicles, and some is demonstrable in cutaneous striated muscle (p. 198).

The usual methods for lipids are applicable to the study of the sebaceous glands. According to Montagna (*Structure and Function of the Skin,* 2d ed, Academic Press, Inc., New York, 1962), human sebum contains cholesterol, free fatty acids, squalene, odd numbered saturated and unsaturated fatty acids (free and esterified), aliphatic alcohols and little glyceride or phospholipid. But histochemically Montagna speaks of positive Smith-Dietrich and Baker hematein stains, osmiophilia and -phobia, birefringence and the Schultz test, and a yellow orange fluorescence excited by light of 360 mμ wavelength.

Chapter 10

Enzymes

The list of localizable enzymes has greatly expanded since the last edition of this book. Many of the procedures still depend on the use of frozen sections of unfixed tissue or on the use of the freezing drying technic advocated by Gersh. A decreasing number are demonstrable in paraffin sections of tissues frozen and "fixed" or, perhaps better, "dehydrated" by cold nondenaturant fluids such as acetone and in some instances alcohol, or by vacuum desiccation while frozen.

The demonstration of enzymes *in situ* depends on their action on a specific substrate in the presence of other substances with which one of the decomposition products resulting from enzyme action will form an insoluble deposit at the site of enzyme action. If this deposit is not already colored, it is needful to render it visible by chemical manipulation.

Further generalization at this point seems futile and redundant, since details must necessarily be given with each method. However, in order to facilitate comparisons as well as to economize on space, rather extensive use has been made of tabular presentation of related variants.

In general it lies beyond the scope of this work to consider the visualization of enzyme activity by electron microscopy, but some mention of procedures will be made where it seems appropriate for comparative histochemical purposes.

PHOSPHATASES

The technics for acid and alkaline phosphatases fall into two classes: (1) the earlier methods, depending on the capture of the liberated phosphate ion by a suitable cation to form an insoluble salt in situ, and permitting the use of varied, more or less physiological phosphate substrates, which are then visualized as lead or cobalt sulfide or similar colored insoluble products; (2) methods using highly artificial substrates of phosphates of various simple and complex naphthols, which are visualized by simultaneous or later coupling with diazonium salts to form insoluble azo dyes.

Both these principles have now been in use for over a decade, but many refinements of technic have been made. Improvements in fixation and sectioning procedures have operated to conserve a higher proportion of enzyme activity, to prevent diffusion artifacts, to produce increasingly insoluble and deeper colored azo dyes and to eliminate staining artifacts in nuclei, axons, fat droplets, etc.

Fixation and sectioning procedures seem equally applicable to the metal phosphate and azo dye methods. It was early observed that much of the activity was lost with the acetone fixation, paraffin imbedding procedures at first used. Fresh frozen sections have been found to lose rather promptly most or all of their acid phosphatase activity by diffusion into the water.

Freeze drying and vacuum paraffin infiltration have given some of the best results so far achieved. Burstone has used this procedure to good advantage in a series of azo dye procedures which have given increasingly sharp localization.

For acid phosphatase Wachstein has used free floating frozen sections of material previously briefly fixed in cold (3°C) neutral formalin. Barka (*J. Histochem.* **10**:741, 1962) also used frozen sections of material prefixed 1–2 days at 3°C in neutral calcium formalin, but he placed them on slides and dried them 2–24 hours before reacting. Allen and Slater (*J. Histochem.* **4**:110, 1956) used 15 μ frozen sections for alkaline phosphatase after 12 hours formalin fixation. The Feder technic (p. 64), freeze substitution in acetone followed by polyvinyl alcohol imbedding, has been used successfully for acid and alkaline phosphatases, 5-nucleotidase and adenosine triphosphatase (Birns and Masek, *J. Histochem.* **9**: 204, 1961). Fresh frozen cryostat sections are quite useful for the nonspecific alkaline and the various adenosine phosphatases (Burgos et al., *J. Histochem.* **3**:103, 1955; Padykula and Herman, *ibid.* **3**:161, 170, 1953; Freiman, *ibid.* **10**:520, 1962); they have not proved useful for acid phosphatase, but if transferred after attachment on slides into cold formalin (3°C) or acetone (0 or −70°C) for postfixation they give very acceptable results. This last procedure has given 72% acid and 92% alkaline phosphatase preservation after 12 hours in acetone at −70°C and 21% acid and 36% alkaline after 18 hours in formalin at 2–4°C. 5'-Nucleotidase, adenosine triphosphatase and glucose 6-phosphatase gave 96, 72 and 22% preservation after acetone; 62, 6 and 0% preservation after formalin (Chang and Hori, *J. Histochem.* **10**:592, 1962). Since 15–30 minutes in formalin vapor is sufficient to prevent diffusion of M-Nadi oxidase in blood smears and 2 hours is enough to prevent diffusion of dopa oxidase even in blocks, it would seem that much shorter formalin postfixation would be adequate for cryostat sections, as it is indeed in the case of the phosphopyridine nucleotide linked dehydrogenases (Hitzeman, *J. Histochem.* **11**:62, 1963). Burstone (*ibid.* **9**:146, 1961) reported good results from postfixation at 25°C for a total of about 5 minutes in absolute and

TABLE 10-1. SUBSTRATES FOR THE NAPHTHOL AS-PHOSPHATE, SIMULTANEOUS AZO COUPLING TECHNIC FOR ACID AND ALKALINE PHOSPHATASES

	Burstone· FD[1]	Burstone[2] OC	Burstone[3] FF	Barka[4] AS-TR, BI	Barka[4] α	Burstone[5] FD	Burstone[3]
Fixing and sectioning procedure	Freeze dry celloidin paraffin	Freeze dry celloidin paraffin	Cryostat postfixed in diacetone alcohol	18 hr formalin attached frozen sections	18 hr formalin attached frozen sections	Freeze dry celloidin paraffin	Cryostat postfixed in diacetone alcohol
Naphthol AS-phosphate[6]	BI(TR,LC)	MX	BI(E,CL,AN)	TR, BI	α-Naphthyl	MX	E(KB,CL, BA,TR,AN)
Amount	5 mg	5 mg	10 mg	10 mg	20 mg	5 mg	10 mg
Dimethyl-formamide	0.1–0.25 cc	0.25 cc	0.25 cc	1 cc	. . . .	0.25 cc	0.25 cc
Distilled water......	25 cc	25 cc	25 cc	q.s. 20 cc	q.s. 20 cc	25 cc	25 cc
Buffer........	0.2 M acetate	0.2 M acetate	0.2 M acetate	0.15 M Veronal acetate[7]	0.15 M Veronal acetate[7]	0.2 M tris	0.2 M tris
pH.........	5.2	5.2	5.2	5	6	8.3	8.3
Vol.........	25 cc	25 cc	25 cc	5 cc	5 cc	25 cc	25 cc
Activator....	10% $MnCl_2$ 0.1 cc = 10 mg	10% $MnCl_2$ 0.1 cc = 10 mg	10% $MnCl_2$ 0.1 cc = 10 mg				
Diazonium salt	Fast red violet LB	Fast blue BB	Fast red violet LB or fast blue BB	Freshly diazotized pararosaniline[8]		Fast red violet LB	Fast blue BB or Fast red violet LB
Amount....	30 mg	30 mg	30 mg	. . . .	. . . .	30 mg	30 mg
Final vol.....	50 cc	50 cc	50 cc	20 cc	20 cc	50 cc	50 cc
Time........	30–60 min	45–60 min	30–120 min	20–90 min	10–30 min	30–60 min	10–30 min
Temperature	25°C	25°C	25°C	25°C	25°C	25°C	25°C

[1] *J. Histochem.* **7:**39, 1959.
[2] *Ibid.* **7:**147, 1959.
[3] *Ibid.* **9:**146, 1961.
[4] *Ibid.* **10:**741, 1962.
[5] *Ibid.* **6:**322, 1958.
[6] Only the qualifying letters of the AS naphthols are given; *e.g.*, for "BI" read "Naphthol AS-BI."
[7] Barka's Veronal acetate contains 9.714 gm sodium acetate (3H₂O) (=5.85 gm anhydrous) and 14.174 gm sodium barbiturate in CO₂ free, glass distilled water to make 500 cc.
[8] Hexazonium pararosaniline, fresh diazotate (Davis and Ornstein, *J. Histochem.* **7:**297, 1959) was used by Barka as the diazo reagent in his acid phosphatase method. The diazotization is done at about 20–25°C, and no diazotization interval is specifically allowed, the process being presumed to be instantaneous. The raw approximately 2.5 N HCl solution containing 4% pararosaniline chloride without allowance for dye content is mixed with 4% NaNO₂ in equal volumes, and the mixture is dumped directly into the alkaline buffered substrate and diluted with water, the pH then being adjusted to 5 or 6, the former for naphthol AS-BI or -TR phosphate, the latter for α-naphthyl phosphate. Excess nitrous acid is not destroyed, though there appears to be about a 50% excess.

descending percentages of diacetone alcohol. [This is a ketone whose members are the methyl radicle and a tertiary butyl alcohol group; $(CH_3)_2$—COH—CH_2—CO—CH_3.]

Since the azo coupling technic for phosphatases is essentially limited to acid and alkaline naphthol phosphatases, these technics will be presented first.

Sections are prepared by one of the foregoing procedures. Adamstone-Taylor cold knife sectioning (p. 63) can be done without elaborate equipment, and postfixation of the attached frozen section with cold acetone probably constitutes the most readily applicable and generally useful procedure. Ordinary frozen sections of material fixed a few hours in cold neutral formalin are useful for acid phosphatase. Wash out acetone or formalin with distilled water and transfer to one of the substrates in the table (10-1), incubate for the indicated time, wash and mount in glucerol gelatin.

Buffer Systems. The buffer used in enzymic reactions is not a matter solely of the proper pH range. In metal ion capture reactions account must be taken of the effect of the buffer anion on the solubility of the capturing metal ion. Also in azo dye technics it is reported that certain buffer systems are better than others for specific enzymic reactions. Hopsu and Glenner (*J. Histochem.* **12**:674, 1964) reported much greater renal esterase activity in guinea pig kidney homogenates with phosphate and acetate buffers than with tris maleate of the same pH and concentration. Hence buffers should be changed only after making a direct comparison of the two systems.

The Gomori Lead and Calcium Phosphate Ion Capture Reactions for Nonspecific and Specific Acid and Alkaline Phosphatases, with Visualization as Lead and Cobalt Sulfides

General Fixation and Sectioning Procedures. Specific applicability of the 4 major procedures noted below and their variants will be noted under the specific enzyme topic.

A. Fix fresh tissue 16 hours in neutral formol calcium (p. 38). Calcium acetate formalin (p. 38) may be used, and with thin blocks (1–2 mm) 1–4 hours could well suffice. Cut frozen sections at 10–20 μ, using a cold knife procedure for thinner sections. Stain loose, or pick up and dry 2 hours or more on slides. Or imbed and section in polyvinyl alcohol (p. 64).

B. Cut fresh frozen sections in a cryostat or by the Adamstone-Taylor cold knife procedure and affix to slides. Pass directly to substrate or keep for short periods at 0–5°C.

C. Cut similar fresh frozen sections and attach to slides. Fix at once for 15–30 minutes in neutral formalin ($CaCl_2$ or calcium acetate) at 2–4°C or in acetone at 2–4°C for 15 minutes, or in acetone at −70°C for several hours. (Short periods do not suffice to extract lipid at this temperature.)

D. Prepare paraffin sections by the freeze drying procedure. Deparaffinize with petroleum ether, wash in low boiling (25–30°C) petroleum ether or isopentane and dry in air.

Nonspecific Acid Phosphatase Procedure. Fixation C with acetone 12 hours at −70°C gives optimal results, method A has been much used and requires no special equipment.

TABLE 10-2. SUBSTRATES FOR THE LEAD, GLYCEROPHOSPHATE ACID
PHOSPHATASE METHOD

	Gomori[2]	McDonald[3]	Barka[4]
Glycerophosphate..	$\alpha + \beta$ 8% 3 cc	$\alpha + \beta$ 3.06% 3 cc	β[1] 1.25% 6 cc (40 mM)
Buffer.............	Acetate	Acetate	Tris maleate
Volume..........	30 cc	27 cc	6 cc
Molarity.........	50 mM	50 mM	0.2 M
pH..............	5, (W: 6)[1]	4.7	5
Distilled water.....	....	....	6 cc
Lead nitrate........	36 mg in 30 cc buffer	10 mg in 27 cc buffer	20 cc 0.2%
Final molarity of lead, mM........	3.5	1	2.4
	Precipitate of excess lead glycerophosphate filtered out		Mix 1st 3 ingredients and add lead dropwise with shaking

[1] $C_3H_5(OH)_2PO_4Na_25H_2O$.
[2] *Stain Techn.* **25**:81, 1950.
[3] *Quart. J. Micr. Sci.* **91**:315, 1950.
[4] *J. Histochem* **10**:741, 1962.
[5] Wachstein, *J. Histochem.* **6**:389, 1958.

Technic.

1. Wash out formalin or acetone with distilled water (80 seconds).
2. Incubate in substrate at 37°C for 40 minutes (Barka substrate; 90 minutes to 24 hours for the Gomori substrate; shorter intervals up to 3 hours with Wachstein's pH 6 variant).
3. Rinse in distilled water and 1 minute in 2% acetic acid.
4. Rinse in distilled water and transfer to a 2% dilution of ammonium sulfide for 2 minutes.
5. Wash, dehydrate and mount in synthetic resin as usual, inserting a safranin, fuchsin or methyl green nuclear counterstain if desired. Hematoxylin eosin may be used.

Results: Sites of acid phosphatase activity, brown.

The acetic acid wash at step 3 was considered important by Gomori in preventing nonspecific lead staining. Acetic acid concentrations of 1–3% are used, and timing is not exact; 2% for 1 minute represents a compromise. Later writers do not stress this step.

Alkaline Phosphatases: The Calcium Cobalt Sulfide (Ca-CoS) Method Staining Procedure. The general histologic technic for handling sections for specific and nonspecific alkaline phosphatase methods follows essentially the procedure of Gomori.

1. From acetone or formalin, sections are washed with distilled water. Paraffin sections from freeze substitution, freeze dry or the older fixation procedures are deparaffinized, preferably with petroleum ether, and either washed in isopentane and let dry (preferable) or hydrated through acetones (preferably ice cold) to water.
2. Introduce into selected substrate, preheated to 37°C, and incubate for prescribed period, perhaps taking out slides at graded intervals.
3. Wash 5 minutes in 2–3 changes distilled water.
4. Immerse 5 minutes in 2% cobaltous nitrate (chloride or acetate will serve).
5. Wash in 4 changes of distilled water, 2 minutes each.
6. Immerse in approximately neutral 1% ammonium or 0.5% sodium sulfide for 1 minute. (2.5 cc saturated Na_2S—about 20% + 0.56 cc glacial acetic acid + 97 cc distilled water yields pH about 6.8–7.5. NaSH may be used, if available.)
7. Wash 5 minutes in running water.
8. Counterstain if desired.
9. Dehydrate, clear and mount, preferably in Canada balsam or ester gum. Cobalt sulfide keeps better in "reducing" resins.

NOTE: If preferred, the von Kóssa silver technic may be substituted for steps 4–7.

Results: Sites of phosphatase activity, dark brown to black.

Watanabe and Fishman (*J. Histochem.* 12:252, 1964) note strong inhibition of intestinal alkaline phosphatase by 50 mM L-phenylalanine, slight inhibition only by D-phenylalanine. The effect is greatest with the calcium cobalt methods, least with naphthol AS-TR and -BI technics.

Cobalt sulfide deposits in sections gradually disappear when they are mounted in certain of the synthetic resins such as old Permount, polystyrene and the Euparal-Diaphane type mixtures. Preservation is best in natural Canada balsam and in β-pinene or piccolyte resins (Bioloid, Permount, HSR, etc.) and in ester gums. Preparations mounted in Apáthy's gum syrup, in glycerol gelatin, Arlex gelatin, syrup and the like fade rapidly. Faded preparations may be fully restored by demounting, hydrating, reimmersing in ammonium sulfide and then remounting as before.

Ammonium sulfide gradually deteriorates on the laboratory shelf. It is desirable to get a fresh bottle about once a year.

Sodium sulfide, in equivalent concentration, or hydrogen sulfide water may be used instead, and the pH adjusted to near neutrality. Sodium sulfide is deliquescent, and crystals should be drained and dried before

TABLE 10-3. GLYCEROPHOSPHATE SUBSTRATE MIXTURES FOR ALKALINE PHOSPHATASE

	Gomori[1] Wts. vols.	Gomori[1] Final mM	Wachstein[2] Wts. vols.	Wachstein[2] Final mM	Padykula[3] Wts. vols.	Padykula[3] Final mM	Burgos et al.[4] Wts. vols.	Burgos et al.[4] Final mM	Feigin and Wolf[5] Wts. vols.	I Final mM	II Final mM	III Final mM	IV Final mM	Allen[6] Wts. vols.	Allen[6] Final mM	Freiman[7] Wts. vols.	Freiman[7] Final mM
Fixation Section method	Acetone Paraffin		Acetone Paraffin		Fresh Frozen		Fresh Frozen		Acetone Paraffin					Fresh Frozen		Fresh Frozen	
Specific substrate	α, β	10–20	α, β(?)	3.3	α, β	12	α, β	13.3		33	33	33	33	β ($5H_2O$) 183 mg	12	β ($5H_2O$) 230 mg	15
Amount	5–10 cc 3%		50 mg		180 mg		10 cc 2%		500 mg								
Calcium salt	$CaCl_2$	70–90	$CaCl_2$	8	$CaCl_2$	18	$CaCl_2$	4.5	$Ca(NO_3)_2$ $4H_2O$ 163.5 mg	13	13	13	0	$CaCl_2$	15	$CaCl_2$	18
Amount	20–15 cc 2%		4cc 0.1 M 0.1 M		5 cc 2%		5 cc 0.5%							5 cc 0.15 M		5 cc 2%	
Magnesium salt	$MgCl_2$	5	$MgSO_4$	10	None		$MgSO_4$ ($7H_2O$)	0.41	$MgCl_2$ ($6H_2O$) 0.102 mg 1.63 gm	0	10	160	160	None		None	
Amount	0.5 cc 10%		5 cc 0.1 M				1 cc 0.5%										
Buffer	Veronal Na	50–100	Ammediol	80	Veronal Na	80(?)	Veronal Na	20	Veronal Na	49	49	49	49	Veronal Na	33	Veronal Na	25
Amount	0.5–1 gm		20 cc 0.2 M 8, 9		10 cc 0.2 M(?)		10 cc 2%		12.5 cc 0.2 M					16.7 cc 0.2 M 9.5(a)		12.5 cc 0.2 M 9.4(a)	
Buffer pH																	
Final volume	50 cc		50 cc 8, 9		50 cc 9.4(a)		50 cc 8.6(a)		50 cc 9.2					50 cc 9.5		50 cc 9.4	
Final pH	9–9.4																
Incubation time	1–4 h		15–60 m		5–180 m		5–20 m 10, 25, 37°C		5–30 m					10 m		60 m	
Temp	37°C		37°C		37°C				37°C					37°C		37°C	

?, Probable, not definitely stated in reference. (a). Adjusted with NaOH or HCl.

[1] Gomori, G., Microscopic Histochemistry, University of Chicago Press, Chicago, 1952, p. 184.
[2] Wachstein, M., and Meisel, E., J. Histochem. 2:137, 1954; Science 115:652, 1952.
[3] Padykula, H., and Herman, E., J. Histochem. 3:161, 170, 1955.
[4] Burgos, M. H., Deane, H. W., and Karnovsky, M. L., J. Histochem. 3:103, 1955.
[5] Feigin, I., and Wolf, A., J. Histochem. 5:53, 1957.
[6] Allen, J. M., J. Histochem. 9:681, 1961.
[7] Freiman, D. G., Goldman, H. and Kaplan, N., J. Histochem. 10:520, 1962

weighing. Or use 2.5 cc of saturated aqueous (about 20%) sodium sulfide and about 0.56 cc glacial acetic acid and 97 cc distilled water to give pH 6.8–7.5. Addition of a few drops of this solution to a small supply of Apáthy's gum syrup or glycerol gelatin should retard fading in these media.

Molnar (*Stain Techn.* **27**:221, 1952) suggests replacing the cobalt bath (step 8) with a 2–5 minute bath in 2% lead nitrate solution; and the ammonium sulfide treatment (step 10) with a 40 minute bath in 0.5% aqueous sodium or potassium rhodizonate solution. Dark brown lead rhodizonate deposits are formed, and hemosiderin does not react.

Gomori (letter, 1953) found the rhodizonate color no better than the sulfide, and suggested instead the use of a very dilute solution of gallamine blue, which colors lead deposits selectively and intensely. Other counterstains may follow the gallamine blue.

Wachstein, Meisel and Ortiz (*Lab. Invest.* **11**:1243, 1962) prescribe overnight fixation at 4°C in 4% formalin with 1% $CaCl_2$ or neutralized 6% formalin without $CaCl_2$ or in Holt's sucrose formalin, and frozen sections at 5–8 μ. Cryostat sections are also used of tissue prefrozen in isopentane

TABLE 10-4. SUBSTRATES OF WACHSTEIN AND MEISEL FOR SPECIFIC PHOSPHATASES AT NEUTRAL pH LEVELS

	Substrate			
	NaβGP[1]	A-5′ P[2]	ATP[3]	KG-6P[4]
Amount	10 cc	20 cc	20 cc	20 cc
Concentration	1.25%	0.125%	0.125%	0.125%
Molarity	8.2 mM	1.4 mM	1.0 mM	1.5 mM
Tris maleate 0.2 M	5 cc	20 cc	20 cc	20 cc
pH	7.2	7.2	7.2	6.7
Lead $(NO_3)_2$, 2%	3 cc	3 cc	3 cc	3 cc
Molarity	3.6 mM	3.6 mM	3.6 mM	3.6 mM
$MgSO_4$ 0.1 M	0	5 cc	5 cc	0
Molarity	....	10 mμ	10 mM	....
Distilled water	32 cc	2 cc	2 cc	7 cc
Total volume	50 cc	50 cc	50 cc	50 cc
Incubation time	30–120 min	5–60 min	5–30 min	10–15 min
Temperature	n.s.[5]	n.s.	n.s.	32°C

[1] Na β GP, sodium β-glycerophosphate, $5H_2O$, M.W. 306.126.
[2] A-5′ P, muscle adenylic acid, adenosine 5′-phosphate, M.W. 347.23.
[3] ATP, adenosine triphosphate, M.W. 507.21.
[4] K G 6 P, K_2, glucose 6-phosphate, M.W. 336.33.
[5] *n.s.*, not stated.
SOURCE: From *J. Histochem.* **5**:204, 1957.

or petroleum ether at −70°C, with or without postfixing in the above CaCl$_2$ formalin for 15–180 minutes.

The substrate for the pH 6 lead sulfide technic contains

	Amount	Final molarity, mM
Pb (NO$_3$)$_2$	600 mg	3.3
0.05 M acetate buffer, pH 6	500 cc	45.0
3% sodium glycerophosphate[1]	50 cc	8.9

[1] M.W. 306.126.

Mix, incubate 24 hours in 37°C incubator, add 5 cc distilled water, filter. Store in refrigerator at 3°C. The filtered solution is usable for 3–4 days only; older solutions, though not turbid, give rise to the nuclear staining artifact. Incubation time was 5–120 minutes.

For glucose 6-phosphatase, unfixed cryostat sections are used in the following substrate, according to the same general technic as on p. 317.

	Amount, cc	Molarity, mM
0.125% glucose 6-PO$_4$K$_2$[1]	20	1.5
0.02 M acetate buffer, pH 6	20	8.0
2% Pb (NO$_3$)$_2$	3	3.6
Distilled water	7	
	50	

[1] M.W. 336.32.

Inhibitors of acid phosphatase were added to the above substrates in the following final concentrations: 5 mM NaF; 2 mM d-tartaric acid. As a preincubation inhibitor, 2.5 mM ethylenediaminetetraacetate in pH 6 (50 mM?) acetate buffer, 60 minutes, to inhibit alkaline phosphatase.

Allen (J. Histochem. 9:681, 1961) lists a considerable number of organic phosphates which liberate phosphate ion in homogenate studies at pH 9.4, using uniformly a final 12 mM substrate concentration in his substrate as given above: adenosine tri-, di- and monophosphates, di- and triphosphopyridine nucleotides, thiamine pyrophosphate, 2-deoxyglucose 6-phosphate, fructose 1- and 6-monophosphates and fructose-1,6-diphosphate, galactose 1- and 6-phosphates, glucose 1- and 6-phosphates, glucosamine 6-phosphate, mannose 1- and 6-phosphates, 6-phosphogluconate, ribose 5-phosphate, O-phosphoserine and -threonine, phosphocholine and phosphocreatinine, as well as the traditional α- and β-glycerophosphates.

Of these, only mannose, glucose and galactose 1-phosphates, ribose 5-phosphate, phosphocholine and α-glycerophosphate gave moderate reactions compared with the strong reaction of β-glycerophosphate in the acid phosphatase method. These lists are by no means exhaustive. Allen's acid phosphatase media contained again 12 mM specific substrate,

TABLE 10-5. MOLECULAR WEIGHTS OF PHYSIOLOGICAL PHOSPHATES FOR
PHOSPHATASE STUDIES

Phosphate	Mol. wt.	mg = 12 mM in 50 cc substrates
Adenosine triphosphate	507.21[1]	304
Adenosine diphosphate (pyrophosphate)	427.22[1]	256
Adenosine 5'-phosphate (muscle adenylic acid)	347.23[1]	208
Adenosine 3'-phosphate (yeast adenylic acid)	347.23[1]	208
Thiamine pyrophosphate (diphosphate)	496.38[1]	297
Diphosphopyridine nucleotide (NAD)	663.2	398
Triphosphopyridine nucleotide (NADP)	743.0	445
2-Deoxyglucose 6-phosphate	244.14	146
Fructose 1-phosphate	260.14[1]	156
Fructose 6-phosphate	260.14	156
Fructose 1,6-diphosphate	340.13[1]	204
Galactose 1-phosphate	260.14	156
Galactose 6-phosphate	260.14	156
Glucose 1-phosphate ($-K_2 2H_2O$: 372.35)[1]	260.14[1]	156
Glucose 6-phosphate ($-K_2$: 336.32)[1]	260.14[1]	156
Glucosamine 6-phosphate	259.16	155
Mannose 1-phosphate	260.14	156
Mannose 6-phosphate	260.14	156
6-Phosphogluconate, $Na_2(H_2$: 276.145)	320.12	192
Ribose 5-phosphate	230.12[1]	138
O-Phosphoserine	171.07	102.6
Phosphocreatine	211.12[1]	126.6
α-Glycerophosphate Na	216.046[1]	129.6
β-Glycerophosphate Na $5H_2O$	306.126	183.5
O-Phosphothreonine	199.107	119
Phosphocholine (phosphorylcholine)	219.61[1]	131

[1] *Merck Index.*

50 mM acetate buffer pH 5 or 5.5 and 3.6 mM lead nitrate (the published 0.036 M was a missed typographical error). His glucose 6-phosphatase medium contained in addition 2 mM d-tartrate to inhibit nonspecific acid phosphatase.

Padylkula and Herman included adenosine 5'-phosphate, adenosine di- and triphosphates as substrates to be used in their alkaline phosphatase medium at the same 12 mM concentration in the substrate mixture as in the table except that they prescribed a 5 mM concentration for the triphosphate.

The addition of d-tartaric acid serves to enhance activity of specific hexose 6-phosphatases, which otherwise react only moderately by acid phosphatase technics, and to inhibit ordinary "nonspecific" acid phosphatases, as demonstrated by the Gomori glycerophosphate lead procedure.

Thiamine Pyrophosphatase, Thiamine Diphosphatase.

$$NH_2 \quad CH_3 \quad O \quad O$$
$$| \quad | \quad || \quad ||$$
$$C \quad C=C-CH_2-CH_2-O-P-O-P-O^- \xrightarrow{+H_2O}$$
$$N \quad \overset{+}{C}-CH_2-N \quad | \quad |$$
$$H_3C-C \quad CH \quad C-S \quad OH \quad OH$$
$$N$$

Thiamine pyrophosphate (Cocarboxylase)[1]

$$NH_2 \quad CH_3 \quad O$$
$$| \quad | \quad ||$$
$$C \quad C=C-CH_2 \cdot CH_2-O-P-O^- + H_3PO_4$$
$$N \quad \overset{+}{C}-CH_2-N \quad |$$
$$H_3C-C \quad CH \quad C-S \quad OH$$
$$N$$

Thiamine orthophosphate

[1] White, Handler, Smith and Stetten, *Principles of Biochemistry*, 2d ed., McGraw-Hill Book Company, New York, 1959, p. 345.

Allen and Slater (*J. Histochem.* 9:418, 1961) and Novikoff *et al.* (*ibid.* 9:459, 1961) refer to this enzyme under the first of the above names. Naidoo (*ibid.* 10:580, 1962) uses the second, in accordance with British usage, but definitely identifies his substrate thiamine diphosphate as cocarboxylase. Hence the terms are to be regarded as synonyms.

Allen and Slater found the enzyme in the well segregated Golgi zone of the lining epithelium of the mouse epididymis. They used cryostat sections of fresh tissue, attached to slides. Novikoff preferred attached frozen sections either of material fixed 12–18 hours at 4°C in neutralized formol calcium (p. 34) or cryostat sections postfixed 5–60 minutes in the same fixative. Acetone postfixation was inferior; formaldehyde improved the intensity of the reaction over that in unfixed frozen sections.

Naidoo used frozen dried paraffin sections of brain, cut at 7–15 μ (procedure D, p. 315) and carried his sections, dry from the final isopentane, directly into substrate.

Naidoo's method (*J. Histochem.* 10:580, 1962) for thiamine diphosphatase (pyrophosphatase): Cut thin (2 mm) slices of brain, freeze in isopentane at −35°C, freeze dry 3 days at −78°C and imbed in paraffin (M.P. 49°C) *in vacuo* (15 minutes). Chill blocks and section at 10–15 μ, transferring onto albuminized slides without water flotation. Store blocks at −10°C for less than 7 days; section on same day as incubation.

TABLE 10-6. SUBSTRATES FOR THIAMINE PYROPHOSPHATASE AND CONTROLS

	Allen and Slater				Naidoo, PbS				Naidoo, Ca—CoS	
	Amount	Molarity, mM			Amount	Molarity, mM			Amount	Molarity, mM
Thiamine pyrophosphate HCl..... (HCl) M.W. 460.789	115 mg	5	.....	.....	11.5 mg	0.5	....	....	184 mg	8
Thiamine monophosphate HCl..... (HCl) M.W. 381.814	95 mg	......	5	......	9.5 mg	....	0.5	....	....	....
Sodium β-glycerophosphate........ (5H₂O) M.W. 306.126	76.5 mg	....	....	5	7.6 mg	....	.....	0.5	....	....
Sodium barbital 0.1 M............	16.7 cc	33	33	35	....	....	.....	.....	12.5 cc	25
Tris maleate 0.1 M, pH 7.1.......	....	....	....	....	25 cc	50	50	50	....	....
CaCl₂ 0.1 M (1.11%)............. (M.W. 110.99 anhydr.)	7.5 cc	15	15	15	....	....	.....	.....	12.5 cc	25
MgCl₂ 0.1 M (2%)................ (6H₂O) M.W. 203.33	....	....	....	....	10 cc	20	20	20	10 cc	20
Pb(CO₂CH₃)₂ 40 mM (1.5%)...... (3H₂O) M.W. 379.35	....	....	....	....	1.25 cc	1	1	1	....	....
Distilled water, to make..........	50 cc	....	....	....	50 cc	....	.....	.....	50 cc	....
Final pH........................	....	9.4	9.4	9.4	....	6.9	6.9	6.9	....	8.7
Incubation time..................	....	2–4 min	10 min	10 min	....	10–80 min	5 hr	5 hr	....	5–50 min
Temperature.....................	....	37°C	37°C	37°C	....	37°C	37°C	37°C	....	37°C

1. Dewax paraffin sections at 20–25°C in 80–100°C petroleum ether, 2 minutes.
2. Wash in 2 changes isopentane (B.P. 27–31°C). Sections dry at once in air.
3. Thrust quickly into warm substrate with sharp movement to dislodge air bubbles.

Substrate:

		Final Concentration mM
0.1 M maleate buffer pH 7.1	15 cc	50
5 mM stock thiamine pyrophosphate (2.4 mg/ 1 cc)	3 cc	0.5
0.1 M MgCl₂ (2.03% MgCl₂·6H₂O)	6 cc	20
0.03 M Pb(NO₃)₂ (or acetate) (993 and 975 mg/100 cc)	1 cc	1.0
Distilled water to make	30 cc	

The final pH is 6.8–7.

4. Incubate in this substrate at 37°C, removing sections at graded intervals.
5. Wash in 4 changes distilled water at 0°C for 10 minutes.
6. Immerse in 1:50 dilution of yellow ammonium sulfide for 2 minutes.
7. Wash in distilled water, dehydrate, clear and mount in synthetic resin or Canada balsam, as for other PbS stains.

Results: Sites of thiamine pyrophosphatase activity, brown to black.

Controls. Results are negative if thiamine orthophosphate or inorganic diphosphate is substituted in the substrate.

The maleate buffer is made by dissolving 5.804 gm dry reagent grade maleic acid in 400 cc glass distilled water, adjusting with 1 N NaOH to pH 7.1 and bringing final volume to 500 cc.

Naidoo wrote me (October 25, 1962) that thiamine pyrophosphate (cocarboxylase C) from Roche or Sigma is about 98% pure. Hence with a molecular weight of 478.81, the above 30 cc substrate mixture contains a total of 7.32 mg of the commercial product, or 15 micromols = 7.18 mg of the pure product.

The further purification of the commercial product was as follows: "Samples used in this work were re-precipitated twice by solution in a little 1 N HCl and the addition of 5 volumes of acetone. Re-precipitation did not lead to any discernible change in the histological results, nor did an independently prepared specimen."

In this series Allen's pH 9.4 preparation and Naidoo's pH 8.6 are visualized as usual by the cobalt sulfide sequence (p. 317), while with Naidoo's lead containing substrate, the acid phosphatase PbS technic is followed (p. 316).

Results: Reaction sites are shown in black CoS or brown PbS. Glycerophosphate and thiamine O-monophosphate give the usual alkaline phosphatase pattern. Sites which are unreactive to these two substrates but which color with thiamine pyrophosphate are considered specific. In Naidoo's lead technic at pH 6.9 with his low substrate concentration, Mg^{++} is required, but neither he nor Allen includes it when an alkaline technic with 5–8 mM substrate is used.

Inhibitors. Naidoo notes inhibition by 0.1 mM UO_2^{++} (acetate) and no effect by 1 mM NaF. Allen and Slater note differential inhibition of glycerophosphatase and thiamine monophosphatase by 4 mM cysteine; the thiamine pyrophosphatase resists this.

Glucose 6-Phosphatase. This phosphatase is distinguishable from ordinary nonspecific acid phosphatase by its thermolability, its sensitivity to formaldehyde and to pH levels below 5. It is destroyed in material fixed in cold alcohol or acetone and imbedded in paraffin.

Tissue may be quickly frozen and stored at −20°C for several days without great loss of activity.

According to Chiquoine (*J. Histochem.* 1:429, 1953) fresh unfixed tissue is frozen and sectioned in the cryostat (p. 63) and dried briefly onto slides.

Substrate. Dissolve 250 mg barium glucose 6-phosphate in 10 cc distilled water, add 0.1 cc 2 N HCl and 120 mg K_2SO_4. Let stand 2 hours with frequent stirring. Centrifuge out $BaSO_4$ and test supernatant for absence of Ba by adding a grain or so more K_2SO_4. If clear, dilute to 30 cc and adjust to pH 6.7 with normal KOH. For the working substrate dilute 1 volume of this solution with 2 volumes of 0.2% lead nitrate (6 mM). Slight turbidity results. Filter and place 0.5 cc quantities in each of the required number of 3 cc beakers. Coat edges of beakers with petrolatum (U.S.P.). Place sections face down over orifice of beaker, invert and incubate 5–15 minutes at 32°C. Rinse successively in distilled water, in 2% acetic acid and again thoroughly in distilled water. Immerse for 2 minutes in 1:50 ammonium sulfide. Wash 2–5 minutes in running water. Stain 2 minutes in 0.1% safranin in 1% acetic, or as desired, dehydrate, clear and mount in balsam. Activity sites are in brown.

Immersion for 10 minutes in Weigert's iodine, or in boiling water, abolishes the activity, as does fixation with formaldehyde. Preparations should be compared with duplicates prepared by the glycerophosphate acid phosphatase method.

PHOSPHAMIDASE

In the course of exploration of a variety of substrates in the acid and alkaline phosphatase methods, Gomori found that *p*-chloroanilidophosphonic acid as substrate gave a quite different distribution picture from that of other substrates when used in the acid range, though the distribution picture was typical of the other alkaline phosphatases when the alkaline to neutral ranges were employed. Gomori (*Proc. Soc. Exp. Biol. Med.* 69:407, 1948) described the method of purification of the crude product made by Otto's synthesis (*Ber. Deutsch. chem. Ges.* 28:617, 1895) (see also Bredereck and Geyer, *Hoppe Seyler Z. physiol. Chem.* 254:223, 1938).

Gomori's Phosphamidase Method. *Substrate.* 0.1 M stock solution of *p*-chloroanilidophosphonic acid. Dissolve 21 gm in an excess (say 150 cc) of a 10% dilution of 28% ammonia water (the equivalent is about 137 cc). Adjust to pH 8 with dilute (say 10%) acetic acid electrometrically (just colorless with phenolphthalein). Add distilled water to make 1000 cc. Store in refrigerator at 0–5°C.

Working substrate is composed of *substrate* and the following solvent:

Solvent
$\begin{cases} \text{MnCl}_2 \text{ 12.5\% (1 } M\text{) aqueous solution 0.4 cc (4 m-mol)} \\ \text{Pb(NO}_3\text{)}_2 \text{ 3.31\% (0.1 } M\text{) aqueous solution 2.5 cc (2.5 m-mol)} \\ \text{Maleate buffer pH 5.6 (5.8\% maleic acid 10 cc, 0.1 } N \text{ sodium} \\ \quad \text{hydroxide 62 cc, distilled water 28 cc) 100 cc (0.1 } N\text{)} \\ \text{Shake to dissolve initial precipitate.} \end{cases}$

To make working substrate add 4 cc stock 0.1 M *p*-chloroanilidophosphonic acid. Preheat in paraffin oven 30 minutes and filter out excess lead phosphate.

Technic. Fix tissues in acetone, 95% alcohol or 100% alcohol at 0°C (for 24 hours?), dehydrate with acetone or 100% alcohol accordingly. "Clear" with petroleum ether, infiltrate in paraffin at 58–60°C *in vacuo* (10–15 mm mercury) for 15 minutes. Imbed and section at 5–10 μ.

1. Deparaffinize and hydrate sections as usual. Inactivate a set of control sections by immersion for 10 minutes in Gram's iodine solution (p. 141).
2. Immerse test sections and iodine inactivated controls in preheated, filtered, working substrate; and a second set of untreated controls in the preheated, filtered solvent without substrate, for 10–24 hours at 37°C, arranging slides all facing in the same direction in Coplin jars so tilted that the slides lean about 30° out of perpendicular with faces obliquely downward.
3. Wipe precipitate off the backs of the slides and rinse in distilled water.
4. Wash slide in 0.1 M citrate buffer of pH 5, until the surface of the glass adjacent to the section appears clean.
   Caution: Undertreatment leaves precipitate on the section; overtreatment may remove part of the lead phosphate deposits at sites of activity.
5. Wash 2–5 minutes in running water.
6. Treat in 1% dilution of yellow ammonium sulfide for 1–2 minutes (or 0.5% Na$_2$S buffered to about pH 7).
7. Wash in water, counterstain as desired. 0.1% safranin in 1% acetic for 5 minutes; or otherwise.
8. Dehydrate in alcohols, clear with xylene and mount in balsam, ester gum or a β-pinene resin.

Results: Carcinoma cells and gray substance of brain and cord show much blackening; other tissues show relatively little. Some benign tumor cells color quite heavily; others do not.

Meyer and Weinmann (*J. Histochem.* 3:134, 1955) modified the sub-

strate by dissolving 2.08 gm p-chloroanilidophosphoric acid in 100 cc
0.15 N NaOH. This is approximately 0.1 M (M.W. 206.578). The lead
nitrate solution is made at 3.3 mM (110 mg/100 cc) in maleate buffer
pH 5.2 containing about 30 mM NaCl (175 mg/100 cc) in place of
Gomori's $MnCl_2$. By using the maleate buffer table on p. 660 and replacing part of the water by 2.25 cc 0.1 M substrate in a 50 cc mixture, the
prescribed concentrations are attained. According to Meyer and Weinmann the alkaline stock 0.1 M substrate is reasonably stable if stored in
the cold.

Meyer and Weinmann still used acetone fixed paraffin sections and
incubated slides alone face down in frequently agitated substrate (inclined turntable). They performed the Gomori iodine inactivation on
undeparaffinized sections, using the stronger Weigert (1% I_2) solution
for 90 minutes or alternatively 10% HNO_3. The reason for the isolation is
that activity transfer from one section to another is observed.

The new substrate and an increase in incubation temperature to 40–
42°C permitted reduction of exposure time to 1.5–4 hours. The ammonium sulfide treatment to visualize the precipitated lead phosphate
by converting it to sulfide is unchanged and is the same as in the Gomori
acid phosphatase methods: 2 minutes in 2% dilution of yellow ammonium
sulfide followed by washing in water.

In a more extended report (J. Histochem. **5**:354, 1957) they spoke of
a pH of 5.15 and of incubation times at 41°C of 1–3.5 hours, but they
still used the same tissue preparation procedure. The iodine inactivation
was now done in 20 minutes after deparaffinizing the control section, still
mounted on the same slide with the test sections.

Pearse (1960) quoted the Gomori and Meyer-Weinmann technics.

DISACCHARASES

It appears that the hexosidases demonstrated by hydrolysis of 6-bromo-
2-naphthol hexosides differ in distribution and thermostability from biochemically isolated lactase, invertase and trehalase.

Dahlqvist and Brun (J. Histochem. **10**:294, 1962) have attempted to
localize histochemically disaccharidase activity by demonstrating the
liberated glucose with a coupled enzymatic reaction yielding an insoluble formazan.

Substrates. Chromogenic substrate, prepared fresh daily.

0.4 M phosphate buffer pH 6	40 cc
Glucose oxidase	4 mg
Nitro blue tetrazolium	10 mg
Phenazine methosulfate	6 mg

Specific Sugar Substrates. 1 gm sucrose, 1.05 gm lactose monohydrate, 1.1 gm trehalose dihydrate, 1.1 gm melibiose dihydrate or 100 mg glucose, dissolved in distilled water and made up to 10 cc.

Working substrates consisted of 2 cc specific sugar solution and 18 cc chromogenic substrate. Note: The glucose mixture turns black in less than 1 hour.

Tissue. Fresh frozen sections are cut at 10 μ by a cold knife process (Adamstone-Taylor or cryostat technic) and attached to slides. The sections are placed in working substrate and incubated 2–20 hours at about 20°C. When color has developed adequately, fix by immersing slides 10 minutes in 5% formaldehyde, rinse 5 minutes in 15% alcohol and mount in glycerol gelatin. Counterstain with nuclear fast red or carmine if desired (formazan blue).

If tetranitro blue tetrazolium were substituted in the chromogenic substrate the red brown formazan should contrast well with alum hematoxylin.

Reactions. The disaccharidase releases glucose, which is oxidized by glucose oxidase to gluconic acid. The reduced oxidase reduces the phenazine methosulfate and is itself reoxidized. The reduced phenazine methosulfate reduces the tetrazolium to insoluble formazan and is itself reoxidized.

The phenazine methosulfate is necessary even in conjunction with the active nitrotetrazoles, in contrast with the case of Krebs cycle dehydrogenases (p. 380).

The method was successful for demonstration of invertase and trehalase in the brush border zone of the intestinal villus and crypt epithelium. Lactose and melibiose substrates demonstrated no activity.

Maltose and isomaltose could not be used as substrates since they directly reduce the tetrazole. Biochemical assay of the rat intestine used revealed no lactase activity. It is probable that this last should be sought in intestine of nursling animals.

β-D-GALACTOSIDASE

The method for this enzyme introduced by Cohen, Tsou, Rutenburg and Seligman, (*J. Biol. Chem.* **195**:239, 1952), has been revised by Rutenburg, Rutenburg, Monis, Teague and Seligman (*J. Histochem.* **6**:122, 1958).

It was found that fresh tissue could be stored 10 days at 2–4°C without serious loss of activity and that fixation in cold neutral 10% formalin up to 3 days caused no demonstrable impairment. Cryostat sections incubated in saline lost enzyme into the solution, which could be demonstrated by its action on substrate solutions, but the sections retained an adequate amount for the histochemical reaction. Hence the following procedure is preferred.

The 1958 Technic of Rutenburg *et al.* for β-D-galactosidase.

1. Fix thin blocks of fresh tissue 16–20 hours in neutral 10% formalin. (Calcium formol, phosphate buffered formalin should be suitable.) Wash blocks about an hour in several changes of distilled water.
2. Cut frozen sections at 15 μ and transfer directly to substrate. (Cryostat sections attached to slides, if required for other concurrent studies, may be used directly or after 15 minutes' fixation in calcium formol.)
3. Incubate 2–8 hours, usually 4, at 37°C in the following substrate.

Substrate. Dissolve 10 mg 6-bromo-2-naphthyl-β-D-galactopyranoside in 1.5 cc absolute methanol, add 20 cc hot distilled water (70°C), let cool and add 8.5 cc McIlvaine buffer pH 4.95 (p. 662) and 10 cc distilled water. (This substrate may be made in 400 cc amounts and kept as long as 6 months at 4°C.)

4. Wash 3 minutes in 3 changes of ice cold distilled water.
5. Postcouple in fast blue B 1 mg/1 cc 1% sodium bicarbonate (pH 7.5–8) for 3–5 minutes.
6. Wash in 3 changes ice cold distilled water and mount in glycerol gelatin.

Results: Sites of enzymatic activity, deep blue, grading to purple and pink in areas of weaker reaction. Epithelia generally react strongly, muscle, pancreas, lymph nodes react weakly or not at all. Leucocytes stain strongly.

α-D-GLUCOSIDASE

Rutenburg, Goldbarg, Rutenburg and Lang (*J. Histochem.* 8:268, 1960) presented a histochemical technic for the localization of this enzyme based on an earlier colorimetric biochemical study by Goldbarg, Tsou, Rutenburg, Rutenburg and Seligman (*Arch. Biochem. Biophys.* 75:435, 1958).

Pearse (1960) prescribes free floating frozen sections of material fixed in cold neutral formalin. Incubate 1–2 hours at 37°C in 9 cc 25 *mM* phosphate buffer pH 6.5 + 1 cc alcohol containing 1–1.5 mg 6-bromo-2-naphthyl-α-D-glucopyranoside. Rinse in distilled water and develop color by a 2 minute immersion in 10 cc 0.1 *M* phosphate buffer pH 7.5 to which 10 mg fast blue B is added just before using. Wash in water and mount in glycerol gelatin.

Wolfgram (*J. Histochem.* 9:171, 1961) points out that the localization of glucosidase and galactosidase in brain is in the myelin sheaths and that defatting with chloroform applied to dried cryostat sections completely prevented this localization. However, enzymatically liberated 6-bromo-2-naphthol was recovered from the solution. Immersion of tissue in solutions of 6-bromo-2-naphthol, with fast blue B postcoupling, showed similar myelin localization.

The effect of prior defatting with chloroform on nonnervous tissues in these hexosidase reactions has not yet been reported.

GLYCOGEN SYNTHESIS

Takeuchi's Amylophosphorylase and Amylo-1,4 → 1,6-transglucosidase Methods. Takeuchi's (*J. Histochem.* 6:208, 1958; 9:304, 1961) technics for the demonstration of phosphorylase synthesize first an amylose, coloring blue with iodine, from glucose 1-phosphate and then constitute it by an amylo-1,4 → 1,6-transglucosidase branching enzyme action into the branched polysaccharide glycogen, which colors purplish to reddish brown with iodine:

Substrates. Dissolve 50 mg potassium glucose 1-phosphate, 10 mg muscle adenylic acid and 2 mg water soluble glycogen in 15 cc distilled water. Then add 10 cc acetate buffer pH 5.8 and one drop of insulin. Warm to 37°C before using.

For inhibition of the branching enzyme action and consequent exclusive production of the straight chain amylose add 5 cc absolute alcohol or 1 mg mercuric chloride (*ca.* 0.1 *mM*) to the foregoing substrate.

Section Procedure.

1. Cut frozen sections of fresh unfixed tissue at 10–40 μ by the cold knife (Adamstone-Taylor) or cryostat procedure and transfer as free floating frozen sections to the above substrate. Friable tissues may be attached directly to slides and air dried at 20–25°C for a few minutes, but the free floating procedure is preferable.
2. Incubate 1–2 hours in the above substrate, using the longer exposure in the presence of the branching enzyme inhibitor.
3. Rinse quickly in 40% alcohol, float free sections onto slides and dry at 37°C for a few minutes. With preattached sections omit this step.
4. Fix 2–4 minutes in absolute alcohol, dry and
5. Apply control digestion in α- and β-amylases at this point.
6. Immerse directly or after amylase digestion in dilute (1:9) Gram's iodine solution (I:KI:HO = 1:2:3000) for 5–10 minutes, until the iodine coloration—red, brown, purple (or blue for amylose)—appears.

7. Mount directly in Takeuchi's iodine glycerol (Gram's iodine 1:9 glycerol) and seal with paraffin or cellulose caprate.

Amylase Digestion.

1. Incubate 30 minutes to 10 hours in 0.5% α-amylase in 4 mM acetate buffer pH 5.7; carry through steps 6 and 7.
2. Use 0.5% β-amylase in 1 mM acetate buffer, pH 4.5, rinse, carry through steps 6 and 7.

Amylose, the result of amylophosphorylase activity alone, is shown in deep blue by the direct procedure and is digested completely by both α- and β-amylase. Glycogen, the result of the sequence action of amylophosphorylase and amylo-1,4 → 1,6-transglucosidase, colors red brown to purple in the direct procedure, is completely digested by α-amylase and resists β-amylase.

URIDINE DIPHOSPHATE GLUCOSE GLYCOGEN TRANSFERASE

Takeuchi and Glenner (*J. Histochem.* **8**:227, 1960; **9**:304, 1961) reported the histochemical application of this recently elucidated (Leloir, *J. Am. Chem. Soc.* **79**:6340, 1957; *Arch. Biochem. Biophys.* **81**:508, 1959; *J. Biol. Chem.* **235**:919, 1960, Hauk and Brown, *Biochem. Biophys. Acta* **33**:556, 1959) pathway of glycogen synthesis.

In this synthesis uridine triphosphate (UTP) reacts with glucose 1-phosphate (G-1-P) to form pyrophosphate (PP) and uridine diphosphate glucose (UDPG), and the latter adds a glycosyl group to preexisting "primer" glycogen in α-1 → 4 linkage. The pathway is demonstrated histochemically by direct use of the intermediate uridine diphosphate glucose (Kornberg in Long, *Biochemists' Handbook,* D. Van Nostrand Company, Inc., Princeton, N.J., 1961, pp. 533–543).

Takeuchi and Glenner showed that activity was promptly and completely inhibited by 0–5°C postfixation of fresh frozen sections (Adamstone-Taylor cold knife) in formalin, more slowly and moderately by alcohol (with some activity remaining at 24 hours), slightly by cold acetone and scarcely at all by drying on slides.

The pH optimum was about 7.6; the presence of glucose 6-phosphate and of Versene in the incubation media enhanced the reaction. With prolonged (10–48 hour) exposure to substrate glycogen again disappeared, but maximal reactions were attained in 20–60 minutes. The synthesized glycogen colored red brown with iodine, resisted β-amylase almost completely and was promptly digested by α-amylase. Addition of as much as 40% alcohol to the substrate still permitted formation of

TABLE 10-7. URIDINE DIPHOSPHATE GLUCOSE GLYCOGEN TRANSFERASE
SUBSTRATES

Substrates	1960	1961	1961 control
Uridine diphosphate glucose.....................	50 mg	50 mg	
Glycogen.......................................	10 mg	10 mg	10 mg
Versene.......................................	20 mg	20 mg	20 mg
Glucose 6-phosphate...........................	.....	10 mg	10 mg
Distilled water................................	15 cc	14 cc	14 cc
Dissolve and add 0.2 M tris buffer pH 7.4.........	10 cc	10 cc	10 cc
Absolute alcohol...............................	.....	1 cc	1 cc
Final volume..................................	25 cc	25 cc	25 cc

glycogen in distinction from the amylophosphorylase, branching enzyme
sequence, where alcohol inhibits the branching enzyme and causes deposits of an amylose which colors blue with iodine and is digested by
β-amylase.

Procedure.

1. Cut frozen sections of fresh tissue by the Adamstone-Taylor cold knife
   method.
2. Transfer directly as free floating sections to substrate. Friable or difficult tissues may be attached to slides directly from the knife and air
   dried before incubation. **Incubate** 1 hour at 25°C.
3. Transfer directly to a 1:9 dilution of Gram's iodine (I:KI:H$_2$O =
   1:2:3000) until color appears.
4. Pick up on slides, mount in 90% glycerol: 10% Gram's iodine. Seal with
   cellulose caprate or paraffin. (Use small drop of glycerol which does
   not quite fill space under coverglass.)

Results: Newly synthesized glycogen, red brown. No-substrate controls,
negative. Preexisting glycogen is apparently lost during the incubation
process.

N-ACETYL-β-GLUCOSAMINIDASE

Enzymes hydrolyzing β-glycosides of N-acetylglucosamine have been
isolated from a variety of sources: mammals, molluscs, molds, emulsin.

By use of α-naphthyl-N-acetyl-β-glucosaminide in a simultaneous azo
coupling technic, Pugh and Walker (*J. Histochem.* 9:242, 1961) have devised a procedure for the histochemical localization of N-acetyl-β-glucos-
aminidase.

Biochemical tests showed 60–80% preservation of the activity of fresh tissue after 20 hour fixation in formol saline (1% NaCl) or formol calcium (1.2% $CaCl_2$) at pH 7 or pH 5.5 formalin containing 0.11 M sodium citrate or acetate or 0.1 M calcium acetate or in acetone or 80% alcohol. Although the last was best, formol calcium and calcium acetate formalin were nearly as good and gave better general histologic preservation.

Fast garnet GBC at 1.5 mg/1 cc proved to be the most satisfactory diazonium salt: fast blue B, fast red RC and fast red TR were also tried.

A substrate concentration of 1.8 mM, almost saturated in water, proved satisfactory. Increasing the concentration of α-naphthyl-N-acetyl-β-glucosaminide by addition of propylene glycol or methyl cellosolve to the solvent was of no benefit.

Method of Pugh and Walker for N-Acetyl-β-glucosaninidase. Fix fresh tissue overnight (16–24 hours) at 3–5°C in formol calcium (pH 7) or calcium acetate formalin (pH 5.5). Soaking in gum sucrose before sectioning is recommended but is optional. Friable and fragmentary tissues should be imbedded in gelatin.

Cut frozen sections at 5–15 μ and transfer to freshly prepared, nearly saturated (1.8 mM), filtered substrate:

α-Naphthyl-N-acetyl-β-glucosaminide 623.5 γ (1.8 μmol) in 1 cc water
Fast garnet GBC 1.5 mg in 0.1 cc water, filtered   0.1 cc water
Citrate buffer 0.2 M pH 5.5   0.1 cc
Final pH about 5.5

Incubate 10–60 minutes at 20°C. Transfer to water, place sections individually in 30% alcohol and then back in water to spread, pick up on clean slides and mount in glycerol gelatin or Gurr's Hydromount. Counterstaining with neutral celestine blue or 0.5% methyl green in 0.1 M pH 4.6 acetate buffer is optional. Locations in renal convoluted tubules, salivary gland and thyroid acini, stomach, intestine, bronchus, uterus, testis and epididymis, chiefly epithelial, are figured, as well as deposits in solid viscera, spleen, thymus and ovary.

Strong inhibition is obtained by inclusion of 0.5–1 μM N-acetylglucosaminolactone in the substrate.

β-GLUCURONIDASE

Ferric Salt, 8-Hydroxyquinoline Method. According to Janigan and Pearse (*J. Histochem.* **10**:719, 1962), the ferric chloride, 8-hydroxyquinoline glucuronide procedure of Friedenwald and Becker, as well as Fishman's modification of it, produces an identical picture, both in the absence of the glucuronide and after Cu^+ inhibition of the β-glucuronidase. Moreover the alleged potassium hydrogen saccharate inhibition of histochemical enzyme activity gives equal inhibition of the staining in the absence of the 8-hydroxyquinoline glucuronide and has been shown to produce complete precipitation of the iron as an insoluble saccharate. Fishman has ably defended the validity of the method (*J. Histochem.* **12:**239, 1964).

The naphthol glucuronide methods with postcoupling are, however, considered valid.

An example of the postcoupling method is that of Seligman *et al.* (*J. Histochem.* **2:**209, 1954), who reported the synthesis of the substrate 6-bromo-2-naphthyl-β-D-glycopyruronoside (commercially available from Borden and K and K).

Method of Seligman, Tsou, Rutenburg and Cohen for β-Glucuronidase.

1. Prepare fresh frozen sections in a cryostat or by the Adamstone-Taylor technic at 6–10 μ.
2. Dry on clean slides for a few minutes. Here, according to Wolfgram, extract 1 minute in chloroform to prevent lipid staining. Usually this step has been omitted.
3. Dry on slides for a few minutes and fix 10 minutes at 3–5°C in phosphate buffered 10% formalin (about pH 7) and wash 15 minutes in cold water.
4. **Substrate solution:** Dissolve 30 mg 6-bromo-2-naphthyl-β-D-glucopyruronoside in 5 cc absolute methyl alcohol and add 20 cc McIlvaine phosphate citric acid buffer pH 4.95 and 75 cc distilled water. Incubate sections 4–6 hours at 37°C in this substrate.
5. Rinse 1 minute in distilled water and azo couple 2 minutes in 0.1% fast blue B in 0.02 *M* phosphate buffer pH 7.5 at 3–5°C.
6. Wash in 2 changes of cold distilled water and 1 of 0.1% acetic acid and mount in glycerol gelatin.

Results: Sites of enzyme activity, blue; lipids, red. To avoid this lipid staining in nervous tissues Wolfgram (*J. Histochem.* **9:**171, 1961) removed lipid by a 1 minute immersion in chloroform, which he stated did not inhibit the enzyme activity but nevertheless totally prevented coloration of central nervous tissues.

Pugh and Walker (*J. Histochem.* **9:**105, 1961) substituted naphthol AS-LC glucuronide and N-acetyl-β-glucosaminide for demonstration of β-glucuronidase and N-acetyl-β-glucosaminidase, respectively, in the foregoing technic.

If both the invalidation of the ferric oxine procedure by Janigan and Pearse and Wolfgram's note of total nonstaining when fat is removed are of general application, the situation for histochemical demonstration of β-glucuronidase would appear somewhat discouraging.

The precoupled azo dye glucuronide method of Friedenwald and Becker, which they reported (*J. Cell. Comp. Physiol.* **31**:303, 1948) simultaneously with the Fe^{+++} oxine method, was totally neglected in favor of the latter. For details, see the second edition of this book or the original reference. The Hayashi and Fishman papers, *J. Histochem.* **12**:239, 293, 298, 1964, should also be consulted.

ZYMOHEXASE (ALDOLASE)

Allen and Bourne (*J. Exp. Biol.* **20**:61, 1943) developed a method for zymohexase. Zymohexase is an aldolase which converts hexose diphosphate (fructofuranose 1,6-diphosphate) to dihydroxyacetone phosphate and phosphoglyceraldehyde, + an isomerase, which catalyzes equilibrium between the 2 products. Inclusion of iodoacetic acid stopped the decomposition at the triose stage. The triose phosphates liberate phosphoric acid in alkaline solution, which is visualized in the usual manner.

This enzyme activity appears to have had no recent attention in histochemistry under the cited nomenclature, and further details are omitted from the present edition. See original reference or p. 213, second edition.

INORGANIC PHOSPHATASES

Berg, in a series of papers (*J. Histochem.* **3**:22, 1955; **4**:429, 1956; **8**:85, 92, 1960; *J. Cell. Comp. Physiol.* **95**:435, 1955; *Anal. Chem.* **30**:213, 1958) has identified the usual substrate of the inorganic polyphosphatase of fishes and amphibia as a cyclic trimetaphosphate and has demonstrated its occurrence in the intestine of rodents. Trimetaphosphate goes through three steps in degradation to orthophosphate, each apparently requiring its own enzyme.

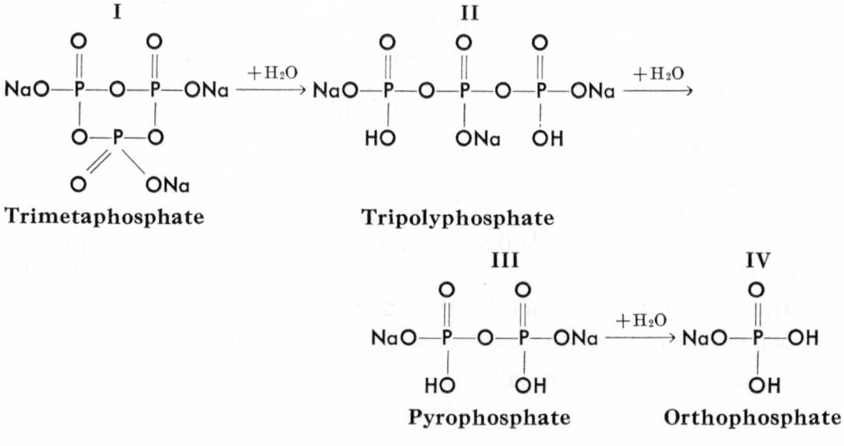

Trimetaphosphate

Tripolyphosphate

Pyrophosphate

Orthophosphate

Reactions. $I + H_2O \rightarrow II$; $II + H_2O \rightarrow III + IV$; $III + H_2O \rightarrow 2IV$.

Enzymes. Trimetaphosphatase; tripolyphosphatase; pyrophosphatase. Assay studies of rat intestine indicated the presence of about 3 times the amount each of pyrophosphatase and tripolyphosphatase as trimetaphosphatase, so there would be no deficiency in the second and third enzymes of the degradation series to limit the potentiality of the trimetaphosphatase.

Berg's Procedure for Trimetaphosphatase. Fix in acetone at 0–4°C or by freeze substitution in acetone, imbed in paraffin, section and float ribbon on 20 *mM* magnesium acetate (285 mg[1]/100 cc) at pH 5.9, mount on slides, drain and dry at 40–45°C. Or acetone containing 0.5% acetic acid and an excess of magnesium sulfate may be used as the fixing fluid.

Substrate.   *mM*

Sodium trimetaphosphate $Na_3P_3O_9$	18.4 mg	0.6
Acetic acid 0.1 *M*	4.5 cc	45
Lead acetate 1.5% (46 *mM*)	10 cc	4.6
Nitric acid to adjust to pH 4.9		
Distilled water		100 cc

Incubations run from 15 minutes to 2 hours. Wash, visualize by a 2 minute exposure to 2% ammonium sulfide, wash, dehydrate, counterstain with 0.2% fast green FCF in 45% alcohol, complete dehydration and clearing and mount in Canada balsam as for Gomori acid phosphatase technics.

ARYL SULFATASE

Rutenburg, Cohen and Seligman (*Science* **116**:539, 1952) reported a method for aryl sulfatase depending on the decomposition of the sulfuric acid ester of 6-benzoyl-2-naphthol and the coupling of the liberated benzoyl naphthol with fast blue B. Rat tissues may be fixed for some days or even months in cold neutral formalin. From these, frozen sections are prepared as usual. Human and monkey tissues are cut by a cryostat technic (p. 63), mounted on glass slides directly and dried in air. With the unfixed tissues it is necessary to incubate in a substrate made up in hypertonic salt solution.

The substrate is prepared by dissolving 25 mg potassium 6-benzoyl-2-naphthyl sulfate in 80 cc hot 0.85% sodium chloride solution and adding 20 cc 0.5 *M* pH 6.1 acetate buffer (p. 661). For unfixed frozen sections the substrate is made hypertonic by the addition of 2.6 gm sodium chloride per 100 cc, thus raising the NaCl content to 3.28%. Unfixed frozen sections

---

[1] 429 mg $Mg(CO_2CH_3)_2 \cdot 4H_2O$.

TABLE 10-8. ARYL SULFATASE ACTIVITY IN ORGANS BY SPECIES

	Man	Monkey	Mouse	Rat	Rabbit	Guinea pig	Hamster	Dog
Liver......	++	++	++	++	±	±	±	±
Kidney....	++	++	++	++	±	±	++	±
Pancreas...	++	++	±	++	±	±	++	±
Adrenal....	±	±	+	+	±	±	+	±

attached to slides are first immersed in 3 baths of NaCl solution of 0.85%, 1% and 2% concentration, and then placed in hypertonic substrate. Fixed frozen sections are transferred first to a small portion of the normal substrate, and then to the regular incubation bath of 20 cc. Sections from each organ are to be incubated in separate containers to avoid transfer to activity. For organs with high activity incubate 2–3 hours at 37°C; for other organs, 4–16 hours in hypertonic substrate.

After incubation, wash formalin fixed tissues in water and unfixed tissues in descending grades of salt solution (2%, 1% and 0.85%); and postcouple 5 minutes in a freshly prepared cold (4°C) 0.1% solution of fast blue B in 0.05 M phosphate buffer of pH 7.6. Then wash in 3 changes of cold 0.85% sodium chloride solution and mount in glycerol or glycerol gelatin.

Areas of high activity stain blue; those of lower activity stain purple to red. On storage even at 4°C the blue gradually changes through purple to red, and some diffusion occurs. Activity is largely cytoplasmic.

Roy (*J. Histochem.* **10:**106, 1962) quotes the method of Rutenburg, Cohen and Seligman (*Science* **116:**539, 1952) as the most widely used histochemical procedure for this group of enzymes and points out procedures for activity due respectively to aryl sulfatases A, B and C.

TABLE 10-9. ARYL SULFATASE SUBSTRATES

	Pearse, 1960		Roy, 1962					
			I		II		III	
	Amount mg	Molarity mM	Amount mg	Molarity mM	Amount mg	Molarity mM	Amount mg	Molarity mM
6-Benzoyl-2-naphthyl sulfate.............	6.25	0.68	6.25	0.68	6.25	0.68	6.25	0.68
NaCl................	650	495	82	56				
Buffer...............	Acetate	100	Acetate	100	Acetate	100	Tris	100
pH................	6.1		6.1		6.1		8.0	
Volume.............	25 cc		25 cc		25 cc		25 cc	

Pearse prescribes a 2–8 hour 37°C incubation and postcoupling in fast blue B as in the Rutenburg method. Pearse prescribes frozen sections of formalin fixed tissue, or fresh frozen sections attached to slides. For the hypertonic saline (2.6% NaCl) substrate, Pearse prescribes baths in graded saline solutions before the substrate. Since 56 mM (0.33%) NaCl is adequate for the chloride dependent sulfatase B, this precaution is unnecessary for the other substrates.

Roy's substrate I, although he used it for biochemical assay, should give essentially the same demonstration of the 2 aryl sulfatases as the original method. Use of substrate III increases the activity of sulfatase C and completely suppresses that of A and B. Substrate II permits activity of sulfatase A but suppresses that of sulfatase B, which is chloride dependent. This distinction can be made only in the absence of sulfatase C, which usually supplies most of the activity.

Roy regards the substrate as satisfactory for aryl sulfatase C, but not for A and B. A 2 hour incubation was adequate for assay of C; a period of 16–18 hours was needed for A and B.

No simultaneous coupling technic has been developed, but the complex naphthol appears to be sufficiently insoluble for use of the postcoupling technic. Hence, after the substrate incubation wash in distilled water, transfer to fast blue B 1 mg/1 cc in ice cold pH 7.5–8 buffer for 5 minutes, wash in water and mount in glycerol gelatin.

ESTERASES

Histochemically localizable esterases comprise nonspecific esterases (which decompose glyceryl and other esters of short chain aliphatic acids), lipases (which attack esters of long chain fatty acids and are found principally in pancreas) and cholinesterases (which hydrolyze fatty acid esters of choline and acetylcholine and are found in motor end organs, neural synapses, nerve cells and erythrocytes).

Following his work on the phosphatases, Gomori (*Proc. Soc. Exp. Biol. Med.* **58**:362, 1945) introduced a method for the demonstration of lipases. In this technic the water soluble palmitic or stearic acid esters of certain polymer glycols or hexitans are hydrolyzed in the presence of a soluble calcium salt, and the calcium soaps formed *in situ* are converted into lead soaps by treatment with lead nitrate. The lead soaps are converted to brown lead sulfide with ammonium sulfide.

The general procedures for preparation of sections for demonstration of esterases can well be substituted for Gomori's acetone paraffin technic. George (*J. Histochem.* **11**:420, 1963) regards Tween 80 or 85 as more specific for lipase than the Tweens prescribed by Gomori. Most later writers who have used the Tween methods simply refer to Gomori's or Pearse's textbooks. Lison (1960) quotes it essentially without change.

The Tween Method for Esterases.

1. Prepare frozen sections of fresh unfixed tissue, attach to slides and postfix 15 minutes in ice cold calcium formalin or in ice cold acetone. Or fix overnight in neutral formol calcium and cut frozen sections. Or prepare paraffin sections by the freeze dry celloidin paraffin or paraffin technic, deparaffinize in isopentane or low boiling petroleum ether and let dry. Wash out formalin or acetone with several changes of distilled water. Generally, prefixation, formalin fixation and frozen sections seem to constitute the preferred procedure.
2. Incubate at 37°C in one of the following substrates:

TABLE 10-10. TWEEN SUBSTRATES FOR ESTERASES

	Gomori, from Lillie, 1954	Pearse, 1953	Lison, 1960
Tween No.[1].....	40 or 60, 2%, 3 cc	60 or 80, 5%, 1.2 cc	20, 80, 5%, 0.6 cc
Solvent.........	30% glycerol, 12 cc	Distilled water, 24.6 cc	Distilled water, 27 cc
$CaCl_2$..........	2% $CaCl_2$, 3 cc	10% $CaCl_2$, 1.2 cc	2% $CaCl_2$, 0.9 cc
Buffer..........	Tris, 0.1 M, 12 cc	Tris, 0.5 M, 3 cc	Tris, 0.05 M, or veronal 1.5 cc
pH.............	7.3	7.3	7.2
Final volume....	30 cc	30 cc	30 cc
Time...........	8–24 hr	3–12 hr	8–24 hr
Temperature....	37°C	Not stated	37°C

[1] Tween numbers: 20, laurate; 40, palmitate; 60, stearate; 80, oleate. Hydrolysis of the oleate was claimed to be a specific property of pancreatic lipase.

3. Rinse in distilled water.
4. Treat with 2% lead nitrate solution for 10 minutes.
5. Rinse repeatedly in distilled water.
6. Treat 2 minutes with a 1:100 dilution of light yellow ammonium sulfide in distilled water. (Gomori said 10 drops, about 0.5 cc, in a Coplin jar of water, or about 50 cc.)
7. Wash in running water. Counterstain 3–5 minutes in alum hematoxylin, dehydrate, clear and mount in synthetic resin. Gomori advises against xylene as a clearing agent and as a solvent for the Clarite resins. alleging fading in xylene media. Instead, use dichlorethylene or ligroin (cf. also p. 444, Timm), or, since any decoloration of the highly insoluble lead sulfide which might occur would be due probably to oxidation to the almost equally insoluble white lead sulfate, use of natural fir balsam or other reducing resin would seem to be indicated.

Results: Sites of lipase activity are evident as dark brown deposits of lead sulfide.

Gomori notes further that treatment for 1 minute with Gram's iodine solution or with 5% phenol, or boiling 10 minutes in water, destroys the enzyme. Addition of 0.2% sodium taurocholate intensifies the action of pancreatic lipase but inhibits that of "all other organs."

Nachlas and Seligman (*J. Biol. Chem.* **181**:343, 1949) reported that in the test tube eserine at 3.5 mM (962 mg/one liter) had only a moderate inhibitory effect both on pancreatic hydrolysis of naphthyl laurate and stearate (lipase) and on hepatic and renal hydrolysis of naphthyl acetate (esterase), especially in man. Sodium taurocholate at 0.1 M (0.54%) accelerated the lipase hydrolysis of naphthyl laurate and stearate, and depressed slightly the esterase decomposition of naphthyl acetate. Quinine hydrochloride at 0.05 M (1.894%) inhibited almost completely the pancreatic lipase hydrolysis of naphthyl laurate and stearate; esterase showed a species variable but lesser grade of inhibition or even (in the dog) acceleration. Atoxyl (sodium arsanilate) at 0.1 M (2.39%) and 0.3% (0.07 M) sodium fluoride tended to inhibit the esterase activity of liver, kidney and pancreas on naphthyl acetate, but they were without effect on the pancreatic lipase hydrolysis of naphthyl laurate and stearate.

In their hands the hydrolysis *in vitro* of the polyglycol stearic acid esters, such as Gomori used, followed more the organ distribution pattern of esterase than that of true lipase. The activity against naphthyl laurate and stearate was similar in organ distribution to that against olive oil.

Unfortunately naphthyl stearate and laurate are too insoluble to use in the histochemical technics (Seligman *et al.*, *Ann. Surg.* **130**:333, 1949); but by including 0.1 M (2.39%) sodium arsanilate (atoxyl) in the naphthyl acetate substrate, they showed that the esterase activity of liver and kidney was inhibited, and they considered the pronounced activity still evident in pancrease as due to lipase.

This finding suggests that the method may actually demonstrate lipase in pancreas and that the activity inhibited by taurocholate may be that of nonspecific esterase, since Seligman *et al.* (*loc. cit.*) showed that the homogenate esterases of other organs were relatively ineffective in hydrolyzing β-naphthyl palmitate and stearate, though pancreatic homogenate enzymes hydrolyzed this substrate readily. Seligman was not able to adapt this palmitate, stearate substrate to histochemical use because of its great insolubility.

THIOACETIC ESTERASE

The cholinesterases of motor end plates (true) and of erythrocytes (pseudo) are reported to hydrolyze noncholine esters, and the acetylcholinesterase of rat brain is active against naphthyl (Ravin, Zacks and Seligman, *J. Pharmacol. Exp. Ther.* **107**:37, 1953) and indoxyl (Barrnett and Seligman, *Science* 114:579, 1951; Pepler and Pearse, *J. Neurochem.* 1:193, 1957) esters. But electrophoretically separated human brain acetylcholinesterase is reported to react with acetylthiocholine substrates and not against thioacetic acid or naphthyl and indoxyl acetates (Barron et al., *J. Histochem.* 11:139, 1963). Thioacetic esterase was concentrated in a zymogram band showing also weak activity against the synthetic protease substrate α-N-benzoyl-DL-arginyl-β-naphthylamide (BANA) but none against other esterase substrates or acetylthiocholine iodide.

However, thioacetic acid as substrate has given good demonstrations of acetylcholinesterase sites in rodents (Wachstein *et al.*, *J. Histochem.* 9:325, 1961). Barrnett and Palade (*J. Biophys. Biochem. Cytol.* 6:163, 1959) and Zacks and Blumberg (*J. Histochem.* 9:317, 1961) reported its use for acetylcholinesterase in both human and mouse muscle.

Wachstein's directions for this technic appear a little more complete and adaptable to routine laboratory use than the others cited. It is to be borne in mind that though usable for demonstration of cholinesterases in human muscle, as well as more generally in rodents, the thioacetic esterase method is not specific for acetylcholinesterase, demonstrating also aliesterases and so-called nonspecific cholinesterase.

The Thioacetic Acid Esterase Method.

1. *Section preparation.* Wachstein (and others) prefer tissue prefixed in neutral formol calcium for 16–24 hours. Section on the freezing microtome or use cryostat or cold knife frozen sections of fresh tissue, directly or, preferably, after 15 minutes fixation at 0–5°C in formol calcium or acetone, or after one of the section freeze substitution technics. Burstone's freeze dry paraffin or celloidin paraffin technic is applicable. Petroleum ether (B.P. 25–40°C) should be used to remove paraffin; acetone is needed to remove celloidin; otherwise sections can be dried in air after petroleum ether and placed directly in the substrate.

2. *Substrate* (Wachstein). A. Thioacetic acid 0.15 cc (= 152.5 mg) in 5 cc distilled water. Adjust to pH 5.5 with about 5 cc 0.1 N NaOH. Add 0.2 M acetate buffer pH 5.5 to make 100 cc.
   Working substrate. To 20 cc solution A add 1 cc 0.5% lead nitrate solution drop by drop, with shaking. Centrifuge and filter. Replace clear solution with fresh every 15–20 minutes during incubation, to minimize precipitation. At pH 6 precipitation becomes more troublesome; at pH 5 the intensity of staining is reduced. The final molarity of this substrate for thioacetic acid is about 19 mM; of lead, 0.7 mM or lower; of acetate buffer, 0.17 M.

3. Incubation times of 30 minutes to 24 hours were used, usually 1 hour.

4. After incubation wash in 2–3 changes of distilled water, dehydrate in

alcohols, clear in xylene and mount in Canada balsam or natural fir balsam.

Results: Sites of activity appear in brown. Inhibitor resistant esterase may be specifically demonstrated by a 1 hour 37°C preincubation in 10 μM E-600. Inclusion of 5 mM sodium taurocholate in the substrate is necessary for demonstration of pancreatic lipase. Eserine at 10 μM was used to inhibit acetylcholinesterase activity.

The method apparently has similar capacities for esterase demonstration with the naphthol AS and AS-LC acetate technics. It would appear to offer advantages in electronmicroscopy in that an electron dense reaction product is engendered.

Thioacetic acid, perhaps listed under the synonym "thiacetic acid" or "thiolacetic acid," is readily available in practical grade from purveyors of organic chemicals. One 1963 quotation was $4.25 per 25 gm.

ESTERASES: AZO DYE TECHNICS

Nachlas and Seligman (*J. Nat. Cancer Inst.* **9**:415, 1949) proposed a nonspecific esterase method utilizing β-naphthyl acetate as substrate and visualizing by simultaneous coupling with α-naphthyl diazonium naphthalene-1-5-disulfonate, which gives a red color; or with the commercial stable tetrazotized diorthoanisidine, fast blue B, which gives a deep blue.

This method, cited in the second edition of this book, has been largely abandoned because of diffusion artifacts; Gomori's α-naphthyl and naphthol AS acetate methods afforded some improvement but have, in their turn, been replaced by more complex naphthyl acetates of the AS series and by the use of improved section preparation procedures.

Following Gomori, Burstone (*J. Histochem.* **4**:130, 1956) used α-naphthyl and naphthol AS acetates, propionates and butyrates on frozen dried paraffin sections, with improvement in localization. The esterase activities were inhibited by 2 mM sodium taurocholate, 2 mM NaF, 0.5 mM diisopropylfluorophosphate (DFP) and 0.5 mM Phemerol, but not by 0.1 mM eserine.

Later Burstone synthesized several new naphthol AS acetates; of these, naphthols AS-D, AS-OL, AS-MX and especially naphthol AS-LC acetates were recommended as suitable substrates for the aliesterase technic as performed on frozen dried paraffin sections.

Burstone's Freeze Dry Esterase Method with Naphthol AS-LC Acetate.

1. Deparaffinize with petroleum ether or isopentane, hydrate through acetone or by drying isopentane in air and passing section directly into substrate.

2. *Substrate:* Naphthol AS-LC acetate 3 mg in 0.3 cc acetone or dimethyl-formamide; add 15 cc distilled water, 15 cc 0.1 M tris buffer pH 7.1 and stir in 15 mg fast garnet GBC or fast blue RR; filter and pour over sections in Coplin jar.
3. *Incubate* 10–30 minutes at 25°C, or until sufficient red or blue color has been developed in sections. A 2 hour trial is adequate for the reporting of a negative reaction, as in the presence of specific inhibitors or of lesions inducing loss of esterase activity.
4. Wash thoroughly in distilled water and mount in glycerol gelatin, polyvinyl pyrrolidone or other suitable medium.

Method of Shnitka and Seligman for Simultaneous Demonstration of Inhibitor Resistant (A) and Inhibitor Sensitive (B) Aliesterases (*J. Histochem.* **9:504, 1961).** It was observed that although diisopropyl-fluorophosphate inhibition was poorly reversible by treatment with certain oximes, inhibition by NaF or by arsanilate was readily reversed by 90–120 minutes washing of sections in distilled water.

1. Fix fresh tissue in thin blocks (3 mm) 16–24 hours in neutral formol calcium at 2–5°C; wash in 4 changes of cold 0.85% NaCl.
2. Transfer to ice cold 30% sucrose (w/v = 0.88 M) containing 0.9% gum acacia (gum arabic) and infiltrate 12–24 hours at 2–4°C. Blot and freeze in petroleum ether or isopentane at −70°C.
3. Transfer blocks to cryostat at −20°C, section at 4–8 μ and transfer sections with needle to surface of 2 M NaCl (11.7%) at 5°C.
4. Transfer at once, lifting on spatula, to first substrate. *First Substrate:* Pour 10 cc 0.1 M phosphate buffer pH 7.3 containing 3% glycol by volume into small beaker containing 0.1 cc of a 2.5% solution of naphthol AS acetate in acetone, swirling to mix thoroughly. Add 30 mg sodium fluoride (*ca.* 70 mM) and 10 mg fast blue BB (C.I. No. 37175), stir to dissolve, filter and incubate sections 10–20 minutes. Instead of NaF, sodium arsanilate 0.1 M (240 mg) may be used as inhibitor.
5. Wash in 3–4 changes of distilled water, 30 minutes each, using 300 cc for each 10 sections, to remove all traces of inhibitor.
6. Transfer to surface of second substrate, made as before, but without inhibitor and using fast red violet LB salt 10 mg in place of fast blue BB (Conn, 7th ed., p. 216).
7. Incubate 20–35 minutes at 37°C.
8. Float in distilled water 10 minutes, pick up on slides and mount in 90% polyvinyl pyrrolidone.

Results: Inhibitor resistant (A) esterases, blue; inhibitor sensitive (B) esterases red.

The same authors also combined mitochondrial staining by the reduced diphosphopyridine nucleotide, nitro blue tetrazolium technic (p. 382) for "diaphorase" in a sequence preceding steps 5–8 of the above procedure.

Following Holt's bromoindoxyl acetate technic, which, by reason of its ferro-ferricyanide redox buffer content, demonstrates only A esterase in rat kidney, by steps 5–8 of the above double stain technic, Shnitka and Seligman also successfully demonstrated the B esterase in red, contrasting with the blue of the bromoindigo method.

ESTERASES: INDOXYL METHOD

Barrnett and Seligman (*Science* 114:379, 1951) introduced indoxyl acetate and butyrate as substrates and described their preparation from sodium indoxyl.

These substrates yield indigo on hydrolysis in the presence of air. This pigment is quite insoluble in water and in fats. The method demonstrates nonspecific esterase, lipase and cholinesterases, which are distinguished by use of the usual inhibitors (p. 347).

Holt and Withers (*Nature* 170:1012, 1952) substituted 5-bromoindoxyl acetate for the above, using ordinary frozen sections of tissue fixed 16 hours at 4°C in neutral formol saline. Finer grained deposits were produced, diffusion decreased and the consistency of performance increased.

Holt reported a series of minor modifications and applications of this technic; see *J. Histochem.* 4:541, 1956, and *Proc. Roy. Soc. [Biol.]* 148: 520, 1958. Shnitka and Seligman (*J. Histochem.* 9:504, 1961) have slightly modified this procedure and reinterpreted it in view of their own experience with it.

Holt's 5-Bromoindoxyl Acetate Esterase Method According to Shnitka and Seligman. Sections were prepared by calcium formol fixation, Holt's gum sucrose infiltration and cryostat sectioning as quoted in the double esterase method of Shnitka and Seligman (p. 343).

Substrate. Mix rapidly 2 cc 0.1 M tris HCl buffer pH 8.3; 5 cc 2 M NaCl (11.7%); 1 cc ferricyanide-ferrocyanide redox buffer 0.05 M for K_3Fe-$(CN)_6$ and for $K_4Fe(CN)_6 \cdot 3H_2O$ (dissolve 1 m-mol of each (329 and 422 mg, respectively) in the same 20 cc portion of distilled water); add 2 cc distilled water. Pour the mixture into a small beaker containing 1.3 mg 5-bromoindoxyl acetate in 0.1 cc acetone, swirling to mix. 5-Bromo-4-chloroindoxyl acetate[1] 1.5 mg may be substituted for the 5-bromo derivative. The final concentrations are 0.5 mM for the indoxyl acetate and 5 mM each for $K_3Fe(CN)_6$ and $K_4Fe(CN)_6$. Incubate free floating sections 30–120 minutes, wash in distilled water, pick up on glass slides and mount in polyvinyl pyrrolidone, or cautiously dehydrate in alcohols, clear in xylene and mount in Permount.

---

[1] Sigma Chemical Co., St. Louis, Mo.

Result: Discrete droplet localization of esterases is seen, shown by Shnitka and Seligman to be *A* esterase, with suppression of *B* esterases by the redox buffer acting as an inhibitor.

CHOLINESTERASE

Gomori (*Proc. Soc. Exp. Biol. Med.* 68:354, 1948) introduced a technic for localization of cholinesterase, for which he preferred myristoylcholine as substrate. He prescribed 12–24 hour fixation in acetone at 0°C, a 1–3 hour bath at 0°C in equal parts of 100% alcohol and ether, a 12 hour infiltration in 4% collodion in alcohol ether mixture at 0°C followed by 2 changes of chloroform of 1 hour each, and imbedding in paraffin (preferably *in vacuo* for 15 minutes. Do not heat more than 2 hours). Section at 5–10 μ.

This procedure should undoubtedly be replaced by one of the later esterase section preparation methods: freeze dry paraffin, cold neutral formol calcium 16–24 hours and frozen sections, cryostat or Adamstone-Taylor cold knife sections attached to slides and, perhaps preferably, postfixed 15 minutes at 3°C in formol calcium or acetone or by the section freeze substitution method of Chang and Hori.

1. Deparaffinize with petroleum ether and hydrate through acetone or by drying in air; wash formalin or acetone fixed frozen sections in distilled water.
2. Incubate 2–16 hours in solvent or in substrate. Since greater activity should be preserved by the newer fixation methods, the shorter interval should be adequate.

   Solvent: 0.1 *M* cobaltous acetate = 2.49% of the tetrahydrate   40 cc

   0.1 *M* tris maleate buffer pH 7.6 (p. 667)   60 cc
   Distilled water   200 cc
   Add 1 mg each of $CaCl_2$, $MgCl_2$ and $MnCl_2$.

   Specific substrate: To 30 cc of solvent add 0.6 cc of 0.02 *M* myristoylcholine (0.663%) in distilled water.
   Store the stock solvent and the myristoylcholine solutions separately in the refrigerator at 4°C, adding a crystal of camphor to each.
3. Wash 2 minutes in running water.
4. Immerse 15 minutes in 0.5% dilution of yellow ammonium sulfide solution or 0.5% sodium sulfide (p. 319). (The cobalt soaps react rather slowly to form the sulfide.)
5. Wash 2 minutes in running water.
6. Counterstain 5 minutes in 0.2% safranin in 1% acetic, if desired.
7. Dehydrate in alcohols, clear in xylene and mount in Canada balsam, ester gum or β-pinene resin.

Results: Sites of cholinesterase activity are shown as dark brown; nuclei, red; cytoplasm, etc., in various shades of pink. Addition of Prostigmine bromide (10 μM: 0.5 cc of a 30 mg/100 cc to a 50 cc Coplin jar) specifically inhibits the hydrolysis of the substrate.

Nachlas and Seligman (*J. Biol. Chem.* **181**:343, 1949) note that cholinesterase is inhibited by 10 μM (2.75 mg/liter) of physostigmine (eserine) but that lipase and esterase are only partly inhibited by 3.5 mM (nearly 0.1%).

Gomori noted species differences in localization with myristoylcholine and the palmitic and lauric choline esters. Dog and mouse tissues reacted best with myristic and lauric esters; human and pigeon tissues, with palmitic. Hard, Peterson and Fox (*J. Neuropath. Exp. Neurol.* **10**:48, 1951) preferred myristoylcholine for their experimental studies on dogs.

Koelle and Friedenwald (*Proc. Soc. Exp. Biol. Med.* **70**:617, 1949) substituted acetylthiocholine as substrate in the cholinesterase technic introduced by Gomori (*loc. cit.*) because the choline fatty acid esters originally employed were found to be only very slowly hydrolyzed by brain and purified cholinesterases from erythrocytes and electric organ, in comparison with acetylcholine. Acetylthiocholine was found to hydrolyze even more rapidly than acetylcholine. This substrate is hydrolyzed by both cholinesterase and by nonspecific esterase, and may be blocked by pretreatment of tissue with the irreversible cholinesterase inhibitor diisopropylfluorophosphate at 1 mM (184 mg/liter).

Koelle and Friedenwald's Technic for Cholinesterase. *Reagents.* Buffer: 1 N glycine 50 cc, 1 N NaOH 18 cc, distilled water 32 cc (pH 9.6). Solvent: Buffer 0.4 cc, 0.1 M copper sulfate (2.5% $CuSO_4 \cdot 5H_2O$) 0.2 cc, distilled water 8.6 cc. Add trace of copper thiocholine, dispersing thoroughly. Preheat to 37°C for at least 15 minutes.

Specific Substrate. Add 0.8 cc acetylthiocholine solution to 9.2 cc solvent, and filter and use at once.

Acetylthiocholine Solution. Dissolve 14.5 mg acetylthiocholine iodide in 0.75 cc distilled water in centrifuge tube.

Add 0.25 cc 2.5% copper sulfate ($CuSO_4 \cdot 5H_2O$). Centrifuge out cupric iodide and decant.

Copper Thiocholine. Dissolve acetylthiocholine in copper glycinate solution, adjust to pH 12 with KOH. Let stand overnight, collect precipitate and wash free of alkali with distilled water.

Technic.

1. Cut frozen sections of fresh unfixed tissue or make teased preparations of fresh muscle. As with the Gomori technic, later preparation methods may be used.

2. Place control preparations in 1 *mM* (0.0184%) diisopropylfluoro-phosphate in 0.85% sodium chloride solution and let stand for 30 minutes, to inactivate.

3. Wash in distilled water.

4. Place untreated preparations and inactivated controls in specific substrate and incubate at 37°C for 10–60 minutes.

5. Rinse in distilled water saturated with copper thiocholine.

6. Transfer to a 1% dilution of ammonium sulfide solution [Koelle says (NH$_4$)$_2$S or 0.5% Na$_2$S buffered to pH 7, p. 319] to convert the deposited copper thiocholine to the dark brown amorphous copper sulfide.

7. Wash in water, float onto slides, blot down.

8. Counterstain if desired, *e.g.*, with 0.2% safranin in 1% acetic for 3–5 minutes, rinse, dehydrate with alcohols or acetone, clear in xylene and mount in balsam, ester gum or β-pinene resin.

Results: Sites of enzymatic activity are shown by dark brown deposits of copper sulfide.

In place of the diisopropylfluorophosphate inhibitor used by Koelle and Friedenwald, it should be possible to use the 10 μM Prostigmine bromide

TABLE 10-11. ESTERASE INHIBITORS, CHEMICAL NAMES, MOLECULAR WEIGHTS AND EXAMPLES OF EFFECTIVE MOLARITIES USED HISTOCHEMICALLY

Inhibitor	Mol. wt.	Acetylcholin-esterase	Aliesterase not qualified	Esterases		Lipase
				A	B	
Eserine { Alkaloid	275.36	10 μM[4,6]	2.5 mM[4]	...	2.5 mM[4]	3.5 mM[4]
Eserine { Salicylate	413.48					
Prostigmine bromide	303.22	10 μM[2]				
Diisopropylfluorophosphate (DFP)	184.15	1 mM[3]; 10 μM[6]	0.5 mM[1]	...	0.5 mM[5]	
Arsanilic acid	217.04	....	0.1 M[4]	...	0.1 M[5]	
Sodium fluoride (NaF)	41.99	1–5 mM[6]	2 mM,[1] 70 mM[4]	...	70 mM[5]	
Sodium taurocholate	537.68	....	0.2 %[4]	...	....	0.1–0.2 %[2,4] activates
Quinine hydrochloride	378.91	....	Less effect than on lipase[4]	...	....	50 mM[4]
Diethyl-*p*-nitrophenylphos-phate (E-600)	275.20	0.1–0.001 μM[6]	....	...	10 μM[6]	
Phemerol · H$_2$O	466.11	0.5 mM[1]				

Note: *A* esterase is generally described as resisting those inhibitor levels which inhibit *B* esterase. Precise levels for its inhibition are not cited.

[1] Burstone, M. S., *J. Histochem.* **4**:130, 1955.

[2] Gomori, G., *Proc. Soc. Exp. Biol. Med.* **68**:354, 1948.

[3] Koelle, G. B., and Friedenwald, J. S., *Proc. Soc. Exp. Biol. Med.* **70**:617, 1949.

[4] Nachlas, M. M., and Seligman, A. M., *J. Biol. Chem.* **181**:392, 1949.

[5] Shnitka, T. K., and Seligman, A. M., *J. Histochem.* **9**:504, 1961.

[6] Wachstein, M., Meisel, E. and Falcon, C., *J. Histochem.* **9**:325, 1961.

(M.W. 303) inhibitor of Gomori or the 10 μM physostigmine (M.W. 275) solution of Nachlas and Seligman.

Rohlich (*Nature* **178**:1398, 1956) finds that acetylcholinesterase may be demonstrated quite well in muscle infiltrated for 2–3 hours at 42°C in polyethylene glycol 1000 and sectioned at 5 μ, using a modified Koelle technic. The material must be sectioned promptly, as the activity deteriorates almost completely in storage for about 1 month in the imbedded state.

The molecular weights for choline, acetyl, butyryl, lauryl and myristyl cholines and acetyl and butryl thiocholines and sample formulation are presented below:

$$HO-CH_2-CH_2-\overset{+}{N}(CH_3)_3 \cdot \overset{-}{Cl}$$
Choline chloride

$$HS-CH_2-CH_2-\overset{+}{N}(CH_3)_3 \cdot \overset{-}{I}$$
Thiocholine iodide

$$CH_3CO-O-CH_2-CH_2-\overset{+}{N}(CH_3)_3 \cdot \overset{-}{Cl}$$
Acetylcholine chloride

$$CH_3CO-S-CH_2-CH_2-\overset{+}{N}(CH_3)_3 \cdot \overset{-}{I}$$
Acetylthiocholine iodide

The butyryl ($CH_3-CH_2-CH_2-CO$), lauryl ($C_{11}H_{23}CO$) and myristyl ($C_{13}H_{27}CO$) groups are substituted for the acetyl (CH_3CO) group in the above cholines and thiocholines.

	Mol. wt.
1. Choline chloride	139.632
2. Acetylcholine chloride	181.670
3. Butyrylcholine chloride	207.708
4. Laurylcholine chloride	319.924
5. Myristylcholine chloride	345.962
6. Thiocholine iodide	247.151
7. Acetylthiocholine iodide	289.189
8. Butyrylthiocholine iodide	315.227

In cases of poisoning by acetylcholinesterase inhibitors, Bergner (*Am. J. Path.* **35**:807, 1959) compares the grade of inhibition of the Koelle acetylthiocholine CuS method (p. 346) in teased intercostal muscle tissue with that obtained in the same muscle after 30 minute immersion in 1 *mM* solutions of TMB-4 (M.W. 478.213) or 2-PAM, (M.W. 264.08) (see "Bergner's Reactivators," below).

Bergner's rat experiments included poisonings by the insecticides Diazinone and Parathion, by TEPP and Sarin and by diisopropylfluorophosphate (DFP) and Tabun. With the first 2, considerable postmortem reactivation occurred when the bodies lay at room temperature for 24 hours; with the last 2 there was little or no postmortem spontaneous reactivation.

2-PAM was quite an effective reactivator after Diazinone, Parathion and Sarin, but it was weak after DFP and Tabun. TMB-4 gave strong reactivation after DFP, Tabun and Sarin.

Although lack of acetylcholinesterase activity of motor end plates in cadavers is not regarded as conclusive evidence of inactivator poisoning, Bergner apparently regards the regeneration of such activity by 1 *mM* 2-PAM or TMB-4 as important evidence for the existence of such poisoning. However, prolonged postmortem delays before autopsy do permit considerable regeneration of acetylcholinesterase activity after some poisons of this type, but not after all of them. See *Merck Index* for descriptions of these compounds, except TMB-4 [1,1'-trimethylene-bis(4-formylpyridinium bromide) dioxime].

BERGNER'S CHOLINESTERASE INACTIVATORS

O,O-Diethyl-O-(2-isopropyl-4-methylpyrimidyl-6)thiophosphate
(Diazinon, M.W. 504.36)

O,O-Diethyl-O-*p*-nitrophenyl thiophosphate
(Parathion, M.W. 297.27)

Tetraethyl pyrophosphate
(TEPP, M.W. 290.198)

Diisopropylfluorophosphate
(DFP, M.W. 184.153)

$$\underset{\substack{\displaystyle\| \\ \displaystyle O}}{\overset{\displaystyle F}{H_3C\!-\!O\!-\!\underset{}{P}\!-\!O\!-\!CH}}\!\!\!\overset{\displaystyle CH_3}{\underset{\displaystyle CH_3}{\diagup}}$$

Methylisopropylfluorophosphate
(Sarin, M.W. 125.124)

$$\overset{\displaystyle H_3C}{\underset{\displaystyle H_3C}{\diagup}}\!\!N\!-\!\underset{\displaystyle CN}{\overset{\displaystyle O}{\underset{}{\overset{\displaystyle \|}{P}}}}\!-\!O\!-\!C_2H_5$$

O-Ethyl-N,N-dimethylcyanophosphamide
(Tabun, M.W. 162.134)
BERGNER'S REACTIVATORS

Pyridine ring with CH=NOH substituent

$$H_3C \overset{+}{} \quad I^-$$

Pyridinium 2-aldoxime methiodide
(2-PAM, M.W. 264.075)

$$HC \!-\!\!\langle ring \rangle\!\!-\!N\overset{+}{}\!-\!CH_2\!-\!CH_2\!-\!CH_2\!-\!N\overset{+}{}\!\langle ring \rangle\!\!-\!CH$$
$$\underset{\displaystyle HON}{\overset{\displaystyle \|}{}} \qquad Br^- \qquad Br^- \qquad \underset{\displaystyle NOH}{\overset{\displaystyle \|}{}}$$

1,1′-Trimethylene bis (4-formylpyridinium bromide)dioxime
(TMB-4, M.W. 478.213)

PROTEASES

Mast Cell Proteases: Chymotrypsin-like Enzyme

Gomori (*J. Histochem.* 1:469, 1953) described in mast cells an enzyme which was quite active against chloroacetyl esters of α-naphthol and naphthol AS. His technic, as presented in the subjoined table, has had to be put together from the above paper and that of Gomori and Chessick (*J. Cell. Comp. Physiol.* 41:51, 1953) on the use of α-naphthyl and naphthol AS acetates as esterase substrates, to which paper I am indebted for the total volume of the substrate solution and the identity and amount of the diazonium salt used. Gomori noted that the mast cell enzyme resisted 10 μM eserine.

Later Benditt (*Fed. Proc.* 13: No. 1, abstr. 1646, 1956) showed that naphthol AS chloroacetate was cleaved both by crystalline chymotrypsin and by extracts of isolated rat mast cells. These 2 *in vitro* reactions and the histochemical reactions were inhibited by 0.1 mM diisoproplfluorophosphate. Later papers by Benditt (*Ann. N.Y. Acad. Sci.* 73:204, 1958) and Benditt and Arase (*J. Histochem.* 6:431, 1958; *J. Exp. Med.* 110:451,

1959) identified further substrates attacked by α-chymotrypsin and iso-lated (as well as *in situ*) mast cell enzyme, such as N-acetyl-L-tryptophan, N-acetyl-L-tyrosine and N-acetyl-L-phenylalanine ethyl esters. *p*-Toluene-sulfonylarginine methyl ester is cleaved by trypsin but not by chymotryp-sin or the mast cell enzyme. Resistance to formaldehyde by chymotrypsin as well as by the mast cell enzyme was noted.

Lagunoff and Benditt (*Nature* **192**:1198, 1961), in kinetic studies of hydrolysis of benzoyl, phenylacetyl, phenylpropionyl and phenylbutyryl naphthol AS esters, using the 310 mμ exc. 515 mμ emiss. fluorescence of released naphthol AS, reported that hydrolysis was rapid for phenyl pro-pionate, slow for phenyl butyrate and negligible for phenyl acetate and benzoate. Histochemical studies using simultaneous fast garnet GBC coupling agreed.

Moloney *et al.* (*J. Histochem.* **8**:200, 1960) seemed unaware of Ben-ditt's studies and referred to the enzyme as an esterase, again stressing its presence in neutrophil leucocytes and myelocytes, as well as in mast cells. Superior results were claimed for the substitution of naphthol AS-D choloroacetate (M.W. 353.813) for Gomori's original preparation.

TABLE 10-12. TECHNICS AND SUBSTRATES FOR MAST CELL PROTEASE/ESTERASE

	Author				
	Gomori	Gomori	Benditt and Arase, 1958	Lagunoff and Benditt, 1961	Moloney *et al.*, 1960
Fixation...........	Formalin	Formalin	Formalin	Cold formalin aca-cia-sucrose	Methanol, 30 sec (smears, imprints)
Section............	Paraffin	Paraffin	Paraffin	Frozen sections defatted with methanol	
Substrate..........	α-Naphthyl chloroacetate	Naphthol AS chloroacetate	Naphthol AS chloroacetate	Naphthol AS phen-ylpropionate	Naphthol AS-D chloroacetate
mg = μM.........	5 mg = 0.9 mM	5 mg = 0.6 mM	0.42 mg (= 50 μM)	0.4 mg (= 40 μM)	25 mg (= 2.9 mM)
Special solvent	Acetone, 0.5 cc	Acetone, 0.5 cc Propylene glycol, 7.5 cc	Acetone, 1.25 cc Propylene glycol, 7.5 cc	Methanol, 10 cc	Acetone, 1.25 cc
Buffer.............	0.2 M phosphate	0.2 M phosphate	0.1 M PO$_4$	0.1 M tris	0.1 M Veronal
Volume..........	2.5 cc	2.5 cc	5 cc	5 cc	12 cc
pH..............	6.4	6.4	6.4	8	7.4
Water to make final volume..........	25 cc	25 cc	25 cc	25 cc	25 cc
Diazonium salt, fast garnet GBC......	20–50 mg	10–50 mg	10 mg	10 mg	25 mg
Incubation time.....	5–20 min	5–20 min	5- 20 min	15–30 min	30 min
Temperature........	20–25°C	20–25°C	20–25°C	20–25°C	20–25°C

Moloney and coworkers studied more inhibitors, in reference particularly to neutrophil leucocyte and myelocyte activity, and reported for eserine strong inhibition at 1 *mM*, none at 100 μM; for taurocholate, complete at 10 *mM*; for arsanilate, complete at 10 *mM*, none at 1 *mM*; for diisopropylfluorophosphate, complete at 10 *mM*; for NaF, partial at 3 *mM*; for CuSO$_4$, complete at 1 *mM*, with no inhibition by 0.1 *M* Lugol's solution, 3 *mM* ZnSO$_4$, 0.1% Zephiran or 3% Versene.

As noted above, none of these substrates was published in complete detail. Some of the data in Gomori's substrates are from Gomori and Chessick (1953); the molarity of the phosphate buffer in Benditt and Arase is set to agree with the estimated concentration of Gomori's. The amount of diazo in Lagunoff and Benditt is supplied from Benditt and Arase, and the amount of tris buffer agrees with that in Burstone's practice, who also worked with Gomori.

Mast Cell Proteases: Trypsin-like Enzyme

Glenner *et al.* (*J. Histochem.* **10**:109, 1962) have noted the presence in the mast cells of dogs and men (but not of rabbits, guinea pigs, rats or mice) of an enzyme hydrolyzing α-N-benzoyl-DL-arginyl-β-naphthylamide and certain naphthol AS esters of ε-amino-caproic acid. This enzyme is inhibited by heparin (1 mg/1 cc), tetrabutylammonium iodide and tosyl and benzoyl-L-arginine methyl esters, in distinction from the mast cell protease of Benditt and Arase, found in all 6 species noted above and demonstrated by its hydrolysis of naphthol AS chloroacetate.

Substrate (*Nature* **185**:846, 1960).

α-N-Benzoyl-DL-arginine-β-naphthylamide	30 mg
Fast Corinth V	10 mg
Tris maleate buffer 50 *mM*, pH 7	20 cc

Fast Corinth V may be replaced by fast garnet GBC, but fast blue B completely inhibits the reaction.

The above substrate is rapidly digested by bovine trypsin, but it resists bovine chymotrypsin for 18 hours.

Fresh frozen sections directly or after Glenner's acetone chloroform freeze substitution procedure are brought into the above substrate for 20–30 minutes, drained and transferred to 1% copper sulfate (0.04 *M*) for 10 minutes, washed and mounted in glycerol gelatin containing a few drops of 1% copper sulfate.

Inhibitors. 0.1 *mM* diisopropylfluorophosphate, 2 *mM* CuSO$_4$, 2 *mM* Pb(NO$_3$)$_2$. Not inhibited by soybean trypsin inhibitor (1 mg/1 cc), 1 *mM* iodoacetate or 0.5 and 10 *mM* KCN.

γ-GLUTAMYL TRANSPEPTIDASE

Glenner *et al.* (*J. Histochem.* **10**:481, 1962) reported a method for the histochemical localization of γ-glutamyl transpeptidase activity which seems interesting, though the substrate may not be immediately available commercially. The synthesis is reported in the same paper.

Attached fresh frozen sections are used according to Glenner's method. Incubate in the following substrate mixture for 20 minutes:

N-(γ-L-glutamyl)β-naphthylamide	3	mg in 0.5 cc acetone
Fast garnet GBC	15	mg in 1 cc distilled water
0.1 M tris maleate buffer pH 7.2	10	cc
Distilled water	28.5 cc	

Sites of activity are shown in red: bile duct epithelium in liver, pancreatic duct epithelium in man, pancreatic acini in rat and guinea pig, brush borders of P-2 and D-1 segments of renal tubules in guinea pigs and in P-1 and P-2 segments in rats, testicular germinal epithelium, epithelial border zone in epididymis and seminal vesicle (man), human endometrial gland epithelium, rat and guinea pig ova and granulosa cells, some duct cells in salivary glands (rodent), tracheobronchial epithelium (rodent), hypophyseal beta cells (?), thyroid follicle epithelium.

Inhibitors. Severe inhibition by Cu^{++}, Zn^{++}, Hg^{++} and Pb^{++} at 1 mM, and by 5 mM Bromsulphalein and 1 mM bromocresol green.

Without effect were Na_2HPO_4, $MgCl_2$, $MnCl_2$, $CaCl_2$, KCN and NaF at 1 mM; diisopropylfluorophosphate, 0.1 mM; Versene, 10 mM; Na pyruvate, 1 mM; Na taurocholate, 4 mM; iodoacetate, 1 mM; acetyltrimethylammonium bromide, 5 mM; p-quinone, 1 mM; atabrine, 1 mM; and p-chloromercuribenzoate, 5 mM.

Activation was seen with glycylglycine and L-methionine, inhibition by L-serine and oxidized glutathione, all at 1 mM.

AMINOPEPTIDASES

There has been some dispute as to whether histochemically demonstrable enzymes releasing β-naphthylamine or other arylamines from amide combinations with amino acid carboxyls should be termed leucine aminopeptidase or simply aminopeptidase. At first it was thought generally that the leucyl naphthylamide gave more specific results. Gomori (*Proc. Soc. Exp. Biol. Med.* **87**:559, 1954) worked with an alanyl derivative in 1954, which did not give especially good histochemical results. Burstone and Folk, and Ackerman used both the alanyl and leucyl derivatives; Nachlas and Seligman and coworkers used chiefly the leucyl. Some investigators have thought the results essentially identical. Ackerman thought the alanyl derivative better, and Seligman's school have adhered to use of the leucyl derivative.

A variety of section preparation procedures noted in Table 10-13 and in the subjoined text have been used. Glenner's recommendations seem well worthwhile in this respect; if $-70°C$ temperatures are not available, Novikoff's recommendations may be followed, or they may be combined with Glenner's acetone chloroform extractions at 0–5°C.

The substrates in Table 10-13 are fairly similar, and incubation times depend in any case on the activity of the particular tissue under study. The temperature is again a matter of convenience. The enzyme activity is greater at 37°C than at 25°C, but so is the rate of decomposition of the diazonium salt.

TABLE 10-13. AMINOPEPTIDASES, COMPARISON OF METHODS AND SUBSTRATES

	Section preparation methods			
	Burstone and Folk: Freeze-dry paraffin, petroleum ether, acetone, water[1]	Nachlas, Seligman, *et al.*: Attached cryostat sections, dried 30 min at 37°C (1957); fresh frozen section (1962)[2]	Burstone and Weisburger: Freeze-dry celloidin-paraffin, petroleum ether, acetone, water; attached fresh frozen (cold knife)[3]	Ackerman: Blood, marrow films, 2 min at $-10°C$ in 1% OsO_4 in dimethylformamide, wash in water[4]
Amides of arylamine......... with	β-Naphthylamine	β-Naphthylamine	3-Aminocarbazole 3-amino-9-ethylcarbazole	β-Naphthylamine
Aminoacid(s) ... Amount and final conc. amide Special solvent..	DL-Alanine L-leucine (Alanyl) 5 mg, 0.93 mM (Leucyl) 5 mg, 0.78 mM	L-Leucine 10 mg, 1.56 mM H_2O, 1.25 cc	DL-Alanine (3-NH_2) 2.5 mg, 0.34 mM (9-Ethyl!) 2.5 mg, 0.35 mM Acetone, 0.25 cc	Alanine 10 mg, 1.87 mM
Buffer .... Amount...... Final molarity pH...........	0.2 M tris 5 cc 40 mM 7.1	0.1 M acetate 12.5 cc 50 mM 6.5	0.2 M tris 7.5 cc 60 mM 7.1	0.1 M phosphate 12.5 cc 50 mM 6.7
Activators ...... Final conc .... Diazonium salt..	.... Fast garnet GBC, 15 mg	1.25 cc 20 mM KCN 1 mM Fast blue B, 12.5 mg	.... Fast garnet GBC, 10 mg	$MgSO_4·7H_2O$, 1 mg 1 mM Fast garnet GBC, 12.5 mg
Additional solvent Final volume....	Water, 20 cc 25 cc	Physiologic saline, 10 cc 25 cc	Water, 17.25 cc 25 cc	Water, 12.5 cc 25 cc
Time range ..... Temperature....	15 min–4 hr 24–25°C	20 min–4 hr 37°C	30 min–18 hr 25(37)°C	Up to 4–6 hr 20–25°C

[1] Burstone and Folk, *J. Histochem.* **4**:217, 1956; **6**:322, 1958.
[2] Nachlas, Seligman *et al.*, *J. Histochem.* **5**:264, 1957; **10**:315, 1962.
[3] Burstone and Weisburger, *J. Histochem.* **9**:349, 1961.
[4] Ackerman, *J. Histochem.* **8**:386, 1960.

Molarities have been computed for convenience on the perhaps unwarranted basis that the substrates are reasonably pure substances. The diazonium salts are probably present in considerable excess, and since commercial samples represent 18–40% or more of the primary amine, computation of molarities seemed futile for them. The molecular weights may be found in Table 6-9, pp. 133–134.

Burstone also used fast black K and fast red B in the first report but later generally preferred fast garnet GBC. Nachlas and Seligman prefer fast blue B in almost all enzymatic azo reaction procedures, but they do compare fast garnet GBC in their 1962 paper.

In their first report Nachlas *et al.* dried their cryostat sections on the slides for 30 minutes at $37°C$; in the later report this drying is not mentioned. Also in the first report they note that colors were at first red and were converted to blue by postchelation in 0.1 M (2.5%) $CuSO_4 \cdot 5H_2O$. This practice is not noted in the later report. Gomori had previously noted diffusion from unfixed frozen sections.

Novikoff (*J. Histochem.* 8:37, 1960), using the Burstone-Folk (1956) substrate, found good preservation of activity in fresh frozen (cryostat) sections which were postfixed in acetone at $2–4°C$ for 15 minutes. Unfixed sections lost activity by diffusion, and postfixation for 15 minutes in formol calcium at $2–4°C$ decreased the activity.

Inhibitors. Strong inhibition has been reported by Burstone and Folk for 10 mM KCN, 10 mM Versene, 1 mM each of Cu^{++}, Pb^{++}, Cd^{++} and (Ackerman) Hg^{++}. Ackerman noted inhibition by 1 mM Zn^{++} in the presence of 0.1 M $CaCl_2$; he reported activation without the Ca^{++}. Inhibition by certain diazonium salts was reported by Nachlas *et al.* (1957) and by Burstone and Weisburger, especially by the borofluorides. Citrate was inhibitory at 10 mM (Nachlas) but not at 5 mM (Burstone and Folk). Ackerman noted activation by Mg^{++}, Co^{++} and Zn^{++} at 0.1 M. Iodoacetate 1 mM, Mn^{++} 1 mM, ethyl maleimide 0.1 M, NaF 2 mM and diisopropylfluorophosphate 0.5 mM have been reported as without effect. Short methanol or ethanol fixation inactivates, as does aqueous formalin (Ackerman).

Since it appears that the azo dyes formed by azo coupling with the naphthylamine released from amino acid amide linkages in the group of peptidase methods are fat soluble basic dyes, diffusion occurs in glycerol gelatin or polyvinyl pyrrolidone and crystallization appears in and around lipid droplets, both much to the detriment of the permanency of the preparations. The freeze dry paraffin technic, with the lipid extraction entailed in deparaffinization with xylene or petroleum ether eliminated part of the difficulties. To overcome these difficulties Glenner (*J. Histochem.* 10:257, 1962) prescribes for alanyl and leucyl naphthylamidases, mast cell protease and γ-glutamyl transpeptidase a modified section freeze substitution technic (p. 43). After freeze substitution for 18–24 hours in acetone at $-70°C$, sections are left in pure acetone 1 hour at $4°C$, then 1 hour each in $2:1$ and $1:2$ acetone/chloroform and in pure chloroform. They are then transferred to slides, coated with 0.5% celloidin and dried in air. After incubation in the appropriate substrate for the prescribed interval, wash in 0.9% sodium chloride and in pH 9.2 0.1 M Veronal buffer and mount in the H-A (Highman variant of the medium of Lillie and Ashburn) gum Apáthy (pp. 109, 111). This variant of the Apáthy gum arabic sucrose medium was specifically designed to prevent diffusion of crystal violet in amyloid stains, and has served to keep aminopeptidase preparations unimpaired as long as 8 months. Sealing of the coverslips with cellulose caprate seems superior to pyroxylin cement; I have used both.

Freeze substitution in acetone followed by polyvinyl alcohol or low melting paraffin may also be used. Naidoo's freeze dry low melting paraffin followed by petroleum ether and isopentane (p. 323) also seems applicable.

Oxidative Aminocarbazole Method of Burstone and Weisburger for Aminopeptidases (*J. Histochem.* 9:712, 1961). This technic offers a different approach than the foregoing azo coupling methods.

Prepare sections by the freeze dry celloidin paraffin technic or fresh frozen sections in the cryostat or by the Adamstone-Taylor technic. Attach to slides and bring to substrate as usual.

Substrate.

	Final concentration, mM
Dissolve 5 mg DL-alanyl-3-amino-9-ethylcarbazole in 0.5 cc ethanol	0.65
Add 25 cc distilled water and 2 cc 50 mM (1.65%) $K_3Fe(CN)_6$	3.5
Add 3 mg 5,6,7,8-tetrahydro-α-naphthylamine in the alcohol	0.7

Burstone comments particularly on the favorable color results when 5,6,7,8-tetrahydro-α-naphthylamine is added to the above substrate, giving a salmon pink color which is converted to deep blue by postchelation with copper. The amount is not stated; 3 mg would furnish more than one equivalent for all the carbazole.

Incubate 15–60 minutes at $25°C$ (Burstone does not specify temperature; this was approximately NIH Bldg. 10 temperature at the time he wrote his 1960 paper there), rinse in distilled water and transfer to 10%

aqueous copper sulfate ($CuSO_4 \cdot 5H_2O = 0.4\ M$) for 1–2 hours, wash in water and mount in glycerol gelatin. A counterstain in 0.1% basic fuchsin in 1% acetic acid, 2–5 minutes, and mounting in Highman's 50% potassium acetate gum Apáthy may be tried if a nuclear stain is needed.

The **nerve cathepsin** of Adams *et al.* or a similarly located amino-peptidase has been found (Adams and Glenner, *J. Neurochem.* **9**:233, 1962) to be well demonstrated by Burstone's aminopeptidase substrates, but biochemically it gives its maximal activity at pH 7–7.5 with L-leucyl-β-naphthylamide as substrate. Relative activities at pH 7 were 90% for DL-alanyl-β-naphthylamide, 33% for DL-phenylalanyl-β-naphthylamide and nil at pH 5, 6 and 7 for benzoyl-DL-arginine-β-naphthylamide, chloro-acetyl-α-naphthylamide and 2-chloroacetyl-3-naphthoic acid anilide (naphthol AS chloroacetate).

Azo Dye Technic of Adams and Glenner for Nerve Aminopeptidase.
Substrate. 3 mg L-leucyl-β-naphthylamide hydrochloride in 30 cc 0.1 *M* tris buffer at pH 7. Preheat substrate to 37°C. Add 15 mg fast garnet GBC just before introducing sections. Incubate fresh frozen 10 μ sections, attached to slides, for 30–60 minutes. Rinse and mount in glycerol gelatin.

Inhibitors. Cysteine 10 *mM*; iodoacetate 10 *mM*; p-chloromercuriben-zoate 1 *mM*; KCN 10 *mM*; ascorbic acid 10 *mM*; diisopropylfluorophos-phate 10 *mM* 58%; with 3 hour preincubation 1 *mM* complete; MnSO$_4$ 1 *mM*. Preheating to 60, 80 or 100°C for 10 minutes inactivated nerve aminopeptidase, as did chloroform methanol and chloroform acetone ex-tractions. Inactivation was noted when fast red B was used as the diazonium salt.

SUBSTRATE FILM METHODS OF ENZYME LOCALIZATION

Perhaps inspired by the statement in Wells's *Chemical Pathology* (3d ed., W. B. Saunders Company, Philadelphia, 1918) that smears of blood or pus on a film of fibrin would digest small holes in the fibrin about each leucocyte, there has arisen in recent years a small series of specific enzyme localization methods wherein a cryostat section of unfixed tissue is closely apposed to a film of the specific substrate and the two are al-lowed to interact for a time and then are separated. The tissue section is then fixed and stained by some appropriate procedure for identification of ordinary morphologic details, and selected areas are photographed. The film is also appropriately fixed and stained for the demonstration of the specific substrate.

The gelatin silver protease (and cathepsin) method of Adams and Tuqan (*J. Histochem.* **9**:469, 1961) seems the most closely allied to Wells's procedure.

Gelatin Silver Protease Method of Adams and Tuqan.

1. Expose panchromatic "quarter" plates to daylight for 15 minutes. Develop, fix in bisulfite hypo, wash and dry as usual. Cut with diamond point from glass side into pieces of convenient size—*e.g.*, cut a 3×5 in. (75×125 mm) plate into 5 strips 1×3 in. (25×75 mm).
2. Fix tissues 1–3 days at 4°C in 10% formalin, cut frozen sections at 15 μ, apply inactivators if they are required, rinse in distilled water and immediately float onto the gelatin side of the blackened photographic plate.
3. Allow to just dry, then moisten with (a) 0.15 M phosphate buffer pH 7.6 or (b) 0.15 M acetate buffer pH 5. No free fluid should be left on the section; the buffer should be entirely absorbed by the gelatin, to prevent diffusion.
4. Incubate in a moist chamber saturated with water vapor at 37°C for 30–60 minutes. The slides may be conveniently enclosed in a large petri dish with wet filter paper in the bottom. The petri dish should be preheated to 37°C. Inspect every 5–10 minutes, replenishing buffer if needed.
5. Dry, dehydrate with alcohols, clear in xylene within 2 minutes to prevent crazing of gelatin film which may ensue on slow dehydration. Mount in balsam or synthetic resin.

Results: Protease activity shown by clear areas where gelatin has been digested and loose silver granules have been washed out. Activity is described about pancreatic zymogen cells, intercalated duct cells of rat and mouse submaxillary gland, over Paneth cells, myelin, renal cortex.

Iodoacetate (1%, 1 hour) inactivated the myelin cathepsin, but not the pancreatic enzyme; diisopropylfluorophosphate (1–10 mM, 1 hour), 6% $HgCl_2$ (1 hour) inactivated both. Pretreatment with alcohol or formalin had no effect, but their presence during the reaction inhibited. This iodoacetate sensitive protease is the myelin cathepsin of Adams and Bayliss (*J. Histochem.* **9**:473, 1961).

The autodigestion procedure reported by Lillie and Burtner (*J. Histochem.* **1**:8, 1953) is of similar nature, with reliance on the digestibility of alcohol fixed cytoplasm.

Leucocyte protease has long been recognized from its lytic action on fibrin of exudates (Wells, *Chemical Pathology*, 3d ed., W. B. Saunders Company, Philadelphia, 1918, pp. 94–96). It resists formaldehyde for long periods.

Histochemically it may be made evident from the selective cytolysis and later karyolysis of the neutrophil leucocytes which occurs in blood films which are first fixed 10 minutes in 75% alcohol and then exposed to distilled water at 60°C. The enzyme is destroyed by fixation in boiling xylene. Formaldehyde fixation renders cytoplasm and nuclei resistant to digestion and also to trypsin. The autolytic digestion occurs readily after fixation in boiling acetone, benzene or toluene.

Daoust's Gelatin Film Deoxyribonuclease Method. For this method (*Exp. Cell Res.* **12**:203, 1957) Daoust directs as follows:

Preparation of Substrate Films. Mix equal volumes melted 5% gelatin and 0.2% deoxyribonucleic acid by heating on water bath. Spread 0.05 cc of mixture with pipet tip over 25 × 40 mm area; leave horizontal until dry. Fix overnight in neutral 10% formaldehyde (25% formalin). Wash in distilled water and let dry.

Preparation of Slides for Carrying Sections. Coat slides to carry the sections with glycerol gelatin (10:7:83 water; premelted on water bath). Deposit 0.3 cc on a slide and spread with the pipet tip over a 25 × 40 mm area. Lay slides horizontal for 10–15 minutes to gel.

Preparation of Sections. Rinse and blot fresh tissue to remove blood, freeze onto cutting stage of cryostat and section at 15 μ in cryostat at −20°C. Transfer sections quickly in cryostat to glycerol gelatin coated slides, remove at once from cryostat to avoid freezing of the coating and lay on horizontally on warm plate at 37°C to melt the glycerol gelatin and spread the sections. Then recool to 20–25°C and allow glycerol gelatin film to gel again (about 20 minutes). This procedure is required to prevent adhesion of the section to the substrate film on reseparation of slides after exposure.

Incubation is accomplished at 20–25°C by apposing the gelated section bearing slide to the dry substrate film slides and pressing the two firmly together for a period of 5–60 minutes. The two slides are then reseparated and the section is fixed by immersion in a horizontal position in neutral 10% formalin for 18–24 hours. The sections are then washed in distilled water, 2 changes, 5 minutes each, and allowed to dry. The substrate film, as soon as separated, is similarly washed and dried. Stain substrate film 10 minutes in 0.2% toluidine blue, wash in distilled water, let dry in air and mount directly in Canada balsam.

Immerse section for 5 minutes in 25:75 acetic:alcohol to prevent staining of the gelatin, transfer directly to 0.1% toluidine blue and stain 1–2 minutes, wash in distilled water, dry in air at 20–25°C and mount in balsam.

Results: Areas of deoxyribonuclease activity appear unstained in the substrate film and may be matched with the section by superimposition of photographic images, or by side to side comparison. The use of a comparison microscope to match areas could be advantageous. For this purpose the 2 slides should be accurately apposed to each other during incubation.

It would appear that the technic of tissue staining could be simplified by incorporating a known amount of acetic acid in the toluidine blue, or by buffering it deliberately at pH 3, omitting the acetic alcohol bath. The use of a synthetic resin to prevent the thiazin dye fading which occurs in balsam, also seems advisable. Azure A or B would undoubtedly serve as well as toluidine blue.

Daoust did not employ acid dyes after his digestion procedure, to demonstrate that the loss of staining was due to destruction of deoxyribonucleic acid and not simply to proteolytic digestion of the supporting gelatin, as in the Adams-Tuqan method. This same objection applies also to the same author's ribonuclease method.

Likewise no provision is made for exploration of the effects of specific inhibitors, and since there is no pH control in the digestion process, it is quite uncertain which of the deoxyribonucleases is being shown.

Substrate Film Method of Daoust and H. Amano (*J. Histochem.* 8: 131, 1960) **for Ribonuclease** (Draining Technic). An equal volume mixture of 5% gelatin and of 5–10% sodium yeast ribonucleate[1] is melted in a water bath. Apply 3–5 drops of the mixture to clean glass slide, spreading it with the pipet tip. Stand slide vertically on a paper towel to drain and dry, wiping off excess from extreme lower end of slide with wet filter paper or gauze. Fix dried film 1 hour at 2–4°C in neutral 20% formalin. Wash out excess formalin in 3 changes of distilled water, 5 minutes each.

Control. Exposure of such films to 0.05% ribonuclease (Worthington) impairs toluidine blue staining in 2 hours and abolishes it in 8 hours.

Procedure. Cryostat sections are applied to glycerol gelatin coated slides, reacted, stained and dried in air according to the same procedure as for Daoust's deoxyribonuclease method, which see (p. 359).

Tremblay (*J. Histochem.* 11:202, 1963) has reported an essentially similar procedure for the demonstration of amylase in tissue sections. In this case the substrate is starch and the demonstration method is the periodic acid Schiff reaction.

Tremblay's Starch Substrate Film Method for Amylase. Heat a 4% aqueous suspension of Hydrolyzed Starch[2] 15 minutes in a boiling water bath. Filter while hot through glass wool and gauze. Deposit about 0.5 cc (8–12 drops) on a slide and spread rapidly over a 25 × 40 mm area. Stand upright on filter paper to drain. Wipe excess off lower end and dry film in air at 20–25°C. Fix film 18–24 hours in methanol:acetic:water —5:1:5 mixture. Wash in 3 changes of distilled water, 5 minutes each, and dry in air at 20–25°C.

Preparation of tissue sections follows that in Daoust's technic for deoxyribonuclease (p. 359).

Incubation. Appose accurately the 2 slides bearing, respectively, the tissue section on glycerol gelatin and the substrate film, face to face, and

[1] Schwartz Laboratories, Inc.
[2] Connaught Medical Research Laboratories, Toronto, Canada.

press firmly together. After 1–20 minutes separate films by insertion of knife edge or razor blade.

Rinse substrate film in distilled water, refix 15 minutes in the methanol:acetic:water mixture, stain by the periodic acid Schiff reaction, wash, dry and mount in resin.

Wash tissue sections, fix in 4% formaldehyde 18–24 hours, wash and stain with 0.2% toluidine blue, as in the deoxyribonuclease technic.

The α-amylase in the control experiments was inhibited by heating 10 minutes to 100°C or by inclusion of 1 mM CuSO$_4$. Heating slides for inactivation was practiced. It is presumed that inclusion of 1 mM CuSO$_4$ ($\cdot$5H$_2$O = 25 mg/100 cc) in the last wash water applied to the starch film before drying and using would act to inhibit the amylase activity, but Tremblay does not mention such a test.

Substitution of a highly branched polysaccharide, such as glycogen, for the starch in the substrate film should serve to distinguish α- from β-amylase.

ACID DEOXYRIBONUCLEASE (DNASE II)

Aronson et al. (J. Histochem. **6**:255, 1958) and Vorbrodt (ibid. **9**:647, 1961) have reported closely related methods for acid deoxyribonuclease (DNase II), based on Gomori's lead sulfide acid phosphatase method. Deoxyribonuclease I is Mg^{++} dependent and has a pH optimum of 7–8. I have not seen a histochemical method for it. Deoxyribonuclease II functions best at pH 4.5–6 and does not require Mg.

Substrate. Vorbrodt prefers a herring sperm deoxyribonucleic acid obtained from Light, Ltd., which is a relatively low polymer and hydrolyzes more rapidly than calf thymus deoxyribonucleic acid from British, Russian and American sources. However, he uses 5–10 times the amount.

		Final concentration
Deoxyribonucleic acid, herring sperm	5 mg	20 mg/100 cc
or calf thymus	0.5–1 mg	2–4 mg/100 cc
Acid phosphatase	2.5 mg	10 mg/100 cc
Acetate buffer 0.2 M pH 5.9 ⎫ for nuclear staining, pH 5.2 ⎭	6.2 cc	50 mM
Lead nitrate 0.1 M (3.31%)	0.5 cc	2 mM
Distilled water to make	25 cc	

Dissolve the substrate and the acid phosphatase in the buffer. Dilute the lead nitrate with 10–15 cc distilled water and add gradually to substrate with shaking. Aronson's substrate contained 2.65 mM Pb and used a pH 5 level. He used 2 mg acid phosphatase for 22.5 cc and 4 mg deoxyribonucleic acid.

Section Preparation. Aronson *et al.* cut fresh frozen sections at 15 μ in a cryostat, attached to slides and postfixed 5 minutes in formalin:water: acetone 10:40:50 at −10 to −12°C and washed 3 minutes in 50% acetone and 5–15 minutes in distilled water at 20–25°C. Novikoff's substitution of 15 minutes in formol calcium at this point could be advantageous. Vorbrodt found 2 minutes inadequate. Vorbrodt prefixed tissue blocks 12–24 hours in formol calcium at 2–4°C, cut frozen sections at 15 μ and affixed to slides. He tried Aronson's procedures, with inferior results.

For routine use Vorbrodt's preferred procedure, overnight fixation and frozen sections, is not only the most practical but apparently the best.

Incubation. Incubate attached frozen sections and formol calcium fixed smears 30 minutes to 4 hours (average, about 2 hours) at 37°C. Rinse in distilled water, then 1 minute in 1% acetic acid and again in distilled water.

Develop in 2% yellow ammonium sulfide 2 minutes. Wash in water, counterstain if desired, dehydrate in alcohols, clear in xylene, mount in balsam or synthetic resin.

Results: At pH 5.9 largely lysosomal type localization is obtained; at 5, one finds largely nuclear localization. This last fact disturbed Aronson, since centrifugate studies had shown cytoplasmic rather than nuclear localization.

Inhibitors. Both nuclear and lysosomal localizations are inhibited by 10 mM NaF, 1 mM CuSO$_4$, 5 mM p-chloromercuribenzoic acid, 5 mM Versene. Na$_2$SO$_4$ at 10 mM inhibits lysosomal but not nuclear staining. Substitution of adenosine 3′- or 5′-monophosphate as substrate gives a SO$_4$ insensitive activity; glycerophosphate activity is sensitive to sulfate.

Some question perhaps remains whether the lysosomal reaction is actually deoxyribonuclease, not just acid phosphatase. However omission of deoxyribonucleic acid does prevent the reaction. (But perhaps glycerophosphate can replace it?)

CYSTEINE DESULFURASE

This enzyme hydrolyzes cysteine to H$_2$S, NH$_3$ and pyruvic acid:
$$HSCH_2CH(NH_2)COOH + H_2O \rightarrow H_2S + NH_3 + H_3C—CO—COOH.$$

Jarrett, *J. Histochem.* **10**:400, 1962 reports a tetrazolium, formazan method for its localization.

Substrate. 20 mg blue tetrazolium (or, preferably, nitro blue tetrazolium) in 10 cc distilled water + 10 cc 0.1 M phosphate buffer pH 7.6. Add slowly 64 mg cysteine hydrochloride in 19 cc distilled water. Then add 1 cc 0.1 M MgSO$_4$ and 10 mg pyridoxine 5-phosphate as activator.

Procedure. Cut fresh frozen tissue in cryostat at 8 μ and attach to coverslip or slides. Immerse in substrate and incubate 18–24 hours at 37°C. When satisfactory color is attained, rinse in distilled water, fix 10–15 minutes in 10% cold formalin and mount in an aqueous mountant. Substituting nitro blue tetrazolium permits reduction of the incubation period to 4 hours, with sharper localization.

Results: In human skin a strongly positive band is seen at the stratum granulosum.

In some manner, not explained by the author, this reaction is supposed to participate in the cystine cross linkage of keratin.

Inhibitors. Smythe (*Biochemist's Handbook,* Long (ed.), D. Van Nostrand Company, Inc., Princeton, N.J., 1961, p. 496) notes that D-cysteine is inert to the animal enzyme, that pyridoxal phosphate is the coenzyme and that KCN and As_2O_3 inhibit.

CARBONIC ANHYDRASE

The enzyme catalyzes the reaction $H_2CO_3 \rightleftharpoons H_2O + CO_2$ over a wide pH range. Its molecular weight has been determined at 30,000, and it contains 1 atom of Zn per molecule.

V. Massey notes in Long 1961, p. 489 marked inhibition by Cu^{++}, Ag^+, Au^{+++}, Hg^{++}, Zn^{++} and V^{+++}; by oxidants ($KMnO_4$), sulfide, NaN_3 and KCN. Animal but not plant carbonic anhydrase is strongly inhibited by sulfanilamide and other sulfonamides. The plant enzyme is apparently SH dependent, being inhibited by *p*-chloromercuribenzoate and similar reagents.

Gomori cited Kurata's method:

1. Fix thin slices in cold acetone for 1 hour.
2. Wash briefly in distilled water.
3. Incubate 45 minutes in a freshly mixed and filtered substrate composed of 50 cc 8% $NaHCO_3$ + 5 cc 10% $CoCl_2$ or $MnCl_2$.
4. Wash in bicarbonate buffer pH 7.2, dehydrate in alcohols, imbed in paraffin and section.
5. Treat deparaffinized, hydrated sections with 2% dilution of ammonium sulfide to reveal the $CoCO_3$ precipitate as CoS, or with 0.5% periodic acid to convert $MnCO_3$ to MnO_2.

Kurata's Reactions. Carbonic anhydrase accelerates liberation of CO_2 from the $NaHCO_3$ and accelerates precipitation of $CoCO_3$ or $MnCO_3$. This appears highly illogical since insoluble carbonates should be more rapidly precipitated at higher pH levels rather than lower, and liberation of CO_2 should decrease the amount of CO_3 ion present.

However, selective staining of erythrocytes and gastric parietal cells was claimed.

Fand et al. (*J. Histochem.* 7:27, 1959), failing to demonstrate carbonic anhydrase by the Kurata method in sites of biochemically demonstrated high activity (endometrium, kidney) and finding the Kurata reaction positive in pancreatic islet beta cells, proceeded to demonstrate that sites yielding the Kurata reaction also reacted with dithizone, including inorganic Zn, insulin and zinc insulin models and tissues previously inactivated at 90°C or with KCN or (Braun-Falco) Diamox. Strong reactions to the Kurata method were given also by gelatin Coujard models containing Cd^{++}, Mn^{++} and Ca^{++}. Fand et al. got strong Kurata staining of renal proximal convoluted tubules in rodents but not in dogs or primates.

In view of Fand's findings, Kurata's method is not to be recommended for localization of carbonic anhydrase.

Pearse, 1960, although agreeing with Fand's conclusions regarding the Kurata method, nevertheless presents Hausler's variant thereof:

Substrate. Mix 1 cc 0.1 M $CoSO_4$ (1.55% = 2.8% $CoSO_4 \cdot 7H_2O$) and 6 cc 0.1 N H_2SO_4. Just before use, pour in 1 gm $NaHCO_3$ dissolved in 50 cc 0.1 M Na_2SO_4 (1.42%), freshly prepared.

Method.

1. Postfix fresh frozen (cryostat or cold knife) sections 1 hour in acetone at 0–4°C.
2. Transfer loose floating sections to substrate at 18–20°C for 90–120 minutes. Keep sections floating.
3. Wash 2 minutes in distilled water.
4. Dilute (1:50) ammonium sulfide 1 minute.
5. Wash and mount in glycerol gelatin.

Results: Activity sites, black.

Inhibitor. 4 mM sodium Diamox (acetazoleamide). (The molecular weight of Diamox is given in the *Merck Index* as 222.25: replacing the sulfonamide NH_2 by ONa gives 245.22.)

Like other CoS preparations, these also could be dehydrated and mounted, preferably in Canada balsam, and counterstains may be applied as with alkaline phosphatase technics.

UREASE

Sen (*Indian J. M. Res.* 18:79, 1930) reported that urease would act in fairly strong alcoholic solution to liberate ammonia and carbon dioxide from urea, and made this the basis of a histochemical method. Of the Co, Ca, Ni, Cu and Pb ions tested for localization of the carbonate formed, the first seemed best. His procedure follows:

Fix animal tissues 1 hour in 60% alcohol containing 1% cobalt nitrate. Add an equal volume of 60% alcohol containing 1% urea and let stand 48 hours at room temperature. Dehydrate with alcohols, imbed in paraffin or celloidin, section, hydrate sections and immerse for some minutes in hydrogen sulfide water or dilute sodium sulfide solution. Wash and mount as usual.

Brief trials of this method have not been satisfactory, and I suggest following Glick's (*J. Nat. Cancer Inst.* **10**:321, 1949) alternate section titrimetric procedure to give approximate localization of urease activity. A block of gastric mucosa is frozen quickly at −25°C. With a large cork borer cut a cylindrical block from the surface down to muscularis. Cut serial frozen sections horizontally from the surface downward. Reserve alternate sections for staining and histologic evaluation in comparison with the results of titrimetric assay of intervening sections.

For the chemical details of this assay the reader is referred to the original paper.

OXIDASES, PEROXIDASES, DEHYDROGENASES

For practical purposes these fall into 3 classes, the relatively stable, moderately formaldehyde resistant hemoglobin peroxidase; the myeloperoxidase or verdoperoxidase—also relatively stable, but somewhat less resistant—of the granular leucocytes and their precursors; and the highly labile tissue oxidases exemplified by cytochrome oxidase (or G-Nadi oxidase of the earlier German writers), succinic dehydrogenase, cysteine desulfurase and other similar enzymes demonstrable by the tetrazolium formazan systems.

The methods for their detection may also be classed according to the substances used to yield colored products in the presence of hydrogen peroxide, or without it, and some of these methods may be used for both the stable and the highly labile enzymes.

Hemoglobin Peroxidase

I will cite 2 general methods for **hemoglobin peroxidase:** Dunn's modifications of the "Zinc leuco" sulfonated triphenylmethane dyes, and one of the nitroprusside benzidine methods.

Lison used first acid fuchsin, and later some patent blue reduced by nascent hydrogen to its leuco state. Dunn (*Stain Techn.* **21**:65, 1946) identified the patent blue as patent blue V (C.I. No. 42051) and later (*Arch. Path.* **41**:676, 1946) substituted the related dye cyanol FF (C.I.

No. 43535), using identical amounts. The latter dye is slightly more violet but otherwise equivalent, and I prefer the patent blue V.

The Lison-Dunn Leuco Patent Blue Method. Fix blocks 3–5 mm thick in buffered 10% formalin (p. 38) for 24 to not more than 48 hours. Prepare paraffin sections at 5–8 μ.

Make a stock 1% aqueous solution of patent blue V. To 100 cc of this add 10 gm granulated metallic zinc and 2 cc glacial acetic acid and boil until completely decolorized. Stopper well and store. This leuco patent blue solution is stable.

For use filter out 10 cc, and add 2 cc glacial acetic acid and 0.1 cc 30% hydrogen peroxide. This must be freshly mixed.

1. Bring sections to water.
2. Stain 3–5 minutes in the leuco patent blue peroxide reagent.
3. Rinse in water.
4. Counterstain 30–60 seconds in 0.1% safranin O in 1% acetic acid or in an aqueous carmine.
5. Dehydrate, clear through a graded alcohol and xylene sequence and mount in synthetic resin.

Results: Nuclei, red; cytoplasm, light pink; hemoglobin, dark blue green; oxidase granules, dark blue.

When aniline blue (C.I. No. 42755) is substituted for patent blue in the foregoing procedure, it decolorizes with zinc and hot acetic acid to a light transparent green. As with patent blue, it also gives a deep blue hemoglobin peroxidase reaction. Mounting is perhaps best in Karo or glycerol gelatin, and preparations may conveniently be examined at once in water. Alcohol tends to extract the color of both the blue dyes on dehydration. (Janigan and Lillie, 1963, unpublished.)

The Lepehne-Pickworth method for demonstration of cerebral capillary distribution is essentially a benzidine and nitroprusside oxidase method for hemoglobin. The technic follows (emended from Mallory):

Fix brain tissue in 10% formalin for 1–3 weeks. Cut frozen sections at 200–300 μ (0.2–0.3 mm).

1. Wash sections 30 minutes in distilled water.
2. Place sections for 30 minutes at 37°C in benzidine and nitroprusside reagent: Dissolve 100 mg benzidine in 0.5 cc glacial acetic acid. Add 20 cc distilled water. Dissolve 100 mg sodium nitroprusside in 10 cc distilled water. Mix the 2 solutions and add 70 cc distilled water. Make this reagent fresh each time. While sections are in this mixture, agitate frequently.
3. Wash 10 seconds in distilled water.

4. Place in 0.04–0.05% hydrogen peroxide at 37°C for 30 minutes, shaking frequently. This dilution must be freshly prepared. Use 0.1 cc 30% hydrogen peroxide in 70 cc water.
5. Wash in distilled water.
6. Dehydrate in 70%, 95% and 100% alcohol, allowing sections to stand in each until diffusion currents are no longer evident. Place in 100% alcohol and xylene, and then in 2 or more changes of xylene until clear. Mount in balsam.

Results: Blood cells in the capillaries are colored black; other structures remain pale gray.

Romeis cites the Doherty, Suh and Alexander (*Arch. Neurol. Psychiat.* **40**:158, 1938) variant of the Pickworth method. Step 2 above is shortened to 10 minutes, step 4 to 20 minutes at 20°C; but if the capillary net is not yet black, incubate further at 37°C until the background is bleached. The benzidine solution is composed of 0.5 gm benzidine dissolved in 50 cc 100% alcohol, mixed with 10 cc 1% aqueous sodium nitroprusside solution (freshly made) and 40 cc distilled water. Deteriorated nitroprusside gives a greenish color on mixing. The peroxide solution contains also 10 cc fresh 1% aqueous sodium nitroprusside, 2 cc glacial acetic acid, 0.5 cc 30% hydrogen peroxide, 50 cc 100% alcohol and distilled water to make 100 cc.

Myoglobin Peroxidase

Drews and Engel have applied the benzidine peroxidase method to the study of muscle and have successfully demonstrated a peroxidase activity which they assign to myoglobin (*J. Histochem.* **9**:206, 1961).

Benzidine Method of Drews and Engel for Myoglobin Peroxidase.

1. Fix fresh muscle 1–14 days in formol saline (p. 37). Surgical material is preferable in man, and in animals it may be desirable to perfuse with 0.85% NaCl to remove blood before fixing. In this case the formol saline may follow the saline perfusion.
2. Cut frozen sections at 10–75 μ and place in benzene for 1 minute.
3. Stain 5–8 minutes in the modified van Duijn solution given below.
4. Rinse in 0.85% saline solution, mount in glycerol gelatin and study at once. The benzidine blue has its usual tendency to fade.

Results: Dark blue microcrystalline deposits are seen at the level of the I bands in striated muscle and in smooth muscle.

Modified van Duijn Solution. Dissolve 0.5% (100 mg) benzidine base in (20 cc) 0.85% NaCl at 80°C. Cool and filter. To 9 cc add 1 cc saturated (about 40% at 25°C) ammonium chloride solution and 1 drop (*ca.* 0.05 cc) 3% hydrogen peroxide solution (freshly diluted from the stock 30% solution). Make benzidine solution fresh every hour.

The postfixation of Villamil and Mancini—5 minutes in saturated alcoholic picric acid solution—directly after step 3, might act to preserve the color (*cf.* p. 371). After picroalcohol, wash in water, dehydrate, clear and mount in synthetic resin as usual.

MYELOPEROXIDASE

This enzyme has been isolated from leucocytes by Agner (*Acta Physiol. Scand.* **2:** Suppl. 8, 1941). It appears to be the enzyme responsible for both the benzidine and naphthol peroxidase reactions and for the Winkler-Schultze M-Nadi oxidase reaction. Certainly there is a very considerable correspondence in reagents effective in inhibiting the Washburn benzidine nitroprusside peroxidase test and the Winkler-Schultze reaction. Apparently the necessary peroxide for the latter reaction must be added if the reagent is quite fresh, or is formed spontaneously in contact with air within the dimethyl-*p*-phenylenediamine and α-naphthol mixture in a fairly short time.

Gomori's statement that leucocyte oxidase is not an enzyme but is fat peroxide ignored Agner's work. It was apparently based on the demonstration by Lison (*Bull. Soc. Chim. Biol.* **18:**185, 1936) that fatty peroxides in adrenal cortical substance were capable of completing the indophenol synthesis from dimethyl-*p*-phenylenediamine and α-naphthol without access of air or addition of peroxide, and the considerable correspondence shown by Sehrt (*München. med. Wschr.* **74:**139, 1927) between the destruction by various reagents of the sudanophilia of leucocytes and of the Winkler-Schultze oxidase reaction.

Recent studies in this laboratory have shown that a number of reagents promptly destroy myeloperoxidase (and M-Nadi oxidase) while conserving sudanophilia, while certain other reagents conserve the enzyme reactions quite well and destroy sudanophilia. There also appears to be no doubt that the sudanophilia of the granules in neutrophil leucocytes is not due to a fat (*J. Histochem.* **1:**8, 1953).

Of all the various technics for leucocyte peroxidase, I generally prefer the Washburn (*J. Lab. Clin. Med.* **14:**246, 1928) method. For this I prefer fixation of films for 10 minutes in 75% alcohol. This has less damaging effect on the enzyme than 100% or 95% alcohol or any of the formaldehyde methods.

The Washburn Method (Lillie, 1952) Modified from Washburn.

1. Fix air dried blood or marrow films 10 minutes in 75% alcohol; or in formaldehyde vapor for 30 minutes as follows: Place a piece of glass rod diagonally in the bottom of a Coplin jar to raise slides a little off the bottom. Add 1–2 cc 40% formaldehyde. Put in slides smear end up. Cover jar. After fixing, wash slides in 2 changes of distilled water.
2. Mix 1 cc 30% aqueous sodium nitroprusside with 99 cc 0.3% benzidine in 95% alcohol. This mixture is said to keep quite well in the cold, though I prefer to keep the benzidine solution alone and add the freshly prepared nitroprusside solution at time of using.

   To the alcoholic benzidine nitroprusside mixture add an equal volume of freshly diluted 0.04% hydrogen peroxide, diluting the 30% stock solution 0.1 cc in 75 cc of distilled water, and pipet at once onto slides and let stand 5 minutes. To exclude negative reactions, double the time. Allow about 2 cc of the final mixture for each slide.
3. Wash 2 minutes or more in running tap water.
4. Counterstain 10 minutes by the "accelerated Giemsa stain" (p. 586).
5. Rinse in water, dry smears and examine in an immersion oil of the mineral oil type. Dehydrate sections with acetone, clear with xylene and mount in neutral synthetic resin.

Results: Peroxidase granules in neutrophils, greenish or bluish black; in eosinophils, somewhat greener or browner in tone; nuclei, violet to red purple; erythrocytes, orange pink. When reagents which inhibit myeloperoxidase are interposed after step 1, erythrocytes often take a browner tone and may present much granular or crystalline black deposit or long needle shaped crystals.

In the foregoing technic Washburn added 0.3 gm basic fuchsin to the alcoholic benzidine nitroprusside solution, and after washing the reaction mixture off, decolorized to faint pink with 95% alcohol, counterstained with Wright's stain (p. 587), rinsed, dried and examined.

The following technics include benzidine and hydrogen peroxide as reactive materials, but no nitroprusside.

The Benzidine Peroxidase Reaction. The following technics for the benzidine peroxidase reaction and statements regarding it are a composite derived from Graham (*J. Med. Res.* 39:15, 1918), the texts of Mallory, Romeis and Schmorl and from Endicott's work in my laboratory. Graham fixed fresh smears in a fresh 10% formalin alcohol for 1–2 minutes and then washed in water. Loele used frozen sections of formalin fixed tissue which are collected from the microtome in water. The staining solution is a saturated aqueous or 40% alcohol solution of benzidine to which 0.2–0.67 cc 3% hydrogen peroxide per 100 cc is added. Loele considered the aqueous solution more stable and prescribed shaking up 0.5 gm benzidine per 100 cc distilled water, filtering and adding 2 cc 1% hydrogen peroxide to each 100 cc filtrate. The 1% peroxide is a 1:30 dilution of the concentrated 30% solution. The technic:

1. Stain smears 5–10 minutes, sections 3–5 minutes in the benzidine peroxide reagent.
2. Wash in water.
3. Counterstain briefly in 0.1–0.5% methylene blue.
4. Wash in water.
5a. Blot smears, dry and examine in modified mineral oil of nΔ 1.515.
5b. Float sections onto slides, blot, dehydrate with 95% and 100% alcohol, and clear with 100% alcohol and xylene mixture and 2 changes of xylene. Blotting between changes is necessary to keep sections on slides. Mount in balsam or synthetic resin.

Results: Peroxidase granules, yellow to brown; nuclei, blue.

Sato's Technic (*Tohoku J. Exp. Med.* 3:7, 1926, cited in Sato: *J. Lab. Clin. Med.* 13:1058, 1928). In this technic the same benzidine and hydrogen peroxide solution may be used, though usually only 0.07–0.13 cc 3% peroxide is added to each 100 cc of filtrate, and Sato's benzidine solution was only 0.25%. The technic:

1. Mordant unfixed fresh air dried smears in 0.5% aqueous copper sulfate ($CuSO_4 \cdot 5H_2O$) solution for 1 minute. Sato used 0.3% copper sulfate in 0.1% acetic acid.
2. Rinse very quickly in water (Mallory dipped films thrice in water; Gradwohl simply drained the films).
3. Stain in the benzidine hydrogen peroxide for 2–8 minutes.
4. Wash in water.
5. Stain 20 seconds to 2 minutes in 1% aqueous safranin.
6. Wash in water, dry and mount in balsam, cedar oil or synthetic resin or examine directly in immersion oil.

Villamil and Mancini (*Rev. Soc. Argent. Biol.* 23:215, 1947, and 24:337, 1948) described a benzidine peroxidase technic for the demonstration of labile oxidases in thyroid epithelial cells. Frozen sections of unfixed tissue are required, and as little as 10–15 minutes' treatment with alcohol or formalin destroys the enzyme, though a similar exposure to physiologic saline solution is tolerated.

Ammonium Molybdate Benzidine Peroxidase Reaction of Villamil and Mancini.

1. Immediately on excision of human surgical or animal specimen cut frozen sections at 10–15 μ.
2. Immerse sections for 3–6 minutes in 1% ammonium molybdate in 0.9% sodium chloride solution.
3. Transfer to a saturated benzidine solution in 0.9% sodium chloride solution, to which a few drops of hydrogen peroxide are added. In about 3 minutes the sections become an intense blue.
4. Transfer directly to saturated (9%) picric acid solution in 95% alcohol and fix for 5 minutes.
5. Wash in water, dehydrate, clear and mount as usual.

Results: Oxidase granules, dark blue in yellow cytoplasm of gland cells, histiocytes and adjacent endothelial cells. To distinguish the more stable leucocyte oxidase, some sections should be immersed in 10% formalin for 15 minutes before step 2.

The Graham α-Naphthol Pyronin Stain (*J. Med. Res.* **35**:231, 1916). This stain for oxidase granules prescribes 1–2 minute fixation of fresh air dried smears in fresh 10% formalin alcohol (p. 39).

1. Then wash in water.
2. Stain 4–5 minutes in 1 gm α-naphthol dissolved in 100 cc 40% alcohol to which 0.2 cc 3% hydrogen peroxide is added shortly before using.
3. Wash 15 minutes in running water.
4. Stain 2 minutes in 0.1 gm pyronin (C.I. No. 45005 = Y or 45010 = B), 4 cc aniline and 96 cc 40% alcohol.
5. Wash in water.
6. Stain 30–60 seconds in 0.5% aqueous methylene blue.
7. Wash in water, blot, dry and mount in balsam.

Results: Neutrophil granules giving the oxidase reaction are purplish red; eosinophil granules are larger, lighter red and more refractile; basophil granules are deep purple; cell nuclei are blue; cytoplasm is pale blue; erythrocytes are greenish yellow to pink.

The above α-naphthol peroxide solution may be used for 4 or 5 days. The aniline pyronin is relatively stable.

Ritter and Oleson (*Arch. Path.* **43**:330, 1947) carried out the α-naphthol pyronin method on blocks of fixed tissue which were then imbedded in paraffin and sectioned. They first fix 24 hours in 10% alcoholic formalin

(p. 39) containing 1 cc of 0.1 N sodium hydroxide per 100 cc. After washing 10 minutes in running water the blocks were immersed for 24 hours in 100 cc fresh 1% α-naphthol in 40% alcohol, to which 0.2 cc 30% hydrogen peroxide is added at the moment of using. Then, after washing 10 minutes in running water they transferred to 0.1% pyronin, 4% aniline, 40% alcohol for 3–24 hours. After this tissues were dehydrated 1 hour in 80%, 2 hours in 95% and 2 hours in 2 changes of xylene of 20 minutes each and imbedded in paraffin. Sections were cut at 4 μ and mounted without counterstaining, or they were counterstained with alum hematoxylin or with a rather bluish Romanowsky stain. Eosin stains, if used, should be kept light to avoid confusion with the red peroxidase granules.

They observed that treatment with 100% alcohol before performance of the α-naphthol peroxide treatment weakens the reaction and that xylene treatment abolishes it.

The Winkler-Schultze reaction and the Nadi reaction depend on the synthesis of indophenol, the indophenol blue of the German writers, from α-naphthol and dimethyl-p-phenylenediamine in the presence of air. Lison referred to the reaction as a phenolase reaction.

The Winkler-Schultze method depends on an alkaline solution of α-naphthol; the Nadi method dilutes a 10% alcoholic solution one hundred-fold with water, and it utilizes preferably somewhat alkaline buffers during the staining procedure.

The Winkler-Schultze Reaction, the M- and G-Nadi Oxidases, Cyto-chrome Oxidase. Person and Fine (*J. Histochem.* 9:190, 197, 1961) used p-dimethylaminoaniline (dimethyl-p-phenylenediamine) and α-naphthol in studies on G- and M-Nadi oxidases.

For the G-Nadi reaction they used fresh frozen sections; for the M-Nadi reaction, the frozen sections were fixed in 10% formalin 20 minutes and washed in 4 changes of distilled water, 2 minutes each.

The substrate was prepared at 10 mM $(CH_3)_2NC_6H_4NH_2 \cdot 2HCl$ and 10 mM α-naphthol dissolved in a minimal amount of alcohol and made up to volume in 0.1 M phosphate buffer.

Positive reactions for M-Nadi oxidase are obtained in parotid and submaxillary glands as well as in cells of the myeloid series.

About 10–20 minute incubation was required for G-Nadi oxidase, an hour or more for the M-Nadi reaction. This is much slower than the Winkler-Schultze reaction on blood and marrow smears.

As far as I have seen at this date the p-aminodiphenylamine of Bur-stone's studies on cytochrome oxidase has not been utilized in the M-Nadi reaction.

Our 1953 technic (*J. Histochem.* 1:8) for the Winkler-Schultze re-action is emended and combined with the Gräff method in accordance with recent papers of Person *et al.* (*loc. cit.*).

1. Prepare fresh frozen sections by the Adamstone-Taylor cold knife method or in a cryostat and affix them to clean slides. Prepare blood, marrow or tissue smears or imprints as usual.
2. For the M-Nadi reaction, fix at once for 20 minutes in ice cold 70% alcohol containing 10% formalin. Wash in 4 changes of distilled water, 2 minutes each. For the G-Nadi reaction for cytochrome oxidase omit this step.
3. Prepare fresh substrate: Dissolve 21 mg p-amino-N,N-dimethylaniline dihydrochloride and 14.3 mg α-naphthol in 0.1–0.2 cc ethanol and add 0.1 M phosphate buffer pH 7.6 (Person 6.4–8.1) to make 10 cc. Lay slides face up on staining rack and deposit 1–2 cc on each. Rock gently to cover smear or section. Or for tissue, lay slides flat in large petri dish and flood and cover to maintain humidity. Stain films 3–10 minutes (sections, up to 2 hours), watching color development. Rinse quickly in distilled water.
4. Preparations may be mounted at this point directly in glycerol gelatin. Immerse in dilute Lugol's solution (0.2% iodine) or in 40% ammonium heptamolybdate $(NH_4)_6 \cdot Mo_7O_{24} \cdot 4H_2O$) for 3 minutes. Wash in distilled water (containing a trace of lithium carbonate (1:20,000) to blue after iodine).
5. Films may be counterstained with Giemsa as usual (p. 586), washed and dried. Mount sections, preferably without counterstain, in glycerol gelatin.

Results: Sites of activity, blue black to dark green.

Omission of formaldehyde from the 75% alcohol enhances activity in neutrophil leucocytes, but permits severe diffusion artifacts.

For G-Nadi oxidase, substitution of Burstone's p-aminodiphenylamine + 3-amino-9-ethylcarbazole substrate is recommended, and preferably his complete technic should be followed (p. 374).

Newer Technics for Cytochrome Oxidase. In the past decade a number of new reagents have been introduced for the indophenol synthesis of the G-Nadi reaction, which is now regarded as a demonstration of cytochrome oxidase activity.

In 1958 Nachlas, Crawford, Goldstein and Seligman (*J. Histochem.* 6:445) replaced the p-amino-N,N-dimethylaniline of the Nadi mixture with 4-amino-1-N,N-dimethylnaphthylamine. On oxidation in the presence of α-naphthol this yielded a purple pigment, indonaphthol purple, which gave satisfactory localization and stability.

Nachlas *et al.* direct: quickly freeze tissue at $-80°C$, section at 6–8 μ in the cryostat at $-20°C$ and thaw sections onto slides in the cryostat. After incubating in the substrate as prescribed, rinse in saline solution and mount in glycerol gelatin.

Burstone (*J. Histochem.* 7:112, 1959) explored further series of amines and phenols as reagents for the indophenol synthesis, and later (*ibid.* 8:63, 1960) he recommended substrates containing 4-amino-diphenyl-amine and either 4-amino-4'-methoxydiphenylamine or 9-ethyl-3-amino-carbazole. With these substrates, addition of cytochrome, required with simple amines, could be eliminated. As in the method of Nachlas *et al.*, a small amount of catalase is still added to eliminate confusing action of peroxidases.

Burstone likewise used fresh frozen sections mounted on slides, which could be stored at —20°C for several days. After incubation, slides are fixed 1 hour in 10% formalin containing 10% cobaltous acetate ($4H_2O$) or similar (0.4 *M*?) solutions containing nickel chloride, ferric ammonium sulfate, cadmium sulfate, uranyl nitrate or lead nitrate. After 5 minutes' washing, sections were mounted in glycerol gelatin or dehydrated, cleared and mounted in Permount. The metal chelation increased the permanency of the stain. Inhibition of the above reaction is accomplished by inclusion of 1 *mM* KCN, Na_2S or NaN_3 in the medium.

In mixing substrates dissolve the naphthol and mix with buffer, then add catalase which inhibits peroxidases, and for rather inactive tissues, the cytochrome c; this may be replaced by the same volume of water with such active tissues as heart, stomach or brain. Just before using, mix in the freshly prepared arylamine.

TABLE 10-14. Substrates for Cytochrome Oxidase

Substrates	Nachlas *et al.*, 1958	Burstone, 1960	Burstone, 1960	Burstone, 1961
Arylamine..........	4-Amino-1-N,N-dimethylnaph-thylamine, 16 mg/8 cc	4-Aminodiphenyl-amine 6–9 mg	4-Aminodiphen-ylamine, 6–9 mg	4-Aminodiphenyl-amine, 6–9 mg
Naphthol............	α-Naphthol, 8 mg/6 cc	4-Amino-4'-meth-oxydiphenylamine, 6–9 mg in alcohol 0.3 cc	9-Ethyl-3-amino-carbazole, 6–9 mg in alcohol 0.3 cc	8-Amino-1,2,3,4-tetrahydroquino-line, 6–9 mg in alcohol 0.3 cc
Cytochrome c.......	30 mg/6 cc			
Catalase............	60 γ/2 cc	1.2 mg	1.2 mg	1.2 mg
Buffer.............	Phosphate 0.1 *M*	Tris HCl 0.2 *M*	Tris HCl 0.2 *M*	Tris HCl 0.2 *M*
Volume...........	6 cc	9 cc	9 cc	9 cc
pH...............	7.4	7.4	7.4	7.4
Final volume........	30 cc	30 cc	30 cc	30 cc
Incubation time	10–30 min	15–60 min	15–60 min	15–60 min
Temperature........	25°C	25°C	25°C	25°C

The pH 7.4 tris HCl buffer contains 21.1 gm tris(hydroxymethyl)amino-methane, 170 cc 1 N HCl and distilled water to make 1 liter.

Montagna and Yun (*J. Histochem.* 9:694, 1961) favored particularly the 8-amino-1,2,3,4-tetrahydroquinoline + N-phenyl-*p*-phenylenediamine substrate of Burstone (*ibid.* 9:59, 1961); Baker and Klapper (*ibid.* 9:713, 1961) also used one of Burstone's methods; Tewari and Bourne (*ibid.* 10:42, 619, 1962) employed both the Nachlas and the Burstone proce-dures.

Pretreatment with 0.1% potassium cyanide solution for a few minutes or inclusion of 1 mM in the substrate abolishes the G-Nadi reaction; the Winkler-Schultze reaction is not affected. The alkali α-naphthol solution of that method cannot be used for demonstration of the labile oxidase (even if buffered to the same pH level?). Ordinary formaldehyde fixa-tion prevents the G-Nadi oxidase reaction but not the Winkler-Schultze; though Gräff found tissues fixed in formalin and buffered with phosphates to pH 7.3–7.6 for an unstated period suitable for his Nadi oxidase reaction.

TYROSINASE, DOPA-MELANASE

According to presently accepted concepts, the chromophore of melanin consists in considerable measure of a sulfur bearing protein into which the indolic oxidation product of tyrosine is incorporated. In the forma-tion of this chromophore L-tyrosine goes through a series of oxidative and rearrangement changes, including a probable decarboxylation, to form a product which is probably a quinhydrone. These changes are enzymatically mediated and exhibit a rather long preliminary phase in which L-tyrosine is converted to L-dopa (3,4-dihydroxyphenylalanine). Hence to expedite the reaction L- or DL-dopa is usually used as the sub-strate; D-dopa is not attacked.

For literature, see Lillie, *J. Histochem.* 4:318, 1956, from which paper the following technic is taken. I have modified the technic slightly from Fitzpatrick and Lerner (*Zoologica* 35:28, 1950) and have elaborated on the description of the results.

1. Quickly freeze skin or other tissue by immersion in petroleum ether containing some fragments of solid carbon dioxide. Slice while frozen parallel to the direction of the hair into slices about 1 mm thick.
2. Fix these slices 1 hour in ice cold calcium acetate formalin.
3. Wash 1 hour in 6 changes of distilled water.
4. Incubate 24 hours at 20–25°C in 0.1% L-(or DL-)dopa in 0.05 M phos-phate buffer pH 7.
5. Wash in water, postfix 1–2 days in calcium acetate formalin, dehydrate, clear, imbed in paraffin and section at 5 μ.

6. Deparaffinize in xylene and mount in cellulose caprate, either directly or after counterstaining as desired. Azure A eosin B at pH 4 gives good contrasts, coloring melanin and dopa melanin dark green.

Results: With positive reaction the cytoplasm of juxtapapillary and hair matrix cells colors a diffuse brown. Melanin granules tend to be larger than in controls and may form confluent globules. Trichohyalin granules remain uncolored in uncounterstained preparations and appear bright red with azure eosin. Dendritic melanocytes in the base of the epidermis and margins of the hair follicles appear to be increased in numbers and contain larger confluent globules of dark brown melanin. The normal basophilia of hair follicle and epidermal cytosplasm is largely lost, from extraction of the relatively unfixed ribonucleic acid during the incubation period. Keratohyalin granules inconstantly give a weak brown color; their eosinophilia to azure eosin is unimpaired. Pigment in more distal hair cortex and medulla remains dark brown and finely granular, as in controls.

Inhibitors. KCN—partial at 0.1 *mM*, complete at 1–100 *mM*; NaN$_3$ 1 *mM*; Na$_2$S 0.1 and 1 *mM*; Na$_2$S$_2$O$_4$ 5 *mM*. Cysteine 1 *mM* appears to enhance the reaction.

It appears probable that Novikoff's recent practice of postfixing cryostat sections in calcium formol at 3°C for 15–20 minutes should prove applicable to this reaction. Blocks fixed at −70°C in alcohol and cold acetone fixed blocks, both imbedded and sectioned in paraffin, have proved inert in the dopa reaction.

Use of L-tyrosine at 0.1% (*ca.* 5.5 *mM*) in the foregoing technic required 24 hours at 3°C followed by a second period in fresh substrate of 24 hours at 37°C (Fitzpatrick and Lerner, *Science* **112:**223, 1950). However, only irradiated skin in the course of active pigment deposit (sun tanning, x-irradiation) gives a positive reaction with tyrosine.

Bloch and Peck (from Mallory) used dopa for the demonstration of M-Nadi oxidase in leucocytes: Fix smears by 20 minute exposure to hot formaldehyde vapor and wash. Then incubate 1–2 hours in 50 cc 0.1% L-dopa in 0.85% NaCl to which 1 cc 0.1 N NaOH is added at time of using. Then wash, dry and examine. Leucocyte granules are brown.

The color of the granules may be intensified by a 2 hour exposure to 2% silver nitrate, followed by thiosulfate and washing. In either variant an alum hematoxylin counterstain may be used.

AMINE OXIDASE AND DECARBOXYLASE

Oster and Schlossman (*J. Cell. Comp. Physiol.* **20:**373, 1942) described a method for the localization of amino acid decarboxylase and amine oxidase in guinea pig kidneys. The decarboxylase first converts the amino acid to the next lower amine, and the amine oxidase converts the amine to the corresponding aldehyde with liberation of ammonia. The aldehyde is then rendered visible by the application of Schiff reagent (p. 270). Because of the natural occurrence of plasmalogen which liberates aldehyde (slowly in the presence of acid, more rapidly with mercuric chloride) it was thought necessary to block these aldehydes first with sulfite before proceeding with the specific enzyme technic. In the latter, tyramine was used as a substrate. When the amino acids L-tyrosine or L-tryptophan were used as substrates instead, the same localization was observed, indicating that the active areas (in distal convoluted tubules) possessed both decarboxylase and amine oxidase activities.

Technic.

1. Incubate frozen sections of fresh kidney in 2% sodium bisulfite solution for 24 hours at 37°C.
2. Wash thoroughly in distilled water.
3. *Plasmal controls:* Take several sections at this point and immerse for 5 minutes in 1% mercuric chloride solution, wash in water and immerse in Schiff reagent for 15 minutes, wash in 2–3 changes of 0.05 M sodium bisulfite, wash in water for 5 minutes, counterstain 1–2 minutes in acetic hemalum (p. 174) and mount in gum syrup. There should be no red color.
   Buffer control: Incubate 24 hours in 0.067 M pH 7.2 phosphate buffer.
   Enzyme inactivation control: First soak some sections in octyl alcohol for 24 hours after the bisulfite treatment, then as in step 3 experimental.
   Experimental: Incubate at 37°C for 24 hours in 0.5% tyramine hydrochloride in pH 7.2 0.067 M phosphate buffer.
4. Wash in distilled water.
5. Place in Schiff reagent until blue color appears, allowing 30 minutes for buffer and inactivation controls.
6. Pass through 3 changes 90 seconds each of 0.05 M sodium bisulfite.
7. Float out and mount in potassium acetate gum syrup. Sections may be counterstained with acetic safranin if desired.

Results: Sites of amine oxidase activity, blue. If L-tyrosine or L-tryptophan is substituted for tyramine in the substrate, the blue color indicates the presence of decarboxylase as well as of amine oxidase.

The above technic has been emended from Oster and Schlossman to supply omitted details. The following method, worked out by Glenner et al. in my laboratory, seems better and has won some measure of acceptance.

TABLE 10-15. MONOAMINE OXIDASE SUBSTRATES AND TECHNICS

	Glenner et al.[1]		Yasuda et al.[2]			
				Concentrations		
	Amounts	Conc.	Amounts	A	B	C
Tryptamine HCl	37.5 mg	6.3 mM	1 cc 0.25 M	8.3 mM	8.3 mM	8.3 mM
Nitro blue tetrazolium	7.5 mg	3.2 mM	7 cc 0.1 %	0.3 mM	0.3 mM	0.3 mM
Phosphate buffer	7.5 cc 0.1 M	25 mM	22 cc 0.1 M	73 mM	73 mM	73 mM
pH	7.6	......	7.6			
Na$_2$SO$_4$	6 mg	1.8 mM				
KCN	......	......	......	......	1 mM	
Marsilid PO$_4$	......	......	......	......	......	100 mM
Final volume	30 cc	......	30 cc			
Incubation time	30–45 min	......	30–60 min			
Temperature	37°C	......	37°C			

[1] Glenner, Burtner and Brown, *J. Histochem.* **5**:591, 1957.
[2] Yasuda and Montagna, *J. Histochem.* **8**:356, 1960.

Technic of Glenner et al. for Monoamine Oxidase. Collect fresh tissue and freeze; cut frozen sections at 10–15 μ by the Adamstone-Taylor method or in a cryostat. Attach to slides.

Immerse sections in preheated substrate and incubate 30–45 minutes at 37°C. Wash 5 minutes in running water, fix 24 hours in neutral buffered 10% formalin, dehydrate in graded alcohols, clear in xylene and mount in Permount or similar resin.

Yasuda and Montagna preferred mounting in glycerol gelatin directly after fixation and water washing, but they noted reddish tinging of fat.

Cyanide (1 mM) inhibits cytochrome oxidase but not monoamine oxidase or succinic dehydrogenase, according to Yasuda and Montagna, but Glenner et al. got inhibition at 0.1 mM. Trichloroacetic acid fixation preserves the SH reduction of nitro blue tetrazolium but inactivates monoamine oxidase. Glenner, Burtner and Brown note inactivation by prior 15 minute exposure to 0.1 M phenylhydrazine, Marsilid (1-isonicotinyl-2-isopropylhydrazine), *p*-chloromercuribenzoate and ethanol. Heating 20 minutes at 60°C inactivates. Incorporation of Marsilid, hydroxylamine, semicarbazide, hydrazine and atabrine at 0.1 M, bisulfite at 1 mM and cyanide at 0.1 mM into substrate inhibited strongly.

CITRIC ACID CYCLE DEHYDROGENASES, DIAPHORASES, SUCCINIC DEHYDROGENASE

Semenoff (*Z. Zellforsch.* **22**:305, 1935) reported a method for demonstration of succinic dehydrogenase depending on the decoloration of methylene blue in the presence of sodium succinate. The quantity of the last was not critical, and increases in concentration accelerated the reaction. The technic follows, purely as a matter of historical interest. It has been replaced by the tetrazolium formazan methods.

1. Cut frozen sections of fresh unfixed tissue.
2. Mount on clean slides in a few drops of substrate, cover with coverglass and seal with petrolatum. Observe periodically. The substrate is composed of

0.05% methylene blue	2 cc
10% sodium succinate	1–2 cc
0.067 M phosphate buffer of pH 7.6–8 to a total of 10 cc	

3. The preparations are decolorized first in the central area of the coverglass; later peripherally. Sites of greatest dehydrogenase activity are the first to decolorize. In liver and muscle, decoloration is complete in 30–80 minutes.

Control sections, heated to 60°C for 10 minutes, fail to decolorize methylene blue. Treatment with potassium cyanide at 10^{-4} or 10^{-5} (M?) completely inhibits the reaction; at 10^{-6} M the reaction is retarded, and at 10^{-7} M no effect is observed. It is presumed that the cyanide is added to the substrate, rather than that pretreatment was practiced. The KCN inhibition raises the suspicion that cytochrome oxidase was involved.

The Tetrazolium Formazan Reaction: Colorless, soluble tetrazolium compounds are converted by the addition of hydrogen into water insoluble deeply colored pigments known as formazans. In tissue, this is accomplished by highly labile enzyme systems which are destroyed by the cold alcohol and acetone fixation processes.

The dehydrogenases of the tricarboxylic (Krebs) and related cycles are now to some extent demonstrable histochemically by the tetrazolium formazan reduction reaction, which was previously used only for "endogenous" and succinic dehydrogenases. The demonstration of several of these enzymes requires (or is facilitated by) the presence as cofactors of the di- and triphosphopyridine nucleotides, commonly called DPN and TPN, and in their reduced forms DPNH and TPNH. Cyanide has been introduced into the substrates to prevent oxidation (= dehydrogenation) by the alternative cytochrome oxidase system (Rosa and Velardo, *J. Histochem.* **2**:110, 1954). But with the introduction of faster reacting tetrazoles, such as nitroneotetrazolium (Pearson, *J. Histochem.* **6**:112, 1958), nitro blue tetrazolium, tetranitro blue and tetronitroneotetrazoles, the use of cyanide was found to be unnecessary (Nachlas *et al.*, *J. Histochem.* **5**:420, 1957). The inclusion in the substrate of minimal amounts of methylene blue, other thiazin dyes which also form reduced leuco compounds, and particularly of phenazine methosulfate was found by Farber *et al.* (*J. Histochem.* 4:347, 357, 1956) to accelerate greatly the blue tetrazolium reactions of the dehydrogenases, but at least the methylene blue addition was found to have no accelerating effect in the succinic dehydrogenase reaction with the faster reacting nitro blue tetrazolium (Nachlas *et al.*, *J. Histochem.* 5:420, 1957; Novikoff, *ibid.* 8:34, 1960).

In 1956 Farber *et al.* (*J. Histochem.* 4:254, 266, 284) showed that by the use of the coenzymes di- and triphosphopyridine nucleotides,[1] a considerable number of other Krebs cycle substances could be used as substrates for tetrazolium reduction in place of succinate. And the reduced forms of the two nucleotides can themselves serve as substrates. The action of these cofactors was referred to as a diaphorase action, and the histochemical tetrazolium reduction pattern seemed to fall into 2 groups, according to which of the coenzymes was used. A considerable number of studies by other workers has shown nonidentity of reduction patterns within the 2 groups, and much current work is being done in this area.

As it became evident from biochemical ultracentrifuge fractionation studies that these enzymes were associated with mitochondria, histochemical studies were increasingly directed toward demonstration of this localization. Two major problems arose: (1) the swelling and distortion of the organelles and possible loss of enzyme by diffusion; (2) false localization on the finer fat droplets of cell cytoplasm.

Some workers, notably Scarpelli and Pearse (*J. Histochem.* 6:369, 1958), have attempted to protect mitochondrial enzymes against swelling and distortion of the mitochondria during the substrate exposure phase by adding 15% sucrose (0.44 M) or, later and preferably, 7% polyvinyl-pyrrolidone (Pyrrolidinone of some manufacturers and PVP of the abbreviators) to the substrate.

Brief fixation procedures, such as that included in the above technic, seem now to be preferred. The formol calcium fixation, 15 minutes at 3°C, preserves activity but does not eliminate lipid staining. Acetone 15–30 minutes at 25°C considerably impairs dehydrogenase activity, but this is largely restored by inclusion of 0.01% Q 10 or menadione in the incubation medium. Acetone 15 minutes at 3°C preserves activity well and prevents the lipid artifact; at −65°C fat remains in the section, but at this temperature the acetone, *n*-butanol, ether mixture of Baker and

---

[1] Recent usage tends to substitute the following new terms for the phosphopyridine nucleotides: nicotinamide adenine dinucleotide (NAD) for diphosphopyridine nucleotide (DPN); dihydronicotinamide adenine dinucleotide (NADH) for reduced diphosphopyridine nucleotide (DPNH): nicotinamide and dihydronicotinamide adenine nucleotide phosphate (NADP, NADPH) for triphosphopyridine nucleotide and its reduced form (TPN, TPNH), respectively.

Klapper (*J. Histochem.* 9:713, 1961) is said to function well, at least for succinic dehydrogenase and diphosphopyridine nucleotide diaphorase reactions.

It was early observed that neotetrazolium, blue tetrazolium and the monotetrazoles tended to produce colored formazan deposits in fat droplets, which were explained at least in part by diffusion of imperfectly water insoluble formazans and their accumulation in fat in the usual manner of Sudan type staining of lipids. The introduction of di- and tetranitro ditetrazoles yielding formazans that are quite insoluble in fats and fat solvents permitted removal of lipids after staining and, it was hoped, any formazan they may have contained. Further, the mounting in resinous media should prevent aqueous diffusion of formazan and the crystallization on the surface of fat droplets which occurred slowly after mounting in glycerol and other aqueous media.

The second approach, pretreatment with fat solvents, as at first practiced, resulted in a considerable degree of enzyme inactivation. However, it has been found that a 15 minute acetone extraction at 0–5°C adequately removed lipids and did not appreciably inactivate. Acetone at dry ice temperature did not adequately remove lipids (Hitzeman, *J. Histochem.* 11:62, 1963). Cold $CaCl_2$ formalin did not prevent the lipid artifact. Wattenberg's (*J. Histochem.* 8:296, 1960) use of coenzyme Q 10 or menadione at 0.01% in the substrate media served to restore essentially all the quantitative succinic dehydrogenase activity loss (two-thirds) ensuing from acetone extraction (15 minutes, 28°C) of cryostat sections, as assayed with iodonitrotetrazolium. Visual effects on nitro blue tetrazolium and iodonitrotetrazolium staining were similar. The required amount of quinone was dissolved in acetone and dried on the coverglass on which the reaction was conducted.

Baker and Klapper (*J. Histochem.* 9:713, 1961) successfully eliminated fat staining with nitro blue tetrazolium by a prior 15 minute extraction at −65°C in a butanol-ether-acetone mixture. This did not impair the succinic or lactic dehydrogenase reactions or the reduced diphosphopyridine nucleotide diaphorase reaction.

To avoid unnecessary duplication, a single technic, basically that of Nachlas, Tsou, de Souza, Cheng and Seligman (*J. Histochem.* 5:420, 1957), is presented, with modifications derived from papers of Allen, Hitzeman, Baker, Wattenberg and others. A table is appended giving compositions of other substrates for other enzymes of the Krebs cycle and for other tetrazoles. In this table I have given amounts of reagent in milligrams on the basis of a total 30 cc volume and the final concentration of the reagent in the whole volume of substrate expressed as molarities to facilitate comparison with journal references. The latter often present data in confusing mixtures of mols, molarities and weight and volume units. A second table giving formulation and molecular weights of reagents has been added for the special benefit of the hard working technicians who have to translate quantities expressed in molarities back into units of mass and volume.

The following nitro blue tetrazolium technic is a composite, based primarily on the method of Nachlas, Tsou, de Souza, Cheng and Seligman (*J. Histochem.* 5:420, 1957) with additions and alterations based on papers of Novikoff, Wattenberg, Allen, Chang and Hori, Cogan and Kuwahara, Hitzeman and others. It is designed also for various of the di- and triphosphopyridine nucleotide linked dehydrogenases by substitution of substrates from the table following it.

The alternative dimethylthiazolyl cobalt formazan technic is offered chiefly as a confirmatory alternative whose reagents are sometimes difficult to obtain. It also seems to be adaptable for various of the Krebs cycle enzymes.

The Tetrazolium Formazan Method for Succinic Dehydrogenase.

1. Quick freeze material (3–5 mm thick blocks of tissue) by placing in a dry test tube and immersing the tube in dry ice and acetone. Animal material is taken as promptly as possible after killing; human surgical material, as soon after excision as possible; autopsy material, at the beginning of the dissection, as soon as possible after death.

2. Transfer still frozen tissue, after trimming, directly onto freezing head or metal chuck of the microtome and cut sections with a cold knife, preferably in a cryostat at 10 μ. Collect sections directly from microtome blade onto cold, clean glass slides and cause to adhere by warming back of slide momentarily with the fingertip.

3. Fix sections 15 minutes in acetone at 2°C. If the Coplin jar with sections is kept in the cryostat, the time may be increased twofold for each 10°C drop in temperature.

4. Originally 15 mg nitro blue tetrazolium (nitro-BT) was used; Pearse and, later, Allen reduced this by half; and Hitzeman in Allen's laboratory now uses 2.5 mg. Dissolve 5 mg nitro blue tetrazolium in 15 cc 0.1 M phosphate buffer pH 7.6 and add 15 cc 0.1 M sodium succinate. Warm to 37°C, if development of color is not prompt at 25°C.

5. Incubate sections at 25 or 37°C 10–30 minutes until adequate blue color is developed (8 minutes at 37°C is reported as adequate).

6. Wash 1 minute in distilled water, dehydrate in 30%, 50%, 70%, 85%, 95% and absolute alcohol, 5 minutes each, absolute alcohol and xylene and 2 changes of xylene. Mount in Permount.

Result: Sites of succinic dehydrogenase activity, in blue.

If a red nuclear stain is desired, counterstain a duplicate section after step 5 in 1% safranin O, rinse in water and dehydrate as in step 6.

Controls.

1. After step 3 immerse sections 30 minutes in 0.01 M iodoacetate (185 mg iodoacetic acid in 100 cc 0.01 N NaOH). Inactivation is complete.
2. Omit succinate from substrate. No staining should result.
3. Heating section to 80°C for 1 hour completely inactivates.

Both the stock succinate solution and the phosphate buffer are stable for some months. Nachlas *et al.* record successful reuse of the final substrate 4 or 5 times for batches of 15 slides over a period of 2 months. It is recommended that such solutions be kept cold and that they be filtered through a coarse paper to remove tissue fragments between usings. Most workers prefer to use fresh solutions, at least for each day's work.

The Scarpelli, Hess and Pearse MTT Co^{++} Method for Diaphorases. This technic uses 2-(4,5-dimethylthiazolyl-2)-3,5-diphenyl tetrazolium chloride or bromide (MTT) with cobalt chelation (from Pearse, 1960, with further variations from Hitzeman, 1962). Because of the high cost of the reagents, the stock solution is prepared in 10 cc quantities which can be kept at 0–4°C for 3–4 weeks, and the working substrate is prepared in 1 cc amounts and used by applying 1–2 drops of the freshly prepared substrate to sections on coverslips.

Stock Solution

	A		B	
0.2 M tris buffer (p. 667) pH 8	2.5	cc	2.5	cc
MTT 1 mg/1 cc	2.5	cc	2.5	cc
Cobaltous chloride 12%				
CoCl$_2$·6H$_2$O (504 mM)	0.3	cc	0.3	cc
Polyvinylpyrrolidone	0.75	cc		
Distilled water to make total of	10.0	cc	10.0	cc

Adjust pH with the tris buffer to pH 7.2 and bring final volume to 10 cc with distilled water. The cobaltous chloride solution is acid.

Pearse substitutes tris buffer for the original phosphate, thereby avoiding the filtration to remove cobalt phosphates which was required in the original medium.

Working Solution. To 1 cc stock solution add 6 mg reduced di- or triphosphopyridine nucleotide. This gives concentrations of about 7 and 6 mM for the 2 nucleotides respectively.

Technic.

1. Quickly freeze fresh tissue with solid carbon dioxide or liquid nitrogen, using small pieces 2–4 mm thick. Transfer to cryostat and cut thin frozen sections. The Adamstone-Taylor procedure may be used. Attach sections to coverglasses.
2. Fix 15 minutes in acetone at 2–4°C, or in cold $CaCl_2$ formalin, or proceed directly with step 4.
3. Rinse off formalin with distilled water. Let acetone fixed sections dry in air.
4. Deposit 0.1–0.2 cc (2–4 drops) of working substrate solution on section and incubate unfixed sections 5–30 minutes at 37°C, using mixture A above. Acetone fixed sections are incubated 20 minutes at 37°C for the diphosphopyridine and 40 minutes for the triphosphopyridine nucleotide diaphorase (DPND, TPND).
5. Fix previously unfixed sections 5–30 minutes in cold formol calcium. Rinse in distilled water.
6. Counterstain if desired, in a one-tenth dilution of Mayer's (or Grenacher's) carmalum or in chloroform extracted 0.5% aqueous methyl green. Rinse in distilled water.
7. Mount in glycerol gelatin.

Results: The cobalt formazan deposit at diaphorase activity sites is black.

TABLE 10-16. GENERAL SUBSTRATE FORMULAE FOR THE DIPHOSPHOPYRIDINE AND TRIPHOSPHOPYRIDINE NUCLEOTIDE (DPN OR NAD; TPN OR NADP) LINKED DEHYDROGENASES OF THE CITRIC ACID CYCLE

	Pearse, 1960			Hitzeman, 1963		Suggested, 1964	
	Amounts		Final conc.	Amount	Final conc.	Amount	Final conc.
	For 1 cc	For 30 cc					
Specific substrate	0.1 cc 1 M	3 cc 1 M	0.1 M	15 cc 0.1 M	50 mM	15 cc 0.1 M	50 mM
Cofactor	0.1 cc 0.1 M	3 cc 0.1 M	10 mM	0.2 cc 0.1 M	0.67 mM	0.3 cc 0.1 M	1 mM
Cyanide (K, Na)	0.1 cc 0.1 M	3 cc 0.1 M	10 mM	1.5 cc 0.1 M	5 mM		
Phosphate buffer	....	....	......	13.5 cc 60 mM	27 mM	......	
Tris HCl buffer	0.25 cc 0.1 M	7.5 cc 0.1 M	25 mM			9 cc 0.1 M	30 mM
Nitro BT	....	....	......	2.5 mg	0.0083 %	5 mg	0.017 %
MTT	0.25 mg	7.5 mg	0.025 %				
Polyvinylpyrrolidone	75 γ	2.25 mg	0.0075 %				
Distilled water, to make	1 cc	30 cc	......	30 cc	......	30 cc	

Tris buffer should be used with the dimethylthiazolyl cobalt tetrazole, usually phosphate with nitro blue tetrazolium.

Pearse lists specifically malic, lactic, α-glycerophosphate, alcohol, glutamic and isocitric dehydrogenases with diphosphopyridine nucleotide and isocitric, glutamic and malic with the triphosphopyridine nucleotide as cofactor. Hitzeman reported specifically on malic, lactic, β-hydroxybutyric and 3-β-hydroxysteroid dehydrogenases with diphosphopyridine nucleotide and isocitric with the triphosphopyridine derivative.

Other specific dehydrogenases studied in recent reports, often with only indicated composition of substrates, include pyruvic (*J. Histochem.* **8:**214, 1960) and glyceraldehyde 3-phosphate (*ibid.* **10:**387, 1962). It is to be presumed that these and other dehydrogenase enzymes not mentioned were or can reasonably be investigated by technics based on those given, employing substrates of the general formulation given in the Table 10-16. Polyvinylpyrrolidone is to be included if fresh frozen sections are employed directly; with cold formol calcium or cold acetone fixation it is apparently unnecessary. The use of cyanide is probably also unnecessary with the newer tetrazoles; its persistence in formulae seems to be a holdover from the neotetrazolium and blue tetrazolium era of enzyme histochemistry.

Hershey *et al.* (*J. Histochem.* **11:**62–67, 224, 1963) in homogenate studies on mouse breast noted a strong activating effect of Mn^{++} on isocitric dehydrogenase: 8 μM quadrupled the activity, and 0.1 mM produced a maximal eight-fold increase.

In regard to the function of phenazine methosulfate in the reactivity of diphosphopyridine linked dehydrogenases, notably lactate and α-glycerophosphate dehydrogenases, Van Wijhe, Blanchaer *et al.* (*J. Histochem.* **11:**505, 1963) find the activity in white muscle fibers much lower than in red muscle in the absence of this agent, and actually greater when 0.1% phenazine methosulfate (N-methylphenazonium methyl sulfate, M. W. 306) is added to the substrates. The lower activity of white fibers in the absence of phenazine methosulfate thus appears due to limitation in diaphorase activity rather than to lack of dehydrogenases.

Balogh (*J. Histochem.* **10:**232, 1962) reported that fresh osseous and dental tissues decalcified in 10% Versene in 0.1 M phosphate buffer at pH 7 with 3 day exposure at 4–10°C; magnetic stirring and daily changes of decalcifying fluid could be used for demonstration of enzyme activities. Di- and triphosphopyridine nucleotide diaphorases, succinic, lactic, malic, isocitric and glucose 6-phosphate dehydrogenases were preserved.

Gomori's tellurite reactions for succinic dehydrogenase, quoted in the second edition of this book now appear to be only of historical interest although still occasionally mentioned in review papers.

Tellurite Reaction for Dehydrogenases (modified in 1962 from

TABLE 10-17. AMOUNTS IN MILLIGRAMS OF DEHYDROGENASE SUBSTRATES
REQUIRED FOR 20, 30 AND 100 CC OF 50 mM SUBSTRATE SOLUTION

Substrates	The salt			For 50 mM substrate			The acid		For 50 mM substrate		
	Cation	H$_2$O	Mol. wt.	20 cc, mg	30 cc, mg	100 cc, mg	H$_2$O	Mol. wt.	20 cc, mg	30 cc, mg	100 cc, mg
Ethanol................	....	...	46.07	46	69	230					
Glucose 6-phosphate	K$_2$[1]	...	336.32	336	504	1682					
Glutamate.............	Na	1	187.14	187	281	936	...[2]	147.13	147	221	736
α-Glycerophosphate.....	Na[1]	...	216.05	216	324	1080					
β-Hydroxybutyrate.....	Na	...	126.09	126	189	630	...[2]	104.10	104	156	520
Isocitrate.............	Na$_3$	1	276.08	276	404	1380	...[2]	192.12	192	288	960
Lactate...............	Na[2]	...	112.06	112	168	560	...[2]	90.08	90	135	450
L-Malate...	Na$_2$[1]	½	187.07	187	281	935	...[2]	134.09	134	201	670
Pyruvate.............	Na	...	110.05	110	165	550	...[2]	88.06	88	132	440
6-Phosphogluconate.....	Ba	...	409.47								
Succinate.............	Na$_2$[2]	6	270.16	270	405	1351	...[2]	118.01	118	177	590
DPN[4] (NAD).........	....	...	663.4								
DPNH[4] (NADH)	Na$_2$	...	763								
TPN[5] (NADP)........	Na	2	801								
TPNH[5] (NADPH) ...	Na	...	834								

[1] *Merck Index.*
[2] *Lange, 10th ed.*
[3] Barka and Anderson.
[4] DPN, DPNH: diphosphopyridine nucleotide and reduced form.
[5] TPN, TPNH: triphosphopyridine nucleotide and reduced form.
Note: 6-Phosphogluconic acid is available as the barium salt (M.W. 409.47) glyceraldehyde 3-phosphate as a bromodioxane addition compound. The chemical manipulations required are not in the scope of this book.

For 20 cc of a 50 mM substrate use the molecular weight (formula weight on many bottle labels) in milligrams, dissolved in a convenient amount of the water in the formula. For 30 cc take 1.5 × the milligram molecular weight. When using the above table always check the molecular weight given in the table against the formula weight on the bottle. The amount of water of crystallization may vary, and sodium and potassium salts, though often interchangeable with the free acid, do not have the same molecular weight. Where differences exist, use the formula weight on the bottle and apply the above rule. Smaller amounts of substrate 1, 2, 3 or 10 cc are readily derived by appropriately shifting the decimal point.

Gomori). Preferably use frozen sections of fresh, unfixed tissue. Postfixation for 15 minutes in acetone at 4°C, as in Novikoff's procedures with the tetrazolium methods, would appear to be indicated. Tissue may be stored at 4°C for several hours without loss of activity. Fixation for 4 hours in cold acetone causes only 40% less activity. The substrate is a 0.1–0.05 M phosphate buffer of pH 7.3–7.6 containing sodium succinate, lactate, etc., in 50 mM to 0.2 M concentration and 0.1% potassium tellurite. Other details from the tetrazolium methods should be readily adaptable, using 0.1% potassium tellurite in lieu of the tetrazoles.

Incubate at 37°C for 20 minutes to 3 hours, inspecting at intervals. Activity sites are shown by deposits of brown to black elementary tellurium. Wash in pH 7–7.3 phosphate buffer. Counterstain as desired (avoiding strong acids or alkalies), dehydrate in alcohol, clear in xylene and mount in balsam. (Tellurium is insoluble in water and in fat solvents, but soluble in strong acids, alkalies and KCN.)

Chapter 11

Endogenous Pigments

THE HEME OR TETRAPORPHIN PIGMENTS

Hemoglobin itself is a relatively basic protein, endowed with or closely associated with peroxidase activities, containing closely bound iron which is usually not reactive for iron ions, and possessing a fairly characteristic absorption spectrum. In hemoglobinurias it is sometimes seen as strongly oxyphilic rhomboidal crystals in the lumina of the proximal convoluted renal tubules and as brightly eosinophilic globules in the distal cytoplasm of the tubule epithelial cells. Similar granules are sometimes found filling macrophages in recently hemorrhagic corpora lutea, and they may be identified in the erythrocyte fragmentation that ensues in erythrophagia. This eosinophilia persists at a higher pH level than that of most other tissue elements. In formalin fixed paraffin sections stained with azure A eosin B at pH 5.5, smooth muscle, connective tissue and most cytoplasm stain blue or green; erythrocytes, eosinophil leucocyte granules and a few other objects retain the eosin stain. This is useful though not highly specific.

Hemoglobin is well stained in erythrocytes by many acid dyes such as the eosins, and often its own yellowish color sufficiently modifies the tinge of red given it by eosin to give it a distinctly different color from that of other cytoplasmic materials. Certain red azo dyes such as azofuchsin G (C.I. No. 16540) and azofuchsin GN (C.I. No. 16535) stain erythrocytes deep red and are rather poor plasma stains; while brilliant purpurin R (C.I. No. 23510) gives good brown cytoplasm and muscle, but rather pale yellowish brown erythrocytes. A mixture of one of the azofuchsins at 1 part of 1% solution to 4 parts of 1% brilliant purpurin R gave red erythrocytes and pinkish brown cytoplasm and muscle. It is probable that with any individual dye samples, varying mixtures would have to be tried to find the most differential one (see p. 542).

Certain basic aniline dyes (notably toluidine blue O and thionin), when used for 30–60 seconds in 1:1000 neutral aqueous solution, stain erythrocytes a brilliant green or yellowish green, nuclei deep blue, cytoplasm light blue, cartilage purple, and mast cell granules deep purplish violet.

Alum hematoxylin counterstains of frozen sections stained for fats with oil red O often present deep olive green erythrocytes. When overstained with neutral iron hematoxylin (either in combined solution or sequence technics), hemoglobin is stained black and is among the more difficult substances to decolorize, losing its color only just before myelin in freshly fixed chromated formalin material.

Allied to these stains is the *Dunn-Thompson* (*Arch. Path.* **39**:49, 1945) method. It apparently requires neutral formalin fixation, for I have had it behave somewhat erratically on mailed in formalin material. However, on tissue fixed in neutral buffered formalin it gives quite consistent results. It may also be used on tissue smears provided these are fixed moist in 10% neutral buffered formalin, or in 3% tannic acid in methyl alcohol (3–5 minutes), or in methyl alcohol and subsequently treated with 3% tannic acid methyl alcohol as above.

The Dunn-Thompson Hemoglobin Stain. Smears and sections are brought to water as usual for sections.

1. Stain 15 minutes in Mallory's aqueous alum hematoxylin (p. 174). (Probably any other unacidified alum hematoxylin will serve.)
2. Wash in tap water.
3. Mordant 1 minute in 4% iron alum.
4. Rinse in tap water.
5. Stain 15 minutes in a picrofuchsin solution composed of 13 cc 1% acid fuchsin and 87 cc saturated aqueous picric acid solution.
6. Dehydrate and differentiate 3 minutes in 1 change or more of 95% alcohol. Dehydrate with 100% alcohol (2 changes), and clear in xylene. Mount in synthetic resin, polystyrene, Depex (etc.).

Results: Cytoplasm, brown to yellow; hemoglobin casts, phagocytosed particles and erythrocytes, emerald green; collagen, red; nuclei, brown to purple to gray black.

The Okajima method (*Anat. Rec.* **11**:295, 1916). This is one of the older differential hemoglobin stains. The following is Dunn's modification, worked out in our laboratory: Fix in buffered neutral 10% formalin, imbed and section in paraffin. Bring to distilled water as usual.

1. Mordant 1 minute in 10% phosphomolybdic acid.
2. Wash in distilled water.
3. Stain 1 hour in 10% phosphomolybdic acid 9.0 cc, saturated aqueous (7.69%) alizarin red S (C.I. No. 58005) 30 cc (Okajima: 20 minutes to 20 hours).
4. Wash in distilled water.
5. Counterstain if desired with an unacidified alum hematoxylin (3–5 minutes).

6. Wash in water, dehydrate and clear through alcohols and xylene. Mount in synthetic resin.

Results: Hemoglobin is light to dark orange red; the background is light brown with hematoxylin, orange without hematoxylin.

Of the derivatives of Lison's zinc leuco method for hemoglobin peroxidase, R. Dunn's patent blue V or cyanol FF (C.I. Nos. 42051 and 43535, respectively) variant is probably the most useful (p. 365).

Photography with violet light, utilizing the strong absorption band at 411 mμ, can be useful for localizing heme pigments photographically. The acid hematins, including formalin pigment, also show this absorption band *in vitro*.

Liberation of the iron ions from hemoglobin by chemical means consistent with good morphologic preservation of tissue seems to be a matter of some difficulty. I have seen Prussian blue reactions in erythrocytes fixed in deliberately acidified formalin (pH 3.5); Gomori reported liberation of ferric ions by strong peroxide solutions. Neither of these procedures seems to be consistent. Prolonged digestion with 0.1 N HCl in the presence of ferricyanide has failed to produce Turnbull's blue in my hands.

A procedure which might prove of interest would be the production of fluorescent antibodies against specific hemoglobins. I have not heard of this having been tried. It might even be possible so to identify fetal and S hemoglobins. This is pure speculation at this time, though I believe that the specific antibodies have been prepared.

Altered Hemoglobins

Methemoglobin is colored bright red by the addition of potassium hydroxide in fresh unfixed material. This reaction is less distinct or absent in fixed tissue. Methemoglobin is partly soluble in alcohol. It is colored by certain basic dyes and stains like hemoglobin with acid dyes. Also like hemoglobin it may be stained by myelin methods. It is bleached by hydrogen peroxide. Silver nitrate and osmium tetroxide do not alter its color. It is best identified by spectroscopic study of fresh material.

Sulfhemoglobin or **sulfmethemoglobin** is a greenish sulfur methemoglobin compound occasioning the greenish discoloration of the abdominal wall of cadavers. It is distinguishable from other hemoglobin derivatives by spectroscopy. (The foregoing statements concerning the altered hemoglobins are derived from Schmorl and Mallory.)

ACID HEMATINS

Of the acid hematins, 3 have been studied in tissue to a greater or less extent: the all too familiar formalin pigment, malaria pigment and an

HCl hematin which forms in small hemorrhagic lesions in the surface of the gastric mucosa. This last I have seen occasionally in animals in certain intoxications, where the fixation was such as to prevent the formation of formalin pigment.

Formalin pigment is formed on fixation in formaldehyde solutions at pH levels below 5.6, and possibly an alkaline hematin is formed at pH levels above 8. I have been told of the presence of formalin pigment in tissue fixed in sodium acetate formalin. Phosphate buffering to pH 7 seems to prevent its formation quite reliably.

The acid hematins are microcrystalline dark brown pigments occurring as tiny birefringent needles or rhomboids. They give no iron reactions; they are dissolved by alcoholic picric acid or alcoholic ammonium picrate solutions and by alkalies. They are quite resistant to strong organic and dilute mineral acids, and they resist even concentrated sulfuric acid for some time. Concentrated nitric acid bleaches them in an hour.

Usually the occurrence of the pigment free in vein lumina, coupled with its birefringence and crystal form, is adequate for identification of formalin pigment. The identification of the other 2 hematins is uncertain in the presence of formalin pigment.

The **formaldehyde pigment** or **acid formaldehyde hematin** is formed when acid aqueous solutions of formaldehyde act on blood rich tissues. It is a dark brown microcrystalline substance which rotates the plane of polarized light. Consequently the individual, minute, rhomboidal particles glow and darken alternately with each 90° rotation of the stage when examined with crossed Nicol prisms or polaroids. The pigment withstands extraction with water, alcohol, acetone, glycols, glycerol, fat solvents and dilute acids. Formalin pigment is bleached promptly or within an hour by concentrated nitric acid, and partially by 90% formic acid. It is bleached in 30 minutes by 3% hydrogen peroxide or by 5% chromic anhydride (CrO_3). Sequence treatment with 5% potassium permanganate (but not 0.5%) and 5% oxalic acid removes the pigment, though neither reagent alone appears to bleach it. It withstands extraction by concentrated sulfuric, hydrochloric, phosphoric and acetic acids. It does not give Prussian blue or Turnbull's blue reactions with ferrocyanide or ferricyanide. It is extracted by treatment with weak alcoholic, aqueous, hydroalcoholic or water-acetone solutions of sodium, potassium or ammonium hydroxide, and by ammonia solutions in glycerol and glycols. It is removed at once by saturated alcoholic picric acid solution. It occurs copiously within vascular spaces among apparently intact or laked erythrocytes and also apparently within phagocytes. It seems more probable that the particles within phagocytes are formed from previously phagocytosed erythrocytes or hemoglobin than that the pigment is ingested as such. Spectroscopically it is similar to but distinct from hydrochloric acid and acetic acid hematins.

Several methods have been suggested for its removal. Verocay immersed sections 10 minutes in 0.01% potassium hydroxide in 80% alcohol, and then washed 5 minutes in 2 changes of water. Schmorl warns that this treatment impairs the alcohol fastness of the Gram stain; he finds Kardasewitsch's method harmless in this respect. This method employed a 5 minute to 4 hour extraction in a 1–5% dilution in 70% alcohol of 28% ammonia water. Subsequent washing with water or alcohol is necessary to remove the excess ammonia. The saturated alcoholic picric acid mordanting (p. 86) before Masson stains (p. 545) should remove formalin pigment, especially if prolonged to 5 minutes. A mixture of 50 cc each of acetone and 3% hydrogen peroxide and 1 cc 28% ammonia water removes the pigment in 5 minutes or less.

More important than methods of removal of formaldehyde pigment is the fact that it is not formed on fixation with formaldehyde buffered to pH levels above 6. Formalin at pH levels from 3–5 forms large quantities of the pigment, with or without obvious lysis of erythrocytes. Fixation in alkaline formalin is said also to produce a formalin pigment. With this I have had no experience. Brief trial of alkaline formalin years ago gave me losses of nucleic acids which I have preferred to avoid.

The foregoing statements on formaldehyde pigment are based largely on studies by Hershberger and myself (*Bull. Int. A. Med. Mus.* **27**:136, 145, 162, 1947).

Malaria pigment occurs in the parasites (especially the quartan *Plasmodium malariae*), about brain capillaries and in littoral phagocytes in spleen, liver, bone marrow and lymph nodes. It is an amorphous, dark brown, granular pigment which does not fluoresce in ultraviolet light but rotates the plane of polarized light, resembling in the latter respect the otherwise quite similar, microcrystalline and doubly refractile acid formaldehyde hematin, the so-called formalin pigment. Kósa (*Virchow Arch. path. Anat.* **258**:186, 1925) stated that that part of the malaria pigment which was free or in erythrocytes was doubly refractile, while that in phagocytes never was. Like formalin pigment it is soluble in dilute aqueous and alcoholic solutions of sodium, potassium and ammonium hydroxides; is bleached within an hour by concentrated nitric acid, by hydrogen peroxide and partially by 90% formic acid; and is insoluble in dilute (5%) aqueous solutions of mineral acids and in concentrated acetic, hydrochloric, phosphoric and sulfuric acids. On direct experiment it was found that both these pigments remained identifiable in slide preparations for 2 weeks if sections were first blotted dry, treated with the 96.5% sulfuric acid (sp. gr. 1.84), covered with a coverglass and sealed with petrolatum. But tissue structure was destroyed (Hershberger, unpublished data).

Schmorl stated that malaria pigment is soluble in 5% alcoholic solutions of sulfuric, nitric and hydrochloric acids at 40–50°C in 1 day or less. It is also soluble in aniline, in pyridine and in a 4% soluton of quinine in chloroform. It is insoluble in fat solvents and is not stained by fat or lipid stains. It is not blackened by osmium tetroxide or silver nitrate. Malaria pigment gives no iron reaction on direct test, but according to M. Kósa (*loc. cit.*) it may give a Prussian blue reaction with potassium ferrocyanide when sections are first treated 10–12 hours with 2% oxalic acid or 1% hydrochloric acid to remove hemosiderin, washed with distilled water, treated for 5–10 minutes with 1% potassium hydroxide and again washed with distilled water. In my experience the prescribed acid treatment may be inadequate to remove the ferric iron from hemosiderin in formalin fixed material. Hence I consider the validity of Kósa's statement questionable. Moreover, I have seen artifactual ferrocyanide staining of smooth muscle, liver cell cytoplasm and other structures after prolonged exposure to oxalic acid used for extraction of iron from hemosiderin, where no iron was seen before.

Brown (*Exp. Med.* **13**:290, 1911) called malaria pigment *hematin;* Mallory used this term for a dark brown amorphous pigment, not more closely described, which occurred in old extravasations of blood. Neither of these usages should be confused with the usual meaning of an acid or alkaline soluble hemoglobin derivative with a characteristic absorption spectrum.

Acid Hematin. Sometimes similar microcrystalline brown pigment is found in material fixed in neutral buffered formalin. This occurs in somewhat autolyzed spleens in the surface adjacent to the stomach, and is also seen in perfectly fresh material fixed in neutral formalin in focal hemorrhages of the gastric mucosa. This pigment would appear to be a hydrochloric acid hematin. This gastric pigment I have observed chiefly in experimental toxicologic material fixed in phosphate buffered formalin, and cannot say whether it would have appeared with other fixations. However, similar pigment may be formed in spleen tissue fixed in 1% acetic or formic acid in 89% alcohol or acetone, without formaldehyde.

BILIVERDIN, BILIRUBIN, HEMATOIDIN

In the destruction of hemoglobin from broken down erythrocytes, the iron containing tetraporphin heme is first separated from the protein globin and then undergoes oxidative scission or opening of the ring between 2 pyrrole ring carbons, the one vinylated, the other methylated. The resulting iron containing compound (or compounds) is known as *verdohemin,* which on loss of iron to ferritin or new hemoglobin molecules becomes biliverdin. Biliverdin is formed particularly in littoral cells of the bone marrow and spleen, and passes through the circulation to the liver. When the ring opening precedes the porphin globin cleavage, the resultant intermediate protein is verdoglobin. This undergoes hydrolysis and iron loss to form again biliverdin. In the liver, biliverdin is normally reduced to bilirubin; on secretion into the intestine it undergoes further reduction to urobilinogen (stercobilinogen) and is later oxidized to urobilin (stercobilin), the yellow brown pigment of feces and urine. In bilirubin and biliverdin the 2 vinyl groups remain; in urobilinogen, urobilin and mesobilirubinogen they are hydrogenated to ethyl groups.

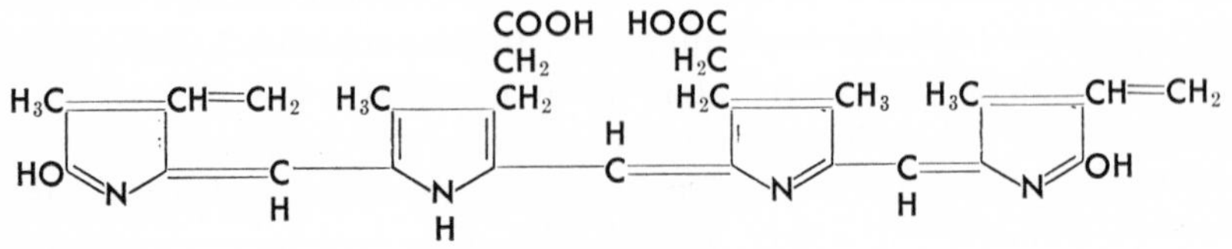

Biliverdin

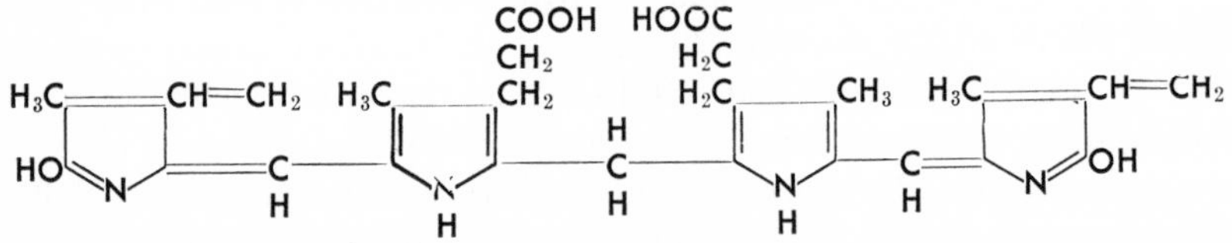

Bilirubin

Bilirubin further forms a mono- or diglucuronide by esterification of one or both of the propionic acid residues with the C-1 hydroxyl of glucuronic acid. These, especially the diglucuronide, are water soluble, and they azo couple to give the direct van den Bergh reaction. Alcohol solubilizes unconjugated bilirubin, thus making it available for the indirect reaction.

Hematoidin is a golden yellow to orange or reddish brown crystalline or amorphous pigment occurring particularly within hemorrhagic infarcts and aging hemorrhages. Rich identified it with bilirubin; Virchow clearly distinguished the two. Of the 2 reports which identify the 2 pigments, the hematoidin in the case of Fischer and Reindel (*Hoppe Seyler Z. physiol. Chem.* **127**:299, 1923) was derived from an echinococcus cyst of the liver; that in Rich's (*Johns Hopkins Hosp. Bull.* **36**:225, 1925) case came from an omental cyst, removed surgically, which had apparently been well encapsulated and unconnected with liver or bile passages. These reports would be more convincing had the hematoidin come from a source more widely separated anatomically from the liver.

These pigments were originally characterized by their Gmelin reaction to concentrated sulfuric or nitric acid, in which a succession of colors develops: brownish red, red, purple, violet, blue and green. This is often performed by adding a crystal or so of sodium nitrite, enough to make 1–2% HNO_2, to concentrated nitric acid. The test is often unsatisfactory but should be repeated on 2 or 3 slides before it is regarded as negative.

T. Dunn (*Milit. Surg.* 109:350, 1951), who questions the identity of hematoidin and bilirubin, describes hematoidin crystals as orange red, yellow or green, rhomboidal, monoclinic, birefringent, readily soluble in chloroform and in pyridine, very slightly soluble in alcohol, insoluble in water, 10% formalin, glycerol, ether or xylene. Carbol-xylene dissolved them. These findings closely parallel Frey's 1860 description.

She reported that the spectrum in chloroform differed from that of bilirubin, that the diazo reaction failed to show a reddish violet color, that application of nitrous acid to fresh tissues dissolved them rapidly without a play of colors. In paraffin sections she found many empty rhomboidal spaces and perceived very little identifiable hematoidin. But in Carbowax sections the rhomboidal form and yellow color of even very small crystals were well preserved. For sectioning in paraffin, I have had fair success with gasoline clearing and brief vacuum infiltration.

Spectroscopically a chloroform solution of bilirubin showed a strong maximum at 430 mμ and slowly increasing absorption from 340 to 250 mμ. The chloroform solution of hematoidin from human infant adrenals and renal papilla (of similar color density to the bilirubin solution) showed no peak at 430 mμ, but a rapidly rising absorption from 450 out to the ultraviolet end of the spectrum.

Dunn reports, as here tabulated, the results of A. S. Mulay's chemical tests.

It is to be observed that Glenner prescribed cryostat sections for his procedure, thus avoiding the losses of bilirubin suggested above and of hematoidin as detailed by T. Dunn. It does not appear to be necessary, however, to avoid the use of formalin, since Dunn found hematoidin well preserved after several weeks in that fluid. I have demonstrated hematoidin in material fixed 1–3 weeks in formalin and carried through an alcohol, petroleum ether, paraffin sequence with 30 minute vacuum infiltration. The use of cold knife frozen sections or Carbowax sections of formalin fixed material would appear to be most convenient for routine autopsy and surgical tissues.

Recently observed reactions common to brain infarct hematoidin and to the bile pigment in small bile passages in obstructive jaundice include a strong ferric ferricyanide reduction, blackening with diammine silver

TABLE 11-1. SOME CHEMICAL REACTIONS OF BILIRUBIN AND HEMATOIDIN

Test	Bilirubin	Hematoidin
Trichloroacetic reaction.........	Blue green	Faint pink
Ehrlich's diazo reaction.........	Red violet	Negative
Rosin's iodine test.............	Green	Negative

in 5–16 hours at 250°C, even after sulfuric acid extraction which removed the iron from concurrently present hemosiderin and liver cell cytosiderin. The green color of the bile in hepatic biliary ductules and capillaries in unstained preparations contrasted with the golden yellow of the hematoidin. Bichromate oxidation at pH 2.2 (below) did not obviously alter the color of bile pigment; perhaps the green was yellower and less pronounced. Nor does brief dithionite reduction (5%, 10 minutes) alter the green color of the bile pigment of obstructive jaundice.

There is a considerable number of oxidative methods purporting to change yellowish brown bilirubin to green biliverdin, e.g., Stein's iodine, Glenner's bichromate, certain peroxide procedures and others. I have long known that bile pigment in Van Gieson stained preparations was often a brilliant grass green. An analysis of the effects of this stain, by leaving out one or another or all of the reagents that went into an iron chloride hematoxylin Van Gieson sequence, led us to the finding that the pigment was green in the unstained paraffin section and required eosin to make it the familiar yellow brown. Delvaux has recently confirmed this finding, using Biebrich scarlet as well as eosin.

When one consults recent biochemical texts it is seen that bilirubin is somewhat more soluble than biliverdin in water and in a number of nonpolar solvents. This would appear to suggest that the principal bile pigment remaining in paraffin sections is in fact biliverdin. It is quite possible that bilirubin may be present and demonstrable in frozen sections, but I have seen no adequate proof of this.

Application of the various oxidative procedures employed in these "bilirubin stains" to hematoidin in a cerebral infarct did not turn it green.

That various oxidative procedures ($K_2Cr_2O_7$, H_2O_2, I_2) convert bilirubin to green biliverdin in vitro is, of course, established.

Stein's method for bilirubin (C. R. Soc. Biol. 120:1136, 1935) depended on its conversion to a green substance, possibly biliverdin, by the action of iodine. Stein found formalin fixed material best, but material fixed in alcohol or in Helly's fluid can be used.

Glenner's (Am. J. Clin. Path. 27:1, 1957) method for bilirubin uses unfixed frozen sections and bichromate oxidation in place of Stein's iodine on formalin fixed tissue.

1. Cut fresh frozen sections by a cold knife procedure (Adamstone-Taylor or cryostat), attach to clean slides and dry in air at about 25°C.
2. Immerse slides for 15 minutes in equal volumes of 0.1 M HCl-KH$_2$PO$_4$ buffer pH 2.2 and 0.1 M (2.94%) potassium bichromate. Wash 5 minutes in running water.
3. Postfix 20 minutes in calcium acetate formalin (p. 38). Wash 5 minutes in running water.
4. Counterstain as desired, dehydrate, clear and mount. Compare with unoxidized controls (omit step 2).

Glenner modified this procedure to precede the bichromate bath with a ferrocyanide reaction for hemosiderin, and follow it with an oil red O stain for fats. Since no lipid extraction procedure is applied, this would show soluble fats as well as lipofuscin. The ferrocyanide reaction was done by preliminary immersion for 5 minutes in 2% $K_4Fe(CN)_6$ in distilled water, followed by 20 minutes in 1% $K_4Fe(CN)_6$ in 25% acetic acid.

Nothing is said about applicability of the method to formalin fixed tissue.

In regard to Stein's and Glenner's oxidation methods to turn bilirubin into green biliverdin, it may be noted that some bile pigment in obstructive jaundice is already quite dark green in formalin fixed tissue and that neither iodine nor bichromate oxidation occasions any change of color in this pigment. It is also to be observed that bile pigments appearing deep green in Van Gieson stains appear quite brown when hematoxylin eosin or azure eosin stains are used. The green color may also be seen in uncounterstained Prussian blue and acid silver nitrate preparations, as well as in unreacted controls.

To prove that the pigment present is in fact bilirubin, it is necessary that it be brown in uncounterstained, unoxidized controls, and that its color be converted to green by the oxidation step. This requirement applies both to Stein's and to Glenner's methods.

Hematoporphyrin gives the same Gmelin reaction as bilirubin, and is insoluble in dilute acids and alkalies.

Lison (1953) recommends use of fluorescence microscopy for the detection of porphyrins in the tissues. With long wave ultraviolet (365 mμ), orange to red fluorescence is observed. Harderian gland of rodents, shell gland of the hen's oviduct, rodent placenta and regressing corpora lutea form good test objects.

As already mentioned, Mallory refers to a dark brown or bluish black pigment occurring in old extravasations of blood as hematin, but does not further characterize it. I infer that it is iron negative.

The foregoing statements regarding hematoidin, bilirubin, and hematoporphyrin have been brought together from Mallory, Hueck, Lison, Schmorl and Romeis, and have been supplemented from direct observations and the journal literature.

THE IRON BEARING PIGMENTS

A golden brown granular pigment originating in sites of hemorrhage and congestion, darker in the lung and intestinal mucosa, soluble in sulfuric acid and yielding red ash on ignition of the granules, which then yielded a Prussian blue reaction, was reported on at length by Rudolf Virchow (*Virchow Arch. path. Anat.* 1:379, 1847). Vogel in 1853 (Hueck, 1912) observed a black pigmentation of the intestinal mucosa which, unlike skin melanin, was removed by acid extraction and which he therefore named *pseudomelanosis coli.* Apparently it was to sections from a case of postmortem hemolysis that Grohe (*Virchow Arch. path. Anat.* **20**:306, 1861) first applied the Prussian blue reaction and noted that if he applied acid first and then ferrocyanide blue haloes appeared about the granules, but that if the sequence was reversed sharply, stained blue granules were seen. It remained for Max Perls (*Virchow Arch. path. Anat.* **39**:42, 1867) to work out a practical mixed ferrocyanide HCl reagent which he applied systematically to a wide variety of tissues and lesions. Quincke added the ammonium sulfide reaction in 1880, although I think Virchow and Vogel had both used this reagent, but apparently on extracts or gross preparations only. Tirmann and Schmelzer (1895; Hueck, 1912) added a ferricyanide demonstration step after the ammonium sulfide. This is what Pearse rather loosely calls the Turnbull's blue reaction. Strictly speaking, that designation should apply to an acid ferricyanide reaction applied to tissue to demonstrate the presence of native Fe^{++}. This occurs sometimes at iron absorption sites in the duodenum and jejunum and in cecal enterosiderosis in the guinea pig. I have occasionally seen it in corpora hemorrhagica of the ovary, and Bunting described it in iron and calcium incrustations of necrotic vessels. Otherwise, as Gomori said, it practically does not occur. Gomori noted gas evolution in the application of the acid ferricyanide of the Tirmann-Schmelzer reaction and warned of the artifacts produced thereby.

It has been objected that ferricyanide is itself an oxidizing agent and would oxidize Fe^{++} to Fe^{+++}. Since it would in this process be reduced itself to ferrocyanide, a blue precipitate of Prussian blue would result. However, ferricyanide exhibits this oxidizing capacity principally in alkaline solutions, while the ferricyanide test for Fe^{++} is carried out in our laboratory at pH 1 or 2. At this pH I have not been able to demonstrate oxidation by ferricyanide, although ferric chloride at pH 1–2 oxidizes SH and diphenols readily.

In mammalian tissues I have not seen positive ferricyanide reactions except in loci where the ferrocyanide reaction was also positive.

There are a number of more recent organic colored chelate reactions for ferrous ions such as Humphrey's 1935 dinitrosoresorcinol reaction (dark green) and the Hukill and Putt recent highly sensitive bathophenanthroline reaction (deep red). The latter produces an alcohol soluble pigment, and the authors require blotting and drying in air before mounting in synthetic resin.

Granick's (*J. Biol. Chem.* **147**:91, 1943) experience with the reduction of ferric iron in ferritin by means of dithionite has been similar to mine with the reduction of hemosiderin iron with sulfide. It is very difficult to achieve complete reduction, and much Fe^{+++} remains demonstrable with ferrocyanide after the ammonium sulfide step of the Tirmann reaction.

For a long time hemosiderin was regarded simply as ferric oxide or hydroxide, though Hueck (1912) spoke of a probable colorless protein carrier substance, and drew attention to the concentrations of acids required to remove the iron from tissue sections.

In 1939 (*Am. J. Path.* **15**:225) I noted enhancement of the resistance of hemosiderin iron to subsequent acid extraction by formaldehyde containing fixatives, as well as the persistence of a brown iron free pigment after certain acid formalin fixations where only iron positive pigment was present in parallel material fixed in neutral formalin. Considerable resistance against extraction by weaker acids was conferred on the iron content by prior fixation in formaldehyde at pH 7, but extraction by sulfuric or oxalic acid or (1963) sodium dithionite was not impeded.

Aposiderin. In 1943 I (*Pub. Health Rep.* **58**:30, 1943) reported the occurrence of a similar iron negative brown renal pigment arising apparently by *in vivo* desiderization of intraepithelial hemosiderin in the later stages of chronic hemolytic intoxicaton. To this iron free phase I applied the name *aposiderin* in 1948, and by extension the same term has been applied also to artificially desiderized hemosiderin. The iron free phase is quite resistant to strong acids and alkalies. Mallory's fuchsin stain is not retained. H_2S does not blacken it, and Fairhall's chromate reaction for lead is negative (Miller, *Pub. Health Rep.* **56**:1610, 1941).

In the same year McManus (*Stain Techn.* **23**:99, 1948) noted a positive reaction of hemosiderin by the periodic aicd Schiff technic. After various isolated reports by me, Goessner and Gedigk, it became evident that a positive periodic acid Schiff reaction appears in new hemosiderins somewhat after the iron reaction has become strongly positive, thus accounting for the negative reaction in some specimens.

Gedigk (*Virchow Arch. path. Anat.* **324**:373, 1953; **326**:172, 1954) also reports on a positive tetrazonium reaction of the iron bearing pigment and iron free phases of the pigment, indicating, as of the early fifties, the presence of aromatic amino acids. Since Burstone (*J. Histochem.* **3**:32, 1955) has shown that cellulose, which contains no protein, also can give a postcoupled tetrazonium reaction, we must regard Gedigk's conclusion as only probable. However, Behrens and Asher (*Hoppe-Seyler Z. physiol. Chem.* **220**:97, 1933) isolated hemosiderin by centrifuging homogenized horse spleen over carbon tetrachloride (sp. gr. 1.594) and over 1,2-dibromoethane (sp. gr. 2.18) and mixtures thereof, thereby obtaining fractions below, between and above those densities. The bulk of the material fell into the second fraction and could be fractionated further by use of mixtures of the 2 halogenated hydrocarbons. The fraction of 1.80–2.18 specific gravity contained 36.1% protein, 3% $CaHPO_4$ and 60.4% $Fe(OH)_3$. Ludewig (*Proc. Soc. Exp. Biol. Med.* **95**:514, 1957) got similar figures and also demonstrated hexosamine, galactose, mannose and fucose chromatographically. These chemical findings agree well with what we presently know of the histochemistry of hemosiderin.

Granick (1949) has conjectured that the protein of hemosiderin may be apoferritin. There are now acceptable amino acid analyses of this latter protein, but none of the glycoprotein remnant of hemosiderin, for which Goessner and I have used the name *aposiderin*. Nor are there any analyses showing the presence of sugars in apoferritin. Dubin (1955), however, seems to regard the identity of apoferritin and the protein of hemosiderin as established, apparently from Granick's 1949 speculation.

From the published analyses of apoferritin it might be of interest to try histochemical tests for tyrosine and arginine. There is an approximate balance between the dicarboxylic and the basic amino acids which would agree with the shift from weak oxyphilia to basophilia at about the same pH levels as collagen and cytoplasms in hemosiderins. Levels of sulfur amino acids, tryptophan and histidine are not remarkable.

Thus the concept has evolved that ionic iron is bound to one or more protein carrier substances. These carrier substances lose their reactive iron readily on acid extraction; but give it up incompletely at pH 4.5 and scarcely at all at pH 7.6 in ethylenediaminetetraacetate solutions, even from 5–10 μ sections in 7 days at 25°C. They are also found iron free in human and animal tissues under a variety of as yet undetermined circumstances. When naturally or artificially deprived of iron they give a series of histochemical reactions which agree in all respects, except the specific iron reactions of the pigment to which they are related.

Histochemically we are able, in 1963, to recognize 2 pairs of such pigments. The one group, comprising the pigments of melanosis and pseudo-melanosis coli and the villus core pigment of villus melanosis (*Zottenmelanose*), is localized almost strictly to the intestinal mucosa and has a suggested relationship to the phenomena of intestinal iron absorption and excretion. The other group comprises the granular pigments resulting from phagocytosis of erythrocytes and resorption of hemoglobin by renal epithelium, and also manifests both iron positive (hemosiderin) and iron free (aposiderin) phases.

The relation of these histochemically demonstrable pigments to the biochemically extractable and crystallizable protein ferritin and its iron free phase apoferritin is uncertain. Physiological and biochemical considerations almost demand the presence of these substances in the intestinal mucosa; much of the isolation work appears to have been done on spleen tissue, where hemosiderin is the characteristic histochemical iron pigment. Ferritin reputedly gives negative reactions for ionic iron (H_2S), which Granick imputes to its high degree of dispersion. His technic in his hands did demonstrate larger granules of hemosiderin in horse spleen as black masses, and it colored erythrocytes gray. The relation of ferritin to the diffuse ferrocyanide staining seen early in the evolution of hemosiderin pigmentation and called *protosiderin* in the 1948 and 1954 editions is also uncertain, but a slight ferrocyanide reaction is easier to recognize than the sulfide test.

A parallel situation may exist in regard to the iron bearing particles observed widely distributed in various rodent epithelial cells by Spicer (*J. Histochem.* **10**:528, 1962) and designated by him as *cytosiderin*. Spicer notes peracetic or permanganate aldehyde fuchsin staining of particles in the same locations, but he does not report whether the aldehyde fuchsin staining particles persist after acid extraction of the iron.

Early in 1963 we found (*J. Histochem.* **11**:662, 1963) that short exposures to fresh 1% fresh aqueous sodium dithionite[1] solutions completely removed demonstrable ferric and ferrous iron from tissues. Test tube experiments indicated that freshly precipitated ferric and ferrous hydroxides were readily dissolved by this reagent at pH 7, but not the sulfides, while at pH 4.5 both sulfides and hydroxides were dissolved. As little as 5 minutes in 1% $Na_2S_2O_4$ in 0.1 M pH 4.5 acetate buffer removed all demonstrable iron in heavily pigmented liver, spleen, lymph nodes (cytosiderin, hemosiderin) and experimental severe enterosiderosis of guinea pigs. Similarly 1% $Na_2S_2O_4$ in acetate and Veronal HCl buffers at pH 5, 5.5, 6, 6.5 and 7 removed all iron from the same tissues in the shortest interval tested (15 minutes).[1]

It was promptly found that dithionite extraction did not impair the periodic acid Schiff reaction of hemosiderin or enterosiderin.

In general, the carrier substance(s) of the intestinal pigments presents stronger protein and lipid reactions, stronger reducing reactions and a rather strong affinity for Nile blue, which after staining is not removed by acetone. These reactions, other than those for iron ions, appear identical in the iron carrying and iron free forms of the respective pigments and also remain unaltered when acid or dithionite extraction of iron salts is practiced.

Cytosiderin. Gedigk and Strauss (*Virchow Arch. path. Anat.* **324**:373, 1953) found the periodic acid Schiff reaction and Sudan black staining both lacking in liver cell cytosiderin, though positive in "mesenchymal hemosiderin." Apparently disregarding the possibility of lipofuscin mixture, they stated further that acid desiderized liver cell hemosiderin was sudanophil, acid fast and positive by Danielli's postcoupled tetrazonium reaction. No simultaneous demonstration of iron and lipid was attempted.

Protosiderin (Lillie, *Histopathologic Technic*, 1948). Diffuse and granular forms of iron positive pigment may often be present in the same cell. The diffuse form is more easily lost on fixation in acid formalin. A similar diffuse Prussian blue reaction is sometimes seen in the contents of renal tubules in the presence of hemoglobinuria. This change is prob-

---

[1] Dithionite should be purchased in small bottles; it deteriorates slowly after opening. Solutions must be freshly prepared, at least daily.

ably related to the positive Prussian blue reaction which may be induced in erythrocytes by fixation in 10% formalin buffered to pH 3.5 or 4, or by immersion of sections of material fixed by neutral formalin in solutions of mineral acids for varying periods.

Heart Failure Cell Pigment. This usually iron positive pigment, found in large phagocytic cells in pulmonary alveoli and in sputum in cases of chronic passive congestion of the lungs, is singly refractile and yellow to dark brown in color. In some cases it is more successfully demonstrated by the hydrochloric acid ferrocyanide technic; in others this procedure produces blue halos about the granules. In some cases a positive periodic acid Schiff reaction is given, in others not. Ferric ferricyanide (p. 211) is not evidently reduced. The pigment is not acid fast in the Ziehl-Neelsen technic. It does not retain iron hematoxylin in the myelin variant method for eosinophils (p. 304), nor fuchsin in the Mallory hemofuscin method. Some of the darker brown examples of this pigment may be largely iron negative with even the hydrochloric acid ferrocyanide method. The iron reaction does not correlate with the periodic acid Schiff reaction. Usually the pigment granules are untinged by oil soluble dyes.

Like some other iron positive pigments, notably that of the involuting corpus hemorrhagicum of the ovary, this pigment may reduce methenamine silver at 60°C while nuclei and red cells are still unblackened. This reaction is probably similar to that of mucins and collagen, which blacken selectively with methenamine silver after treatment with ferric chloride (p. 242). Diammine silver solutions as used for reticulum impregnation (p. 526) do not blacken the iron positive pigments mentioned above.

Extraction of the iron by a 24 hour bath in 10% sulfuric acid does not remove much of the darker brown material, though the iron reaction is negative. The periodic acid Schiff reaction of the granules is not decreased by the acid extraction. The amount of material which is dark brown to black after 3–3½ hours at 60°C in methenamine silver (p. 240) is much reduced by the acid extraction. This supports the thesis that the methenamine silver reaction is due to the iron itself.

Other Iron Positive Pigments. The iron positive pigment in apocrine gland cells is of uncertain origin. That in renal epithelium I regard as granular hemosiderin.

The iron positive pigment in cutaneous xanthomata often appears to be related to the lipids.

In all these lipid associated iron pigments the use of combined lipid and iron technics is needed to determine whether the lipid and the iron occur in separate granules or in the same granules.

The hemosiderins are by definition pigments which exhibit one or more of the reactions of ionic iron. Traditionally 3 principal reactions have been used: the formation of ferric ferrocyanide (Prussian blue) when the material is treated with acid solutions of ferrocyanides (Perls's reaction); the formation of black iron sulfides, probably both FeS and Fe_3S_4, perhaps also unreduced Fe_2S_3, when material is treated with ammonium sulfide (Quincke's reaction); and the formation of ferrous ferricyanide (Turnbull's blue) from the ferrous sulfide thus formed, by treatment with a ferricyanide and acid (the Tirmann-Schmelzer reaction). In addition, Mallory has proposed a reaction with fresh unoxidized hematoxylin without mordant salts (p. 441), which gives black with iron salts (probably Fe^{+++}) and clear dark blue with copper. The 2 colors are comparable to those attained in Heidenhain type hematoxylin procedures on tissues premordanted with $FeCl_3$ and $CuSO_4$ respectively. I have included also 2 more recent metal chelate reactions, both apparently for Fe^{++} and used after reduction with sulfide or thioglycolate: Humphrey's and the reaction of Hukill and Putt (p. 405).

It is often stated that the fixative of choice for demonstration of hemosiderin is alcohol. On comparative tests of the same material with various fixatives, I have found that positive Prussian blue reactions are most often obtained when 10% formalin buffered to pH 7 is the fixing agent. This is definitely superior to alcohol, alcoholic formalin, Orth's fluid and unbuffered 10% formalin. However, in more or less autolyzed human liver the iron positive pigment in liver cells may be better preserved with alcohol.

According to Schmorl, Hall has proposed fixation of fresh tissue in alcoholic solutions of ammonium sulfide containing 70 parts of 100% alcohol. For liver, spleen and bone marrow he made up the remaining 30 parts with strong ammonium sulfide solution; for other tissues he used 5 parts of ammonium sulfide and 25 of distilled water. The fixation interval was 24 hours. This amounts to a Quincke reaction done in the block on tissue during fixation. Hall prescribed a ferrocyanide reaction to follow on the paraffin sections. A ferricyanide test could also be used, as in the Tirmann-Schmelzer reaction.

The **Quincke** (*Deutsch. Arch. klin. Med.* **25**:567, 1880) (omit steps 4 and 5) and **Tirmann-Schmelzer** (Hueck; Schmorl; Mallory) reactions: Formalin or alcohol fixation and celloidin or paraffin sections may be used.

1. Bring sections to distilled water as usual.
2. Impregnate sections 1–2 hours, or as long as 1–2 days in strong, slightly yellow ammonium sulfide solution. Mallory prefers to dilute this with 3 volumes of 95% alcohol, to avoid loss of sections. Otherwise it would seem indicated to soak sections first in 1% collodion for 5–10 minutes after deparaffinizing, drain 1 minute and harden 5–10 minutes in 80% alcohol before bringing to water. Highman (*Int. A. Med. Mus. Bull.* **32**:97, 1951) impregnates instead for 24 hours in saturated hydrogen

sulfide water for hematite and other refractory iron ore dusts which fail to react to the usual procedure. Buffered Na_2S at pH 7 (p. 319) can be used to avoid the alkali detergent effect.

3. Wash thoroughly in distilled water.
4. Soak sections 15 minutes in equal volumes of 1% hydrochloric acid and 20% potassium ferricyanide, freshly mixed. This step is omitted in the Quincke method. (The 1% HCl is presumably 0.12 N, not 0.3 N).
5. Wash thoroughly with distilled water.
6. Counterstain with 0.5% basic fuchsin in 50% alcohol for 5–20 minutes, wash in water, differentiate in alcohol according to Mallory; or with alum carmine for 1–24 hours and wash in water according to Schmorl.
7. Dehydrate with alcohols, clear in xylene, mount in polystyrene, Depex, cellulose caprate or other nonreducing resin.

Results: Quincke's reaction gives a dark brown to black color to the iron pigment; that of Tirmann and Schmelzer, a dark blue.

The brown color of the sulfide is less readily distinguished from other brown colored substances than the blues of the Prussian and Turnbull blue reactions. Silver, lead and mercury also give dark brown to black deposits with this method. Other brown and black insoluble sulfides are noted on p. 431. Unless special precautions are taken sections are often lost in the alkaline sulfide solution. The same objection applies also to the Tirmann-Schmelzer reaction. Further, if instead of potassium ferricyanide the ferrocyanide is applied to the sections treated with ammonium sulfide, a positive Prussian blue reaction is still obtainable. This indicates that only a portion of the ferric iron orignally present was converted to ferrous sulfide, or perhaps it indicates a conversion to Fe_3S_4. It might be objected that Perls's reaction was open to the same criticism; *i.e.*, that it demonstrated only ferric iron. However, with numerous tests of hemosiderin containing material, I have only rarely obtained a direct positive Turnbull's blue reaction on an intrinsic hematogenous pigment with acidulated potassium ferricyanide, when that salt is substituted for potassium ferrocyanide in the technic given on p. 406. Bunting, however, reports positive diffuse ferricyanide staining as well as ferrocyanide staining in the mixed calcium iron deposits occurring in necrotic areas (*J. Nat. Cancer Inst.* **10**:1368, 1950).

I have occasionally seen ferricyanide positive pigment in phagocytes in human ovaries, and part of the demonstrable iron in the epithelial cells of the distal extremities of the intestinal villi, especially in the duodenum, may be ferricyanide reactive, though most of it is ferrocyanide positive.

Other Ferricyanide Reactions. Other insoluble ferricyanides include cobaltic and cobaltous—which are brown and red; cupric and cuprous— greenish yellow and brownish red; lead—red and soluble in hot water; nickel—brown; silver—orange; and stannous—white (Lange).

Dinitrosoresorcinol gives a dark green color with iron salts. Humphrey (*Arch. Path.* **20**:256, 1935) substituted this reagent for the ferricyanide of the Tirmann-Schmelzer procedure, directing as follows:

After a 1 minute bath in 30% ammonium sulfide, rinse in water and stain 6–20 hours in dinitrosoresorcinol; either saturated aqueous or a 3% solution in 50% alcohol. Wash in the same solvent, dehydrate, clear and mount in Canada balsam. The dark green color is quite permanent in balsam.

Bathophenanthroline.[1] Hukill and Putt (*J. Histochem.* **10**:490, 1962) have reported a method utilizing the highly sensitive Fe^{++} reagent, bathophenanthroline (4,7-diphenyl-1,10-phenanthroline).

1. Fix in buffered 10% formalin (pH 7), imbed in paraffin, section at 5 μ and mount on slides using distilled water to float out. Deparaffinize and hydrate to distilled water as usual:
2. Stain sections 2 hours in bathophenanthroline reagent. Dissolve 100 mg bathophenanthroline in 100 cc 3% acetic acid by heating to 60°C overnight, shaking well to suspend evenly at the start. Store at room temperature or in cold (stable for 4 weeks). For use, to 40 cc bathophenanthroline solution add 0.2 cc thioglycolic acid and mix well. The used solution may be returned to stock. It is necessary to add more thioglycolic acid each day that it is used, since this reagent oxidizes readily in air.
3. After staining, rinse in distilled water, counterstain 3 minutes in 0.5% aqueous methylene blue and wash in 3 changes distilled water, 1 minute each.
4. Blot and dry thoroughly in oven at 60°C and mount in Permount.

Results: Iron, red; nuclei, blue.

Note that this reagent demonstrates only Fe^{++} and that if used without thioglycolic acid it will serve as a specific reagent for Fe^{++}. It does not permit separate demonstration of Fe^{+++} in distinction from Fe^{++}, thus sharing the deficiency of the Quincke and Tirmann-Schmelzer methods. However, bathophenanthroline is claimed to be more sensitive than ferrocyanide in detecting minimal amounts of iron. The authors do not recite the color reactions, if any, with other metal ions. The metal dye complex is readily soluble in alcohols and most lipid solvents, though essentially insoluble in water. The effect of gum syrup, glycerol gelatin and similar mounting media was not reported.

The Ferrocyanide Reaction of M. Perls (*Virchow Arch. path. Anat.* **39**:42, 1867). The following technic works well on the hemosiderins and

---

[1] Bathophenanthroline was obtained from the Frederick Smith Chemical Co., Columbus, Ohio.

most mineral iron. Hematite dust deposits may require more drastic treatment to obtain the reaction.

1. Fix 48 or more hours in 10% formalin buffered with phosphates to pH 7 (p. 38).
2. Dehydrate, clear, imbed in paraffin and section as usual.
3. Make up fresh 2% solution of potassium ferrocyanide in distilled water and add an equal volume of 0.25 N (2% by volume of concentrated HCl) hydrochloric acid (Bunting) or 5% acetic acid (Highman). Heat sections 30 minutes at 60°C in this mixture; or, preferably (Bunting), let stand an hour at room temperature. Gomori used a 30 minute bath at room temperature in a solution containing 2 gm potassium ferrocyanide, 36 cc distilled water and 4 cc concentrated hydrochloric acid (*ca.* 1.2 N).
4. Rinse in distilled water.
5. Counterstain 2 minutes in 0.2% safranin O or basic fuchsin in 1% acetic acid.
6. Wash in 1% acetic acid.
7. Dehydrate with 95% and 100% alcohols, 100% alcohol + xylene; clear in 2 changes of xylene and mount in polystyrene or other nonreducing resin (p. 97).

Results: Reaction sites, blue or green; nuclei, red; background, pink. Freshly formed deposits of iron pigment react well with the acetic variant and are less likely to be dissolved out. Older deposits may require the stronger acid for adequate reaction. See also p. 433 for the demonstration of hematite and other highly insoluble iron. Heating to 80°C in the ferrocyanide, as in the Abbott variant or even 60°C, is apt to produce a finely granular, blue deposit throughout the section. I have abandoned the practice of heating ferro- or ferricyanide reagents for iron. The Abbott variant was quoted in the eighth edition of Mallory and Wright; the other references are Bunting, *Stain Techn.* 24:109, 1949; Highman, *Arch. Path.* 33:937, 1942; Gomori, *Am. J. Path.* 12:655, 1936.

Recent experiments indicate that the optimal pH for the ferrocyanide reaction may be about pH 1.5 Cytosiderins of intestinal epithelia and of liver cells appear to be sensitive to more acid solutions. Such solutions as in Highman's methods for refractory iron ore dusts or Gomori's 1.2 N HCl solution or even 1 N HCl may completely remove these pigments, and even the 0.125 N HCl concentration traditionally used may give blurred borders to granules both of cytosiderin and of the phagocyte pigments hemosiderin and pseudomelanosis pigment. At high pH levels (7–5) all these pigments retain their native yellow brown colors, even on prolonged exposures. At pH 3–4 a variable proportion reacts with green to blue colors.

The variant of this reaction currently in use in my laboratory in the study of hepatic and intestinal epithelial cytosiderins as well as the phagocyte pigments hemosiderin and aposiderin, pseudomelanosis and melanosis coli pigments, and natural and experimental enterosiderosis of guinea pigs conforms to the foregoing requirements.

Lillie's 1964 Technic for the Prussian Blue and Turnbull's Blue Reactions for Fe^{+++} and Fe^{++}.

1. Bring paraffin or frozen sections to distilled water as usual. Interpose desiderization or decalcification procedures at this point if required.
2. Dissolve 400 mg potassium ferrocyanide [$K_4Fe(CN)_6 \cdot 3H_2O$], yellow crystals, in 40 cc 0.06 N hydrolychloric acid,[1] when testing for Fe^{+++} (ferric iron). For testing for Fe^{++} (ferrous iron), substitute 400 mg of the red crystals of potassium ferricyanide $K_3Fe(CN)_6$. Make this solution fresh daily. Expose sections 1 hour. Positive reactions are often obtained in 10–15 minutes, but the longer exposure should be required before reporting a negative reaction.
3. Wash in 1% acetic acid or 0.01 N HCl.
4a. Stain 5–10 minutes in 0.5% basic fuchsin in 1% acetic acid, wash, dehydrate and mount in polystyrene, Depex, cellulose tricaprate or similar resin. Reducing resins (p. 96) tend to decolorize Prussian blue after a time.
4b. Stain by oil red O technic for concurrent demonstration of lipofuscin in paraffin sections or for lipids in frozen sections (p. 457), wash and mount in Apáthy's gum arabic medium.
4c. Traditionally, counterstain with alum carmine, nuclear fast red or the like.
4d. For critical work omit counterstains, dehydrate in alcohols, clear in xylene and mount in cellulose tricaprate.

Results: Fe^{+++} is demonstrated as dark blue Prussian blue; Fe^{++}, as dark blue Turnbull's blue. With low concentrations of iron, and with reactions done at pH 3–4, the color becomes less intense and appears more green, especially when the weak reaction is due to high pH action on considerable amounts of yellow brown pigment. Variant 4b is particularly useful where iron positive and lipid pigments are present in the same cell, to show whether separate or the same granules are giving the two reactions. If frozen sections are used, the various lipids, as well as iron pigment, may be shown in so-called xanthomata. Polarized light should be used on these tumors, as well, since they may contain birefringent lipids.

[1] 1 cc 12 N (conc.) HCl + 199 cc H_2O.

Other Ferrocyanide Reactions. Uranium potassium ferrocyanide is dark brown; cupric and cuprous ferrocyanides, red brown; cobaltous, gray green; cobaltic, dark brownish red; mercuric, white; lead, yellowish white; nickel, greenish white; silver, yellow; barium, yellow; ferrous, bluish white; manganese, greenish white; and zinc, white. These are most of the insoluble ferrocyanides listed (Lange). Most of these reactions have not been used histologically.

MELANOSIS AND PSEUDOMELANOSIS PIGMENTS OF THE INTESTINE

These are coarsely granular pigments contained in large phagocytic cells of macrophage type occupying in greater or less numbers the stroma of the tips of the villi in the small intestine, especially the duodenum, and the stroma of the cecal, appendiceal and colonic mucosa, particularly surrounding the mouths of the glands, thus giving rise to a tortoise shell appearance when viewed from the surface.

The condition was apparently seen by Virchow (*Virchow Arch. path. Anat.* **1**:379, 1847); it was described by Vogel about 1853 (Hueck, 1912) as pseudomelanosis coli because the black pigment, unlike skin melanin, was soluble in sulfuric acid and contained iron. Solger (Inaug. Diss. Greifswald, 1898; Hueck, 1912) described a morphologically similar condition, in which the pigment lacked demonstrable iron, and named it *melanosis coli*. Pick (*Berlin klin. Wschr.* **48**:840, 1911) and Hueck (1912) sharply distinguished pseudomelanosis and melanosis on the basis of the iron reaction of the former. Lubarsch described the homologous condition in guinea pigs in 1917 (*Berlin kl. Wschr.* **54**:65) and 1922 (*Virchow Arch. path. Anat.* **239**:491). In this species the pigment is not infrequently partly iron positive, a fact which led Lubarsch to the position that transitions existed between melanosis and pseudomelanosis. This was denied by most workers, Hueck (1922) taking the position that where iron negative and iron positive granules existed there were two distinct processes. As long as the iron reactions and their abolition by acid extraction were the sole criteria for identification of pseudomelanosis pigment this position could not be successfully controverted.

While all these studies of the pigment of human melanosis and pseudomelanosis and of the homologous guinea pig pigment were going on, and various theories were evolved as to its (or their) causation, involving such factors as chronic constipation, drug absorption (notably of cascara sagrada), chlorophyll intake (particularly in the guinea pig), a few studies on intestinal iron absorption were made by physiologists and hematologists. Macallum (*J. Physiol.* **16**:268, 1894) fed certain ferrous salts to guinea pigs and observed pronounced uptake of granules of ferric iron in intestinal villus epithelium and in large phagocytic cells in the lamina propria of the mucosa. This condition appeared soonest in the duodenum, but on heavy feeding it extended through the jejunum and much of the ileum. Later studies by Gillman and Ivy (*Gastroenterology* **9**:162, 1940) and by Endicott, Gillman *et al.* (*J. Lab. Clin Med.* **34**:414, 1949) also demonstrated iron but failed to connect it definitely with the iron absorption mechanism. Their studies seem to have been limited to duodenum, cervical and mesenteric lymph nodes, spleen and liver. Other parts of the intestine were not specifically mentioned.

There has been apparently no correlation between these physiological studies and the studies of guinea pig melanosis, at least not up to 1954 (Hieronymi, *Zbl. allg. Path.* **91**:428).

Over the past decade I have made a considerable number of studies of various reactions on human melanosis pigment, on a single case of pseudo-melanosis encountered coincidentally with a carcinoid tumor of the appendix and on guinea pig small and large intestine. Iron pigmentation appears to have been distinctly more frequent in guinea pigs studied at the National Institutes of Health than at Louisiana State University, perhaps because of the practice of giving green fodder in addition to pellets at the former institution. In New Orleans, where pellets only are fed, very small amounts of iron, limited to the duodenum and cecum, are found in most animals.

In general the pigments yield slowly positive diammine and methenamine silver reactions, but a negative reaction to acid silver nitrate. Ferric ferricyanide is reduced, perhaps more strongly in man, but apparently equally in iron positive, iron negative and acid extracted pigment. The periodic acid Schiff and Bauer reactions are positive in iron positive, desiderized iron positive and natively iron negative pigments. Diazo-safranin colors the human and guinea pig pigments dark red to black, regardless of the native presence or absence of ferric iron or of its extraction by sulfuric acid. The postcoupled benzylidene reaction for indoles (tryptophan) is negative in human melanosis and pseudomelanosis and in iron positive and negative pigments of the guinea pig. The sulfuric Nile blue technic gives a strony dark blue coloration which resists immediate acetone extraction. The pigment colors gray green with Sudan black, losing this color in acetone.

The cytosiderin of the duodenal epithelium of the guinea pig appears to lack all the foregoing reactions, at least in readily discernible grade. Like the phagocyte iron, it colors dark blue with hydrochloric or acetic acid ferrocyanide mixtures, black with 0.01% hematoxylin in pH 7 phosphate buffer (0.01 M) on 24–48 hour exposure at 23–25°C, and occasionally and only in the duodenum and cecum gives a moderate dark blue coloration with 1% potassium ferricyanide in 0.125 or 0.01 N hydrochloric acid. The bathophenanthroline reaction (p. 405) has also been reported as positive after reduction.

The pigment produced in guinea pigs fed ferrous carbonate in the stroma of the mucosa of the small and large intestine is iron positive and much larger in amount than in normal animals. In these animals cytosiderin may also be seen in villus epithelium of the jejunum.

OCHRONOSIS

But few modern histochemical observations of this pigment have been reported. Friderich and Nikolowski (*Arch. Derm. Syph.* **192**:273, 1951) recorded gold yellow fluorescence with ultraviolet, basophilia to nuclear fast red (p. 114) and to cresyl violet and negative iron, silver and elastica reactions. Gomori thought the cresyl violet stain the most characteristic one and noted absence of an argentaffin reaction.

Oberndorfer's (*Erg. allg. Path.* 19:47, 1921) review notes the occasional iron staining of cartilage as well as hemosiderosis in the bone marrow. In Moran's material (*Am. J. Path.* 33:591, 1957) I found diffuse ferrocyanide and ferricyanide reactions of the cartilage matrix.

Dr. L. B. Thomas at the Clinical Center, National Institutes of Health, supplied me with material from a case studied there in 1957. In this case the pigment did not reduce diammine silver in 10 minutes to 16 hours at 25°C, even after dithionite reduction (2% $Na_2S_2O_4$ 2 hours), though it did moderately reduce ferric ferricyanide. It stained strongly with 0.05–0.1% Nile blue and azure A at pH 0.9–1, and the Nile blue stain was not removed by acetone (p. 281). The Fe^{++}uptake reaction for melanin was negative. The pigment was unstained by Clara's (Mallory's) hematoxylin and yielded no Prussian blue or Turnbull's blue by treatment with HCl + potassium ferrocyanide or ferricyanide. Extraction with alcohol saturated with picric acid or ammonium picrate did not remove it.

LIPOFUSCINS

These pigments have been variously designated by the terms "wear-and-tear pigment," *Abnutzungspigment,* aging or waste pigment, lipochromes, chromolipoïdes, ceroid, yellow pigment and probably others. The term "lipochrome" is more correctly applied to the readily ether soluble carotinoid pigments which give blue colors with strong sulfuric acid. The term "chromolipoïdes," though of itself unequivocal, I consider too apt to be confused with "lipochrome." The terms "wear-and-tear pigment," and *Abnutzungspigment,* besides being cumbersome, imply a terminal pathologic physiologic process, which may not be so firmly established as was thought a generation ago. The latter objection applies also to "aging" or "waste pigment." The term "lipofuscin," despite its hybrid Greco-Latin etymology, is unequivocal in meaning and is widely used, both in English speaking countries and in Europe and Latin America. The term "ceroid" was introduced to designate a usually, though not always, acid fast sudanophil pigment occurring as granules up to several micra in diameter and as borders of large fat globules in experimental rat liver cirrhosis.

These yellow to brown pigments are generally characterized by sudanophilia which characteristically persists in paraffin imbedded tissue, by a moderate basophilia manifest usually at pH levels above 3 in formalin fixed tissue and by a staining blue with Nile blue at pH 1 and lower which is of oil soluble dye type and is promptly extracted by acetone applied immediately after staining. However, if a 5–10 minute wash in tap water is interposed, the dissolved dye forms salt unions, and acquires the same acetone resistance as usual basic dye stains at pH 4–7.

In addition to these fatty acid reactions, they usually show reactions for ethylene groups, blackening with osmium tetroxide and coloring red in performic and peracetic acid Schiff sequence stains.

In addition they usually reduce ferric salts in the ferric ferricyanide reduction test and blacken slowly in ammoniacal silver solutions without following photographic development; this occurs more rapidly in hot ammoniacal and methenamine silver solutions. Lipofuscins do not reduce acid silver nitrate. They would be expected to give the bromination silver reactions of Norton et al. and of Mukherji et al., but specific reports of these reactions have not been made at this writing. As recorded by Hueck, their basophilia and hence their Nile blue staining is not impaired by 24–48 hour bleaching with hydrogen peroxide. It is often difficult to discern whether they lose any of their often light native color in this process. Their ready oxidation by organic peracids and by potassium permanganate has been referred to above under performic Schiff reaction.

These oxidants, applied beforehand, will prevent other reduction reactions, such as ferric ferricyanide and alkaline silver reductions. Peracetic acid for 2 hours will induce the indophenol reaction for peroxides (p. 187) in some pigments (e.g., ovary).

In regard to diammine silver technics, most of those designed for the impregnation of reticulum commence with a permanganate or similar oxidation which tends to destroy the argentaffin reaction. In the original Maresch technic (p. 530) the exposure to diammine silver is probably too brief for an argentaffin reaction of lipofuscins, though melanins should be demonstrated. The diammine silver method to be used for lipofuscin is the Masson-Hamperl or a basically similar procedure of mine (p. 240).

Lipofuscins also usually give the periodic acid Schiff reaction. Since the oxidation of unsaturated fatty acids with peracids results predominantly in the production of glycolic fatty acids (oleic acid yields 9,10-dihydroxystearic acid, and polyene fatty acids yield corresponding polyglycolic acids), it is not necessary to postulate sugar conjugates to account for this reaction. Of course, galactolipids do exist, but the fatty acids in them are attached to the sphingosine group by an amide linkage, and such lipids would lack the free carboxyl which seems to be identified in the lipofuscins.

Methylation (*ca.* 6 hours, 60°C, 0.1 *N* HCl/methanol) destroys the Nile blue reaction and the basophilia of lipofuscins; saponification (1% KOH/70% alcohol, 20 minutes) restores it; the sudanophilia to oil red O and to Sudan black B is unimpaired by methylation, and methylated lipofuscin stains red to pink with Nile blue. These reactions seem to confirm the fatty acid nature of the lipofuscins.

The resistance to paraffin imbedding mentioned above has long been known. However, it does not, as with the myelins and similar lipids, depend on prior fixation in bichromate, bichromate formalin or formalin. I have fixed fresh human autopsy tissues, brain, spinal cord, ganglia, liver, heart, scalp and axillary sweat glands as well as the ceroid of experimental liver cirrhosis in hot methanol chloroform and demonstrated lipofuscins with Nile blue and with Sudan black B in amounts not strikingly different from those in control formalin fixed tissues. In other instances Carnoy's fluid or methanol chloroform preserves distinctly less pigment than does formaldehyde. Hence for practical purposes the fat solvent fixations are not recommended except for the specific purpose of demonstrating insolubility of usually only a part of the total amount of pigment present in life.

In fluorescence microscopy, the lipofuscins of the liver, adrenal, testicular germinal epithelium and heart muscle give a red brown fluorescence. Hepatic lipofuscin fluoresces brown before extraction with alcohol, and red brown after; and the extract gives the labile green fluorescence of vitamin A (cited from Popper, *Arch. Path.* **41**:766, 1941).

In man lipofuscins do not characteristically give reactions for iron ions, though sudanophilic granules may appear in the same cells together with hemosiderin granules in preparations stained to demonstrate lipofuscin with oil red O and hemosiderin with acidified ferrocyanide (p. 407). This double staining is often readily demonstrable in macrophages in the margins of cerebral hemorrhages ("compound granule cells") and in involuting hemorrhagic corpora lutea. In such cases I do not consider that other reactions of granules in the cells in question can surely be imputed to one or the other of the 2 pigments.

I do not imply here that no sudanophil pigment can be an iron carrier at the same time, but that caution should be exercised in reaching the conclusion that a given pigment falls into that class.

Certain of these pigments, notably that of heart muscle and of the smooth muscle of the seminal vesicles, the intestine and of arteries, are distinctly less sudanophil than those of gland cells, nerve cells and other epithelial structures. Here tinging by orange red Sudan dyes may be difficult to discern, especially with browner pigments, and the use of blue, green and black oil soluble dyes is preferable since green or blue discoloration is easier to discern in a yellow brown pigment than orange.

On the other hand some lipofuscins are quite strongly sudanophil, notably that arising in involuting corpora lutea, in the reticular zone of the adrenal, in neurons of the brain, spinal cord and ganglia. Here it is possible that the clearer red staining with red Sudan dyes correlates with paler native color of the pigment.

In the brain three morphologic subtypes may be distinguished. In the inferior olive and in the subthalamic nucleus one finds single rounded mulberry-like masses lying more or less centrally in the cell, with the nucleus to one side, composed of small rounded globules of dust-like particles of sudanophil material. In the major thalamic nuclei (anterior, lateral, median and pulvinar) one finds about a dozen or two coarse sudanophil globules, perhaps the size of eosinophil leucocyte granules. In most other nerve cells lipofuscin granules are relatively fine, perhaps more accumulated to the central side of the somewhat excentric nucleus but not forming any distinct globular mass.

Some histochemical peculiarities exist as well. The olivary granules tend to stain metachromatically with thionin and azure A at pH 3–3.5 after bromination (p. 185), a peracetic acid oxidation of 10–120 minutes or both in sequence. The coarse thalamic granules seem more likely than other lipofuscins to give a direct Schiff reaction for free aldehyde after relatively brief exposures. The nerve cells of the Gasserian ganglion contain sudanophil granules which stain with azure A at pH 1, rather than at a minimum of pH 3 as with most other nerve cell lipofuscins in formalin fixed tissue. The acid fastness of nerve cell lipofuscin noted by Wolf and Pappenheimer (*J. Neuropath. Exp. Neurol.* 4:402, 1945) has been a rather inconstant characteristic in my hands. Similarly, on extended experience the ceroid of dietary liver cirrhosis of rats has shown acid fastness in varying grade and frequency. Hence this characteristic for separating ceroid from the rest of the lipofuscins seems to break down, and I see no reason for continued use of the word except as a short, readily pronounced synonym for lipofuscin.

Adrenal lipofuscin pigment is seen as variably numerous, usually fine brown granules in the parenchyma cells of the reticular zone of the cortex; and as coarser, usually darker brown granules staining similarly but more deeply and contained in scattered, small interstitial phagocytes in the reticular and inner fascicular zones of the cortex. This pigment is colored green to deep blue in the ferric ferricyanide reduction test (p. 211), blackens with methenamine silver in the argentaffin method (p. 240) and colors reddish brown to red purple with the periodic acid Schiff method (p. 198). The coarser globules, both in phagocytes and in parenchyma cells, are often peracetic acid Schiff (p. 183) positive, and while some granules react even after Carnoy fixation, there appears to be more reaction after bichromate fixations.

The capacity to reduce ferric ferricyanide is abolished by bromination (p. 185) and by oxidation for 1 hour in 5% chromic acid for 20 minutes in 0.5% potassium permanganate; but not by the usual SH blocking reagents, nor by periodic acid. Conversely, the periodic acid Schiff reaction is unaffected by bromination, weakened by chromic acid and permanganate oxidations and abolished by 24 hr acetylation in 40% acetic anhydride/pyridine. It may often be colored with oil soluble dyes after paraffin imbedding. For this purpose the Sudan black method (p. 480) is recommended. Acid fastness may be demonstrated in some cases. Here a night blue or Victoria blue technic may be more convincing than the usual fuchsin method because of the greater difficulty of distinguishing reddish brown from brown than blue or green from brown (p. 578).

It is probable that the adrenal and testicular ceroid pigment described in mice by Firminger (*J. Nat. Cancer Inst.* **13**:225, 1952) is closely related to the foregoing pigment.

Seminal Vesicles. Two pigments are seen in this organ; the one in the smooth muscle which is similar in most respects to that described in intestinal smooth muscle, the other occurring in the epithelial cells between the basally placed nuclei and the cell border against the lumen.

This epithelial pigment stains dark green with Sudan black B and dark blue with Nile blue. The sulfuric Nile blue stain is extracted by immediate application of acetone or alcohol, and the preparations may be restained by the same technic. Methylation for 4–8 hours at 60°C in 0.1 N HCl/methanol prevents the staining by Nile blue, but 32 hours has no effect on the sudanophilia. Slight staining is shown at pH 3, moderate at pH 4, with 0.1–0.05% solutions of thionin or azure A. Diazosafranin (p. 224 colors it dark red brown to reddish black. Saturated iodine/methanol 1 hour at 3°C, acetylation (10% in pyridine 20 hours 25°C), benzoylation (5% benzoyl chloride pyridine 20 hours 25°C), and prolonged methylation (24 hours 60°C but not 4 hours) prevent the azo coupling reaction; performic acid (1 hour) and 2,4-dinitrofluorobenzene (24 hours) do not. The periodic acid Schiff reaction is positive (red purple), blocked by benzoylation or acetylation. Prolonged exposure (3 days) to Schiff reagent yields a direct (autooxidative) positive reaction; the usual 10 minute exposure gives only a faint pink color. The peracetic Schiff reaction is positive.

Treatment for 1–2 hours in 5% CrO_3 at 25°C largely destroys seminal vesicle epithelial pigment, at least in some cases, so that the native brown color disappears and the granules largely or completely lose sudanophilia to Sudan black B. Partial blackening is seen in an hour in diammine silver at 60°C; this would indicate a 25°C reaction in 10–14 hours. The ferric ferricyanide reaction is positive.

The Leydig cell lipofuscin is colored by Sudan black B and by oil red O in paraffin sections of formalin fixed material. It reduces ferric ferricyanide (p. 211). Part of it is acid fast by the Ziehl-Neelsen method, and more retains the basic fuchsin in Mallory's hemofuscin stain (p. 417). Methenamine silver is reduced in the argentaffin technic (p. 240). A minority of the granules are Schiff positive after peracetic acid (p. 184) and on 48 hour exposure to Schiff reagent directly (p. 419). The granules color red purple in the periodic acid Schiff method (p. 198), and the reaction is not impaired by a diastase digestion which removes all glycogen from germinal epithelium. In azure eosin stains the pigment is brown to dark green, and the basophilia is destroyed by 1 day methylation at 25°C (p. 282) but not by methanol extraction for 7 days. Ferrocyanide reactions for iron are negative, and iron hematoxylin is not retained in the eosinophil myelin technic.

A quite similar *pigment* occurs in the epithelial cells of some tubules of the *epididymis*. It is basophilic, readily methylated and periodic acid Schiff positive with or without diastase digestion, as is the cuticular border of the epithelium. It is occasionally Schiff positive on direct 48 hour exposure and after peracetic acid oxidation. It is partly acid fast and positive by the Mallory hemofuscin technic. It reduces methenamine silver and ferric ferricyanide. The ferrocyanide reaction for iron and the Weigert-Lillie myelin tests (p. 304) are negative.

Ovarian lipofuscin pigment occurs in phagocytes near involuting corpora lutea and perhaps in their walls. It colors light to dark green with thionin and with azure eosin. It stains greenish black and greenish blue respectively with Sudan black and spirit blue in paraffin sections (p. 480). The periodic acid Schiff (p. 198) reaction is moderately strongly positive. Part of the granules give the peracetic acid Schiff reaction as well (p. 184). The granules are only partially acid fast with Ziehl-Neelsen and Victoria blue technics (p. 578). In myelin technics iron hematoxylin is retained longer than in nuclei, but not so well as in erythrocytes. The ferrocyanide test for ferric iron is negative (p. 407). Ferric ferricyanide is sometimes reduced (p. 211), the granules becoming green to deep blue; and the granules in part blacken with methenamine silver. With Mallory's hemofuscin method, retention of the dye is inconsistent.

In corpora hemorrhagica, iron positive pigment is also seen, associated with strongly eosinophilic iron negative granular material which is perhaps only partly degraded hemoglobin. It is not clearly evident that the iron positive pigment is necessarily unrelated to the lipofuscin.

It is just in this situation that the ferrocyanide oil red O combined stain (p. 407) is particularly valuable.

Occasionally in later stages some of this pigment reacts for Fe^{++} as well as Fe^{+++}. One employs 1% $K_3Fe(CN)_6$ in 1% acetic or 0.125 N hydrochloric acid, 30–60 minutes at 25°C, washing in 1% acetic, then in alcohols and in xylenes and mounting in cellulose caprate. A fuchsin counterstain may be employed; safranin gives brown crystalline precipitates after ferricyanide methods.

In some instances both the iron positive and the iron negative pigments blacken with methenamine silver (p. 240). Sudan black B and oil red O clearly differentiate the 2 pigments, even when granules of both are present in the same cell. Likewise diammine silver (p. 240) blackens the lipofuscin pigment and not the iron bearing granules. This last is a true argentaffin reaction, since the blackening is observed with no following reduction bath after as little as 2 minutes' exposure to the silver solution.

Although the Winkler-Schultze indophenol synthesis is not usually effected by unaltered ovarian pigment, a preliminary 2 hour oxidation by peracetic acid (p. 187) followed by thorough washing in water causes many ovarian pigment granules to stain a definite blue green with the Winkler-Schultze procedure. This probably indicates the formation of (fatty acid?) peroxides from unsaturated compounds.

Lutein. Apparently the lutein described by Schmorl was a mixture of lipofuscin and a carotenoid pigment (see p. 429).

Cardiac lipofuscin pigment often stains better than the other lipofuscin pigments with oil soluble dyes after paraffin imbedding. Sudan black or oil blue technics are preferred to Sudan IV or oil red O, because a green discoloration of the brown pigment is easier to discern than an orange discoloration. Ferric ferricyanide reduction is observed in some but not all cases. Part of the pigment gives the periodic acid Schiff reaction; a minor proportion gives the peracetic Schiff. The pigment is not definitely acid fast. It does not retain the myelin stain with iron hematoxylin (p. 304). With ferrocyanide it does not react for iron. A minor proportion of the granules reduce methenamine silver (p. 240). When the permanganate oxidation is omitted, a minor proportion of the granules blacken in the diammine silver reticulum technics; after $KMnO_4$ no silver reduction occurs (p. 530). The pigment stains green with thionin at pH 3.

Von Recklinghausen's hemofuscin (*Versamml. Gesell. Natürf. Ärzte* **62:**324, 1889) was described as a finely granular yellow pigment not reacting to the iron methods. It occurred along with hemosiderin in the liver and certain other tissues in cases of hemochromatosis. Hueck classified it as a lipofuscin, as do I, and later Gillman and Gillman (*Arch. Path.* **40:**239, 1945) called it *cytolipochrome.* In frozen sections it may be stained with oil soluble dyes, but according to Endicott and Lillie (*Am. J. Path.* **20:**149, 1944) it does not so stain after paraffin imbedding and is not acid fast. The material of Endicott and Lillie had been stored for several years in formalin; and it is possible that, like myelin, hemofuscin may lose part of its resistance to decolorization on long storage in formalin. However, the hemofuscin in this material still resisted decolorization with alcohol after prolonged staining with basic fuchsin according to Mallory's technic for the demonstration of this pigment.

Mallory's Hemofuscin Method.

1. Fix in Zenker's fluid, alcohol or 10% formalin. Make paraffin or celloidin sections and bring to water as usual, including an iodine sodium thio-sulfate sequence in the case of Zenker fixation.
2. Stain 5–10 minutes in Mallory's alum hematoxylin (p. 174; other alum hematoxylins will serve).
3. Wash well in water.
4. Stain 5–20 minutes in 0.5% basic fuchsin solution in equal volumes of distilled water and 95% alcohol.
5. Wash in water.
6. Differentiate in 95% alcohol.
7. Dehydrate with 100% alcohol, clear in xylene and mount in poly-styrene.

Results: Nuclei, blue; hemofuscin, bright red; melanin and hemosiderin, unstained in their natural browns.

Ceroid is also stained by this procedure, and it is not impossible that various other myelin like substances would be.

Post, Benton, and Breakstone (*Arch. Path.* **52:**67, 1951) report a similar cytoplasmic pigment of normal, predominantly centrolobular *human* liver cells, which is insoluble in water, alcohols, aromatic and aliphatic solvents, acetone, acids and alkalies. It is stained by the Mallory hemofuscin tech-nic and resists alcohol decolorization but is not acid fast. It gives negative reactions by the periodic acid Schiff method, by the ferric ferricyanide reduction test, by the Feulgen technic, by the acid ferrocyanide method for ferric iron, by Stein's methods for bile pigment and by Gomori's alkaline phosphatase method. It resists digestion by ribonuclease, deoxy-ribonuclease, amylase and trypsin. Unlike hemofuscin as characterized by Mallory, it is not dissolved by 5% hydrogen peroxide. It is considered to be otherwise similar to hemofuscin and is thought to be a functional metabolic complex.

In view of the high solubility of rosaniline base in fatty acids (oleic 20%, stearic 15%) recorded in the *Colour Index* as compared with its solubility in ethanol (0.3%), it is suspected that hydrolysis of the rosani-line chloride occurs in this procedure, and that we are probably seeing a differential solubility reaction. This would tend to support Hueck's views as to the lipofuscin nature of this pigment.

Intestinal Smooth Muscle Pigment. This condition is seen occasionally as a dark brown coloration of the muscularis of the ileum, and appears to have been relatively commoner in the earlier German autopsy experi-ence. Its causation is obscure.

The pigment occurs in formalin fixed tissue as fine to coarse droplets in the muscularis and as coarser globules in macrophages in the sub-mucosa. The muscularis mucosae is not involved.

The pigment colors moderate gray green with Sudan black and moderately deep greenish blue with sulfuric Nile blue. The latter reaction is prevented by 6 hour methylation in 0.1 N HCl methanol and is restored by demethylation (saponification) in 1% potassium hydroxide in 70% alcohol for 20 minutes.

In 1/5000 azure A (0.7 mM) it stained strongly at pH 4 and above, moderately at pH 3, and remained almost unstained at pH 1–2. The pigment reacts slowly and lightly with Schiff reagent, attaining a fair pink color in 24 hours, similar to that obtained after 10 minute oxidation in peracetic acid. A 2 hour peracetic acid oxidation followed by 10 minutes in Schiff reagent yields a red color. A similar sequence of 10 minutes each in 1% periodic acid, Schiff reagent gives a dark red purple.

With a myelin procedure a brown to black color is retained when erythrocytes are still black and nuclei are decolorized.

Acid silver nitrate (pH 4) is not appreciably reduced in 2 hours directly or after dithionite reduction. This reaction excludes melanin. Ammoniacal silver is strongly reduced in 24 hours but is only slightly reduced in 3 hours. Hot methenamine silver (60°C) is reduced in 3 hours. The ferric ferricyanide test is positive.

The ferrous ion uptake reaction for melanins is very faint and is to be regarded as negative. Ferro- and ferricyanide reactions for Fe^{+++} and Fe^{++} ions are negative, excluding the hemosiderins.

Oxidation by potassium bichromate at pH 2.2 gives no color reaction (bilirubin is said to give green).

Moderate acid fastness to the Ziehl-Neelsen method is shown.

Only a yellow color is seen with diazotized p-nitroaniline; a deep red purple is seen with diazosafranin and is prevented by prior acetylation. The Morel-Sisley reaction for tyrosine is completely negative (Paneth cells reacted strongly).

The postcoupled benzylidene reaction for tryptophan is negative.

The pigment remains strongly basophil to azure eosin after 6 hour peptic digestion, although basic protein is largely destroyed.

The reactions parallel closely those observed in the more familiar and much more frequent smooth muscle pigment seen in human seminal vesicles.

The carboxylic acid and aldehyde nature of the pigment, together with the presence of ethylenic and 1,2-glycol groupings, and the colorability with fat and fatty acid stains point to a lipofuscin pigment.

CEROID

Since the original description of ceroid as an often, but inconstantly acid fast brown pigment occurring in experimental liver cirrhosis of rats (Lillie, Daft and Sebrell, *Pub. Health Rep.* **56**:1255, 1941; and Edwards and White, *J. Nat. Cancer Inst.* **2**:147, 1941) and mice (Lee, *J. Nat. Cancer Inst.* **11**:339, 1950), similar acid fast pigments have been described in vitamin E deficiency of rats and monkeys, which apparently arise in muscle tissue. A similar pigment apparently evolves from adrenal and testicular Leydig cell lipofuscins (Firminger, *J. Nat. Cancer Inst.* **13**:225, 1952).

As characterized by Endicott and Lillie (*Am. J. Path.* **20**:149, 1944), ceroid possesses a bronze brown color in gross preparations, and occurs microscopically as yellow globules 1–20 μ in diameter, located sometimes in liver cells, most often in large phagocytes, and also as rims of acid fast material surrounding large fat globules. Fluorescence microscopy of frozen sections shows a greenish yellow fluorescence which fades to pale yellow. In paraffin sections the fluorescence is golden brown. It retains myelin stains, acid fast stains, and Mallory's hemofuscin stain. It usually stains green in the azure eosin technic (p. 162), and is stained by oil soluble dyes, both in frozen and paraffin sections. The oil soluble dyes are readily removed by acetone, alcohol and the like; and preparations may be restained and decolorized repeatedly. With the usual brief hemalum and iron chloride hematoxylin stains it does not color. Though it is Gram negative, if crystal violet staining is prolonged or accelerated by heat, the violet is retained with or without iodine treatment.

Ceroid is insoluble in dilute acids and alkalies but is saponified by boiling 10% NaOH (gross chemical procedure), and fatty acids are precipitated from the solution by acid. It is insoluble in alcohols, acetone, ether, aliphatic and aromatic hydrocarbons, chloroform, carbon tetrachloride, pyridine, acetic anhydride, glycols and glycerol. It is not bleached by permanganate, chromic acid, hydrogen peroxide, or bromine or chlorine water.

It is blackened by osmium tetroxide, blackens slowly with diammine silver carbonate (p. 528). Most of it fails to reduce ferric ferricyanide; but definite deposits of blue pigment are formed in isolated globules and foamy masses. The Prussian blue (Perls) reaction is usually negative; but iron positive pigment is sometimes associated with it, and necrotic foci containing ceroid exhibit both iron and calcium deposition.

Much of the pigment is colored red purple in the periodic acid Schiff procedure (p. 198), but often clear, unstained, small globules are seen inclosed in foamy red purple masses. The peracetic and performic acid Schiff reactions are also positive in small globules, in part of the foamy masses and in some of the large globules. In parallel preparations it appears as if part of the material gave the HIO_4 reaction, part the CH_3CO_3H reaction and part both reactions.

Bromination prevents the peracetic Schiff reaction. Benzoylation or acetylation prevents the periodic Schiff reaction and retards but does not prevent the peracetic Schiff reaction. Ceroid is colored red by 2–3 day exposure to Schiff reagent, and yellow by similar long exposures to phenylhydrazine.

The basophilia of ceroid is abolished by benzoylation but not by bromination. Ferric ferricyanide reduction is prevented by benzoylation but not by bromination. Acid fastness is unaffected by bromination, benzoylation or strong halogen acids. Hydrochloric and hydriodic acids (16 hours, sp. gr. 1.19 and 1.70 respectively) reverse the peracetic and periodic acid Schiff reactions but do not destroy acid fastness or sudanophilia. Exposure to 5% phenylhydrazine or to molar aniline chloride for 24 hours prevents both the peracetic Schiff reaction and the Schiff reaction which occurs directly in 2–3 days. The periodic acid Schiff reaction is unaffected by these blockades.

Sudan Black B Methods for Lipofuscins. In this case any of the commonly used Sudan black technics may be used. Since the lipid substance under study is quite insoluble, the usual objection that the 70% alcohol and the propylene glycol technics remove much of the birefringent (steroid) lipid and perhaps part of the phospholipids as well does not apply.

I usually use the following Sudan black B method.[1]

Dilute 20 cc saturated Sudan black B in absolute alcohol with an equal volume of distilled water. Let stand 10–20 minutes and filter.

1. Bring paraffin sections to water. Attached cryostat sections may be used if lipid solubility tests are contemplated. Lipofuscin is at least partly insoluble in an equal volume methanol chloroform mixture (ranging from 2:1 to 1:2) at 25–60°C for as long as 2–3 days.
2. For a Feulgen nucleal counterstain, hydrolyze sections in 1 N HCl at 60°C. With routinely fixed formalin material in paraffin sections the optimal time varies between 10 and 20 minutes; 3 minutes is enough for films or cryostat sections fixed a few minutes in methanol.
3. Transfer to Schiff reagent for 10–30 minutes; the 0.5% solutions take longer than the 1%, especially if they are not fresh.
4. Wash in 3 changes of 0.5% sodium metabisulfite ($Na_2S_2O_5$) and 10 minutes in running water. I use the bisulfite washes to avoid any oxidative recoloration of leucofuchsin by chlorinated city water.
5. Stain 10–20 minutes in the filtered Sudan black.
6. Wash in water and mount in Apáthy's gum syrup or in glycerol gelatin.

To confirm the oil soluble nature of the lipofuscin stain, decolorize in acetone (20 seconds to 5 minutes), examine in water or glycerol, wash

[1] Note, 6/10/64. A strong lipofuscin stain without precipitation on sections is produced by 30 minutes' staining in Sudan black B 500 mg, ethylene glycol 30 cc, ethanol 30 cc, and distilled water 40 cc.

and restain (step 5). Lipofuscins decolorize by acetone and may be restained by the original technic. This decolorization and restaining may be repeated several times without evident loss in either stainability or decolorizability.

OTHER COMBINED PIGMENT STAINS

The oil red stain for lipofuscins has also been successfully combined with the diammine silver method on central nervous tissues, to stain the neuromelanin of the substantia nigra and locus coeruleus in black or very dark brown and the nerve cell lipofuscins in nearby nuclei in red. The exposure to ammoniacal silver is purposely kept short to avoid the reduction of silver by lipofuscins which ensues on prolonged exposures.

We make the diammine silver by placing 2 cc 28% ammonia in a 100 cc beaker and then adding about 35 cc 5% silver nitrate, quickly at first, shaking between each addition to dissolve the dark brown silver oxide, and cautiously in the last 5 cc, adding just enough silver to produce a faint but definite permanent turbidity.

1. Paraffin sections are brought through xylene and alcohols to 2 changes of distilled water.
2. Immerse 15 minutes in diammine silver at 20–25°C in the dark.
3. Wash in distilled water and immerse 5 minutes in 0.2% gold chloride ($HAuCl_4$). The gold toning is included to increase stability of the melanin stain.
4. Rinse in distilled water and place in 0.2 M (5%) sodium thiosulfate for 2 minutes. Wash 10 minutes in running water.
5. Stain with oil red O or by the Feulgen Sudan black B technic, as above in the normal technics. Mount in Apáthy's gum syrup, Farrants's gum arabic or glycerol gelatin.

For cutaneous and ocular melanins the ammoniacal silver step may be decreased to 2 minutes, or it may be replaced by an hour in 2% silver nitrate in pH 4 acetate buffer. This makes the silver reaction more nearly specific for true melanins.

The Feulgen Sudan black B variant should give red nuclei, black neuromelanins, dark green lipofuscin and lighter green myelin and red corpuscles. In the oil red O technic the black neuromelanin contrasts well with the red lipofuscin. Although I have not specifically tested the use of an alum hematoxylin nuclear stain in this combined procedure, I believe it should work.

The more sensitive ferric ferricyanide reaction can not thus be successfully combined with oil red O for lipofuscin. These reducing pigments also color blue with the ferric ferricyanide reaction, leaving the oil red O effect visible only as an orange staining of myelinated fibers.

Such technics as these should prove useful in helping to resolve the question of whether certain ganglion cell pigments are "lipomelanins" or a mixture of separate granules of lipofuscin and neuromelanin. The production or storage of multiple organic substances of a secretory nature in the same cells seems quite well documented in other locations; *e.g.*, the presence of heparin, histamine and serotonin in mast cells, along with a number of enzymes.

THE MELANINS

A variety of pigments have at one time or another been classed under this heading. The first, to which the name properly belongs, is the black to brown pigment found in epidermis, hair follicles and hairs and in cutaneous melanoma. The iron containing, acid soluble pigment of human red hair is excluded, as is the yellow, readily alkali soluble pigment of hair follicles and hairs seen in guinea pigs (trichoxanthin, *J. Histochem.* **5:**346, 1957) and possibly in mice (so-called "phaeomelanin," which is a misnomer, for this pigment is yellow, *xanthos*, not brown or dusky, *phaios*).

Second, we include the yellowish brown to black epithelial and connective tissue pigments of the iris, ciliary body, choroid and retinal pigment epithelium. The last occurs in rod shaped granules and may be chemically and functionally as well as morphologically distinct. It is sometimes called *fuscin*. The pigment of ocular melanoma appears to derive from that of the choroid and is histochemically similar to it.

Also quite similar histochemically to choroidal pigment is the melanin occurring in patches in the piarachnoid in some human brains. It is often quite prominent in ruminant brains and is seen in other mammals. The pigment found in vertebrate chromatophores in the derma and elsewhere and in blue nevi is also classed as melanin.

The pigment found normally in the human substantia nigra, locus coeruleus and nucleus dorsalis vagi is histochemically distinct from ocular, pial and cutaneous melanins and has been called recently *neuromelanin*. It occurs with less constancy and lesser amounts in other primates, including Old World monkeys as well as the great apes, and has been reported also in Canidae and Felidae.

The brown to black pigment occurring in neurons of certain sensory nerve root ganglia and in some sympathetic ganglia is (or are) sometimes classed with lipofuscins, sometimes with melanins. The histochemical reactions applied to them have not been, perhaps, sufficiently critical to give a definitive answer to this question.

Finally the iron free phase of the granular phagocyte pigment of the intestinal mucosa of man has also been classed as melanin by some workers, as lipofuscin by others and as a substance closely related to the iron bearing pseudomelanosis and villus melanosis pigments. This pigment has been discussed in full under the last mentioned category (p. 408).

Much chemical study has been devoted to the elementary analysis and destructive fractionation of melanins isolated by enzymatic or alkali digestion of black hair and wool, from epidermis of Negroes, from eyes of various species (mostly oxen) and from melanomata of cutaneous and ocular origin in man and the common melanoma of white horses. These melanins were alkali soluble acidic substances of undetermined molecular weight, containing 50–60% C, 4–6.5% H, 9–14% N and a percentage of S ranging from 1 to 12%. The balance was assigned to O. That the sulfur was not assignable to contaminating keratins is shown by its presence in tumor and eye melanins. Amino acid analyses have been few; Serra (*Nature* **157**:771, 1946) identified chromatographically in hydrolysates of alkali extracted hair melanin the amino acids arginine, histidine, tyrosine, tryptophan, cystine, cysteine and methionine, as well as an acid insoluble black "melanoid" residue. Block *et al.* (*Amino Acid Handbook*, Charles C Thomas, Publishers, Springfield, Ill., 1956) do not list melanin.

The study of animal tyrosinase started around 1902; Otto von Fürth and his students were prominent in this work. In 1917 Bloch introduced the dopa reaction into the study of cutaneous melanogenesis. The dopa reaction is not, properly speaking, a reaction of any of the melanins. It is rather the enzyme histochemical reaction which produces a dark brown pigment from L-3,4-dihydroxyphenylalanine (dopa), the first oxidation product of tyrosine. The enzyme tyrosinase, in the presence of oxygen, oxidizes tyrosine slowly to dopa, and oxidizes that substance more rapidly to an indolic quinone or semiquinone-like substance which possesses a deep brown color and is considered to be the coloring matter of melanin.

Since decarboxylation is accomplished at stage VII, the acid nature of the melanoprotein is presumed to depend on coincident oxidation of cystine residues to protein bound cysteic acid. Lorincz (chap. 22, pp. 515–563, in Rothman's *Physiology and Biochemistry of the Skin*, University of Chicago Press, Chicago, 1954) adds step VIII to the original Raper (*Biochem. J.* **21**:89, 1927) sequence, considering the final state to be a quinone. I (*J. Histochem.* **5**:325, 1957) added IX, to account for reducing capacity still present in melanogenic sites. Mild oxidations: I_2, H_5IO_6, $K_2Cr_2O_7$, $FeCl_3$ *et al.* carry IX to VIII, while dithionite reduction carries melanin in stage VIII or IX to VII. Melanin in stage VII can be acetylated with consequent marked retardation of acid silver reduction. Acetylation is without effect on the reactions of native or oxidized melanins. Stage VII presents very rapid metal reduction reactions, like those of isolated catechols *in vitro.*

The dopa reaction occurs in skin, especially in stages of melanogenesis, as after radiation and in initial fetal and infantile pigment production.

The Raper Cycle

I $+O \rightarrow$ II $-2H \rightarrow$ III

Tyrosine   Dopa   Dopa quinone

$\rightarrow$ IV $-2H \rightarrow$ V $\rightarrow$ VI $-CO_2 \rightarrow$

VII $-2H \rightarrow$ VIII   VII $+$ VIII $\rightarrow$ IX

Raper final   Lorincz quinone   Lillie quinhydrone

It is reported also in the fetal eye in early stages, and after irradiation. It occurs in cutaneous melanoma and probably also in melanoma of ocular origin, though I do not recall having found a report of the latter. I have made several trials of the dopa reaction on infant locus coeruleus and substantia nigra, within the period of pigment appearance, with consistently negative results.

Foster has reported the formation of the yellow pigment of mouse skin when tryptophan is used as substrate in place of tyrosine (*J. Exp. Zool.* 117:214, 1951). In my hands guinea pig hair follicles containing trichoxanthin are dopa negative, though Langerhans cells in the same area and black or brown pelage areas in the same animal give positive dopa reactions (*J. Histochem.* 5:346, 1957).

Metal Reduction Reactions. These reactions depend on the reducing capacity of the melanins.

The crucial histochemical test for cutaneous, ocular and pial melanins is the reduction of 0.1 *M* silver nitrate (1.7%) in pH 4 0.1 *M* acetate buffer in 1 hour or less at 25°C in the dark. This is followed by 1–2 minutes' washing in distilled water and in 0.2 *M* thiosulfate (5% hypo) and then in running water (10 minutes).

This procedure blackens guinea pig skin melanin in as little as 10 minutes. Monkey and human skin pigments require 30–60 minutes.

The trichoxanthin of yellow guinea pig skin is resistant to acid silver nitrate, requiring 18–24 hours at 25°C to acquire a deep red brown color, and 24 hours at 60°C for complete blackening. Neuromelanin of the human substantia nigra is similarly resistant, requiring 3 days in the dark at 25°C for blackening.

Masson's ammoniacal silver technic, which I simplify by placing 2 cc 28% ammonia in a 100 cc beaker and adding gradually 35–40 cc 5% $AgNO_3$, swirling to redissolve the dark brown silver oxide and stopping at the point where the solution remains faintly turbid or opalescent, is more rapid and much less specific. Although it blackens the skin and eye melanins in about 2 minutes, it also blackens neuromelanin in 2–15 minutes; trichoxanthin may blacken in 2 minutes or may completely and irreversibly disappear, by reason of its alkali solubility. With longer exposures (8–24 hours), lipofuscins, intestinal melanosis-pseudomelanosis pigment, hematoidin, bile pigment, enterochromaffin and other substances also blacken.

The same is true of Gomori's methenamine silver used alone as an argentaffin reagent (p. 240).

The ferric ferricyanide reaction (p. 211) is also sensitive but relatively nonspecific, and being an acid reagent it preserves trichoxanthin well.

Blockades. The foregoing metal reduction reactions are prevented by moderately active oxidants: 2% $FeCl_3$ 1 day 24°C, 5% CRO_3 3–30 minutes, 5% $K_2Cr_2O_7$ 2–3 days, 1% H_5IO_6 3–6 hours for ferric ferricyanide, less for diammine silver, 10% I_2 in methanol 1–2 days. If after these oxidations reduction for 1 hour in 1% sodium dithionite ($Na_2S_2O_4$) is applied, the metal reduction reactions are restored. This is true for melanins, trichoxanthin and neuromelanins.

After dithionite reduction, melanin, but not neuromelanin or trichoxanthin reduces silver nitrate at pH 4 in 1–2 minutes. This behavior is observed with or without a preceding oxidation.

Acetylation is without effect on the metal reduction reactions of native melanin, but after dithionite reduction acetylation greatly retards (18–24 hr) the pH 4 silver nitrate reaction. Acetylated catechol is similarly retarded in its reduction of acid silver nitrate.

One point about these oxidation studies is that dichromate or dichromate sublimate fixations are apt to prevent the metal reduction reactions.

In combinations of the silver reaction with oil red staining or the periodic acid Schiff reaction, the silver reduction should be done first and followed by 10–15 minute gold toning in 0.2% $HAuCl_4$ after thiosulfate removal of unreduced silver, to render the metal stain more permanent.

Other Reactions of the Melanins. Cutaneous and ocular melanins and trichoxanthin color dark green on 20 minute staining in 0.05% azure A at pH 1. Methylation in 0.1 N HCl/methanol at 60°C is resisted 24 hours or more, as with the cysteic acid of oxidized hair cortex. Neuromelanin does not stain below pH 3, where only a weak green color appears. Strong staining occurs at pH 4 and above.

After prolonged (24–32 hours at 25°C or 2 hours at 60°C) exposure to weak (1 mM) solutions of ferrous salts at pH 4–5, melanin, trichoxanthin and neuromelanin color blue green and enterochromaffin colors blue when reacted with ferricyanide at pH 1 (cf. p. 427). Lipofuscins and heme pigments do not react (*Arch. Path.* **64:**100, 1957, *J. Histochem.* **9:** 44, 1961).

Melanin and trichoxanthin give no tryptophan or tyrosine reactions. The Gibbs reaction for phenols is negative, as is Clara's staining with dilute unmordanted hematoxylin at pH 7 (1–2 days). No azo coupling is demonstrated with diazosafranin. Neuromelanin reacts moderately to the periodic acid Schiff reaction; cutaneous and ocular melanins and trichoxanthin do not.

Melanins are insoluble in water, alcohol, fat solvents and dilute acids and alkalies. Though freed from the choroidal and retinal epithelial cells and partly dispersed as granules and rods by peptic and tryptic digestions, the individual granules appear to resist digestion long after cytoplasms and nuclei have disappeared. Likewise, digestion with ribonuclease, with malt diastase and with chondromucinase is resisted. Whether the alkali removal mentioned by Mallory is actually a solution of the pigment or is a dispersal from digestion of the cytoplasmic matrix, I am still uncertain.

Melanin is slowly bleached by 10% hydrogen peroxide; it may require 1–2 days, and is not visibly affected by 3% peroxide in 24 hours. Although slow bleaching with ferric chloride is reported, a 24 hour exposure to a 1% solution has no evident effect. Similarly, no evident bleaching occurs with 24 hour exposures to 1% sodium iodate in 0.3% nitric acid, to 3% potassium bichromate, to Weigert's iodine, to 0.5% sodium bisulfite, to 5% hydroquinone, to normal hydrochloric acid, to 5% formic acid, to 5% trichloroacetic acid or to 5% acetic acid. Appreciable though often irregular and unpredictable bleaching occurs with 5% chromic acid (CrO_3) in 1–3 hours, and with 0.5% potassium permanganate in intervals of 20 minutes up to several hours. Chlorine water bleaches melanin, though treatment with 1 cc bromine in 39 cc carbon tetrachloride for an hour does not. The most pronounced bleaching occurs with performic and peracetic acids (p. 183), even on 1–2 hour exposures, and with 16–24 hour exposures ocular melanin may be completely removed. This effect may be due to the large amount of hydrogen peroxide present in these reagents. Even 30 hours' exposure to 0.03 M periodic acid does not bleach ocular melanin. (See Table 11-2.)

Melanins are commonly said to reduce osmium tetroxide. Melanin remains the same shade of dark brown after the ammonium sulfide treatment used in the Gomori Ca-Co alkaline phosphatase method (p. 317).

Ocular melanins do not evidently tinge with oil soluble dyes. They do not retain the iron hematoxylin of the Weigert-Smith-Dietrich type technics, nor the basic fuchsin of the Mallory hemofuscin or Ziehl-Neelsen

TABLE 11-2. BLEACHING OF MELANINS

	Skin melanin	Tricho-xanthin	Ocular melanins	Neuro-melanin
0.25% KMnO$_4$, 25°C......	20 min	0–5 min	2–4 hr	1–5 min
70% HNO$_3$, 25°C........	6–8 hr	30 sec	3–4 hr	4–6 min
5% CrO$_3$, 25°C..........	2 hr	15 min	......	1 hr (40°C)
1% H$_5$IO$_6$, 60°C..........	4 hr	Unchanged, 4 hr		
0.05 M HIO$_4$, 25°C........	Partial, 4–24 hr	Unchanged, 24 hr		
Bromine water, hr.........	8	3		
Peracetic acid, 25°C.......	2–12 hr	1 hr (3°C)		

acid fast methods. Lack of acid fastness is also specifically recorded for cutaneous melanin and for that of the nerve cells of the substantia nigra. Perls's Prussian blue reaction with ferrocyanide is negative.

I have recorded (*J. Histochem.* **5**:346, 1957) bleaching of cutaneous and ocular melanins, neuromelanin and trichoxanthin as follows. The experiments on eyes and brains were only fragmentary and have not been reported previously.

It is of interest that prior fixation in bichromate fixatives prevents the prompt CrO$_3$ bleaching.

Neuromelanin gives negative iron reactions with ferrocyanide (p. 407) and with the Tirmann-Schmelzer technic. Schiff reactions are negative on direct brief or prolonged exposure, after warm normal hydrochloric acid hydrolysis (Feulgen procedure, p. 149) and after oxidation with KMnO$_4$, or CrO$_3$ (Casella, Bauer procedures, p. 199) or with peracetic acid (ethylene reaction, p. 184). However, peracetic acid oxidation for 2 hours causes the pigment to become oxidase positive by the Winkler-Schultze indophenol method (p. 187). This indicates probable formation of peroxides from unsaturated compounds. Neuromelanin is not tinged by Sudan black B or oil red O. Its color is not altered in myelin stains differentiated to the point where nuclei are decolorized but red corpuscles are still black. Osmium tetroxide is not evidently reduced in formalin fixed tissue. The pigment does not retain fuchsin in the Mallory hemofuscin or Ziehl-Neelsen acid fast stains.

Fe^{++} Ion Uptake Reaction of Melanin (R. D. Lillie). *Technic.* Avoid all chromate fixatives. Other fixations, mercurial, formaldehyde, alcoholic, etc., are well tolerated.

1. Paraffin sections: deparaffinize and hydrate as usual.
2. Immerse for 1 hour in 2.5% ferrous sulfate (FeSO$_4$·7H$_2$O).
3. Wash 20 minutes in distilled water (4 changes).

4. Immerse 30 minutes in 1% potassium ferricyanide $[K_3Fe(CN)_6]$ in 1% acetic acid.
5. Wash in 1% acetic acid.
6. If desired, counterstain 5 minutes in Van Gieson's picric acid, acid fuchsin mixture (100 mg acid fuchsin: 100 cc saturated aqueous picric acid solution). Do not use hematoxylin.
7. Dehydrate in 2 changes each of 95% and 100% alcohol, clear in alcohol xylene (50:50) and 2 changes of xylene.
8. Mount in synthetic resin. If not counterstained, use cellulose caprate.

Results: Melanins of skin, eye and pia, neuromelanin and trichoxanthin, dark green; background, faint greenish or unstained; with Van Gieson, usual red collagen, yellow and brown muscle and cytoplasm. Lipofuscins and heme pigments are unreactive.

Chapter 12

Metals, Anions, Exogenous Pigments

Carotenes. The carotenoid pigments are defined by Lison (1960) as long chain hydrocarbons with conjugated double bonds. They range from red to yellow in color.

They are insoluble in water, glycerol, dilute acids and alkalies and formalin. They are soluble in cold alcohol, more so in chloroform, acetone, xylene, toluene, benzene, petroleum ether and carbon bisulfide. They give a green fluorescence in ultraviolet light.

They are quickly decolorized by oxygen and by dilute chromic acid or potassium bichromate. They yield a transient blue color with concentrated sulfuric acid and a brown green to violet or black color with Weigert's iodine. Ferric chloride and hydrogen peroxide solution decolorize them, but they are said not to reduce diammine silver.

Lison believes that the term *lipochrome* applied to these pigments should be abandoned. Inasmuch as it is also applied by some workers to the lipofuscins, I agree thoroughly. Its continued use produces confusion.

Vitamin A. For demonstration of vitamin A, Popper (*Arch. Path.* 31: 766, 1941) recommends brief fixation in 10% formalin, preferably in the cold and not over 10–12 hours. Blocks are cut 3 mm thick. Frozen sections are examined in water within 3 hours of cutting, with ultraviolet light at 365 mμ in a fluorescence microscope (p. 13). Vitamin A presents a brilliant green fluorescence which fades quite promptly in 10–60 seconds or more, depending upon the amount present.

Vitamin A is soluble in fat solvents and occurs dissolved in body fats as well as in liver cells, Kupffer cells, lutein cells, adrenal cortex and other places. It resists treatment with 0.1 N hydrochloric acid, 0.1 N ammonium hydroxide and saturated sodium dithionite (hydrosulfite) ($Na_2S_2O_4$) solution. The fluorescence of vitamin B_2 is destroyed by the last. Hydrogen peroxide produces a blue fluorescence of fats but does not destroy the green vitamin A fluorescence.

Vitamin A, like the carotenes, gives a green to blue color with sulfuric acid. It gives a blue color with antimony trichloride.

Riboflavin. Gomori quotes a method of Chèvremont and Comhaire. After reduction of riboflavin to leucoflavin it reoxidizes in air to red rhodoflavin.

Place frozen sections of formalin fixed tissue in 1–2% hydrochloric acid containing enough zinc dust to give a steady evolution of hydrogen, and stir about gently for 30 minutes. Then wash in water and expose to air in a shallow vessel for several hours. Mount in glycerol gelatin. Flavoproteins are stained red. I have small faith in the efficiency of hydrogen reduction away from the immediate site of nascence. Gomori suggests replacing the hydrogen reduction with sodium dithionite.

Vitamin C. For the demonstration of ascorbic acid, Deane and Morse (*Anat. Rec.* **100**:127, 1948) recommended immediate fixation for 30 minutes in the acetic alcohol silver nitrate solution of Barnett and Bourne (*J. Anat.* **75**:251, 1940), followed by transfer directly to an acid fixing solution for 2 hours, then overnight washing in running water.

The fluid of Barnett and Bourne was ambiguously stated to be a "saturated solution of silver nitrate in ethyl alcohol (5 parts), water (4 parts) and glacial acetic acid (1 part)" and to give a concentration of slightly less than 10% silver nitrate. Since silver nitrate is only slightly soluble in pure alcohol, it seems that saturation in the mixture was meant. The following emended formula is suggested: Silver nitrate 10 gm, distilled water 40 cc. Dissolve, and add glacial acetic acid 10 cc and 100% alcohol 50 cc. This fluid does not keep.

The acid fixing solution contained sodium thiosulfate crystals ($Na_2S_2O_3 \cdot 5H_2O$) 5 gm, sodium bisulfite ($NaHSO_3$) 1 gm, distilled water 100 cc.

After washing, the material is dehydrated, cleared, infiltrated and imbedded in paraffin as usual, and sectioned at 5 μ.

Deane and Morse deparaffinized and mounted for examination in the unstained state; or counterstained with paracarmine (p. 179) or hematoxylin and eosin (p. 176).

Barnett and Bourne varied the procedure by simply washing in distilled water after fixation, imbedding and sectioning, and then toning sections 4–10 minutes in "very dilute gold chloride solution," fixing in sodium thiosulfate solution 4–10 minutes, followed by dehydration, clearing and mounting.

Cater (*J. Path. Bact.* **63**:269, 1951) claimed superior results by a 3 hour fixation in aqueous 10% silver nitrate, 10% acetic acid solution, followed by 3 changes of distilled water of 30 minutes each and a 90 minute bath in 5% sodium thiosulfate, all in the dark. Washing in water is presumed. Dehydration, clearing, paraffin imbedding and sectioning at 5 μ were followed by a light counterstain with neutral red.

I have not used these procedures.

Clara (*Mikroskopie* **7**:387, 1952), though admitting the effectiveness of the acid silver nitrate method in demonstrating ascorbic acid, points out that a number of other substances also reduce silver under the prescribed conditions. He names melanin, pheochrome substance, enterochromaffin substance, pancreatic alpha granules and the neurosecretory granules of the supraoptic and paraventricular nuclei of the thalamus.

Langeron cites Massa's (*Soc. Pharm. Montpelier* **5**:14, 1945) use of the ferric ferricyanide reduction test (p. 211) for the demonstration of ascorbic acid in plant tissues. Massa made up his potassium ferricyanide at 0.2% and his ferric chloride at 3.24%, both in 15% acetic acid, and mixed equal volumes at the time of using. The reaction time should be restricted to 5–10 minutes. Because of the solubility and diffusibility of ascorbic acid, only fresh tissue can be used.

Ascorbic acid gave immediate blue coloration; phenols, tannoids, anthocyanins and flavones gave green colors or green black precipitates. He noted the reaction of glutathione and cysteine (p. 209), and used the nitroprusside reaction as a control. The reaction of carotenoids, tocopherols and vitamin A was noted as much slower than that of ascorbic acid.

The method should be applicable to Adamstone-Taylor or Linderström-Lang frozen sections of fresh animal tissue, transferred directly into the freshly mixed reagent from the microtome. Even brief drying should be avoided.

Pneumonyssus Pigment. Sometimes difficult to distinguish from carbon is the pigment deposited in monkey lungs about cysts and remnants of the acarid parasite *Pneumonyssus foxi*. This includes particles of a rather deep brown color which stain practically black with azures. However, examination of unstained preparations reveals angular black particles, brown granules and doubly refractile needles.

Exogenous Pigments. Hueck lists the following, classified according to color. I have abbreviated, translated and supplemented his list, chiefly from the mineral pigments in the *Colour Index*, and from the colored ores noted in Lange. Not all these have been reported as pigments in tissues.

Black. Carbon as soot, coal and graphite. Coal occurs as irregularly angular and jagged particles. Graphite crystallizes as hexagonal crystals.

Brownish, Greenish and Grayish Black. Oxides and sulfides of various metals, not specified by Hueck, but including iron, cobalt, nickel, lead, silver, copper, antimony, chromium, gold, iridium, manganese, mercury, molybdenum (MoS_2), palladium, platinum, rhodium, tin, tantalum, thallium, thorium, tungsten, uranium and vanadium.

Brown. Bismarck brown used in tattooing; manganite, umber and cupric ferrocyanide.

Brownish Red. Iron and copper compounds, notably iron oxide.

Red. Cinnabar, carmine and other dyes used in tattooing; alizarin and madder; to which I might add the native arsenic sulfides realgar and orpiment, the iron ore hematite (Fe_2O_3) and mercuric oxide.

Blue. Vivianite [$Fe_3(PO_4)_2 \cdot 8H_2O$], ultramarine (a mixed silicate and sulfide of aluminum and sodium), steatite (a colored talc), azurite [$Cu(OH)_2 \cdot CuCO_3$], azure blue ($CoAl_2O_4$), smalt (potassium cobaltous silicates), copper blue (CuS), blue dyes used in tattooing, etc.

Green. Casalis green (Cr_2O_3) and its hydrates; Kinmann's green and related products resulting from the fusion of varying proportions of zinc and cobaltous oxides; turquoise green (similarly made from chromium, cobaltous and aluminum oxides); verdigris (basic copper acetates); Schweinfurt green (cupric acetoarsenite); Scheele's green (copper arsenite); and ultramarine green (a sodium aluminum silicate and sulfide); also green dyestuffs used in tattooing.

Yellow. Chromates of lead, barium and zinc; cadmium and stannic sulfides; Naples yellow [$Pb_3(SbO_4)_2$].

Violet. Chiefly dyestuffs used in tattooing.

Gray. Chiefly various silicates.

White. Various lead, zinc and bismuth pigments, as well as barite ($BaSO_4$) and titanium oxide (TiO_2).

Carbon

Carbon is one of the commonest extrinsic materials appearing as a pigment. Carbon is commonly deposited in the lungs and mediastinal lymph nodes, but may appear in axillary nodes as well, and sometimes in the skin as a result of tattooing or sterilization of hypodermic needles in sooty flames. It is distinguished by its black color and resistance to all solvents and bleaching agents.

The statements that carbon is insoluble in acids, alkalies and nonpolar solvents and that it is not bleached by oxidizing agents should be considered in the light of Table 11-2 on melanin bleaching (p. 427).

Metallic silver is readily removed by a 20 minute exposure to 5% potassium cyanide solution or to a Gram-Weigert iodine potassium iodide (1:2:100) solution followed by thiosulfate to remove the excess iodine. Most metallic sulfides are soluble in nitric acid even in moderate dilution.

Iron

Various ores may be black (magnetite, hematite), blue (vivianite), green (siderite), gray (siderite), red (hematite) and brown or yellow (siderite, goethite). Some react in acid solutions to ferrocyanides, others to ferricyanides, some to both (see pp. 405–407). Iron ore dusts may be removed by treatment with oxalic or dilute nitric acids. Generally, however, petrographic examination may be necessary to identify precisely the dusts in question. See also below.

Highman (*Int. A. Med. Mus. Bull.* 32:97, 1951) finds that some of the less soluble iron ore dusts (notably hematite, Fe_2O_3) fail to react to the usual ferrocyanide test, p. 405. He notes that by increasing the concentration of the hydrochloric acid to 4 N or to even higher concentration (11 N), and heating to 60–80°C, positive Prussian blue reactions may be obtained even with the more refractory ores. For the Quincke and Tirmann-Schmelzer reactions a prolonged exposure (1–2 days) to saturated hydrogen sulfide water is substituted for the usual ammonium sulfide step, p. 403.

Aluminum

Aluminum has been demonstrated after aluminum dust therapy of silicosis as globules and mulberry like aggregates of dark red material lying in the center of the fibrous nodules, by the aurine technic of P. C. Irwin (personal communication, 1948).

Fix in formalin, cut frozen or paraffin sections and bring to water as usual.

1. Stain 5 minutes at 75°C in 2% aurine tricarboxylic acid (NH_4 or Na salt) in a pH 5.2 buffer composed of 3.8 parts 5 M (267.5 gm/liter) ammonium chloride, 3.8 parts 5 M (385.3 gm/liter) ammonium acetate and 1 part 6 N (500 cc/liter) hydrochloric acid.
2. Rinse for a few seconds in cool distilled water.
3. Decolorize 3 seconds in pH 7.2 buffer composed of 3.6 parts of above buffer and 10 parts 1.6 M (15.36%) ammonium carbonate.
4. Rinse quickly in distilled water.
5. Counterstain briefly in saturated aqueous picric acid solution or in 1:10,000 methylene blue.
6. Dehydrate, clear and mount by alcohol, xylene, balsam (or synthetic resin) sequence.

Pearse (*Acta Histochem.* 4:95, 1957) has used a dye introduced as chromoxane pure blue B, C.I. No. 43830, and usually designated as pure blue B with various trade name prefixes, under the ICI[1] trade name Solochrome Azurine BS, for the demonstration of aluminum and beryllium in tissue.

An 0.2% solution of pure blue B is used, in distilled water for Al and Be, in 1 N NaOH for Be alone, the Al being dissolved at this pH level.

Deparaffinize (remove mercury precipitate) and hydrate as usual. Stain 15–20 minutes, rinse in distilled water, dehydrate in alcohols, clear in xylene and mount in synthetic resin.

Beryllium colors almost black in the alkaline solution; in the neutral

[1] ICI, Imperial Chemical Industries, Ltd.

bath, Al and Be are blue. (The *Colour Index* notes a quite stable dark blue barium lake used in printing.)

Alcoholic morin gives an intense green fluorescence in ultraviolet light tests. The fluorescence, after formation, is stable in 2 N HCl, which dissolves out the morin compounds of beryllium, indium, gallium, thorium and scandium. Although the aluminum salt is formed only in acetic acid or neutral conditions, the similar green fluorescence of **zirconium** is formed even in strong hydrochloric acid.

Feigl[1] used 0.001% morin in alcohol, 1 drop + 1 drop test solution + 5 drops concentrated HCl, and he detected 0.1 γ Zr (1/500,000). For Al he used 1 drop saturated morin in methanol, 1 drop test solution, 1 drop 2 N acetic acid, detecting 0.2 γ (1/250,000).

Asbestos

It occurs in tissues as fine, white, doubly refractile fibers and as the so-called asbestosis bodies. The latter occur as beaded rods with large rounded ends, as fusiform bodies with beaded centers, as rosettes and in other similar forms. They are golden yellow in color and give the Prussian blue reaction for ferric iron. Also some of the fine asbestos fibers are colored blue by acidulated potassium ferrocyanide solution (pp. 405–407). The asbestosis bodies and the fine fibers giving the Prussian blue reaction are dark under crossed Nicol prisms. (J. W. Miller, *Pub. Health Bull.* 241, pp. 96–101, Government Printing Office, Washington, 1938.)

Titanium

One drop (0.025 cc) of a saturated methanol solution of morin gives an intense brown spot with 1 drop of 0.5 N HCl solution containing titanium salts. The sensitivity is 0.01 γ or 1/5,000,000, (Feigl,[1] IST 199). Since titanium oxide is now being used extensively in white paints, the problem of its identification may arise. The morin test seems adaptable to histochemical use.

Beryllium

Denz's (*Quart. J. Micr. Sci.* **90**:317, 1949) test for reactive beryllium compounds, utilizes naphthochrome green B (Clayton Aniline Co.), described as pheno-oxy-dinaphtho-fuchsondicarboxylate of sodium. The dye forms a green beryllium lake, optimally at pH 5. The dark blue green ferric lake and the yellowish green aluminum lakes are formed only at relatively high metal concentrations at this pH level. See p. 113, C.I. No. 44530.

---

[1] References to Feigl's Spot Tests are abbreviated IST and OST for inorganic and organic volumes, respectively, followed by page numbers.

Denz's Beryllium Method.

1. Fix tissues in formol saline or alcoholic formalin (p. 39). Dehydrate with alcohols, clear in xylene or cedar oil, imbed in paraffin, section, deparaffinize with xylene and hydrate through descending alcohols.
2. Mix equal volumes of a phosphate buffer of pH 5 (*sic*) and of a freshly prepared 0.5% aqueous solution of naphthochrome green B. Place slides in this mixture in a Coplin jar and incubate 30 minutes at 37°C.
3. Wash in distilled water.
4. Differentiate 30 minutes in 100% alcohol.
5. Wash in distilled water.
6. Counterstain 5 minutes in 1% aqueous acridine red.
7. Wash in distilled water.
8. Differentiate rapidly in 100% alcohol.
9. Clear in xylene and mount in Canada balsam.

Results: Beryllium compounds, apple green; background, red.

The method demonstrates protein combinations of soluble beryllium salts, which apparently remain in place for fairly long periods. Beryllium oxide and silicate dusts in tissues fail to react.

The acridine red referred to may be acridine red 3B (C.I. No. 45000), which is a basic dye of the pyronin class. Probably one of the latter could be substituted.

Beryllium gives a specific yellow green fluorescence in ultraviolet when treated with 3 drops Versene solution + 1 drop 0.02% morin in acetone + 1 drop concentrated ammonia. The precipitate is washed successively with Versene, water and acetone. The test is sensitive to 0.07 γ Be and is selective in the presence of 200 parts Al, Fe, Mg or Ca. This spot test method appears readily adaptable to histochemical use.

Barium and Strontium

According to Waterhouse's (*Nature* **167**:358, 1951) method first fix tissue in neutral 10% formalin in 70% alcohol. Then soak the blocks for 30–60 minutes in a freshly prepared 1–2% solution of sodium rhodizonate in distilled water or pH 7 phosphate buffer. Then wash out excess rhodizonate in 50% alcohol. Tissues can then be sectioned as usual, and permanent preparations may be obtained. Barium and strontium compounds both give intensely red reaction products. Treatment with aqueous potassium chromate solution before the rhodizonate prevents formation of the color with barium salts, and chromate treatment after coloration removes the color from barium but not from strontium.

McGee-Russell (*J. Histochem.* **6**:22, 1958) fixes, imbeds in paraffin and sections at 8–10 μ, deparaffinizes and brings through descending alcohols to 50%. Then rinse quickly in distilled water and immerse section in a saturated solution of sodium rhodizonate for 1 hour or longer. Examine in distilled water. Calcium deposits containing Sr or Ba color reddish orange; background is unstained. Spectroscopically pure calcium salts do not react. If desired, sections may be counterstained 5–10 seconds in 0.5% toluidine blue, dehydrated and cleared through acetone and xylene and mounted in a resinous mount.

McGee-Russell finds the K_2CrO_4 tests above equally applicable to sections; he notes further that dilute HCl removes the Sr rhodizonate but not the Ba salt.

Calcium

The procedure of feeding madder or injecting alizarin compounds to mark in red newly deposited calcium salts during life, and the recently observed intravital fluorochrome staining with tetracycline are considered on p. 636.

Allied to these procedures are the chelate staining with alizarin red S, purpurin, calcium red, chloranilic acid and similar mordant dyestuffs.

Alizarin Red S. Langeron prescribed 80–90% alcohol fixation. I have found phosphate buffered 10% formalin satisfactory. **Avoid calcium in fixatives.** Stain 1 hour in 0.1% aqueous alizarin red S, rinse and counterstain briefly in 0.1% thionin, azure A, toluidine blue or methylene blue, rinse briefly in 1% acetic acid, dehydrate with acetone, clear in xylene and mount in synthetic resin. Dahl (*Proc. Soc. Exp. Biol. Med.* **80**:479, 1952) added 1/1000 volume of ammonia water to 1% alizarin red S to give pH 6.4, stained alcohol fixed paraffin sections 2 minutes, washed with distilled water 5–10 seconds, dehydrated in alcohols, cleared in xylene and mounted in cedar oil. McGee-Russell's 1958 variation of these technics seems superior and is cited in detail.

McGee-Russell Alizarin Red S Procedure for Calcium (*J. Histochem.* **6**:22, 1958). Make a 2% aqueous solution of alizarin red S (C.I. No. 58005) and adjust to pH 4.2 with dilute ammonia. Fix material in alcoholic formalin. Bring paraffin sections through xylene and alcohols to 50% alcohol, rinse quickly in distilled water, cover section with the alizarin red S and watch under microscope until red calcium lake forms over deposits (30 seconds to 5 minutes). Drain, blot with filter paper, dehydrate quickly (10–20 seconds) with acetone, acetone + xylene, xylenes, balsam or synthetic resin. Ca^{++} deposits are orange red, except oxalate. McGee-Russell did not consider sulfate or fluoride. The former should probably react, the latter probably will not.

The purpose of microscopic control is the avoidance of diffusion artifacts. Calcium deposits are orange red on a colorless background. Toluidine blue counterstains tend to react with the deposits and are not recommended.

Alizarin red S forms a crimson lake with calcium, and scarlet lakes with aluminum and with barium. Magnesium gives a clear scarlet solution; mercury, a clear dark red solution.

Purpurin of Grandis and Mainani. Schmorl recommended a similar method employing purpurin (C.I. No. 58205) or anthrapurpurin (alizarin SX) (C.I. No. 58255) in saturated alcoholic solution (they are respectively very sparingly soluble in water and insoluble in water). He prescribed fixation with strong alcohol or neutral 10% formalin. Paraffin sections are deparaffinized and brought through 100% alcohol into

1. The saturated alcoholic stain for 5–10 minutes. The anthrapurpurin solution should contain also 1% sodium chloride and a trace of ammonia water.
2. Wash in 0.75% aqueous sodium chloride solution for 3–5 minutes.
3. Wash thoroughly in 70% alcohol until no more color clouds come out of sections.
4. Dehydrate, clear and mount as usual.

Results: Calcium deposits are stained red.

It is probable that sodium anthrapurpurin monosulfonate (C.I. No. 58260), which is water soluble, can be substituted as an aqueous solution in this technic.

Kernechtrot, Nuclear Fast Red, Calcium Red. This is an aminoanthraquinone sodium sulfonate which gives a red precipitate with soluble calcium salts. I am using the last term because of the occasional confusion with *Kernechtrotsalz* B, which is fast red B salt (p. 114). McGee-Russell (*loc. cit.*) reports that lakes are formed with Pb^{++}, Fe^{+++}, Cu^{++}, K^+, Sn^{++++} and Sr^{++}, as well as with Ca^{++}, but not with Ba^{++} or Mg^{++}. In tissue, selective staining of $CaCO_3$ and $—PO_4$ deposits is achieved, but oxalate remains unstained.

McGee-Russell directs purifying a sample of the dye by first washing in 3 small washes of distilled water and then making a saturated solution of the residue (about 0.25%) in distilled water. The pH should be about 4.9.

Technic. The technic is simple. Bring paraffin, ester wax, celloidin, gelatin or frozen sections (2–10 μ) to distilled water. Flood sections on slides with saturated aqueous calcium red. Stain with microscopic control until deposits are deep red (5–55 minutes). Drain and blot, dehydrate with acetone 20 seconds (2–3 changes or dropper bottle), acetone + xylene, xylene, balsam or other suitable resin.

Eisenstein *et al.* (*J. Histochem.* 9:154, 1961) report a method producing yellow brown rhomboidal and needle shaped microcrystals of calcium chloranilate at Ca^{++} sites. Fe^{++}, Fe^{+++} and Mg^{++} do not precipitate with neutral Na chloranilate. In large amounts Cu^{++} reacts, and small amounts of heavy metals give more macrocrystalline deposits.

Eisenstein's Chloranilate Method for Calcium. Dissolve 4 gm sodium hydroxide in 600 cc distilled water. Add 11 gm chloranilic acid (2,5-dichloro-3,6-dihydroxy-*p*-benzoquinone (Eastman 4539, M.W. 209) and bring total volume to 1000 cc. Shake to dissolve. Adjust pH to 7 with additional chloranilic acid if necessary. Store in refrigerator. Filter before using. The reagent is stable for some 6 months.

Deparaffinize and hydrate sections as usual; wash in distilled water. Immerse sections for 1 hour with constant vigorous agitation. Wash in two 30 minute changes of 50% isopropyl alcohol. Counterstain with Giemsa or other suitable stain, dehydrate in alcohols, clear in xylene and mount in balsam or synthetic resin.

The fine yellow brown crystals are readily identified and are brilliantly birefringent under polarized light. Iron deposits do not react. Crystal size is such that very precise cytologic localization is not accomplished. The function of the agitation during the reaction is to reduce crystal size.

Von Kóssa's Method. (Beitr. path. Anat. **29:**163, 1901). Widely used for demonstration of calcification is the von Kóssa silver nitrate method, which actually demonstrates the presence of phosphates, soaps and amorphous but not crystalline carbonates, rather than calcium itself.

McGee-Russell (*loc. cit.*) notes also the reaction of calcium oxalate, and Cogan *et al.* (*J. Histochem.* **6:**142, 1958) report intense blackening over gypsum ($CaSO_4 \cdot 2H_2O$) crystals. See also p. 635. Pizzolato (*J. Histochem.* **12:**333, 1964) cites negative reactions of experimentally produced deposits of CaC_2O_4, CaF_2 and gypsum.

Alcohol fixation is often recommended for calcium methods, but neutral 10% formalin works well in practice. Calcium carbonate, calcium acetate and calcium chloride formulae are, of course, to be avoided, because of the possibility of false positive reactions.

1. Wash in several changes of distilled water.
2. Immerse in 5% silver nitrate for 10–60 minutes (von Kóssa: 5 minutes) and expose to bright daylight (Mallory, Romeis, Langeron), not direct sunlight. Schmorl used 1–5% silver nitrate for 30–60 minutes; Cowdry, 10% for 30 minutes or more.
3. Wash well in distilled water.
4. Treat for 2–3 minutes in 5% aqueous sodium thiosulfate solution.
5. Wash in water.
6. Counterstain 20–60 seconds in 0.5–0.1% aqueous safranin O.
7. Differentiate and dehydrate in 95% and 100% alcohol.
8. Clear with 100% alcohol and xylene and 2 changes of xylene. Mount in synthetic resin.

Results: Calcium deposits, black; nuclei, red; other tissues, pink.

In place of safranin other counterstains may be used. In case of hard calcium deposits, ragged sections may require the collodion treatment outlined on p. 55. With larger deposits it may be better to use the procedure of silvering before decalcification (p. 635).

It should be recalled that melanin may also become black or very dark brown by this technic. Although ascorbic acid should also react, this material is not preserved in sections except with very special precautions.

The most widely used criterion for the detection of small calcareous deposits in their staining deep blue with alum hematoxylin or gray violet with iron hematoxylin. This is not specific but is very useful.

Some calcareous deposits are encrusted or admixed with ferric salts, which may be detected by the usual ferrocyanide reaction (p. 407).

Cretin's Reaction. Lison regarded this reaction as very sensitive and highly specific. Gomori agreed as to specificity but found the reaction so capricious as to be almost useless. I have always regarded it as too complicated for practical use and have not tried it; it was given in detail in the second edition of this book.

The most specific chemical tests are those with sulfuric and oxalic acids. In the unstained state the calcium deposits are granular, opaque and white. By mounting the sections in water and running in acetic acid under one edge of the coverglass while drawing water out with a piece of filter paper from the other, the deposits may be seen to dissolve; if carbonates, with the formation of gas bubbles; if phosphate only, without gas bubbles. If sulfuric acid is used in place of acetic, the deposits dissolve as before, but monoclinic gypsum crystals are formed; but if 5% or 10% oxalic acid is used, the characteristic cubic calcium oxalate crystals appear.

Although it seems to be generally accepted that calcium oxalate deposits do not react to the organic colored chelate reactions for Ca^{++}, reports on the von Kóssa reaction of oxalates and sulfates are conflicting. Silver oxalate is fairly insoluble, though less so than the calcium salt, and silver sulfate is moderately soluble (*ca.* 0.8%, 22°C, Lange). Hence pure deposits of calcium oxalate and of gypsum crystals could well be unreactive to the von Kóssa test. Although x-ray diffraction studies have assured the identification of the two crystal forms, I do not believe that they afford assurance of the absence of carbonate, phosphate or other reactive salt. Since it is well known that 1 N solutions of acetic and formic acid are efficient decalcifying agents for bone and other calcified tissue and that calcium oxalate is promptly precipitated from these solutions, though not from hydrochloric acid above about 0.5 N, it would appear that if the positive von Kóssa reaction of a given oxalate deposit is due to the presence of contaminating carbonate or phosphate, for example, a 24 hour extraction in 1 N acetic acid should render a following von Kóssa test negative. Pizzolato's H_2O_2 von Kóssa variant could then be applied to demonstrate the calcium oxalate, as usual.

The microincineration methods for calcium oxalate are presented in Chapter 19, p. 652.

Stimulated by these successes in conversion of calcium oxalate to carbonate by 450°C microincineration, with the resultant development of reactivity to usual calcium tests, Pizzolato was led to search for an oxidant which would convert oxalate to carbonate *in situ*, without solution of the product. The chemical method of titration in acid permanganate solution was naturally inapplicable. After a number of trials, strong hydrogen peroxide used in the presence of silver nitrate was found to yield the desired results (*J. Histochem.* **12**:333, 1964).

Pizzolato's Peroxide Silver Method for Calcium Oxalate. Routine paraffin sections of formalin fixed tissue are usable. It is preferable to use a minimal amount of albumen fixative, since this is apt to occasion excessive bubble formation on the slides.

1. Deparaffinize in xylene, hydrate through graded alcohols as usual.
2. Mix equal volumes of 30% hydrogen peroxide and 5% silver nitrate, allowing 2 cc for each slide. The pH of this mixture is about 6.
3. Lay slides face up on 2 glass rods over a glass bowl and deposit on each slide 2 cc of the fresh peroxide silver mixture, rocking slightly to spread the reagent over the section.
4. Expose to a 60 watt tungsten filament electric lamp or a 25 watt fluorescent bulb at a distance of 15 cm (6 in.) above the slides for a period of 15–30 minutes. If excessive bubbling develops, pour off reagent and replace with fresh.
5. Wash thoroughly in distilled water, counterstain 2–3 minutes in 0.1% safranin in 1–2% acetic acid if desired.
6. Dehydrate in 2 changes each of 95% and absolute alcohol, absolute and xylene, clear in xylene, mount in Permount or cellulose caprate.

Results: Nuclei, red; calcium oxalate, black; calcium fluoride and barium sulfate did not react. *In vitro* tests with calcium sulfate were also negative.

Magnesium

A blue magnesium compound is formed from alkaline solutions of *p*-nitro-benzeneazoresorcinol. An excess of KCN in the solution decreases interference of Cu, Zn and other metals which form complex cyanides (McNary, *J. Histochem.* **8**:124, 1960).

Make a 1% solution of the dye in 0.5% (or 0.1 N) NaOH. Deposit a drop of this on the section or smear; add a drop of 1% KCN. Cover with a coverslip and seal with paraffin. The method detects 1.3 γ Mg in spot tests.

The same author has also adapted Glick's (*J. Biol. Chem.* **226**:77, 1957) titan yellow (C.I. No. 19540) method for the staining of leucocytes in blood smears.

Rinse smear in distilled water to lake red cells and remove plasma magnesium. Dry. Place on smear a drop of 0.1% titan yellow in 1 N NaOH, cover with coverslip and seal with paraffin.

Magnesium is demonstrated by a flame red color. Sensitivity is about 1 γ.

McNary also notes a green magnesium reaction with zincon (p. 451).

Silver

Appearing as dark brown to black granules which are turned black by soluble sulfides, silver deposits are removed by treatment with a solution containing 1 gm potassium ferricyanide and 22.5 gm sodium thiosulfate ($Na_2S_2O_3 \cdot 5H_2O$) per 100 cc, or by treatment for 1–2 hours with Weigert's iodine solution (p. 141) followed by rinsing and immersion in 5–10% sodium thiosulfate until white (Schmorl). According to Timm (*Virchow Arch. path. Anat.* **297**:502, 1936), silver sulfide is also removed by potassium cyanide solution (p. 444). It is not dissolved by ammonium hydroxide or by sodium sulfide solution.

It is here to be noted that a 20 minute exposure to Weigert's iodine, followed by thiosulfate, or a simple 20 minute treatment with 5% potassium cyanide will completely decolorize Masson-Hamperl preparations, even when they are quite dark. The presence of oxygen is, of course, necessary to convert metallic silver to the soluble double cyanide $KAg(CN)_2$ (*J. Histochem.* **9**:184, 1961).

Copper

Copper (cupric?) sulfide is also a dark brown to black material which is soluble in potassium cyanide solution (p. 444, Timm), but is not removed by sodium sulfide or ammonium hydroxide. Copper ferrocyanide is red, and Lison quotes this as a specific reaction (p. 408). According to Mallory copper compounds give a light to clear dark blue color with unoxidized fresh aqueous hematoxylin solution.

Mallory's Hematoxylin Stain for Iron and Copper. Fix in alcohol. After formalin fixation only yellow to brown colors are obtained with iron. Imbed in paraffin or celloidin. Hydrate sections as usual.

1. Dissolve 5–10 mg hematoxylin in 0.5–1 cc 100% alcohol. Add 10 cc distilled water which has been boiled 5 minutes to drive off carbon dioxide. Stain sections 1 hour or more in the hematoxylin solution.

2. Wash 1 hour in several changes of tap water.

3. Dehydrate, clear and mount with alcohol, xylene and balsam.

Results: Nuclei, bluish gray; hemosiderin, black; copper, light to clear dark blue. I have had no experience with this method, but the prolonged staining of tissues in Clara's 1/10,000 hematoxylin demonstrates enterosiderin and hemosiderin iron in 1–2 hours, and tissue premordanted with 1 mM $CuSO_4$ gives beautiful blue green nuclear staining.

Okamoto and Utamura used rubeanic acid (dithio-oxamide) for the demonstration of copper. Romeis directs: Bring frozen, paraffin or celloidin sections to water as usual. Add 2–5 cc 0.1% alcoholic rubeanic acid to 100 cc 10% aqueous sodium acetate solution. Incubate sections 12–24 hours at 37°C in this solution in a tightly covered vessel. Wash in water, counterstain in alum carmine, alcohol, xylene and balsam as usual.

Results: Copper rubeanate, greenish black; cobalt, yellowish brown; nickel, blue violet. Silver and lead yield black sulfides. According to Feigl (1949) copper rubeanate is formed also from weak acid solutions; for cobalt and nickel the sodium acetate is required.

Poulson and Bowen quote (*Exp. Cell Res. Suppl.* **2**:161, 1952) Waterhouse's use of sodium diethyldithiocarbamate as a histochemical reagent for copper in blowflies. They applied equal volumes of an 0.2% solution of this reagent and of 2% HCl (0.25 N?) to freshly dissected *Drosophila* larvae. Copper gives a yellow brown color. Waterhouse (*Counc. Sci. & Indust. Res. Bull.* 191, 1945) used 0.1% in either acid or neutral solution, both on fresh tissue and on material coagulated by heat, alcohol or formalin. Iron also forms a brown carbamate compound, but the sensitivity to iron is much lower than to copper. The blowfly material failed to react to the rubeanic acid method.

McNary (*J. Histochem.* **8**:124, 1960) reports a positive (blue) zincon reaction (p. 451) with copper. Posttreatment with a solution of Versene decolorizes the blue reactions of zinc but leaves the copper reaction unaltered.

Copper forms a red brown dithizone complex but not from the zinc specific dithizone complex forming buffer solution. Sensitivity is high, 0.03 γ, 1:660,000.

Wilson's Disease. Schaffner, Sternlier, Barka and Popper (*Am. J. Path.* **41**:315, 1962) reported the presence in (cirrhotic) liver cells of yellow brown pigment granules which fluoresce golden brown in ultraviolet, stain with oil red O and Nile blue in paraffin sections and in part red with periodic acid Schiff after diastase digestion. Acid phosphatase in formol calcium frozen sections was much reduced in the pigmented liver cells and was almost normal in other cells. Acid phosphatase activity was increased in Kupffer cells, as was that of alkaline glycerophosphatase and adenosine triphosphatase. Intranuclear glycogen deposit was often prominent. (Most of the recited pigment reactions are those of the usual hepatic cell lipofuscin.—R.D.L.)

High assay figures for copper in hepatic tissue were reported, ranging in the 10 cases from 60 γ to 1.56 mg/gm dry weight.

Cobalt

Despite the wide use of cobaltous sulfide to demonstrate the precipitation of phosphate ions in calcium phosphate, little other histochemical information is available concerning this metal. Its phosphate reacts with solutions of 1-nitroso-2-naphthol to form a red brown deposit. Iron phosphate does not react. The more reactive iron salts form brown black with this reagent. Copper salts give a brown color but may be rendered nonreactive by conversion to cuprous iodide by an iodide sulfite mixture. Cuprous iodide is soluble in potassium iodide solution.

Alcoholic thioglycolic acid anilide yields a red brown, acid insoluble cobalt compound from ammoniacal solution. Black precipitates are yielded by 4-methyl- or 4-chloro-1,2-mercaptobenzene with copper, cobalt and nickel; red with tin, bismuth and molybdenum; yellow with lead, silver and antimony; and pale yellow with cadmium, mercury and arsenic.

The foregoing account is gleaned largely from Feigl (1949).

McNary (*J. Histochem.* 8:124, 1960) notes also a violet complex with dithizone (p. 450), a blue green zincon complex which is unstable in acid, and a yellow brown rubeanic acid complex (p. 442). Rubeanic acid detects 0.03 γ Co (1:660,000).

Ethylenediaminetetraacetate at about pH 10 produces blue to violet complexes with Co and Fe. Place a drop of 10% Versene in 1% Na_2CO_3 on the slide, add a drop of 1% H_2O_2, put on coverglass and watch for color reaction.

Nickel

According to Lison a fresh alcoholic pure hematoxylin solution stains nickel salts lilac, grading to blue in thicker sections. He prescribes fixation in formalin 30 cc, saline solution (*sérum physiologique*) 100 cc, and ammonium sulfide 0.3 cc. Soak in ammonium phosphate solution to produce the insoluble double nickel ammonium phosphate. Decalcify, imbed and section. Stain in fresh alcoholic hematoxylin.

Nickel sulfide (NiS) is black, soluble in nitric acid and aqua regia and partly in hydrochloric acid, and insoluble in ammonia water and in sodium sulfide solution. Its ferrocyanide is greenish white; its ferricyanide, rusty brown (Lange). Since nickel phosphate is insoluble in water, the phosphate buffered neutral formalin (p. 38) should serve as well as the sulfide for preservation of relatively soluble nickel salts.

Choman (*Stain Techn.* 37:325, 1962) has adapted the dimethylglyoxime method for nickel from Feigl for the histochemical demonstration of this element.

1. Transfer Adamstone-Taylor cold knife sections (or cryostat sections) directly to clean slides.
2. Expose face down for 10 seconds to fumes of concentrated ammonia water in small beaker.
3. Deposit on section, face up, a drop of 1% dimethylglyoxime in 95% alcohol.
4. After 30 seconds wash off reagent gently with 70% alcohol.
5. Dehydrate and clear by dropping onto sections successively a few drops each of 95% and absolute alcohols and xylene. Mount in balsam. Superior tissue detail will be seen by use of cellulose caprate.

Results: Nickel is demonstrated as red acidular crystals. Sensitivity is about 1 in 10,000,000.

Lead

The Lead Sulfide Method. For the detection of lead, Timm (*Virchow Arch. path. Anat.* **297**:502–508, 1936) fixed tissues, especially bone, in absolute alcohol saturated with hydrogen sulfide gas. He decalcified in 30% formic acid in water, also saturated with hydrogen sulfide. Acid was removed by several changes of 5% sodium sulfate and of water, all saturated with hydrogen sulfide. Frozen sections were cut and treated with potassium cyanide solution to remove copper and silver sulfides and with yellow ammonium sulfide to remove tin. Sections were washed in water, mounted on slides, dehydrated in alcohols and cleared in bromobenzene. Mount in bromobenzene balsam. Lead remains as brown granules of sulfide. Lead sulfide is converted into white lead sulfate by hydrogen peroxide. The crucial test is the restoration of the brown color at the same sites by a fresh 5–10 minute application of dilute ammonium sulfide.

The Chromate Method. Fairhall treated paraffin sections of formalin fixed lung for several days in a solution of potassium chromate acidified with acetic acid. The lead salts are converted into yellow monoclinic lead chromate crystals (*Pub. Health Bull.* 253, pp. 22–24, Government Printing Office, Washington, 1940). Fixation in Orth's or Möller's (Regaud's) fluid yields the same result according to Lison, who attributes the general method to Frankenberger and to Cretin.

The Hematoxylin Method. Mallory (1938, p. 143) prescribed fixation in alcohol or 10% formalin and imbedding in celloidin or paraffin.

1. Stain 2–3 hours at 54°C in fresh 0.05–0.1% solution of hematoxylin in water saturated previously with calcium carbonate.
2. Wash 10–20 minutes in running water (or several changes).

3. Dehydrate with 95% alcohol, clear in terpineol and mount in terpineol balsam.

Results: Lead is stained bluish gray to black. Even slightly aged hematoxylin gives a brown color and is useless. Old xylene balsam also immediately turns the stain brown. I suggest the use of one of the nonreducing synthetic resins.

Rhodizonate Test for Lead. Following Molnar's suggestion (*Stain Techn.* 27:221, 1952) for improving phosphatase technics by substituting a lead nitrate bath for the cobalt and a rhodizonate treatment for the ammonium sulfide, it would appear that a simple 40 minute bath in 0.5% sodium or potassium rhodizonate solution should demonstrate lead deposits in dark brown.

According to Feigl (1949) neutral rhodizonate metal salt mixtures yield precipitates as follows: lead, blue violet; zinc, brown violet; cadmium, bismuth, calcium, strontium and barium, red brown to brown red; uranyl salts, brown; and thallium, dark brown. Silver is reduced to a black (metallic?) state. Iron gives a soluble blue green color and hence does not confuse. At pH 2.8 only silver (black), tin (violet), thallium (brown black), cadmium and mercurous salts (brown red), barium (red brown) and lead (scarlet red) yield precipitates. Prior treatment with sulfuric acid should render barium nonreactive and should extract mercury, tin, cadmium, thallium and silver. If the silver is, however, in the metallic state, application of the iodine thiosulfate sequence, or of cyanide (p. 441) would remove it. Under these conditions the test should be specific for lead.

Arsenic

For **As** fix in 10% formalin containing 2.5% copper sulfate ($CuSO_4 \cdot 5H_2O$) for 5 days. Wash 24 hours in running water. Imbed in paraffin. Deparaffinized sections present green granules of Scheele's green ($CuHAsO_3$) which, though insoluble in water, is dissolved by acids and by ammonium hydroxide. By substituting cupric acetate for the sulfate, the green granular paris green or cupric acetoarsenite is produced. Its solubilities are similar (Castel's method, *Bull. Histol. Appliq.* 13:106, 1936). I suggest a light safranin counterstain.

Bismuth

The Christeller- (*Med. Klin.* 22:619, 1926) Komaya (*Arch. Derm. Syph.* 149:277, 1925) bismuth reaction uses Leger's reagents which are a 4% aqueous solution of potassium iodide and a 2% solution of quinine sulfate [3 gm quinine sulfate, 1 cc concentrated nitric acid (30 drops), 150 cc distilled water]. Mix 5 cc of each, add 2 drops (0.067 cc) nitric acid for use. Cut frozen sections of formalin fixed material; prestain with carmine, fuchsin or crystal violet; wash in water; apply the mixed Leger's reagent for 1 minute; rinse in water containing 2 drops nitric acid to each 10 cc. Mount, blot dry, treat with carbol xylene + alcohol, carbol xylene, xylene and balsam in sequence. Christeller describes the bismuth compound as bright yellow; according to Schmorl the needle shaped crystals are orange yellow. Cowdry refers to brown granules and cites a modification of Castel's (*Arch. Soc. sci. med. biol. Montpelier* **16**:453, 1934–1935), which utilizes a few drops of sulfuric acid in place of the nitric acid to dissolve the quinine sulfate. This gives red quinine iodobismuthate.

Bismuth deposits are blackened by hydrogen sulfide water or with ammonium sulfide solution.

Gold

According to H. Elftman and A. G. Elftman (*Stain Techn.* **20**:59, 1945) gold may be demonstrated by simple incubation of paraffin sections of formalin fixed tissue in 3% hydrogen peroxide at 37°C for 1–3 days. The hydrogen peroxide bleaches other interfering pigments; and gold appears as rose, purple, blue and black deposits. For critical evaluation omit counterstains. An alum hematoxylin stain may be used to aid in topographic studies and interferes only slightly. Probably light green SF (C.I. No. 42095) interferes least of the cytoplasmic stains.

The Stannous Chloride Reaction. The same authors also recommend the following modification of Christeller's (*Verhandl. Deutsch. path. Ges.* **22**:173, 1927) stannous chloride reaction, which produces the purple of Cassius. Make a stock aqueous solution of 5% stannous chloride ($SnCl_2 \cdot 2H_2O$) in which some pieces of metallic tin are placed to prevent oxidation to $SnCl_4$. For use, mix 40 cc stannous chloride and 4 cc concentrated hydrochloric acid. Incubate paraffin sections of formalin fixed tissue at 56°C for 24 hours in a covered Coplin jar. Wash repeatedly in distilled water, dehydrate, clear and mount. Gold is evident as purple to brown particles, and the red, blue and black of colloidal gold may be present as well.

G. Brecher tells me that the Christeller reaction may also be applied to tissues fixed in Zenker's fluid, provided that the thiosulfate treatment is omitted after the customary iodizing to remove mercury precipitates.

Mercury

For Hg Almkvist (Schmorl) prescribed fixation in: 100 cc saturated aqueous picric acid solution to which is added 3 gm 25% (0.75 cc 70%) nitric acid. The mixture is allowed to stand 1 day, shaken, filtered and saturated with hydrogen sulfide: Fix for 8–24 hours or up to 3 days for maximal effect. Imbed in paraffin. Mercury appears as fine yellow to brown granules of mercury sulfide. This is soluble in sodium sulfide solution but not in sodium thiosulfate. Other heavy metal sufides are also precipitated by this fixative solution, as iron, silver, cobalt and others. The precipitate should be tested with acidulated potassium ferricyanide as in the Tirmann-Schmelzer reaction (pp. 403–404) to exclude iron (blue) and cobalt (red). Mercuric ferricyanide is soluble, and potassium ferricyanide solution does not dissolve mercuric sulfide.

Christeller's fixative (Schmorl) consisted of 15 cc distilled water, 2 gm tin chloride and 1 gm nitric acid, and produced a black granular precipitate.

Brandino's method (Lison, 1st ed., p. 102) tests sections of alcohol or formalin fixed tissue with 1% 1,5-diphenylcarbohydrazide ($C_6H_5NH \cdot NH)_2CO$ (in alcohol?: very slightly soluble in water). A violet precipitate is formed.

Voigt (*Acta Histochem.* **14**:315, 1962) has modified the Timm silver sulfide method to make it specific for *mercury*. Fe, Zn, Cu, Pb, Co and perhaps Cd are also demonstrable, but of all these sulfides HgS is the least easily oxidized. Hence paraffin sections of material fixed in H_2S alcohol are treated 15 minutes in 15% hydrogen peroxide.

The balance of the technic follows Timm's usual silver procedure for heavy metals (*Deut. Z. ges. gerichtl. Med.* **46**:706, 1958) as presented in the Timm zinc method, p. 451.

Manganese

From Lison's 1953 account the suggested methods for manganese appeared unsatisfactory. Pearse, 1960, notes in his Table 52 the color reactions of $Mn(NO_3)_2$ with diethyldithiocarbamate (brown), dithizone (light brown) and pure blue B (Solochrome Azurine) (red), but otherwise does not discuss histochemical demonstration of the metal. Barka and Anderson do not consider Mn.

The lower oxides are insoluble and colored: MnO, gray green; Mn_2O_3, dark brown; and MnO_2, black. MnS is green or pink, MnS_2 is black, and there is also a pink native silicate.

Feigl (IST, pp. 175–177) uses the benzidine blue reaction for the detection of MnO_2, reporting a sensitivity of 0.15 γ (1:330,000). MnO_2 acts as the oxygen source to produce benzidine blue from solutions of benzidine or its halogen acid salts. Manganous salts in 0.05 N NaOH in the presence of air spontaneously oxidize to MnO_2, which is black and insoluble. Rinse and apply benzidine solution and observe the formation of a blue color. The color fades on drying but may be redemonstrated by a fresh application of benzidine solution.

This spot test seems to be of such nature as to be readily used histochemically. MnO_2 promptly disappears in 2% oxalic acid.

Feigl also notes the rapid reduction of diammine silver by Mn^{++}.

$$Mn(OH)_2 + 2(NH_3)_2AgOH \rightarrow MnO_2 + 2Ag + 4NH_3 + 2H_2O$$

In view of the ready air oxidation of Mn^{++}, this test seems less applicable to histochemistry, despite its high sensitivity (0.05 γ or 1/1,000,000). Melanin also reacts promptly with diammine silver.

McNary (*J. Histochem.* 8:124, 1960), however, has used it successfully on blood films. He prescribes adding 0.900 sp. gr. (28%) ammonia to saturated silver nitrate until precipitate is redissolved, then adding an additional equal volume of ammonia. Saturated $AgNO_3$ at 25°C takes about 25 gm to 10 cc water. I suggest taking 5 cc 28% ammonia and adding this strong silver solution to it drop by drop until a slight turbidity remains on shaking. Then add an additional 5 c ammonia water. Place a drop or two of this ammoniacal silver solution on the section or smear, put on a coverslip, seal with paraffin and wait 10 minutes for formation of MnO_2 and metallic silver.

Potassium

Lison rejected Macallum's potassium method as of little value, Gomori considered it a usable reaction. He modified it as follows: Dissolve 2 gm cobalt nitrate in 5 cc 20% acetic acid. Dissolve 6 gm sodium nitrite in 10 cc distilled water. Mix. Allow most of fumes to escape. Chill to 5°C. Immerse small fragments of fresh tissue (or Adamstone-Taylor frozen sections) in cold reagent for 2 minutes. Rinse in ice cold distilled water and wash in 4–5 changes of ice cold 50–70% alcohol. Convert cobalt to sulfide by immersion in 0.5–1% yellow ammonium sulfide for 2 minutes. Wash in water; counterstain with safranin, hemalum, carmine or the like; dehydrate with alcohol, clear in xylene, spread out and mount in Canada balsam.

The specific precipitate of potassium cobaltinitrite is converted to dark brown cobalt sulfides, and these serve to localize potassium. It is uncertain whether this demonstrates ionic or bound potassium or both. The alleged nonspecific creatine reaction has been shown to be due to potassium contamination.

Ryder (*J. Histochem.* 7:133, 1959) used frozen dried sections for the method of Poppen *et al.* (*ibid.* 1:160, 1953), who used alcohol formalin fixation and paraffin imbedding. Poppen *et al.* modified Macallum's cobaltinitrite method as follows:

Cobaltinitrite Reagent.

1. Dissolve 25 gm cobaltous nitrate in 50 cc distilled water; add 12.5 cc glacial acetic acid.
2. Dissolve 120 gm sodium nitrite (K free) in 180 cc distilled water. Of this solution take 210 cc and add to the acid cobaltous nitrate solution.
3. Bubble air through the mixture until no more brown fumes evolve.

Store in refrigerator and refilter before each use. The reagent remains potent for 3–4 months at 0–5°C.

Technic.

1. Cut paraffin sections at 7 μ. Press directly onto slides or float on warm absolute alcohol to flatten, drain and dry. Or, according to Poppen, transfer ribbons directly into 2 changes of xylene and 2 of absolute alcohol. With attached paraffin sections I suggest Naidoo's method (p. 323) of deparaffinizing in petroleum ether, washing in isopentane and drying instantly in air.
2. Transfer directly to cobaltinitrite reagent. Loose sections are rolled on a glass rod in the last alcohol and immersed below the surface of the aqueous reagent until diffusion turbulence subsides. They will then float on the reagent smoothly. Leave in reagent 3 minutes or longer.
3. Wash quickly in 2–4 changes of ice cold distilled water until yellow color stops coming out.
4. Float loose sections onto slides, let dry, blot with 2 changes each of 95% and absolute alcohol, clear in xylene and mount in synthetic resin. This leaves the potassium cobaltinitrite compound as birefringent chrome yellow crystals.

Alternatively, the cobalt may be converted to black cobalt sulfide, thus: Immerse 20–30 minutes in 2% dilution of yellow ammonium sulfide, wash in several changes of distilled water (float onto slides) dehydrate, clear and mount as above. As usual for CoS preparations, Canada balsam may be a better mounting medium.

Control slides are immersed 2–5 minutes in distilled water before immersion in cobaltinitrite reagent. This removes potassium salts.

Thallium

Thallium deposits form yellow crystals of iodide (TlI) on fixation of tissues in alcohol colored with Lugol's solution (Barbaglia, from Lison, 1953). Gomori suggests 2.5 gm iodine, 5 gm KI in 50–100 cc 95% alcohol; tincture of iodine (U.S.P.), diluted with an equal quantity of alcohol, should serve. The yellow thallous iodide is insoluble in alcohol, acetone, potassium iodide solution or water but is soluble in aqua regia.

Zinc

Lison's 1953 text cited a method of Mendel and Bradley (*Am. J. Physiol.* 14:311, 1905) for the demonstration of zinc. Treat paraffin sections 15 minutes at 50°C in 10% sodium nitroprusside solution. Wash in gently flowing water for 15 minutes. Cover section with a coverglass and introduce at one side a drop of sodium or potassium sulfide solution. An intense purple color is produced. Lison regarded the reaction as specific.

Mager, McNary and Lionetti (*J. Histochem.* 1:493, 1953) propose the following variation of the dithizone method for zinc.

Reagents.

1. Stock dithizone: Dissolve 10 mg diphenylthiocarbazone in 100 cc reagent grade anhydrous acetone. Store at 3°C in brown glass bottle.
2. Complexing buffer: Dissolve 55 gm sodium thiosulfate ($Na_2S_2O_3 \cdot 10H_2O$), 9 gm sodium acetate ($NaCO_2CH_3 \cdot 3H_2O$) and 1 gm potassium cyanide (KCN) in 100 cc distilled water. Shake in separatory funnel with several successive portions of dithizone in carbon tetrachloride, until the CCl_4 layer remains clear green, to remove traces of zinc.
3. Normal acetic acid.
4. Rochelle salt: a 20% aqueous solution of sodium potassium tartrate [$NaK(CO_2CHOH)_2 \cdot 4H_2O$].

Reaction Mixture. Mix 24 cc stock acetone dithizone with 18 cc distilled water, adjust with normal acetic acid to pH 3.7, add 5.8 cc complexing buffer and 0.2 cc Rochelle salt solution. Use at once.

Procedure.

1. Fix thin tissue fragments 1 hour in 2 changes cold 100% ethanol or, preferably, methanol (Rixon and Whitfield, *J. Histochem.* 7:262, 1959).
2. Cut frozen sections at 15 μ, or clear in xylene, infiltrate 1.5 hours in paraffin, imbed and section at 6 μ, or prepare paraffin sections by the freezing drying procedure (p. 60). Attached cryostat sections may be postfixed 10 minutes in cold alcohol.
3. Dry frozen sections onto slides, deparaffinize paraffin sections in xylene and let dry.
4. Flood sections with dithizone reaction mixture and stain 5–10 minutes, drain.
5. Wash off excess dye by flooding with chloroform, drain.
6. Rinse quickly in distilled water and mount in Karo, fructose syrup, or Arlex gelatin. Rixon and Whitfield used glycerol; glycerol gelatin should serve.

Results: Zinc is demonstrated as red to purple granules or diffuse red. The complexing buffer serves to render nonreactive the other metals which normally react with dithizone: Mn, Fe, Co, Ni, Cu, Ag, Pd, Pt, Cd, Sn, In, Au, Hg, Tl, Pb, Bi. Yellow crystals of dithizone resulting from evaporation of acetone are readily distinguished.

Haumont (*J. Histochem.* 9:141, 1961) used this method on undecalcified sections of ossifying young rat bones, and on ground sections of adult bone, using 95% alcohol fixation in both cases. Longer exposures, up to 1 hour in dithizone, were used for the 50 μ ground sections.

McNary (*J. Histochem.* 8:124, 1960), besides several variants of the dithizone method, used zincon (2-carboxy-2-hydroxy-5-sulfoformazylbenzene).

Zincon Method for Zinc, Copper, Cobalt, Magnesium.

1. Mix 2 cc 0.15% zincon in 0.1 *N* NaOH with 8 cc borate buffer pH 8.8 (this should result in a pH about 9.1–9.2).
2. Flood slides with this mixture; let stand 3 minutes.
3. Rinse and mount in Karo.

Results: Zinc and copper yield deep blue complexes; cobalt, a blue green; magnesium, green. The zinc complex is decolorized by 5–10% Versene; the cobalt, by dilute acid.

The Timm-Gesswein Silver Sulfide Method for Zinc. Gesswein (*Virch. Arch.* 332:481, 1959) used a variant of the silver sulfide method of Timm (*Deutsch. Z. ges. gerichtl. Med.* 47:428, 1958) and Voigt (*Acta Path. Microbiol. Scand.* 44:146, 1958).

Method. Fix small pieces 10–20 hours in H_2S saturated 70% alcohol. Then 10 hours 95% and 10 hours absolute alcohol, xylene 2 changes 30 minutes each, to paraffin imbedding. Cut 4–6 μ sections, float on preboiled double distilled water and attach to coverglasses. Silver 1½–2 hours in artificial light under close microscopic control, wash in running water, stain nuclei with *Kernechtrot* or hematoxylin, ascending alcohols, xylenes; mount in resin.

The following solutions are stored in quartz glass containers:

Gum arabic: 40 gm well ground gum arabic suspended in 100 cc double distilled water, with daily stirring with glass rod for 14 days.

Silver nitrate: 10 gm dissolved in 100 cc double distilled water and kept 14 days in dark before using.

Reduction fluid: dissolve 0.4 gm hydroquinone and 0.9 gm citric acid in 20 cc double distilled water; shake hard for 5 minutes. Let stand in dark for 12 hours before using.

Working silver solution: to 60 cc 40% gum arabic add 0.5 cc 10% $AgNO_3$ and shake well for 10 minutes. Then add 5 cc reduction solution, shake about 30 seconds and pour at once over sections.

Uranium

The several oxides of uranium are insoluble in water, as is uranyl phosphate (Lange). Hence, the phosphate buffered formalin (p. 38) should be adequate for fixation. Lison cites Schneider's fixation in 50 cc saturated aqueous picric acid, 50 cc 5% potassium ferrocyanide and 10 cc hydrochloric acid. This was followed by washing in 4% hydrochloric acid, then hydrochloric acid alcohol. Dehydration and imbedding as usual follow, and uranium salts appear as the deep brown double ferrocyanide of potassium and uranium. Gerard and Cordier (*Arch. Biol.* **43**:367, 1932) used the Prussian blue reaction as for iron, obtaining the same dark brown double ferrocyanide.

The alpha particle autoradiographic technic (second edition of this book p. 439) might be used to study the distribution of uranium salts in tissues.

Thorium

Thorium was used at one time in roentgenography of blood vessels, and it has occasionally been demonstrated in tissues. The most probable form is the insoluble dioxide ThO_2. Thorium 232 is almost the only naturally occurring isotope, with a half life of 1.39×10^{10} years. It is also an alpha and gamma emitter and should be localizable by the autoradiographic method for those emanations.

Feigl notes the reactivity of Th in the quinalizarin test for Mg (IST 225).

Thorium, along with Be, In, Ga and Sc, forms fluorescent morinates in the morin test for Al, which, in distinction from those of Al and Zr, are unstable in 2 *N* HCl.

According to Pavelka (*Mikrochemie* **4**:199, 1926; Feigl IST 201), spot testing with alizarin and then exposing the spot to ammonia gives violet red with Ti (sensitivity 0.18 γ, 1/166,000); purple red ("raspberry"), with Zr (sensitivity 0.29 γ, 1/103,000); and violet with Th (sensitivity 0.24 γ, 1/125,000).

Sulfates

Gomori cites Macallum's (*Abderhaldens Handbuch der biologischen Arbeitsmethoden,* vol. 2, pp. 1145–1146, 1912) sulfate method: Treat frozen sections (Adamstone-Taylor or Linderström-Lang technics should be more successful) of fresh tissue with 0.1 *N* lead acetate for 10 minutes or more. Wash thoroughly in water and then in 0.1 *N* nitric acid to remove lead phosphate, carbonate and chloride. Wash in water and treat with equal volumes of glycerol and ammonium sulfide, converting the lead sulfate to the brown sulfide. Molnar's suggestion of substitution of a 40 minute bath in 0.5% sodium rhodizonate for the sulfide treatment might be tried. According to Feigl neutral sodium rhodizonate reacts with lead sulfate or sulfide to give an insoluble deep violet, while rhodizonic acid, at pH 2.8, gives a red precipitate.

Macallum's ammonium sulfide is produced by saturating 16% ammonia (sp. gr. 0.96) with hydrogen sulfide gas.

See also Chapter 8, pp. 275–284, for identification of sulfuric and sulfonic acid residues.

Phosphates

For phosphates Bunting (*Arch. Path.* **52**:458, 1951) used a variant of the molybdenum blue reaction adapted by him from Feigl and from Serra and Queiroz-Lopes for paraffin sections of formalin fixed tissues.

Bunting's Molybdenum Blue Technic for Phosphates.

1. Deparaffinize and hydrate as usual.
2. Cover section with few drops of 5% ammonium molybdate and add an equal volume of 1% nitric acid. Let stand 5 minutes.
3. Wash thoroughly with water.
4. Cover with benzidine solution for 1 minute. (Dissolve 50 mg benzidine base in 10 cc glacial acetic acid, and dilute to 100 cc with distilled water.)
5. Flood with 45% (saturated) sodium acetate solution. Apply coverglass and examine at once.

Results: Sites of phosphate ion, blue. The color fades and diffuses in a few hours.

Serra and Queiroz-Lopes (*Portugaliae Acta Biol.* **1**:111, 1945) hydrolyzed small blocks of tissue for 2–3 weeks at 10–12°C in a solution containing 1 gm ammonium molybdate in 100 cc 2 N HCl and then continued the hydrolysis for 2–3 days in the same fluid at 20–25°C. They then added an equal (small) volume of the same benzidine solution as Bunting (step 4), reacted for 3 minutes, and added 2 volumes of saturated sodium acetate. By mounting in glycerol and sealing with Romeis's rosin lanolin (p. 91) they were able to preserve the reaction for some months.

Chapter 13

Lipids

NEUTRAL FATS

The most ancient method for coloration of fatty substances in tissues is the reduction of osmium tetroxide (commonly called osmic acid). This reagent is reduced to a black substance by unsaturated fats and fatty acids and by a variety of other reducing agents, such as eleidin and tannin; and if osmium tetroxide is followed by 60–70% alcohol, stearin and palmitin are also blackened. Myelin is also blackened by osmium tetroxide; but if previously treated with chromate solutions, only degenerating myelin is so blackened (pp. 180–182).

Generally speaking, the oil soluble dye methods are much less troublesome and more satisfactory for the demonstration of fatty substances. The first of these was Sudan III, C.I. No. 26100, introduced by Daddi (*Arch. Ital. Biol.* **26**:143, 1896). Michaelis (*Virchow Arch. path. Anat.* **164**:263, 1901) later introduced the use of Sudan IV or Scharlach R, C.I. No. 26105, which has been the most popular of the oil soluble dyes.

Following the long use of these 2 Sudans, III and IV, the property of staining with oil soluble dyes generally has come to be referred to as sudanophilia, even though the oil soluble dye used may not have the word Sudan included in its name.

FAT STAINS WITH OIL SOLUBLE DYES

The findings of Kay and Whitehead (*J. Path. Bact.* **53**:279, 1941) indicate that stronger staining of fats is obtained when 2 or more homologs or isomeres of the naphthol Sudans are saturated in the same stock staining solution. This they explain on the basis that each of the chemical individuals dissolves to its own saturation point, more or less independently of the other dyes present, both in the hydroalcoholic dye solvent and in the fats themselves. Since the absorption maxima of the red Sudans lie fairly close together in the 510–530 mμ range, denser coloration is thus achieved in that range. This principle seems equally applicable to the various solvents employed for Sudan staining, since it is the final optical density in the demonstrated oil or fat that is significant.

Since oil red O (C.I. No. 26125) is also a group of isomeric homologs of Sudan III (C.I. No. 26100), Sudan IV (C.I. No. 26105) and oil red 4B (C.I. No. 26120), admixture of commercial samples of all 4 should yield more potent staining mixtures of very similar chemical behavior. For histochemical use it is not recommended that naphthol type dyes of this sort be mixed with the chemically distinct naphthylamine and aminoanthraquinone oil soluble dyes (see pp. 129–133).

Staining with oil soluble dyes is based on the greater solubility of the dye in lipid substances than in the usual hydroalcoholic (and other) dye solvents. Michaelis so described it in Ehrlich's *Encyklopädie*, Lison (1936) so characterized it and Cain and Harrison (*J. Anat.* 84:196, 1950) still state that these substances operate "not as a dye, but only as an oil soluble colorant."

This staining has long been regarded as quite specific for lipids. Cain and Harrison make the important exception that fats of high melting point do not color with Sudan dyes unless heated to near or above their melting points. Thus cholesterol and its esters, carotenoids, tristearin and high melting paraffins may be stained when melted, but not at room temperature.

There is an important corollary to this theory of staining by oil soluble dyes. The dye should be again extracted by an excess of a suitable dye solvent which does not dissolve the lipid, and the lipid should then be again restainable by the original technic. Most of the lipids which survive paraffin imbedding can thus be completely decolorized in a matter of a few seconds to 1 or 2 minutes with acetone, and stained again with oil soluble dyes. The decolorization and restaining can be reperformed repeatedly. Similarly, frozen sections dried onto slides and stained by Sudan black B, C.I. No. 26150, or oil red O C.I. No. 26125, can be decolorized by 3 or 4 hour extraction in diethylene glycol, restained and decolorized repeatedly. It is found, however, that some substances, such as the sudanophil granules of leucocytes, cannot be decolorized by prolonged exposure to acetone, xylene, chloroform and the like, even at elevated temperature. Erythrocytes stain intensely on prolonged heating with Sudan black B, but not with oil red O or Sudan IV, and the stain is not extracted by acetone or xylene.

It is evident that the Sudans are not inert chemically (Lillie and Burtner, *J. Histochem.* 1:8, 1953), as had been supposed, but are capable of forming firm unions with certain tissue elements, some of which, at least, are probably not lipids. These combinations occur less promptly than with ordinary fat stains, and may require elevation of temperature for their accomplishment. Hence any Sudan or other oil soluble dye staining is suspect in which one dye is allegedly much better as an oil soluble dye than another or in which resistance to immersion oil or to xylene or absolute alcohol has been noted; and the lipid nature of the stained substance needs confirmation by the extraction and restaining tests mentioned above.

Particularly dye bases of arylamine dyes are suspect in this regard (Table 6-8, pp. 130–131) and have actually been observed under some circumstances to stain chromosomes, cartilage matrix and other acid tissue components.

It is perhaps noteworthy that acetylated and benzoylated Sudan dyes still stain ordinary fats quite effectively but fail to color leucocyte granules. It is possible that these ester dyes may be useful in discriminating true fats from chemically sudanophilic substances.

The original method of Daddi's (1896) called for a saturated solution of Sudan III in 70% alcohol. This takes a half hour or more to stain, gives a rather light orange color and dissolves out an appreciable amount of fat, in some instances all of the demonstrable fat that was present.

Herxheimer's Technic (*Zbl. allg. Path.* 14:891, 1903). Employing a saturated solution of Sudan IV (scarlet or Scharlach R) in a mixture of equal volumes of acetone and of 70% alcohol, this technic gave deep orange red staining in a few minutes but also removed a considerable amount of fat, and in some cases all of the fat present.

Herxheimer's Alkaline Sudan IV (*Deutsch. med. Wschr.* 27:607, 1901). This saturated dye solution has been much used by neurohistologists. It contained 1% (Conn) or 2% (Mallory) sodium hydroxide in 70% alcohol. The solution is said to be unstable and must be discarded after 2 or 3 days. Globus (*Practical Neuroanatomy*, William Wood & Company, Baltimore, 1937, p. 256) used 3.33% sodium hydroxide in 50% alcohol, again saturated with the dye.

Technic.

1. Place sections in a covered watchglass and heat until condensation droplets appear on the lid, and then allow to stand 15 minutes.
2. Wash 5 minutes in distilled water.
3. Counterstain in dilute Ehrlich's hematoxylin (pp. 174, 175).
4. Wash in distilled water.
5. Mount in glycerol.

Results: Fats, bright red.

This variant of Globus's method preserves some fats which are lost in the original Herxheimer solution, probably because of its lower (50%) alcohol content, as compared with the 70% of the original.

Romeis used a solution of Sudan IV in 40% alcohol and avoided fat losses but took some 18–24 hours to stain.

Gross's (*Z. wiss. Mikr.* 47:64, 1930) technic, which used a saturated solution of Sudan IV in 50% diacetin, stained fats deep red promptly and did not dissolve out lipids. However, the solvent gradually decomposed and impaired the stain.

Lillie and Ashburn (*Arch. Path.* **36**:432, 1943) developed the principle of using fresh aqueous dilutions of a saturated 99% isopropanol stock solution to 60% or 50% strength. These solutions were supersaturated with dye and stained vigorously and promptly in the first few hours after dilution, later becoming slow and relatively inefficient stains. Sudan IV, first used in this procedure, was soon replaced by dyes giving more stable supersaturated solutions and better color effects.

Oil red O, C.I. No. 26125, introduced by French (*Stain Techn.* **1**:79, 1926) in the Herxhmeimer technic, is found to be one of the best fat stains available in this supersaturated isopropanol method (*Stain Techn.* **19**:55, 1944). It gives a deep scarlet color to fats. Oil red 4B, C.I. No. 26120, is similar.

Sudan II (C.I. No. 12140) gives a bright orange yellow in this technic which contrasts well with a Weigert myelin stain. Sudan brown (C.I. No. 12020) gives a deep brownish red.

Coccinel red (*Stain Techn.* **20**:73, 1945) stains successfully from as low as 30% isopropanol, and also gives a deep scarlet color. This dye is 1,5-bisamyl-amino-anthraquinone, and its 1,4 isomer oil blue N (C.I. No. 61555, *Stain Techn.* **20**:7, 1945) gives deep blue fats from 40% isopropanol solution.

Supersaturated Isopropanol Method. The following technic may be used with *Sudan brown, oil red 4B* or *oil red O,* any of which is better than Sudan IV or Sudan III.

Prepare a stock saturated solution in 99% isopropanol using 250–500 mg of dye per 100 cc.

1. Dilute 6 cc of stock solution with 4 cc water.
2. Let stand 10–15 minutes and then filter. The filtrate can be used for several hours.
3. Stain thin frozen sections for 10 minutes.
4. Wash in water.
5. Stain 5 minutes in an acid alum hematoxylin of about 0.1% hematoxylin content (undiluted Mayer, 1 part of Lillie's to 4 of 2% acetic, or 1 of Ehrlich's to 5 of 2% acetic, see p. 174).
6. Blue in 1% disodium phosphate or in tap water.
7. Float out in water, mount on slides and
8. Drain and mount in gum syrup or glycerol gelatin (p. 101).

Results: Fats and lipofuscins are deeply stained red or brown according to the color of the dye. Birefringent lipids color less deeply but are conspicuously bright in polarized light.

Rinehart (*Arch. Path.* **51**:666, 1951) used oil red O, Sudan IV, Sudan black B and coccinel red as supersaturated 60% ethanol solutions made in the same way. His staining interval was 5 minutes.

The amylamino anthraquinone dyes oil blue N, coccinel red and carycinel red were quite satisfactory in the supersaturated isopropanol technics. The first stained well from a final 40% isopropanol concentration; the other 2, from as low as 30% isopropanol. Deep blue, scarlet and deep crimson colors respectively were imparted to fats (*Stain Techn.* **20**:7, 73, 1945). For relatively alcohol soluble birefringent lipids it would appear that dye solvents containing 40–50% water should be preferred, and that carbowax imbedding should be avoided.

Chiffelle and Putt (*Stain Techn.* **26**:51, 1951) strongly recommend propylene or ethylene glycol as a solvent for fat stains. These solvents virtually do not attack aliphatic fatty acid esters but are said to have some solvent capacity for aromatic compounds, such as cholesterols and ketosteroids. The dyes recommended are Sudan IV and Sudan black B. These are soluble to about 0.5% in propylene glycol.

Propylene Glycol Method of Chiffelle and Putt. Dissolve 0.7 gm of Sudan IV or Sudan black B in 100 cc pyropylene glycol at 100–110°C. Do not exceed 110°C. Filter hot through Whatman No. 2 filter paper. Cool and refilter with vacuum through a medium porosity fritted glass filter.

Technic.

1. Cut frozen sections, wash in water 2–5 minutes to remove formaldehyde.
2. Dehydrate 3–5 minutes in pure propylene glycol, moving sections at intervals.
3. Transfer to the dye solution for 5–7 minutes. Agitate occasionally.
4. Differentiate in 85% propylene glycol for 2–3 minutes.
5. Wash in distilled water 3–5 minutes.
6. Counterstain if desired.
7. Float onto slides, drain and mount in glycerol gelatin.

Results: Neutral fats, myelin, mitochondria and other lipids, orange red or greenish black; cytoplasm, unstained. No data are presented regarding preservation of birefringent lipids.

To avoid the dye precipitation often seen with supersaturated 50–60% alcohol solutions of oil soluble dyes, and the losses of birefringent crystalline lipids seen with glycol solutions, we have recently employed with encouraging results a solution of 500 mg Sudan black B in 30 cc glycol +

30 cc ethanol + 40 cc distilled water. The solution is approximately saturated and can be used with 15–30 minute staining intervals for 2–3 days. Stains are very clean and limited to lipids while the solution is fresh, but more or less diffuse gray staining of muscle and cytoplasm appears in week old solutions. Hence it has been our practice to make the solution fresh every second day (Gutiérrez and Lillie, Stain Techn. 40: 178, 1965).

STAINING OF LIPIDS WITH ESTERIFIED SUDAN DYES

Benzoylated oil red O was made for me by the National Aniline Division, Allied Chemical & Dyestuffs Corp. Acetylated Sudan IV and Sudan black B can be made quite simply. Dissolve 2–2.5 gm of dye in 60 cc pyridine, then add 40 cc acetic anhydride and let stand overnight. Then pour into 3 or 4 liters of distilled water, let stand a few hours and filter out the precipitated dyestuff on a Buchner funnel with vacuum. Dry the precipitate, the funnel and the glassware used in the precipitation. Dissolve the precipitate from glass, funnel and filter paper with acetone and evaporate to constant weight at 60°C. Yields range from 75% up to nearly theoretical. While acetylated oil red O may also be prepared, the resultant ester is a tarry red mass at room temperature.

Acetylated Sudan black B appears to give less background staining and just as intense lipid staining as the untreated dye. Acetylated and benzoylated oil red O and acetyl Sudan IV fail to stain human neutrophil leucocytes in 16 hours at 37°C, but at 60°C there is apparently some hydrolysis of the esters, and some coloration results on prolonged staining.

Observing the precaution of staining at 37°C or lower, and using a control human blood film fixed either with formaldehyde gas or with 75% alcohol for 10 minutes, these esterified dyes can be used to aid in discriminating lipid staining from stable sudanophilia.

The technics used are those usual for fat stains. We have employed stock solutions at 550–600 mg per 100 cc in 100% ethanol, diluting at time of use to 60% or 50% alcohol content with distilled water. Filtration of the freshly diluted mixture reduces precipitation on sections, and washing after staining in 50–60% alcohol is helpful.

Fluorescence Microscopy. For the demonstration of fats in fluorescence microscopy, Popper (Arch. Path. 31:766, 1941) used either a 10 second stain in 1% aqueous methylene blue (C.I. No. 52015) or a 3 minute stain in 0.1% aqueous phosphine (C.I. No. 46045). The first gave a blue fluorescence which suppressed green fluorescences other than that of vitamin A. The second produced a silvery white fluorescence and demonstrated more fats than traditional strong alcoholic Sudan methods.

Both these dyes are basic, and both have been used also for demonstration of free or bound nucleic acids. Hence the specificity is questionable.

As with stains with Sudan dyes, the fluorescence color should be extractable by a dye solvent which does not dissolve the lipid, and the fatty substance should be restainable, if the fluorescence demonstration is to be regarded as evidence of lipid nature of the stained substance.

3,4-Benzpyrene is a colorless oil soluble hydrocarbon which is highly fluorescent (blue) in ultraviolet light. Lison (3d ed., pp. 479–480) recites that it is the only lysochrome (oil soluble dye) known which is certainly completely lacking in polar groups, that it is highly sensitive and that it is the most specific colorant for lipids. He apparently considers it completely unreactive to form other types of staining than simple oil solubility.

However, it must not be forgotten that 3,4-benzpyrene is one of the most chemically reactive hydrocarbons known (Fieser and Fieser, *Organic Chemistry*, 3d ed., D. C. Heath and Company, Boston, 1956). It azo couples readily at 5 even with *p*-nitrophenyldiazonium chloride, it forms a 5-acetoxy derivative with lead tetraacetate in acetic acid and a 5-thiocyano derivative with thiocyanogen. Moreover, this carcinogenic hydrocarbon is readily metabolized *in vivo* to noncarcinogenic phenolic derivatives. It would seem to be a mistake to assume from its hydrocarbon structure that it is not capable of chemical reactivity under staining conditions.

According to Lison, Berg (*Acta Path. Scand. Suppl.* 90, 1951) used a 0.00075% solution in 0.75% caffeine in water. Apparently observation is done directly in water, and no permanent preparations result. The fluorecence is blue to bluish white.

In my judgment, if the preparations cannot be destained with an appropriate solvent and then restained as before, the lipid nature of the material stained is just as questionable as with phenolic and amine dyes.

Lison's explanation of stable sudanophilia as true oil soluble dye staining, despite the nonextractability of the dye, directly controverts the whole theory of differential oil solubility of dyes as the basis of fat staining. Many organic reactions are accomplished better in nonpolar than in polar solvents.

Myelin Stain with Sudan II and Iron Hematoxylin. Use frozen sections at 10–15 μ of material fixed in formalin and chromated in 2.5% potassium bichromate for 2–4 days, then washed in water.

1. Make fresh mixture of 5 cc of fresh 1% aqueous hematoxylin and 5 cc of 4% iron alum in covered dish. Stain sections 45 minutes at 55–60°C, agitating dish gently from time to time to insure even staining.
2. Wash sections in water. Save out some sections in water.
3. Decolorize in 0.5% iron alum for 1 hour, agitating from time to time.

4. Wash in water. (Steps 3 and 4 can probably be omitted; see p. 489.)
5. Treat with 1% borax, 2.5% potassium ferricyanide solution 10 minutes, agitating several times. (This is Lillie's variant of Weigert's borax ferricyanide, formula 15, p. 491.) At start of this step dilute the Sudan II for step 7. If step 3 is omitted, time variation is done in this step.
6. Wash in water.
7. Take 6 cc of a stock solution of Sudan II (C.I. No. 12140) saturated in 99% isopropanol, and dilute with 4 cc water, let stand 7–8 minutes, filter. Stain sections 10 minutes in the fresh filtrate.
8. Wash in water.
9. While a nuclear stain with a red, green or brown dye might be useful at this point, I have had little success in attempting to insert one.
10. Float onto slides, drain and mount in gum syrup.

Results: Normal myelin, blue black; nerve cells, gray; nuclei, deeper gray; red corpuscles, yellow to black; fats, orange yellow.

The persistence of black in nerve cells indicates underdifferentiation; loss of color in myelin indicates overdifferentiation. If sections are not satisfactory, those saved at step 2 may be differentiated for a shorter time in 0.5% iron alum if the myelin was too pale, or an hour in 1% iron alum if other structures were too dark. With freshly fixed formalin or Orth material chromated not over 4 days, this should not be necessary.

Feyrter developed a staining technic which is said to be specific for the so-called "onkocytes." Hamperl (*Arch. Path.* **49**:563, 1950) performs it as follows:

1. Fix in 10% formalin and cut frozen sections at 10–15 μ.
2. Float from distilled water onto a clean slide.
3. Cover with 1% thionin or 1% cresyl violet in 0.5% tartaric acid solution. (Let stand a few days before using. Do not filter.)
4. Place coverglass on the stain drop, and seal with cellulose caprate, polystyrene or lanolin rosin (p. 91).

Results: Nuclei, blue; myelin, red purple; other lipids, onkocytes and mucus, pink to red. Cardiolipids show blue metachromasia with cresyl violet. The onkocytes owe their metachromasia to poorly sudanophilic lipids in their cytoplasm. The full color of the staining develops only after some hours. Hamperl states that the preparations are stable for years. Romeis comments on their limited life.

Consideration of the special requirement of Feyrter (Romeis) that the thionin of only one German firm is suitable for his metachromatic staining of myelin, and of the fact that some materials staining metachromatically by Feyrter's method are themselves removed from frozen sections by brief (2 hour) alcohol extraction (Thorén, *Acta Soc. Med. Upsal.* **55**:125,

1950) suggests that the dye concerned may contain a good deal of a relatively fat soluble dye, such as Bernthsen's methylene violet. The solutions of this dye in chloroform are red. It would appear that the procedure may be closely related to the Ciaccio type methods insofar as it applies to myelin.

PARAFFIN

Paraffin may occur in sections as a result of incomplete deparaffinization, as birefringent, often intranuclear crystals. The birefringence disappears at the melting point of the paraffin. In the cold these crystals do not stain appreciably with oil soluble dyes; but if the staining solution is heated to above the melting point of paraffin, staining occurs (Nedzel, *Quart. J. Micro. Sci.* 92:343, 1951). Xylene, alcohol, water, alcohol, xylene sequence treatments are more effective in removal of these birefringent crystals than a similar exposure to xylene alone, both at 23–25°C.

FATTY ACIDS

Fatty acids are readily soluble in ether and alcohol. They form calcium soaps when fixed in a 10% formalin which has been saturated with calcium salicylate (about 1.5%). These calcium soaps are insoluble in ether and 100% alcohol mixture and in dilute hydrochloric acid when tested with these reagents separately, but they dissolve in a hydrochloric acid solution in ether and alcohol. After mordanting with copper acetate, fatty acids and their calcium soaps form a black hematoxylin lake which is very resistant to decolorization with Weigert's borax ferricyanide mixture. This forms the basis of Fischler's (*Zbl. allg. Path.* 15:913, 1904) method for fatty acids.

Fischler's Technic (modified slightly from Mallory).

1. Fix in 10% formalin and cut frozen sections.
2. To differentiate fatty acids from calcium soaps, extract some of the sections with 2 or 3 changes of 100% alcohol ether mixture (50:50), first dehydrating through 95% and 100% alcohol, and afterwards rehydrating through 100%, 95% and 80% alcohol. Only the soaps will remain in these. The specific colored metal chelate reactions for Ca^{++} should be applicable.
3. Treat both extracted and unextracted sections with saturated (perhaps 10%?) aqueous cupric acetate solution for 2–24 hours at 20–30°C.
4. Wash in distilled water.

5. Stain 20 minutes in Weigert's lithium carbonate hematoxylin (p 491).
6. Differentiate in Weigert's borax ferricyanide mixture (p. 491) "greatly diluted" with distilled water, until red corpuscles are decolorized.
7. Wash thoroughly in distilled water and mount in glycerol, glycerol gelatin or gum syrup. If desired, one may add a counterstain with a yellow or red oil soluble dye before mounting (cf. p. 460).

Mallory notes that iron, hemoglobin and calcium may stain as well. If differentiation be carried to the point where red corpuscles are thoroughly decolorized, hemoglobin should give no difficulty. Pretreatment of a few sections with dilute hydrochloric acid in place of step 2 should serve to eliminate calcium as a source of error, but adds the soap fatty acid to the free form. Similarly, overnight extraction in 5% oxalic acid or (15 minutes) sodium dithionite solution should serve to remove iron. Or a control section may be subjected to the ferrocyanide test (p. 407).

Since Wigglesworth's iron sulfide method (p. 171) is said to demonstrate carboxylic acids as well as phosphoric acid complexes, this method might also be applicable to the demonstration of fatty acids.

Tandler's lead sulfide methods are said to demonstrate fatty acids (*Cien. e Invest.* 8:44, 1952) and phosphoric acids (*Arch. Histol. Norm. y Pat.* 4:275, 1951). He employs a primary 12 hour fixation in 10% neutral lead acetate, with or without about 0.2% picric acid included, or in 5% lead acetate with a few drops up to 1% acetic acid. After this, tissues are washed thoroughly in water.

At this point tissues intended for demonstration of phosphoric esters are dehydrated, cleared, imbedded in paraffin, sectioned, deparaffinized and brought either into 70% alcohol containing 2% yellow ammonium sulfide or into saturated hydrogen sulfide water.

Tissues intended for demonstration of fatty acid esters are treated with very dilute (0.7–0.5%) ammonium sulfide without prior alcohol treatment and washed and mounted in glycerol.

Lead phosphate esters are insoluble in alcohol, chloroform, xylene and alcohol ether, but soluble in dilute acetic acid. Even 0.5% will remove them in a short time. Unsaturated fatty acid lead soaps are soluble in alcohol (70–80%), while saturated fatty acid lead salts resist alcohol but are dissolved by xylene, chloroform, etc. Both types of lead soaps resist extraction in 40% acetic acid.

Substitution of Molnar's rhodizonate method (p. 445) should give a darker color in both technics, and permit final dehydration and mounting in a resinous medium.

I question whether the differential solubilities of the lead soaps are sufficiently great to permit their histochemical differentiation.

Meyer-Brunot (Z. *wiss. Mikr.* 60:476, 1952) adapts the Gomori lead sulfide lipase technic for the differentiation of fatty acids and neutral fats.

1. Fix smears by heating on an albumen glycerol smeared slide over a small flame.
2. Immerse in 0.5% calcium chloride in 0.5% Veronal sodium solution (pH 9.4) for 10 minutes, thereby converting free fatty acids to calcium soaps.
3. Wash thoroughly and immerse for 10 minutes in 2% lead nitrate solution, converting the calcium soaps to lead soaps.
4. Wash thoroughly in water and immerse for 30 seconds in dilute ammonium sulfide—I suggest 1:50 dilution—thus converting lead soaps to sulfide; or in 0.5% potassium bichromate, forming the yellow lead chromate (p. 444).
5. For neutral fats, counterstain with Sudan III as usual (pp. 456–458).

Undoubtedly the method can be applied to frozen sections of formalin fixed material. Treatment with 1% acetic acid after step 3 to dissolve lead phosphate would tend, according to Tandler (p. 463), to eliminate lead phosphate derived from cell nuclei. Use of rhodizonate (p. 445) in place of ammonium sulfide could give a darker color to the lead deposits.

Cain (*J. Anat.* 84:196, 1950) again stresses the view (from which I strongly dissent, agreeing rather with Smith's original report) that Nile blue sulfate solutions containing the red oxazone which Lison calls Nile red behave simply as mixtures of a (rather inefficient) oil soluble dye and a blue basic dye which colors nucleic acids and other acid bearing tissue elements as well as the open carboxyl groups of free fatty acids. Staining with the red oxazone component does not indicate unsaturation, but appears to be governed by the staining temperature and the melting point of the specific fats and fatty acids concerned. Solid fats do not readily stain with oil soluble dyes at temperatures far below their melting points. The melting points of the fatty acids are: oleic 14°C, palmitic 63°C, and stearic 70°C; of their glyceryl esters, respectively, 4°C, 65°C and 71°C.

The technics are simple. Fix in formalin, cut frozen sections, stain 20–30 minutes in 0.1–0.15% aqueous solution of Nile blue, differentiate 1–20 minutes in 1% acetic acid, wash well in tap water and mount in lukewarm glycerol gelatin, or in a buffered neutral gum syrup (p. 100). (Modified from Romeis.) To include the high melting fats in the stained substances, raise the staining temperature to 70°C. I suggest buffering the Nile blue to pH 2.5 or 3 with acetates to eliminate if possible the necessity for regressive differentiation. Staining for 20 minutes in 0.1% Nile blue in 1% acetic acid, followed by washing in water and mounting in glycerol gelatin, has given sharply selective staining of certain lipofuscin pigments.

Further exploration (*J. Histochem.* 4:377, 1956) disclosed that the method could be made more specific for fatty acids by doing it at a pH level below that at which carboxylic and phosphoric acid residues stain with basic dyes. It was found that lipofuscins, pepsinogen granules and *in vitro* fatty acids stained dark blue when exposed to 0.05% Nile blue in 1% sulfuric acid by volume (pH about 0.9). If such sections are dehydrated directly with acetone, the blue staining is at once lost from the pigment and peptic zymogen granules, only mast cells and perhaps cartilage retaining the stain. But if, instead, mounting is done in glycerol gelatin or syrup, the fatty acid residues remain dark blue. The latter staining does not occur with the usual blue thiazin dyes of the thionin, azure, methylene blue group. However, if the pH level of staining is raised to 3 or 3.5 (H_2SO_4—KH_2PO_4 buffer, p. 659), staining of carboxylic acid residues occurs alike with Nile blue and the thiazins, and preparations may be dehydrated and mounted in resins. The staining of lipofuscins is green, however, and easily distinguished from the dark blue of the glycerol gelatin mounts.

Liquid neutral fats, shaken with this sulfuric acid Nile blue solution, color red. Addition of a drop or two of anhydrous acetic or propionic acid changes the color to dark blue; shaking with distilled water takes the acetic acid out of the oil and restores the red color. Methyl esters of fatty acids also color red when shaken with Nile blue, but the technic of methylation is applicable only to the histochemical study of such lipids as are insoluble in hot methanol.

Not all samples of Nile blue are satisfactory for this technic, even when certified. Naturally, the above procedure on staining of fatty acid materials which are then dehydrated applies only to the insoluble or relatively insoluble fatty acid complexes.

Lillie's Sulfuric Nile Blue Technic for Fatty Acids (*Stain Techn.* 31: 151, 1956). Use frozen, attached cryostat or paraffin sections, according to the nature of the material under study. Bring sections to water.

1. Stain 20 minutes in 0.05% Nile blue in 1 cc concentrated sulfuric acid +99 cc distilled water. (Dissolve dye in water and add acid.)
2. Wash 10 minutes in running water. Mount in glycerol gelatin.

Results: Fatty acids, dark blue. Neutral fats, pink to red.

It is to be noted that all technics using acid Nile blue solutions will decompose calcium soaps and stain their fatty acid residues.

Acid Fastness. The mechanism of acid fastness of mycobacteria has been much discussed. It has been attributed to mycolic acid, to a hypothetical capsule, to a peculiar deoxyribonucleic acid or to an oil solubility phenomenon similar to fat staining. The sudanophilia of the organisms supports this. Lartigue and Fite (*J. Histochem.* 10:611, 1962) support the last theory and stress the need for some phenol or phenol-like substances in the staining solution to facilitate the penetration of the dye. They also note the resistance to fat solvents shown in Table 13-1, but do not mention hot pyridine.

TABLE 13-1. ACID FASTNESS AFTER VARIOUS BLOCKADE REACTIONS[1]

Blocking agent	End group	Hair cortex	Rat liver ceroid	*Mcb. tuberculosis*
5% Phenylhydrazine hydrochloride	—CHO	24 hr, 25°C Unimpaired	24 hr, 25°C Unimpaired	24 hr, 25°C Unimpaired
1 *M* Aniline chloride.....	—CHO	24 hr, 25°C Unimpaired	24 hr, 25°C Unimpaired	24 hr, 25°C Unimpaired
40% Acetic anhydride/ pyridine	—OH, —NH₂	60 hr, 60°C Unimpaired	4 hr, 60°C Unimpaired	4 hr, 25°C Lost
1 *N* NaNO₂/1 *N* HAc...	—NH₂	4 hr, 25°C Unimpaired	4 hr, 25°C Unimpaired	4 hr, 25°C Unimpaired
0.1 *N* HCl/MeOH......	—COOH —PO₄H —SO₄H	3–7 days, 25°C 24 hr, 60°C Impaired	7 days, 25°C Lost	2 hr, 25°C Lost
CCl₄.................	Lipid	24 hr, 25°C Unimpaired	24 hr, 25°C Unimpaired	24 hr, 25°C Unimpaired
Pyridine..............	Lipid	6 hr, 60°C Unimpaired	24 hr, 60°C Unimpaired	2–4 hr, 60°C Lost
Methanol..............	Lipid	7 days, 60°C Unimpaired	7 days, 60°C Unimpaired	7 days, 60°C Unimpaired

[1] The tissues used were fixed in formalin and imbedded in paraffin.
SOURCE: From Lillie and Bangle, *J. Histochem.* **2**:300, 1954.

Our 1954 data indicate that the acid fastness of lipofuscins, as typified by ceroid, and of hair cortex and mycobacteria are not necessarily identical. However, in all three the reaction is impaired or abolished by methylation, while hot methanol is without effect.

It is perhaps worthy of note that the *Colour Index* records a number of amine dye bases as much more soluble in fatty acids than in neutral fats. Rosaniline base affords a particularly striking example. Its solubility in oleic and stearic acids is recorded as 20 and 15%; other solvents dissolve either none (linseed oil, paraffin, mineral oil, "white spirit," toluene) or quite small amounts (ethanol 0.3, acetone 0.6, benzene 0.2, butyl acetate 0.5, ethyl acetate very slightly soluble).

CARBONYL LIPIDS

This class probably includes ketosteroids, as well as plasmalogens and various ill defined, readily soluble lipids which give aldehyde and ketone reactions. Verne derives them from ethylenic oxidation products. Since ethylenic linkages readily oxidize in air to epoxides and peroxides which hydrolyze respectively to 1,2-glycols and to aldehydes, this derivation is not improbable.

Cain (*Quart. J. Micr. Sci.* **90**:411, 1949) considers this latter group distinct from true plasmalogens, which become Schiff positive promptly on treatment with mercuric chloride solutions, while ethylenic derivatives oxidize slowly to aldehydes and the ethylenic linkages themselves react slowly with Schiff reagent. This last I question.

The lipids demonstrated by Liang (*Anat. Rec.* **97**:419, 1947) in axis cylinders of nerves are believed by Chu (*Anat. Rec.* **108**:723, 1950) to be unsaturated fatty acid lecithin esters, which he says react directly with Schiff reagent. In view of the slow reaction of ethylenic groups observed by Cain and by us, it seems more probable that Chu was dealing with intermediate peroxidation products of the unsaturated fat.

Seligman considers that his hydroxynaphthoic acid hydrazide method demonstrates ketones as well as aldehydes, and gave two supplemental tests for the distinction of the latter.

The following carbonyl method of Seligman and Ashbel (*Cancer* **4**:579, 1951) has been altered slightly to accord with the report of Herman and Dempsey (*Stain Techn.* **26**:185, 1951), with certain variations of our own and with Seligman and Ashbel (*Endocrinology* **50**:338, 1952).

M. L. Karnovsky and H. W. Deane (*J. Histochem.* **3**:85, 1955) have shown reasonably conclusively that the supposed histochemically demonstrable ketosteroids are actually autoxidation artifacts: aldehydes arising by oxidation of unsaturated lipids during formalin (and other) fixations. Nevertheless I retain the method as the only reasonably workable strongly chromogenic one which should show ketones as well as aldehydes. A comparison should always be made with the Schiff reaction and with the *m*-aminophenol fast black K technic which should show aldehydes alone. The latter, unfortunately, is not applicable to readily soluble lipids as at present developed, since these are readily soluble in the glacial acetic acid in which the Schiff's base condensation reaction is effected. It is probable that if the amine were treated with a stoichiometric equivalent of concentrated HCl a water soluble chloride would be formed, as with aniline.

The Seligman-Ashbel Method for Active Carbonyl Groups.

1. Fix in 10% formalin, cut frozen sections at 10–20 μ, float onto slides and dry for 10 minutes to make sections adhere.
2. Wash in water for 2 hours to remove formaldehyde.
3. Stain controls by oil red O as usual (p. 457). Perform solvent tests on experimental material and bring sections back to water. Omit this step in plain demonstration technic.
4. Immerse extracted and unextracted sections for 2 hours at 25°C in a fresh 0.1% solution of 2-hydroxy-3-naphthoic acid hydrazide. (Dissolve

40 mg in 2 cc hot glacial acetic acid, add 38 cc freshly prepared 50% alcohol.)

5. Wash in 4 changes each of 5% acetic in 50% alcohol, of 50% alcohol, and of distilled water, of 2 minutes each (total 12 washes, 24 minutes). Or (Seligman and Ashbel, 1952) 6 washes of 50% alcohol, 20 minutes each; and 1 of 30 minutes in 0.5 N hydrochloric acid; followed by rinses in water and in 1% sodium bicarbonate.

6. Mix 25 cc of 0.67 M pH 7.4 phosphate buffer with 25 cc of 100% alcohol. Introduce slides, dissolve 50 mg fast black B or fast blue B, pour at once over slides in a Coplin jar, and let stand 2 minutes.

7. Wash in 0.1% acetic acid and in water.

8. Counterstain in 0.1% safranin in 0.1% acetic acid for 1–2 minutes, if desired. Wash in water.

9. Mount in glycerol gelatin, Arlex gelatin or the like; *or* dehydrate quickly with alcohol, clear with xylene and mount in polystyrene or other synthetic resin.

Results: "Active" carbonyl in dark blue or greenish blue. Myelin and ceroid from frozen sections are stained. Compare with similar sections reacted 20 minutes at step 4 with Schiff reagent and treated with bisulfite as usual. Ketones react only slowly with Schiff reagent.

Pearse (1960, p. 867) cites a method for "α-ketol groups of corticoids" from Khanolkar (*Indian J. Path. Bact.* 1:84, 1958), stating that the theoretical specificity is high, and is supported by *in vitro* tests.

1. Attach cryostat section of fresh tissue to slides and immerse 20 minutes in aniline 10 + glacial acetic acid 90, to block preexisting aldehydes.

2. Wash gently for 1–3 minutes in distilled water.

3. Oxidize 30 minutes at 50°C in 5% ferric chloride.

4. Rinse gently in distilled water.

5. Immerse 20 minutes in Schiff reagent.

6. Wash in 3 changes of bisulfite water as usual.

7. Mount in glycerol gelatin.

Corticosteroids stain magenta; androgens, estrogens, pregnanediol and cholesterol do not react.

Comments. Step 1 or a similar immersion in glacial acetic acid appears to remove all the birefringent crystals of adrenal cortex and all lipids stainable by Sudan black B except lipofuscins. Substitution of phenylhydrazine or its 2,4-dinitro derivative in this step blocks not only the direct Schiff reaction of adrenal cortex and atheroma but also the essentially equal one produced by ferric chloride. I suspect that the aldehydes demonstrable by the Schiff reaction, with or without ferric chloride oxidation, are the usual lipid aldehydes from oxidation of unsaturated fats, and that when these are blocked by *adequate aqueous* blockade methods, such as phenylhydrazine hydrochloride (0.5 *M*, 24 hours), the amount of new aldehyde producible by ferric chloride oxidation will be too small to permit histochemical detection.

In any case it is to be noted that after a 24 hour phenylhydrazine blockade of the periodic acid Schiff reaction of gastric mucosa, a similar ferric chloride treatment reengenders a partially positive Schiff reaction of the epithelial mucin. So the possibility of a positive lipid aldehyde reaction arising by reoxidation or hydrolysis of previously blocked aldehyde is not to be disregarded.

PLASMALOGENS

Plasmalogens are phosphatidalcholines or -ethanolamines in which the γ fatty acid is replaced by an unsaturated ether group. On hydrolysis of the ether an α-β-unsaturated alcohol is formed and promptly converts to aldehyde by enol-ketol shift. The alcohol soluble aldehyde may then be demonstrated with Schiff reagent as in Feulgen's plasmal reaction, or with a phenylhydrazine as in Bennett's reaction (*Am. J. Anat.* **67**:151, 1940).

These plasmalogens occur in adrenal cortex, corpus luteum, mammary and preputial glands, myelin sheaths and fat cells. They also are found in some tissues showing no sudanophilic substances, such as muscle, kidney, liver, thyroid epithelium, prostatic and seminal vesicle epithelium and elastic fibrils generally. They are readily soluble in alcohol and other fat solvents. Nuclei react neither to the Feulgen plasmal method nor to the dinitrophenylhydrazine method.

The technics generally used employ Schiff reagent or a hydrazine to couple with the open carbonyl group. The first group includes the technic of Feulgen and its modifications: the use of frozen sections of unfixed tissue oxidized or hydrolyzed with mercuric chloride to release *plasmal* from *plasmalogens;* the technic of Verne—the use of tissue fixed in mercuric chloride or platinum chloride without controls; and the technic of Gerard—in which frozen sections of formaldehyde fixed tissue are carefully washed in water and then treated with mercuric chloride. Untreated controls are used with the Feulgen and Gerard methods.

The second group includes the methods of Bennett, employing phenylhydrazine or dinitrophenylhydrazine, which form yellow aldehyde complexes; and those of Seligman and Ashbel, in which 3-hydroxy-2-naphthoic acid hydrazide is first reacted with tissue carbonyls and then coupled with a stabilized diazonium salt to yield a colored compound.

For the dinitrophenylhydrazine reaction Albert and Leblond prescribe 48-hour fixation in 10% formalin (neutralized with magnesium carbonate), 24 hours' washing in running water, and frozen sections at 10–15 μ. (1)

Extract frozen sections for 4 hours in 17% alcohol. (2) Soak overnight in saturated 30% alcohol solution of 2,4-dinitrophenylhydrazine 17 cc plus 0.2 N (1.64%) aqueous sodium acetate 13 cc (emended; authors stated simply "enough to raise the pH to neutrality,"[1] noting a decrease of alcohol content to 17%). (3) Wash 20 minutes in 17% alcohol to remove excess stain. (4) Wash in distilled water and mount in glycerol gelatin. The positive reaction is a yellow color.

For the Feulgen plasmal reaction Albert and Leblond fix, wash and section as above.

Comment. The use of such a long formaldehyde fixation without inclusion of a reducing agent should provide ready opportunity for spontaneous autooxidation of unsaturated fats, with formation of peroxides and aldehydes. Substitution of attached cryostat sections, treated with $HgCl_2$, as in the method of Ferrans and Hack for step 1 in the foregoing dinitrophenylhydrazine reaction, should operate to restrict it to plasmal lipids. A Seligmen-Ashbel technic using the 3-hydroxy-2-naphthoic acid hydrazide fast blue B sequence as the demonstration reaction could be similarly modified.

Hayes (*Stain Techn.* **24**:19, 1949) has redefined the plasmal reaction to make it more specific for acetal lipids.

The Plasmal Reaction of Feulgen and Voit, Hayes' 1949 Modification.

1. Cut frozen sections of tissues at 15 μ either unfixed or fixed in neutral 10% formalin for *less than 6 hours*. Or use unfixed smears or impression preparations. [Immerse unfixed tissue in (15%) aqueous gum arabic solution for 5–10 minutes and freeze in a drop of the same to facilitate sectioning; or use Hack's polyethylene glycol method, p. 65.] The use of attached cryostat sections of unfixed tissue is suggested.
2. Wash in several changes of 0.9% sodium chloride solution. (Use distilled water if sections are formalin fixed.)
3. Place sections in 1% mercuric chloride solution for 2–10 minutes to allow complete penetration. For controls omit this step. Rinse glass section lifters before going into mercury solution.
4. Transfer mercury treated and control sections directly to separate small, closed dishes of Schiff reagent and let stand 5–15 minutes. Controls should remain negative. (Discard used Schiff reagent daily.)
5. Wash in 3 changes of 0.5% $NaHSO_3$ in 0.05 N HCl, of 2 minutes each.
6. Wash in several changes of water, float onto slides and blot down.
7. Counterstain briefly in 0.5% methyl green in 0.5% acetic or in acetic hemalum (0.1% hematoxylin 2% acetic) for 2 minutes. Wash in water. Blot.

[1] Cf. Walpole's buffers, p. 661.

8. Treat successively with 95% alcohol, 100% alcohol, 100% alcohol + xylene (1:1) and 2 changes of xylene. Blot between changes if necessary. Mount in synthetic resin: polystyrene, Permount, HSR, etc.

Results: Aldehyde sites (plasmal ?) in red. It is not clear how the alcohol soluble aldehyde is insolubilized to resist step 8, and no alcohol extraction control before step 3 is prescribed.

Norton *et al.* (*J. Histochem.* **10:**375, 1962) fix ox adrenals and rat brains in Baker's calcium cadmium formalin with an excess of calcium carbonate pH 5.7–5.8 or in calcium acrolein: Freshly distilled acrolein 10 cc, water 90 cc, calcium chloride 1 gm, hydroquinone 50 mg, calcium carbonate in excess (pH 6.4–6.8). The mixture is stable for several days at 3–5°C. Fixation intervals should be short, 1–3 hours, and blocks should be 3–4 mm thick only. Norton and coworkers used the Hayes technic for their histologic studies. From concurrent chemical work it appeared that 90% of plasmalogen was phosphatidal ethanolamine. **Acrolein** was so bound as to give **much additional (artifactual) aldehyde reactivity** (see "Acrolein Schiff Reaction," p. 40). The use of acrolein fixation in plasmal studies seems contraindicated.

Ferrans, Hack and Borowitz (*J. Histochem.* **10:**462, 1962) now identify the actual aldehyde producing substance as an α,β-unsaturated glyceryl ether and consider that the acetal phosphatides are degradation products formed during isolation. They used cryostat sections or freeze dry Carbowax sections of unfixed tissue.

1. Immerse sections 2 minutes in 1.358% (50 mM) mercuric chloride.
2. Distilled water 1 minute.
3. Schiff reagent 10 minutes.
4. Wash in 3 changes 0.05 M sulfurous acid.
5. Mount in glycerol and seal with lacquer.

Controls. A, omit step 1; B, extract with 2:1 chloroform methanol before step 1. A reveals native, including lipid, aldehydes. B reveals nonlipid or insoluble lipid aldehyde.

West and Todd formulate the plasmalogen as phosphatidal cholines or phosphatidal ethanolamines in which the γ fatty acid is replaced by an unsaturated ether group, which on hydrolysis

undergoes an enol-ketol shift to form an alcohol soluble aldehyde.

BIREFRINGENT LIPIDS

Polarized Light. When examined in the dark field produced by crossing polaroids or Nicol prisms, neutral fats ordinarily remain dark. Substances forming Lehmann's "liquid crystals," such as cholesteryl esters, phosphatides and cerebrosides, may exhibit the black cross of polarization with luminous quadrants between the arms of the cross filling out a circle. This phenomenon is suppressed if the temperature is above that at which the liquid crystals in question can exist and the globules remain dark. Any fatty substance in solid crystalline form may be luminous under polarized light. Sections showing such crystals should be compared with paraffin sections of the same tissue, where the luminous crystals should be absent if they are fatty in nature. Or a control frozen section may be extracted 10 minutes in methanol + chloroform.

The use of polarized light has been suggested by Prickett and Stevens (*Am. J. Path.* **15**:241, 1939) as a means of differentiating between normal birefringent myelin and degenerating singly refractile myelin. In practice I have not found this method particularly helpful.

In cutaneous xanthomata, this means of examination reveals more or less numerous, fine, needle shaped, doubly refractile crystals associated with more plentiful isotropic sudanophilic fat droplets. These tumors often contain iron positive pigment as well, and the fat may be cholesterol positive. Here it would be of interest to apply the combined ferrocyanide + oil red O technic (p. 407).

CHOLESTEROL

Cholesterol is often manifest in necrotic tissue and in the granulomatous tissue replacing it as long rhomboidal crystals which glow under polarized light and are extinguished and light up alternately once in each 90°C of rotation of the stage.

The Schultz Method. Cholesterol may be more definitely identified by Schultz's (*Zbl. allg. Path.* **35**:314, 1924) adaptation to histology of the Liebermann-Burchardt sterol reaction. The technic as modified by Mallory follows:

1. Cut thin (10–15 μ) frozen sections of formalin fixed tissue.
2. Mordant sections in a closely stoppered bottle for 3 days (Schmorl: 2–4 days) at 37°C in 2.5% iron alum solution (or 1.4% $FeCl_3 \cdot 6H_2O$). (Hershberger, in my laboratory, finds that 1–3 minutes in 3% hydrogen peroxide or in 1% sodium iodate will suffice in place of the iron alum.)

3. Rinse in distilled water, float onto slides and blot dry.
4. Treat with a few drops of acetic sulfuric mixture made as follows: Place 2–5 cc glacial acetic acid in a small test tube and immerse in ice water. Then add gradually the same volume of concentrated sulfuric acid while the tube is still in the ice water.
5. Cover with a coverglass and examine at once. The preparations may be kept for a few days if sealed with petrolatum.

Results: A blue green color appears in a few seconds, becoming stronger in the first few minutes and often turning to brown in half an hour. Or the blue green color may persist as long as 24 hours. Positive controls such as sections of previously tested adrenal cortex should always be used. At least 2 sections (3 would be better) of the material under test should be treated with the acetic sulfuric mixture and examined, before considering the test negative. The presence of glycerol inhibits the test; but if stearic acid is present as well, the inhibition is destroyed. Both cholesterol and cholesteryl esters react.

Lewis and Lobban (*J. Histochem.* 9:2, 1961) modified the traditional Schultz test by using a sulfuric acid mixture containing 0.5% iron alum (or 0.28% $FeCl_3 \cdot 6H_2O$), 20–30% water and no acetic acid. With this modified reagent cholesterol itself reacts weakly, yielding a weak red color only after some 15 minutes, but other steroids react more promptly and with stronger colors. Premordanting 2–3 days in 2.5% ferric alum enhances the color.

Method of Lewis and Lobban for Sterols.

1. Cut frozen or polyvinyl alcohol or gelatin sections as usual. Cryostat sections should be thawed onto slides and dried a few minutes to insure adhesion.
2. Treat sections in 2.5% ferric ammonium alum (or 1.4% $FeCl_3 \cdot 6H_2O$) at 37°C for 1–3 days; at 25°C, 2–4 days may be tried.
3. Blot firmly onto slides and apply a drop of sulfuric acid iron alum reagent and cover at once with coverslip. Examine.

Reagent. Add cautiously 4 cc concentrated sulfuric acid (sp. gr. 1.84) to 1 cc 2.5% iron alum[1] in distilled water. Cool the mixture by immersing test tube in cold water. The mixture is stable for a week or two.

[1] An 0.84% solution of anhydrous ferric chloride = 1.4% $FeCl_3 \cdot 6H_2O$ (0.05 M) should serve, if ferric ammonium alum is not readily available.

Results: Testosterone, Δ^4-androstene-3,17-dione, dihydrotestosterone, dihydro-iso-androsterone and androsterone yield blue green colors developing in 6–10 minutes. The androsterone color is the weakest and is more of a brown green. Pregnenolone, pregnanedione, methyl testosterone and α-estradiol yield strong to moderate purple red to pink colors, developing in 4–10 minutes. Pink to weak red colors develop in 10–12 minutes with progesterone and 11-dehydro-17-hydroxycorticosterone; after 15 minutes cholesterol gives a weak red, which is weakened further as the water content of the reagent is increased.

Controls. Unmordanted frozen sections are treated as above with iron free 80% (v/v) sulfuric acid. If the red colors seen in the test were due to steroids, they should fail to appear.

Apparently the **Golodetz reaction** (Schmorl, Romeis) was a procedure closely related to the foregoing. In it frozen sections were treated 1–2 minutes in a mixture of 5 cc concentrated sulfuric acid and 2 cc 30% formalin, and "cholesterol" developed a brown red color. Romeis questioned the specificity of the reaction, since a blackish brown color was given also by various phenols, fats and oils.

Windaus's Digitonin Reaction (Hoppe Seylers Z. *physiol. Chem.* **65:** 110, 1910). This is a reaction for free sterols. All writers caution about absolute cleanliness of slides and coverslips, since cholesterol is present in sweat, and hence fingerprints give positive reactions. This is particularly important when the reaction is carried out on the slide under a coverglass on fresh or formalin fixed material. Cowdry recommends a variant of Lison's which seems to avoid this difficulty, thus: Fix in formalin and cut frozen sections. Immerse sections in a 0.5% solution of digitonin in 50% alcohol in a small covered dish for several hours. Rinse in 50% alcohol. Counterstain part of the sections only, by the usual hematoxylin Sudan IV or oil red O technic. Mount all sections as usual in Apáthy's gum syrup or a glycerol gelatin.

Examine the uncounterstained sections under polarized light with crossed nicols. Needles or rosettes of complex cholesteryl digitonids are formed. In the counterstained preparations the cholesterol compound remains doubly refractile and does not stain, but the cholesteryl ester compound colors with the oil soluble dye and loses its birefringence.

The digitonin cholesterid crystals are insoluble in cold 95% alcohol, acetone, ether or water; slightly soluble in hot ethyl alcohol and in methyl alcohol; readily soluble in glacial acetic acid; and very soluble in pyridine and in chloral hydrate.

Cholesterol is not blackened by osmium tetroxide. It is soluble in acetone, ether, benzene, xylene and strong alcohol. There is some loss of doubly refractile material from adrenal cortex after treatment with 70% alcohol, more loss with 80%, and complete loss with 95–100%.

MYELIN LIPIDS

Chemical Considerations. A number of papers have appeared recently bearing on the alteration of extractable brain lipids occasioned by exposures to formaldehyde for a varying period of time. The inference is fairly plain that those lipids which do not appear in extracts and are not converted into others which do must represent those retained in tissue and are demonstrated by various largely empirical histologic procedures.

Heslinga and Deierkauf (*J. Histochem.* **9**:572, 1961; **10**:79, 704, 1962) have published a series of papers on human, ox and rat brain lipids and their chromatographic distribution as modified by the action of formaldehyde and other fixatives. Fresh brain yielded 7 fractions: F, near the front, of cholesterol, cholesterin esters and glycerides; E, phosphatidylethanolamine; D, phosphatidylserine; C, lecithins; B, sphingomyelin and lysophosphatidylethanolamine; A, a double spot of lysolecithin and the larger half of phosphoinositides and cerebrosides. The starting spot was not characterized.

Formaldehyde fixation, even in 19 hours, largely suppresses the phosphatidylethanolamine spot; in 93 hours this change is further advanced.

Prolonged fixation, over a year, also decreases lecithin but increases the lyso compounds in spots A and B (lysolecithin and lysophosphatidylethanolamine).

Mercuric chloride apparently forms addition complexes with the more unsaturated lipids, so that spots E, C and B also appear double (phosphatidylethanolamine, lecithin and lysophosphatidylethanolamine).

Chromic acid and dichromate render 50% or more of the lipids insoluble and partly polymerize lipids bound to an insoluble aggregate of chromous hydroxides (Heslinga, Thesis, Leiden, 1957). It is undoubtedly this chromous hydroxide which serves to bind hematoxylin in the Weigert-Smith-Dietrich-Baker-Elftman myelin and phospholipid methods which do not employ an iron hematoxylin. The various fractions in the chromatograms exhibit oxidation "tailing" and a decrease of distinguishable fractions.

With osmium tetroxide the fusion and the tailing of the spots are even more pronounced and extend back to the starting spot. Spots D and E (phosphatidylserine and phosphatidylethanolamine) have disappeared.

Later studies indicated considerable diminution of both amount and mobility of phosphatidylethanolamine and its lyso derivative. About a third of the lecithin is changed to lysolecithin. Other lipids seem little altered by formaldehyde. Sulfatides are now recognized as present in the same fraction as cerebrosides. The front spot F is increased by an increment of free fatty acids almost corresponding to the losses in the 2 ethanolamine fractions.

Altogether, little if any lipid is insolubilized by formalin. In this regard the histochemical and chemical findings appear to conflict. But the chemical report nowhere relates the total amount of extractable lipid to fresh wet weights, to dry weights or to total protein nitrogen, and it is not clear that the total amount of extractable lipid has not decreased.

The papers of Riemersma and Booij (*J. Histochem.* 9:560, 1961; 10:89, 1962) establish spectrophotometrically and gravimetrically that lecithin binds osmium tetroxide in the proportion of 1 mol per double bond. This was true also for oleic acid, methyl oleate, decene and octadecene.

Classification. Besides a small amount of neutral fat, cholesterol esters and cholesterol, the myelin lipids include phospholipids: lecithins, cephalins, diphosphoinositides and sphingomyelin, as well as readily extractable plasmalogens; and cerebrosides, sulfatides, gangliosides, strandin and proteolipid. Altogether these make up about 27.7% of white substance and 9.87% of gray (West and Todd).

The **lecithins,** or phosphatidylcholines, are generally α-phosphate esters of a glycerol residue which also carries in ester linkage 2 fatty acid residues, joined by the phosphate to a choline residue.

The fatty acids found in lecithins are palmitic, stearic, oleic, linoleic, linolenic and arachidonic. The 2 residues are commonly dissimilar and may be one saturated and one unsaturated, both saturated or both unsaturated. Lecithins are precipitated by acetone from their colloidal aqueous solutions, but they are soluble in other fat solvents.

$$\gamma \qquad H_2C\text{—O—CO—R}$$
$$\beta \ RCO\text{—O—}CH \qquad O$$
$$\alpha \qquad H_2C\text{—O—}P\text{—O—}CH_2CH_2N(CH_3)_3^+$$
$$O-$$

Glyceride   Phosphate Choline

In the course of formaldehyde fixation part of the lecithin is converted to lysolecithin, a compound in which the γ-fatty acid residue is lost, probably by hydrolysis, since there is an increase in the fat, cholesterol and fatty acid portion in chromatograms.

The lecithins (Baker, *Quart. J. Micr. Sci.* 87:441, 1946) react to the Smith-Dietrich-Baker type of procedure. The suggested mechanism is that the unsaturated fatty acid residues undergo oxidation by bichromate, with polymerization and consequent loss of solubility. Concurrently with this process Cr^{+++} is bound to the oxidation sites and serves to bind such mordant dyes as hematoxylin in a colored lake.

The **cephalins** include phosphatidylethanomalines and phosphatidylserines, in which the 2 nitrogenous compounds replace the choline of the lecithins in an otherwise similar structure.

$$
\begin{array}{c}
H_2C\!-\!O\!-\!CO\!-\!R' \\
| \\
R^2\!-\!CO\!-\!O\!-\!CH \qquad O \\
| \qquad\qquad \parallel \\
H_2C\!-\!O\!-\!P\!-\!O\!-\!CH_2CH_2\!-\!\overset{+}{N}H_3 \\
| \\
O\!- \\
\end{array}
$$

| Glyceride | Phos-
phate | Ethanolamine
(colamine) |

$$
\begin{array}{c}
H_2C\!-\!O\!-\!CO\!-\!R' \\
| \\
R^2\!-\!CO\!-\!O\!-\!CH \qquad O \\
| \qquad\qquad \parallel \\
H_2C\!-\!O\!-\!P\!-\!O\!-\!CH_2CH\!-\!COOH \\
| \qquad\qquad\quad | \\
O\!- \qquad\qquad \overset{+}{N}H_3 \\
\end{array}
$$

| Glyceride | Phosphate | Serine |

Like the lecithins the cephalins also lose γ-fatty acid residues during formaldehyde fixation to form lysophosphatidylethanolamine and -serine. They are among the lipids stained black by Baker's procedure.

The **plasmalogens,** which are also included among the phospholipids, have already been considered (pp. 469–471).

On **diphosphoinositides** we have no information regarding behavior toward histochemical staining procedures. From their structure the inositol groups should probably form aldehyde with periodic or chromic acid, but unless the fatty acid residue, which is unidentified, should prove to be polyene, the compound might well remain soluble in fat solvents despite formaldehyde or chromate fixation.

In **sphingomyelin** the fatty acid glyceride residue of lecithin is replaced by sphingosine (1,3-dihydroxy-2-amino-4-trans-octadecene), in which the amino group forms an amide with a fatty acid. Such sphingosine amides are called "ceramides."

The **cerebrosides** are galactosides or ceramides and are named by the fatty acid residue forming the amide group. Phrenosine, or cerebron, contains cerebronic acid; kerasin, lignoceric acid; nervon, nervonic acid; and oxynervon, oxynervonic acid.

When carbon 6 of the galactose residue is sulfated, the resultant lipids are called **sulfatides,** which occur in both gray and white substance.

Holländer (*J. Histochem.* 11:118, 1963) proposes a method for demonstration of sulfuric esters of cerebrosides based on their metachromatic basophilia at low pH levels.

Cerebroside Sulfuric Esters in Brain.

1. Fix in 10% formalin, cut frozen sections at 20–30 μ.
2. Stain 6 minutes in 1/20,000 (5 mg/100 cc) acriflavine in 0.1 M citrate HCl buffer, pH 2.5.
3. Wash 1 minute in 70% isopropanol.
4. Transfer to mixture of 15 cc 2% p-dimethylaminobenzaldehyde in 6 N HCl and 35 cc isopropyl alcohol for 75 seconds.
5. Wash in distilled water.
6. Counterstain 6 minutes in Mayer's acid hemalum.
7. Wash 15 minutes in running water.
8. Isopropyl alcohol 70%, 80%, 90%, 96%, 100%.
9. Clear in xylene, mount in resin.

For fluorescence microscopy, omit steps 4–7 and use nonfluorescent resin for mounting. The full procedure yields carmine red sulfolipids and blue nuclei. The fluorescence procedure gives golden yellow to orange sulfolipids on light green myelin.

In **gangliosides** the ceramide residue is linked by its terminal alcohol group in glycosidic linkage to a tetrasaccharide consisting in series of 2 hexose residues, N-acetylgalactosamine and sialic acid.

The class of proteolipids makes up about a tenth of the myelin lipids extracted from white substance. They are insoluble in water, soluble in fat solvents and readily cleaved to protein and lipid fractions. Proteolipid A is about 20% protein, 70% cerebroside and a little phosphatide; B is about 50% protein, 20% cerebroside, 15% sphingomyelin and 15% other phosphatides; C is 70–75% protein and 25% phosphatides.

The staining procedures applicable to the foregoing myelin lipids depend on a variety of factors, some common to the group, others restricted to certain members thereof.

Aside from sudanophilia in material untreated with fat solvents, (p. 454) which appears generally applicable to the whole group, the persistent sandanophilia in chromated material after paraffin or celloidin imbedding and sectioning is probably the most generally applicable to the group, though specific data are lacking on some individual lipids. About half the total myelin lipids are thus rendered solvent resistant, and our own experience indicates that there is also much binding of chromium to the soluble fraction coupled with the extensive oxidative changes which occur also in the soluble as well as the insolubilized fractions. I have seen quite extensive sudanophilia of mesenteric fat in formalin fixed human carcinoid material which was postchromed 24 hours at 60°C in pH 3.5 3% $K_2Cr_2O_7$ before paraffin imbedding through an alcohol chloroform sequence.

Although chemical extraction studies do not indicate any extensive insolubilization of myelin lipids by formaldehyde fixation without chromates or other metallic oxidants, there is still quite extensive sudanophilia, particularly well demonstrated with Sudan black B after neutral or acid formalin fixation and routine paraffin imbedding.

That this sudanophilia is due to myelin lipids is indicated by its total abolition when primary fixation is done in hot methanol chloroform or other purely fat solvent fixatives.

For total extraction of lipids I now use a 48 hour fixation at 60°C in methanol chloroform mixtures. The first 18–24 hour period is divided between 2 changes of 2:1 methanol:chloroform; the second working day uses a 4–6 hour bath in 1:1 methanol:chloroform; and the remaining period is divided between 2 changes of 1:2 methanol:chloroform. The extraction is done in tightly sealed screw capped bottles with metal foil solvent resistant inner caps. The fluid level is marked on the outside of each container with a grease pencil, and the bottles are inspected at intervals to see that no evaporation loss is occurring. Heating is normally done in a 60°C paraffin oven. At the end of the heating period blocks are transferred through two 30–60 minute chloroform baths into paraffin directly, or after a sequence of two 1 hour baths in absolute alcohol and alcohol ether into a 1–3 day bath in 1% celloidin in ether alcohol. The thin celloidin infiltrated tissue is then carried through chloroform into paraffin as before. The double imbedding permits thinner sections than the plain paraffin. We have cut 2 cm blocks of human cerebellum serially at 3 μ, without skipping sections.

Ciaccio Positive Lipids. The methods used for demonstration of sudanophilia or staining by oil soluble dyes after paraffin (or celloidin) imbedding and sectioning are all essentially variants of Ciaccio's original method.

It is perhaps of interest that when linseed oil or cod liver oil, which present iodine numbers of 175–202 and 137–166 respectively are oxidized with dichromate *in vitro,* they yield insoluble, basophilic, acid fast lipids. Cod liver oil contains no phosphorus. When these oils are parenterally administered they provoke inflammatory reactions in which after a time the offending oils are identified in nonchromated paraffin imbedded formalin fixed tissue as globules of sudanophil, acid fast, basophilic material coloring blue to violet with Nile blue, black with osmium tetroxide, brown to black with ammoniacal silver carbonate and *gray to black* with the Weil-Weigert myelin stain (Endicott, *Arch. Path.* 37:49, 1944).

Ciaccio's Method (*Anat. Anz.* 35:17, 1909). This method depends on simultaneous formaldehyde and chromate treatment of fresh or formalin fixed tissue, followed by prolonged chromation, dehydration, clearing and paraffin imbedding. Sections are stained in a supersaturated solution of Sudan III or Sudan IV, counterstained in hemalum and mounted in gum syrup. This method stains myelin red; *Ciaccio positive* lipids, orange;

and nuclei, blue. By introducing an osmium tetroxide step just after chromation, Ciaccio stained neutral fats (probably oleins) black.

Simple chromation for 2–4 days after 2 days' or more fixation in 10% formalin seems as effective as Ciaccio's rather elaborate schedule, and nuclear staining is less impaired with the shorter chromation.

Though this and other variants of the classical Ciaccio procedure using Sudan III and Sudan IV are often quite satisfactory for uncolored insoluble lipids, in lipid pigments possessing natural brown colors, the orange tingeing of the native color is often difficult to discern with any degree of certainty. With such lipids it is better to use a blue or dark green, oil soluble dye. Blue to green colorations are easily distinguished from unmodified yellows and brown.

The following technic, devised by Lillie and Laskey (*Bull. Int. A. Med. Mus.* **32**:77, 1951) for the demonstration of the rod acromeres in the retina, works very well on cardiac, ovarian and other similar lipofuscins and ceroid pigments.

Modified Ciaccio Procedure of Lillie and Laskey with Sudan Black B.

1. Fix in calcium acetate formalin or calcium chloride formalin (p. 38). For those lipids which require chromate oxidation, soak in 3% potassium bichromate for 4–8 days, changing every 2 days. Wash out chromate overnight in running water (or siphon washer). For many lipids chromation is unnecessary; and with some, it renders the material useless for other histochemical procedures by oxidizing their reactive groups. Prepare paraffin sections, deparaffinize and hydrate as usual. Frozen (or attached cryostat) sections may be used for comparison or for special multiple solubility tests.
2. Hydrolyze 15 minutes at 60°C in preheated 1 N hydrochloric acid.
3. Transfer directly to Schiff reagent (p. 270) for 10 minutes.
4. Wash 5 minutes in 0.5% sodium metabisulfite, 3 changes of ½–1, 2 and 2 minutes.
5. Wash in running water or in several changes of water.
6. Dilute 20 cc of a 1% solution of Sudan black B in 99% isopropanol with 20 cc of a 1% aqueous solution of borax, (0.026 M). Let stand 10–15 minutes. Filter into a Coplin jar. Stain sections 5 minutes. (See also pp. 420, 459.)
7. Wash 5 minutes in running water.
8. Mount in Arlex gelatin, glycerol gelatin or other aqueous mountant.

Results: Nuclei, red purple; lipids, dark gray green with brown pigments, definitely altered in color toward green or greenish black if lipid positive; background, light greenish gray.

Several batches of slides may be stained successively in the same Coplin jar within the first hour or so after the dilution and filtration of the Sudan black B. Fresh dilutions must be made each day, as further precipitation occurs on longer standing, and the solution loses its supersaturated state.

Longer staining in Sudan black B increases the density of background staining and decreases the contrast. The 50% alcohol solution turns brown in a few days and stains cytoplasm and various other structures gray green, but fails to stain fats.

Oil red O, similarly supersaturated in 50% alcohol, may be used for a red lipid stain in the above technic but requires 1–2 hours for adequate staining. With this a *following* dilute alum hematoxylin counterstain is used in place of the *preceding* Feulgen procedure, steps 1–5.

If the alcoholic Sudan black solution and the aqueous diluent are preheated to 60°C, and then mixed and filtered in the paraffin oven as above, a 5 minute stain at 60°C will color erythrocytes and the granules of eosinophil and neutrophil leucocytes and myelocytes dark gray green, even after formalin fixation and routine paraffin imbedding.

Thomas (*Quart. J. Micr. Sci.* **89**:333, 1948) gives a technic basically similar to the Lillie-Laskey, using 3 day chromation in saturated aqueous potassium bichromate (12% at 20°C) before imbedding and a 7–10 minute stain in a saturated solution of Sudan black B in 70% alcohol, a quick rinse in 50% alcohol, a 3–5 minute counterstain in alum carmine and mounting in Farrants's glycerol gum arabic (p. 101).

The Klüver-Barrera Luxol Fast Blue MBS for Myelinated Fibers. Although at first sight this myelin stain with Luxol Fast Blue MBS or MBSN (duPont) (Azosol Fast Blue HLR, General Dystuffs) C.I. Solvent Blue 38, might appear to be related to the Sudan staining of myelin, since the dye is classed as a solvent (oil soluble) dye, it requires overnight staining at an elevated temperature and prolonged 70% alcohol extraction to remove it from other structures while leaving it in myelin. Since the chemical structure of the dye has not been revealed, it is not proper to regard the method as anything other than an empirical method for myelinated fibers, without histochemical significance. For this purpose it seems to be effective. The *Armed Forces Institute of Pathology Manual* cites a report by Klüver and Barrera (*J. Neuropath. Exp. Neurol.* **12**:400, 1953), which I summarize as follows:

1. Use 15–30 μ celloidin or 15–20 μ paraffin sections of formalin fixed tissue. Deparaffinize and wash in several changes of absolute (2) and 95% (3–4) alcohol.
2. Stain 18–24 hours in 0.1% Luxol fast blue in 95% alcohol, 0.05% acetic acid at 55–60°C.
3. Wash in 95% alcohol and in distilled water and immerse briefly in 0.05% Li_2CO_3.

4. Differentiate in 70% alcohol until gray substance is paler than white, return again briefly (20–30 seconds) to Li_2CO_3 and resume 70% alcohol differentiation (several changes) until colorless gray substance contrasts sharply with blue green white substance.
5. Wash thoroughly in distilled water.
6a. Add 0.4 cc 10% acetic acid to 40 cc 0.1% cresyl echt violet (Chroma) in distilled water, warm (35–40°C?) and counterstain sections 6 minutes (celloidin sections 3 minutes). Differentiate in 95% alcohol, dehydrate in 2 changes of absolute alcohol, clear in xylene and mount in synthetic resin.
6b. Carry through periodic acid Schiff procedures: 0.5% periodic acid, 5 minutes; 2 changes distilled water, Schiff's reagent, 10–30 minutes; bisulfite, 3 changes, 2 minutes each; running water, 5 minutes; alum hematoxylin, 1 minute; tap water (or 0.5% sodium acetate) 5 minutes; acid alcohol 16–30 seconds; alcohols, xylene, Permount.

Results: Myelin, blue green; variant A: Nissl substance, violet; variant B: fungi, basement membranes, other periodic acid Schiff positive substances, red; nuclei, dark blue.

The Traditional Weigert Hematoxylin Methods for Myelin. These depend on chromate oxidation producing polymerization and insolubilization of myelin lipids with concomitant binding of chromium in one of its lower valences. Although I cannot follow Lison's (1960, p. 469) exact formulation of the process, it appears quite probable that a chemical process similar to that which he postulates has occurred, and that the end product is a chelated Cr^{++} or Cr^{+++} ion bound to a complex lipid polymer. Elftman (*J. Histochem.* 2:1, 1954) clearly identifies the bound metal as Cr^{+++}, but does not indicate how it is bound. Empirically the reaction seems to be restricted to phospholipids, but no specific reaction of the phosphate group seems to be involved. It is questionable whether a cephalin or lecithin containing only saturated fatty acids would react.

Of the reactivity of unchromated formalin fixed tissue I shall speak later.

With the **Smith-Dietrich procedure** (*Verhandl. Deutsch. path. Ges.* 14:263, 1910) there is a sequence formalin chromate treatment and an overstaining with ripened acetic hematoxylin followed by differentiation with Weigert's borax potassium ferricyanide and mounting in fructose syrup. In this procedure frozen sections are made after the formalin fixation, and actually no test of solubility in fat solvents is made. Dietrich states that sections may be carried through alcohol and xylene into balsam, with loss of part of the lipids. Mallory notes that the procedure may also stain iron, hemoglobin and blood pigments. Baker (*Quart. J. Micr. Sci.* 85:1, 1944) used it as a reagent for demonstration of the Golgi substance, reducing the borax ferricyanide time from 15 to 8 hours, as follows:

1. Add 1% calcium chloride to 10% formalin and neutralize it with suspended calcium carbonate. Fix tissue in this for 3 days.
2. Imbed tissue in 25% gelatin; or if thinner sections are desired, evaporate it 30 hours in a desiccator over anhydrous calcium chloride at 37°C, stopping the evaporation while the gelatin solution is still liquid.
3. Cool in refrigerator (5°C), cut out tissue block, and harden 1 day in 1% calcium chloride, 1% cadmium chloride, 10% formalin solution.
4. Cut frozen sections at 15 μ from the 25% gelatin, or as thin as 5 μ if the concentration procedure has been used.
5. Attach sections by floating onto slides previously coated with 2.5% gelatin, drained and dried.
6. Expose slides to the fumes of concentrated formalin for 10 minutes to harden the gelatin, and put back into calcium cadmium formalin until required.
7. Wash the slides to be stained by the Smith-Dietrich procedure for 3 minutes in water and
8. Place in cold 5% potassium bichromate solution in a Coplin jar and then place the jar in an oven at 60°C (not 57°C) for 48 hours.
9. Slides should be lifted out of the solution a few times during the first few hours to get rid of air bubbles.
10. Then take out the jar and allow it to cool.
11. Wash slides in several changes of distilled water, and
12. Stain 5 hours in a modified Kultschitzky's hematoxylin (hematoxylin 1 gm, distilled water 98 cc, sodium iodate 0.2 gm,[1] glacial acetic acid 2 cc) at 37°C. The hematoxylin forms a resistant black lake with the chromium held by the lipids.
13. Normally one differentiates in Weigert's 1% borax, 2.5% potassium ferricyanide solution for 15 hours; for Golgi substance, only 8 hours.
14. Then wash slides 5 minutes in running water and mount in glycerol gelatin.

In vitro tests indicate that cephalin and sphingomyelin are stained black. Lecithin is black in the presence of other Smith-Dietrich negative lipids, but not when alone. Galactolipids (cerebrosides) are gray (J. R. Baker, *Quart. J. Micr. Sci.* **85**:1, 1944).

Like Dietrich's method, the foregoing procedure makes no prestaining test of the solubility of the reacting lipids.

Ciaccio (*Bull. Micr. Appl.* **4**:45, 1954) proposes the following modifica-

[1] For usual American hematoxylin, the 200 mg NaIO₃ is excessive; use 50 mg.

tion of the Baker technic: Fix 2–3 hours in Zenker formol, wash (1 hour) in running water, chromate in 5% $K_2Cr_2O_7$ at 60°C for 1 hour, wash in water and cut frozen sections. Or, alternatively, dehydrate in five 1 hour changes of 50%, 60%, 70%, 80%, 90% acetone containing 1% cadmium chloride, then 2 changes, 1 hour each, of anhydrous acetone, and then 1–2 hours in petroleum ether (2 changes?) and infiltration and imbedding in paraffin.

Lipids thus preserved may be stained by the Smith-Dietrich hematoxylin procedure, differentiating in a 1/10 dilution of Weigert's borax ferricyanide mixture, by the periodic acid Schiff procedure, directly with Schiff reagent or by diammine silver hydroxide. They are also stained by basic aniline dyes.

Baker's Acid Hematein Test (*Quart. J. Micr. Sci.* **87**:441, 1946).

1. Fix 6 hours in Baker's calcium chloride formalin (p. 38).
2. Transfer for 18 hours to 5% potassium bichromate containing 1% calcium chloride ($CaCl_2$).
3. Transfer to a second bath of 1% $CaCl_2$, 5% $K_2Cr_2O_7$ for 24 hours at 60°C.
4. Wash 6–18 hours in running water.
5. Cut frozen sections at 10 μ directly, or after Baker's gelatin imbedding (p. 67). Harden the gelatin block 18 hours in calcium chloride formalin, and wash the gelatin block in running water for 30 minutes before sectioning.
6. Incubate sections 1 hour at 60°C in 1% $CaCl_2$, 5% $K_2Cr_2O_7$ solution and wash in several changes of distilled water (5 minutes total).
7. Incubate in acid hematein solution for 5 hours at 37°C. [Acid hematein: Boil 50 mg hematoxylin with 10 mg sodium iodate (1 cc of 1%) in 49 cc distilled water. Cool and add 1 cc glacial acetic acid. Prepare fresh daily.] (The $NaIO_3$ can probably be decreased to 3–5 mg, and used cold.—R.D.L.)
8. Rinse in distilled water and leave 18 hours at 37°C in borax ferricyanide [250 mg each of borax ($Na_2B_4O_7 \cdot 10H_2O$) and of potassium ferricyanide $K_3Fe(CN)_6$ in 100 cc distilled water].
9. Wash in distilled water (4–5 changes, 10 minutes total).
10. Mount in Farrants's or Kaiser's medium (pp. 101, 103); *or* dehydrate, clear and mount in balsam.

Results: Phospholipids: lecithin, cephalin and sphingomyelin, dark blue to blue black; galactolipids from brain, blue black to pale blue; gelatin,[1] black or brown; mucin, dark blue to pale blue or brown.

[1] See p. 66 about avoiding the gelatin staining artifact.

Baker's Pyridine Extraction Test. Fix 20 hours in dilute Bouin's fluid: saturated aqueous picric acid 50 cc, formalin (40% formaldehyde) 10 cc, glacial acetic acid 5 cc, water 35 cc. Extract 1 hour in 70% alcohol, 30 minutes in 50% alcohol, 30 minutes in running water. Dehydrate in 2 changes of pyridine at 20–25°C, 1 hour each, and extract for 24 hours in fresh pyridine at 60°C. Wash 2 hours in running water. Transfer to 1% $CaCl_2$ 5% $K_2Cr_2O_7$ at step 2 of the acid hematein test and proceed as before with that test.

Results: Lecithin, cephalin, sphingomyelin and galactolipids remain unstained. Mucin, gelatin, chromatins are stained black, blue black or dark brown. Erythrocytes stain black both with and without pyridine extraction. Mitochondria and myelin are positive without extraction, negative after pyridine. Nuclei stain after extraction but not before.

I would regard sudanophilia to Sudan black B as a more critical test of the adequacy of the pyridine extraction than Baker's hematein reaction. Besides the lipofuscins, which remain sudanophil after primary hot methanol chloroform fixation and in formalin fixed tissue remain sudanophil after 24 hours 60°C extraction with pyridine, rat liver ceroid resisted 3 days at 60°C; I have noted that formalin fixed human brain and nerve root myelin quite regularly stains almost as well with Sudan black B after 24 hour 60°C extraction in pyridine. In the same experiment the periodic acid Schiff (galactolipids) and peracetic acid Schiff (unsaturated lipids) reactions remained at most slightly impaired after similar pyridine extraction.

Elftman's Controlled Chromation Hematoxylin Method for Phospholipids (*J. Histochem.* 2:1, 1954). Elftman considerably simplified the rather complicated Baker acid hematein method and further controlled it by setting the pH of the bichromate solution at 3.5.

1. Place fresh tissue in 2.5% $K_2Cr_2O_7$ buffered to pH 3.5 (see Table 3-4, p. 54 and substitute 5% $K_2Cr_2O_7$ for the 6% in the table) and heat 18 hours at 56°C.
2. Wash 6 hours in running water or in a siphonage device.
3. Dehydrate in alcohols, clear in xylene or other solvent, imbed in paraffin.
4. Section at 5–25 μ, deparaffinize and hydrate as usual.
5. To 50 cc 0.1 M acetate buffer pH 3 add 0.5% potassium ferricyanide and 50 mg hematoxylin. Warm to 56°C. Stain sections in this solution 2 hours at 56°C.
6. Wash in distilled water, dehydrate in alcohols, clear in xylene, mount in synthetic resin.

Results: Phospholipid sites: myelin sheaths, Golgi lipids, dark blue. The function of the ferricyanide in the staining bath is to prevent background staining. This does away with the necessity for the traditional borax, ferricyanide differentiation.

If the available oven or water bath is not regulated to 56°C, the chromation time should be adjusted. Add or subtract 0.030103 to the logarithm of 18 for each 1°C below or above 56°C, so as to decrease the time in hours at higher temperatures or increase it at lower temperatures.

The applicability of such methods as this to material previously fixed in formalin needs further study. Hence for routine fixed material the more traditional methods are preferred.

Bevan *et al.* (*J. Chem. Soc.* 1951, 841) used phosphomolybdic acid to identify choline containing lipids in paper chromatograms, developing the molybdenum blue color with stannous chloride. Levine and Chargaff (*J. Biol. Chem.* 192:465, 1951) used a similar method. Landing *et al.* (*Lab. Invest.* 1:456, 1952) adapted this procedure to tissue staining.

1. Frozen sections of formalin fixed tissue are floated on gelatin coated slides, drained, blotted and exposed to formaldehyde vapor for 10–15 minutes. Fresh frozen sections are thawed onto slides and dried briefly. Paraffin sections are deparaffinized.
2. Dry sections thoroughly, dip in acetone and ether (50:50).
3. Immerse 15 minutes in 1% phosphomolybdic acid in ethanol and chloroform (50:50). Rinse in ethanol chloroform and 2 changes of chloroform; dry.
4. Immerse for few seconds in fresh 1% stannous chloride in 3 N hydrochloric acid (1 volume concentrated HCl, 3 volumes H_2O).
5. Wash in water, counterstain in aqueous eosin, dehydrate, clear and mount in balsam or synthetic resin.

Results: Gaucher lipid (kerasin), deep blue; Niemann-Pick lipid (sphingomyelin), lighter blue green; Tay-Sachs ganglion cells, deep blue; normal myelin, deep blue. Faint to moderate staining is seen in adrenal cortical cells, lymphocyte and leucocyte cytoplasm, some squamous epithelial cells, margins of striated and cardiac muscle fibers, "endothelium" of alveolar and glomerular capillaries, ganglion cells, cytoplasm of renal, hepatic and basal epithelial cells. In cryostat sections, myelin stained strongly, the other structures stained less strongly. Paraffin sections showed strong staining of myelin, cytoplasm of liver, adrenal cortical and ganglion cells, some muscle fibers, erythrocytes and collagen in many areas. Weak staining appeared in smooth muscle, mucous glands, lingual epithelium, pancreas, fat, lymph nodes, spleen, bladder epithelium, testicular, gastric and intestinal epithelia and adrenal medulla.

The binding to known lipids is much decreased or prevented by prior extraction with fat solvents, but binding by other structures, as noted above under paraffin sections, seems relatively increased.

This procedure cannot be regarded as a binding of Mo by intrinsic PO_4 groups, since the phosphoacid is used. Phosphomolybdic acid is known to bind many basic organic reagents and is used in the dye industry to convert soluble basic dyes into insoluble pigments. Kerasin, the Gaucher lipid, contains neither choline nor phosphate.

However, strong staining of sudanophilic materials may well be associated with phosphatide nature of the fat concerned.

The other reactions observed in myelinated fibers are probably attributable to specific groupings in certain of the foregoing lipids.

Reactions for ethylenes (pp. 180–186), the peracetic Schiff and the direct osmic acid reaction, and probably also the bromine silver methods, can be assigned to unsaturated fatty acid groupings in the phosphatides, lysophosphatides and ceramide groups. The sphingosine double bond should also prove as reactive as that in oleins.

Reactions for carbohydrates, notably the periodic acid Schiff reaction, should be expected in the galactoside and glucoside cerebrosides and in the sulfatides, since sulfation of galactose carbon 6 should not interfere with a Criegee cleavage in one of the vicinal glycol sites. The linkage, whether 1,3 or 1,4, in the tetrasaccharide residue of the gangliosides could determine whether or not these would react to periodic acid. Lison has no hesitation about assigning a positive periodic acid Schiff reaction to gangliosides.

For the Gaucher lipid kerasin, Morrison and Hack (*Am. J. Path.* **25:** 597, 1949) have specifically reported a positive periodic acid Schiff reaction in the foam cells. Bauer and Casella reactions were negative in my hands, using Morrison's material.

The Niemann-Pick lipid, sphingomyelin, which lacks hexose, is periodic acid Schiff negative according to Morrison and Hack (*loc. cit.*) Wolman's conflicting report was based on a 24 hour periodic acid treatment and is explained on the assumption that the ceramide bond was hydrolyzed, thus leaving a 2-amino-3-hydroxy grouping for a positive Nicolet-Shinn reaction. With the normal short periodic acid treatment the reaction is negative (Lison, 1960).

As noted before, diphosphoinositides should give a positive periodic acid Schiff reaction, if insolubilized by the fixation employed.

Basophilia, as Lison says, should be shown by gangliosides because of the sialic acid residue, and by sulfatides on account of the SO_4H residue on galactose carbon 6. The same behavior toward methylation and demethylation would be expected as with the sialic acid mucins and the sulfated aminopolysaccharides (pp. 282–284). But hot methanol controls must be performed.

The traditional myelin technics include fixations in bichromate alone, in formalin bichromate, in formalin followed by bichromate and in formalin alone, without subsequent use of bichromate. Sometimes copper salts and trivalent chromium salts have also been interposed as "mordants." The hematoxylin used for staining has in some instances lacked any mordant metal, in some cases it follows treatment by a ferric salt, and in some it is mixed with ferric alum or ferric chloride.

In all cases, however, successful technics have required treatment by bichromate or by a ferric salt before extraction with fat solvents, and the hematoxylin, if uncombined with a ferric salt at the time of using, has to depend on prebound chromium or iron to form a blue to black lake complex.

Some myelin staining can be achieved with iron hematoxylin on material fixed in formalin and imbedded in paraffin without prior chromation or ferric chloride oxidation, but the stain is generally weaker and of poorer quality.

Despite successes with sequence iron hematoxylins on frozen sections, the technics requiring chromation before imbedding have been generally favored, either with unmordanted hematoxylins, depending on the chelated chromium, or with sequence or mixed iron hematoxylins.

It appears in my experience that primary fixation in formalin followed by cutting of thin blocks which are then chromated some days at 25°C in 2.5% $K_2Cr_2O_7$ before paraffin imbedding is the preferable procedure. Primary dichromate formalin fixations appear to give less even myelin preservation in brain blocks.

Hot bichromate treatments, as in the Baker and Elftman procedures, induce rather pronounced changes in staining with acid and basic dyes. Brain and root ganglion tissue which normally gives a satisfactory red blue balance with azure A eosin B at pH 4 or 4.5 after formalin or Kose's bichromate formalin (p. 55) fixation, after a 24 hour chromation at 60°C in 5% $K_2Cr_2O_7$ requires a pH of 6.5–7 to get any nuclear staining. It is, of course, recognized that the lowering of tissue pK from the pH 6 which is useful for azure eosin after simple methanol or ethanol fixation to 4 or 4.5 is due probably to the attachment of $=CH_2$ or $—CH_2OH$ groups to tissue amine residues, thereby decreasing their oxyphilia and consequently increasing their basophilia. It appears probable that their $=CH_2$ or $—CH_2OH$ groups are oxidized to formic acid or carbon dioxide by the hot bichromate, thereby restoring the basicity of the reliberated amine groups. Perhaps

$$RN{=}CH_2 + 2O \rightarrow RNH_2 + CO_2 \quad \text{or} \quad RN{=}CH_2 + H_2O + O \rightarrow RNH_2 + HCOOH$$
$$RNH{-}CH_2OH + 2O \rightarrow RNH_2 + CO_2 + H_2O \quad \text{or}$$
$$RNH{-}CH_2OH + O \rightarrow RNH_2 + HCOOH$$

I have not been too well satisfied with the density of the blue staining of myelin achieved by Baker and Elftman technics, as compared with more traditional myelin procedures. I have made some further alterations in the procedure first published by me in 1944 (*Arch. Path.* **37**:392), and

I am indebted to Drs. Windle and Rassmussen at the National Institutes of Health for their kindly evaluation of results at some stages in the differentiation procedure.

Lillie's Myelin Method. Fix routinely in buffered formalin (p. 38, formula 4 or 5) for 2 days for small blocks, up to 2–3 weeks for whole human brains. Cut blocks 3–5 mm thick and chromate at 20–25°C in 5% $K_2Cr_2O_7$ for 4–8 days. Wash in running water or in a siphonage chamber for 4–6 hours or overnight if more convenient. Dehydrate as usual through graded alcohols to absolute alcohol, 2 changes, 1 hour each, then alcohol + ether 1 hour and 1% celloidin 2–4 days. Transfer through 2–3 changes of chloroform to paraffin and infiltrate 20 minutes *in vacuo* (10–20 mm mercury) or 3 hours in 3 changes of paraffin, 1 hour each. Section at 3–25 μ as desired.

Deparaffinize and hydrate through xylene and graded alcohols, using isopropanol if conservation of the supporting celloidin is desired. Acetone can be used to remove it completely.

1. Stain 1 hour at 60°C in a fresh mixture of 1% alcoholic hematoxylin solution and either 4% iron alum or 2.25% ferric chloride [NH_4Fe $(SO_4)_2 \cdot 12H_2O$; $FeCl_3 \cdot 6H_2O$]. The 2 ferric iron solutions are equivalent, and the hematoxylin is at once oxidized on mixing, so the solution need not be aged.
2. Rinse in water. At this point we formerly differentiated 1 hour in 0.5% iron alum; 0.3% ferric chloride would serve. Now I usually omit this step and prolong slightly the borax ferricyanide differentiation.
3. Rinse in water and differentiate in 1% borax containing 1.25% potassium ferricyanide. About 10–15 minutes suffices to yield blue black myelin and brown to black erythrocytes and to decolorize glia nuclei. Microscopic control is advisable on new or varied material; results remain very constant on similar sections of the same type of material. On first trial one may try 5, 10, 15 and 20 minute differentiation and select the interval giving best results for further sections; or the process may be followed microscopically.
4. Wash thoroughly and counterstain as desired: 0.1% safranin in 1% acetic acid, 0.1% basic fuchsin in 0.01 N HCl or the usual cresyl fast violet (p. 156) should afford usable contrasts.
5. Dehydrate with isopropanol, alcohol or acetone, as desired, clear in xylene, mount in synthetic resin.

Comment. Although this method may be used on primary dichromate formalin material and on unchromated formalin fixed tissue, the results are more uneven in the first case and less complete in the second.

Material fixed in formalin, alcoholic formalin or any formalin mixture and imbedded in paraffin without chromation will give fairly good myelin

TABLE 13-2. SCHEDULES FOR TRADITIONAL MYELIN STAINS

	Weigert	Pal	Kultschitzky	Wolters	Wright	Spielmeyer	Weil	Lille 1944
Fixation	Formalin or Orth 2–3 days	Formalin 2 days or Müller 2–3 wk	Formalin 2+ days	Formalin 2 days or Müller 2–3 wk	Formalin 2+ days	Formalin 3+ days	Formalin 2+ days	Formalin or Orth 2 days
Washing						1 hr		Rinse
First mordant	Weigert 1st 4–6 days or 2–3 days 37°C	Müller 2–3 wk	Weigert 2d. 4–5 days	Müller 2–3 wk				Bichromate 2–4 days
Washing								Rinse
Second mordant	Weigert 2d 1 day 37°C							
Section method	Graded alcohols to celloidin	Graded alcohols to celloidin	Graded alcohols to celloidin	Graded alcohols to celloidin	Frozen sections	Frozen sections	Graded alcohols to paraffin	Graded alcohols to paraffin or frozen sections
Hematoxylin method	Combined Weigert's neutral iron, p. 168	Combined Weigert's lithium, p. 491, No. 5	Combined, Kultschitzky's acetic, p. 491, No. 8	Combined, Wolters' acetic, p. 491, No. 10	Sequence, 5 min 10% FeCl₃ and Wright's, p. 491, No. 11	Sequence, 6 min 2–5% iron alum and Spielmeyer's, p. 491 No. 12	Combined, Weil's iron, p. 168	Combined, Lillie-Weil, p. 489, step 1
Staining time	24 hr	6–48 hr	12–24 hr	24 hr	30 min	10–24 hr	15 min	40 min
Temperature	15–20°C	15–20°C	15–20°C	"Warm"	20°C	20°C	50°C	58°C
Washing	30–60 min tap	Water and 2–3 drops sat. aq. Li₂CO₃		Müller few sec	Rinse	Rinse	Rinse	Rinse
First differentiator	Weigert's borax ferricyanide 15–30 min	0.25% KMnO₄ 15–20 sec	Kultschitzky's decolorizer 3–4 changes 4–12 hr	0.25% KMnO₄ 20–30 sec	10% FeCl₃ brief	2.5% iron alum microscopic control	4% iron alum to gross differentiation Weil's borax ferricyanide	0.5% iron alum 1 hr
Second differentiator		Pal's bleach few sec		Pal's bleach 30 sec to 3 min				Lillie's borax ferricyanide 10 min
Washing	24 hr tap	Thorough	Thorough	Thorough	Thorough	2 changes distilled 1–2 hr tap	Water	Water
Counterstain		(Carmine optional)						Acetic safranin, 5 min, wash
Mounting procedure[1]	Alcohol, aniline xylene or carbol xylene, balsam	95% alcohol, carbol xylene, xylene, balsam	95% alcohol, terpineol or origanum oil, xylene, balsam	95% alcohol, terpineol or origanum oil, xylene, balsam	95% alcohol, terpineol or origanum oil, xylene, balsam	95% alcohol, carbol xylene or xylene (blot), balsam	Alcohols, xylene, balsam	Acetone xylene, xylene, balsam.

[1] Routine synthetic mounting media may be substituted for balsam.

TABLE 13-3. FORMULAE OF REAGENTS USED IN VARIOUS MYELIN TECHNICS

1. The formalin is a 10% dilution in water of 40% formaldehyde solution.

2. **Weigert's first mordant**
Potassium bichromate	5 gm
Chromium fluoride	2.5 gm
Distilled water to make	100 cc

3. **Weigert's second mordant**
Cupric acetate	5 gm
Chromium fluoride	2.5 gm
Glacial acetic acid	5 cc
Distilled water to make	100 cc

4. **Weigert's borax ferricyanide**
Borax ($Na_2B_4O_7 \cdot 10H_2O$)	2 gm
Potassium ferricyanide	2.5 gm
Distilled water to make	100 cc

5. **Weigert's lithium hematoxylin**
Hematoxylin	0.75–1.0 gm
Alcohol	10 cc
Distilled water to make	100 cc
Saturated aqueous lithium carbonate	1–2 cc

6. **Müller's fluid**
Potassium bichromate	2.5 gm
Sodium sulfate crystals	1 gm
Distilled water to make	100 cc

7. **Pal's sulfite oxalic bleach**
Potassium sulfite	0.5 gm
Oxalic acid	0.5 gm
Distilled water	100 cc

8. **Kultschitzky's hematoxylin**
10% alcoholic hematoxylin, aged 6 mo.	10 cc
Glacial acetic acid	2 cc
Distilled water to make	100 cc

9. **Kultschitzky's decolorizer**
1% potassium ferricyanide	10 cc
Saturated aqueous lithium carbonate	100 cc

10. **Wolters's hematoxylin**
Hematoxylin	2 gm
Alcohol to dissolve	10–20 cc
Glacial acetic acid	2 cc
Distilled water to make	100 cc

11. **Wright's hematoxylin** was an extempore solution of a few crystals in 15 cc distilled water.

12. **Spielmeyer's hematoxylin**
5% alcoholic hematoxylin (aged)	4 cc
Distilled water	36 cc

13. **Weil's borax ferricyanide**
Weigert's formula	50 cc
Distilled water	50 cc

14. **Lillie's bichromate**
Potassium bichromate	5 gm
Water	100 cc

15. **Lillie's borax ferricyanide**
Borax	1 gm
Potassium ferricyanide	2.5 gm
Distilled water	100 cc

16. **Lillie's acetic safranin**
Safranin O (C.I. No. 50240)	100 mg
Glacial acetic acid	1 cc
Distilled water to make	100 cc

by this method, but the demonstration of fine fibers requires chromation before exposure to lipid solvents. Strangely enough, chromate fixatives not containing formaldehyde are ineffective in the usual 1–3 day fixation periods. It is to be noted that the older writers required 2–3 weeks' hardening in Müller's fluid, and that Endicott found about 3 weeks' treatment with chromate necessary to render certain unsaturated fats insoluble and myelin positive *in vitro*. It is further to be noted that Kaufmann and Lehmann insisted that the chromation in the Smith-Dietrich procedure be done at 60°C at least. This again follows a formaldehyde fixation.

References for Myelin Technics. Weigert's iron chloride hematoxylin method is taken from his article in Ehrlich's *Encyklopädie*, pp. 937–944, and is quoted essentially without change by Mallory. Pal's method I have taken from Weigert's article, from Schmorl and from Mallory. Kultschitzky's and Wolters's technics are as given by Romeis, Schmorl and Mallory. Wright's technic is given as included in the eighth edition of *Pathological Technic*, by Mallory and Wright, W. B. Saunders Company, Philadelphia, 1924, which varies somewhat from that in the sixth edition (1918). Spielmeyer's technic is essentially as it appeared in Mallory, Romeis and Schmorl. Weil's is as published: *Arch. Neurol. Psychiat.* **20**: 392, 1928. Lillie's first appeared in *Arch. Path.* **37**:392, 1944. The current revision has not been published until now, and is not tabulated.

In frozen sections, myelin of peripheral nerves is stained vividly red to red purple by the periodic acid (pp. 196, 197, 198) and peracetic acid (p. 183) Schiff procedures. These reactions are obtained (though less vividly) in material fixed with formaldehyde and chromated before dehydration and imbedding, and the peracetic reaction is still strong in brain fixed 2 weeks in formalin and sectioned in paraffin without chromation.

Chapter 14

Polysaccharides, Mucins

The staining reactions of the polysaccharides fall into 6 general classes. The first and oldest are the more or less transient color reactions with iodine, exemplified by the blue reactions of starch, amylose and amylopectin; the red brown reaction of the glycogens and amyloid; the violet with chitin in the presence of $ZnCl_2$; the blue of cellulose with iodine and sulfuric acid, and others. Of these the glycogen and starch reactions are currently in use in pathology.

The second group is the often metachromatic staining with basic dyes. This depends on the presence in the polysaccharide of sulfate ester residues, of uronic acid residues and of sialic acid groups. Some discrimination is possible with this group of methods by regulation of the pH of staining and by the responses to methylation and alkali saponification procedures in sequence. Open —SO_4H radicals take up basic aniline dyes at lower pH levels than do the carboxylic acids, and on application of methylation reagents of the Fraenkel-Conrat type they form acid methyl sulfate, which goes into solution in the methylation reagent, leaving the unsulfated polysaccharide behind. The carboxylic acids, sialic and uronic, form methyl esters which are unreactive to basic dyes. But on saponification the methyl esters are converted to soaps and free methanol, and on reacidification the carboxylic acids are again liberated and stainable with basic dyes. But the sulfated polysaccharides, having completely lost their sulfate groups to the solution, do not regain stainability on saponification and acidification.

Acetylated aminopolysaccharides, such as the chitins, and the hexose polysaccharides themselves, both lacking acid groups, are not stained by these methods, and there are a few unacetylated aminopolysaccharides such as *Aspergillus* polysaccharide and deacetylchitin (Evans and Kent, *J. Histochem.* **10**:8, 1962) which are actually basic.

A third group comprises largely empirical stains with mordant dyes such as hematoxylin and carmine in the presence of aluminum chloride (mucihematein, mucicarmine) or alkaline ammoniacal hydroalcoholic carmine (Best). One suspects an Al^{+++} chelation complex in the first 2 instances, binding perhaps to the acid groups of the polysaccharide,

493

though mucihematein stains also the neutral mucopolysaccharide of gastric surface epithelium. Best's solution undoubtedly contains the oxidation form carmein, which probably has more quinone groups than the 2 normal anthraquinone groups of carminic acid.

The reason for the recent revival of popularity of mucicarmine to identify mucins in tumors is not clear. Perhaps it has a connection with the 1961 reprinting of F. B. Mallory's 1938 *Pathological Technique.*

The mechanism of staining with these preparations, as well as the significance of positive staining, remains obscure.

The fourth group of methods, perhaps allied to the Al^{+++} mordant methods, are those depending on uptake of ferric iron in an ionically reactive state by various mucins and other substances. The more commonly used variants, derived from Hale's (*Nature* **157**:802, 1946) dialyzed iron method, depend on the use of colloidal solutions of ferric hydroxide in the presence of acetate ion at pH levels ranging from about 2 to about 4.5. The more acid solutions are said to be more selective for the more strongly acid mucopolysaccharides, and to depend on direct reaction of the acid radicle with the ferric hydroxide. The Lillie-Mowry (*Bull. Int. A. Med. Mus.* **30**:91, 1949) acid variant of their ferric mannitol technic depends on the same reactivity. It would appear probable that in the alkaline ferric mannitol reaction the iron is present as ferrate anion and that only surface cell gastric mucin and esophageal or proventricular keratohyalin granules develop a blue color on treatment with ferrocyanide. The mechanism of this latter reaction has not been explored with blockade reactions. Methylation prevents the acid iron uptake reactions.

P. Mayer (*Mitth. Zool. Station Neapel* **12**:303–330, 1896, footnote p. 326) reported brown staining of mucus by several days exposure to very dilute ferric acetate solution in a thin layer in a moist chamber. He converted the brown stain to Prussian blue with acid and potassium ferrocyanide. Iron alum and $FeSO_4$ solutions did not work. Mayer's findings seem to have escaped notice.

The fifth group, the Criegee reactions for vicinal glycols and amino alcohols, comprises the most definitely chemically based reactions in common use for the histochemical study and histologic demonstration of polysaccharides with 1,4 linkages. Substitution of an amino group at position 2 leaves the hexosamine reactive, since a 2-amino-3-hydroxy configuration is present, but an acetylamino group instead makes the hexosamine unit unreactive. Sulfation of the hydroxyls at 2 or 3 or both has a similar effect, whether artificially induced or occurring *in vivo*, but 6-sulfo groups do not prevent the 2,3 Criegee cleavage. Should the glycosidic linkage be 1,3 instead of 1,4, such 1,3 linked units are unreactive.

The reagents employed are chromic acid (Bauer, 1933), periodic acid

(McManus, 1946) or, less commonly, $KMnO_4$ (Rossman, 1942; Casella, 1942), lead tetraacetate (Crippa, 1951; McManus, 1952; Lhotka, 1952; Leblond, 1952; Shimizu, 1952) and sodium bismuthate (Lhotka, 1952). Chromic acid has the theoretical disadvantage of destroying part of the aldehyde formed in the Criegee cleavage reaction. In practice, for histologic purposes this property is often advantageous in suppressing the weaker background reactions of collagen fibrils, basement membranes, etc., and leaving reactive to the Schiff reagent only glycogen, mucins and bacterial and fungal cell walls.

Perhaps the least specific reaction is that of low pH basophilia (and metachromasia) after sulfation (188). This renders many otherwise non-basophilic mucins, such as that of the gastric surface epithelium, and weakly metachromatic mucins, such as that of Brunner glands, intensely basophilic and metachromatic, even at pH 1. However, the sulfation reaction seems to be general for aliphatic hydroxyls, so that collagen and reticulum react intensely, rather than relatively weakly as with the periodic acid Schiff reaction. It seems quite probable that this reaction is at least in part assignable to hydroxyproline hydroxyls. At this writing it seems indicated that amine groups are also readily sulfated, so that their normal oxyphilia is lost, and under some conditions may be replaced by an intense basophilia, which is again removable by methylation. The possibility of sulfation of tyrosine phenolic residues has also suggested itself.

GLYCOGEN

Glycogen is a highly branched polysaccharide derived from, and decomposing into, glucose. It is stored in liver cells, certain cells of the parathyroid, muscle, cartilage and other locations. It is likely to hydrolyze post mortem, and consequently prompt fixation is especially required. However, prompt refrigeration, followed by adequate fixation, may avail. I have had good glycogen preservation in material refrigerated for 12–24 hours or even 56 hours before fixation. Formerly, strong alcoholic fixatives were recommended as it was believed that glycogen itself was readily soluble in water, except in cartilage. Much work was done with 100% alcohol alone, which on a comparative basis now seems to be one of the poorest glycogen fixatives because of its poor penetration. Preservation seems adequate only in the relatively badly shrunken surface layers. Neutral aqueous formalin solutions often preserve glycogen quite well, especially in fresh animal livers, but the action of certain acid alcoholic fluids seems prompter and more reliable.

I can recommend Carnoy's fluid (p. 42), alcohol formalin and acetic alcohol formalin (p. 39). Picric acid variants of the alcohol formalins are often recommended (p. 59) but seem to offer no distinct advantage over the corresponding fluids without picric acid.

For simultaneous studies of glycogen and fats, aqueous fixations and frozen sections are required: they may be used also when the fat stains are not desired. Usually, however, nitrocellulose or paraffin sections are preferred, and the latter give better results if collodionized before applying the specific stain. With the periodic acid Schiff method I now regularly omit collodion (p. 198).

For *digestion tests* nitrocellulose sections are to be avoided, and on paraffin sections the test must be performed before collodionizing. I have seen glycogen resist digestion for 18 hours in collodionized sections, when the same enzyme solution removed it completely from uncollodionized control sections in 30 minutes. Apparently the larger enzyme molecules are unable to penetrate the collodion film.

Human saliva has been used as a digestant by many workers, but I have found malt diastase or ptyalin more convenient. The latter was unavailable commercially for some time. Malt diastase in 1/1000 solution buffered to pH 6 with phosphates is an entirely adequate digesting fluid. Some samples are still active at 1/1,000,000. In addition to an α-amylase, human saliva, beef salivary gland ptyalin and barley malt diastase contain a ribonuclease. In malt diastase this action is evident in 0.02–0.1% concentrations, and resists boiling in 0.1 N acetic acid. Consequently, if pure glycogenase action is desired it is necessary to use malt diastase solutions at 1/100,000 or higher dilution. In 1/1000 dilutions at pH levels of 5–8 both the diastatic and ribonuclease actions are destroyed at temperatures of 55–60°C. Hence digestion tests should be done at 35–45°C for maximal action.

The foregoing account is based on the author's papers: Stain Techn. **22**:67, 1947; Bull. Int. A. Med. Mus. **27**:23, 1947; Anat. Rec. **103**:611, 635, 1949, in which previous pertinent literature is reviewed.

Diastase Digestion Test. Make a 0.1% solution of malt diastase in 0.02 M phosphate buffer of pH 6. Sodium chloride up to 0.8% may be added if desired, but larger quantities should be avoided as they may inhibit the enzyme action. Filter before using, to remove starch granules.

Technic.

1. Bring paraffin sections to water as usual.
2. Digest 30–60 minutes at 45–35°C in 1/1000 malt diastase.
3. Wash in water.
4. Dehydrate with alcohols or acetone.
5. Soak 5–10 minutes in 1% collodion in ether:alcohol (50:50).
6. Drain 1 minute.
7. Immerse in 80% alcohol for 5–10 minutes to harden the collodion.
8. Proceed with the glycogen demonstration method chosen, using an undigested control section along with the digested one.

Goetsch, Reynolds and Bunting (*Proc. Soc. Exp. Biol. Med.* **80**:71, 1952) report successful digestion of glycogen from liver cells by amylase, using undeparaffinized sections. This procedure could well avoid some of the section losses. In our hands diastase solutions required 6–12 hours to effect fairly complete digestion of liver glycogen, compared with about 10 minutes for the usual deparaffinized ones. Heating of the sections to the melting point of the paraffin before digestion almost totally inhibits digestion, probably by forming a continuous paraffin film over the section.

Purified α- and β-amylases are now commercially available. Takeuchi (*J. Histochem.* **6**:208, 1958) uses them at 0.5% in distilled water, buffering with 4 *mM* acetates to pH 5.5–6 for α-amylase and to pH 4–5.7 for β-amylase. Digestion periods range from 30 minutes to 10 hours at 37°C. The β-amylase promptly digests amylose, starch and similar unbranched polysaccharides, but it attacks glycogen only slightly; α-amylase promptly digests both.

McManus and Saunders (*Science* **111**:204, 1950) reported on the use of *pectinase, pectinol O, pectin esterase, polygalacturonase* and *β-glucuronase*, as microdissection agents for the study of tissues fixed in cold acetone (p. 43). The enzymes were used in 0.4% solution in acetate buffer of pH 4 (p. 661), probably Waipole's.

Pectinase and polygalacturonase remove periodic acid Schiff positive materials: mucin, glycogen, splenic and lymphadenoid reticulum, cartilage matrix, hyalin, etc. Pectinol O gave qualitatively similar though less complete removals. Pectin esterase and β-glucuronase did not attack the periodic acid Schiff positive materials. Incubation periods were 48 hours at 37°C.

Glycogen Demonstration Methods

The traditional methods for the demonstration of glycogen are the iodine method, which is applicable also to amyloid, corpora amylacea, starch, amylose and other substances; and the alkaline carmine solution of Best. More recently we have added the aldehyde reaction with Schiff's reagent after oxidation with chromic acid or potassium permanganate (p. 199), periodic acid (p. 198), lead tetraacetate (p. 202) and sodium bismuthate (p. 203).

Iodine Methods. I omit the Langhans method cited in the first edition of this book, since it is now demonstrated that ordinary aqueous formalin will preserve glycogen. I prefer to fix in my acetic alcohol formalin (p. 39), alcoholic formalin or Carnoy's fluid. Complete dehydration with ascending alcohols. Changes of 1 hour each suffice for the 100% alcohol; the lower grades should have 8–16 hours each. Clear in cedar oil and imbed in paraffin as usual (Schedule VI, p. 72). Carry sections through 2 changes each of xylene and of 100% alcohol into 1% collodion in equal volumes of ether and 100% alcohol. Soak 5–10 minutes, drain 1 minute and harden in 80% alcohol for 5–10 minutes. Transfer to water and proceed.

1. Gram's iodine for 5–10 minutes.
2. Dehydrate in 2 changes of 2% iodine in 100% alcohol.
3. Clear and mount in origanum oil. Seal with pyroxylin cement.

For the demonstration of newly formed amylose and glycogens (p. 330) Takeuchi immerses sections after incubation for a few minutes in a ten-fold dilution of Gram's iodine and then mounts in iodine glycerol and seals with paraffin. Amylose and starch color blue, glycogens color red purple to red brown.

The staining solution is $I:KI:H_2O$, 1:2:3000; the iodine glycerol is 9 parts pure glycerol and 1 part Gram's iodine.

Lower's (*Stain Techn.* **32:**127, 1957) silver conversion procedure renders iodine preparations permanent. It was used chiefly for the study of insect cuticle and muscle but seems readily adaptable to other tissues.

1. Deparaffinize and hydrate sections as usual, removing mercury deposits with iodine, thiosulfate and water washes. This avoids carrying any mercury over to the silver bath.
2. Immerse 10 minutes in Weigert's iodine ($I:KI:H_2O$, 1:2:100). Wash thoroughly in distilled water.
3. Immerse 10 minutes in 1% silver nitrate. Wash thoroughly in distilled water.
4. Develop in a fine grain photographic developer or fresh 1% hydroquinone for 10 minutes. Wash thoroughly in distilled water.
5. Tone 15 minutes in 0.1% gold chloride in distilled water. Wash thoroughly in distilled water.
6. Fix 2 minutes in 0.2 M sodium thiosulfate (5% $Na_2S_2O_3 \cdot 5H_2O$). Wash 10 minutes in running water.

7. Differentiate 2 minutes in 1% $K_2S_2O_5$ in 0.125 N HCl. Wash, dehydrate, clear and mount in balsam, Permount, cellulose caprate or the like.

Results: Iodophil material, purple to black.

Glassware should be cleaned with concentrated nitric acid to remove silver after each use for this method, and then washed thoroughly in distilled water.

Since the whole operation is conducted apparently in daylight it is probable that the silver iodine compounds formed are at least partly reduced without development. Since the silver exposure is brief, iodine is probably not liberated from aliphatic substitutions as in Norton's procedure (p. 185), but only the loosely bound iodine in (oxidized) elementary form is shown. This is removed in the Norton procedure by the bisulfite bath which follows halogenation.

Takeuchi writes me (1963) that he finds it better to use Gomori's CrO_3-methenamine silver technic when permanent preparations are required. In any case Lower's method does not preserve the differential color reactions with iodine.

Best's carmine solution is prepared by gently boiling 2 gm carmine, 1 gm potassium carbonate and 5 gm potassium chloride in 60 cc distilled water for several minutes or until the color darkens. Cool and add 20 cc 28% ammonia water. Ripen for 24 hours and store in refrigerator at 0–5°C. The carmine should be certified by the Biological Stain Commission. The stock solutions may be kept for several weeks only. The foregoing directions are derived from C. Bensley and from Mallory, and vary materially from Best's as cited in Ehrlich's *Encyklopädie*.

The staining solution is composed of 8 cc of the stock solution above, 12 cc 28% ammonia water and 24 cc methyl alcohol, total 44 cc. Mallory used 10 cc, 15 cc and 15 cc respectively, total 40 cc, and directed filtration of the stock solution before mixing. C. Bensley directed thorough mixing and warned strictly against filtration. This dilute solution is good for 1 or 2 days only, and it is preferable to use it only once.

1. Mallory prescribes celloidin sections, Bensley paraffin, and I generally take the paraffin sections from 100% alcohol into 1% collodion for 5–10 minutes, drain 1 minute, harden 5 minutes in 80% alcohol and transfer thence to water.
2. Stain 5 minutes in an acid alum hematoxylin (Ehrlich's, Lillie's or other, p. 174).
3. Wash briefly in tap water and
4. Stain 20 minutes in the freshly diluted staining solution.
5a. Rinse *paraffin* sections with 3 changes of fresh methyl alcohol (preferably using a dropper bottle) then
6a. Dehydrate and remove collodion with 2–3 changes of acetone.

7a. Pass through acetone and xylene into 2 changes of xylene and mount in synthetic resin.
5b. Wash *celloidin* sections in several changes of a mixture of water 10 cc, 100% ethyl alcohol 8 cc and methyl alcohol 4 cc.
6b. Dehydrate in 80% and 95% alcohol.
7b. Clear in origanum oil and mount in balsam.

Results: Glycogen, red; nuclei, blue.

The periodic acid Schiff procedure, with diastase digestion controls, is far simpler and appears to be quite uniformly successful.

The Bauer and Casella oxidation Schiff methods are discussed on p. 195, and their results are included in the detailed discussion on pp. 200–201. The preferred method for demonstration of glycogen is the periodic acid Schiff leucofuchsin technic (p. 198). Variations and results are discussed in detail on pp. 195–201. A useful method, giving red purple glycogen and other periodic Schiff positive substances (but blue collagen and reticulum), is the allochrome procedure (p. 549).

It may be noted here that prolonged bromination (1 cc bromine in 39 cc carbon tetrachloride for 3–6 hours at 25°C) completely prevents the reaction of glycogen by the periodic acid Schiff method, without evidently affecting the reactivity of any other tissue substances. The reaction is probably analogous to the chlorination of starch, bromine replacing the hydrogen on carbons 1 and 4, and removing both hydrogens, leaving O= on carbons 2 and 3 (Kerr, *Chemistry and Industry of Starch,* Academic Press, Inc., New York, 1950). This bromination effect is reversed by a 3 day immersion in 5% silver nitrate.

Mitchell and Wislocki (*Anat. Rec.* 90:261, 1944, cited in *J. Tech. Methods* 25:159, 1945) reported on the demonstration of glycogen by an *ammoniacal silver* nitrate technic. Gomori (*Am. J. Clin. Path., Tech. Sect.* 10:177, 1946) explained this as an aldehyde reduction of ammine silver (cf. p. 533) and extended the method to the demonstration of mucus. I dissent from this explanation (p. 275).

The Methenamine Silver Method. For this purpose Gomori found best a methenamine silver nitrate solution: Add 5 cc 5% silver nitrate to 100 cc 3% methenamine. A heavy white precipitate appears and easily redissolves on shaking. This stock solution may be kept for months in the refrigerator, or for about 2 weeks at room temperature.

Gomori prescribed an alcoholic fixative for glycogen. Mitchell and Wislocki used an alcoholic picroformalin. Grocott prescribed 10% formalin. Grocott's (*Am. J. Clin. Path.* 25:975, 1955) variant is much used for fungi in tissues. Gomori's technic follows:

1. Deparaffinize and collodionize in 0.5% collodion. For mucin omit collodion.

2. Bring sections to water.
3. Treat 1–1½ hours in 5% chromic acid. (Grocott; 1 hour.)
4. Wash 10 minutes in running water (this can be reduced to 1 minute).
5. Treat 1 minute in 1–2% sodium bisulfite ($NaHSO_3$) to remove traces of chromic acid. (Grocott, 1%.)
6. Wash 5 minutes in running water.
7. Rinse in distilled water, 3–4 changes.
8. Silver at 37–45°C (Lillie, AFIP, 58–60°C) in stock methenamine silver solution 25 cc distilled water 25 cc, 5% borax 1–2 cc. (Grocott 2 cc.) Observe slides at intervals under the microscope until mucin, glycogen and fungi are dark brown while background remains yellow. This may take 1–3 hours (30–60 minutes at 60°C).
9. Rinse in several changes of distilled water.
10. Tone 5 minutes in 0.1% gold chloride.
11. Rinse thoroughly in 2–3% sodium thiosulfate solution to remove excess silver. (Grocott used 2%; I prefer 5%.)
12. Wash in running water.
13. Counterstain as desired (Grocott stained 40 seconds in 0.2% light green SF in 0.2% acetic acid), dehydrate, clear and mount as usual. The collodion membrane sometimes stains rather intensely. It may be removed by acetone or by ether alcohol mixture during dehydration.

Results: Mucin, glycogen and melanin color deep gray brown to black. Insoluble calcium salts may also blacken. In comparison with the Bauer method this technic appears rather laborious, and on brief trial the visual contrasts appear inferior. I have had a number of failures with it on Bauer positive material. It shares with the Bauer reaction the staining of mucin which gives difficulties in the study of glycogen in muciparous cells.

Many investigators have used Grocott's variant with good results for the demonstration of fungi in tissues, notably *Histoplasma*. Grocott increased the temperature to 45–50°C and reduced the time to about 1 hour. The *AFIP Manual* gives 58°C and 30–60 minutes as Grocott's method.

McLean and Cook (p. 40) state that staining for 15–20 minutes in a saturated solution of *chlorazol black E* in 70% alcohol demonstrated nuclei in black; cytoplasm and inclusions, gray; chitin, green; and glycogen, red. If sections are overstained, differentiate with terpineol.

I have tried this with American chlorazol black E. Chitin of cestodes is fairly well shown in green, but much of the connective tissue is also gray green, and (to say the most for the method) it requires a certain amount of imagination to discern a reddish fluorescence where the glycogen ought to be. The carmine and periodic acid methods are much better for glycogen.

CHITINS

Chemical studies have been done largely on crustacean carapace material; it should be remembered that other phyla than arthropods and other classes within arthropoda also elaborate exoskeletal material which bears the anatomical name of chitin. It appears quite clear that these chitins are not all chemically identical, and indeed it would be extremely surprising if they were. Those of most interest in pathology constitute the cell walls of some fungi and bacteria and the exoskeletons and egg shells of various parasitic and commensal worms and other less frequent parasites. Lobster shell is probably infrequent in human pathology.

Pearse (1960, p. 229) takes the view that there is a single chitin, composed of N-acetylglucosamine in pairs linked by β-1,4 linkages, and notes its presence in arthropods, annelids and molluscs "and also in insects" and in certain lower plants.

Pearse, 1960 (p. 264) notes that all varieties of chitin on which he has tried it give a blue coloration with his alkaline tetrazolium method for SH. "Tanned chitin" (quinonized) does not react. He notes further that chitins may be sulfated by one of the Kramer-Windrum methods and are then strongly basophil (pp. 188–190).

Pearse further commented on the histochemical inapplicability of the alkaline *p*-dimethylaminobenzaldehyde reaction for N-acetylhexosamines, even when the preferred pH 9.8 borate buffer is used. Chitin is normally periodic acid Schiff negative (*ibid.*, p. 237); Gomori stated specifically (1953, p. 62) that chitin reacted to both the Bauer and the periodic acid Schiff reactions. Lison (1960, p. 403) comments that the N-acetylglucosamine polymer should *not* react. However, sclerosed insect chitin softened with NaOH is strongly positive, and that of mushroom (champignon) membrane reacts strongly. I noted (1954, p. 279) a negative reaction in cestodes and adult schistosomes and in the egg walls of ascarids and trichurids, but a positive Bauer and periodic acid Schiff reaction in schistosome egg cuticle. The cell wall material of *Bacillus anthracis*, many other bacteria, fungi and yeasts reacts.

In a recent paper Runham (*J. Histochem.* 9:87, 1961; 10:504, 1962) reported strong periodic acid Schiff, Hale, alcian blue and metachromatic staining reactions in the radula of the mollusc *Patella vulgata* and newly formed puparia of *Calliphora*. However, α-chitin from crab shells and β-chitin of the *Aphrodite chaete* and the *Aloteuthis* pen did not so react. Preliminary chromatographic studies yielded only N-acetylglucosamine; the author suggests a highly branched structure with many terminal residues. In cockroaches in various stages of chitin formation, Salthouse (*ibid.*, **10**:109, 1962) reported negative reactions to the Hale, alcian blue and periodic acid Schiff methods.

The chitin of the exoskeleton of arthropods is insoluble in water, alcohol, ether, alkalies, dilute acids and ammine copper hydroxide. It dissolves in hot concentrated hydrochloric acid or sulfuric acid.

When tested with the iodine and zinc chloride test it yields a violet color. Add 3–5 drops of concentrated iodine potassium iodide solution to 10 cc 33% zinc chloride solution. Apply this to chitin which has previously been treated with potassium hydroxide and thoroughly washed. The chitin is colored brown on the surface, violet within.

A solution of iodine 50 mg, potassium iodide 500 mg, calcium chloride (probably $CaCl_2 \cdot 6H_2O$ was meant) 16 gm and distilled water 4 cc stains chitin red violet.

Zander directed as follows for sections: Mount (frozen or paraffin) section in water under a coverglass. Simultaneously draw water out from one side of the coverglass with filter paper and introduce Weigert's iodine solution (p. 141) on the other. Tissues are stained brown. Then draw out the iodine solution with filter paper and at the same time introduce (33%) zinc chloride solution. The brown tissues are partly decolorized. In the same way replace the zinc chloride solution with distilled water. Chitin now assumes a violet color. The foregoing tests for chitin are derived from Ehrlich's *Encyklopädie*.

CELLULOSE AND STARCH

Cellulose colors violet when treated with a solution composed of 25 parts zinc chloride, 8 parts potassium iodide and 8.5 parts distilled water, saturated with iodine crystals (Behrens, from Ehrlich's *Encyklopädie*).

If cellulose is treated with Lugol's solution and then with a mixture of 2 parts (by weight) of concentrated sulfuric acid and 1 part of water, it gives an intense blue color (*ibid.*).

Cellulose fibers and vegetable tissue fragments in intestinal contents stain red to purple by the permanganate, chromic acid and periodic acid Schiff technics. Some fibers are Schiff positive without oxidation, and more, but not all, react after peracetic acid treatment (p. 182). These perhaps contain lignin. They still rotate the plane of polarized light after application of these methods. With other stains these fibers may give striking color alterations when rotated under crossed Nicol prisms.

Cellulose resists ptyalin and malt diastase digestions; raw starch is digested quite slowly, but by both β- and α-amylases (p. 497). When treated with Lugol iodine solutions, starch granules give the familiar dark blue color. While this fades soon in usual mounts, Takeuchi's iodine glycerol helps (p. 498), and Lower's iodine silver method (p. 498) can be tried.

Starch granules remain almost unstained with most ordinary stains but are doubly refractile, exhibiting the black cross of polarization separating 4 bright quadrants. On rotation the orientation of the black cross follows the position of the plane of polarization, not that of the starch granules. Also on rotation it is seen that in certain positions alternate quadrants are respectively yellowish and bluish white, and that on rotation these colors fade in some granules but are maintained in others.

On Gram-Weigert staining, starch granules stain black and transmit no polarized light. After Casella or Bauer staining the anisotropy is maintained, the quadrants appearing bright red purple on a dark background. On direct illumination with nonpolarized light these 2 methods give red purple starch granules. After the periodic acid leucofuchsin technic the granules are dark purple and may remain dark under crossed Nicoll prisms, or give a dark red illumination. I assign the total extinction of polarized light noted above simply to the density of the stains, not to any alteration in molecular structure.

LIGNIN, INULIN, PECTIN

According to McLean and Cook (*op. cit.*, p. 77) a basic fuchsin solution decolorized by addition of strong ammonia water, drop by drop, is a test reagent for aldehyde and may be used for the demonstration of lignin, which gives a purple color.

Plant cuticle and lignin, because of their aldehyde content, react also with Schiff's reagent.

Lignin (*op. cit.*, p. 78) according to McLean and Cook, also gives Maule's reaction. Treat first with aqueous potassium permanganate (I suggest 0.5% for 10 minutes). Wash with dilute hydrochloric acid (10% HCl anhydrous, *ca.* 3 N) and then with dilute ammonia. A red color develops in lignified tissue only.

McLean and Cook describe the orcin test for *inulin*. Soak sections first in 0.5% orcin in 90% alcohol. Then transfer to strong hydrochloric acid and warm. An orange red color is developed at sites of inulin deposit.

McLean and Cook (*op. cit.*, p. 77) state that ruthenium red ($Ru(OH)$ $Cl_2 \cdot 3NH_3 \cdot H_2O$) (M.W. 258.75) colors pectin substances and pectic mucilage deep red.

Deparaffinize sections and soak 24 hours in 1 part hydrochloric acid and 3 parts alcohol. Then place in dilute ammonia for some hours. Then place in 1:5000 aqueous ruthenium red in the dark until adequately colored.

DEXTRAN

This highly water soluble glucose polysaccharide may be demonstrated in the renal epithelium and in casts in the collecting tubules by using the periodic acid Schiff method. However, it is necessary to fix in strong alcoholic fixatives, to float paraffin sections on 95% alcohol and to use alcoholic reagents at least through the periodic acid step, and preferably throughout.

Mowry's Periodic Acid Schiff Method of Dextran (*Am. J. Path.* **29**:523. 1953).

1. Fix 48 hours at —5°C in 100% alcohol.
2. Transfer to fresh 100% alcohol for 18 hours.
3. Clear in petroleum ether or other paraffin solvent.
4. Infiltrate and imbed in paraffin. Section at 5 μ.
5. Float sections on clean slides without albumen with warm 95% alcohol to flatten.
6. Dry sections in an incubator at 37°C for 24 hours and then transfer to a paraffin oven for 20 minutes.
7. Deparaffinize in xylene, transfer to 2 changes of 100% alcohol.
8. 1% periodic acid (H_5IO_6) in 90% alcohol for 2 hours (80 minutes is less adequate; 3 hours is no better than 2). Keep alcoholic periodic acid in the dark. Discard when a brown color appears.
9. Wash in 95% alcohol for 5 minutes.
10. Hydrate quickly through graded alcohols.
11. Immerse in Schiff reagent (p. 270) for 10 minutes.
12. Wash in 3 changes 0.5% sodium metabisulfite of 1, 2 and 2 minutes.
13. Wash 2–3 minutes in running water.
14. Counterstain in a 25% aqueous dilution of Weigert's iron hematoxylin (p. 168) or by the same iron hematoxylin picric acid sequence as for the aqueous method (p. 199), alcohol, alcohol xylene, xylene, polystyrene, Permount, etc.

Results: Dextran, glycogen and starch show dark red purple; other periodic acid Schiff positive substances, much as usual (pp. 200–201). Glycerin albumen, if used on slides, may react quite intensely. The method may be useful for other highly water soluble substances which contain HIO_4 reactive groupings.

Control sections stained by the routine aqueous periodic acid Schiff procedure (p. 198) should be compared. Dextran deposits are lost when the aqueous method is used.

By use of the iron dextran "Imferon" (M.W. 10,000–20,000), which contains 50 mg ferric hydroxide per cubic centimeter, Jasmin and Bonin (*J. Histochem.* 9:104, 1961), in cryostat sections, were able to demonstrate the localization of the dextran with the Prussian blue reaction (Lison, 1953); they used the common mixture of equal parts of 2% potassium ferrocyanide and 2% hydrochloric acid, 15–30 minutes.

MUCIN, CARTILAGE, MAST CELLS

Mucin is precipitated by dilute acetic acid and rendered insoluble in water. Pseudomucin and gastric mucin are not precipitated by acetic acid. When precipitated by alcohol, mucin will redissolve in water. Dilute alkalies readily dissolve it.

Consequently alcoholic and acid fixatives are preferred. Formalin is quite serviceable if not alkaline, as it would become from magnesium carbonate neutralization. Tellyesniczky's acetic formalin alcohol (p. 39) should be excellent. I have used most of the following methods on routine material fixed in formalin that was probably acid.

The most uniformly successful method for demonstration of epithelial mucins is the periodic acid Schiff method (p. 198). Mucin in the gastric surface epithelium stains most intensely by this method; then that in intestinal goblet cells. The mucins of intestinal glands, trachea and bronchi, minor salivary and buccal glands, female genital tract, and prostatic gland and seminal vesicle contents are generally quite well stained. The mucins of the rabbit's pharyngeal glands, those of the basal portion of the colonic glands of some rodents and connective tissue mucins may stain quite poorly or not at all. Cartilage matrix, however, usually stains quite well, and more densely in the pericellular capsular areas than between them.

Bauer and Casella methods are generally successful on those mucins which color intensely with the periodic acid Schiff method; they fail where this method colors them lightly.

Technics for these procedures appear on pp. 198–199. The allochrome procedure (p. 549) gives excellent contrasts for epithelial mucins—red purple, contrasting with gray green or greenish yellow epithelial cytoplasm and blue connective tissue.

Metachromatic Dyes. Perhaps the simplest stains are those using simple aqueous solutions of certain basic dyes which stain mucin and cartilage matrix *metachromatically* (pp. 119–120). Of these perhaps the best are thionin (C.I. No. 52000), azure A, azure C, toluidine blue O (C.I. No. 52040), Bismarck brown Y (C.I. No. 21000), and safranin O (C.I. No. 30240). Highman recommends especially new methylene blue N (C.I. No. 152030) in his buffer technic.

With these, one stains perhaps 30–60 seconds in a 1:1000 aqueous solution, dehydrates with acetone and clears in xylene. The azures, thionin and toluidine blue give deep blue nuclei, light blue cytoplasm, green erythrocytes, red purple to violet mucus and cartilage matrix and deep violet mast cell granules. With the Bismarck brown Y, nuclei are brown; mucin and cartilage matrix, brownish yellow. With safranin O, mucin and cartilage are orange; nuclei, red; mast cell granules, orange red. However, gastric mucus is said to stain with these dyes only when freshly formed (Mallory). It is readily observed that in the mucin in cardial and pyloric glands stain metachromatically, while that of the surface epithelium does not.

Iron Hematoxylin and Metachromatic Dyes. A useful variant of this simple procedure is made by combining an acid iron hematoxylin nuclear stain and a simple, contrasting plasma stain with it. Other basic dyes may be used which do not of themselves exhibit metachromasia.

The following technic of ours may be followed. Paraffin sections of formalin fixed material are deparaffinized and brought to 80% alcohol as usual.

1. Weigert's acid iron chloride hematoxylin (p. 168) 6–8 minutes.
2. Wash in water.
3. 1:5000 aqueous fast green FCF (C.I. No. 42053) for 3 minutes.
4. Wash in 1% acetic acid.
5. Stain 4–6 minutes in 0.1% safranin O (C.I. No. 50240) in water.
6. Dehydrate with 95% and 2 changes of 100% alcohol, clear with 1 change of 50:50 alcohol xylene mixture and 2 changes of xylene. Mount in synthetic resin.

Results: Nuclei, black; cytoplasm, gray green; mucus, cartilage and mast cell granules orange red. If cytoplasms, collagen, muscle, etc., do not stain green, reduce the time in step 5.

By using 0.2% eosin Y in step 3 and 0.1% crystal violet (C.I. No. 42555) or malachite green (C.I. No. 42000) in 1% acetic acid in step 5, pink cytoplasm and violet or green mucus may be obtained. Other dye combinations also give good results, such as sequences of picric acid and basic fuchsin or new fuchsin; or 1:5000 methyl blue (C.I. No. 42780) or aniline blue (C.I. No. 42755) in place of the fast green FCF before safranin.

Safranin, Bismarck brown and basic fuchsin variants with fast green FCF also do well on connective tissue mucus and cartilage in mixed tumors, and often on the mucoid ("basophilic") degeneration of the derma seen near some skin cancers. For mast cells I prefer the safranin variant. This variant is perhaps the most vivid of all methods for demonstration of nucleus pulposus mucin.

I have found brief staining with 1:2000 thionin (or German toluidine blue) buffered to pH 4 with 0.01 M acetate buffer very successful for connective tissue mucins in connection with chondromucinase studies (*Arch. Path.* **52**:363, 1951).

Buffered Thionin or Azure A Stain.

1. Deparaffinize and hydrate sections as usual.
2. Stain 30 minutes in 0.05% thionin in 0.01 M acetate buffer.
3. Rinse, dehydrate in alcohol, clear with xylene, mount in polystyrene.

Results: Connective tissue mucins, purplish red; mast cell granules, red purple; nuclei, blue violet; red corpuscles, pale yellow; basophil cytoplasm, blue; muscle and connective tissue, faint greenish or unstained.

Using a pH 5 buffer demonstrates muscle and connective tissue in light blue greens, while pH levels of 3 and 2 cause red corpuscles to remain unstained. Cytoplasm stains more poorly. Mucins appear to be only partly demonstrated at pH 3, and at pH 1–2 metachromatic staining seems restricted to cartilage and mast cells. Nuclear basophilia of formalin fixed tissue persists to about pH 1.5–1.2. (Note: Phosphates precipitate thionin; use acetate and citrate buffers with this dye.)

This method of staining with buffered thiazin dyes is based on that of Highman (*Stain Techn.* **20**:85, 1945); and a basically similar procedure has been extensively used by Dempsey *et al.* (*Anat. Rec.* **98**:417, 1947).

Mota (*Blood* **6**:81, 1951) counts mast cells in rat bone marrow by making a 1:100 dilution of marrow in 3% acetic acid containing 1/50,000 toluidine blue. The mast cells are readily distinguished by their red purple granules, and chamber counts of mast cells are readily compared with total nucleated cell counts.

Vassar and Culling (*Arch. Path.* **68**:487, 1959) report bright yellow fluorochrome staining of mucin in 0.5% atabrine (quinacrine HCl) in pH 3.95 or 8.6 buffer, staining 3 minutes, washing in water and mounting in glycerol. Apáthy's syrup prevents the specific fluorescence. Magdala red, used similarly at pH 3.95, gave a light green fluorescence.

HEMATOXYLIN AND CARMINE METHODS

Two of the traditional methods for mucus are *Mayer's mucihematein* and *mucicarmine* stains. I have not used them to any great extent but cite them because the first is said by Mallory to be excellent for connective tissue mucin and the second for epithelial mucin. For both, 100% ethyl alcohol fixation is prescribed. Paraffin and celloidin (nitrocellulose) sections may be used.

Mucihematein. For the mucihematein dissolve 0.2 gm hematein (not hematoxylin) and 0.1 gm aluminum chloride in 100 cc of either 40% glycerol or 70% alcohol. To the alcoholic solution 1 or 2 drops of concentrated nitric acid are added. The latter is preferable when the mucus tends to swell in aqueous stains. With either solution stain sections 10–60 minutes or more, wash in several changes of distilled water for 5–10 minutes, dehydrate, clear and mount with alcohols, xylene and balsam or synthetic resin. Mucus stains violet blue; other tissue elements remain unstained. Gastric mucin is not stained. Cowdry suggests prestaining with alum carmine to give red nuclei.

Laskey (*Stain Techn.* **25**:33, 1950) uses hematoxylin and ripens with 40–100 mg sodium iodate per gram. Solutions are ready to use at once and remain useful for over 6 months. Her directions for preparation of the solution read: Dissolve 1 gm hematoxylin in 100 cc 70% alcohol. Add 0.5 gm aluminum chloride and 5 cc 1% aqueous sodium iodate solution, and make up to 500 cc with 70% alcohol.

Laskey's Technic for Mucihematein Staining.

1. Deparaffinize and hydrate as usual.
2. Lay slides face up on staining racks and flush off several times with distilled water.
3. Deposit 2 cc of mucihematein on each slide and stain for 5–10 minutes.
4. Wash 15 minutes in distilled water (3 changes).
5. Dehydrate with 95% and 100% alcohols, 2 changes each, and clear with alcohol + xylene and 2 changes of xylene. Mount in polystyrene or other resin.

Results: Epithelial mucins stain deep blue violet; connective tissue mucins and cartilage matrix, lighter violets. Gastric surface epithelial mucus is unstained.

Mucicarmine. For mucicarmine heat a mixture of 1 gm carmine (alum lake), 0.5 gm aluminum chloride crystals and 2 cc distilled water over a small flame, agitating constantly, until the color darkens, about 2 minutes. Then add with constant stirring 100 cc 50% alcohol. Let stand 24 hours and then filter. This stock solution is stable. According to Mallory, take 1 cc stock mucicarmine and dilute with 10 cc distilled water or 50–70% alcohol and stain 10–15 or more minutes, rinse in water, dehydrate with alcohols, clear with xylene and mount in balsam. Cowdry first stained sections in alum hematoxylin, washed and stained 5 minutes in undiluted mucicarmine. Only mucus, including gastric mucus, is stained red; other structures are unstained or stained with hematoxylin, according to the variant chosen.

Acid methyl blue and aniline blue stains in the various collagen technics (pp. 540, 541, 546, 548) often stain epithelial mucus, including gastric mucus, selectively a light blue, contrasting well with counterstains and with the deep blue collagen. Mucus may remain deep violet by Gram-Weigert variants (p. 262).

Alcian Blue. Steedman (*Quart. J. Micr. Sci.* **91**:477, 1950) reported a technic for staining chondroitin and mucoitin sulfuric acid mucins with the phthalocyanine dye Alcian Blue 8GS.[1] This dye stains mucin a clear blue green color. Mast cells are not stained. Prolonged staining will color almost all nonnuclear components of tissue. Treatment (after step 3) for 2 hours or more with alkaline alcohol (pH 8 or higher) converts the dye into the insoluble pigment monastral fast blue, which is highly resistant to decolorization, and thus permits the subsequent use of various histologic reagents.

Steedman's Alcian Blue 8GS for Mucins. Material fixed in Bouin, susa, Zenker's fluid is recommended. Formalin fixed tissue is considered unsuitable.

1. Deparaffinize and hydrate as usual.
2. Stain 10–40 *seconds* in 1% aqueous Alcian Blue 8GS.
3. Rinse in distilled water.
4. If required, treat 2 hours in 80% alcohol containing 0.5% borax.
5. Counterstain with alum hematoxylin and eosin, or otherwise as desired.
6. Dehydrate, clear in xylene and mount in synthetic resin or balsam.

NOTE: The alcian blue solution should contain thymol to prevent mold growth and should be filtered every 7–10 days.

According to Mowry (*Ann. N.Y. Acad. Sci.* **106**:402, 1963), about 1958 Imperial Chemical Industries changed the composition of Alcian Blue 8GX to improve its water solubility and textile dyeing characteristics. This change has necessitated alterations of the histologic technics employing it as the principal dyestuff.

The following schedule combines *Mowry's alcian blue method* (**AB**) and his combined *alcian blue periodic acid Schiff* (**AB-PAS**) schedule.

Deparaffinize and hydrate as usual.

1. Wash 3 minutes in 3% acetic acid.
2. Stain 2 hours in 1% alcian blue in 3% acetic acid, rinse and
3. Wash 3–5 minutes in 3% acetic acid to decrease background staining.
4. Wash 3 minutes in running water, rinse in distilled water.
5. 0.5% periodic acid, 10 minutes.
6. Running water, 5 minutes, rinse in distilled water.
7. Schiff reagent (0.5% fuchsin, cold Schiff method) 10 minutes.
8. 50 *mM* $NaHSO_3$ (0.45% $Na_2S_2O_5$ will serve), 3 changes, 2 minutes each.
9. Wash 5 minutes in running water, dip in distilled water.
10. Stain 5 minutes in alum hematoxylin (Harris or similar formula).
11. Rinse in running water.
12a. Stain 1 minute in saturated aqueous picric acid, rinse quickly in water.

[1] Imperial Chemical Industries, Ltd.

12b. Differentiate 10–20 seconds in acid alcohol (1 cc concentrated HCl + 99 cc 70% alcohol) and wash 3 minutes in water.
(Steps 10–12 can be omitted for critical studies.)
13. Dehydrate, clear and mount.

Results: For the alcian blue method (omit steps 5–9)—acid mucopolysaccharides, turquoise blue. This includes all connective tissue mucins, most epithelial mucins, some bacterial cell walls and often mast cell granules. For the alcian blue periodic acid Schiff method (the full schedule)—neutral polysaccharides: glycogen, Brunner gland mucin (man), magenta; acidic mucins, turquoise blue. Mucins reacting to both alcian blue and periodic acid Schiff blue, violet or purple.

The alcian blue solution should be filtered before use, and a crystal of thymol should be added to prevent growth of molds. The pH is about 2.6. The solution is reasonably stable but may become exhausted from repeated use.

Periodic Acid Alcian Green, Blue or **Yellow Sequence for Gastric Mucin.** According to A. Maxwell (*Stain Techn.* 38:286, 1963), Alcian green 2GX, Alcian Blue 8GX 300 and Alcian Yellow GXS may be used. These dyes are excellent mucin stains for most types of mucin but fail to stain the mucin of human gastric surface epithelium. However, if sections are first oxidized in periodic acid, staining occurs.

Maxwell's Periodic Acid Alcian Green for Gastric Mucus. Fix in formalin or formol sublimate, imbed in paraffin, cut thin sections, deparaffinize and hydrate as usual, using the iodine thiosulfate sequence for the mercurial fixation.

1. Oxidize 5 minutes in 0.5% periodic acid and rinse in water.
2. Immerse 5 minutes in 10% $Na_2S_2O_5$ in 0.1 N HCl.
3. Transfer directly to 1% aqueous alcian green (blue or yellow). The exposure is apparently brief; author gives no timing.
4. Rinse in water, counterstain in Mayer's acid hemalum, wash in tap water, dehydrate, clear and mount in balsam or synthetic resin.

Results: Gastric mucin, green (blue or yellow if blue or yellow is used).

If a 5 minute stain in 1% alcian green is interposed before the periodic acid oxidation of step 1 and alcian yellow is substituted in step 3, intestinal and metaplastic intestinal mucins stain green while gastric mucin is yellow.

One is led to speculate that the alcian dyes, whose end groups remain secret, are possessed of reactive primary amino groups and that a Schiff type reagent is formed *in situ* on the direct transfer from bisulfite to alcian dye bath. This is reminiscent in some ways of the Arzac use of basic fuchsin, though the technics are not parallel.

The technic seems worthy of trial, though I have not had opportunity to test it.

The Hale Colloidal Ferric Oxide or Dialyzed Iron Procedure for Acid Mucopolysaccharides. This technic has undergone considerable evolution since its introduction. Mowry (*Ann. N.Y. Acad. Sci.* **106**:402, 1963) has adapted Müller's preparation of colloidal iron and further controlled its behavior by a moderate dialysis to remove most of the free hydrochloric acid and, by adding acetic acid, to achieve a pH level of about 1.6–1.9 for optimal selectivity.

Preparation of Colloidal Iron Solution. Boil 250 cc distilled water. Into the boiling water pour 4.4 cc of the official iron chloride solution (U.S.P. XI) and stir. (The equivalent in iron content of this solution would be 2.73 gm $FeCl_3 \cdot 6H_2O$ dissolved in 4–5 cc distilled water, and such an extempore solution may be used if the official solution is not readily available.) Keep boiling during the addition of the iron solution. When the solution becomes dark red let it cool.

Remove free acid and unhydrolyzed (ionizable) iron salts by dialysis. Transfer the red solution to 41 mm dialysis tubes containing a glass marble as a weight at the lower end in about 25 cc portions. Suspend each tube in a 250 cc cylinder and add distilled water to fill the cylinder outside the tube. Dialyze 24 hours, changing the water twice during the dialysis interval. Filter contents of dialysis tube through Whatman No. 50 or similar very fine paper, to remove particulate iron oxide. This filtrate is the *stock colloidal iron solution* and is stored at room temperature (20–25°C).

Working Colloidal Iron Solution. Distilled water 18 cc, glacial acetic acid 12 cc, stock colloidal iron 10 cc. Prepare fresh daily, or oftener if many slides are to be stained.

Like the Alcian blue procedure, the **colloidal iron technic** is also often combined with other methods giving contrasting colors. Such a procedure is the valuable **colloidal iron periodic acid Schiff method.** The following is Mowry's technic. For the simple colloidal iron method, omit steps 6–10.

Staining Procedure. Deparaffinize and hydrate paraffin sections as usual. Defat frozen sections and smears. Remove mercury from material fixed in mercurial fixatives.

1. Immerse sections 2 hours in working colloidal iron solution.
2. Wash 30 minutes in 30% acetic acid, using 3 changes, 10 minutes each.
3. Wash 5 minutes in running tap water and in deionized distilled water.
4. Immerse 20 minutes in a fresh mixture of 20 cc 0.15 N hydrochloric acid and 20 cc 2% potassium ferrocyanide [$K_4Fe(CN)_6 \cdot 3H_2O$]

5. Wash 5 minutes in running water (this should not be alkaline) and rinse in distilled water.

6. 0.5% periodic acid, 10 minutes.

7. Running water, 5 minutes; dip in distilled water.

8. Schiff reagent (0.5% fuchsin, cold Schiff method), 10 minutes.

9. 50 mM NaHSO$_3$ (about 0.45% Na$_2$S$_2$O$_5$ will serve), 3 changes, 2 minutes each.

10. Wash 5 minutes in running water, dip in distilled water.

11. Counterstain 5 minutes in alum hematoxylin (Harris or formula of similar strength). Rinse in running water.

12a. Stain 1 minute in saturated aqueous picric acid, and rinse in water, or

12b. Differentiate hematoxylin 20–30 seconds in acid alcohol (1 cc concentrated HCl plus 99 cc 70% alcohol) and wash 2–3 minutes in running water. Hematoxylin should remain reddish brown.

13. Dehydrate, clear and mount.

Results of the simple colloidal iron procedure: Sialomucins, goblet cell mucins, carcinoma mucins, connective tissue and their tumor mucins, blue; nuclei, cytoplasms, generally unstained except by counterstains. Mast cell granules and some microbial cell walls react.

Control preparations introduced at step 3 show no iron staining except of hemosiderin and other ferric iron deposits.

The suggestion of prior dithionite desiderization arises. However Gedigk states that desiderized hemosiderin becomes again iron positive on exposure to Hale's colloidal iron (*Arch. path. Anat.* **326**:172, 1954).

With combined colloidal iron periodic acid Schiff method: Hale negative polysaccharides which are periodic acid Schiff positive color magenta; Hale positive mucin which is periodic acid Schiff negative colors pure blue. Most epithelial mucins, which are normally reactive to both methods, color violet to purple.

SIALOMUCIN, SIALIDASE

In 1960 Spicer and Warren (*J. Histochem.* **8**:135) reported the identification of sialic acid containing mucins in sublingual gland of mouse, rat and guinea pig. The mucin was identified by digestion with sialidases prepared from cultures of *Clostridium perfringens* or of *Vibrio cholerae*. Commercial polyvalent (A + B) influenza vaccine also exhibited sialidase (neuraminidase) activity.

Sections were digested with 0.05 cc enzyme (0.1% protein) in 0.1 M phosphate buffer pH 6 for unstated periods. The digestion fluid and washings were assayed for sialic acid, as were digested and undigested sections, thus demonstrating the liberation of sialic acid.

Histologic preparations were stained either 30 minutes in 0.02% azure A at pH 3 or by the alcian blue periodic acid Schiff technic. Sialomucins, strongly metachromatic before sialidase digestion, failed to stain afterward. Alcian blue periodic Schiff staining of sialomucins is changed from a strong blue before digestion to purple red after.

Quintarelli included the ox submaxillary gland as another locality for sialomucin (*J. Histochem.* 9:176, 1961), identifying the constituents as sialic acid and N-acetylgalactosamine in 1:1 molar proportions.

Quintarelli used apparently a 24 hour digestion in a dilution of influenza vaccine with 4 parts 5 mM phosphate buffered 0.85% sodium chloride solution; the pH was not stated, but the composition of the buffer indicates perhaps pH 7.5 (2.72 gm KH_2PO_4 + 30 gm Na_2HPO_4 + 170 gm NaCl in 1 liter, diluted 1/20 for use).

After digestion, preparations were stained by the iron hematoxylin, fast green FCF, safranin O technic (p. 507), by the alcian blue periodic acid Schiff method (p. 510) or by a simple periodic acid Schiff method. Metachromatic and alcian blue staining were lost by sialomucins; the periodic acid Schiff reaction persisted.

In a later report by Warren and Spicer (*J. Histochem.* 9:400, 1961) they used a 2500-fold sialidase concentrate from *V. cholerae* cultures (method of Ada and French, *Nature* 183:1740, 1959). Sialomucin is identified also in the vaginal epithelium of pregnant rats and mice, as well as during mucification periods of the estrus cycle. Sialidase failed to release sialic acid from the sialomucins of the vagina and salivary gland of the pregnant rat, though assays revealed the presence of copious sialic acid. Both *V. cholerae* and *C. perfringens* enzymes were used.

In methylation saponification sequences and in minimum pH levels of basic dye staining, the sialic acid mucins behave as carboxylic acid mucins.

CHONDROMUCINASE AND HYALURONIDASE DIGESTIONS

The chondromucins or chondroitin sulfuric mucins are further identified by the fact that their metachromatic staining wtih thionin, toluidine blue, azure A, safranin O and the like may be prevented by chondromucinases or chondroitinases.

The chondromucinases so far characterized are enzymes which resist boiling for 10 minutes in 0.1 M acetic acid, and may thus be separated from the hyaluronidase of bovine testes and from the amylase of barley malt, both of which are destroyed by this treatment.

Since the metachromatic staining of umbilical cord and nucleus pulposus mucins and of cartilage matrix are destroyed apparently equally by raw and by acid boiled testicular "hyaluronidase," it would appear that these metachromatically stained mucins are chondromucins, not hyaluronic acid. The Hale and ferric mannitol reactions of the same mucins are likewise equally impaired by raw and acid boiled hyaluronidase digestions. Hence it appears that these methods, too, demonstrate chondromucins rather than hyaluronic acid.

Hotchkiss (*Arch. Biochem.* **16:**131, 1948) listed hyaluronic acid among the substances giving a strongly positive spot test with his (alcoholic?) periodic acid Schiff method. Others have denied this reaction (using aqueous periodic acid?).

The vitreous humor, which contains a considerable amount of hyaluronic acid, exhibits a weblike coagulum, more copious after alcoholic fixations, which stains red with the periodic acid Schiff method (p. 198) and blue by the allochrome procedure (p. 549). It also colors blue with spirit blue and this blue staining is retained after alcohol dehydration, clearing and mounting in xylene polystyrene, as are those of ceroid and cartilage matrix.

Blue staining of this vitreous webwork is seen also with the Lillie-Mowry ferric mannitol method in the pH 5 variant (p. 205).

The periodic acid Schiff positive material in the fibrillar stroma of the umbilical cord is not reduced in amount by 18 hours' digestion in a bovine testicular hyaluronidase which completely destroyed the metachromatically staining material in 1 hour.

Technic of Hyaluronidase and Chondromucinase Digestions.

1. Fix in alcohol, alcohol acetic formalin, Carnoy, lead or mercury salt mixtures or the like. Dehydrate, imbed in paraffin and section as usual. Bichromate fixatives impair the digestibility of cartilage matrix.
2. Deparaffinize and hydrate through alcohols, treating with iodine and thiosulfate to remove mercury precipitates if necessary. Do not collodionize, for this greatly retards digestion. Fragile material may be digested without removal of paraffin, but the digestion may then require days rather than hours.
3. Digest for graded intervals in hyaluronidase or malt diastase buffered to pH 5.5–6.5 (0.1 M) with phosphates or acetates. I have used testicular hyaluronidase concentrations of 25–2 mg per 100 cc. Digestion times vary from 1–18 hours. Steps of 1, 2, 4, 6 and 18 hours are convenient. Malt diastase is used at 1:1000 dilution in pH 6 buffer (0.1 M acetate or phosphate). Digest at 37–45°C.
4. After digestion, wash in water and stain with toluidine blue, thionine (p. 508), the iron hematoxylin, fast green safranine method (p. 507) or one of the iron methods (pp. 205–512), as usual. Dehydrate, clear and mount by methods prescribed for the staining technic employed.

Hyaluronic acid and chondroitin sulfates A and C are digested.

MAST CELLS

Besides their ready staining with basic aniline dyes and the basic components of neutral stain mixtures, and their variable behavior under the periodic acid Schiff procedure (p. 201), it is specifically recorded that mast cell granules are nonacid fast (p. 577), Gram negative and Gram-Weigert negative, and iron negative with ferrocyanide and ferricyanide technics. They do not usually blacken selectively in the Masson argentaffin or the Gomori-Burtner methenamine silver technics. They usually do not reduce ferric ferricyanide (p. 211). In ferric mannitol procedures at pH 5 and pH 8, the granules (in mice) do not take up iron selectively, but their staining with safranin is irregularly permitted or prevented.

When frozen dried material is fixed by formaldehyde gas before infiltration with paraffin, mast cells are then reported to give positive azo coupling reactions, presumably because of their content of histamine (Lagunoff et al., *J. Histochem.* 9:534, 1961; see p. 229). After this treatment rat mast cells give positive ferric ferricyanide and methenamine silver reductions and positive azo coupling in alkaline reaction mixtures. I have seen these reactions positive in presumed mast cells in the gastric and proventricular submucosa and muscularis of the mouse after routine calcium acetate formalin fixation and paraffin imbedding.

The granules are not stained by iron or alum hematoxylin or by alum or borax carmine, by mucicarmine or mucihematin, or by alcian blue.

Metachromatic staining has been attributed by Lison and others to the presence of sulfate esters of mucopolysaccharides, and the metachromasia of mast cells has been attributed to heparin (Jorpes, *Heparin,* Oxford University Press, New York, 1939; also Sylvén, *Acta. Path. Microbiol. Scand.* 29:197, 1951). The metachromasia is readily abolished by even brief methylation (p. 283) and can be restored by demethylation with $KMnO_4$ (p. 285) only if methylation in 0.05 N HCl methanol did not exceed 6 hours at 60°C.

The usual brief saponification demethylation does not restore the metachromasia.

AMYLOID

Amyloid is a chondroitin sulfuric acid protein complex which is colored mahogany brown by iodine + potassium iodide solution in the fresh state. This reddish brown color is changed to violet or blue by sulfuric acid. Amyloid is insoluble in water, alcohol, ether and dilute acids. Like mucin, it exhibits metachromatic staining with certain basic dyes, and it stains light blue with aniline blue and methyl blue methods for collagen fibers. It gives a dim blue fluorescence under ultraviolet light (p. 17).

Mallory's Iodine Reaction (emended).

1. Stain paraffin or frozen sections of formalin or alcohol fixed material in 1:10,000 iodine solution for 10–15 minutes. (Dilute 1 cc Weigert's iodine solution (p. 141) with 99 cc water or 3 cc Gram's iodine solution with 97 cc water.)
2. Wash in water, and examine in water or glycerol. Or mount in Takeuchi's iodine glycerol (p. 498).

Results: Amyloid is mahogany brown. Postmortem tissues should be rinsed in 1% acetic acid before the iodine is applied.

According to Langhans (Ehrlich's *Encyklopädie*) permanent mounts may be made thus:

1. Prestain 10–15 minutes with carmine.
2. Stain 5–10 minutes in Gram's iodine solution (p. 141).
3. Dehydrate with 100% alcohol containing 1–2% of iodine crystals.
4. Clear and mount in origanum oil.
   Lower's silver procedure for the iodine reaction of glycogen (p. 498) also seems applicable.

Bennhold's (*München. med. Wschr.* **2**:1537, 1922) Congo red method for amyloid is given here in Puchtler's (*J. Histochem.* **10**:355, 1962) modification. Alcoholic fixatives such as Carnoy's fluid and absolute alcohol permit better stains, but good results are obtainable after aqueous formalin, formol Zenker or Kaiserling's fluid. Imbed in paraffin as usual and section at 5 μ.

1. Hydrate through graded alcohols, removing formalin pigment and mercury precipitates as usual.
2. Stain 10 minutes in Mayer's acid hemalum.
3. Wash in 3 changes of distilled water.
4. Transfer to alkaline NaCl alcohol for 20 minutes. To 40 cc saturated sodium chloride solution in 80% alcohol (*stable stock solution*) add 0.4 cc 1% NaOH just before using.
5. Stain 20 minutes in freshly alkalized Congo red solution. To 40 cc of the stable stock saturated solution of Congo red in 80% alcohol saturated with NaCl add 0.4 cc 1% NaOH, filter at once and use alkalinized solution within 15 minutes.
6. Dehydrate quickly in 3 changes of absolute alcohol, clear in xylene and mount in Permount.

Results: Amyloid, red to pink; elastic tissue, lighter red; nuclei, blue; other structures, largely unstained.

The stock 80% alcohol saturated with sodium chloride is stable for at least some months. It is conveniently made by dissolving 2 gm NaCl in 20 cc distilled water and adding 80 cc alcohol, when immediate precipitation of the excess NaCl occurs. The stock Congo red solution is readily made by saturating a quantity of the foregoing solvent with the dye. It also keeps for months. But the alkaline staining solution deteriorates promptly.

The dyeing of amyloid by sulfonated benzidine, tolidine and dianisidine dyes appears to depend on a mechanism similar to that in the direct textile dyeing of cotton. The linearity of the dye configuration permits hydrogen bonding of the azo and amine (and naphthol) groups of the dye to similarly spaced carbohydrate hydroxyl radicals of cellulose and amyloid. It is to be noted that prior acetylation of tissue prevents Congo red staining of amyloid by blockade of the carbohydrate hydroxyls, while deamination of tissue amine groups, which are the natural targets of the dye sulfonic acid groups, does not.

Permanganate and chromic acid oxidations have a greater suppressing effect on Congo red staining of amyloid than does periodic acid, since their action is not limited to 1,2-glycols, attacking primary alcohols as well.

Saturation of the dye solvent with sodium chloride tends to depress dye ionization and acid-base type staining, as does also the high alcohol content. The presence of free alkali also acts to inhibit union of tissue amine groups with the sulfonic acid groups of the dye. The high alcohol percentage also protects sections against the detergent action of the alkali.

The function of the pretreatment with alkaline alcohol is to release native internal hydrogen bonding between adjacent polysaccharide chains and thus render more potential sites available for binding of dye. This is particularly effective on the more highly birefringent deposits of amyloid. The alkali pretreatment also has a greater enhancement effect on amyloid fixed in formalin, Zenker-formol or Kaiserling's fluid, in contrast to that fixed in alcoholic fixatives.

Other dyes of the same series, Congo Corinth (C.I. No. 22145), benzopurpurin 4B (C.I. No. 23500), vital red (C.I. 23570) and trypan blue (C.I. 23850) are only slightly less effective than Congo red (C.I. 22120). Acid dyes of other classes could not be substituted. For a fuller discussion, see Puchtler's 1962 paper.

According to Herzenberg (*Virchow Arch. path. Anat.* **253**:656, 1924), amyloid may be stained intravitally by injection of 0.1–1 mg Congo red in 1 cc intravenously in mice.

The Crystal Violet Method. Mallory cites a crystal violet method which I have modified by adding methyl violet 2B to give a redder color.

Formalin or alcohol fixation, and frozen or paraffin sections may be used. From water:

1. Stain sections 3–5 minutes in crystal violet (C.I. No. 42555) 1 gm, methyl violet 2B (C.I. No. 42535) 0.5 gm, alcohol 10 cc, distilled water 90 cc.
2. Wash in 1% aqueous acetic acid.
3. Wash thoroughly in tap water.
4. Examine directly in water or mount in glycerol, glycerol gelatin, fructose syrup or Apáthy's gum syrup (p. 101).

Results: Nuclei and cytoplasm, varying shades of blue violet; amyloid and fibrinoid, red purple. The preparations fade after a time (Mallory, 1938; Conn and Darrow, 1943). Water mounts may be sealed temporarily with petrolatum.

Highman's Crystal Violet Method (*Arch. Path.* **41**:559, 1946).

1. Stain 5 minutes in Weigert's acid iron hematoxylin.
2. Wash in water.
3. Stain 1–30 minutes in 0.5–0.1% crystal violet or methyl violet in 2.5% acetic acid (I suggest 5 minutes in 0.2% crystal violet).
4. Wash in water.
5. Mount in Highman's potassium acetate Apáthy gum syrup, glycerol gelatin or Alex gelatin (pp. 101–102).

Results: Red purple amyloid, cartilage and certain types of mucus, in a bluish background with blue black nuclei. The acetic acid in the crystal violet prevents overstaining of cytoplasm, and the salt added to the syrup prevents diffusion or "bleeding" of the violet. Omission of the iron hematoxylin (step 1) renders the stain less dense.

Lieb (*Am. J. Clin. Path.* **17**:413, 1947) used about 0.3% crystal violet (10 cc saturated alcoholic solution in 1 cc hydrochloric acid and 300 cc water), stained 5 minutes to 24 hours and mounted from water in a solution of 50 gm Abopon in 25 cc water (p. 105).

Fernando varies the crystal violet method by staining 10 minutes in 3% formic acid, 1% crystal violet solution, differentiating amyloid to red with 1% formic acid about 2–3 minutes, washing and mounting in a dextrin sucrose sodium chloride solution of n∆ 1.54 and pH 3.75 (p. 104). He prescribes blotting with filter paper after each step (*J. Inst. Sci. Techn.* **7**: No. 2, 1961).

Iodine green is stated by Conn to color mucin and amyloid red, while it stains nuclei and basophil cytoplasms green. Mallory cited the following technic for frozen sections of fresh or formalin fixed material: stain 24 hours in 0.33% aqueous iodine green, wash in water and examine in water or glycerol.

The so-called *paramyloid* is characterized by inconstancy and irregularity of staining with Congo red and with crystal violet. Commonly colors are displayed between that of typical amyloid and that of serum or plasma, and considerable variability is evident even in the same section. The Van Gieson stain gives a yellow color to paramyloid, whereas it stains typical amyloid more orange. Paramyloid bodies often present concentric lamination, like that of corpora amylacea in prostatic acini, and may show central calcification. Its distribution is not that of typical amyloidosis. It occurs in bone, fat, fascia, etc., rather than in the liver, spleen, pancreas, kidney, adrenal and heart (Bauer and Kuzma, *Am. J. Clin. Path.* **19**:1097, 1949).

King (*Am. J. Path.* **24**:1108, 1948) has applied a Del Río-Hortega silver carbonate method for demonstration of both usual and atypical amyloid in frozen section of formalin fixed tissues.

1. Cut thin frozen sections; wash in distilled water.
2. Add concentrated (28%) ammonia water drop by drop to 5 cc 10% silver nitrate until the brown precipitate is just dissolved; then add 6–8 cc 3.5% sodium carbonate (Na_2CO_3), and dilute to 75 cc with distilled water. Store surplus solution in a dark, cold place. To 10 cc of the stock diammine silver carbonate solution in a small beaker add a few drops of pyridine. Introduce the sections with a glass rod and warm gently to about 45°C with continuous gentle agitation until sections become a rather deep brown ("tobacco brown").
3. Transfer directly with a glass rod to (5%) sodium thiosulfate ($Na_2S_2O_3 \cdot 5H_2O$) solution for 2–4 minutes.
4. Wash in several changes of tap water.
5. Float onto slides, smooth out and blot down with hard filter paper.
6. Counterstain lightly if desired.
7. Dehydrate and clear by the usual alcohol xylene sequence, and mount in Canada balsam or an unsaturated synthetic resin.

Results: Amyloid, nuclei and lipochrome (lipofuscin?) pigment show dark brown to black. Some collagen may impregnate, and cytoplasm is often light brown, as are hyaline casts in the renal tubules.

The periodic acid Schiff procedure (p. 198) colors amyloid light red; and in its allochrome variant (p. 549) the color remains predominantly red, though with a bluish cast. The pinacyanole technic of Humason and Lushbaugh (p. 159) gives carmine red amyloid.

Vassar and Culling (*Arch. Path.* **68**:487, 1959) stain tissues 3 minutes in 1% aqueous thioflavine TCN (C.I. No. 49005) and differentiate 10 minutes in 1% acetic acid to reduce background fluorescence. Wash and mount in Apáthy's medium. Nuclear fluorochrome staining sometimes occurs; this can be prevented by a 2 minute prestain in alum hematoxylin.

Both primary and secondary amyloid fluoresce strongly in near ultraviolet illumination, and the authors consider the stain superior to both Congo red and methyl violet.

For **corpora amylacea the Langhans iodine** method for glycogen may be used. Schmorl recommends a variant of Siegert's (no reference) in which Müller or alcohol fixation is recommended:

1. Wash sections well in water, then
2. Stain deep brown with strong iodine potassium iodide solution.
3. Decolorize with strong alcohol and then
4. Immerse in 20% hydrochloric acid (2.4 N?) until the corpora amylacea reappear as darkly colored points.
5. Wash out acid quickly with water.
6. Dehydrate in tincture of iodine diluted with 4 volumes of alcohol (1.4% I_2).
7. Mount in origanum oil.

Results: Corpora amylacea in prostate, brain, lung and urinary tract are stained deep brown; other tissues are colorless.

Toluidine blue O stains the corpora amylacea of the central nervous system metachromatically reddish purple. They are red to purple with the periodic acid and chromic acid leucofuchsin methods (pp. 198–199) and resist diastase digestion (p. 496).

The periodic acid Schiff method colors prostatic secretion pink to purplish red, and corpora amylacea appear in deeper purplish red. Diastase digestion does not alter these reactions. When prostate sections are incubated about 3½ hours in methenamine silver (p. 240) by the Gomori-Burtner technic, to the point where stroma reticulum and nuclei begin to blacken, prostatic secretion still stains pink by the safranin counterstain and the corpora amylacea are peripherally or (more often) completely blackened.

Congo red (p. 517) colors prostatic corpora amylacea purplish to orange red and the secretion gray violet to pink. The crystal violet amyloid technic (p. 519) colors them red purple, while the secretion remains violet.

HYALIN

Mallory's "alcoholic hyalin" is said to give reactions for phosphates and to stain by Mallory's hematoxylin method for lead (p. 444). After

Zenker fixation it stains intensely red with Mallory's phloxine methylene blue method (pp. 160–161) and blue with his phosphotungstic acid hematoxylin (p. 537). With alcohol or formalin fixation it is stained deep blue by Mallory's (regressive sequence) iron chloride hematoxylin method (pp. 166–167).

Mallory's Phloxine Method. When overstained with phloxine and then decolorized with lithium carbonate, hyalin remains red: Fix in alcohol or formalin, section in paraffin or celloidin.

1. Stain nuclei in Mallory's or other alum hematoxylin (p. 174).
2. Wash in water.
3. Stain 20–60 minutes in 0.5% phloxine B (C.I. No. 45410) in 20% alcohol.
4. Wash in tap water.
5. Decolorize 30–60 seconds in 0.1% aqueous lithium carbonate.
6. Wash in tap water.
7. Dehydrate and clear through an alcohol xylene sequence and mount in balsam.

Results: Nuclei appear blue; fresh hyalin appears as red droplets and threads; older hyalin, pink to colorless. Hyaline droplets in renal epithelium are also well shown, and hyaline casts color purplish red more than pink. Amyloid stains pale pink.

Mallory's Thionin Method. Similar material is used.

1. Stain 5–10 minutes in 0.5% thionin (C.I. No. 52000) in 20% alcohol.
2. Differentiate several minutes in 80% alcohol and then
3. 95% alcohol and
4. Clear in terpineol and mount in terpineol balsam.

Results: Granules and networks of red to purple material; old hyalin, blue; nuclei, blue.

Laqueur (*Am. J. Clin. Path.* **20**:680, 1950) recommends a combination of Altmann's aniline acid fuchsin with a Masson trichrome procedure for formalin or Zenker fixed material.

1. Hydrate deparaffinized sections as usual, using the iodine thiosulfate sequence of Zenker fixed tissue.
2. Stain 5 minutes in alum hematoxylin.
3. Wash in water.
4. Flood with 20% acid fuchsin in aniline water (shake 2 cc aniline thoroughly with 100 cc distilled water; filter) and heat with a small flame to fuming. Let stand 5 minutes.
5. Wash in water.
6. Differentiate in a mixture of 7 parts 20% alcohol and 1 part saturated

alcoholic picric acid (about 1% picric acid in 30% alcohol) until only hyalin and red corpuscles remain red, and collagen is faint gray or unstained.

7. Wash thoroughly in water.
8. Mordant 4–18 hours in 1% phosphomolybdic acid solution.
9. Transfer directly to 1% light green SF in 1% acetic acid for 1 hour.
10. Wash in water.
11. Differentiate in 80% alcohol until collagen fibrils appear discrete. This occurs quickly, so care is needed.
12. Clear through 95% and 100% alcohol, xylene; mount in synthetic resin.

Results: Mallory's alcoholic hyalin, brilliant red; cytoplasm, pale brown; bile pigment, green; collagen, green; hemosiderin and hemofuscin, unstained or yellowish brown in their natural color.

Renal hyaline droplets and casts appear red purple with the periodic acid leucofuchsin technic (p. 198). Casts also react to the Casella and Bauer methods (p. 199), though less strongly. With the allochrome procedure (p. 549) the droplets and casts assume an orange color similar to that given by intravascular fibrin and that of pneumonic exudates. It contrasts well with the gray green or gray yellow of renal epithelial cytoplasm. Both droplets and casts often color red with Mallory's phloxine technic (p. 522) and may color violet with Weigert's fibrin method (p. 262). They are eosinophilic with azure eosin methods.

The hyalin of intimal degeneration of small renal arteries gives a positive Sudan IV (p. 456) and a Liebermann-Burchard cholesterol reaction (p. 472) in frozen sections. It is often periodic acid Schiff positive (R. D. Baker, *Am. J. Path.* **27**:680, 1951).

GARGOYLISM MUCOPOLYSACCHARIDE

For the metachromatic staining of the acid mucopolysaccharide of Hurler's disease, Haust and Landing (*J. Histochem.* **9**:77, 1961) recommended fixation of fresh frozen sections for 20–30 minutes in equal volumes of acetone and tetrahydrofuran and staining for 2 minutes in 0.5% toluidine blue in 25% acetone. Rinse *directly* in acetone, *clear in xylene* and mount.

Lagunoff, Rosa and Benditt (*Am. J. Path.* **41**:273, 1962) applied their technic of freeze drying followed by formaldehyde gas fixation for 48 hours at 50°C and subsequent imbedding in paraffin. Sections of this material were brought through xylene and alcohols to 1% toluidine blue in 75% alcohol, 0.01 acetates, pH 3.5 (p. 661). With this technic gargoyle cells contained intensely metachromatic material, whereas with aqueous formalin fixation no toluidine blue metachromasia is preserved. These cells give a weak periodic acid Schiff reaction and light Sudan black B staining. A few cells contain intensely sudanophilic granules. Luxol fast blue staining paralleled the Sudan black results. With ordinary aqueous formalin fixation the lipid is not demonstrable in paraffin sections, only in frozen sections. Sudan black and Luxol fast blue gave strong staining in frozen sections; oil red O gave weak staining. Most "gargoyle" cells contain either metachromatic or sudanophilic material; a few possess both.

Chapter 15

Connective Tissue Fibers and Membranes

Although the methods for collagen, reticulum, basement membranes and elastin are different in some respects, it is profitable to discuss them together, since it is often desirable to stain 2 types of fibers simultaneously.

Four basic processes exist for the selective demonstration of basement membranes and collagen and reticulum fibers: the silver impregnation from ammoniacal solutions, the staining with acid aniline dyes from strongly acid solution, the phosphotungstic and phosphomolybdic acid hematoxylin methods and the periodic acid leucofuchsin method.

THE SILVER METHODS

The variations of the Bielschowsky-Maresch diammine silver technic for reticulum impregnation are far more numerous than the few samples quoted here. Maresch apparently got quite acceptable preparations in his original study, but since the process depends on a silver impregnation usually done in diffuse daylight at varying temperatures, variations in results are to be expected. Various pretreatments have been introduced to attempt to control the variability of these results. Each has its devotees and the tendency has been to add more steps and make the process increasingly complex.

The use of preoxidants which oxidize tissue elements tending to give spontaneous argentaffin reactions probably does serve a useful purpose. But temperature control has generally been very crude, and usually little attention is paid to the amount and quality of light present during the silvering process. I have noted a material difference in optimal impregnation time when the working area was moved to another less well lighted room.

It is questionable whether the various methods of preparing diammine silver oxide have any influence, provided the same final point of approximate saturation is reached. Carbonate technics do appear to be slightly different, and a few attempts to use diammine silver chloride which we made at one time never reached a measurable degree of success.

The most important factor appears to be experience in appraising the proper grade of section color change during impregnation. This experience is often acquired painfully.

It seems dubious that any considerable amount of reducible silver remains in the tissue by the time the final thiosulfate step is reached, but this step is traditional, and no one omits it.

The silver methods purport to differentiate between reticulum and collagen fibers. The former are colored black; the latter brown, lavender and gray in varying shades and tones. These methods are often uncertain in their action. One learns by experience to discern whether or not a given preparation has afforded a reasonably complete demonstration.

On account of the high alkalinity of the silver solutions, paraffin sections are often partially or completely loosened from the slides. To combat this tendency Masson used a gelatin glue which I have found no more uniformly successful in keeping sections on than was Mayer's albumen glycerol. Mallory, however, recommended it highly.

Masson (*J. Tech. Methods* 12:75, 1929) dissolved 50 mg gelatin in 25 cc distilled water and floated out sections on a large drop of this placed on the slide on a warm plate. When the sections were smooth, the excess gelatin water was drained off, and the section was blotted dry with filter paper and placed in a large, closed, moist chamber with formaldehyde vapor at 40–50°C for several hours to overnight. Shorter periods are said to be adequate for other than alkaline silver methods.

With the Foot silver carbonate method Mallory recommended alcohol as the final diluent of the silver solution in place of water, to prevent sections from floating off the slides in the alkaline silver solution.

Personally I prefer to use the routine paraffin sections which are deparaffinized with xylene and transferred to 100% alcohol. They are then soaked 5–10 minutes in 1% collodion. The collodion is then drained for 1–2 minutes and the preparations are next immersed in 80% alcohol for 5 or more minutes and then transferred to water.

The Bielschowsky-Maresch method, the Perdrau-Da Fano, one Foot variant, the Wilder method, the Gomori variant and a method of ours depend on silver oxide (or hydroxide) dissolved in ammoniacal solution. The Del Río-Hortega method and Foot's and Laidlaw's variants use ammoniacal solutions of silver carbonate. Except Foot's 2 technics, which specified Zenker material but work well after formalin fixation, and Laidlaw's, which specified Bouin's fluid as an alternative method, all methods specify formalin fixation. The details of manufacture of the ammoniacal silver solution vary somewhat, but in all except our oxide method one produces a precipitate from silver nitrate with sodium or potassium hydroxide, with ammonium hydroxide and then sodium hydroxide, or with lithium or sodium carbonate. One then barely dissolves the precipitate with ammonium hydroxide, except in Gomori's, in which one back titrates with more silver nitrate. In all, the re-solution in ammonium hydroxide is done in quite concentrated solution; and, except in Laidlaw's method, the solution is considerably diluted for use.

In the following formulae solutions are expressed in grams per 100 cc of solution, except in the Bielschowsky-Maresch and Del Río-Hortega formulae, where it is presumed that the continental European custom of expressing solutions in percentage by weight was followed. Thus the 10% silver nitrate solution with a specific gravity of 1.088 contained 10.88 gm per 100 cc in Bielschowsky's laboratory, while according to American custom 100 cc of 10% silver nitrate solution contains 10 Gm.

Maresch's Bielschowsky Silver Solution (*Zbl. allg. Path.* 16:641, 1905). Add 5 drops of 40% sodium hydroxide (4 gm NaOH, 6 gm H_2O) (this would be about 0.3 cc and would contain about 172 mg NaOH, the equivalent of 731 mg $AgNO_3$) to 10 cc 10% (10 gm $AgNO_3$, 90 gm H_2O) silver nitrate solution (1088 mg $AgNO_3$). The brown precipitate is then redissolved by constant shaking while adding 28% ammonia water drop by drop (perhaps 1 cc). It is best to leave the last few granules undissolved, as an excess of ammonia inhibits the impregnation. Dilute to 25 cc with distilled water for use. Use once.

Gridley (*Am. J. Clin. Path.* 21:207, 1951) and Couceiro and Freire (*Acad. Brasil. Cien.* 24:11, 1952) use the Maresch solution diluted to 60 cc instead of 25 cc.

Perdrau-Da Fano Silver Solution. Perdrau (*J. Path. Bact.* 24:117, 1921) used Da Fano's silver solution, which I have cited from Bailey and Hiller (*J. Nerv. Ment. Dis.* 59:337, 1924). Add 2 drops of 40% sodium hydroxide (40 gm NaOH in 100 cc solution) to 5 cc of 20% (20 gm in 100 cc solution) silver nitrate and 28% ammonia drop by drop (about 1.1 cc) with constant shaking until precipitate is almost or just dissolved. Dilute to 50 cc. Use once.

Foot's Silver Oxide Solution (*J. Lab. Clin. Med.* 9:777, 1924). Add 20 drops of 40% sodium hydroxide to 20 cc 10% silver nitrate. Dissolve the brown precipitate by adding strong (28%) ammonia water drop by drop with constant shaking until only a few granules remain. About 2 cc (theoretically 1.7 cc) is required. Dilute to 80 cc with distilled water. Use once. Assuming 17 drops per cc for the sodium hydroxide solution, an exact equivalent of the silver nitrate is used in this variant.

Wilder's Silver Oxide Solution (*Am. J. Path.* 11:817, 1935). Add 28% ammonia water drop by drop (about 0.5–0.6 cc) to 5 cc 10.2% silver nitrate until the precipitate is dissolved. Then add 5 cc 3.1% sodium hydroxide and redissolve the precipitate with a few drops of ammonia water. Make up to 50 cc with distilled water.

Gomori's Silver Oxide Solution (*Am. J. Path.* 13:993, 1937). To 20 cc

10% silver nitrate add 4 cc (3.3–5 according to Gomori) 10% potassium hydroxide. (This amount precipitates 1–1.5 gm of the total 2 gm silver nitrate as oxide.) Then add 28% ammonia water drop by drop to dissolve the precipitate completely. Then again add 10% silver nitrate drop by drop until the precipitate formed dissolves easily on shaking. Dilute the solution with an equal volume of distilled water. It can be kept stoppered for 2 days.

The end point in the addition of silver nitrate is not clear in the above directions, which are as Gomori originally published them, and as they were copied by Mallory. Gomori wrote me (1945) that he added silver until the precipitate dissolved only on vigorous shaking or even to faint permanent opalescence. In the last case he again added 1 drop of about 2% ammonia water to clear.

Lillie's Silver Oxide Method (*Stain Techn.*, **21**:69, 1946, modified, 1954). Place 1 volume of 28% ammonia water in a small flask and add rapidly 14–16 volumes of 5% silver nitrate solution, shaking the flask constantly. Then cautiously add more silver nitrate, shaking until the brown precipitate completely dissolves between each addition. Continue the addition of silver nitrate until a faint permanent opalescence is produced. This takes a total of 19–20 volumes of silver nitrate solution. Use the solution by placing 2 cc on each slide, and discard. The solution is good for 1–2 days after mixing.

Krajian employed the silver solution produced by adding concentrated ammonia water to 10% silver nitrate solution until the precipitate is almost completely dissolved. This should yield essentially the same mixture as the preceding 10% silver solutions.

The Del Río-Hortega Silver Carbonate Solution (Cited from Romeis). To 5 cc 10% silver nitrate add 15 cc 5% sodium carbonate. Then carefully add (28%) ammonia water drop by drop (about 0.4 cc) with constant shaking until the precipitate is just dissolved. Then add 55 cc distilled water. The solution may be kept a long time in brown glass.

Foot-Menard Silver Carbonate Solution (*Arch. Path.* 4:211, 1927). To 10 cc 10% silver nitrate add 10 cc saturated (about 1.3%) aqueous lithium carbonate solution. (The solubility of lithium carbonate is less in hot water than in cold; do not heat to saturate.) Wash the precipitate 3 times with distilled water by decantation. Add 25 cc distilled water and then add 28% ammonia water drop by drop (about 0.8 cc) until the precipitate is almost dissolved, shaking vigorously the while. Make up to 100 cc with distilled water. Mallory modified this by making the final dilution to 100 cc with 95% alcohol instead of water and adding a few more drops of ammonia water to dissolve the resultant precipitate.

Laidlaw's Concentrated Silver Carbonate Solution (*Am. J. Path.* **5**: 239, 1929). Dissolve 12 gm silver nitrate in 20 cc distilled water in a 250 cc graduate. Add 230 cc saturated (1.33%) aqueous lithium carbonate solution. Shake well and let precipitate settle to the 70 cc mark. Carefully decant supernatant fluid, refill with distilled water, shake and again let settle to 70 cc and decant, repeating to a total of 3 or 4 washes. Again let settle to 70 cc, decant and add 28% ammonia water with constant shaking until almost clear (about 9.5 cc). Dilute to total volume of 120 cc, filter through a Whatman 42 or 44 filter and store in stock bottle. This solution may be kept for months and may be filtered and reused a dozen times or more.

A modification of Foot's silver carbonate solution used for years in my laboratory was prepared thus: To 5 cc 10% silver nitrate add 5 cc saturated (16–20%) aqueous sodium carbonate. Let settle and wash 5 times with 35–40 cc portions of distilled water by decantation. Then add 15 cc distilled water and 28% ammonia water drop by drop (about 0.4 cc) with constant shaking until precipitate is almost dissolved. Dilute to 50 cc with distilled water.

The relative virtues of sodium, potassium and ammonium hydroxides as precipitants are difficult to evaluate, and all solutions should contain diammine silver, hydroxyl, nitrate and ammonium ions as well as the potassium or sodium ions that may have been added. The alkalinity is controlled with fair precision by limitation of the excess ammonia to the amount just sufficient to form the diammine silver radical.

The use of lithium or sodium carbonate in the Foot, the Laidlaw and our variants of the Del Río-Hortega method seems to be a matter of indifference, since in all 3 of these methods the silver carbonate is carefully washed free of soluble salts before the diammine compound is formed.

General Considerations of the Technics. The technics follow a quite uniform general pattern, with quite pronounced variations in duration of individual steps and in concentration of some of the reagents.

The *iodine sodium thiosulfate sequence* in the 2 Foot technics is to be regarded simply as the usual treatment for mercury fixed tissues, and I have always omitted it with the carbonate method on formalin fixed material. The function of this iodine thiosulfate treatment in Laidlaw's variant is not clear, but Laidlaw seems to have regarded it as an integral part of the Mallory bleach. The thiosulfate in any case should be thoroughly washed out before proceeding with the next step.

Weigert's Bleach. The sequence treatment with potassium permanganate and oxalic acid, or a substitute for it, appears in all the variants after the Bielschowsky-Maresch and the Del Río-Hortega. Its introduction into diammine silver methods is due to Perdrau (*J. Path. Bact.* 24:117, 1921) and appears to be purely pragmatic. Omission of the permanganate step results in failures of impregnation, and omission of the oxalic acid step causes irregularities of impregnation, so that both excellent impregnations and failures are obtained on similar material. Perdrau, Foot, Laidlaw and Wilder prescribed 0.25% potassium permanganate for 10, 5, 3 minutes

TABLE 15-1. SCHEDULES FOR DIAMMINE SILVER HYDROXIDE RETICULUM METHODS

	Maresch	Perdrau	Foot	Wilder	Gomori	Lillie	Gridley	Krajian	Couceiro & Freire
Fixation	Formalin or alcohol	Formalin	Zenker or formalin	Formalin, Zenker or Helly	Formalin	Formalin or Orth	Formalin, Zenker, Bouin, alcohol, Carnoy	Formalin (?)	Formalin, alc. form., Helly, Orth, Carnoy, Gendre
Section method	Wash several hours, cut frozen sections	Wash 1 day tap, 1 day dist. water. Frozen or paraffin sect.	Paraffin sections	Paraffin or loose or mounted frozen or celloidin sections	Paraffin sections. Use gelatin glue	Paraffin sections collodionized	Paraffin sect. well dried	Frozen sect. 7-10 μ	Frozen (12-15 μ) or paraffin 6 μ
Iodine	....	....	0.5% alc, 5 min	....	....	....	Only for Zenker	Formalin (?)	
Wash	....	....	Water	....	....	....	Only for Zenker		
Thiosulfate	....	....	0.5% aq., 5 min	....	....	....	Only for Zenker		
Wash	....	....	Tap water	....	Tap water	Tap water	Tap and dist. water	Distilled water	Dist. water 3-5 min, 2-3 changes
Oxidant	....	0.25% KMnO₄ 10 min	0.25% KMnO₄ 5 min	0.25% KMnO₄ 1 min or 10% phosphomolybdic acid 1 min	0.5-1.0% KMnO₄ 1-2 min	0.5% KMnO₄ 2 min	0.5% H₅IO₆ aq., 15 min	15 cc 0.3% KMnO₄ + 5 cc 28% NH₃, 5 min	4% CrO₃, 40 min
Wash	....	Dist. water	Tap water	....	Rinse tap	Tap water	Distilled water	Dist. water, few sec	Dist. water 3-5 min, 4-5 changes
Reducer	....	Pal's bleach (p. 533) until white	5% oxalic acid 15-30 min	10% HBr 1 min (see p. 533) or none	1-3% K₂S₂O₅ 1 min	5% oxalic acid 2 min	None	2% oxalic to decolorize	None
Wash	Dist. water	Dist. water 5 min	Dist. water	Dist. water	Tap, several min	Tap water	....	2 changes dist. water	
Sensitizer	2% AgNO₃ 24 hr	2% AgNO₃ 24 hr	2% AgNO₃ 48 hr	1% uranyl nitrate 5 sec	2% iron alum 1 min	3% H₂O₂ 2 min or 1.24% (46 mM) FeCl₃·6H₂O² 2 min	2% AgNO₃ 30 min	None	None
Wash	Dist. water 1-3 sec	Dist. water less than 5 min	Dist. water brief	....	Tap, few min Dist. water 2 changes	Tap, 3 min Dist. water 2 changes	Dist. water, 2 changes	None	
Silver	2-30 min 20°C until yellow brown p. 527	40-60 min 25°C, p. 527	30 min 25°C, p. 527	1 min 25°C, p. 527	1 min 25°C, p. 527	3 min 25°C, p. 528	15 min 25°C, p. 527	15 min 60°C, p. 528	20 min 25°C, p. 527

530

TABLE 15-1. SCHEDULES FOR DIAMMINE SILVER HYDROXIDE RETICULUM METHODS (*Continued*)

	Maresch	Perdrau	Foot	Wilder	Gomori	Lillie	Gridley	Krajian	Couceiro & Freire
Wash	Dist. water 2-3 sec	Dist. water quick	Dist. water quick	95% alcohol quick	Dist. water 5-10 sec	Dist. water 5-10 sec	Dist. water, quickly	Dist. water, 2 changes	Dist. water, 10-15 sec, 2 changes
Developer	20% formalin 5-30 min	20% formalin 30 min	5% formalin 2 changes 30 min	1% formalin 0.03% uranyl nitrate, 1 m, in p.533	10 to 20% formalin 3 min	10% formalin 2 min	30% formalin, 3 min	20% formalin, 55°C, 2 min	30% formalin, 5 min
Wash	Dist. water	Dist. water	Tap, rinse	Dist. water	Tap, few min	Tap, 3 min	Wash well dist. water	Rinse, dist. water	Distilled water
Gold chloride	5 drops 1% 1 drop glacial acetic in 10 cc water, until violet; 10 min	0.2% until violet	1%, 1 hr	0.2%, 1 min	0.1-0.2% 10 min, rinse dist. water	0.2%, 2 min	0.5%, 5 min	1/300, 2 min	0.1%, 3-4 min
					Reduce 1 min 1-3% $K_2S_2O_5$				
Wash	Dist. water	Dist. water, rinse	Tap, rinse	Dist. water	....	Tap, rinse	Dist. water	Rinse, dist. water	Distilled water
Sodium thiosulfate[1]	5%, 15-60 sec	5%, 2 min	5%, 2 min	5%, 1-2 min	1-2%, 1 min	5%, 2 min	5%, 3 min	5%, 2 min	5%, 2 min
Wash	Running water	Thorough, dist.	Tap, several hr	Tap water	Tap water	Tap water	Running water	Wash	Prolonged, water
Counterstain	....	....	Hematoxylin Van Gieson	Hematoxylin and eosin, or Van Gieson	....	Hematoxylin and eosin, or Van Gieson, acid fast or others			
Mounting	Alcohols to 95% or 100%, carbol-xylene or xylene, balsam	Alcohols, carbol-xylene or creosote-xylene, balsam	Alcohols to 100%, xylene, balsam	Alcohols, xylene, balsam	Alcohols, xylene, balsam	95% alcohol, acetones, acetone-xylene, xylene, balsam	Alcohols, xylene, balsam	Glycerol gelatin	Alcohols, xylene, balsam

[1] Crystals, $Na_2S_2O_3 \cdot 5H_2O$.
[2] Original—$\frac{1}{60}$ U.S.P. Liq. Ferr. Chlor.

TABLE 15-2. SCHEDULES FOR DIAMMINE SILVER CARBONATE
RETICULUM METHODS

	del Río-Hortega	Foot-Menard	Laidlaw	Lillie
Fixation	Formalin	Formalin or Zenker	Bouin or Formalin	Formalin
Section method	Frozen sections	Paraffin sections	Paraffin sections. Wash Bouin 20 min, formalin 5 min	Paraffin sections collodionized
Iodine		0.5% alc., 5 min	1% alc., 3 min	
Wash				
Thiosulfate[1]		0.5% aq., 5 min	5% aq., 3 min	
Wash		Tap water	Tap water	Tap water
Oxidant		0.25% KMnO₄ 5 min	0.25% KMnO₄ 5 min	0.25% KMnO₄ 5 min
Wash				Tap water
Reducer		5% oxalic acid 10 min	5% oxalic acid 3 min	5% oxalic acid 10 min
Wash		Tap water	Tap water, 10 min	Tap water
Wash	Dist. water	Dist. water	Dist. water, 3 changes	
Silver	1–2 min 45–50°C p. 528	10–15 min 37°C p. 528	5 min, 50°C p. 528	5 min, 60–70°C, until golden brown p. 529
Wash		Dist. water, rinse	Dist. water, rinse	Dist. water, rinse
Developer	1% formalin until yellow	20% formalin 5 min	1% formalin several changes 3 min	20% formalin 2 min
Wash		Thorough, tap	Dist. water, rinse	Tap water
Gold chloride	0.2%, 30 sec	0.2%, 5 min	0.2%, 10 min	0.2%, 2 min
Wash		Tap water	Dist. water	Tap water
Sodium thiosulfate[1]	5%, brief	5%, 2 min	5%, 10 min several changes	5%, 2 min
Wash	Tap water	Tap water	Tap water	Tap water
Counterstain	Van Gieson	Hematoxylin Van Gieson	As desired	Hematoxylin Van Gieson
Mounting[2]	95% alcohol, carbol-creosote-xylene, xylene, balsam	Alcohols, xylene, balsam	Alcohols, xylene, balsam	95% alcohol, acetones, acetone-xylene, xylene, salicylic balsam

[1] Na₂S₂O₃·5H₂O.

[2] Usual synthetic resins are substituted for balsam.

and 1 minute respectively; Gomori used 0.5–1.0% for 2–1 minute; and I
have used 0.5, 0.33 and 0.25% solution for 2–5 minutes. In any case the
sections are colored fairly deep brown, and the reaction is probably completed in a few seconds. Wilder's substitution of a 1 minute 10% phosphomolybdic acid treatment probably serves the same purpose, as the hexa-
valent molybdenum of the molybdic acid is easily reduced to a lower
valence. The washing after this step serves to remove the excess reagent.
The reducing agent in Foot's methods, and Laidlaw's and our variants
has been 5% oxalic acid, varying in time thus: 15–30 minutes in Foot's
oxide method, 10 minutes in his and our carbonate methods, 3 minutes
in Laidlaw's, and 2 minutes in our oxide method. Actually the brown

permanganate stain disappears in a few seconds in this reagent, and what benefit may accrue from further exposure is difficult to discern. Gomori used a 1–3% potassium metabisulfite ($K_2S_2O_5$, which hydrates to $KHSO_3$ in water) solution for 1 minute, and Perdrau used Pal's 0.5% oxalic acid, 0.5% acid potassium sulfite ($KHSO_3$) solution until the sections were white. Wilder prescribed a 1 minute bath in one-fourth dilution of concentrated hydrobromic acid to follow the permanganate step and stated that this could be omitted if phosphomolybdic acid was substituted for permanganate. The hydrobromic acid removes the brown permanganate stain instantly. Couceiro and Freire oxidized 40 minutes in 4% chromic acid solution, Gridley used a 15 minute bath in 0.5% aqueous periodic acid (H_5IO_6). The latter should lead to greater constancy of results, since periodic acid carries oxidation of 1,2-glycols and 1,2-aminoalcohols only to the aldehyde stage, while permanganate and chromic acid both produce aldehyde and oxidize it further.

Sensitizers. Maresch employed a 24 hour bath in silver nitrate solution, with no antecedent oxidation. Wilder substituted 1% uranyl nitrate for 5 seconds. Gomori prescribed 1 minute in 2% iron alum as preferable to several other metal salt impregnations tried by him. I have substituted a 2 minute bath in a 1:50 dilution of U.S.P. ferric chloride solution (*ca.* 46 *mM* or 1.24% $FeCl \cdot 6H_2O$) as equivalent, and have found a number of oxidant solutions also successful: 3% H_2O_2, 1% $NaIO_3$, 1% iodine or a 1% acetic acid, 5% potassium bichromate mixture. After Orth fixation this sensitizing step is better omitted. Since ferric chloride treatment also sensitizes connective tissue fibrils so that they more or less specifically reduce the methenamine silver of the argentaffin cell method (p. 240), it would appear that there may be actual metal organic compounds formed, in which the silver later replaces the metal. Aldehyde sites do not appear to reduce ammine or methenamine silver complexes selectively, perhaps because the aldehyde is bound with amino groups under alkaline conditions.

However, aldehyde sites, engendered by permanganate or periodic acid, may well operate to initiate silver deposition from the 2% silver nitrate of the Maresch, Perdrau-Da Fano, Foot and Gridley methods and thus afford nuclei for further deposit in the alkaline ammine silver solutions. Gomori found that the same effect could be achieved in 10 minutes with 10% silver nitrate, and noted that thorough washing in distilled water after sensitization was preferable to the brief rinses prescribed by the Bielschowsky-Maresch and the Foot silver oxide technics. Bailey and Hiller washed not over 5 minutes with distilled water, using the Perdrau-Da Fano method.

Sensitizing agents have not been commonly employed in diammine silver carbonate technics. All technics prescribe washing with distilled water before the silver bath.

Silver Bath. Times in the silver oxide baths vary thus: 1 minute at room temperature prescribed by Gomori and Wilder, the 2–30 minutes' interval of the Bielschowsky-Maresch technic, Foot's 30 minutes, and Perdrau's 40–60. These methods vary in concentration in grams of silver nitrate used to make 100 cc of solution thus: 4 gm for the Bielschowsky-Maresch; 4–5 gm for our oxide method and the Gomori; 2.5 gm for the Foot; 2 gm for the Perdrau-Da Fano; and 1 gm for the Wilder. With carbonate methods concentrations are 10 gm for Laidlaw's; 1 gm for Foot's and ours; and ⅔ gm for Del Río-Hortega's; and times and temperatures are respectively 5 minutes at 50°C, 10–15 minutes at 37°C, 3–5 minutes at 60–70°C and 1–2 minutes at 45–50°C. Sections turn yellow to brown during silvering by the carbonate methods and in the original Bielschowsky-Maresch oxide technic. With the other oxide methods they remain unchanged in color until developed. Though little correlation is seen among time, temperature and concentration, nevertheless, when the same variant is employed, increase in temperature accelerates the process, and variation of dilution alters the time requirement in the expected direction.

Most technics prescribe a quick rinse of 1–10 seconds in distilled water between the silver bath and the reduction bath. Wilder used alcohol, and Del Río-Hortega carried sections direct from his weak silver bath to weak formalin.

Reduction. All methods use formaldehyde in concentrations varying from a 30% dilution of the concentrated 37–40% formaldehyde down to 1%. Gridley used 30% formalin for 3 minutes; Couceiro and Freire used the same for 5 minutes; Bailey and Hiller, 20% formalin for 30 minutes for the Da Fano technic used by Perdrau; Maresch, for 5–30 minutes; Foot's carbonate method, for 5 minutes; ours, for 2 minutes; Foot's oxide method used two changes of 5% over a 30 minute period; Gomori required 10–20% for 3 minutes; Laidlaw, 1% for 3 minutes; Del Río-Hortega, 1% until yellow; and Wilder, a 0.03% uranyl nitrate, 1% formalin solution for 1 minute. Actually reduction occurs visibly in the first few seconds after adding formalin, and no further darkening is evident after 30 seconds or so. I have used a 2 minute period in 10% formalin for the oxide variant, and in 20% formalin for the carbonate.

Washing after the formalin is usually in tap water, though Wilder and Laidlaw prescribe distilled water.

Toning. All technics use a toning in yellow auric chloride (which is 1:500): until violet according to Bailey and Hiller in Perdrau's method, 1 minute in Wilder's method, 30 seconds in Del Río-Hortega's, 5 minutes in Foot's carbonate method, 10 minutes in Laidlaw's, 2 minutes in our carbonate and oxide variants. Foot's silver oxide method used 1% for 1 hour, while the Bielschowsky-Maresch technic called for 5 drops of 1% solution with 1 drop of glacial acetic acid in 10 cc distilled water until the sections turned violet, and Gomori used either 1:500 or 1:1000 for 10 minutes. Couceiro and Freire used 0.1% for 3–4 minutes, controlling microscopically; and Gridley employed 0.5% for 5 minutes and insisted that golden brown tones be replaced by pale yellowish gray (taupe) or lavender. Actually the sections change color in a few seconds and probably even Wilder's 1 minute interval is longer than necessary.

Following gold toning usually a brief wash or rinse in tap or distilled water is recommended. Gomori prescribes a second reduction with 1–3% potassium metabisulfite for 1 minute, followed by another wash.

Fixing. Then all methods remove unreduced silver by means of sodium thiosulfate. Gomori prescribes 1–2% for 1 minute, the rest use 5% for 15–60 seconds (Bielschowsky-Maresch), brief (Del Río-Hortega), 1–2 minutes in Wilder's, 2 minutes in Perdrau's and Foot's 2 cited methods and our carbonate and oxide variants, and Couceiro and Freire's method, 5 minutes in Gridley's technic, and 10 minutes with Laidlaw's strong silver carbonate method.

Counterstains, etc. Thorough washing follows in all technics, and then counterstains are inserted by Foot, Wilder, Del Río-Hortega and our carbonate and oxide variants. Usually a brief hemalum stain, tap water bluing, and a 45–60 second Van Gieson technic are recommended; they have been quite successful in our hands. If Gomori's iron alum sensitizer or our iron chloride bath is used before the silver oxide bath, an iron hematoxylin effect is produced. This I find too dense and prefer to omit the hematoxylin with this variant. I have had very interesting results by following the reticulum method with a Ziehl-Neelsen acid fast stain or by a periodic acid Schiff reaction (p. 198).

Alcohol dehydration, clearing with xylene, carbol xylene, or carbol creosote xylene and inclusion in balsam are recommended. With our collodion film technics we find it advisable to complete the dehydration with acetone (thus removing the collodion and any precipitate which may have formed on it) and then pass through acetone and xylene into 2 or 3 changes of xylene.

The following **reticulum technic** is based on *Wilder's, Gomori's* and *our variants* of the *Bielschowsky-Maresch method.*

Place 1 cc 28% ammonia water in a small flask. Add 5% silver nitrate, the first 14–16 cc fairly rapidly, the rest of the 19–20 cc total cautiously, shaking between each addition to clear the brown clouds of silver oxide until a faint permanent turbidity remains. This diammine silver hydroxide solution can be used for 1 or 2 days, and is discarded after one use.

The procedure of impregnation is as follows:

1. Fixation in formalin or Orth's fluid. Dry 5 μ paraffin sections several hours in 58°C oven, then take through 2 changes of xylene and 2 of 100% alcohol into

2. 1% collodion in ether and absolute alcohol (equal volumes) for 5–10 minutes.
3. Drain 1–2 minutes.
4. 80% alcohol 5 minutes or more.
5. Rinse in tap water.
6. 0.5% potassium permanganate 2 minutes.
7. Wash in water.
8. 5% oxalic acid 2 minutes.
9. Wash in water.
10. Wilder's 1% uranyl nitrate 5–10 seconds, or Gomori's 2% iron alum 1 minute, or liquor ferri chloridi, 1:50 (46 mM $FeCl_3$) in distilled water 2 minutes, or 3% hydrogen peroxide 2 minutes. With Orth fixed material omit this step.
11. Wash 3 minutes in running water and then rinse in 2 changes of distilled water. Wilder omitted this wash, but it does not interfere even after uranyl nitrate.
12. Lay slides face up on glass rods over a large pan and deposit on each about 1.5–2 cc of the diammine silver hydroxide. Let stand 3 minutes, decant and
13. Rinse quickly in distilled water.
14. Reduce 2 minutes in 10% formalin.
15. Wash 3 minutes in running water.
16. Tone 2 minutes in 0.2% acid gold chloride ($HAuCl_4$).
17. Rinse in tap water.
18. Fix 2 minutes in 5% sodium thiosulfate (0.2 M).
19. Wash in tap water.
20. Counterstain as desired. For example, acetic alum hematoxylin (p. 174) 2 minutes, tap water 2 minutes, Van Gieson's picrofuchsin (p. 540) 1 minute. Differentiate in 2–3 changes of 95% alcohol. Or stain by Ziehl-Neelsen for acid fast organisms (p. 578). Or stain 5 minutes in 0.1% safranin, thionin or toluidine blue, differentiate 1 minute in 5% acetic acid, wash well in tap water. Or use the periodic acid Schiff for red basement membranes.
21. Complete dehydration and decollodionization in 3 changes of acetone, clear with 1 change of acetone and xylene (50:50) and 2 or more changes of xylene. Mount in synthetic resin. The acetone removes the collodion film; if this is to be preserved, use isopropanol.

ACID AND BASIC FLUOROCHROME METHOD

Vassar and Culling (*Arch. Path.* **68**:487, 1959) found good differential fluorochrome staining of collagen, reticulum and basement membranes by staining 3 minutes in equal volumes of 1% alcoholic solutions of rhodamine B and fluorescein, differentiating in 1% acetic alcohol, dehydrating, clearing and mounting in Harleco resin (HSR). The photo-micrograph shows moderate (red?) fluorescence of proximal tubule cytoplasm, with strong fluorescence of glomerular stroma, presumably yellow. The authors neglect to give the colors.

THE HEMATOXYLIN METHODS

Mallory's phosphotungstic acid hematoxylin stains nuclei, centrioles, spindles, mitochondria, fibrin, fibrils of neuroglia and the so-called my-oglia and fibroglia and the contractile elements of striated muscle blue; collagen, reticulum, elastin, cartilage and bone matrix are yellowish to brownish red.

For staining of mitochondria Mallory prescribed (p. 289) a prolonged oxidation with ferric chloride before dehydration of the formalin fixed blocks, and prolonged the staining interval. For other elements the following general technic is prescribed. The solution is the same in either case and is prepared by dissolving 1 gm hematoxylin and 20 gm phosphotungstic acid in 1000 cc distilled water. This ripens in several weeks and the naturally ripened product is thought to be best. However, Mallory states that the addition of 177 mg potassium permanganate will ripen it at once. (50 mg $NaIO_3$ might serve better.)

Zenker fixation was prescribed by Mallory. Earle has told me that he has had satisfactory staining of material fixed in buffered formalin, without subsequent mercury treatment. Peers (*Arch. Path.* **32:**446, 1941) stated that sections of formalin fixed material should be brought to water as usual and then mordanted 3 hours at 57°C (paraffin oven temperature) in saturated aqueous mercuric chloride solution. Sections thus mordanted are then treated just as though Zenker fixation had been employed, thus:

The Mallory Phosphotungstic Acid Hematoxylin (PTAH) Technic.

1. Iodine in 95% alcohol (0.5%), 5 minutes.
2. 0.5% sodium thiosulfate, 5 minutes (or 5% for 1 minute).
3. Wash in tap water.
4. 0.25% potassium permanganate, 5 minutes.
5. Wash in water.
6. 5% oxalic acid, 5 minutes (Mallory 10–20 minutes).
7. Wash in running water 1–2 minutes.
8. Stain in phosphotungstic acid hematoxylin overnight (12–24 hours).
9. Dehydrate rapidly in 95% and 100% alcohol or in acetone, clear with a 50% mixture of the dehydrating agent and xylene, then 2 changes of xylene. Mount in balsam or synthetic resin.

Lieb (*Arch. Path.* 45:559, 1948) introduces mordanting in ferric ammonium alum after step 7 thus: Rinse in distilled water, mordant 1 hour in 4% iron alum, rinse in tap water and in distilled water and stain in the hematoxylin solution 2–24 hours. The color of normally blue staining elements is intensified by this treatment.

Linder (*Quart. J. Micr. Sci.* 90:427, 1949) has described a hematoxylin method for collagen, reticulum and capillary basement membranes. It appears to be limited in its usefulness to material fixed with mercuric chloride fixatives. The hematoxylin solution requires 10 weeks' ripening to stain basement membranes well, though collagen and reticulum are stained by the fresh solution. The lake retains its staining potency up to at least 7 months. I have had no experience with this method.

Thomas's phosphomolybdic acid hematoxylin was made by Linder as follows.

Dissolve 2.5 gm hematoxylin in 49 cc dioxane and 1 cc aerated water. Dissolve 16.5 gm phosphomolybdic acid in 44 cc distilled water and 11 cc ethylene glycol or glycerol, and filter. Mix equal volumes of the 2 solutions and ripen the mixture at (British) room temperatures (18–20°C) for 10 weeks. The similarity of the solution to Mallory's phosphotungstic acid hematoxylin is noteworthy.

The Linder-Thomas Phosphomolybdic Acid Hematoxylin Technic.

1. Fix in 9 volumes saturated aqueous mercuric chloride and 1 volume commercial formalin.
2. Imbed in paraffin by usual technics, section at 3 μ, deparaffinize and hydrate as usual.
3. Treat with Weigert's iodine solution (p. 141) for 1 minute.
4. 5% sodium thiosulfate (0.2 M) 1 minute.
5. Wash in distilled water.
6. Barely cover section with phosphomolybdic acid hematoxylin and stain for 10 minutes.
7. Wash with distilled water.
8. Dehydrate, clear and mount.

Results: Collagen, reticulin and basement membranes of pulmonary capillaries, deep violet; red corpuscles, purple; nuclei, blue but lightly stained; cytoplasm, bluish. A counterstain with 0.02% acriflavine in 1% acetic acid for 30 seconds gives a greenish background that contrasts well.

THE ACID ANILINE DYE METHODS: PICRIC ACID MIXTURES

The general subject of collagen staining with acid aniline dyes I have reviewed (*J. Tech. Methods* 25:1, 1945), and the reader may find there many details and methods for which I have not found space in this account.

The selective collagen stains with acid aniline dyes apparently depend on the selectivity of collagen for certain acid dyestuffs from fairly strongly acid solutions. With one group of methods a mixture of aniline blue, methyl blue, indigocarmine, acid fuchsin or other dyestuffs is made in appropriate proportion with picric acid, which acts both as the acidifying agent and as a counterstain for muscle, cytoplasm and other materials. In another group the counterstain precedes the fiber stain and the latter is mixed with or preceded by an acid such as phosphotungstic, phosphomolybdic or picric acid, or even hydrochloric acid.

Stains in the first group are the simplest in application, and are widely used also as general stains.

Picroindigocarmine was the first differential connective tissue stain reported (by Jullien in 1872). In Ramón y Cajal's (*Rev. Cien. Med. Barcel.* **22**:97, 1896; *Histology*, 1933) modification it is still widely used. In this technic one first stains nuclei red with carmine, then washes in water and stains 5–10 minutes with a solution of 250 mg (originally 333 mg) indigocarmine (C.I. No. 73015) in 100 cc saturated (1.2%) aqueous picric acid solution. Rinse in weak (perhaps 0.5%) acetic acid and dehydrate and differentiate in absolute alcohol. Connective tissue is blue green; muscle, greenish yellow; nuclei are red.

An iron hematoxylin stain, such as Weigert's (p. 168), for 3–6 minutes can be substituted for the carmine, and a sequence of 95% and absolute alcohol is just as satisfactory for differentiation and dehydration. This method on the whole is less selective and less complete for fine fibers than are its methyl blue or acid fuchsin counterparts.

Van Gieson's mixture consists of acid fuchsin (C.I. No. 42685) and picric acid. (See *J. Tech. Methods* **25**:1, 1945, for literature.) The usual proportion is 5 cc 1% acid fuchsin (50 mg of dye) to 95 cc saturated aqueous picric acid solution. The proportion of acid fuchsin can profitably be raised to 100 mg per 100 cc picric acid solution (**Weigert**). Ad-

TABLE 15-3. VAN GIESON PICRO ACID FUCHSIN MIXTURES

	Van Gieson	Weigert	Unna	Lillie	Freeborn-Van Gieson glia[1]
Acid fuchsin, mg/100 cc	50	100	250	100	150
Picric acid saturation..	95%	Saturated	Saturated	Saturated	Half saturated
Other additives........	....	....	1.5 HNO₃ 10 glycerol	0.25 cc conc. HCl	

[1] Mallory uses 15 cc 1% acid fuchsin, 50 cc 1.22% picric acid and 50 cc water for Freeborn's glia mixture.

dition of 0.25 cc concentrated hydrochloric acid to the last mixture sharpens the differentiation, so that muscle is purer yellow and collagen is deeper red (**Lillie,** *loc. cit.*) **Unna's variant,** containing 250 mg acid fuchsin, 1.5 gm nitric acid [the P. G. 1884 was 30%, sp. gr. 1.185, and the 1.5 gm would equal 0.5 cc of present day concentrated (70%) acid, sp. gr. 1.42], 10 cc glycerol, 90 cc water and picric acid to saturation, gives deep crimson collagen and bright yellow muscle.

Technic. Bring sections to water as usual.

1. Stain 5 minutes in Weigert's acid iron chloride or other similar hematoxylin (p. 168).
2. Wash in water.
3. Stain 5 minutes in the picrofuchsin mixture.
4. Dehydrate and differentiate with 2–3 changes each of 95% and 100% alcohol.
5. Clear with a mixture of 100% alcohol and xylene followed by 2–3 changes of pure xylene. Mount in polystyrene.

Kattine (*Stain Techn.* 37:193, 1962) substitutes alum hematoxylin in step 1. She stains 7–10 minutes, washes in water, acid alcohol (1 cc concentrated HCl:99 cc 70% alcohol) and again in water. Then she immerses sections 30–60 seconds in phosphotungstic phosphomolybdic acid mixture (1.25% each) and washes with water before proceeding with the Van Gieson step. Nuclei are then stained black.

Picro-methyl blue mixtures were used by Dubreuil, Curtis, Ohmori and others. I find that 100 mg methyl blue (C.I. No. 42780) or aniline blue (C.I. No. 42755) per 100 cc saturated aqueous picric acid solution is a suitable proportion (*J. Tech. Methods* 25:1, 1945).

1. Stain first with iron hematoxylin (Weigert's acid iron chloride) for 5 minutes.
2. Wash with water.
3. Stain in picro-methyl blue or picro-aniline blue for 5 minutes.
4. Differentiate briefly in 1% acetic acid or directly in 95% alcohol.
5. Then 100% alcohol, 100% alcohol and xylene, 2 changes of xylene and mount in polystyrene, Permount or similar resin.

Results: Connective tissue, including much reticulum, mucosal and renal glomerular basement membranes, is deep blue; muscle and cytoplasms, varying shades of yellowish green to gray; mucus, pale blue; nuclei, black.

Violamine R (C.I. No. 45190) is a good substitute for acid fuchsin in the Van Gieson methods, yielding a similar color picture, with less tendency to fade than with acid fuchsin. Amido black 10 B (C.I. No. 20470) can be used in place of methyl blue, giving a very precise dark bluish green color to collagen. It is one of the most selective and precise collagen stains that I have encountered. For the best contrasts, use 20–40 mg of this dye to the 100 cc of saturated picric acid solution.

Masson's Van Gieson variant (*J. Tech. Methods* **12:**75, 1929) introduced a plasma stain with 2 cc saturated aqueous metanil yellow (C.I. No. 13065) diluted to 100 cc in 1% acetic acid between the iron hematoxylin and the picrofuchsin. Thus:

1. Stain nuclei black with Regaud's iron hematoxylin (p. 166).
2. Wash.
3. Differentiate in two-thirds saturated alcoholic picric acid.
4. Wash 15 minutes in running water.
5. Stain 5 minutes in the acetic metanil yellow.
6. Rinse in distilled water.
7. Mordant 5 minutes in 3% potassium bichromate.
8. Stain 30–60 seconds in 1% acid fuchsin in saturated aqueous picric acid.
9. Rinse quickly in distilled water.
10. Differentiate 5 minutes in 1% acetic acid.

I see no particular advantage to this method over an acidified Van Gieson stain such as Unna's, in which there are fewer steps.

Biebrich Scarlet Picro-Aniline Blue. In 1940 I reported a similar method (*Arch. Path.* **29:**705, 1940).

1. Weigert's acid iron chloride hematoxylin for 5 minutes in place of Regaud's.
2. Wash.
3. 0.2% Biebrich scarlet (C.I. No. 20905) in 1% acetic acid for 4 minutes in place of the metanil yellow.
4. Wash, omitting the chromation, and
5. Stain for 4–5 minutes in 0.1% aniline blue in saturated aqueous picric acid, instead of in picro-acid fuchsin, and
6. Transfer directly to 1% acetic for 3 minutes.
7. Dehydrate, clear and mount in polystyrene.

Results: Connective tissue was stained blue, including renal glomerular stroma, basement membranes and much reticulum; erythrocytes, orange scarlet; muscle, pink; cytoplasm, pink to gray; nuclei, gray to black; mucus, light blue.

Further experimentation with this method corrected some of its defects and apparently increased its completeness of staining connective tissue (*J. Tech. Methods* **25:**1, 1945), thus:

Picro-Amido Black 10B.[1] Bring sections to 80% alcohol as usual.

---

[1] Called Naphthol Blue Black in the second edition of this book and in the original publication. See p. 124.

1. Stain 6 minutes in acid iron hematoxylin (Weigert's or similar formula).
2. Wash in tap water.
3. Stain 5 minutes in: brilliant purpurin R (C.I. No. 23510) 0.6 Gm, azofuchsin G (C.I. No. 16540) 0.4 gm, glacial acetic acid 1 cc and distilled water to make 100 cc.
4. Rinse in water.
5. Stain 1–5 minutes in: amido black 10B (C.I. No. 20470) 50–100 mg, saturated aqueous picric acid 100 cc.
6. Differentiate directly in 1% acetic acid for 2 minutes.
7. Dehydrate, clear and mount by an alcohol, alcohol xylene, xylene, synthetic resin sequence.

Results: Dark green collagen, reticulum, basement membranes and renal glomerular stroma; pale greenish blue mucus; brown to greenish brown epithelial cytoplasm; light brown muscle; red erythrocytes.

Since with fresh samples of brilliant purpurin R and azofuchsin G it may be necessary to adjust the proportions so as to maintain the brown red balance between muscle and erythrocytes, it is well to prepare these 2 dyes in 1% solutions in 1% acetic acid and mix them in 6:4 proportion for use. This permits of ready variation to increase or decrease the red. Aniline blue or methyl blue at the same concentration can be used in place of amido black 10B, with only slightly inferior results and somewhat better demonstration of mucus.

Fast Green Van Gieson. A similar method giving red connective tissue, gray green cytoplasm and muscle, green erythrocytes and brown nuclei is done thus (*J. Tech. Methods* **25**:1, 1945). I have found it a useful method.

Technic. Bring sections to water as usual.

1. Stain 6 minutes in an acid alum hematoxylin (p. 174).
2. Wash in tap water.
3. Stain 4 minutes in 0.1% fast green FCF (C.I. No. 42053) in aqueous 1% acetic acid.
4. Wash in 1% acetic.
5. Stain 10–15 minutes in 0.2% acid fuchsin in saturated aqueous picric acid.
6. Wash 2 minutes in 1% acetic acid.
7. Dehydrate, clear and mount through alcohols, alcohol and xylene, xylene to polystyrene, or cellulose tricaprate.

Results: Nuclei, brown; collagen, reticulum and basement membranes, deep purplish red; ocular lens capsule and Descemet's membrane, a deeper red purple; muscle, grayish or yellowish green after formalin fixatives and a deeper and purer green with nonformalin fixatives; cytoplasm, ellipsoids of retina and red corpuscles, green; Paneth cell granules, sometimes red; hypophyseal alpha granules, light green; beta granules, brownish red; adrenal cortex cells, green; medulla cells; pink to gray pink except after chromate fixatives when they are a darker and grayer green than cortex cells. Mucus is almost unstained.

In step 3 I have substituted 0.3% wool green S (C.I. No. 44090) with good results. The greens are bluer. In step 4, 0.2% violamine R (C.I. No. 45190) or 0.1–0.5% ponceau S (C.I. No. 27195) may be substituted for the acid fuchsin with good results.

The mechanism of the foregoing group of stains remains obscure. The dyes usable in picric and related acid mixtures are generally di- to tetrasulfonic acids, they often, but not regularly, contain one or more primary, secondary or even tertiary amino groups and they belong to several distinct classes of dyes, the disazo, triphenylmethane, rhodamine and indigo groups all being represented.

Unlike what happens with many other structures stained by acid dyes, the staining of collagen fibers by Van Gieson mixtures is not prevented by deamination and is only poorly prevented by pyridine acetylation. Sulfation in acetic anhydride acetic acid solvent mixtures prevents acid dye staining of the usual type and also prevents the selective collagen stains by Van Gieson stains. This blockade is resolved by methanolysis in the same manner as (and concurrently with) the destruction of sulfation induced metachromatic basophilia at pH 1–2. Since both O and N acylations appear to occur in such mixtures, this does not aid greatly in elucidating the staining mechanism.

The selectivity of the Van Gieson type stains for collagen fibers appears to be enhanced by addition of mineral acids to the stain mixtures (see also Lillie, *J. Histochem.* **12**:821, 1964).

PHOSPHOMOLYBDIC AND PHOSPHOTUNGSTIC ACID METHODS

It appears perhaps indicated by Puchtler's work (*J. Histochem.* **6**:265, 1958) that the selectivity of the following group of methods may be due to specific uptake of molybdenum or tungsten acids by the fibers, and subsequent binding of the usual sulfonated aminotriphenylmethane dyes by their NH_2 groups. Puchtler indicates that the same structures are demonstrated if after the phosphomolybdic acid bath, sections are reduced with stannous chloride to produce molybdenum blue, and she finds further that basic dyes may be used in place of the usual water soluble aniline blue or light green SF. If this mechanism is accepted it relates this group of stains more to the phosphotungstic acid hematoxylin group (p. 537) than to the Van Gieson stains, to which they have sometimes been regarded as equivalent.

These methods include technics in which the acid and the fiber stain are used in sequence, as in the 1900 Mallory method and in the Heidenhain and Masson variants; and those in which the acid and the fiber stain are used together, as in the 1905 and 1936 Mallory methods. Often Zenker, Helly, Regaud, Bouin or other mercurial or picric acid fixations are prescribed for these methods, and if the material has been fixed with formalin, mordanting in Zenker's or Bouin's fluid or in saturated mercuric chloride or picric acid solution is prescribed, either of blocks of unimbedded tissue or of sections before staining. I have found saturated mercuric chloride in water and saturated picric acid in alcohol acceptable means of accomplishing this end. The effect of these fixations and aftertreatments is to enhance the staining of cytoplasm and to render connective tissue somewhat more difficult to stain fully.

Although there has been considerable dispute both as to the relative efficiency of phosphomolybdic and phosphotungstic acids and as to the proper concentration and exposure time, it seems to make little difference whether one uses one, the other, a combination of both or neither, as long as sections are treated with acid before and during the fiber stain. I have used picric acid, ferric chloride and other reagents successfully in place of phosphomolybdic acid (*J. Tech. Methods* **25**:1, 1945).

Numerous variants of the Mallory technics have been published, and the tendency of recent years seems to have been in the direction of greater complexity of method and introduction of more visually controlled differentiations. Although I do not question the efficacy of such methods in the hands of those who have had long experience with them, they are difficult of execution for the new or occasional user and require a familiarity with the results to be attained which is not general among other than specially trained technicians.

Of the group, the most widely used have been Mallory's 1905 and 1936 variants, Heidenhain's 1916 "azan" method and Masson's 1928–1929 "trichrome" methods.

Mallory's 1905 Method (*J. Med. Res.* **13**:113, 1905).

1. Zenker fixation.
2. Usual iodine and thiosulfate sequence.
3. Wash in water.
4. Stain 5 minutes in 0.5% acid fuchsin.
5. Drain and transfer to: aniline blue (C.I. No. 42755) 0.5 gm, orange G (C.I. No. 16230) 2.0 gm, phosphomolybdic acid 1 gm, distilled water 100 cc. Stain 10–20 minutes.
6. Dehydrate and differentiate in several changes of 95% alcohol, then 100% alcohol, xylene and balsam.

Mallory's 1936 Method (*Stain Techn.* 11:101, 1936). As above, but use 1 gm phosphotungstic acid in place of the phosphomolybdic in the aniline blue stain. Stain with this for 20–60 minutes or longer. In 1936 Mallory recommended 0.25% acid fuchsin for 30 minutes, but in his 1938 text he reverted to a 1–5 minute stain in 0.5%, as in the 1905 technic.

Results: With both Mallory's variants collagen fibrils are deep blue; cartilage and bone matrix, mucus, amyloid and some hyaline materials, varying lighter shades of blue; fibrin, nuclei, glia fibrils, "fibroglia and myoglia" and axis cylinders, red; erythrocytes and myelin, yellow.

Heidenhain's "Azan"[1] Variant (*Z. wiss. Mikr.* 32:361, 1916). This technic gave red nuclei and erythrocytes, orange muscle, reddish glia fibrils, blue mucin, and dark blue collagen and reticulum, including glomerular stroma.

Technic: Fix in Zenker's, Helly's, Bouin's or Carnoy's fluid.

1. Stain 30–60 minutes in a covered dish at 50–55°C and then 1–2 hours at 37°C in: 0.25–1 gm azocarmine B (C.I. No. 50090) in 100 cc cold water and 1 cc glacial acetic; or 100 cc water saturated by boiling with 0.1 gm azocarmine G (C.I. No. 50085), cooled and acidified with 1 cc glacial acetic acid.
2. Wash in distilled water.
3. McGregor (*Am. J. Path.* 5:545, 1929) inserted the step of differentiating in 0.1% aniline in 95% alcohol and rinsing in 1% acetic acid in 95% alcohol.
4. Heidenhain then mordanted 30 minutes to 3 hours in 5% phosphotungstic acid.
5. Rinse in distilled water.
6. Stain 1–3 hours in a 50–33% (Mallory: 25%) dilution of a stock solution of aniline blue 0.5 gm, orange G 2 gm, glacial acetic acid 8 cc, distilled water 100 cc.
7. Rinse in water.
8. Dehydrate and differentiate in 95% alcohol; then 100% alcohol, xylene and balsam as usual.

I have not used this method, regarding a 3–9 hour technic as too cumbersome for frequent use, and having found some of the picric acid and hydrochloric acid methyl blue methods fully effective. The periodic acid leucofuchsin technic and its allochrome variant (pp. 198, 549) are suggested for kidney and lung.

Masson's Trichrome Stain (*J. Tech. Methods* 12:75, 1929). This also followed a sequence procedure. Thus: Fix in Bouin's or Möller's (Regaud's) fluid or premordant formalin or alcohol material with Bouin's

---

[1] The term "Azan" is derived from the first syllables of "Azokarmin B" and of "Anilinblau W," the names of the principal dyes used.

or Möller's fluids, respectively. Paraffin sections are fastened to slides with Masson's gelatin (p. 526).

1. Stain with Regaud's iron hematoxylin (p. 166) and
2. Differentiate to a pure nuclear stain in two-thirds saturated alcoholic picric acid solution (6%).
3. Wash 15 minutes in running water (3 minutes is adequate to remove the picric acid).
4. Stain 5 minutes in 2 parts 1% "xylidene ponceau" (ponceau 2R, C.I. No. 16150) and 1 part 1% acid fuchsin (C.I. No. 42685), both in 1% acetic acid.
5. Rinse in distilled water.
6. Mordant 5 minutes in 1% aqueous phosphomolybdic acid.
7. Drain and stain 5 minutes in 2.5% aniline blue (C.I. No. 42755) in 2.5% acetic acid or in 2% light green SF (C.I. No. 42095) in 1% acetic acid.
8. Return aniline blue stains to the phosphomolybdic acid for another 5 minute period. (I find this step unnecessary.)
9. Take the aniline blue stains from the phosphomolybdic acid and the light green stains directly from the stain and differentiate 2 minutes in 1% acetic acid. Dehydrate, clear and mount by an alcohol, xylene, balsam sequence. Masson recommends Curtis's salicylic acid balsam or natural acid balsam. Polystyrene, Permount or other resin—should serve well.

Results are similar to those of other Mallory stains, depending on the colors of the plasma and collagen stains used.

Other writers have substituted the simpler Weigert's acid iron chloride hematoxylin (p. 168) for Regaud's. Fast green FCF (C.I. No. 42053) and wool green S (C.I. No. 44090) have been found (Lillie, *J. Tech. Methods* **25**:1, 1945) to be good substitutes for light green, giving green and blue green collagen respectively and staining mucus in paler tones of the same colors. Biebrich scarlet (C.I. No. 26905), Bordeaux red (C.I. No. 16180), chromotrope 2R (C.I. No. 16570) in the reds, brilliant purpurin R (C.I. No. 23510) as a brown are good substitutes for the ponceau 2R and acid fuchsin mixture. Saturated alcoholic picric acid and saturated aqueous mercuric chloride are good premordants for formalin material.

A single solution stain giving muscle and cytoplasms in pink, with blue collagen, reticulum and hypophyseal beta granules, is our buffered Mann stain (p. 302).

Gomori (*Am. J. Clin. Path.* **20**:661, 1950) found that one solution trichrome mixtures can be made from blue or green acid triphenylmethane or diphenylnaphthylmethane dyes as collagen stains with red sulfonated azo or disazo dyes as plasma stains, and acetic and phosphotungstic or phosphomolybdic acids. Phosphotungstic acid tends to intensify the plasma stain: phosphomolybdic, the fiber stain; and alcohol weakens the plasma stain. Pretreatment with hot Bouin's fluid intensifies staining of muscle and plasma. Water washing extracts plasma stains more than fiber stains, whereas acetic rinsing makes the preparation more transparent without altering the color balance. Gomori recommended the following technic:

Gomori's Trichrome Stain.

1. Fix smears in alcohol or alcohol ether. Imbed tissue blocks in paraffin and section at 3–5 μ.
2. Bring smears or sections to water as usual.
3. Stain nuclei 5 minutes with alum hematoxylin (Delafield, Harris, Lillie-Mayer or Ehrlich, p. 174).
4. Wash in water.
5. Stain 5–20 minutes in

Chromotrope 2R	0.6	gm
Fast green FCF	0.3	gm
Phosphotungstic acid	0.6	gm
Glacial acetic acid	1	cc
Distilled water	100	cc

6. Rinse in 0.2% acetic acid.
7. Dehydrate and clear by the usual alcohol xylene sequence. Mount in polystyrene, Permount, HSR or other synthetic resin.

Results: Connective tissue, green; muscle and cytoplasm, red; nuclei, gray blue.

Like other fast green methods of the Masson type, it gives a rather diffuse and incomplete picture of the more finely fibrillar stroma. Much of the reticulum of liver and spleen is difficult to discern.

THE HYDROCHLORIC ACID METHODS

An **HCl orange G methyl blue method** of mine (*loc. cit.*) omits all so-called mordants and yields deep blue reticulum, fine collagen fibrils, renal glomerular stroma and basement membranes; blue to brown coarse collagen bundles, lighter blue epithelial mucus, orange pink erythrocytes, orange to gray cytoplasm, orange yellow muscle and black nuclei. Brush borders of renal epithelium sometimes stain differentially blue. Aniline blue can be used instead of methyl blue.

Formalin material is used. Paraffin sections are brought to water.

1. Stain 6 minutes in Weigert's or similar acid iron hematoxylin.
2. Wash in water, and stain 10 minutes in 1% aqueous phloxine B (C.I. No. 45410).
3. Wash 2 minutes in 1% acetic acid and stain 10 minutes in methyl blue 100 mg, orange G 600 mg, concentrated hydrochloric acid (37%) 0.25 cc, distilled water 100 cc.
4. Wash in 1% acetic acid 5 minutes, dehydrate, clear and mount by an acetone, acetone and xylene, xylene sequence in synthetic resin.

The **HCl Biebrich scarlet methyl blue variant** of this technic, giving a denser overall stain with more brilliant colors, may be done as follows (*loc. cit.*):

1. Stain paraffin sections of formalin fixed material 6 minutes in Weigert's acid iron chloride hematoxylin.
2. Wash in water, and stain 5 minutes in 1% Biebrich scarlet in 1% acetic acid.
3. Wash 2 minutes in 1% acetic acid and stain 5 minutes in a 0.5% dilution of concentrated hydrochloric acid containing 0.5% methyl blue or aniline blue or 0.2% amido black 10B. Satisfactory results can also be attained by reducing the methyl blue to 0.1% or the amido black 10B to 0.05% in the same HCl solution, if the staining time is prolonged to 20–40 minutes.
4. Dehydrate with 95% and 100% alcohol, clear with 100% alcohol and xylene mixture and 2 changes of xylene and mount in synthetic resin.

Results: Muscle, red with darker cross striae; erythrocytes, scarlet; cytoplasm, gray pink; brush borders of renal epithelium, sometimes blue or green; mucus, pale blue or blue green; collagen, reticulum, basement membranes and renal glomerular stroma, deep blue or blue black.

PERIODIC ACID OXIDATION METHODS

Another method for the demonstration of collagen, reticulum and basement membranes is the periodic acid leucofuchsin method (p. 198). This procedure is apparently unrelated chemically to the silver methods or to the acid aniline dye collagen methods. Basically it is supposed to depend on the presence of hydroxyl groups or one hydroxyl and one primary or secondary amine group on adjacent carbon atoms. It now appears that this reaction in the case of collagen and reticulum (and gelatin) is due in small measure to the presence of hydroxylysine in the protein molecules, and, more largely, to the presence of a closely bound, nonglucosamine saccharide (Bangle and Alford, *J. Histochem.* 2:62, 1954).

The periodic acid Schiff reaction of collagen and reticulum is quite readily blocked by sulfite treatment after periodic acid oxidation; that of basement membranes, somewhat less so. Immersion after periodic acid for a 2 hour period in 0.05 M $NaHSO_3$ followed by a 10 minute bath in Schiff reagent results in positive reactions of glycogen, starch, cellulose, most mucins, renal casts, yeasts, lens capsule, Descemet's membrane, rod acromeres and vitreous coagulum. The connective tissues including collagen, reticulum, basement membrane, bone and cartilage matrix, zymogen granules and thyroid colloid fail to react.

Acetylation with a 40% acetic anhydride 60% pyridine mixture before periodic acid oxidation prevents the aldehyde formation in most substances, if adequately prolonged. Cartilage matrix and starch resist acetylation the longest, 18–24 hours at 25°C being required to block this reaction. Contrariwise, much shorter periods are adequate to prevent the reaction in collagen, reticulum and basement membranes (2 hours). Glycogen and the mucins are intermediate in their requirements.

The reaction of renal reticulum and glomerular basement membranes with the periodic acid leucofuchsin technic is not abolished by 16 hours digestion in 1:4000 bull testis hyaluronidase at pH 5 and 37°C, but the metachromatic staining of umbilical cord matrix was completely destroyed by the same solution in 2 hours.

The usual periodic acid Schiff procedure used after the above chemical treatments is given on p. 198. A useful variant specifically valuable for the differentiation of the connective tissues is the allochrome procedure (*Am. J. Clin. Path.* 21:484, 1951). This method colors most collagen and reticulum bright blue; lens capsule, suspensory ligament, Descemet's membrane, renal tubule basement membranes and many other epithelial basement membranes, capillary basement membranes and part of the medial stroma of arteries, deep red. It depends on the use of a picromethyl blue counterstain after a usual periodic acid Schiff sequence. The technic follows.

Lillie's Allochrome Connective Tissue Method.

1. Deparaffinize and hydrate paraffin sections through xylene, alcohols and water as usual. Treat with iodine and thiosulfate (p. 85) if required for removal of mercury precipitates. Wash frozen sections with 2 changes of water to remove excess formaldehyde.
2. Oxidize 10 minutes in 1% aqueous H_5IO_6.
3. Wash 5 minutes in running water.

4. Immerse 10 minutes in Schiff reagent (p. 270).
5. Wash 2, 2 and 2 minutes in 3 changes of 0.5% sodium metabisulfite.
6. Wash 5 minutes in running water.
7. Stain 2 minutes in Weigert's acid iron chloride hematoxylin (p. 168).
8. Wash 4 minutes in running water.
9. Stain 6 minutes in saturated aqueous picric acid containing 40 mg methyl blue (C.I. No. 42780) per 100 cc.
10. Dehydrate and differentiate in 2 changes each of 95% and 100% alcohol. Wash in 50:50 alcohol xylene mixture and clear in 2 changes of xylene. Mount in synthetic resin: polystyrene, Permount, HSR, cellulose caprate, Depex or the like.

Kattine (*Stain Techn.* **37**:192, 1962) substitutes alum hematoxylin in step 7, staining for 10 minutes, washing in water, differentiating briefly in acid alcohol (1 cc concentrated HCl, 99 cc 70% alcohol), washing again and converting the hematoxylin stain to a black lake by immersing 30–60 seconds in phosphotungstic phosphomolybdic acid mixture (1.2% each). Preparations are again washed in water.

Results: Nuclei, black, gray or brown; cytoplasms and muscle cells, gray green to greenish yellow; most reticulum, blue; ring fibers of splenic reticulum, typically red purple; basement membranes of glomerular, renal and many other capillaries, red purple; medial stroma of arteries, red with fewer blue fibrils; epithelial basement membranes, characteristically red purple in the kidney, where they are relatively thick, perhaps deep violet in other organs where they may be quite thin; but usually one can find at least small areas where an inner red lamina is slightly separated from an adjacent blue reticulum fibril. Amyloid varies from fairly deep to quite pale purplish red to lavender. Arterial hyalin colors orange red to purple red. Fibrin is red to orange. Bone matrix colors gray orange; cartilage, red purple. The collagen of areolar tissues is colored bright blue; that of denser masses may retain some coarse pink or greenish yellow fibers among the predominant blue or greenish blue fibers. Glycogen, starch, cellulose, Descemet's membrane; lens capsule and suspensory ligament; bacterial, yeast and mold chitins; epithelial mucins and that of acute torulosis; thyroid and hypophyseal colloids; follicle fluid and zona pellucida in the ovary, prostatic secretion and corpora amylacea; intestinal melanosis and adrenal and ovarian lipofuscin pigments—all retain the red purple colors of the Schiff reaction. Renal brush borders remain purplish pink, hyaline or colloid droplets color orange and casts color deep red purple.

The "black periodic acid procedure" (p. 273) is useful for demonstration of the stroma of smoth and striated muscle, mucosal basement membranes and reticulum, as well as glycogen, starch, periodate reactive mucins and other substances.

ELASTIC FIBERS

Though elastic tissue in arterial walls is often stained brilliantly pink with azure eosin methods and the like, elastic fibers are less easily discerned in the derma, the pulmonary parenchyma and other locations. In fresh material containing collagen and elastin fibers, the former are distinguished by their wavy course and their pronounced swelling and clearing in dilute acids such as acetic, citric and oxalic. Elastic fibers remain as slender, straight fibrils, anastomosing at intervals in such preparations. Normally elastic fibrils stain with acid dyes but may be rendered basophilic by treatment with chromic acid or chromates. They quickly blacken with osmium tetroxide. In the presence of ferric salts they stain with basic fuchsin with or without resorcin. From acid solution they are selectively stained by the weak acid orcein.

Elastic fibers in some species, notably rodents, color red purple with Schiff reagent in a variety of procedures in which this reagent is employed: The Feulgen nucleal and plasmal reactions; the 1,2-glycol reactions after oxidation with periodic acid, chromic acid, potassium permanganate, lead tetraacetate and sodium bismuthate; the ethylene reactions with performic and peracetic acids; and finally, with brief (10 minute) exposures to Schiff reagent alone. A brief (30 minute) treatment with 5% phenylhydrazine before periodic or peracetic acid prevents the red coloration of elastica in these methods, and prevents their direct Schiff and Feulgen reactions as well. It is indicated that the reactive material is an aldehyde insoluble in fat solvents.

Verhoeff's Iodine Iron Hematoxylin

Verhoeff's procedure is an overstaining with an iodine + ferric chloride + hematoxylin mixture, followed by a ferric chloride differentiation (Mallory). It seems to be quite permanent. I have seen a section stained by Verhoeff nearly 50 years before which was still excellent. The elastic tissue was deep violet, nuclei were blue violet, the acromeres of the rods and cones were a good violet.

Verhoeff's Method, According to Mallory. Fix in Zenker or in formalin, imbed in paraffin or celloidin, bring sections to 80% alcohol. Do not iodize before staining.

Dissolve 1 gm hematoxylin in 20 cc hot 100% alcohol. Add 8 cc 10% ferric chloride solution. Mix and add 8 cc Lugol's solution containing 2% iodine and 4% potassium iodide. This solution is best fresh but can be used for 2–3 weeks. Immerse sections in this mixture for 15 minutes or more, until quite black.

Differentiate a few seconds in 2% ferric chloride, observing microscopically in water. If overdifferentiated, restain at once. Wash in water; then in 95% alcohol to remove the excess iodine; then again in water. Counterstain in 0.5% aqueous eosin, dehydrate in alcohols, clear in origanum oil, mount in balsam.

Results: Elastin, black; nuclei, blue black; collagen, fibrin, glia and myelin, pink; erythrocytes, orange red. The acromere staining noted above is probably a lipid stain.

Orcein

The Taenzer-Unna Acid Orcein Method. Bring paraffin sections to 70% alcohol by the usual sequence.

1. Stain 1–18 hours at room temperature or 10–30 minutes at 30–37°C in a freshly filtered solution of 1 gm orcein (natural or synthetic) in 100 cc alcohol of 65% (Stutzer), 70% (Mallory, Romeis), 75% (Taenzer), 80% (Merk), 90% (Kornhauser, from Conn and Darrow), 100% (Cowdry, Schmorl, Lee) to which 1 cc of official P.G. or concentrated hydrochloric acid is added. (Stutzer, Taenzer and Merk are cited from Ehrlich's *Encyklopädie.*)
2. Wash in alcohol (70–100%) and in water, either first.
3. Counterstain briefly in polychrome methylene blue (Unna), 1:1000 azure A or toluidine blue for 1 minute, or alum hematoxylin for 3–6 minutes, if desired.
4. Dehydrate and clear by an alcohol or acetone xylene sequence and mount in balsam or synthetic resin.

One may further add a connective tissue stain of Van Gieson or Mallory type, or a picroindigocarmine. The foregoing technic is a composite from the various modern texts.

Fraenkel's Method (Schmorl).

1. Stain nuclei red with (Orth's) lithium carmine. Differentiate in hydrochloric acid alcohol (1%).
2. Stain 24 hours: Of a stock solution of 1.5 gm orcein, 120 cc 95% alcohol, 60 cc distilled water, 6 cc nitric acid, add sufficient to a 3% alcoholic hydrochloric acid solution to give a dark brown color. This is the staining solution.
3. Differentiate in 80% alcohol.
4. Stain 10–15 minutes in 0.25% indigocarmine in saturated aqueous picric acid solution.
5. Rinse in 3.5% acetic acid.
6. Dehydrate quickly in 95% and 100% alcohol, clear in oil or xylene—I suggest the 100% alcohol + xylene 50:50 mixture first, then 2 changes of xylene. Mount in balsam (or synthetic resin).

Results: Red nuclei, dark brown elastin, blue green collagen, greenish yellow muscle.

Romeis's Method. Bring paraffin sections to 70% alcohol.

1. Stain 1 hour in 1% orcein in 0.125 N hydrochloric acid, 70% alcohol.
2. Wash thoroughly in 2 changes distilled water.
3. Stain heavily with Ehrlich's acid hematoxylin, acid hemalum or 3 minutes in Hansen's iron alum hematoxylin (p. 170).
4. Wash 10 minutes in distilled, tap and distilled water.
5. Stain in 60 cc 0.1% acid fuchsin in saturated aqueous picric acid solution to which is added 0.25–0.3 cc 2% acetic acid (5 minutes should suffice).
6. Rinse in 60 cc distilled water containing 2.5 cc of the acidified picro-fuchsin solution above, for not more than 2–4 seconds.
7. Blot dry.
8. 95% alcohol 1 minute.
9. 100% alcohol 3 minutes, then clear with xylene and mount in balsam.

Results: Black to red brown elastica, yellow muscle, bright red collagen, dark brown nuclei.

Weigert's acid iron chloride hematoxylin can probably be used in place of Hansen's formula, and any alum hematoxylin would undoubtedly serve. The addition of the few drops of 2% acetic acid (pH probably above 2) to the Van Gieson stain already at pH 1.95 seems rather futile; and it seems that the technic could be simplified by direct transfer from the Van Gieson mixture to alcohol.

Resorcin Fuchsin

Another important group of elastin stains are the iron resorcin lakes of basic fuchsin, crystal violet and other basic dyes. Weigert (*Zbl. allg. Path.* 9:289, 1898; Ehrlich's *Encyklopädie*) directed thus: To 200 cc 1% basic fuchsin solution add 4 gm resorcinol and boil until dissolved. Then add 25 cc liquor ferri sesquichlorati P.G.[1] (the modern U.S. official solution of iron chloride is the same) and boil 2–5 minutes longer. Cool and collect the precipitate on a filter. Take up the precipitate from the sides and bottom of the original vessel as well as from the filter paper with 200 cc 95% alcohol (by boiling as necessary). Add 4 cc concentrated hydrochloric acid and filter, washing the filter through afterward with enough fresh alcohol to restore the total volume to 200 cc. Commercially prepared resorcin fuchsin is available.

Weigert directed 15–30 minutes' staining in this solution, followed by alcohol differentiation and clearing in xylene. This gave black elastic fibrils on a pale violet background.

One may use 2 gm crystal violet in 200 cc water in place of the basic

[1] 25 cc P.G. or U.S. = 62 cc Br. 1932 = 29 cc Fr. 1905 = 27 cc Spain 1905 = 16.5 cc Netherl. 1905. U.S.P. Liquor Ferri Chloridi is about 2.3 M $FeCl_3$.

fuchsin. In this case 0.5–2 gm dextrin should be added, according to French (*Stain Techn.* 4:11, 1928; also personal communications). The resulting stain is green. Or if 1 gm basic fuchsin and 1 gm crystal violet are used, a deep blue green color is achieved. If 2 gm safranin is used, elastic fibrils are stained brownish red. The resorcinol used should be fresh and crystalline. When heating the alcohol to dissolve the precipitate a closed electric hot plate or a steam table is preferred because of the fire hazard. Romeis specified the hydrochloric acid as the P.G. official 25%, sp. gr. 1.126; Ehrlich specified it as concentrated. Most writers have followed the latter, and some even add additional hydrochloric acid for staining.

Usually this procedure is combined with other stains which, because of the high acidity and alcohol content of the resorcin fuchsin stain, must follow it rather than precede. Silver impregnations for reticulum, however, should precede the elastic tissue stain. In this case the crystal violet compound is preferable to resorcin fuchsin, because the green contrasts better than blue black with the black silver deposit. The more common combinations are with fibrin or collagen stains. Some simply precede the elastin stain with a carmine stain for nuclei.

For combination with staining of tubercle bacilli, one first stains as usual with hot (1 hour at 55–60°C) carbol fuchsin (pp. 577–578), washes off in water and then stains 20–30 minutes in the acid alcoholic resorcin fuchsin solution, which decolorizes cells and other structures at the same time. Then differentiate in alcohol, counterstain 5 minutes in 0.1% methylene blue in 1% acetic acid, dehydrate with alcohol or acetone and clear with a 50% xylene mixture with 100% alcohol or acetone followed by 2 changes of xylene. Mount in synthetic resin.

For Hornowski's (*Z. wiss. Mikr.* 26:128, 1909) Weigert's elastica Van Gieson's collagen stain I have substituted variations of Hart (*Zbl. allg. Path.* 19:1, 1908) and Kattine (*Stain Techn.* 37:193, 1962).

1. Deparaffinize and bring to 70% alcohol. Rinse in acid alcohol (1 cc concentrated HCl, 99 cc 70% alcohol).
2. Stain 24 hours in Weigert's resorcin fuchsin solution diluted with 9 volumes acid alcohol.
3. Rinse in acid alcohol and place for 1–3 minutes in 95% alcohol.
4. Stain 7–10 minutes in alum hematoxylin (Ehrlich, Harris, Delafield or other).
5. Rinse in water, differentiate briefly in acid alcohol, rinse 1 minute in running water.
6. Form black dye lake by immersing 30–60 seconds in phosphomolybdic phosphotungstic acid mixture (1 gm each in 80 cc distilled water).
7. Rinse in distilled water and counterstain 2–5 minutes in Lillie's HCl Van Gieson (0.25 cc concentrated HCl, 100 cc saturated aqueous picric acid, 100 mg acid fuchsin).

8. Rinse briefly in distilled water, dehydrate and differentiate in 2 changes each of 95% and absolute alcohol, clear in xylene, mount in synthetic resin.

Puchtler and Sweat (*Stain Techn.* **35**:347, 1960) use commercial prepared resorcin fuchsin obtained from Chroma, staining 4–5 hours at 20–25°C in 0.2% resorcin fuchsin in 70% alcohol containing 1% by volume of concentrated hydrochloric acid. Distilled water rinsing and a Van Gieson counterstain follow, then alcohols, xylene and synthetic resin.

Higher concentrations gave less selective staining; lower concentrations required longer staining, 24, 48 or more hours for 0.1, 0.05 or 0.02%.

The Volkman-Strauss Method. Others have combined the resorcin fuchsin with one of the aniline blue methods, such as the Volkman-Strauss (*Z. wiss. Mikr.* **51**:244, 1934) combination with the Mallory-Heidenhain procedure (see p. 545); and no doubt picro-methyl blue and similar procedures, with or without a red plasma stain, could be used (p. 541).

An elastic tissue fibrin combination is sometimes useful and such a method is quoted by Schmorl. A variant of this which I have found useful is quoted:

Elastin Fibrin Technic. Bring paraffin sections to 95% alcohol.

1. Stain 20–40 minutes in resorcin fuchsin or the resorcin fuchsin crystal violet. Mercury fixed tissue should be stained 1–2 hours.
2. Wash in 95% and 80% alcohol.
3. Stain 20 minutes in carmine (p. 179), 5 minutes in acid iron hematoxylin (p. 168) or 10 minutes in 1% Bismarck brown R in 1% acetic acid.
4. Wash in water.
5. Stain 2–3 minutes in aniline methyl violet (saturated methyl violet in distilled water 9 cc and 1 cc saturated methyl violet in 20% aniline, 80% alcohol mixed at time of using). See also pp. 262, 566–567; any methyl violet or crystal violet solution will serve.
6. Rinse quickly in 0.9% aqueous sodium chloride solution.
7. Flood with Weigert's (p. 141) iodine, pour off and again flood, giving total exposure of 20–30 seconds.
8. Rinse in water.
9. Blot dry.
10. Clear and decolorize in equal volumes of aniline and xylene as long as a fresh drop of mixture is colored violet by the section.
11. Wash in 2–3 changes of xylene. Mount in balsam.

Results: Nuclei, red, gray or brown; elastin, blue black; fibrin, violet; Gram positive bacteria, blue black.

Resorcin Fuchsin Oil Red O. The resorcin fuchsin method may also be combined with a fat stain if a suitable quantity of the stock stain is diluted with water to bring its alcohol content down to 60%. The frozen sections are stained 1–2 hours in a covered dish, then rinsed with 60% alcohol and stained with oil red O for 5 minutes (dilute 3 cc of stock saturated isopropanol solution with 2 cc distilled water; let stand 7–8 minutes, filter and use at once). Then wash in water, counterstain 3–5 minutes in 0.1% aqueous Janus green B (C.I. No. 11050) and wash 1 minute in 5% acetic acid. Wash in water, float onto slides and mount in gum syrup. Or one may use an alum hematoxylin nuclear stain for 5 minutes, wash and mount.

Orcinol New Fuchsin

Fullmer's Orcinol New Fuchsin (*Stain Techn.* **31**:27, 1956). This reagent appears to be more selective for elastic fibers than the preceding ones. The reagent is prepared in a manner similar to that for Weigert's resorcin fuchsin.

Add 2 gm new fuchsin (Magenta III C.I. No. 42520) and 4 gm orcinol (reagent grade) to 200 cc distilled water, boil 5 minutes and add 25 cc Liquor Ferri Chloridi U.S.P. IX and boil 5 minutes more. (Or use 15.5 gm $FeCl_3 \cdot 6H_2O$ and water to make 25 cc, if the U.S.P. solution is not available.) Cool, collect precipitate on a filter and dissolve it in 100 cc 95% alcohol. This is the staining solution.

Sections are deparaffinized, brought to absolute alcohol, stained 15 minutes at 37°C in the above solution, differentiated in 3 changes of 70% alcohol, 5 minutes each, dehydrated, cleared and mounted in resin as usual. Only elastic tissue stains, deep violet.

Various counterstains may be combined with it. A Van Gieson stain may be interposed either before or after the alcohol differentiation.

Staining in a 50:50 mixture of redox buffered iron hematoxylin (p. 169) and orcinol new fuchsin gives excellent results.

Gallego's Iron Fuchsin Method. See the second edition of this book, pp. 363–364, or German (*Am. J. Clin. Path., Tech. Suppl.* **3**:13, 1939). It was also included in Langeron, and was attributed by them to Gallego. The cited modification is essentially in the form in which I contributed it to Conn and Darrow, with emendations.

Aldehyde Fuchsin

Gomori's Aldehyde Fuchsin Method for Elastic Fibers (*Am. J. Clin. Path.* **20**:665, 1950). Dissolve 0.5 gm basic fuchsin (C.I. No. 42510) in 100 cc 70% alcohol. Add 1 cc concentrated hydrochloric acid and 1 cc U.S.P. paraldehyde. In 24 hours the mixture becomes a deep violet and is ready to use. Store at 0–5°C. (The molar ratio of acetaldehyde to rosaniline is nearly 15:1.)

Avoid chromate fixations. Formalin and Bouin's fluid give colorless backgrounds, mercury fixatives give a pale lilac.

1. Deparaffinize and hydrate paraffin sections as usual.
2. Treat 10–60 minutes with 0.5% iodine.
3. Decolorize 30 seconds with 0.5% sodium bisulfite.
4. Wash 2 minutes in water.
5. Transfer to 70% alcohol.
6. Stain in aldehyde fuchsin: for elastic fibers, 5–10 minutes; for pancreatic islet cells, 15–30 minutes; for hypophysis, ½–2 hours. Rinse in alcohol (70%) and inspect microscopically from time to time.
7. Wash in several changes of 70% alcohol.
8. Counterstain with hematoxylin and orange G (p. 176) or with the Masson trichrome or Mallory-Heidenhain method (pp. 546, 545). The latter two are preferred for hypophysis. Fast green FCF or light green SF should be substituted for the aniline blue in these methods.
9. Dehydrate, clear and mount through an alcohol, xylene, synthetic resin sequence.

Results: Elastic fibers, mast cell granules, gastric chief cells, beta cells of pancreatic islets and certain of the hypophyseal beta granules—violet to purple. Alpha granules of the hypophysis stain orange red, delta granules stain green to greenish blue and chromophobe cells present pale gray green cytoplasm. Collagen is stained green, using the fast green Mallory-Heidenhain variant.

According to Vassar and Culling (*Arch Path.* **68:**487, 1959), elastic fibers show quite a strong autofluorescence in unstained sections or in hematoxylin eosin stained preparations. The fluorescence is enhanced by a 3 minute stain in a 1% alcoholic solution of acriflavine, followed by dehydration, clearing and mounting in Harleco resin (HSR).

Elastase

Recrystallized trypsin (Armour and Co.) has no effect on elastin, according to Lansing *et al.* (*Anat. Rec.* 114:555, 1952), but commercial trypsin does digest elastin on overnight exposure at 37°C. This difference is due to the presence of an elastase in the cruder product, which is extractable by pH 6, 0.1 M phosphate buffer and is salted out by 0.4 saturated ammonium sulfate. Lansing's group used digestion at pH 9 for 1 hour at room temperature, or for less time at 37°C. Baló and Banga (*Biochem. J.* **46:**384, 1950) prepared an elastase concentrate from defatted and powdered pancreas.

Recrystallized elastase is now available from a number of commercial sources.

Fullmer (*J. Histochem.* **6:**425, 1958) prescribed 6 hour digestion at 37°C in 0.015% "elastase" in 0.1 M Veronal HCl at pH 8.8, staining afterward with orcein, resorcin fuchsin, orcinol new fuchsin or aldehyde fuchsin.

The Worthington preparation available at that time exhibited some proteolytic action. Fullmer later (*J. Histochem.* **8**:290, 1960) reported quite satisfactory results with the 2× crystallized Worthington product at 8 mg/30 cc 0.2 *M* borate buffer pH 9, using a 6 hour 37°C digestion.

OXYTALAN FIBERS

These fibers, which are apparently distinct from reticulum, collagen and elastin fibers in their staining reactions and histochemical behavior, were described and named by Fullmer in 1958 (*Science* **127**:1240; *J. Histochem.* **6**:425) as occurring in tendons, periodontal membranes, etc.

These fibers are morphologically similar to elastic fibers but do not stain with orcein, resorcin fuchsin, aldehyde fuchsin, orcinol new fuchsin or Verhoeff's hematoxylin and are not digested by elastase (0.015%, 6 hours, 37°C 0.1 *M* Veronal pH 8.8). They, like elastin fibers, resist hot formic acid treatments sufficient to completely gelatinize surrounding collagen; they are destroyed by alkali treatment which is resisted by both collagen and elastin.

After 10–30 minute oxidation in peracetic acid (p. 183) they become stainable with orcein, resorcin fuchsin and aldehyde fuchsin, but not with Verhoeff's stain or with orcinol new fuchsin. Likewise the peracetic oxidized fibers are digested by elastase.

β-**Glucuronidase** (Worthington) at 30 mg/100 cc 0.1 *M* acetate buffer pH 4.5 for 24–48 hours at 37°C, when applied after peracetic oxidation, digests oxytalan but not elastic fibers, so that aldehyde fuchsin staining is lost. When it is applied before peracetic oxidation the staining of oxytalan fibers is unaffected (Fullmer, *J. Histochem.* **8**:113, 1960).

Chapter 16

Smear Preparations, Bacteria, Protozoa and Other Parasites

For the study and demonstration of these, a variety of special methods are prescribed: some of them use the usual fixed material, but some perhaps function better with special fixations.

PREPARATIONS OF SMEARS AND FILMS

In place of sections or to supplement them it is often desirable to utilize spread films or smears of tissues, blood and exudates. Films are preferable for the study of the cytology of the blood, the red bone marrow, the spleen pulp and various inflammatory exudates. For the demonstration of bacteria, protozoa and rickettsiae they are often preferable to sections. For the demonstration of scarce blood protozoa, thick blood films are made and hemolyzed before or during staining so that a relatively large volume of blood can be scanned quickly for the presence of malarial plasmodia, trypanosomes, leishmaniae and even microfilariae.

Endicott's Marrow Smear Method. For the staining of spleen and marrow Endicott's (*Stain Techn.* **20**:25, 1945) technic for the preparation of films is recommended. Dip a capillary pipet into a tube of human serum or plasma and take up a column about 10 mm in length. Then immediately place the point of the pipet in the red marrow or spleen pulp and aspirate about 2 mm of tissue. Blow the tissue and serum onto a clean slide near one end, and mix thoroughly by repeated aspiration and expulsion with the same pipet. Finally, leaving the drop on the slide, smear it in the usual manner by placing another slide against the first at an angle of 30–45° over the drop and between it and the center of the first slide. Then draw the slide back toward the drop until it makes contact and the fluid spreads along the acute angle between the 2 slides. Then push the second slide along the first away from the original site of the drop so that the fluid film follows in the acute angle. The thickness of the film can be regulated by varying the angle of contact; the more acute the angle, the thinner the film.

Impression Films. Useful tissue films can also be prepared by simply pressing a clean slide lightly on a freshly cut surface of the tissue in question. These films are called *impression films*. The method is often used for brain.

Thin blood films are simply prepared by depositing a small drop of blood near one end of the slide and drawing it along in the acute angle made by a second slide, as above.

Thick blood films are made by depositing several large drops of blood near one end of a clean slide and spreading them with a glass rod, the corner of a clean slide or a match into a circular area about 10–15 mm in diameter. It is often useful to make a thick film on one end of a slide and a thin film on the remaining two thirds. Since the value of thick films depends on the removal of the hemoglobin from the red corpuscles by hemolysis in distilled water or some other agent, one should be careful with such combined films not to allow the fixative to come in contact with the thick film before hemolysis.

Smears of thick pus may perhaps require dilution with serum (as on p. 559 for spleen and marrow smears). Thinner exudates can be smeared as is blood. Relatively clear or even turbid fluids may require centrifugation and resuspension of the sediment in a small drop of serum or serous exudate for the preparation of satisfactory films. With serous inflammatory exudates of relatively high protein content the supernatant fluid is satisfactory for resuspension of the sediment; but with urine and spinal fluid, serum is a more satisfactory diluent.

Centrifugates. According to Arcadi (*J. Urol.* **61**:814, 1949) centrifuged urinary sediments may be smeared on slides, air dried and then fixed by immersion for 1 minute in 99% isopropyl alcohol. After this fixation he stained 2 minutes in alum hematoxylin (Harris's, p. 174), washed in water, counterstained 1 minute in 2% aqueous eosin Y, washed 15 seconds in water, dehydrated with isopropyl alcohol, cleared in xylene and mounted in Permount, dammar or other suitable resin.

Undoubtedly other stains can be applied after this fixation technic.

Aspirated material and washings from hollow viscera may be fixed by mixing with an equal volume of 15% formalin and then centrifuging. Addition of alcohol to precipitate mucus may be necessary with gastric washings. The sediment can then be dehydrated after some hours in formalin, dealcoholized and imbedded in paraffin. Paraffin sections may be prepared as usual and stained in a variety of ways. The method, according to Wollum *et al.* (*J. Nat. Cancer Inst.* **12**:715, 1952) is superior to smears in cancer diagnosis, in avoiding thick areas, in preserving cell relationships of small tissue fragments and in permitting multiple stains.

Fixation. Thin blood films and marrow films, tissue smears and exudate smears should be fixed at once in methyl alcohol for 3–5 minutes and then allowed to dry until it is convenient to stain them. Such films can be stained successfully for 2–3 weeks, whereas films not fixed at the time of taking soon deteriorate, so that staining becomes inferior.

Sometimes special procedures are better served by fixing still moist films by the vapor of osmium tetroxide or by gaseous formaldehyde (films are placed face down over a shallow vessel containing a 1–2% osmium tetroxide solution or a little concentrated formalin) or, perhaps more conveniently, by depositing 1–2 cc of strong formalin in a Coplin jar and then standing the films in it, film end up, and putting on the lid.

In the case of quite thin smears, where focusing may be difficult, it may be useful to draw a line, or more than one, on the slide with a grease pencil or, if the preparation is to be covered with a coverglass, with black marking ink to establish a readily visible plane of focus.

Thick blood films should ordinarily be dried in a place protected from dust, flies and roaches for 18–24 hours before staining. Staining should not be delayed any longer after drying than necessary. If staining cannot be carried out within 24 hours, it is preferable to hemolyze with distilled or even tap water for 5–10 minutes and then fix 5 minutes in methyl alcohol.

Such films may be stained by a variety of methods, including simple solutions of basic aniline dyes, Gram's stain, the acid fast stain, Macchiavello's stain, Goodpasture's, Giemsa's, Wright's, Leishman's and many others. After staining they may be allowed to dry or mounted in synthetic resin.

In place of the ether alcohol mixture recommended by Papanicolaou (*Diagnosis of Uterine Cancer by the Vaginal Smear*, The Commonwealth Fund, New York, 1945), Davidson, Clyman and Winston (*Stain Techn.* **24**:145, 1949) highly recommend 3:1 mixtures of tertiary butyl alcohol with ethyl alcohol and with ethyl phosphate, and report excellent results with Papanicolaou's stain.

Papanicolaou Stain for Cancer and Precancer Diagnosis. There has appeared a considerable number of single solution methods giving the general color effects of the Mallory aniline blue connective tissue stain. Several of them have been applied, mainly to the staining of smears of desquamated epithelia, and notably in the study of the variations of vaginal contents during the estrus cycle, in the diagnosis of uterine cervical carcinoma and the like. Some are applicable also to paraffin and celloidin sections. They have also been widely applied to smear and exudate material from other organs, to Millipore filtrates of ureteral urine, spinal fluid and thin exudates, gastric washings, etc.

In the Papanicolaou (*J. Lab. Clin. Med.* **26**:1200, 1941; *Science* **95**:438, 1942; *J. Nat. Cancer Inst.* **7**:357, 1947) technics for staining smears for cancer diagnosis, ether alcohol (50:50 *or* 1:2) or isopropyl alcohol fixation (2 minutes) is usually recommended. Smears are then brought through descending alcohols to water and stained 5–10 minutes in an alum hematoxylin with or without added acetic acid; washed, blued and dehydrated through ascending alcohols; counterstained 30–100 seconds in a phosphotungstic acid orange G solution in alcohol (OG-5, 6 or 8);

washed in 3 changes of alcohol; stained in an alcoholic solution of light green SF, Bismarck brown and eosin Y for 1½ minutes (designated as EA 25, 31, 36, 50 or 65); and washed 3 times in 95% alcohol, then 100% alcohol, alcohol xylene, 2 changes of xylene and balsam.

Some of these technics are presented in quite elaborate detail. Gates and Warren (*Handbook for Diagnosis of Cancer of the Uterus*, Harvard University Press, Cambridge, 1947), for example, prescribe dipping 5 times into each of the descending and ascending graded alcohols.

The subjoined technic now used at the Charity Hospital in New Orleans was kindly furnished me by Dr. Nelson Holmquist. Part of the timings are given in "dips," which take about 1 second each, and in "slow dips," which take about 5 seconds. These are not translated into seconds, since the motion implied in the word "dip" is an essential part of the process.

Routine Papanicolaou Stain, Charity Hospital.

1. 80%, 70% and 50% alcohols and distilled water, 30 seconds each.
2. Harris's alum hematoxylin (without acetic acid), 5 minutes.
3. Distilled water, 6 dips.
4. 0.03 N HCl (1/400 dilution of concentrated acid), 8 dips.
5. Running water, 6 minutes.
6. Distilled water, 50%, 70%, 80% and 95% alcohols, 30 seconds each.
7. OG-6: 0.5% orange G in 95% alcohol containing 15 mg phosphotungstic acid per 100 cc; stain 1½ minutes.
8. 2 changes 95% alcohol, 2 slow dips each.
9. Stain in EA-50 (Table 16-1, p. 564) 1½ minutes.
10. 3 changes 95% alcohol, 2 slow dips each.
11. Absolute alcohol, 30 seconds.
12. Absolute alcohol + xylene equal parts; and 2 changes xylene: 4, 2 and 3 minutes.
13. Mount in Permount or similar resin.

Millipore technics offer a convenient method of concentrating the cells from sparsely cellular body fluids and washings. Millipore is a cellulose plastic material of unstated composition, furnished in filter discs 150 μ thick and of varying diameters. Discs of 15 mm diameter have been found convenient for filtrations of quantities of about 10 cc. Slight suction is used to expedite filtration. An open manometer attached to the suction line by a T tube should read not over 10 mm mercury.

The Millipore discs are conveniently labeled with a single typewriter character which serves both to identify the case and to mark the upper surface bearing the cell film. They can then be attached to a carrier assembly by small spring hemostats strung by the spring end on the carrier and holding the Millipore discs in their jaws. Larger, 40–50 mm discs can be similarly carried through the stain baths, but they require larger staining vessels and are mounted finally on 50 × 75 mm (2 × 3 in.) slides.

Apparatus, instructions and Millipore discs are obtainable from the Millipore Filter Corp., Bedford, Massachusetts. Similar material is available from the Gelman Corp., Chelsea, Michigan.

Millipore Stain Technic.

1. 80%, 70% and 50% alcohols and 2 changes distilled water, 10 slow dips each, agitating slowly (about 50–60 seconds each bath).
2. Harris's alum hematoxylin (without acetic acid); immerse 20 seconds, drain 10 seconds.
3. Wash in 3 changes distilled water, 1 slow dip each, and 20 minutes in running water.
4. 50% alcohol about 1 minute, agitate slowly with 10 slow dips.
5. 0.22 N ammonia (1.5 cc 28% NH_3, sp. gr. 0.898 + 98.5 cc 70% alcohol), 5 minutes.
6. 70%, 80% and 95% alcohols, 5 minutes each.
7. OG-6, 50 seconds (above, p. 562, step 7).
8. EA-50 (see Table 16-1, p. 564), 75 seconds.
9. 3 changes 95% alcohol, 10 slow dips each and agitate slowly.
10. 2 changes n-propanol and n-propanol + xylene 50:50, 5 minutes each.
11. Xylene, 3 changes, 2 minutes each.
12. Xylene + Permount 50:50, 5 minutes. Mount in Permount.

The orange G solutions as used are supersaturated in 95% alcohol and must be freshly diluted. For OG-5 take 1 cc 10% aqueous orange G and 19 cc absolute alcohol and add 5 mg phosphotungstic acid. For OG-6 reduce the phosphotungstic acid to 3 mg; for OG-8, to 2 mg. Except for the phosphotungstic acid the solutions are identical.

(I am indebted to Dr. N. Holmquist for the two foregoing technics, Papanicolaou and Millipore.)

The Shorr (*Science* 94:545, 1941) stains are also used principally for smears. Shorr also fixed in ether alcohol for 2 minutes; then stained 1 minute in "S-3," washed (10 dips each) in 70%, 95% and 100% alcohol, cleared in xylene and mounted. Foot (in *Pathology in Surgery*, J. B. Lippincott Company, Philadelphia, 1945, p. 11) brought smears (or sections) to water, stained in alum hematoxylin, washed, blued and counterstained 5 minutes in his modified Shorr stain, and carried through ascending alcohols to xylene and balsam or synthetic resin.

TABLE 16-1. COMPOSITION OF PAPANICOLAOU EA STAINS

	EA 25	EA 31	EA 50[1]	EA 65[2]
Light green SF 0.5% alcoholic......	44 cc	50 cc	45 cc	4.5 cc
Bismarck brown 0.5% alcoholic....	12 cc	8 cc	10 cc	10 cc
Eosin Y 0.5% alcoholic............	44 cc	42 cc	45 cc	45 cc
Phosphotungstic acid..............	170 mg	170 mg	200 mg	200 mg
Li_2CO_1 saturated aqueous..........	1 drop	1 drop	1 drop	1 drop
95% alcohol.....................	...	...	...	40.5 cc

[1] EA 50 was originally described as EA 36
[2] The amount of light green in EA 65 has been further reduced since the last edition.

TABLE 16-2. COMPOSITION OF SHORR STAINS

Ingredient	Shorr, 1941	Foot, 1945
Biebrich scarlet, C.I. No. 26905........	500 mg	300 mg
Aniline blue WS, C.I. No. 42755.......	...	75 mg
Orange G, C.I. No. 16230............	250 mg	125 mg
Fast green FCF, C.I. No. 42053.......	75 mg	25 mg
Glacial acetic acid..................	1 cc	1 cc
Phosphotungstic acid................	500 mg	25 mg
Phosphomolybdic acid...............	500 mg	250 mg
Alcohol...........................	100 cc	50 cc
Water.............................	...	50 cc

Dart and Turner (*Lab. Invest.* 8:1513, 1959) use an acridine orange fluorochrome technic for exfoliative cytology.

Fix smears in equal parts of diethyl ether and 95% ethyl alcohol for 1 hour or longer. Stain as follows:

1. 5 dips each in 80%, 70% and 50% alcohol and in distilled water.
2. 4 dips in 1% acetic acid.
3. Distilled water, 2 minutes.
4. pH 3.8 buffer, 3 minutes (Walpole or McIlvaine, pp. 661, 662).
5. Buffered 0.01% acridine orange, 3 minutes, with initial agitation. Mix 1 cc 0.1% acridine orange in 9 cc distilled water containing 0.2% "Tween 80" in pH 3.8 buffer. The working stain is refrigerated when not in use. The stock 0.1% acridine orange is stable at room temperatures of 20–25°C.
6. Differentiate 4 minutes in pH 3.8 buffer.
7. Wipe ends of the slides, then gently blot with coarse blotting paper to remove excess buffer.
8. Mount under a coverslip in pH 3.8 buffer and examine. Let each smear stand 2 minutes after application of coverslip.

Immediately before screening blot excess buffer from the slide with a towel. It is convenient to store the buffer used as a mounting medium in a small dropper bottle that is cleaned frequently. If the slides dry during examination add more buffer. After screening remove coverslips gently. The slides may be reexamined within 3 months by fluorescence microscopy after remounting with buffer. Beyond that time, decolorize and restain in acridine orange. Or slides may be decolorized with 50% alcohol and restained by the usual Papanicolaou method.

Results: Normal superficial squamous cervical epithelial cells show fluorescent green nuclei and gray green transparent cytoplasm; basal and intermediate cells present green or yellow green nuclei and greenish or reddish cytoplasm; endocervical cells present green nuclei, blepharoplasts and cilia and reddish cytoplasm.

Bacteria, yeasts, yeast spores and monilia stain red; trichomonads, red with a yellow nucleus. Leucocytes are bright green; mucus is pale dull green.

Atypical and dyskaryotic cells present increased green nuclear staining. Atypical hyperplastic and hyperchromatic cells present brillant green to orange red nuclear fluorescence and gray green to red cytoplasm. Atypical brilliant red nucleoli are often present.

GRAM POSITIVE BACTERIA

Fibrin, certain *hyaline* droplets seen in degeneration of renal epithelium and *keratohyalin* granules share to a greater or less extent the property of *Gram positive bacteria* of retaining the dye complex formed by the action of iodine upon crystal violet when certain solvents are applied. Gram positive bacteria, however, are more resistant to solvent extraction than are fibrin and hyaline droplets. Thus ethyl alcohol, acetone and their mixtures usually leave Gram positive bacteria blue black, and decolorize fibrin and hyaline droplets. Keratohyalin is intermediate in its resistance. Aniline and aniline xylene mixtures leave fibrin as well as bacteria stained violet.

Various other substances are usually added to crystal violet or methyl violet solutions in mixtures of water and alcohol. The dye concentrations are usually high, and some solutions are apparently supersaturated when made. The function of the added phenol or aniline is not clear. I am not inclined to credit the alleged mordant action of these substances, since the Hucker-Conn ammonium oxalate variant seems as good as any and is considerably more stable than the aniline water solutions, or even the phenol water solutions. Many of these solutions were formerly described as gentian violet solutions. Inasmuch as gentian violet seems to have been a variable mixture of dextrin, crystal violet (hexamethylpararosaniline) and methyl violet (its tetra- and pentamethyl homologs), and crystal violet alone serves the same purpose better (Conn), this dye is here prescribed in all formulae.

Ehrlich's Aniline Crystal Violet as Emended by Conn. Crystal violet (C.I. No. 42555) 1.2 gm, dissolve in 12 cc 95% alcohol and add 100 cc freshly prepared and filtered aniline water made by shaking 2 cc aniline in 100 cc water. This keeps about 2 weeks. Weigert (Ehrlich's *Encyklopädie*) used methyl violet (C.I. No. 42535) in a similar formula.

Stirling's Aniline Crystal Violet, as Emended by Conn. Crystal violet 5 gm, 100% alcohol 10 cc, aniline 2 cc, distilled water 88 cc. This solution is quite stable.

Nicolle's Carbol Crystal Violet, as Emended by Conn. Crystal violet 1 gm, 95% alcohol 10 cc, phenol 1 gm, distilled water 100 cc. Dissolve the dye in alcohol, the phenol in water, and mix; or, perhaps easier, dissolve both in alcohol and add the water. Schmorl cites a carbol crystal violet containing 2.5 gm phenol, and Mallory cites one with 3 gm, both attributed to Nicolle. Both these authors give the amount of gentian or crystal violet as 10 cc of saturated alcoholic solutions. According to Conn this would be about 1 gm of most commercial samples.

The Hucker-Conn Ammonium Oxalate Crystal Violet, Modified (*Arch. Path.* 5:828, 1928). Crystal violet 2 gm, 95% alcohol 20 cc, ammonium oxalate 800 mg, distilled water 80 cc. Dissolve the dye in the alcohol, the oxalate in the water, and mix. The solution keeps at least 2 or 3 years.

Gram's Iodine. Dissolve 2 gm potassium iodide in 2–3 cc distilled water, dissolve 1 gm iodine crystals in this solution. Dilute with distilled water to 300 cc for Gram's solution, or to 100 cc for Weigert's.

Gram Staining of Smears for Bacteria. *Technic.*

1. Fix by quickly passing the smear face down through the blue flame of a Bunsen burner or alcohol lamp 3 times.
2. Stain with crystal violet 20–60 seconds. Acid fast bacilli require at least 1–2 minutes, and perhaps it is safer to heat to 60–80°C as well.
3. Wash in water. Conn blots off excess dye and does not wash.
4. Cover with Gram's iodine for 1–2 minutes or with Weigert's for 20–30 seconds.
5. Decolorize 30–60 seconds by dropping alcohol on the film or by agitation in 2–3 changes of alcohol until color clouds no longer come out and the film, if of an exudate, is largely decolorized. Instead of alcohol, one may use acetone from the dropper bottle. With this reagent decolorizing is complete in 5–10 seconds.
6. Wash in water.
7. Counterstain 30–60 seconds in a 0.1–0.5% solution of safranin O (C.I. No. 50240), basic fuchsin (C.I. No. 42510), Bismarck brown Y or R

(C.I. No. 21000 or 21010), or pyronin Y or B (C.I. No. 45005 or 45010).

8. Wash in water, dry and examine in immersion oil.

I prefer the Hucker-Conn crystal violet formula, the Weigert iodine, acetone decolorization and 0.2–0.5% safranin as counterstain.

Results: Gram positive organisms are blue black; Gram negative, red or brown, according to the counterstain used.

Bartholomew's (*Stain Techn.* **37**:139, 1962) directions, designed for staining of thin culture suspension smears, are perhaps not directly applicable to tissue smears or sections. He used the Hucker-Conn ammonium oxalate crystal violet formula (p. 566), the Burke formula for iodine, which is identical with Weigert's (p. 566), and 0.25% safranin in 10% alcohol. He compared 99% ethanol, acetone, methanol, *n*-propanol, *n*-butanol and *n*-amyl alcohol as decolorizers, and appraised the effect of water dilution on them.

Lower concentrations of crystal violet and of iodine were less effective in achieving proper Gram differentiation. Overwashing in water after crystal violet and iodine steps is to be avoided. Washing after safranin counterstains also needs to be brief.

Methanol is too rapid and unselective as a decolorizer, and butyl and amyl alcohols are too slow and ineffective for practical use. *n*-Propanol gave the widest time range between under- and overdecolorization; although slower than acetone it had a wider margin of safety. Addition of small amounts of water (5–10%) to the decolorizers accelerated destaining. At 95% *n*-propanol gave fully adequate decolorization over a far wider time range than ethanol; though slower than acetone, its time range was moderately wider.

The recommended procedure follows. It should be usable for tissue and exudate smears and can probably be adapted for sections.

Heat fixation is recommended.

1. Flood slide with crystal violet 1 minute.
2. Wash 5 seconds in running water.
3. Weigert's iodine, 2 changes, 5 seconds and 1 minute.
4. Wash 5 seconds in running water.
5. Decolorize in 3 changes *n*-propanol, 1 minute each. (Discard propanol No. 1 after each 10 slides, putting in fresh at No. 3 and moving the others forward.)
6. Wash 5 seconds in running water.
7. 2 changes of safranin, 5 seconds and 1 minute.
8. Wash 5 seconds, dry and examine.

Results: Blue black Gram positive organisms; red Gram negative organisms.

Gram Stain for Sections. The acetone technic may be applied to sections (*Arch. Path.* **5**:828, 1928), thus:

1. Bring paraffin sections through xylene and alcohols to water as usual.
2. Stain 30 seconds in Hucker-Conn crystal violet.
3. Rinse briefly in water.
4. Treat 20–30 seconds with Weigert's iodine.
5. Decolorize with acetone 10–15 seconds.
6. Wash in water.
7. Counterstain 30 seconds in 0.5% safranin.
8. Differentiate and dehydrate (10–15 seconds) with acetone from a dropper bottle.
9. Clear by acetone and xylene and 2 changes of xylene. Mount in polystyrene, Depex or other resin.

Results: Gram positive bacteria, blue black; nuclei, deep red; Gram negative bacteria and fibrin, red; cytoplasm, pink.

Glynn's method (*Arch. Path.* **20**:896, 1935) differs from the foregoing in using Nicolle's carbol crystal violet (p. 566) for 2 minutes, and in counterstaining (step 7) first with 1:2000 basic fuchsin in 0.002 N hydrochloric acid for 3 minutes and then for 30–60 seconds in saturated aqueous picric acid. Cytoplasm and red corpuscles are yellow; serum, fibrin and collagen are pale pink; myelin is violet; and Gram positive bacteria are blue black.

The **Kopeloff-Beerman** formula for crystal violet has given more intense Gram positive reactions than the ammonium oxalate formula (Bartholomew and Mittwer, *Stain Techn.* **25**:103, 1950). I cite the method from Conn and Darrow.

1. Hydrate sections or use air dried films.
2. Stain 5 or more minutes in a fresh mixture of 4 parts 5% sodium bicarbonate and 15 parts 1% aqueous crystal violet solution.
3. Wash off with sodium hypoiodite. (Dissolve 2 gm iodine crystals in 10 cc 1 N NaOH, and dilute to 100 cc.)
4. Immerse in or cover with hypoiodite for 2 minutes.
5. Wash in water, blot lightly and at once.
6. Decolorize with acetone or 30% ether acetone, dropping onto slide until color stops coming out (10 seconds or less). A higher proportion of ether (50%) slows the differentiation.
7. Counterstain 5–10 seconds in 2% safranin or 0.1% basic fuchsin.
8. Wash in water, dry and examine. Sections can probably be dehydrated by dripping on acetone and xylene in sequence as in the Gram acetone technic (above).

The Brown-Brenn Procedure for Gram Positive and Negative Bacteria in Tissues (from the Armed Forces Institute of Pathology, *Manual of*

Histologic and Special Staining Techniques, 2d ed., McGraw Hill Book Company, New York, 1960). Paraffin sections of formalin fixed tissues (4–6 μ) are brought through xylene and alcohols to water as usual.

1. Stain flat, face up, for 1 minute by depositing on each slide 1–1.5 cc of a fresh mixture of 4 cc 1% crystal violet and 1 cc 5% sodium bicarbonate.
2. Wash in water and flood with Gram's iodine for 1 minute.
3. Rinse in water and blot dry.
4. Decolorize individually with equal volume ether acetone mixture from dropper bottle until no more color comes out.
5. Stain 1 minute in a 0.1% dilution of saturated aqueous basic fuchsin (25 mg/1000 cc final dilution).
6. Wash and blot gently.
7. Dip in acetone and then differentiate to yellowish pink color with 0.1% picric acid in acetone.
8. Acetone, acetone and xylene, 3 changes xylene, Permount.

Results: Blue black Gram positive bacteria; red Gram negative bacteria; red nuclei, mast cell granules; yellow background.

Perhaps the most used Gram technic for tissues has been the Gram-Weigert method for fibrin and bacteria (p. 262).

FUNGI

Mallory's variant of Weigert's fibrin stain for the demonstration of actinomyces seems worthy of note:

1. Stain paraffin sections of formalin or alcohol fixed material for 3–5 minutes in alum hematoxylin.
2. Wash in water.
3. Stain 15 minutes at 57°C in 2.5% phloxine B (C.I. No. 45410) or 5% eosin Y (C.I. No. 45380).
4. Wash in water.
5. Stain in Ehrlich's or Stirling's aniline crystal violet (p. 566) for 5–10 minutes.
6. Wash in water.
7. Treat with Gram's iodine for 1 minute (or Weigert's for 20–30 seconds) (p. 566).
8. Wash in water and blot dry with filter paper.
9. Differentiate with several changes of aniline until no more color is removed.
10. Wash in 3 or 4 changes of xylene and mount in balsam (or synthetic resin).

Results: Mycelia, blue; clubs, red.

General Information on Fungi. The same method is useful for other ray fungi in mycetoma, Madura foot and allied conditions. Mycelia are often well brought out in light blue by azure eosin methods (p. 162) which are much better for study of tissue cellular reactions. The Bauer chromic acid leucofuchsin and the periodic acid Schiff methods (pp. 198, 199) can be recommended for mycelial fungi and yeasts in tissues. With the latter, it is desirable to suppress the background staining of collagen and reticulum by use of a sulfite blockade procedure (p. 275), by use of highly diluted (20–50 mg fuchsin per 100 cc) Schiff reagent or by use of a triphenylmethane sulfonic acid dye counterstain as recommended by Kligman, Mescon and DeLamater (*Am. J. Clin. Path.* **21**:88, 1951), who used a brief counterstain with light green.

The allochrome method (p. 549) has given us brilliant results, particularly with *Cryptococcus neoformans* (*Torula histolytica*). *Coccidioides immitis, Histoplasma capsulatum,* the organisms of cutaneous blastomycoses and various mycelial fungi have been successfully demonstrated by this method. Anthrax bacilli are well stained. The granules of mycetoma, actinomycosis and botryomycosis are densely stained by this method; quite thin sections are required if any internal detail is to be discerned. All these organisms retain the red purple in their cell walls.

Contrasts are better with the Bauer method or with the Kligman-Mescon-DeLamater periodic acid Schiff variant, but tissue structure is much better shown by the allochrome method. In the Bauer method a brief nuclear stain with Weigert's acid iron hematoxylin is preferable to alum hematoxylin, as it seems less apt to overpower the red of the smaller fungi such as *Histoplasma*.

Cryptococcus neoformans is also well shown by simple brief stains with metachromatic dyes, such as 1:1000 toluidine blue or thionin for 30 seconds. Organisms are blue violet, the copious mucin of acute torulosis is red purple; cell nuclei and tigroid granules are deep blue; and mast cell granules, violet to purple.

Use of safranin O in the Gram acetone technic (p. 568) gives red nuclei, pink cytoplasm, orange red and blue black yeast cells, orange mucus and orange red cartilage and mast cell granules.

Kligman, Mescon and DeLamater (*Am. J. Clin. Path.* **21**:88, 1951) prepare skin scrapings for examination for fungi by first applying a drop of Mayer's glycerol albumen to the surface of the lesion and then scraping with a blunt knife. The scales are then smeared on a slide, and the smear is fixed 30 seconds in 95% alcohol. Then pass through periodic acid (1% H_5IO_6) for 1 minute, and wash in water; then Schiff reagent for 5 minutes. Wash 5–10 minutes in 0.5% $K_2S_2O_5$ in 0.05 N HCl, using 2–3 changes. Wash in water, dry and examine. The fungi appear red purple.

The internal filamentous structure of botryomyces granules should be well shown by this technic, as it is by the Bauer method (p. 199). The staphylococcal component is better demonstrated by Gram-Weigert variants, which do not, however, stain the filaments (*J. Lab. Clin. Med.* **32**: 76, 1947).

Kligman's periodic acid fuchsin stain is probably derived from Arzac's and may well depend on the aldehyde binding capacity of the arylamine of the basic fuchsin. The Schiff bases formed by the complexing of aldehyde with fuchsin are highly resistant to acid and alcohol decolorization. Kligman's technic has variants for smears and for sections (letter from Dr. Kligman, January 31, 1952).

Kligman's Periodic Acid, Fuchsin Method. Fix smears 1 minute in 95% alcohol. Deparaffinize sections and immerse briefly in 100% alcohol.

	Smears	*Sections*
1. Rinse in distilled water	No	Few seconds
2. Immerse in aqueous periodic acid	5%, 1 min	1%, 10 min
3. Wash in running water	No	5–10 min
4. Stain in 0.1% fuchsin in 5% alcohol	2 min	2 min
5. Wash in tap water	Rinse	30 sec
6. Immerse in a 0.5% tartaric acid, 1% zinc hydrosulfite solution	10 min / Sputum 1 min	10 min & 30 min to 3 hr
7. Wash in tap water	Rinse	3–5 min
8. Saturated aqueous picric acid solution	2 min	6 min

9. Dehydrate in 95% and 100% alcohol, 10 seconds and 1 minute respectively, clear in 2 changes of xylene, 1 minute each, and mount in HSR or other synthetic resin or in Canada balsam.

The color of the positive reaction is somewhat more purple than a plain basic fuchsin stain. In a similar procedure utilizing 0.5 N alcoholic hydrochloric acid as the decolorizing reagent in place of the tartaric acid + zinc hydrosulfite mixture, I have interposed also a 5 minute stain in Weigert's acid iron chloride hematoxylin before the picric acid step.

Gridley (*Am. J. Clin. Path.* **23**:303, 1953) has modified the Bauer stain for demonstration of fungi in tissues by adding counterstains with Gomori's aldehyde fuchsin and metanil yellow.

Gridley's Technic for Fungi in Tissue Sections.

1. Paraffin sections at 6 μ are deparaffinized and hydrated as usual. Rinse in distilled water.
2. Oxidize 1 hour in 4% chromic acid.
3. Wash 5 minutes in running water.
4. Immerse in Schiff reagent (0.5% fuchsin, p. 270) for 15 minutes.
5. Rinse in 3 changes of 0.5% sodium metabisulfite $Na_2S_2O_5$ in 0.05 N hydrochloric acid, 2 minutes each.

6. Wash 15 minutes in running water.
7. Stain 15–20 minutes in Gomori's aldehyde fuchsin (p. 556).
8. Rinse in 95% alcohol and wash well in water.
9. Counterstain 2–5 minutes in 0.25% metanil yellow in 0.25% acetic acid.
10. Wash in water, dehydrate, clear and mount in Permount.

Results: Hyphae, deep blue; conidia, rose to purple; elastin and mucin, deep blue; yeast capsules, deep purple; general background, yellow.

The simple Bauer method, with or without an iron or alum hematoxylin counterstain (p. 199), is to be preferred to histochemical study of fungus cell walls.

Perhaps the most popular of the carbohydrate methods adapted for finding of fungi in tissues has been Gomori's chromic acid, methenamine silver sequence (p. 500) as used by Grocott (*Am. J. Clin. Path.* **25**:975, 1955).

The Black Bauer Method: Another chromic acid variant which seems useful is the *"black Bauer"* method reported by Lillie, Gilmer and Welsh (*Stain Techn.* **36**:361, 1961).

1. Formalin fixed tissue, 5 μ paraffin sections through xylenes and alcohols to water as usual.
2. Oxidize 15–60 minutes (usually 40) in 4% chromic acid.
3. Wash in running water 10 minutes and in glacial acetic acid 1 minute.
4. Immerse 1½ hours in 11% (1 M) m-aminophenol in glacial acetic acid.
5. Wash 10 minutes in running water, rinse in distilled water.
6. Azo couple 2 minutes at 3°C in a freshly prepared solution of fast black K (3 mg/1 cc) in ice cold 0.1 M Michaelis Veronal-HCl buffer pH 8.
7. Wash 15 minutes in 0.1 N HCl (3 changes, 5 minutes each) and 10 minutes in running water.
8. Dehydrate in alcohols, clear in xylene, mount in cellulose tricaprate or Permount.

Results: Cytoplasms and nuclei, pink to red; glycogen, epithelial mucins, starch, cellulose, fungus cell walls, black. Organisms are less conspicuous than with the chromic methenamine silver technic, but they show more internal structure. *Candida albicans, Blastomyces dermatitidis, Coccidioides immitis, Cryptococcus neoformans, Toxoplasma gandii,* and *Histoplasma capsulatum* were demonstrated by this method; *Endamoeba histolytica* is also well shown by reason of its glycogen content (Gilmer).

For staining nuclear chromatin in certain yeastlike fungi, DeLamater (*Stain Techn.* **23**:161, 1948) recommends a procedure of acid hydrolysis and aldehyde mordanting followed by staining in basic fuchsin.

DeLamater's Formaldehyde Fuchsin Method.

1. Fix (cultures) in Schaudinn's fluid (p. 47).
2. Hydrolyze 5 minutes at 30°C, 5 minutes at 60°C, and then 5 minutes at 30°C in 1 N HCl.
3. Wash in 1–3 changes of distilled water.
4. Mordant in 2% formalin 4 minutes (2 cc 40% HCHO + 98 cc H_2O).
5. Wash in distilled water.
6. Stain 15 minutes with 0.5% basic fuchsin in 0.04 N hydrochloric acid.
7. Wash in distilled water.
8. Dehydrate and decolorize in graded alcohols.
9. Clear in xylene and mount in balsam or synthetic resin.

Results: Nuclei stain an intense magenta red, cytoplasm stains light pink.

The **streptothrices** are usually Gram positive and may be acid fast, hence the technics for Gram positive (pp. 565–569) or acid fast (pp. 576–581) organisms may be used. Their reaction to the formaldehyde fuchsin methods of Goodpasture and of Fite I do not know.

Baker and Smith's Picroindigocarmine: Baker (*Am. J. Path.* **32**:287–307, 1956) on p. 299 recommends a previously unpublished picroindigocarmine stain of Baker and Smith for *Mucor* in tissues:

1. Deparaffinize and hydrate as usual, rinse in 0.5% acetic acid.
2. Stain 5–10 minutes in Goodpasture's aniline carbol fuchsin.[1]
3. Wash in running water and in 0.5% acetic acid.
4. Stain 5–10 minutes in Ramón y Cajal's picroindigocarmine (p. 539).
5. Wash in 0.5% acetic acid.
6. Dehydrate rapidly in 95% and 2 changes of 100% alcohol, clear in xylene and mount in Permount.

Results: Nuclei, red; fungi and collagen, blue green; other tissues in varying colors.

Other mycelial fungi in tissues may be studied with Gram-Weigert, with azure eosin technics and with the Bauer method.

The Alkali Method. A useful quick method for epidermal fungi is to

---

[1] Goodpasture's aniline carbol fuchsin: To 100 cc 30% alcohol add 0.59 gm basic fuchsin, 1 cc aniline, 1 gm phenol.

scrape off material from the suspected area and macerate on the slide under a coverglass in 20% (Mallory) or 15% (Schmorl) sodium (or potassium) hydroxide solution. The epidermal cells are dissolved or cleared, leaving the fungal mycelia as refractile, perhaps branching and often septate filaments and spores. Reduced illumination is often desirable for study of details by this method. This technic may be used for identification of the fungi of ringworm, favus, epidermophytosis and the like.

DIPHTHERIA ORGANISMS

Christensen (*Stain Techn.* **24**:165, 1949) recommends a method with sequence of acid toluidine blue, iodine and safranin to replace Albert's method for diphtheria organisms. I have not tried Christensen's method.

Christensen's stain for *Corynebacterium diphtheriae*. Use air dried, heat fixed smears of the usual Loeffler medium cultures.

1. Stain 1 minute in 0.15% toluidine blue (52% dye content),[1] 5 cc glacial acetic acid, 2 cc ethyl alcohol and 100 cc distilled water.
2. Wash with water and apply Albert's iodine solution (iodine 2 gm, potassium iodide 3 gm, water 300 cc) for 1 minute.
3. Wash with water and counterstain with safranin.

Results: Cell bodies in light pink; protoplasmic striations in red or brownish red; metachromatic granules in black.

Excellent results may also be attained by simple, brief (1–2 minutes) staining in polychromed methylene blue. Loeffler's solution when aged several years performs excellently. For a freshly prepared solution I suggest 0.1% azure A in the same solvent. The orthochromatic color is blue violet; the metachromatic, red purple. Loeffler's methylene blue: 0.3 gm methylene blue in 30 cc alcohol + 1 cc 1% potassium hydroxide and 90 cc distilled water.

INFLUENZA BACILLI AND ENCEPHALITOZOA

The **Goodpasture-Perrin** (*Arch. Path.* **36**:568, 1943) method for influenza organisms, encephalitozoa and toxoplasmata:

1. Zenker or Orth fixation preferred, but Perrin found 10% formalin material postchromated with 2.5% potassium bichromate for 2 days quite satisfactory.
2. Paraffin sections to water as usual, including iodine and thiosulfate sequence if Zenker material is used.
3. Stain in Goodpasture's carbol aniline fuchsin (p. 573) for 5 minutes at 70°C—steaming on hot plate.

[1] For zinc free toluidine blue of 80–90% dye content, 0.1% should serve.

4. Rinse quickly in tap water.
5. Decolorize with strong formalin (40% formaldehyde), a few drops at a time, until no more color is removed, 15–20 minutes.
6. Rinse in tap water.
7. Counterstain 1 minute in saturated aqueous picric acid solution.
8. Dehydrate with 2 changes of 95% and 2 of 100% alcohol. Clear with 100% alcohol and xylene followed by 2 changes of vylene. Mount in synthetic resin.

Results: Encephalitozoa are blue black; the chromatin of toxoplasma is brownish red; cell nuclei are light red; cytoplasm is pinkish yellow; erythrocytes are bright yellow; influenza bacilli are blue.

The **Wright and Craighead method** as modified by Perrin (*loc. cit.,* above) for encephalitozoa and toxoplasmata: Formalin fixation with 48 hours' postchromation in 2.5% potassium bichromate, or Orth fixation. Paraffin sections to water as usual.

1. Stain 10 minutes at 70°C in carbol fuchsin (p. 577).
2. Rinse in tap water.
3. Differentiate with concentrated formalin (40% HCHO) from dropper bottle until no more color is removed.
4. Rinse in tap water.
5. Stain 4 minutes in methylene blue 1 gm, alcohol 20 cc, glacial acetic acid 0.5 cc, distilled water 80 cc.
6. Dehydrate with acetone, clear with 50:50 acetone xylene mixture followed by 2 changes of xylene. Mount in synthetic resin.

Results: Encephalitozoa are stained deep bluish red; cell nuclei and toxoplasmata are blue; cytoplasm is light blue to pink.

ACID FAST STAINS

By "acid fastness" we refer to the property of retaining stains when other stained elements of tissues are decolorized by treatment with dilute solutions of mineral acids in water or alcohol. This property is shown by *Mycobacteria* and by certain other organisms to a less extent, by bacterial spores, by hair cortex and sometimes keratohyalin and by some of the lipofuscin pigments, notably the coarsely granular one called ceroid. The dyes used have generally been basic aniline dyes, and usually the term "acid fastness" is understood to mean retention of these dyes. Although the coupling of active diazonium salts with tissue phenols yields acid resistant dye tissue compounds, this reaction is not generally included in the meaning of the term "acid fastness."

The dyes used have generally been basic triphenyl or diphenylnaphthylmethane dyes, with pararosaniline (C.I. No. 42500), rosaniline (C.I. No. 42510, Magenta I, basic fuchsin) and new fuchsin (C.I. No. 42520) being the most used. Night blue (C.I. No. 44085) and auramine O (C.I. No. 41000) have also been used considerably, and Koch first used methylene blue. The basic nature of these dyes has naturally directed attention to the possibly acid nature of the substance demonstrated.

Lillie and Bangle (*J. Histochem.* 2:30, 1954) found that acid fast staining of ceroid, hair cortex and tubercle bacilli was not prevented by 24 hour exposure to 5% phenylhydrazine or to 1 *M* aniline hydrochloride. Tubercle bacilli lost their acid fastness on 2–4 hour extraction in pyridine at 60°C and on 4 hour acetylation in acetic anhydride/pyridine (40/60) but resisted methanol 7 days at 25, 37 or 60°C and carbon tetrachloride 6 hours at 60°C; ceroid and hair cortex resisted all these. Methylation at 60°C in 0.1 *N* HCl/methanol destroyed the acid fastness of tubercle bacilli in 2 hours, ceroid lost its acid fastness in a week at 25°C, and hair cortex showed moderate impairment on 24 hours 60°C or 7 day 25°C methylation. Reversal of methylation effects by saponification was not known at that time. Nitrosation in 1 *N* NaNO$_2$/1 *N* acetic acid 4 hours had no effect on acid fastness.

Lartigue and Fite (*J. Histochem.* 10:611, 1962) failed to obtain successful acid fast stains with new fuchsin in 9.5% alcohol but succeeded when various other phenols were substituted for phenol or aniline. On the basis of these studies and on the known sudanophilia of tubercle and lepra bacilli they felt that the oil solubility theory of Lamanna's (*J. Bact.* **52**:99, 1956) was the most probable.

The *Colour Index* records that rosaniline base exhibits solubilities of 20% and 15% in oleic and stearic acids, but only 0.5% in butyl acetate, no solubility in linseed oil and mineral oil, and 0.3% and 0.6% in ethanol and in acetone. But rosaniline chloride is soluble in water 0.39% and in alcohol 8.16% (Conn).

The oil solubility theory would seem to require hydrolysis of the chloride (or acetate) during the staining procedure and solution of the free base in the fatty acids whose presence was indicated by the successful methylation blockade.

Carbol Fuchsin Methylene Blue Method. In this method for acid fast organisms, the stock carbol fuchsin is traditionally composed of saturated alcoholic solution of basic fuchsin (C.I. No. 42510) 10 cc and 5% aqueous phenol solution 90 cc. This solution may keep for years. Rosaniline chloride is soluble to about 6% in alcohol; pararosaniline chloride is soluble to about 3.5% of commercial samples and to 8.16% and 5.93% of the pure substances according to Conn. Neelsen [*Zbl. med. Wiss.* **21**:497, 1883; *Fortschr. Med.* **3**:200 (footnote), 1885] prescribed first 0.75, later 1.0 gm fuchsin in 100 gm 5% phenol, adding "a little" alcohol, which he later specified as 10 gm. Conn prescribes 300 mg fuchsin, 10 cc alcohol, 5 gm phenol and 95 cc distilled water. Kinyoun's (*Am. J. Pub. Health* **5**:867, 1915) formula—fuchsin 4 gm, phenol 8 gm, alcohol 20 cc; heat to dissolve and then add water 100 cc—is far stronger and is said to be a more energetic stain. This may well be true when the stain is freshly prepared, but it soon deposits a considerable quantity of excess dye, and thereafter is probably no better than other formulae.

Mallory recommended Verhoeff's formula. This is kept as a stock solution which is diluted at the moment for use. Dissolve 26.8 gm phenol (25 cc melted crystals) in 50 cc 100% alcohol. Add 2 gm fuchsin and heat at 37°C with occasional shaking for 18–24 hours. Filter and store. For use dilute 1 cc of stock solution with 6 cc water. This represents a final dilution of 0.281% fuchsin, 9.53% alcohol and 4.76% phenol. The main advantage seems to be in the permanency of the stock solution. In view of the usual stability of the ordinary formula, this advantage may be outweighed by the disadvantage of having to dilute it for use.

Fite (*Am. J. Path.* **14**:491, 1938) recommended new fuchsin and prescribed thus: 1 gm dye, 5 gm phenol, 10 cc methyl alcohol; dissolve completely, and then add gradually, with shaking, enough distilled water to make 100 cc. Later he reduced the dye to 0.5 gm and used ethyl or methyl alcohol.

My own 1954 directions read: dissolve 25 gm phenol in 50 cc alcohol, add and dissolve 5 gm fuchsin and then dilute to 500 cc with distilled water.

Carbol fuchsin solutions gradually form a dark red caked deposit which fails to redissolve on warming and shaking. This deposition results in progressive weakening of the solution. Consequently positive controls should be used at frequent intervals to avoid false negatives from stain failure. Although some batches of solution have remained effective for years, others become useless in as little as a year.

With any of the carbol fuchsin or carbol new fuchsin solutions the sections are heavily stained either by means of heat or by prolonged exposure, and then decolorized with acids, alcohol or usually both. The heating methods occasion somewhat more section shrinkage and definitely more dye precipitation from evaporation. I have tried adding glycerol to carbol fuchsins to prevent drying while heating, but abandoned it because bacilli appeared less well stained. Fite's observation that previously heated and cooling or cooled carbol fuchsin stains more brilliantly than unheated, just as does hot carbol fuchsin, appears to indicate that supersaturation plays an important part in brilliancy of staining. This would also account for the greater vigor of staining obtained with the freshly prepared (and supersaturated) Kinyoun's solution.

Technic for Carbol Fuchsin and Methylene Blue.

1. Bring paraffin sections to water as usual. (Smears are prepared as usual and heat fixed.)
2. Stain 10 minutes at 70°C, 30 minutes at 55°C, 2 hours at 37°C or 4–16 hours at 25–20°C, with any of the carbol fuchsins.
3. Wash in water.
4. Decolorize with 2 cc concentrated hydrochloric acid + 98 cc 95–70% alcohol. This ordinarily takes 20 seconds or more and may be extended to several minutes without harm.
5. Wash 2–3 minutes in running water.
6. Counterstain with acid hemalum (p. 174) for 2–5 minutes, or with 1% methylene blue or 1% Janus green B in 1% acetic acid, 20% alcohol for 3 minutes. (The latter 2 counterstains are suitable for smears.)
7. Wash in water. (At this point smears are dried in a warm air stream and examined directly in immersion oil.)
8. Dehydrate and clear with an acetone xylene sequence and mount in a suitable nonreducing resin, such as polystyrene, Dopex or cellulose caprate.

Results: Acid fast bacilli, red; ceroid, red; nuclei, blue or green; mast cell granules, blue violet with methylene blue but unstained by hematoxylin. Red corpuscles are often pink in formalin material; and hair shafts and keratohyalin may retain more or less red.

By acidifying the counterstain the dense staining seen with ordinary methylene blue counterstains is avoided. This was at least part of the value of the Gabbett (*Lancet* 1:757, 1887) solution (2 gm methylene blue in 25 cc concentrated sulfuric acid and 75 cc distilled water: 48.8 gm sulfuric acid per 100 cc), which was recommended for simultaneous decolorization and counterstaining. Gabbett did not specify the amount of methylene blue. This was supplied in the 1901 and later editions of Mallory and Wright. Its omission of alcohol was its most serious defect. Picric acid counterstains have been used by some workers, with good contrast, but give no tissue detail, fail to show leucocytes and non-acid fast organisms and, according to Fite, cause fading of the fuchsin stain.

In clearing of sections, carbol xylene should be avoided. It decolorizes nearly all the previously well stained tubercle bacilli and even impairs the acid fast staining of ceroid.

Similar acid fast stains may be achieved, with opposite color effects, by substituting night blue (C.I. No. 44085) or Victoria blue R (C.I. No. 44010) for fuchsin in my carbol fuchsin formula on p. 577), and using 0.1% safranin in 1% acetic acid as a counterstain. The technic follows that above. Acid fast bacilli appear in dark blue, cell nuclei in red.

Hagemann's Phenol Auramine. Hagemann's (*München. med. Wsch.* **85:**1066, 1938) technic of staining smears with phenol auramine and examining with fluorescence microscopy (pp. 14–17) has been widely used. The principal advantages claimed are that organisms are readily discerned at lower magnifications than with Ziehl-Neelsen technics, and hence larger areas can be scanned in the same time. Use of magnifications as low as 180 × is claimed for scanning; but to determine morphologic characteristics 600 × was needed. Lempert (*Lancet* **247:**818, 1944) used a 16 mm (⅔ in.) objective for focusing the lamp and condenser system, and a 6 mm (¼ in.) objective for identification. The use of immersion objectives is unnecessary, but should one desire to use them for higher magnification, Lempert advises the use of glycerol for immersion, because of the fluorescence of cedar oil. Our white modified mineral oils (Shillaber's, Crown) are designated "low fluorescence" and "very low fluorescence" for high and low viscosities, and should be usable.

Hagemann dissolved 1 gm auramine (C.I. No. 41000) in 100 cc 5% phenol; Lempert used 300 mg in 100 cc 3% phenol and filtered after vigorous shaking and warming to 40°C. The technic follows:

1. Stain heat fixed films 8–10 minutes at room temperature in Lempert's phenol auramine.
2. Wash well in tap water.
3. Decolorize in 2 changes of 2 minutes each of hydrochloric acid alcohol. Lempert used 0.5 cc concentrated hydrochloric acid, 0.5 gm sodium chloride, 25 cc distilled water and 75 cc methanol. Fite used his usual 2 cc concentrated hydrochloric acid and 98 cc 95% alcohol mixture.
4. Wash well in tap water.
5. Treat for 20 seconds with 0.1% potassium permanganate solution.
6. Wash in water, dry at room temperature in an air current and examine.

Results: The bacilli appear as bright yellow rods on a very dark red background. The method has not been found adaptable for histologic study. Part of the alleged superiority of the method disappears when one uses acetic methylene blue as a counterstain for Ziehl-Neelsen stains, either of smears or of tissues. We have often readily found tubercle bacilli by this latter technic with an 8 mm objective, and the tissues and other non-acid fast organisms are seen as well.

Fite's New Fuchsin Formaldehyde. Except for the acid alcohol step contained therein, Fite's (*Am. J. Path.* **14:**491, 1938) method for acid fast bacilli was quite similar to DeLamater's Chromatin method (p. 573) and the Wright-Craighead procedure (p. 575).

1. Stain paraffin sections 30–60 minutes or more at room temperature (22–25°C) in phenol 5 gm, ethyl or methyl alcohol 10 cc, new fuchsin 1 gm; dissolve and add distilled water to make 100 cc.

2. Immerse in concentrated formalin (40% HCHO) for 5 minutes.
3. Decolorize nearly completely with acid alcohol (2 cc concentrated hydrochloric acid, 98 cc 95% alcohol).
4. Immerse again in concentrated formalin for a few seconds.
5. Counterstain with hematoxylin and Van Gieson's picrofuchsin. Dehydrate, clear and mount through 95% and 100% alcohol, 100% alcohol and xylene, and 2 changes of xylene to polystyrene or Permount.

Results: Acid fast bacilli are stained violet; hair shafts, keratohyalin and mast cell granules are decolorized. The behavior of ceroid with this stain has not been reported.

The Fite Oil Fuchsin Method. Lepra bacilli sometimes fail to stain by the foregoing procedures. *Fite* recommended a procedure based on protection of organisms from oil solvents, which Wade (letter, May 21, 1956) regards as an entirely new procedure, perhaps suggested by Faraco's oil restoration step but actually completely original. Wade (*Stain Tech.* **32:** 287, 1957) has further modified this oil fuchsin method of Fite's by combining it with the formaldehyde fuchsin method, thus achieving effects which Fite considers very superior for lepra bacilli.

The Wade-Fite Oil Formaldehyde New Fuchsin Procedure for Lepra Bacilli. Fix preferably in Zenker's fluid or in formalin. Dehydrate with alcohols, clear in cedar oil and imbed in paraffin as usual. Section at 6–8 μ and mount on slides with Mayer's glycerol albumin. Dry overnight at 37°C.

1. Deparaffinize in 2 parts rectified turpentine + 1 part heavy liquid petrolatum (paraffin oil), 2 changes in 5 minutes.
2. Drain, wipe back and edges of slide, blot with filter paper until section appears opaque. Let stand in water until rest of slides are ready.
3. Stain 16–24 hours in Fite's carbol new fuchsin (later formula, p. 577). Wash in water.
4. Immerse 5 minutes in reagent grade 37–40% formaldehyde to blue bacilli. Section color remains red or may turn blue.
5. Extract 5 minutes in 5% (v/v) sulfuric acid. Wash in water. No obvious color change occurs.
6. 1% potassium permanganate, 3 minutes.
7. Bleach individually by agitation in 2% oxalic acid, preferably less than 30 seconds, not more than 60 seconds. Use 5% oxalic acid if sections do not decolorize readily.
8. Stain 3 minutes in a dilute van Gieson stain: 10 mg acid fuchsin, 100 mg picric acid, 100 cc distilled water (a 10% dilution of Weigert's formula in distilled water should serve).

9. Dehydrate directly and rapidly without aqueous rinse, in 95% and 100% alcohol. Clear in xylene.
10. Mount in synthetic resin: Permount, HSR or the like.

Results: Acid fast bacilli and free granules, dark blue; connective tissue, red; background, yellowish.

In some cases it may be necessary to soak sections several hours in the turpentine oil mixture; 6 hours should suffice, 10 may occasionally be needed, to "refat" "decrepit" bacilli.

Blanco and Fite (*Int. J. Leprosy* 16:367, 1948) found that aqueous formalin fixation gave fair to good staining of lepra bacilli in biopsy material from human skin, using the Ziehl-Neelsen and oil fuchsin (above) technics. Excellent results were obtained with Zenker fixation, poor with Bouin and fair with alcoholic 20% formalin.

For preservation of the acid fast material in lepra bacilli, Wade (*Stain Techn.* 27:71, 1952) recommends Carbowax imbedding and sectioning (p. 64) and one of the oil fuchsin technics.

Blanco and Fite (*Arch. Path.* 46:542, 1948) have used a modified Jahnel procedure for the demonstration of lepra bacilli in tissues. Although much too prolonged for regular diagnostic use, the procedure is said to afford a truer picture of the relations of the organisms to the tissues than most of the commoner methods.

Blanco-Fite Silver Method for *Mycobacterium leprae.*

1. Fix in 10% formalin for 2 or more weeks.
2. Soak blocks in pyridine 1–3 days.
3. Wash 24 hours in several changes of distilled water.
4. Immerse in 10% formalin 4 days.
5. Wash 24 hours in several changes of distilled water.
6. Treat with 95% alcohol 3–8 days, changing alcohol daily.
7. Transfer to distilled water until blocks sink.
8. Incubate at 37°C in the dark in 0.5% silver nitrate for 5–8 days.
9. Wash 10 minutes in distilled water.
10. Reduce 2 days in pyrogallol 4 gm, formalin 5 cc, distilled water 95 cc.
11. Dehydrate, clear and imbed in paraffin as usual.
12. Section, deparaffinize and mount.

Results: Most lepra bacilli are black, some are brown. Melanin and keratohyalin are also blackened. Tubercle bacilli and spirochetes should also blacken by this method.

BACTERIAL SPORES

Bartholomew and Mittwer (*Stain Techn.* **25**:153, 1950) modified the bacterial spore stain of Schaeffer and Fulton (*Science* **77**:194, 1933) with some simplification, thus:

	Schaeffer and Fulton	Bartholomew and Mittwer
1. Fix smears on slides by passing through flame	3 times	20 times
2. Stain in malachite green	5%, 4 or 5 times in 1 min	Sat. sol. (7.6%) 10 min cold
3. Rinse in water	30 sec	Rinse
4. Stain in safranin	0.5%, 30 sec	0.25%, 15 sec
5. Rinse, blot dry and examine		

Results: Bacterial bodies, red to pink; spores, green.

BACTERIAL CELL ENVELOP

Hale (*Lab. Pract.* **2**:115, 1953) stains bacterial cell envelops by first mordanting unfixed smears for 5–10 minutes in 1% phosphomolybdic acid and then staining for a few seconds in 1% methyl green or 0.1% Janus green.

BACTERIAL MITOSIS

DeLamater and Mudd (*Exp. Cell Res.* **2**:499, 1951) demonstrate bacterial mitosis by the following procedure:

1. Cut a small slab of agar from a 2 hour old 37°C culture. Place on a small glass plate (slide), stand upright in a Coplin jar containing a little 0.5% osmium tetroxide and cover the jar for 5 minutes.
2. Cut small fragments of the agar and press face down on coverglasses or slides to make impression preparations.
3. Hydrolyze 6 minutes in 1 N hydrochloric acid at 60°C (preheated).
4. Rinse in distilled water.
5. To 10 cc 0.25% aqueous thionin add 1 drop thionyl chloride, mix well and stain preparations in this for 2 or more hours.
6. Rinse once in distilled water to remove stain particles, drain on filter paper and
7. Immerse in 100% alcohol in jars surrounded by solid carbon dioxide to maintain a temperature below −50°C. Let stand 12 hours to complete dehydration.

8. Dip in fresh 100% alcohol at +25°C. Clear in xylene, drain on filter paper and mount in synthetic resin.

The reaction of thionin (or azure A, which may also be used in the foregoing technic) in the presence of the HCl and H_2SO_3 formed by hydrolytic decomposition of the thionyl chloride $SOCl_2$ is considered by the authors to be an aldehyde reaction. In a sense, the procedure parallels the Feulgen method, but it uses an undecolorized thionin sulfurous acid complex in place of Schiff reagent.

GRAM NEGATIVE BACTERIA AND RICKETTSIAE

Gram negative bacteria and rickettsiae in tissues are generally best studied with stains of the azure eosin type, such as Mallory's phloxine + borax methylene blue, Maximow's hematoxylin azure II eosin or our buffered azure eosinate and azure A eosin B variants. Giemsa's blood stain in 1:40 to 1:50 dilution has been much used. Wolbach added 5 drops of 0.5% sodium carbonate to 100 cc final stain mixture and differentiated after staining with colophonium alcohol. I prefer to buffer to a relatively acid level, say pH 4 for formalin material, and thus obviate the necessity for differentiation. Except for Wolbach's variant, these methods have been given under general methods (pp. 160–165).

Wolbach's Giemsa Variant (*The Etiology and Pathology of Typhus,* Harvard University Press, Cambridge, Mass., 1922, pp. 13–14). Fix thin slices of tissue 24–48 hours in Zenker's or Möller's (Regaud's) fluid (p. 56). Cut thin paraffin sections and take to water as usual.

1. Stain 1 hour in Giemsa's stain (pp. 585–587) 1 cc, methyl alcohol 1.25 cc, 0.5% sodium carbonate solution 0.1 cc (2 drops), distilled water 40 cc.
2. Pour off and replace with 2 further changes of the same mixture during the first hour and leave in the third change overnight.
3. Differentiate in 95% alcohol containing a few drops of 10% colophonium alcohol.
4. Dehydrate with 100% alcohol, clear in xylene and mount in cedar oil.

Results: Rickettsiae stain an intense reddish purple; nuclei, dark blue to violet; cytoplasm, in varying lighter blue shades; collagen and muscle, pale pink; erythrocytes, gray to yellow or pink. Further differentiation occurs after mounting in cedar oil; and exposure to sunlight for prolonged periods has been used to bring sections to the proper point. I have not used this method extensively but would caution against identifying as rickettsiae the metachromatic granules of tissue mast cells, which also stain in redder shades than nuclear chromatin.

There are a number of methods used for the identification of rickettsiae in smears. Among them one of the most useful has been the Macchiavello technic (*Zinsser's Epidemiology and Immunity in the Rickettsial Diseases*, Harvard University Press, Cambridge, Mass., 1940, p. 896).

The Macchiavello Method. The following is Bengtson's variant, as used at the National Institutes of Health:

1. Fix thin films by passing quickly, face down, through a blue flame 3 times.
2. Stain 5 minutes in basic fuchsin 0.5 gm (saturated), 0.1 M disodium phosphate 3.6 cc, 0.1 M sodium acid phosphate ($NaH_2PO_4 \cdot H_2O$) 1.4 cc, distilled water 95 cc. Filter. This buffer corresponds to pH 7.2 (p. 664).
3. Rinse rapidly with 0.5% aqueous citric acid solution.
4. Wash thoroughly in tap water.
5. Counterstain 1–2 minutes in a 0.1% aqueous methylene blue, or 10 seconds in a 1% solution.
6. Rinse with water, dry and examine in immersion oil.

Results: Rickettsiae, red; cells and bacteria, varying shades of blue. Thus far this method has not been adapted to tissue sections.

The other method most often used is the Giemsa stain. With this one may stain at pH 7–7.2 and then differentiate with faintly acid water until red corpuscles are pink, or one may stain at pH 6.5–6 and simply rinse and dry smears. Smears of blood, marrow, pus or exudates should be spread thin so that in most areas cells lie separated from one another. These smears should be fixed at once with methyl alcohol or 100% ethyl alcohol for 2 and 5 minutes respectively.

Nyka (*J. Path. Bact.* **67**:317, 1945) recommends a relatively simple methyl violet metanil yellow technic for typhus rickettsiae in mouse lungs:

Fix in 10% neutral formalin. The usual imbedding and sectioning procedures are presumed, and sections are deparaffinized and hydrated as usual.

1. Stain 30–60 minutes in 1:10,000 aqueous methyl violet.
2. Differentiate in weak acetic acid (0.03–0.04%: 2 drops glacial acetic acid in 100 cc distilled water) until cell cytoplasm is decolorized.
3. Counterstain a few seconds in 1:10,000 aqueous metanil yellow.
4. Dehydrate and clear with an acetone xylene sequence.
5. Mount in synthetic resin. Gurr's Xam and the Media Manufacturing Centre's DPX4 are mentioned by the author. Our American synthetic resins such as Permount, polystyrene, etc., will probably serve.

In the few preparations that I have seen stained by this method, rickettsiae are still difficult to distinguish from other basophilic granules and mast cell granules.

BLOOD, TISSUE AND PROTOZOA

Giemsa's stain is also widely used for the study of the morphology of blood, spleen and marrow cells and for the identification of protozoan parasites such as trypanosomes, leishmaniae, plasmodia and bartonellae.

The stain is best purchased from a reputable dye manufacturer. Insist on certification by the Biological Stain Commission. Either the prepared glycerol methanol solution or the dry mixed powder may be obtained. The latter should be dissolved in equal volumes of glycerol and methanol (methyl alcohol) at 800 mg per 100 cc of the mixed solvent. Although a small undissolved residue is found on dissolving Giemsa stains in amounts over 300 mg per 100 cc, the solution increases in strength, staining capacity and optical density with further addition of dye—the last in proportion to the total amount of dye added, up to 1.1 gm per 100 cc. Consequently the presence of a small residue is not to be taken as evidence of saturation of the glycerol methanol solvent. Quantities in excess of 1.1 gm per 100 cc occasion no further increase in staining power or optical density.

The best solvent appears to be an equal volume mixture of C. P. methanol and neutral C. P. glycerol. Special treatment of the methanol to render it acetone free is expensive and of no discernible value. Glycerol may be of either 95% or 98% strength without affecting the quality of the stain. More important than traces of acid in the reagents are traces of alkali. A trace of acid actually acts more as a stabilizer of the azures and methylene blue against the alteration which occurs spontaneously in glycerol methanol solutions, and is readily overcome in staining by the use of the appropriate buffers. Traces of alkali, on the other hand, fairly rapidly convert methylene blue and azure B into lower azures and methylene violet and alter the staining effect profoundly.

The older German texts required equal weights of glycerol and methanol. This corresponds nearly exactly to 60 volumes of methanol and 40 of glycerol. Giemsa stain deteriorates somewhat more rapidly in this mixture than in the equal volume mixture. The 75:25 mixture used for MacNeal's stain appears to be little or no better for preserving the stain than plain methanol.

An equal volume mixture of 100% ethyl alcohol and 98% glycerol appears to be as good a solvent for Giemsa stain as the corresponding methanol mixture, and to preserve the stain at least as well.

The recommended composition of Giema stain, using American dyes, is as follows: methylene blue eosinate 4 gm, azure B eosinate 5 gm, azure A eosinate 1 gm and methylene blue chloride (85–88% dye content) 2 gm. The mixture should be kept in a cool dry place, tightly stoppered.

It is not recommended that the eosinates be made in the laboratory, particularly not from commercial azure B, or from methylene blue unless special precautions are taken.

Commercial azure B is apparently a variable substance, containing varying proportions of methylene blue and azure A, often with an adequate amount of one or the other to modify considerably the character of the Giemsa stain. Further, eosinates of azure B and of methylene blue are quite susceptible to partial demethylation ("polychroming") on drying even at moderate (55–60°C) temperatures.

Directions for synthesis of azure A and B eosinates were included in the previous editions of this book. This no longer seems necessary.

The Giemsa Stain for Films.

1. Thin films should be fixed as soon as taken in methyl alcohol for 3–5 minutes (see pp. 559–561 for preparation of films). Thick films are first hemolyzed and then fixed or stained without fixation.
2. Stain 40–120 minutes in 1 cc Giemsa stain, 2 cc stock buffer and 47 cc distilled water. For marrow a phosphate buffer (p. 664) of pH 5.8–6 is preferable; for blood cytology, pH 6.4 or 6.5; for both blood and protozoa some prescribe pH 6.8; and for malaria survey work on thick films pH 7–7.2 is prescribed. For most things I use a pH 6.5 buffer.
3. Rinse in distilled water, dry and examine. For thick film malaria staining Wilcox used a pH 7.2 stain and prolonged the distilled water washing for some minutes. This takes out some of the excess basic dye deposited at the higher pH level. Use of a pH 6.5–6.8 buffer obviates this differentiation.

The 40 minute stain is adequate for blood work and for tertian and quartan parasites. For staining of Schüffner's granules or undulating membranes, longer staining, up to 2 hours, is often desirable. Platelets are often well demonstrated by these technics (better than by Wright's stain), with purple central granule and pale blue periphery.

Accelerated Giemsa Stain for Thick Films. Stain unfixed thick films, after 1 hour's drying, in Giemsa stain 4 cc, acetone 3 cc, pH 6.5 buffer 2 cc, distilled water 31 cc. Stain 5–10 minutes, rinse in distilled water, dry and examine. By this brief staining one avoids the loss of thick films so often suffered with brief drying periods.

Some malariologists find it advantageous to cover positive thick films with coverslips after staining, to protect them from roaches. Polystyrene (p. 96) appears to be excellent for this purpose. Dr. J. A. (Johnnie)

Walker writes me that he has found good color preservation in films so mounted after a 10 year interval. It is presumed that the film collection was kept in the dark under ordinary tropical temperature conditions.

Methods for protozoa in sections are discussed on pp. 164, 168, 200, 572 and 583–584.

Wright's and **Leishman's stains** are compounds of eosin Y with methylene blue altered by the action of alkalies so as to contain a variable amount of azure B, azure A and methylene violet. The stains are best procured as dry powders from commercial manufacturers, and should bear the certificate of the Biological Stain Commission.

As so certified, these stains usually consist chiefly of the eosinates of azure B and of methylene blue, regardless of the method of manufacture. Spectroscopically they should present 2 absorption bands of nearly equal density, the one at about 517 mμ (eosin) in a proportion of about 0.9:1 of the other, which represents the blue component, lying preferably between 652 and 658 mμ. A satisfactory stain with these characteristics may be made by mixing equal parts of the methylene blue and azure B eosinates as prepared for the Giemsa stain (p. 585).

The solvent recommended is C. P. methyl alcohol (methanol), which meets American Chemical Society specifications. Redistillation from silver oxide and sodium hydroxide to prepare a neutral, acetone free and aldehyde free methyl alcohol has been found to be unnecessary.

I prefer Wright's original prescription of 0.5 gm per 100 cc methanol to the weaker solutions in vogue. Although some residue remains undissolved when as little as 150 mg per 100 cc is used, the solution increases in optical density and staining power up to 600 or 700 mg per 100 cc, and it is probable that the solubility lies in that range.

One of the advantages usually urged for Wright's and Leishman's stains is that the undiluted stain may be used for fixation, and water may then be added for the staining period. I prefer to have films fixed at once at the bedside in methanol, and then later, on return to the laboratory, mix stain and water in a test tube in a proportion of 1 cc stain to 3 cc water, allowing 2 cc total for each slide to be stained. The water should be buffered by addition of 1 cc of 0.1 M phosphates at pH 6.5 for each 30–40 cc water (p. 664). If it is necessary to use other than distilled or rain water, a larger amount of stock buffer may be needed, or a solid buffer (*ibid.*) may be added in such quantity as is found necessary under local conditions.

The Technic for Wright Stain.

1. Fix films in methanol for 2–3 minutes (or deposit 0.5 cc stock stain on each slide and let stand 2 minutes).

2. Deposit 2 cc of a 25% dilution with buffered water of the stock stain on each slide (or add 1.5 cc water to the stock stain on the slide). Let stand 3–5 minutes.
3. Rinse in water, dry in an air stream (or with compressed air) and examine in immersion oil. Modified mineral oils preserve the stain if left on; cedar oil decolorizes the blue and purple elements.

Lillie's Wright Stain Technic. Superior results in regard to the sharpness of nuclear and parasite chromatin staining may be achieved by using a 1% solution in equal volumes of glycerol and methanol. Thus: Fix films 2–3 minutes in methanol. Stain 5 minutes in 4 cc stock stain, 3 cc acetone, 2 cc 0.1 M pH 6.5 phosphate buffer and 31 cc distilled water in a Coplin jar. Rinse, dry and examine. Such a mixture may be used *at once* for a second group of 10 slides with only slightly inferior results.

A slower, similar method uses 2 cc of stock 1% stain, 2 cc of pH 6.5 buffer and 46 cc water, and requires 20–30 minutes.

General Results of Romanovsky Stains on Films. With all these Giemsa, Wright, Leishman and similar Romanovsky stains, the cytoplasm of lymphocytes should be a clear medium blue; their nuclei, a deep purple to violet; chromatin of malaria parasites and of trophonuclei of trypanosomes, red purple; of blepharoplasts, a darker, perhaps more violet purple; undulating membranes, pink; cytoplasm of plasmodia and trypanosomes, light blue; nuclei of monocytes, lighter red purple; their cytoplasm, an opaque, faintly bluish gray; central granules of blood platelets, red purple; periphery, light blue; the granules of mast leucocytes are deep blue violet; eosinophil granules are orange pink; neutrophil granules, purple to violet. Bartonellae appear faintly blue with red purple chromatin dots and are best discerned when stained with Giemsa stain at pH levels between 6.2 and 6.8. Bacteria stain deep blue to violet. Diphtheroids may exhibit deeply stained bars and polar granules in a light blue body. The color of erythrocytes varies with the pH of the diluting water from pink at pH 6 through yellowish pink at 6.5, pinkish or grayish yellow at 6.8, grayish yellow to greenish yellow or even gray blue at 7–7.2. Differentiation with distilled water which is often faintly acid or with very dilute (0.1–0.05%) acetic acid displaces the color of erythrocytes from the gray blue toward the pink limit of the color series above. Eosinophil granules are often best stained when chromatin is much understained and pale blue in color.

SUDANOPHIL GRANULES OF LEUCOCYTES

These granules occur in neutrophil and eosinophil leucocytes, monocytes and probably basophil granulocytes as well, in general in much the same cells as show peroxidase and indophenol oxidase activities. They do not stain in the cold with the usual oil soluble dye methods which suffice for the staining of true fats and lipids. At temperatures of 20–25°C they require prolonged exposures to the naphthol type oil soluble dyes such as oil red O, Sudan III and Sudan IV. Naphthylamine and aminoanthraquinone dyes act more rapidly but still do not stain in the usual 5–10 minute intervals used for lipids. Reasonably rapid staining, 1–2 hours for oil red O for example, may be attained at 37°C, but elevation of temperature to 55–60°C or higher appears to be positively deleterious in comparison with 37°C staining.

After Savini's and Sehrt's papers (*Wien. med. Wschr.* **46**:1964, 1921; *C. R. Soc. biol.* **87**:744, 1922; *Münch. med. Wschr.* **74**:139, 1927) these granules were generally accepted as lipid in nature, though a number of writers commented on the resistance of Sudan black stains to extraction with 100% alcohol or with xylene. Lillie and Burtner (*J. Histochem.* **1**:8, 1953) demonstrated their water soluble nature, their resistance to extraction with a variety of fat solvents (aromatic and aliphatic hydrocarbons, pyridine, carbon tetrachloride, etc.), their unstainability with esterified Sudans (p. 459) and their capacity to react with alcohols and phenols; and concluded that they were not lipid. Since they are readily rendered unstainable by alcohol of 60% concentration or higher at 60°C, staining is preferably done at 50% alcohol concentration. Indeed I have seen decolorization of previously well stained preparations in the customary saturated 70% alcohol solutions of Sudan dyes.

Lillie-Burtner Technic for Staining Sudanophil Granules in Leucocytes.

1. Fix air dried blood films 10 minutes in 75% alcohol, in 75% alcohol containing 10% formalin or with formaldehyde gas over a little strong formalin (p. 561). Wash briefly in water to remove excess formaldehyde.
2. Mix 0.5% oil red O in 100% alcohol or, better, 99% isopropanol with an equal volume of distilled water and place in oven or water bath at 37°C. Stain smears 2–4 hours. (Fewer but larger granules are shown by staining 30–60 minutes in dye mixture preheated to and kept at 60°C.)
3. Wash in water.
4. Counterstain 5 minutes in Lillie's acetic hemalum or other alum hematoxylin.
5. Wash 5 minutes in running water.
6. Blow dry with air stream. Wash 1–2 minutes in xylene or acetone to remove dye precipitate. Mount in polystyrene with coverglass, or again blow dry and examine in immersion oil.

Results: Nuclei, blue; numerous fine to moderately numerous medium bright red granules in unstained to pale yellowish cytoplasm of neutrophil leucocytes; fewer similar granules in monocytes; granules of eosinophils largely pale gray green to brownish yellow, usually with a few to moderately numerous bright red to orange red, medium to coarse granules. Erythrocytes vary from greenish gray to very pale gray. Often erythrocytes and plasma show globules to fine granules of red deposit, which is also highly resistant to solvents. This deposit varies from none to copious from one slide to another, and in different areas of the same slide. It seems to be uninfluenced by filtration of the stain mixture and is extracted by alcohol of 60–90% in much the same way as the coloration of the leucocyte granules.

By substituting Sudan black B for oil red O in the foregoing technic the color of granules in the leucocytes is changed to greenish black; the granules of the eosinophils stain quite uniformly in dark gray green, often appearing more lightly colored centrally. The erythrocytes assume varying shades of gray green, becoming dark gray to black if staining is prolonged, especially at 60°C. Staining time with Sudan black B is shorter than with oil red O. A half-hour at room temperature, 5–10 minutes at 60°C (preheated) or 15 minutes at 37°C suffice. Counterstains for nuclei are less satisfactory than with the hemalum of the oil red stain. A 2 minute stain in 0.5% safranin in 1% acetic acid is fairly satisfactory. Feulgen staining, as practiced on tissue sections (p. 149), gives rather pale colors.

Blood films fixed with formaldehyde (either gaseous or in aqueous solution) and stained with oil soluble dyes for the demonstration of leucocyte granules are quite apt to show areas of partial detachment, wrinkles running in mosaic fashion and irregular precipitates both of oil soluble dye and of the hematoxylin counterstain. These precipitates and the droplets stained in red corpuscles may be quite difficult to remove, whether with alcohol, acetone or xylene, after staining. They seem to be prevented in considerable measure by prior treatment with 60–80% alcohol, and are much less conspicuous in films fixed for 10 minutes in 75% alcohol.

The sudanophil granules of polymorphonuclear leucocytes, though quickly destroyed by 60–100% alcohol at 60°C, resist 90% and lower alcohol concentrations for quite long periods at room temperatures and lower. They are water soluble at 60°C after brief 75% alcohol fixation but are rendered insoluble in water by mercuric chloride, lead nitrate and formaldehyde.

Their sudanophilia is destroyed by treatment with ferric chloride, ferrous chloride, potassium bichromate, potassium permanganate, periodic acid and hydrogen peroxide.

Though it is uncertain whether Sudan staining demonstrates preexisting granules or whether the granules simply represent deposition of dye complex at sites of reaction, it is convenient to refer to these sites as the sudanophil granules.

PERIODIC ACID SCHIFF REACTION

After alcohol fixations, a 10 minute oxidation in 1% H_5IO_6, 5 minutes' washing, 10 minutes in Schiff reagent, 5 minutes' washing in 3 changes of 0.5% sodium metabisulfite, 10 minutes' washing, 5 minutes in acetic hemalum as counterstain, and 5 minutes' washing in tap water, films are blown dry in an air stream and examined in immersion oil or mounted in synthetic resin.

Nuclei stain deep blue; erythrocytes, pale yellow to gray; cytoplasm of neutrophils, purplish red; granules of eosinophils, clear and unstained in foamy pink cytoplasm. Dark red purple glycogen granules occur in lymphoid cells and sometimes in neutrophil leucocytes. Platelets contain purplish red oval granules.

Pretreatment with diastase solutions weakens the cytoplasmic staining of neutrophil leucocytes but does not destroy it. Glycogen is removed by diastase digestion (p. 496). The staining of platelets is unaffected. Treatment of films with water or pH 6 buffer weakens cytoplasmic staining of leucocytes only slightly.

For glycogen digestion tests, films fixed in formaldehyde gas or alcoholic formaldehyde solutions (p. 39) should be employed, since after simple alcoholic fixations, the proteolytic enzymes in the polymorphonuclear leucocytes selectively autolyze these cells, destroying first their cytoplasm and then their nuclei. This leucocyte protease is quite active at 60°C and is not destroyed by 10 minutes in boiling acetone, benzene, toluene or xylene.

Acetylation for 4 hours at 60°C in 40% acetic anhydride + pyridine mixture renders leucocytes and platelets periodic acid Schiff negative, and a 16 hour deacetylation in 20% ammonia water, 80% alcohol solution restores the reactivity of platelets and in part that of neutrophils. Benzoylation in 1:19 benzoyl chloride: pyridine (p. 278) is less successful at 25 or 37°C, and at 60°C, the reagent completely destroys the capacity of nuclei to stain with alum hematoxylin or Giemsa stain.

Fluorescence Microscopy. Primulin, berberin and rivanol have been used for the demonstration of protozoan parasites in fluorescence microscopy. They give respectively blue, bright yellow and yellowish green fluorescence to leucocyte nuclei; yellow, yellow and bright yellow to leucocyte cytoplasm; and blue white, golden yellow and yellowish green color to malaria parasites (*Haemoproteus, Plasmodium nucleophilum,* and *P. vivax*). One stains methyl alcohol fixed smears 2–5 minutes in saturated aqueous or alcoholic solutions of the fluorochromes. Parasites and leucocytes stand out as brilliantly fluorescent objects against a dark field and are readily discerned at 200 diameters under dry lens systems. Nothing is said about the behavior of blood platelets with this method, and most of Patton and Metcalf's work was done on the 2 avian parasites (*Science* 98:184, 1943). I have had no experience with this method.

Catechol Mordant Dyes. When Gomori's variant of Clara's method for enterochromaffin cells using very dilute aqueous solutions of hematoxylin, brazilin, gallocyanine or celestine blue is applied to alcohol fixed or formaldehyde fixed human blood films, the granules of the eosinophil leucocytes are selectively stained. Gallocyanine gives brilliant purplish violet eosinophil granules with 48 hour staining in a 1/20,000 solution. The red corpuscles appear in pale yellowish gray; nothing else stains. With celestine blue at 1/20,000 for 2 days, white cell nuclei appear in pink; red cells, faint yellow; eosinophil granules, blue green; and neutrophils, unstained. Hematoxylin gives blue gray, brazilin and alizarin pink, but the contrasts are inferior to those with the oxazin dyes. In sections, however, 0.01% hematoxylin, 32–48 hours, gives blue black eosinophil granules.

Perhaps the most contrastful results are obtained with a 1/100,000 aqueous solution of celestine blue, staining 6 hours at 60°C. This yields light red purple nuclei, blue green eosinophil granules, unstained neutrophil cytoplasm and pale yellow erythrocytes. It is necessary to employ alcoholic formaldehye or formaldehyde vapor fixation to avoid the autolytic digestion of the neutrophils which occurs in distilled water at 60°C.

In tissue sections a safranin counterstain may be used after 1/20,000 gallocyanine (2 days, 37°C), but the staining is variable and generally less successful than in blood films.

RETICULOCYTES

Brecher (*Am. J. Clin. Path.* 19:895, 1949) prefers **new methylene blue N** (C.I. No. 52030) to the more commonly used brilliant cresyl blue for the staining of reticulocytes in blood. Various lots of brilliant cresyl blue vary considerably in staining properties and spectroscopic characteristics, indicating differences in composition. As Conn states, brilliant cresyl blue is not used in industry and must be specially manufactured in small lots for biological staining. This fact undoubtedly explains the variations. New methylene blue, on the other hand, is manufactured by several manufacturers for textile dyeing and appears to be quite constant both in its absorption spectrum ($\lambda = 630 - 632.5$ mμ) and in staining performance.

Brecher's New Methylene Blue Technic for Reticulocytes.

1. Dissolve 0.5 gm new methylene blue and 1.6 gm potassium oxalate in 100 cc distilled water.

2. Mix approximately equal drops of stain and of fresh or oxalated blood on a slide.
3. Draw up the mixed drop into a capillary pipet and let stand for 10 minutes.
4. Expel the mixture in small drops on several slides and make thin smears as usual. Dry in air and examine with oil immersion.

Results: Erythrocytes are light greenish blue; reticulum is a deep blue and sharply outlined.

Deeper blue staining of erythrocytes indicates that an excess of dye was used. Generally the blood drop should equal or slightly exceed the stain drop in size.

As an example of a brilliant cresyl blue dry smear technic I quote the Cunningham-Isaacs technic from Conn and Darrow, 1948 (ID3-8):

Brilliant Cresyl Blue Method for Reticulocytes.

1. Dry a drop of 0.3% alcoholic solution of brilliant cresyl blue (C.I. No. 51010) on a cleaned and polished slide or coverglass.
2. Deposit a drop of fresh blood 2–3 mm in diameter on a similarly cleaned slide or coverglass.
3. Appose the stain covered area on the first slide or coverglass to the blood drop and move this slide up and down hinge fashion until the dye film is all dissolved and the blood appears blue black.
4. Allow the 2 slides or coverglasses to cohere in parallel position and spread the blood drop.
5. Draw apart along the plane of contact and allow the 2 films to dry.

Results: Sharply stained blue reticulum and pale blue erythrocytes. If desired the films may be counterstained with Wright's or Giemsa's stain by one of the usual technics (pp. 586–588). In this case the background is the usual one with these stains, and the reticulum appears deep blue.

Phase microscopy reveals a number of erythrocyte containing rods and granules which appear dark under dark contrast phase illumination, and which Brecher (*Bull. Int. A. Med. Mus.* **30**:99, 1949) finds to be associated with but not identical with the stainable reticulum in the same cells.

Since the presence of the hemoglobin largely obscures these rods and granules, hemolysis is a necessary part of the technic for their phase contrast demonstration. Phenylhydrazine intoxication renders reticulocytes more numerous and more conspicuous under phase microscopy, perhaps because of *in vivo* hemolysis, so that under these conditions they may be found without artificial hemolysis.

Brecher's Technic for Phase Microscopy of Reticulocytes.

1. Mix a drop of blood with a drop of hypotonic ammonium oxalate solution (1.2%) on a clean coverglass.
2. Pick up the blood and coverglass by bringing a clean slide down on top of it.
3. Turn over and apply petrolatum U.S.P. (paraffinum molle B.P.) along the edges of the coverglass to seal the preparation. This is done conveniently from a 5 cc syringe fitted with a large bore needle.

INCLUSION BODIES

Oxyphil inclusion bodies such as Negri bodies, Guarnieri bodies, herpes, varicella and molluscum inclusions and the like are often quite well shown by azure eosin (pp. 161–163) and phloxine azure sequence (p. 160) methods. I have seen them excellently demonstrated in hematoxylin eosin preparations which had been mounted in Canada balsam for 2 or 3 years. Such old preparations appear to be distinctly superior to fresh stains for this purpose. The safranin O eriocyanine A method (p. 297) has given good results.

Most of the so-called specific Negri body methods depend on balanced mixtures of 2 basic or 2 acid dyes, or on sequence procedures using an acid and a basic dye. The preferred material for Negri bodies is hippocampus and cerebellar cortex. The major lesions of rabies, however, are found in the brain stem.

Stovall-Black Method (*Am. J. Clin. Path.* **10**:1–8, 1940). Stovall and Black used acetone fixation and a sequence stain:

1. Stain 2 minutes in a 1% alcoholic solution of ethyl eosin (C.I. No. 45386, sodium ethyl eosinate) adjusted to pH 3 with 10.1 N hydrochloric acid.
2. Rinse in water.
3. Stain 30 seconds in 10 cc 1% methylene blue in 95% alcohol, 10 cc 0.2 M acetate buffer of pH 5.5 (p. 661), and 20 cc water.
4. Then differentiate in 0.38% acetic acid in water (13 drops in 60 cc) until sections are brownish red.
5. Wash, dehydrate and clear.
6. Mount in balsam.

Results: Negri bodies are brownish to pure red; nucleoli, pale blue; other structures, pink.

A variant of this method which we have used successfully:

1. In 90 cc 100% alcohol or 94 cc 95.5% alcohol, 3.25 cc 1% acetic acid and water to make 100 cc, dissolve 950 mg ethyl eosin. Stain in this for 2 minutes.

2. Then wash in alcohol and in water.
3. Counterstain formalin material in 0.5% methylene blue in 25% alcohol; alcohol fixed material, in alum hematoxylin.
4. Differentiate in 0.25% acetic acid for 2–5 minutes.
5. Wash, dehydrate and clear.
6. Mount in balsam.

Gerlach's Method (Kraus, Gerlach and Schweinburg).

1. Stain paraffin sections of formalin fixed material in a fresh mixture of 3 cc carbol fuchsin, 6 cc Loeffler's methylene blue (about 0.35% in 22% alcohol containing 1:10,000 potassium hydroxide) and 50 cc distilled water. Heat sections to steaming 4 times in 4 changes of this mixture.
2. Wash in water.
3. Differentiate and dehydrate in alcohols and clear in xylene.
4. Mount in synthetic resin or mineral oil; the stain fades rapidly in balsam.

Results: Negri bodies, red; chromatin and nucleoli, rather light blue.
Mann's Methyl Blue Eosin Technic (Kraus, Gerlach and Schweinburg). This method is classical: Zenker fixation was prescribed. Paraffin sections are carried through 0.5% iodine and 5% sodium thiosulfate as usual and washed in water.

1. Stain 24 hours in 6 cc 1% aqueous eosin Y (C.I. No. 45380), 6 cc 1% aqueous methyl blue (C.I. No. 42780) and 28 cc distilled water.
2. Wash in water and differentiate in 100% alcohol containing 4 mg sodium hydroxide per 100 cc (0.001 N; add 0.1 cc 1% NaOH in alcohol to 25 cc 100% alcohol).
3. Wash in 100% alcohol.
4. Then wash in water containing a few drops of acetic acid—say 0.1%.
5. Dehydrate and clear through alcohols and xylene and mount in polystyrene or cellulose caprate.

Results: Negri bodies and erythrocytes are stained red; nuclei and inner granules of the inclusions, blue.
Schleifstein's Rapid Method (*Am. J. Pub. Health,* **27**:1283, 1937) (emended). Schleifstein prescribed 4 hours' fixation in Zenker's fluid at 37°C, 30 minutes' washing in water, dehydration 1 hour at 37°C in dioxane over anhydrous calcium chloride, infiltration 1 hour in dioxane paraffin 50% mixture at 56°C and in pure paraffin for 1 hour. In place of the dioxane schedule I suggest substitution of the rapid acetone benzene schedule (p. 72).
Schleifstein's stain consists of 1.8 gm basic fuchsin (rosaniline chloride)

and 1 gm methylene blue, dissolved in 100 cc glycerol and 100 cc methyl alcohol. For use it is diluted 1:80 (Mallory, 1 drop to 2 cc) with 1:40,000 potassium hydroxide.

1. Paraffin sections are brought to water as usual.
2. Steam gently for 5 minutes (70°C?) in the diluted stain.
3. Then wash in tap water.
4. Differentiate to a faint violet color in 90% alcohol.
5. Dehydrate rapidly with 95% and 100% alcohol, clear through 100% alcohol and xylene (50:50) and 2 changes of xylene. Mount in Permount or other resin.

Results: Negri bodies, deep magenta red; erythrocytes, coppery red; nucleoli, blue black; cytoplasm, blue violet.

Zlotnik's Method for Negri Bodies in Fixed Tissue (*Nature* **172**:962, 1953).

1. Bring paraffin sections to water as usual.
2. Stain 5 minutes in Ehrlich's hematoxylin (p. 174).
3. Blue 2 minutes in tap water.
4. Counterstain 1 minute in saturated aqueous picric acid containing 0.5% orange G (C.I. No. 16230).
5. Wash in water until only erythrocytes remain yellow. Rinse in distilled water.
6. Stain 10 minutes in 0.5 gm acid fuchsin, 0.5 gm phosphotungstic acid, 100 cc 1% acetic acid.
7. Rinse in distilled water.
8. Differentiate 5 minutes in 2 gm phosphotungstic acid, 2 gm phosphomolybdic acid, 30 cc 100% alcohol and 70 cc saturated aqueous picric acid.
9. Rinse in distilled water and in 1% acetic acid.
10. Stain 15 minutes in 1% aniline blue in 2% acetic acid.
11. Rinse in 1% acetic acid, dehydrate and clear by the alcohol xylene sequence, mount in synthetic resin.

Results: Negri bodies, purplish red with blue inner granules; nerve cell cytoplasm, bluish; nucleoli, dark purple; erythrocytes, yellow.

This is essentially a somewhat complicated variant of the Masson-Mallory trichrome procedure and should yield blue connective tissue as well. I have not had occasion to use it.

For various oxyphil inclusion bodies, notably Guarnieri and Kurloff bodies, the inclusions of infantile giant cell pneumonia and others (but not Negri bodies) A. C. Lendrum (*J. Path. Bact.* 59:399, 1947) recommended his phloxine tartrazine stain. Fluorane dyes are required, and of these phloxine B (C.I. No. 45410) and rose Bengal (C.I. No. 45440) appear to be the best. Eosin Y and erythrosin are too readily extracted. Calcium chloride is used as an intensifier for the fluorane staining. As a differentiator Lendrum specifies the tartrazine NS of Imperial Chemical Industries, dissolved in Cellosolve (ethylene glycol monoethyl ether). It is presumed that this is C.I. No. 19140 and that the tartrazines of other manufacturers will serve. This particular letter designation was no longer listed by I.C.I. in the second edition of the *Colour Index.*

Lendrums's Phloxine-Tartrazine Method (emended).

1. Fix preferably in mercuric chloride formalin (9 parts saturated aqueous mercuric chloride solution and 1 part formalin) for 24 hours, dehydrate with iodized 70% alcohol and ascending alcohols, clear, infiltrate and imbed in paraffin as usual.
2. Bring paraffin sections to water as usual, including iodine and sodium thiosulfate steps if tissue was not iodized before imbedding.
3. Stain as usual in Mayer's hemalum or in Weigert's acid iron chloride hematoxylin.
4. Blue and wash as usual.
5. Stain 30 minutes in 0.5% phloxine B or rose Bengal in 0.5% (0.045 M) aqueous calcium chloride solution.
6. Rinse in water.
7. Differentiate with saturated tartrazine solution in Cellosolve, either briefly from a dropper bottle, or with strongly phloxinophil objects for as long as several hours in a Coplin jar.
8. Rinse in 60% alcohol, dehydrate with 95% and 100% alcohol, then 100% alcohol and xylene, and clear in 2 changes of xylene. Mount in balsam or other suitable resin.

Results: Kurloff bodies in guinea pig lung, Guarnieri bodies, inclusions of infantile giant cell pneumonia and others (but not Negri bodies) are stained (red) by the phloxine; collagen, yellow; nuclei, according to the hematoxylin stain selected.

I have not tried this method. It has been used by a number of British workers.

According to Wolman (*Proc. Soc. Exp. Biol. Med.* 74:85, 1950) the elementary bodies of smallpox may be demonstrated by fixing smears of scrapings from incised recent papules or vesicles in ether and alcohol (50:50) for a few minutes, drying in air and staining by the Feulgen procedure (p. 149).

The strongly acidophil intranuclear inclusion bodies seen in some cases of chronic lead and bismuth poisonings may be acid fast when stained by the Ziehl-Neelsen technic. Sections were stained in carbol fuchsin for 3 hours at 56°C, washed in water and decolorized 3–5 minutes in 3 cc concentrated HCl: 97 cc 70% alcohol and counterstained with Harris's alum hematoxylin. Those seen in lead poisoning failed to react to ammonium sulfide. (M. Wachstein, *Am. J. Clin. Path.* **19**:608, 1949.)

Perrin and Littlejohn (*J. Clin. Path.* **3**:40, 1950) detail a rapid method which may have some value in the cytologic examination of fresh sputum for tumor cells. Their carbol fuchsin methylene blue stain is composed of 4 volumes of a 0.5% methylene blue solution in 20% glycerol (by volume), mixed extempore with 1 volume of a 1% fuchsin solution in 10 parts alcohol to 90 parts 5% aqueous phenol solution. Purulent or bloody particles are picked out of the morning sputum, mixed thoroughly with a drop of the stain and warmed gently over a Bunsen burner for 30 seconds. The uniformly stained, sticky specimen is then covered with a large coverglass and spread by gentle pressure. Specimens may be examined at once or allowed to stand a while. Staining continues and in 5 or 6 hours becomes so intense as to obscure nuclear detail.

Improved nuclear detail was obtained by substituting 2% iodine green (C.I. 42556) for the fuchsin methylene blue mixture. It is probable that the commoner, closely related dyes ethyl and methyl green can be used in the same way.

With the fuchsin methylene blue, cytoplasm of squamous and columnar cells stains bright pink; nuclei and bacteria, violet to purple. Leucocyte and lymphocyte cytoplasm is pale pink or green; that of macrophages, purplish red; and of plasma cells, violet to purple. Tumor cell cytoplasm is red when well keratinized, and violet to blue green in more anaplastic cells.

Russell Bodies

Russell bodies are colorless spheres, polyhedra, rods or ovoids occurring singly and in clusters in the cytoplasm of cells of the plasma cell type, ranging upward in size to spheres twice the diameter of surrounding plasma cells. In fixed tissue they are strongly oxyphil on staining with mixtures of the azure eosin type (pp. 160–165) but, according to Kindred (*Stain Techn.* **10**:7, 1935), they differ from hemoglobin in not staining with eosin at pH levels of 6.2–6.6 when in the unfixed state.

Russell (Ehrlich's *Encyklopädie*) prescribed Müller fixation and stained 10–30 minutes in saturated fuchsin solution in 2% aqueous phenol, then washed 3–5 minutes in water and 30 seconds in 100% alcohol, counterstained in 1% iodine green (C.I. No. 42556) in 2% aqueous phenol for 5 minutes, dehydrated with 100% alcohol, cleared in xylene and mounted in balsam. Nuclei stained green; the fuchsin bodies, red. Klien (*ibid.*) prestained with alum hematoxylin, stained in warm carbol fuchsin and differentiated in a strong fluorescein solution in alcohol. The usual alcohol, xylene, balsam sequence followed. Schmorl quotes Russell's original method without change; Cowdry refers to Kindred's paper (above); other recent authors make no reference to these bodies. Askanazy, writing in Aschoff's *Pathologische Anatomie* (Fischer, Jena, 1936), noted that they are Gram positive. This is true with the Gram-Weigert method, but with acetone differentiation they are Gram negative. With hemalum and oil red O they do not take the fat stain in frozen sections. On application of the Weigert myelin technic they become deep gray while red corpuscles are still black; and they retain some gray for a little while after the erythrocytes decolorize. The periodic acid Schiff leucofuchsin technic (p. 198) colors them red, with or without antecedent diastase digestion (p. 496); but after oxidation with chromic anhydride (p. 199) or with 1% potassium permanganate, only a pink or gray pink color is produced by the leucofuchsin. They do not blacken with diammine silver (pp. 239–240) and are iron negative.

Welsh (*Am. J. Path.* **40**:285, 1962) notes also the occurrence of periodic Schiff negative forms and finds a correlation between the degree of reactivity and of intracisternal electron density. The grade of eosinophilia also varies from quite strong to inappreciable. Using 0.2 *mM* methylene blue and 0.1 *mM* eosin at pH ranges from 3–9.5, Goldberg and Deane (*J. Histochem.* **8**:327, 1960) found the pK of formalin fixed Russell bodies to lie at about 6–7.5. Congo red and crystal violet amyloid stains were negative; the periodic acid Schiff stain was positive.

For Russell bodies of cancer cells (and plasma cells) Bangle (*Am. J. Path.* **43**:437, 1963) records slight to strong acid fastness (Ziehl-Neelsen) unaltered by prior 2 hours 60°C 2:1 chloroform:methanol extraction or HCl hydrolysis (1 *N*, 60°C, 20 minutes); a positive Gram-Weigert and negative Gram acetone stain; positive periodic acid Schiff reaction, also after diastase and in the allochrome method (orange to red); orthochromatic basophilia above pH 4 with 0.01–0.05% thiazin dye solutions, oxyphilia to eosin, acid fuchsin and Biebrich scarlet only in the acid range (pH 5, 6); a positive Millon reaction but negative SH and SS reactions with ferric ferricyanide and the peracetic thionin method; negative fat stains with oil red O and Sudan black B, negative peracetic Schiff and direct 72 hour Schiff reactions; a negative benzidine nitroprusside test for hemoglobin and a negative phosphotungstic acid hematoxylin stain for so-called alcoholic hyalin.

SPIROCHETES

Spirochetes are generally demonstrated in tissues by one of the numerous reported silver methods. For fresh clinical material the dark field technic is preferable, and this may be applied also to fresh autopsy material. For smears, various methods using Wright's and Giemsa's stains as well as silver methods and "negative" methods have been used.

The methods employing Wright's and Giemsa's stains either add a small quantity of an alkali carbonate or heat the staining solution or both. Heated stains are replaced 3–5 times and allowed to act 15 seconds to 3 or 4 minutes each time.

Giemsa's Method (modified slightly from *Deutsch. med. Wschr.* **31**: 1026, 1905).

1. Fix films 15 minutes in 100% alcohol.
2. Dilute 1 cc Giemsa stain with 38 cc distilled water and 2 cc 0.1% potassium carbonate. Stain smears 10–30 minutes.
3. Rinse, blow dry with compressed air or blot dry with filter paper and examine in immersion oil.

Wright's (?) Rapid Method. Fix films 15 minutes in 100% alcohol or by passing thrice through a blue flame. Make a 1:40 dilution of Giemsa stain in distilled water. Flood slide with 2–3 cc of this, heat to steaming, let stand 15 seconds, decant and repeat flooding and heating 5 times more. Let cool for 1 minute the last time, rinse with distilled water, dry and examine. This technic appeared in the 1908 edition of *Pathological Technique,* by Mallory and Wright, apparently as an original modification of Wright's. With both the foregoing methods spirochetes are stained dark purplish red.

Negative methods are derived from Burri's India ink method, which itself, according to Conn and Darrow, has largely been abandoned on account of difficulties in obtaining ink free of bacteria. Dorner (*Stain Techn.* **5**:25, 1930) introduced nigrosin for the same purpose, and Harrison (*Brit. Med. J.* **2**:1547, 1912) used collargol. Congo red posttreated with hydrochloric acid to turn it blue has been similarly employed, but Cumley (*Stain Techn.* **10**:53, 1935) notes that after the slides are made they may again turn red or fade altogether.

Mallory recommended a 10–25% suspension of India ink in distilled water, which is to be autoclaved before use. Dorner prescribed dissolving 10 gm water soluble nigrosin (C.I. No. 50420) in 100 cc distilled water by heating 30 minutes in a bath of boiling water. Harrison prepared a 5% suspension of collargol in distilled water. This is good for months.

Technic. Mix a bacteriologic loopful of exudate on a clean slide with a loopful of one of the above fluids and spread into a thin smear. Dry and examine. Spirochetes and bacteria appear unstained in a dark brown, gray or reddish brown background respectively for the ink, nigrosin and collargol.

Silver Methods

Fontana's Method. This is the traditional silver method for smears:

1. Conn and Darrow prescribe heat fixation, Mallory a 1 minute treatment with Ruge's 1% acetic acid, 2% formalin solution using several changes, followed by rinsing in water.
2. Steam 30 seconds in· phenol 1 gm, tannic acid 5 gm, distilled water 100 cc. Use only a few drops.
3. Rinse 30 seconds in distilled water.
4. Steam (70–80°C) 30 seconds in Fontana's ammoniacal silver hydroxide: To 5% silver nitrate add 28% ammonia water drop by drop until the dark brown precipitate just dissolves (about 0.5 cc for 10 cc of 5% silver nitrate), then add more silver nitrate, shaking to dissolve the brown clouds of silver oxide between drops, until a faint permanent turbidity is attained. This is identical with our usual diammine silver solution, except that we put the 0.5 cc ammonia in first. Conn and Darrow state that this solution is good for several months; but judging from experience with similar solutions for reticulum, it seems preferable to prepare a small quantity fresh each time.
5. Wash, dry and mount in balsam.

Levaditi's Method. This is the traditional method for spirochetes in blocks of tissue (Conn and Darrow). Except for preparation of teaching material it is not recommended. It is slow and cumbersome, as well as being capricious and uncertain. Slide methods are preferred for diagnosis.

1. Fix blocks about 1–2 mm thick in 10% formalin for 1–2 days. Older material stored in formalin can be used.
2. Rinse in water and soak in 95% alcohol for 1 day.
3. Place in distilled water until the tissue sinks.
4. Impregnate in 2% silver nitrate at 37°C for 4 days, changing the solution daily.
5. Wash in distilled water.
6. Reduce 48 hours in 3 gm pyrogallol, 5 cc 40% formaldehyde and 100 cc distilled water.
7. Wash in several changes of distilled water.
8. Dehydrate with graded alcohols, clear in cedar oil and imbed in paraffin. Section at 5 μ. Deparaffinize with xylene and mount in balsam or synthetic resin.

Results: Tissues, varying shades of yellow and brown; spirochetes, black.

The Warthin Technic. Of the numerous proposed single paraffin section methods, I have finally selected a *modification of Warthin's* (*Am. J. Syph.* 4:97, 1920) technic which has given us more consistent results than any previously tried. *Faulkner* (*Stain Techn.* **20**:81, 1945) substituted an acetate buffer for Kerr's (*Am. J. Clin. Path.* **8**:63, 1938) dilute citric acid solution which seems to control the process better. The technic:

1. Bring paraffin sections of formalin fixed material to water as usual.
2. Wash with 0.01 *M* pH 3.6–3.8 acetate buffer (p. 661).
3. Impregnate 45 minutes at 55–60°C in a Coplin jar filled with 1% silver nitrate in water buffered to pH 3.6–3.8 as above.
4. While slides are incubating, heat and mix the developer solution. Make in advance a stock gelatin solution by dissolving 10 gm gelatin in 200 cc distilled water buffered as above (pH 3.6–3.8), heating in paraffin oven for 1 hour. Add 2 cc 1:10,000 Merthiolate (sodium ethyl-mercurithiosalicylate) as preservative. Cool and store. Melt the stock gelatin solution, take 15 cc and heat it to 60°C. Heat 3 cc 2% silver nitrate buffered as above at pH 3.6–3.8 to 60°C and add to the gelatin. Then add 1 cc freshly prepared 3% hydroquinone in the same buffered water. Use the mixed developer at once.
5. Place slides face up on glass rods and pour on the warm developer. When sections become golden brown to grayish yellow and developer begins to turn brownish black, pour off and rinse with warm (55–60°C) tap water, then with distilled water.
6. Tone 3 minutes in 0.2% gold chloride. (For greater permanence.)
7. Wash in water and counterstain with hemalum and eosin or by other methods. This step may be omitted.
8. Then dehydrate, clear and mount as usual.

Results: Underdevelopment gives a pale background and slender or pale spirochetes; overdevelopment gives thick spirochetes, dark background and precipitates; optimal development gives pale yellowish brown tissue and black spirochetes. At the lower pH level, tissue staining is less; at the higher, organisms are denser. This method has performed well on syphilitic fetal liver, on yaws lesions, on Weil's disease, on Vincent's fusospirillosis mouth lesions and on other spirochetoses.

TRICHINAE

The Unfixed Muscle Spread. The usual technic for examination for trichinae in muscle is taken from *Nolan and Bozicevich* (*Pub. Health Rep.* **53**:652, 1938). Take about 1 gm of fresh muscle in the aggregate, as small fragments snipped with scissors from various areas, best from the diaphragm near the tendinous portions. Lay these in rows on one or more 50 × 75 mm slides. Place a second slide on top and press the fragments out flat. Heavy spring paper clips may be used to supply the pressure, one on each side, or heavy rubber bands. The muscle fragments should be pressed out to a state of transparency. Examine directly with a dissecting microscope or with the low power of the microscope with reduced illumination. The preparations do not keep.

The Formic Acid Method. Even more satisfactory crush preparations can be made after preliminary fixation in 20% formic acid for 12–24 hours. This method has the advantage of allowing removal of the material to the laboratory and working up at leisure. The muscle swells greatly. Small snips are cut off, teased and crushed out to transparency. Stains may be applied, and permanent preparations mounted. My technic is this:

Cut small pieces of muscle from various locations at autopsy, especially diaphragm and intercostal muscles. Pectoralis and rectus abdominis muscles can be used. Deltoid and gastrocnemius are favorable sites for biopsy. Masseter is also a good muscle for biopsy, if cosmetic considerations can be disregarded. Immerse these at once in a 1:3 or 1:4 dilution of concentrated (90%) formic acid in distilled water and leave overnight. Wash 30–60 minutes in running water and transfer to a mixture of equal volumes of glycerol and of 50% alcohol for at least 18 hours. The material can be kept in this mixture.

When desired snip off small fragments of muscle with scissors, taking at least a dozen from various pieces of muscle. Drop these into 30 cc 1% acetic acid to which 0.3–0.6 cc of Lillie's acid hemalum (p. 174) has been added. Other hematoxylins can be used, if diluted in 1% acetic acid to give a final concentration of about 5–10 mg hematoxylin per 100 cc. Stain overnight. Place the fragments on coverglasses in 2 rows of 2 or 3 pieces each and tease and crush gently with needles. Add a few drops of Apáthy's gum syrup (p. 101). Lay the coverglass on a blotter on a flat surface. Put a slide down on top of the preparations and press down firmly with a slight rotatory motion, so as to crush and spread the muscle fragments. The excess gum syrup is squeezed out into the blotter. The preparations may be examined at once, using a 32 mm objective for finding and an 8 mm objective for detailed study; but they clear further on standing.

Muscle nuclei and cross striae are well shown; the nuclei of the giant cells surrounding recently encysted parasites are readily identified.

If the preparations acquire air bubbles after release of the pressure, run in a little more syrup from one edge, but do not press on the coverglass directly. It is likely to break. The syrup dries hard.

Use of very dilute safranin in dilute acetic acid solution in place of the hematoxylin yields more transparent preparations with a purer nuclear stain. Use a 1:1000–1:10,000 safranin O (best, about 1:2000) in 1% acetic acid and stain overnight as with the hematoxylin.

Muscle previously fixed in formalin does not yield satisfactory crush preparations.

The **digestion technic,** quoted from Bozicevich (*Pub. Health Rep.* **53:** 430, 1938), is more sensitive but requires more apparatus. Set up a 3 liter glass funnel with a large rubber tube on the stem. Into the open end of this tube fit a 15 cc centrifuge tube with conical bottom. Between the bottom of the funnel and the centrifuge tube attach a screw clamp for closing the tube when the centrifuge tube is to be removed after the digestion is complete. Support the whole in a suitable circular hole in an inch plank. Lay in the funnel a 15 cm (6 in) perforated porcelain plate. (See illustration from Bozicevich.)

Make up the digestion fluid by dissolving 15 gm pepsin in 3000 cc of warm (40°C) tap water. Add 21 cc concentrated hydrochloric acid. Place this solution in the funnel with attached centrifuge tube.

Grind 70 gm fresh muscle, preferably from the diaphragm; place the ground muscle a little at a time on a quadruple thickness of 40 mesh gauze or cheesecloth which is previously laid in the funnel over the porcelain plate. Place the whole apparatus in a 37°C incubator and digest for 15–18 hours (overnight). During the digestion the living larvae are liberated from the muscle and pass through the gauze, settling into the bottom of the centrifuge tube. Then clamp off the rubber tube, remove the centrifuge tube and take up larvae with a pipet from the bottom of the tube. Most of the fluid may be decanted off first.

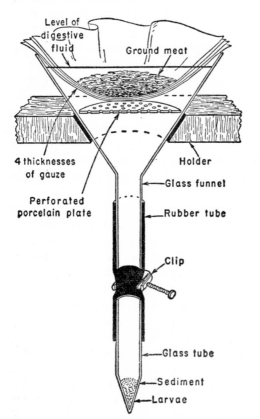

Fig. 16-1. Modified Baermann apparatus. (*Courtesy, J. Bozicevich, Public Health reports,* 53:430, 1938, *Washington, D.C., Government Printing Office.*)

Chapter 17

Glia and Nerve Cells and Fibers

Valuable as the silver methods may be in the study of reactive gliosis, it is often even of more value to study brain tissues stained by general oversight methods such as the azure eosin technics (pp. 160–165), which reveal cellular gliosis, perivascular infiltration, hemorrhages, necroses, bacteria, inclusion bodies and tigrolysis. Use of diammine silver technics for reticulum may aid in establishing the relation of focal gliosis to blood vessels. I have successfully used the picric acid and hydrochloric acid methyl blue methods for this purpose. The periodic acid Schiff leucofuchsin and allochrome methods (pp. 198, 549) seem worthy of trial. Fat stains and myelin technics have their place. Perivascular and interstitial macrophages can well be studied with iron reactions as well as with fat stains, separately or in the same preparation.

Ependyma is quite well shown with the above general methods for cells and fibers. Some of the special glia procedures can be of value in the study of ependymitides. Choroid plexus and their epithelium are well shown by the azure eosin methods. The usual stroma methods of general histology are applicable to these essentially vascular and epithelial structures. Fat stains may be of value, especially for the plexal epithelial lipid.

The meninges may require almost any of the methods applicable to the general tissues. The azure eosin methods are useful for the cytology of exudates; the bacterial methods, collagen methods, pigment methods, fibrin and other methods may all have their specific applications.

Generally the amateur has indifferent success with the metallic impregnation methods, but many workers have used them and secured useful preparations. Unfortunately special fixations and very fresh material are often required, and this limits their usefulness. I have endeavored to select methods which are adaptable to routine formalin fixed material when possible, and have relied to a considerable extent on the selection made by Davenport, Windle and Rhines for Conn and Darrow. These authors have supplied a number of valuable emendations, as well as modifications.

Block impregnations have been used with considerable success by many neuroanatomists. Since these often prevent the use of other, perhaps unexpectedly more significant methods on adjacent sections, I have omitted them here. Davenport discusses them to some extent.

Generally collodionization of paraffin sections (p. 85) should be employed when alkaline silver solutions are to be used. Frozen or loose celloidin or nitrocellulose sections should be handled with glass needles during the metal impregnation stages. Paraffin coated forceps [dipped in smoking hot (100–120°C) paraffin] may be used for handling tissue blocks.

GLIA CELLS AND GLIA TUMOR CELLS

General

Weil and Davenport (quoted from Conn and Darrow) prescribe 10% formalin fixation for several days and paraffin sections at 10 μ.

1. Deparaffinize sections and bring through 100% alcohol into a 1.5% celloidin solution in ether alcohol mixture for 2–3 minutes.
2. Drain partially and then hold horizontal face down with slight tilting movements, both lateral and longitudinal, until the remaining film congeals.
3. Then harden the film in 80% alcohol.
4. Impregnate 6–48 hours at 37°C in 8 gm silver nitrate dissolved in 10 cc distilled water and diluted with 90 cc 95% alcohol.
5. Rinse quickly in 95% alcohol.
6. Reduce in 5 gm pyrogallol, 5 cc 40% formaldehye and 95 cc 95% alcohol for about 1 minute, more or less according to desired intensity.
7. Wash thoroughly in running water.
8. Tone 5–10 minutes in 0.2% aqueous gold chloride solution.
9. Wash in distilled water.
10. Fix in 10% sodium thiosulfate (0.4 M) 1 minute.
11. Dehydrate with alcohols; dissolve the celloidin with 100% alcohol and ether, and clear in xylene. I suggest substitution of an acetone and xylene sequence; methanol also dissolves celloidin.

Results: Pathological glia, gray to black; axis cylinders, black or gray; background, gray violet.

Addition of 0.25–0.5 cc 1 N nitric acid (p. 672) to the silver bath may be required to inhibit staining of normal glia cells.

Weil and Davenport (*ibid.*) also cite a modification of *Stern's* diammine silver hydroxide method for *microglia* and *oligodendroglia*. Fixation in 10% formalin and celloidin sections at 15 μ are prescribed.

1. Wash sections in distilled water. If it is desired to increase the relative density of impregnation of oligodendroglia, add 0.5 cc 28% ammonia water to 100 cc distilled water and soak 3 minutes.

2. Impregnate 10–20 seconds; the longer intervals favor the impregnation of oligodendrocytes, in a diammine silver hydroxide prepared by adding 10% silver nitrate to 2 cc 28% ammonia water until a faint permanent opalescence is produced. This requires 18–20 cc. Dilute to 40 cc with distilled water. This solution is essentially identical with that used in Lillie's argentaffin technic (p. 535).

3. Transfer sections directly to fresh 15% formalin and agitate until deep brown. For oligodendrocytes use 10% formalin and commence agitation only after celloidin is blackened and section begins to turn brown.

4. Wash in tap water and dehydrate with 2 changes of isopropyl alcohol, clear in 1 change of a 50% mixture of isopropyl alcohol with xylene and 2 changes of xylene. Mount in balsam or synthetic resin. Introduction of gold toning at step 4 tends to prevent fading in xylene (Davenport).

Oligodendrocytes

The following methods are designed especially for oligodendrocytes but often impregnate microglia as well.

Del Río-Hortega's silver carbonate method, slightly altered from Conn and Darrow: Fix in Ramón y Cajal's formalin ammonium bromide (p. 38) for 12–48 hours.

1. Heat the block in fresh formalin ammonium bromide at 45–50°C for 10 minutes. Ramón y Cajal heated at 50–55°C.

2. Cut frozen sections at 15–20 μ.

3. Wash in 1:100 dilution of 28% ammonia water and then in distilled water.

4. Impregnate 1–5 minutes in an ammoniacal silver carbonate solution prepared as follows: To 5 cc 10% silver nitrate add 20 cc 5% sodium carbonate solution (a threefold excess) and then drop by drop add 28% ammonia water to barely dissolve the precipitate (about 0.4 cc should be required). Add about 20 cc distilled water and filter, bringing volume to 45 cc. Keep in a brown bottle.

5. Wash sections 15 seconds in distilled water.

6. Reduce 30 seconds in a 1:100 dilution of strong formalin (Davenport: 2–3 minutes).

7. Wash thoroughly in tap water.

8. Tone in 0.2% gold chloride until gray. Ramón y Cajal specified 10–15 minutes in cold (15°C?) solution; less time if solution is warmer.

9. Fix in 5–10% sodium thiosulfate (2–5 minutes). Ramón y Cajal specified 5%.

10. Wash thoroughly in tap water, float onto slides, blot down with filter paper, dehydrate and clear by a 100% alcohol xylene sequence, and mount in balsam or synthetic resin.

Results: With this method cytoplasm and processes of oligodendrocytes should be black; cell nuclei, unstained; and general background, gray. Since the exposure to the diammine silver carbonate is brief and at a lower temperature than in the same author's reticulum method and a considerably greater excess of sodium carbonate is present, reticulum should not be impregnated.

Longer fixation than that prescribed is said to make the impregnation less selective and to favor impregnation of astrocytes.

Penfield's variant (Conn and Darrow) of this method gives both oligodendrocytes and microglia. By increasing the volume of the silver solution above from 45 to 75 cc with distilled water and by taking out sections after 20, 45 and 120 seconds in the silver, the rest of the technic being the same, microglia and processes are black, other glia cells are dark gray to black and background is pale.

Astrocytes

Large protoplasmic astrocytes are often well demonstrated with azure eosin stains (pp. 160–163); and with Mallory's aniline blue (pp. 544–549) or his phosphotungstic acid hematoxylin (p. 537) both astrocytes and glia fibrils may be well shown. The classical method, however, is:

S. Ramón y Cajal's Gold Sublimate Method. The following technic follows Conn and Darrow for the most part.

Fix about 5 days (not less than 2 nor more than 25) in Ramón y Cajal's formalin ammonium bromide (p. 38). Cut frozen sections at 15–30 μ, and store in the same fixative.

1. Wash in 2 changes of distilled water.
2. Impregnate well-spread-out sections 3–4 hours in 5 cc 1% yellow or brown gold chloride, 5 cc 5% mercuric chloride and 30 cc distilled water. Ramón y Cajal used 5 cc 1% gold chloride, 4–5 gm mercuric chloride (saturated solution?) and 20–25 cc water. Temperatures around 25°C are preferable; 18–40°C is permissible. Check impregnation from time to time by examination of a wet section under the microscope. Astrocytes should appear dark with a relatively light background, and sections acquire an overall purple coloration. When impregnation is satisfactory,
3. Wash in distilled water and
4. Fix in 5–10% sodium thiosulfate solution ($Na_2S_2O_3 \cdot 5H_2O$) for 5–10 minutes. Ramón y Cajal preferred a saturated solution with an added 2% of a normal sodium bisulfite solution.

5. Wash thoroughly in several changes of tap water, float onto slides, blot down with filter paper, dehydrate with 100% alcohol and clear with xylene, blotting between changes. Mount in balsam or synthetic resin.

According to Globus (*Arch. Neurol. Psych.* **18**:263, 1937) material stored in formalin for a long time may be used if one soaks frozen sections 24 hours in a 10% dilution of 28% ammonia water, rinses twice in distilled water and then immerses for 2–4 hours in a 10% dilution of concentrated (40%) hydrobromic acid. Following this treatment rinse in 2 changes of a 1:2000 dilution of strong ammonia water, and proceed as above.

Achúcarro's Tannin Silver Method according to Del Río-Hortega, emended slightly from Conn and Darrow. Fix 10 days or more in 10% formalin (alkalinized to litmus with ammonia, according to Ramón y Cajal). Cut frozen sections (not over 10 μ: Ramón y Cajal).

1. Wash in distilled water.
2. 3% aqueous tannic acid at 50°C for 5 minutes. Ramón y Cajal used 10% tannin and cites Del Río-Hortega as using 3% tannin rather than tannic acid.
3. Wash in a 1% dilution of 28% ammonia water until sections become pliable.
4. Impregnate sections a few at a time in 3 changes of diammine silver hydroxide. The recommended solution is made by precipitating silver oxide from 30 cc 10% silver nitrate by the addition of 2 cc (40 drops) 40% sodium hydroxide drop by drop (a slight excess). The precipitate is then filtered out on hard filter paper and washed free of excess alkali with 10 or more washes of distilled water. (Ramón y Cajal omitted this filtration and washing.) Then transfer precipitate to a 250 cc flask with 50 cc distilled water and dissolve by adding 28% ammonia water drop by drop [2–2.38 cc; the latter is the theoretical quantity for $Ag(NH_3)_2OH$, presuming no loss of silver], avoiding any excess of ammonia and preferably leaving a few granules undissolved. Dilute to 150 cc with distilled water and store this stock solution in a brown glass bottle. For use, dilute 5 cc with 45 cc distilled water. (This would correspond to perhaps a 1:25 dilution of Lillie's diammine silver solution, (p. 240).

Sections become yellowish brown when sufficiently impregnated. The weak silver solution requires frequent renewal.
5. Wash in 3 changes of distilled water.
6. Tone 20 minutes at 40–45°C in 0.2% gold chloride solution.
7. Wash in water.
8. Fix in 5–10% sodium thiosulfate (for 2–5 minutes). (Ramón y Cajal specified 5%.)

9. Wash in (several changes of) water. Float onto slides and blot down. Dehydrate and clear with a 100% alcohol xylene sequence, blotting between changes to keep sections in place and to accelerate clearing. Mount in balsam or synthetic resin.

Results: Protoplasmic astrocytes should be dark gray to violet; fibrils, black; connective tissue, pale; other tissue elements, reddish to violet. This method is considered less selective than the gold sublimate method.

NERVE CELLS AND THEIR PROCESSES

Procedures which randomly select individual nerve cells and display them with all (or most of) their cell processes are generally derived from the chromate silver procedure introduced by Camillo Golgi in 1873–1878. They are of necessity block impregnation methods and have rather small use in pathology. Variants have been numerous. I have selected Fox's zinc chromate method for presentation here because it can be applied to the routinely formalin fixed material which is left over after gross sectioning and selection of blocks for regular histologic procedures have been done.

Fox's Zinc Chromate Golgi Technic for Nerve Cells and Their Processes:

1. Cut thin (2–5 mm) slices of brain which has been fixed in formalin 2 months to 2 years. Longer fixations, over 4 months, are preferable.
2. Soak blocks 2 days in zinc chromate 6 gm, 90% formic acid 4 cc, distilled water to make 100 cc. Davenport reduces the time to 18 hours at 25°C.
3. Blot free of excess chromate, agitate in 0.75% silver nitrate until all surfaces are deep red.
4. Pass a thread through each block and suspend in 0.75% $AgNO_3$, 2 changes, 24 hours each. Brush off silver chromate precipitate with camel's hair brush after each change.
5. Dehydrate with 2 changes each of 95% and absolute alcohol, 15 minutes each, clear in xylene 10 minutes and infiltrate 10 minutes in paraffin. Here the use of vacuum should give much better infiltration, but this has apparently not been tried, or perhaps thorough infiltration is not desired (see step 7).
6. Section entire block serially at 90–100 μ and store sections serially in 95% alcohol.
7. Dehydrate sections with absolute alcohol, several changes, clear with alcohol xylene and several changes of xylene, washing off loose silver chromate in the process. Mount on slides.
8. Coat the sections with several applications of Permount and let dry 5–7 days. Davenport omits step 7 and drys in Permount 3–7 days.

9. Moisten surface of Permount with toluene, apply coverglass and place slides in warm place for few hours with small lead weights on the coverglasses.

Results: Background, pale yellow; isolated cells and processes, black. Klatzo (*Lab. Invest.* 1:345, 1952) recommends a shorter Golgi variant for glia cells and processes.

1. Fix in fresh chloral hydrate formalin bichromate: 5 gm $K_2Cr_2O_7$ in 90 cc distilled water; add 10 cc formalin and then 3 gm chloral hydrate. For fibrillary astrocytes fix 18–48 hours; for protoplasmic astrocytes, 12–17 hours; for oligodendroglia, 18–24 hours; for microglia, 12–18 hours. At 24 hours, rinse blocks in 10% formalin and place in fresh fixing solution if a second day is required.
2. Wash rapidly in 3–4 changes of distilled water.
3. Pass blocks individually through 4 baths of 25 cc 1% silver nitrate, allowing about 2 minutes in each, handling with paraffin coated forceps.
4. Impregnate 18–24 hours in 1.5% silver nitrate.
5. Rinse in distilled water and brush off surface precipitate.
6. Cut frozen sections at 60–100 μ. Collect in 30% alcohol (2 changes).
7. Dehydrate in 95% alcohol and 100% alcohol, and clear in toluene. I suggest use of alcohol toluene mixtures to facilitate the clearing.
8. Float onto slides, blot, cover liberally with toluene Permount and apply coverglass.

NEUROFIBRILS, AXONS AND NERVE ENDINGS

These methods generally require special fixations or fresh tissue and hence are often not applicable in pathologic studies. Davenport's method and Foley's variant of Bodian's protargol method utilize material fixed in 10% formalin.

Davenport (*Arch. Neur. Psychiat.* 24:690–695, 1930) preferred nitrocellulose sections at 15–30 μ, but stated that paraffin sections could be used.

1. Celloidin or nitrocellulose sections are to be spread on slides and then immersed in 2% collodion and drained. Paraffin sections are to be passed through xylene and 100% alcohol into 2% collodion in ether alcohol mixture and drained.
2. When the collodion film has set, immerse in 80% alcohol for 5–10 minutes or as much longer as convenient.
3. Immerse sections in 10 gm silver nitrate, 0.5 cc 1 N nitric acid (p. 672), 10 cc distilled water and 90 cc 95% alcohol. Let stand until

sections are light brown at 37–40°C. Formalin fixed material usually requires about an hour. With other fixations longer intervals may be necessary. Avoid exposure to bright light.

4. Rinse in 95% alcohol.
5. Reduce in 5 gm pyrogallol, 5 cc strong formalin, 100 cc 95% alcohol, watching under the microscope. This may take as little as 2 minutes. The reduction may be slowed by adding more alcohol. To avoid precipitates, the preparation should be kept moving. Addition of 100 mg glucose in 0.5 cc water (0.125 cc corn syrup, 0.375 cc water) also aids in preventing precipitates. One 50 cc portion of reducer is sufficient for at least 20 slides.
6. Rinse in 2–3 changes of 95% alcohol, agitating constantly.
7. Dehydrate with 100% alcohol, remove collodion with ether + 100% alcohol mixture, clear in xylene and mount in balsam.

Results: Nerve cells, yellow to brown; fibers, dark brown to black.

For demonstration of peripheral nerve endings in frozen sections the following variant of the **Bielschowski-Gros method** appears useful (Garven and Gairns, *Quart. J. Exp. Physiol.* 37:134, 1952; Davenport, p. 252). It is probable that material fixed routinely in sodium acetate formalin or phosphate buffered formalin can be used, but Davenport prescribes a $MgCO_3$ formalin.

Shake 25–30 cc formalin with 1–2 gm $MgCO_3$, filter off 24 cc and dilute to 200 with distilled water. Fix blocks 5–7 mm thick in 3 daily changes of this 12% formalin.

1. Wash blocks 5 minutes in running water. Cut frozen sections at 15 μ. Wash sections individually in 3–4 changes of distilled water, 5–10 seconds each.
2. Float sections individually on 25% silver nitrate, in small, flat staining dishes, spreading well with glass needles to avoid wrinkles. Cover with tin can or cardboard box to exclude light and let stand 10–120 minutes, inspecting periodically for darkening to a shade of brownish yellow which must be learned by experience. On first trial of this method, inspect at 10 minute intervals up to 2 hours, taking out 1–2 sections each time after some color change appears.
3. Wash in 4 changes of formalin diluted to 20% with distilled water containing 1 mg NaCl to each 200 cc. Davenport suggests 5, 10, 20 and 60 seconds duration for the 4 baths. No AgCl cloud should form around the section in the last bath.
4. Treat with ammoniacal silver solution, watching under microscope for proper blackening of nerve fibers.

To 5 cc 20% silver nitrate add 28% ammonia (sp. gr. 0.890–0.900) drop by drop until only 1 or 2 black granules of silver oxide remain.

Use 1 cc of this solution for each section, picked up on a slide, adding 1 drop 28% ammonia to each 1 cc.

5. When impregnation is adequately developed, transfer section to a 20% dilution of 28% ammonia to stop the impregnation.
6. Rinse in distilled water and tone 2–10 minutes in 0.2% gold chloride, if desired.
7. Dehydrate, clear and mount in Permount or cellulose tricaprate.

Bodian Copper Protargol Method, Foley's variant (*Stain Techn.* 18: 27, 1943). Dehydrate and infiltrate with celloidin or low viscosity nitrocellulose as usual, and section at 15–25 μ; or infiltrate 24 hours at 58°C in 5% agar and cut frozen sections at 20–40 μ.

1. Soak 24 hours in 1 cc 28% ammonia and 99 cc 50% alcohol.
2. Drain and place in 1% protargol (silver albumose) in distilled water for 6–8 hours at 37°C. In the protargol solution, but not in contact with the sections, place a 200–300 mg piece of 0.002 in. (50 μ) electrolytic copper foil which has been thinly coated with collodion. Use no metallic instruments.
3. Drain and transfer sections to a mixture of 50 cc 1% aqueous protargol, 50 cc 95% alcohol and 0.5 cc pyridine (0.1–2 cc: higher quantities of pyridine accentuate impregnation of thin fibers; lower quantities accentuate that of cell bodies and dendrites). Put in another piece of copper foil, very thinly coated with collodion. Incubate 24–48 hours at 37°C.
4. Rinse 5 seconds in 50% alcohol.
5. Reduce 10 minutes in the following reducer: Dissolve 1.4 gm boric acid in 85 cc distilled water; then add and dissolve 2 gm anhydrous sodium sulfite; then add and dissolve 0.3 gm hydroquinone; then add 15 cc C. P. acetone and mix well.
6. Wash in several changes of distilled water.
7. Tone 10 minutes in 0.2% gold chloride in about 0.3% acetic acid (20 drops of glacial acetic acid to 100 cc).
8. Wash in several changes of distilled water.
9. Reduce 1–3 minutes in 2% aqueous oxalic acid solution.
10. Rinse in distilled water.
11. Fix 3–5 minutes in 5% sodium thiosulfate (0.2 M) solution.
12. Wash in distilled water.
13. Stain 18–24 hours in Einarson's chrome alum gallocyanine (p. 178).
14. Wash thoroughly in distilled water.
15. Mordant 30 minutes in 5% aqueous phosphotungstic acid and
16. Transfer directly to the following stain: Aniline blue 10 mg, fast green FCF 500 mg, orange G 2 gm, glacial acetic acid 8 cc, distilled water to make 250 cc. (I fail to see the function of the minute amount of aniline blue.) Stain 1 hour.

17. Dehydrate and differentiate with 70–95% alcohol.
18. Complete dehydration with normal butyl alcohol and clear in cedar oil. (Or use the isopropyl alcohol xylene sequence for dehydration and clearing.)

Results: Nerve fibers, neurofibrils, blue black; nuclei, variable—blue black if high pyridine concentration was used; tigroid, light blue; collagen, blue to green; myelin, yellow.

The essential part of the foregoing method is comprised in steps 1–12. The counterstains can well be varied according to taste, as with other silver methods where gold toning and thiosulfate fixation are employed. For instance, an acid picrofuchsin stain, giving red collagen and yellow cytoplasm, might well provide better contrast between collagen and nerve fibers than the blue green prescribed.

Romanes (*J. Anat.* 84:104, 1950) recommends a very dilute silver chloride ammonia procedure for staining nerve fibers in paraffin sections. Fix in alcohol, Bouin's fluid, Carnoy's fluid, acetic alcohol or acetic alcohol formalin. Treat blocks for a few hours in 2 cc "0.880 ammonia" (35.3%) in 98 cc 70% alcohol (= 2.5 cc 28% NH_3 + 97.5 cc 70% alcohol). Decalcify if necessary, dehydrate, clear and imbed in paraffin. Section and attach to slides with albumin fixative. Deparaffinize and hydrate as usual. The following directions are as emended by Powers (*J. Dent. Res.* 31:383, 1952; and in letters).

1. Incubate at 58°C for 16 hours in the dark in a fresh ammoniacal silver chloride. Mix with 2.9 cc 0.1% silver nitrate with 100 cc distilled water, add 1 cc 0.1% sodium chloride and adjust to pH 7.8 with 0.7 cc of a 1% dilution of 28% ammonia water. This fluid does not keep.
2. Drain and transfer without washing to 1% hydroquinone in 10% sodium sulfite (crystals, $Na_2SO_3 \cdot 7H_2O$ or 5% of the anhydrous salt) for 5 minutes at 20°C.
3. Wash well in running water, and rinse in distilled water.
4. Tone in 0.5% gold chloride for 2 minutes or (Powers) 0.2% for 10 minutes. Wash 1 minute in 2 changes of distilled water. Reduce not more than 3 minutes in 2% oxalic acid. Wash in running water. Fix 3–5 minutes in 5% sodium thiosulfate. Dehydrate, clear and mount in unsaturated synthetic resin or balsam.

Results: Nerve fibers, purple to black; nuclei, red; neurofibrils, purple; keratin, yellow; bone cells, black. Raising the pH to 8.3 and introducing 5 gm fine copper wire gives black nerve fibers throughout. Powers replaces this step by premordanting 18 hours at 37°C in 0.5% cupric nitrate [*ca.* 24 *mM* $Cu(NO_3)_2 \cdot 3H_2O$].

Powers (*loc. cit.*) recommends use of both Romanes and Ungewitter silver variants for the demonstration of nerve fibers in dentine. For the Romanes method she prefers fixation for 1–3 days in 10% formalin containing 10% chloral hydrate; for the Ungewitter method 3 or more days' fixation in a Bouin fluid containing 1 gm trichloroacetic acid, 75 cc saturated aqueous picric acid and 25 cc 40% formaldehyde (w/v).

After either fixation, wash 16–24 hours in running water, decalcify in the Evans-Krajian formic acid citrate mixture (p. 633) or in 5% trichloroacetic acid in 50% alcohol. Wash 24 hours in running water, dehydrate in successive 24 hour changes of 30%, 50% and 70% ethyl alcohol, in a mixture of 95% alcohol and *n*-butanol, and finally in two 24 hour changes of *n*-butanol. Infiltrate 12–24 hours in hard paraffin (56–58°C melting point), imbed and section serially at 10–15 μ.

For the Romanes procedure, deparaffinize, hydrate and mordant 18 hours at 37°C in 0.5% cupric nitrate [crystals, $Cu(NO_3)_2 \cdot 3H_2O$, *ca.* 20 *mM*]. Wash in 4 changes of distilled water, and carry through the Romanes-Powers procedure (above). The copper mordanting reduces the amount of background staining and obviates the need for the copper wire in the silver solution.

For the Ungewitter method, deparaffinize and bring to 80% alcohol. Transfer directly to cold 1% aqueous silver nitrate containing 20–30% urea and 1–3 drops (0.1 cc) per 100 cc of a 1% picric acid, 1% mercuric cyanide solution. Incubate in a paraffin oven for 60–90 minutes. Rinse quickly in 2 changes of distilled water and reduce 3–5 minutes in a urea hydroquinone solution containing 1–2 gm hydroquinone, 20–30 gm urea, and 10 gm anhydrous sodium sulfite in 100 cc distilled water, agitating gently for the first 2 minutes. Wash in 5 changes of distilled water and examine microscopically in 80% alcohol. If not adequately silvered, repeat silvering and reduction as before. Finally dehydrate, clear and mount.

The **Nonidez method** (*Am. J. Anat.* 65:361, 1939) is highly recommended by Davenport, Windle and Rhines in Conn and Darrow:

1. Fix 1–3 days in 25 gm chloral hydrate in 100 cc 50% alcohol.
2. Drain and blot and place in ammoniated alcohol (95% alcohol 30 cc, 28% ammonia water 0.1 cc or 2 drops) for 24 hours, changing once or more if there is much fat.
3. Distilled water 5 minutes.
4. 2% silver nitrate (aqueous) at 37°C for 5–6 days, changing after 1–2 days or sooner if the solution becomes yellowish brown.
5. Wash 2–3 minutes in distilled water.
6. Reduce 24 hours in pyrogallol 2.5–3.0 gm, 40% formaldehyde 8 cc, distilled water 100 cc.
7. Wash in 6 changes 20–30 minutes each of distilled water. Imbed, section and mount.

Nonidez prescribed graded alcohols, amyl acetate clearing and paraffin imbedding. Other methods can undoubtedly be used. This method is used for nerve endings, both peripheral and central, and for neurofibrils and axis cylinders generally. They appear in shades of brown.

Nauta and Gygax (*Stain Techn.* **26**:5, 1951), observing that increasing amounts of NaOH in ammonia silver nitrate mixtures increase the sensitivity and decrease the selectivity of silver impregnation, explored the effect of varying mixtures on impregnation of degenerating axons.

For axon degenerations in the rat brain they recommend the following modification of the Glees method.

Bielschowsky-Glees Method for Degenerating Axons (Nauta and Gygax).

1. Fix in neutral 10% formalin for 14 days to 6 months.
2. Cut frozen sections at 15–20 μ.
3. Soak sections 6–12 hours or more in 50% alcohol containing 1% of 25% ammonia water. Handle sections only with glass rod from steps 3–10.
4. Wash in 3 changes of distilled water.
5. Soak 24 hours in 1.5% silver nitrate solution in 5% aqueous pyridine solution (a 10 cc lot is adequate). Transfer directly to step 6.
6. Impregnate 2–5 minutes in a covered vessel in diammine silver: $AgNO_3$ 490 mg in 20 cc distilled water + 10 cc 95% alcohol. Let cool and add 2 cc 27–28% ammonia water and 1.5 cc 1 N NaOH. (Emended slightly for American reagents.)
7. Transfer directly to a mixture of 45 cc 10% alcohol, 2 cc 10% unbuffered formalin and 1.5 cc 1% aqueous citric acid (crystals) solution. The sections spread on the surface and turn golden brown rapidly.
8. Fix 1–2 minutes in 2.5% sodium thiosulfate.
9. Wash in 3–5 changes of fresh distilled water.
10. Dehydrate with graded alcohols, clear with xylene, mount in synthetic resin—Caedax, Depex, polystyrene, etc.

The Glees Method for Axons in Paraffin Sections (Marsland, Glees and Erikson, *J. Neuropath. Exp. Neurol.* **13**:587, 1954).

1. Fix in 10% formalin or formalin saline, dehydrate in alcohols, clear in xylene and imbed in paraffin. Section at 6–8 μ.
2. Deparaffinize in xylene, bring through 100% alcohol.
3. Collodionize 1 minute in 0.5% celloidin, drain off most of celloidin and allow surface to *gel* but not *dry*.

4. Immerse 1 minute in 70% alcohol.
5. Wash in distilled water.
6. Incubate 15–30 minutes in 20% silver nitrate at 37°C in incubator, until the section turns amber.
7. Wash off directly with 10 % formalin in tap water from dropper bottle until solution comes off clean. Flood with formalin for another 10–15 seconds, until a fine white precipitate rises to the surface. The section should now be yellow.
8. Wash off directly with the Glees ammonia silver solution. Flood with ammonia silver and let stand 30 seconds. *Glees Ammonia Silver Solution.* Mix 30 cc 20% aqueous silver nitrate solution and 20 cc 95% alcohol. Add concentrated (28%) ammonia water drop by drop until precipitate just dissolves and add 3–4 more drops of ammonia (use dropper bottle).
9. Drain and wash off with 10% formalin (tap water) for 1 or more minutes. The section becomes brownish yellow, the solution turns black. Check impregnation microscopically. If section is underimpregnated repeat steps 8 and 9 using shorter intervals in each.
10. Wash in distilled water, fix 30–60 seconds in 5% sodium thiosulfate and wash 10 minutes in running water.
11. Dehydrate, clear and mount by alcohol, xylene, balsam sequence.

Results: Axons and degenerate boutons terminaux are in black. For intracellular and intraaxon detail, reduce concentration of formalin and silver solutions.

Proceeding from studies on acid phosphatase (*J. Neurophysiol.* **9**:121, 1946), Lassek evolved a method (*Stain Techn.* **22**:133, 1947) for the demonstration of normal axons in myelinated tracts (letter, March 29, 1951).

Brain tissue fixed in 10% formalin for 2–3 days may be used.

Lassek's Lead Method for Axons.

1. Imbed in paraffin, section and hydrate section as usual.
2. Immerse in buffered lead nitrate at 37°C for 1–96 hours.

Molar acetate buffer pH 4.7	5 cc
5% aqueous lead nitrate solution	2 cc
Distilled water	36 cc
At time of using add 50 mg ascorbic acid.	

3. Wash in distilled water.
4. Immerse in H_2S water or in 1% ammonium sulfide for 1–5 minutes.
5. Wash in water, counterstain as desired; 0.1% safranin or thionin in 0.1% acetic acid for 5 minutes is suggested. Rinse in 1% acetic acid.

6. Dehydrate, clear and mount in balsam through alcohol xylene sequence. Axons should appear in brown.

Methenamine Silver. In the use of the Burtner argentaffin cell variant (p. 240) for the study of nerve cell pigments I have seen in oversilvered preparations excellent demonstration of axons, along with generally blackened nerve cell bodies. This occurs with formalin material after about 3–3½ hours' incubation at 60°C or in about a half hour less in material chromated before imbedding.

Prior methylation of formalin fixed material greatly accelerates the silvering of axons. I have seen excellent, perfectly black axons and brown to black tigroid substance after a 24 hour methylation at 60°C in anhydrous methanol containing 0.1 N hydrochloric acid. The silvering period in the same Gomori methenamine silver solution as above should be 1½–2½ hours at 60°C. This methylation completely inhibits the usual safranin counterstain, as it does all other basic aniline dye stains. If any counterstain is desired, it would be necessary to use the Feulgen procedure or alum hematoxylin for nuclei, since these nulcear stains are not prevented by methylation.

Ranvier's Method. The classical method for **motor end plates** and other **peripheral nerve endings** is that of Ranvier. I have had some excellent preparations and some utter failures in a rather brief experience with this method. Carey has used this method with quite consistent success, and I quote here his variant. (*Am. J. Path.*, 18:237–289, esp. 242, 1942):

Ranvier's Gold Chloride Method for Peripheral Nerve Endings (Carey).

1. Cut tissue (muscle) in 3–5 mm slices and immerse in filtered fresh lemon juice for 10–15 minutes (they become transparent in 5–10 minutes, according to Ranvier), handling tissues with glass or paraffin coated instruments.
2. Pour off lemon juice and add 1% gold chloride (HAuCl$_4$) without rinsing. (Ranvier rinsed in water.) Let stand 10–60 minutes until a uniform golden yellow tone is reached, not *brown*. (Ranvier gave 20 minutes' immersion and then washed in water.)
3. Transfer directly to a 25% dilution of concentrated (90%) formic acid and reduce in the dark for 8–12 hours (Ranvier used 20% for 1 day).
4. Wash in water and store in a 50:50 mixture of C. P. neutral glycerol and 50% alcohol.
5. Snip out a small fragment and tease gently in glycerol or crush out under a coverglass. Mount in glycerol sealed with cellulose caprate or in glycerol gelatin.

Results: Nerve fibers and endings appear black; other tissues, in varying shades of red, purple and violet.

Other writers have used a 20% dilution of formic acid in distilled water in place of the lemon juice, and reduced in a fresh portion of the same fluid for 24 hours. Tissues after spreading can be dehydrated, cleared and mounted in balsam or synthetic resin. I have tried formic, acetic and citric acids, and the last seems to give the cleanest impregnations. With these, 30–60 minutes in the gold chloride seems to be necessary. I have used Apáthy's syrup for mounting these preparations.

Various attempts have been made to apply this method to material previously fixed in formalin, but with poor success.

Peters's Protein Silver for Nerve Fibers. Peters (*Stain Techn.* 33:47, 1958) gives methods for nerve fiber impregnation said to be applicable to routine paraffin sections of material fixed in aqueous formalin, acetic alcohol formalin, Bouin's or Huber's fluid (omit usual iodine treatment of sections), p. 47. These methods avoid the inconstancies of manufactured silver proteinates by the direct use of proteins with silver nitrate.

1. Attach paraffin sections with albumen fixative, dry, deparaffinize and hydrate through xylene and graded alcohols as usual.
2. Impregnate sections 16–24 hours at 37°C or 56°C in the dark in albumen silver or casein silver, made as follows: Dissolve 300 mg dried egg albumen or casein by sprinkling powder onto surface of 60 cc distilled water. Filter through Whatman No. 1 paper. To 50 cc filtrate add 1.8 cc 2% silver nitrate and adjust to pH 8.2–8.5 by adding drop by drop a 5% dilution of 28% ammonia (instead one may use a boric acid sodium borate buffer of pH 8.2 or 8.5 as the solvent for the albumen or casein). This amount of silver solution suffices for 5 slides only.
3. Wash slides in 2–3 changes of distilled water.
4. Develop in 1% hydroquinone in 10% sodium sulfite (Na_2SO_3) for 5–10 minutes.
5. Wash 10 minutes in running tap water.
6. Wash in distilled water and tone 10 minutes in 0.2% gold chloride.
7. Rinse in distilled water and reduce 10 minutes in 2% oxalic acid.
8. Wash 5 minutes in running water.
9. Fix 10 minutes in 5% sodium thiosulfate (0.2 M).
10. Wash 10 minutes in running water.
11. Dehydrate in graded alcohols, clear in alcohol xylene and 2–3 changes of xylene. Mount in synthetic resin.

For embryonic tissue increase 2% silver nitrate to 2.5 cc; in adult tissue greater intensity is attained with 2 cc. With casein silver use only 1 cc 2% silver nitrate.

The borate buffer may be replaced by 0.2% ammonium hydrogen tetra-borate ($NH_4HB_4O_7 \cdot 3H_2O$).

Impregnation time may be prolonged to 48 hours without harm.

For the method of Rogers, Pappenheimer and Goetsch (*J. Exp. Med.* **54:**167, 1931), see the second edition of this book, p. 417, or the original reference.

Ehrlich's Supravital Methylene Blue Method. This is the other classical method for study of peripheral nerve endings. I have had no personal experience with this method, but have relied largely on Romeis, Lee and Mallory for the following. The solution should be made from medicinal, zinc free methylene blue. The dye should be dissolved in 0.9% sodium chloride of C.P. grade (0.6% for amphibia), not in Ringer's or Locke's or similar fluids, as these produce precipitates. The methylene blue is introduced into the tissues by intravascular perfusion, by instillation into body cavities, by injection into loose connective tissues or simply by immersion of small fragments. Within the tissues the methylene blue is reduced to leucomethylene blue and then reoxidized by atmospheric oxygen. Tissues must be taken as soon after cessation of circulation as possible. Human autopsy tissues are ordinarily not usable. Blood must first be washed out with saline solution before the perfusion methods are used, though some workers use an intravital perfusion in living animals. The strength of methylene blue solution varies between 0.5 and 0.06%.

For perfusion and injection technics use about 0.2% methylene blue at 37°C, and perfuse with sufficient volume to replace the salt solution used to wash out the blood; or inject with enough to distend the tissues moderately. After 30 minutes remove the tissues to be studied and place on glass wool moistened with 0.06–0.1% methylene blue in a loosely covered container in a 37°C incubator. Tissue should be taken in small fragments or thin slices. Leave in the incubator until tissues become bluish—perhaps 15–120 minutes.

For the immersion technic immerse thin slices or small fragments of tissue in 0.1–0.25% methylene blue at 37°C. Romeis prefers to lay them on glass wool moistened with 0.05–0.1% methylene blue and to drip onto the surface of the fragments (which may measure 5–20 mm in thickness) a 0.1–0.25% dye solution to flood the surface. Keep the preparations at 37°C for 1–2 hours, observing under low magnification from time to time until nerves are stained blue.

Sectioning and Fixation. After staining by the variants above has reached its optimum, Romeis prescribes cutting fresh sections with a razor and immediate study; or fixation with ammonium molybdate according to Dogiel—a freshly prepared 5–8% solution, which is to be filtered if not clear. Thin membranes are adequately fixed in 30–60 minutes. Thicker tissue sections may require up to 24 hours. This requires 50–100 volumes of solution. Then wash 1–6 hours in several changes of water according to size and thickness. Preparations are to be dehydrated rapidly in several changes of 95% and 100% alcohol during a total period of 10 minutes to 2 hours—again according to thickness. Alcohol tends to extract the stain. Clear in terpineol, changing once. Wash out in xylene and mount in balsam (or Permount).

Romeis also suggests the preparation of thick frozen sections after washing out the ammonium molybdate, with or without gelatin imbedding. Paraffin imbedding extracts the color badly.

Dogiel also proposed a fixation in saturated aqueous ammonium picrate solution (p. 123) for 2–24 hours, followed by mounting in equal volumes of glycerol and ammonium picrate solution.

Schabadasch (Z. Zellforsch. **10**:221–385, 1930) proposed addition of 50–700 mg resorcinol (or in some instances p-aminophenol) per liter of methylene blue, and buffering of the methylene blue solution with phosphates to various pH levels ranging from 5.7 for colon to 7.2 for isolated nerve. The methylene blue concentrations ranged from 150–350 mg per liter for the most part. He fixed in a mixture of ammonium iodide or ammonium thiocyanate ("rhodanid") in ammonium picrate. The latter is to be impure and contaminated with enough "ammonium picraminicum" (picramate?) so that the crystals are large, orange needles, not the fine, yellow needles of the pure salt. Either a 2.11% solution of ammonium iodide or a 1.12% solution of ammonium thiocyanate is saturated with this ammonium picrate at 60°C, and then allowed to stand several days at 15–20°C. One fixes the stained preparations 3–6 hours at 35°C and mounts directly in a mixture of equal volumes of C.P. glycerol saturated with ammonium picrate and of 10% gelatin solution. Thicker pieces may require preliminary clearing in saturated ammonium picrate glycerol.

Apáthy uses his gum syrup as a mounting medium for crushed or spread whole mounts.

Bethe proposes fixation in 5% ammonium molybdate containing either 0.25% osmium tetroxide or 1% chromic anhydride (CrO_3). In either case add 1 drop (0.05 cc) of concentrated hydrochloric acid to 20 cc of the fixative. Fix 4–12 hours in the osmium tetroxide variant, 45–60 minutes in the chromic; then wash, dehydrate quickly in alcohols, clear in benzene and imbed in paraffin; or clear in xylene for direct mounting in balsam or Permount (cited from Romeis).

The acetylcholinesterase methods (pp. 34–349) are also much used now for the study of nerve endings.

Liang's Sulfurous Acid Leucofuchsin Method. H. M. Liang's (*Anat. Rec.* **97**:419, 1947 [Proceedings]) method utilizing Schiff reagent to demonstrate nerve endings is interesting but requires further study as to its significance.

Liang prescribed 1 hour fixation in 1% acetic or formic acid, followed by 2 rinses in sulfurous acid of unspecified strength and 1–3 hours' immersion in Schiff reagent (p. 270) until nerves are deep purple. He then washed in several changes of sulfurous acid, rinsed with distilled water, counterstained 15 minutes in 1% aqueous methyl green solution, dehydrated, cleared and mounted as whole mounts. Or after the washing following the second sulfurous acid bath, he dehydrated, cleared and imbedded in paraffin, sectioned, brought sections to water, stained 5 minutes in 1% methyl green, dehydrated quickly with alcohols, cleared and mounted.

For the paraffin sections, an acid hemalum or iron hematoxylin picric acid counterstain can be used and renders other structures more visible. Elastic tissue of blood vessels sometimes stains red purple by this method, and myelin shows red purple vacuolation figures around the solid red purple axon.

RETINA

Apparently 3 lipid substances are demonstrable (Lillie, *Anat. Rec.* 112:477, 1952) in the rods and cones. One is relatively insoluble, is located in the acromeres, is apparently partly protein bound and is preserved in paraffin sections even after some partly alcoholic fixations; but it is removed by alcohol ether and alcohol chloroform extraction from fresh unfixed tissue. It is best demonstrated by the periodic acid Schiff reaction after various aqueous fixations. It retains iron hematoxylin poorly in myelin type technics (pp. 471, 489), and retains it best after formalin bichromate sequence fixations; and may be demonstrated with oil soluble dyes in Ciaccio type technics (p. 480). It was thought that this lipid might be kerasin.

The second lipid substance, also located in acromeres, required aqueous formaldehyde or bichromate fixations for its preservation in paraffin sections, and was best demonstrated by peracetic acid or performic acid Schiff technics after formalin bichromate sequence fixations. Conditions which produce Kolmer's droplets give also fine droplets between the rod acromeres which are performic acid Schiff positive. It is probably largely responsible for the positive myelin stains which are obtained after formalin bichromate combination or sequence fixations. It is assumed that this lipid also stains with fat stains in paraffin sections. That it is not identical with the periodic acid Schiff positive material is indicated by its presence in Kolmer's droplets and by its loss from sections first fixed in lead or mercury salts without chromates or formaldehyde and then dehydrated and imbedded by an alcohol-gasoline-paraffin sequence. This lipid is perhaps an unsaturated fatty acid lecithin.

The third lipid is demonstrated by oil soluble dyes and by iron hematoxylin methods after aqueous formaldehyde or chromate fixations, but not by the periodic, performic or peracetic acid Schiff methods. It is localized in the ellipsoids and is associated with a strongly eosinophilic (p. 162, 543) basic protein, which is especially well shown after Carnoy and alcoholic formalin fixations.

Glycogen is demonstrated in the retina by the periodic acid Schiff method, removed by diastase digestion and localized chiefly in the myoid segments of rods and cones and in the zones of synapsis. Sometimes entire granule cells seem to be outlined by heavy glycogen deposits.

Myelin seems more difficult to demonstrate in the nerve fiber layer of the retina than in the optic nerve or in the small oculomotor branches seen outside the bulb. It reacts with the performic acid Schiff as well as with hematoxylin methods and oil soluble dyes.

For the demonstration of Kolmer's droplets the preferably dark adapted retina should be fixed 12–24 hours in Held's fluid. This is a vague mixture composed of 4 volumes each of saturated aqueous potassium bichromate solution and of 10% formalin, with the addition of 1 volume of glacial acetic acid. By increasing the amount of acetic acid, droplets can be shown in relation to cones as well as to rods. After fixation, the tissues are washed overnight in running water, dehydrated through alcohols and imbedded in paraffin, not celloidin. Staining is done with an iron hematoxylin procedure of the Heidenhain type, and preparations are differentiated, according to Kolmer, to the point where rod acromeres become colorless. At this point ellipsoids as well as the Kolmer droplets should still be rather darkly stained. According to Walls (*Anat. Rec.* **73:** 373, 1939) these lipid droplets are artifactual, produced by high concentrations of acetic acid from acromere and pigment epithelial substances and oxidized to an insoluble state by chromation.

For the demonstration of rhodopsin (visual purple) fix retina in 2.5% platinic chloride solution for 12–24 hours (Romeis), dehydrate in alcohols and imbed in paraffin as usual. The rod acromeres are colored an intense orange. This is essentially the method of Stern (*Arch. Ophth.* **61:**561, 1905), who prescribed the use of animals dark adapted for at least 2 hours and the use of red light only, during dissection, blocking and fixation.

Lipid Droplets in Human Retinal Pigment Epithelium. Ciaccio positive lipid (p. 480) is almost regularly demonstrable with Sudan black B in routine paraffin section of formalin fixed surgical specimens removed for a wide variety of conditions, as well as in normal eyes. Only in retinal detachments with atrophy and of considerable apparent duration and in phthisis bulbi have I noted pronounced diminution or absence of the lipid.

According to Streeten (*Arch. Ophth.* **66:**391, 1961) these droplets first appear in children about 16 months of age and gradually increase in number. They vary in size from barely visible to 0.5 μ or more. Faint staining with Sudan IV and oil red O is recorded; staining is rapid and intense with Sudan black B. The Sudan black may be extracted with acetone or alcohol and the preparations restained with little or no loss of intensity, even after repeated decolorization and restaining. Schultz cholesterol reactions are negative; Baker's acid hematein test is essentially negative, as was the Luxol fast blue myelin stain. With Nile blue the granules stain violet, or more reddish in older eyes, and a purer blue after permanganate bleaching of pigment.

The lipid is slowly extracted by hot methanol ether, after formalin fixation, but no data are available about solubility on primary alcoholic-fixations. The direct Schiff reaction was negative even in 48 hours, but peracetic and performic acids, though not periodic acid, engendered a definitely positive Schiff reaction (purple). The lipid is not acid fast. Methenamine silver and ferric ferricyanide are not reduced by the lipid, though the pigment reacts.

I have noted lipid droplets up to 4–5 times the diameter of the retinal fuscin granules and in one series of cases found the lipid still strongly stainable with Sudan black after a 24 hour extraction in pyridine at 60°C.

It is of interest also that Sudan black demonstrates quite well in paraffin sections of formalin fixed eyes the lipid in the more or less numerous macrophages which appear in and near the nerve head in chronic glaucoma.

Other Ocular Structures

The vitreous humor contains a webwork of coagulum staining red by the periodic acid Schiff procedure and blue by the allochrome method. It colors blue with spirit blue in the Ciaccio type method using this dye (p. 480) but not with Sudan black B. It does not stain with basic thiazin dyes, either ortho- or metachromatically. It sometimes colors blue by the Lillie-Mowry ferric mannitol method (p. 204). Its staining is not evidently affected by bovine hyaluronidase chondromucinase preparations (p. 515).

The suspensory ligament of the lens merges into this vitreous web in periodic acid Schiff preparations, but, like lens capsule and Descemet's membrane, remains red in allochrome preparations.

Corneal connective tissue differs from that of the sclera and various ocular areolar tissues in its metachromasia to thionin, which may be demonstrable after lead nitrate or mercuric chloride fixatives (pp. 44–52), and in its pure deeper red color with periodic acid Schiff procedures when a picric acid counterstain is used.

Under polarized light corneal and scleral collagen are strongly birefringent; lens capsule is moderately so and requires rotation for its demonstration; lens fibers are scarcely visible.

Conjunctival epithelium may show quite pronounced alkaline phosphatase activity (p. 317) as well as moderate amounts of glycogen and some melanin. The conjunctival goblet cell mucin is rather weakly stained by metachromatic dyes and alcian blue (pp. 507, 509); it is stained quite well by HIO_4 and CrO_3 Schiff procedures (pp. 198, 199).

The allochrome method (p. 549) often fails to distinguish a distinct red basement membrane, though one is often shown under the corneal epithelium and the retinal pigment epithelium over choroid and ciliary.

Ocular pigments are considered on pp. 422–427.

Chapter 18

Hard Tissues, Decalcification

Bones, teeth and other calcified tissues are sometimes studied by the preparation of ground sections of the macerated specimen (p. 634), but usually the removal of most of the calcium salts is required to permit the preparation of sections thin enough for the study of cellular detail.

Adequate fixation of hard bone is facilitated by sawing thin slices with a fine toothed bone saw or hacksaw. This procedure produces a narrow zone of mechanical distortion adjacent to the saw cut. Mallory discarded the first half dozen sections; I have preferred to slice off this zone with a razor blade after decalcification and then section from the fresh cut surface. Making such a cut through the center of a block further serves as an adequate test of completion of decalcification.

When the marrow of the cancellous bone is the primary objective of study, time may be saved and the acid damage to marrow cells reduced by cutting off the cortical bone as soon as the cancellous portion is soft enough.

Fixatives for bone and marrow should be chosen with the primary objective of study in mind, and are much the same as for soft tissues. Chromate fixatives such as Orth's, Kose's and Möller's potassium bichromate formalin mixtures (p. 53) and formalin Zenker variants such as the Spuler-Maximow fluid (p. 49) are preferred by many for the study of marrow cells. They render the nucleic acids less susceptible to hydrolysis either by ribonuclease or by acids (pp. 143–148) and engender moderate resistance even to normal hydrochloric or nitric acid.

When preservation of iron bearing pigments is important, and for routine diagnostic purposes, formalin is the fixative of choice. The calcium phosphate of the bone substance serves as a fully adequate buffer to keep the pH level of the fixative probably above 6 within the tissue. If the action of the formaldehyde is not prolonged beyond the 2–3 days recommended for adequate fixation, nucleic acids are left quite susceptible to ribonuclease digestion or hydrolysis by mineral acids. Hence formalin fixed bone is preferably decalcified with 1 N acetic or formic acid or with buffer mixtures of pH 2 or higher.

For general diagnostic purposes, 5–7.5% nitric acid has been found effective over many years of trial. Recently the 8% hydrochloric, 10% formic acid fluid of Richman, Gelfand and Hill (*Arch. Path.* 44:92, 1947) has had considerable vogue (p. 633). This fluid is 1 *N* HCl containing 2.4 *N* HCOOH. It is a quite active and effective decalcifying agent. It will decalcify 1–2 gm pieces of compact bone in 12–24 hours at 24°C and in 6–8 hours at 37°C.

The effect of the electrolytic bath recommended by these authors for use with this fluid seems to be purely that of the heat produced by the passage of the current, since equally rapid decalcification occurs with external heating to the same temperature or in bones suspended in the electrolyte at the maximum possible distance from either electrode.

Decalcification at 55–60°C is hazardous. Loss of calcium salts occurs rapidly and is followed promptly by swelling and hydrolysis of the bone matrix collagen, which soon results in complete digestion. This occurs in as little as 24 hours in the 8% hydrochloric, 10% formic acid mixture and in 2–3 days in 5% formic acid.

Decalcification at 37°C impairs alum hematoxylin staining and Weigert's iron hematoxylin staining of nuclei to some extent. Eosin stains of cytoplasm are well preserved. Feulgen staining of nuclei is unsuccessful, and azure eosin stains give pink cytoplasms and nuclei. Both the formic hydrochloric mixture and 5% formic acid produce these results. The latter also impairs Van Gieson and Masson staining of collagen and bone matrix. Mineral acid decalcification is 2–3 times faster at 37°C than at 20°C; formic acid is actually somewhat slower.

With decalcification at 15–25°C, either in mineral acids or in formic acid or in mixtures of formic and hydrochloric acids, satisfactory hematoxylin eosin, Van Gieson, Masson and azure eosin stains may be obtained, if exposure to the mineral acids is not prolonged. Feulgen staining of nuclei is well preserved after formic acid decalcification at 24°C, but with mineral acids at 20°C or even at 3°C it is impaired or destroyed.

Altogether, for other than enzyme demonstration, 1 *N* acetic and formic acids seem the best general decalcifying agents. They are more economical reagents than the Kristensen and other buffer mixtures and seem equally effective. The preferred procedure is to use 2 changes daily of about 25 cc per gm bone, testing the removed fluid at each change to determine the presence of calcium ion by mixing 5 cc of it with 1 cc of 5% sodium or ammonium oxalate. When a negative test is obtained—wait several minutes for the development of delayed turbidity—the specimens may be considered decalcified. This test seems more objective and less liable to underdecalcification than the common practice of testing with a pin. It coincides well with the cessation of weight loss. It is equally applicable to decalcification with mineral acids, but it must be recalled that calcium oxalate will not precipitate from hydrochloric or nitric acid above about

0.7 N or 0.8 N final dilution. The concentration of stronger acid must be reduced by dilution or by addition of an amount of 2 N NaOH which will not quite neutralize; a drop of Congo red solution will give a color change at about pH 4–5.

Following this procedure 1–2 gm blocks of compact bone 3–4 mm thick decalcify in 4–5 days in 5% formic acid; similar blocks of cancellous bone, in 2–3 days. In 5% nitric acid it takes about half that time, and in the 8% hydrochloric, 10% formic acid mixture, even less: some 4–8 hours for cancellous bone and 12–24 hours for compact bone.

C. E. Jenkins (*J. Path. Bact.* **24**:166, 1921) recommended an alcoholic acid solution which fixes and decalcifies human rib in 48 hours, permits normal blue nuclear staining with Ehrlich's hematoxylin and occasions no swelling of collagen fibers in Van Gieson preparations. A 17–20°C temperature in Glasgow is presumed.

Jenkins's Decalcifying Fluid.

Concentrated hydrochloric acid	4 cc
Glacial acetic acid	3 cc
Distilled water	10 cc
Alcohol, 100%[1]	73 cc
Chloroform	10 cc

Fix bones until soft; wash in 2 changes absolute alcohol, 4 hours each; chloroform to remove alcohol, 2 changes, 30 minutes each; paraffin.

A. J. Schmidt (*J. Exp. Zool.* **149**:171, 1962) used this solution after freeze substitution for salamander legs, 5 days at −70°C in absolute alcohol saturated with picric acid. His decalcification interval was 5 days at 20–25°C (*J. Histochem.* **11**:443, 1963). He reported demonstration of glycogen by the periodic acid Schiff method equal to that in similarly freeze substituted but undecalcified tissue.

In not exposing tissue to water before or during decalcification this procedure meets the requirements which I have specified for the preservation of glycogen through decalcification (*J. Histochem.* **10**:763, 1962).

Our findings (*Am. J. Clin. Path.* **21**:711, 1951) of very slow decalcification of dog femur by 0.5 N HCl in 80% alcohol, 8 days at 25°C or 12 weeks at −23°C, indicate that decalcification of compact bone may take considerably longer than stated above by Jenkins for human rib.

Trichloroacetic acid is also a fully satisfactory decalcifying agent which

---

[1] If 95% alcohol is used, the proportions are 76 cc alcohol and 7 cc distilled water.

permits just as satisfactory nucleai and marrow cell staining as does formic acid. However, on account of its high molecular weight (163) as compared with that of formic acid (46), much larger quantities (3.55 times) are needed for efficient decalcification.

Sulfurous acid, available as a 5–6% solution of sulfur dioxide in water, is also a prompt decalcifying agent, but if its action is prolonged more than 48 hours, nuclear staining is seriously impaired.

After decalcification with nitric, formic, trichloroacetic or sulfurous acid, tissues should be washed 18–24 hours in gently running water to remove acid, then hardened in 80% alcohol, dehydrated and imbedded as usual in paraffin or nitrocellulose. Frozen sections of decalcified bone for the study of fats and myelinated nerves are readily prepared on the freezing microtome. In this case, naturally, all contact with alcohol or other fat solvents is to be scrupulously avoided.

Alcoholic solutions of acids are quite inefficient decalcifying agents. Solutions in 70% or 80% alcohol are slow: 0.5 N HCl took 8 days at 25°C, compared with 4 days for 0.5 N HCl in 40% alcohol and 2 days for aqueous 0.5 N HCl. With formic acid 5% solutions took 3–5 days in water, about 4 months in 30% alcohol, and failed to decalcify in several months in 80% alcohol. This occurs probably more because of the suppression of ionization by alcohol than because of insolubility of certain calcium salts in alcohol. Calcium nitrate, calcium chloride and calcium bromide are listed as soluble to very soluble in alcohol; calcium acetate is slightly soluble; the formate is insoluble; but addition of 5% of either glacial acetic acid or of 90% formic acid to a saturated 70% alcohol solution of calcium chloride occasions no precipitation, though small quantities of oxalic or sulfuric acids give copious precipitates.

In the study of fractures, periosteal hemorrhages and similar lesions where preservation of precise anatomic relationships is of more importance than cytologic preservation, it is often desirable to imbed in nitrocellulose either after or preferably before decalcification. Imbed before decalcifying to make sure that soft tissues are not displaced from hard.

For the gross opening of long bones in scurvy, rickets and similar conditions it may be desirable to imbed the bones temporarily in a plaster of paris matrix before sawing in two lengthwise. Procedural fractures at the epiphyseal line are thus avoided. This imbedding may be done either before or after fixation.

When imbedding the bone in plaster, its position may be marked by inserting toothpicks in the soft plaster to mark the plane of sawing. Allow the plaster to set for about an hour. Saw with a thin bladed hacksaw. Then break off the plaster and wipe the surface with gauze or with a brush moistened in 5% acetic acid. The bones are usually greasy enough to separate readily from the plaster. If difficulty is encountered in this respect, the bones may be first dipped in light mineral oil before imbedding in plaster. I am indebted to Drs. J. H. Peers and T. H. Tomlinson for this note.

Mechanical agitation appears to have no great effect on the speed of decalcification, so that apparatus designed for this purpose seems scarcely worth the trouble or expense.

The use of vacuum during decalcification does not materially expedite the process, but it does prevent the formation of large gas bubbles in the marrow in large pieces of bone. With small bones it has no evident value.

Prolonged, slow decalcification with fluids of relatively high pH level (5), such as 5–10% solution of ammonium chloride, ammonium nitrate or potassium or sodium acid phosphate, gives excellent preservation of marrow cells after 2–3 weeks; but cortical bone is still hard at the end of 3 weeks.

Frank and Deluzarche (*Bull. Histol. Appliq.* **27**:35, 1950) recommended for the decalcification of enamel and dentin in the crowns of human teeth first a primary fixation in 10% formalin followed by a 12 hour refixation in Bouin's fluid. Then the crown is rinsed in water, in alcohol and in ether, and coated with 3 layers of collodion on the enamel surface. Decalcification follows in a fluid composed of 2 gm nitric acid (sp. gr. 1.38) (1.23 cc of our 69–70% acid, sp. gr. 1.42), 8 gm trichloroacetic acid, 20 cc Bouin's fluid and 70 cc water. Maintenance of partial vacuum (about 100 mm) during decalcification is recommended. Dehydration, clearing and infiltration through graded alcohols, cedar oil, toluene and paraffin should be fairly rapid.

Hahn and Reygadas (*Science* **114**:462, 1951) report the use of a solution of sodium ethylenediaminetetraacetate for demineralization of hard tissues. This solution is alkaline, and the evolution of carbon dioxide is thereby prevented. Complex soluble electronegative calcium containing ions are formed. If the ethylenediaminetetraacetic acid is neutralized with quaternary sodium pyrophosphate instead of hydroxide, the demineralization effect for iron salts is increased. No further details as to concentration of solutions have been published. Since iron salts were also removed along with calcium salts, this process was not recommended in those cases where demonstration of iron containing pigments might be important.

Retention of Hemosiderin Iron in Decalcified Tissue. Various expedients have been adopted in the past to retain in the tissues as much iron as possible. Some of these seem particularly applicable in the case of tissue which is to be decalcified, either with acids or with Versene. It is true that much hemosiderin remains demonstrable in marrow littoral cells when formic acid decalcification is practiced. But both of the iron formates are soluble in water; the ferric is somewhat more soluble than the ferrous, which is only slightly soluble. It is probable that protein and polysaccharide chelate bonding of the iron ions protects them to some extent, at least in the pH 2.5–4.5 range of acid treatment. The question of iron retention is usually disregarded by the Versene decalcification enthusiasts.

However, use of a soluble sulfide, buffered to neutrality to prevent deleterious alkali effects on tissue, as a component of the fixing fluid should act to keep iron undissolved. $Ca(SH)_2$ is very soluble in water. FeS has a solubility of 6.16 mg per liter; Fe_3S_4 is also quite insoluble, though both dissolve in strong mineral acids. Hence nitric and hydrochloric acids should be avoided as decalcifying agents under these circumstances.

It is probable that much of the tissue hemosiderin, normally ferric in state, is reduced to Fe_3S_4 by H_2S. In the Tirmann-Schmelzer method after sulfide reduction it is known to react with $K_3Fe(CN)_6$. The existence of a ferrocyanide reaction in sulfide treated tissue is evidence of the preexistence of Fe^{+++}. Ferrous salts are comparatively uncommon in tissue, and their prior existence cannot be proved in sulfide treated tissue or in tissue subjected to other reducing agents.

To apply this method, fix bone with red marrow in 10% formalin to which 2% yellow ammonium sulfide is added or 1% NaSH. Na_2S yields strongly alkaline solutions which should be adjusted electrometrically to pH 7, or saturated with hydrogen sulfide gas. After usual fixation intervals decalcify with 5% formic acid (p. 633) or by Christensen's solution, or perhaps with Versene.

1 N Acetic acid decalcifies effectively, though perhaps not quite so rapidly as 1 N formic acid, according to A. Gutiérrez in my laboratory. Hemosiderin iron resists 1–2 N acetic acid for prolonged periods (*Am. J. Path.* **15**:225, 1939) and is readily shown by ferrocyanide after acetic acid decalcification. The decalcification technic is the same as with 5% formic acid.

Ethylenediaminetetraacetic Acid, Disodium, EDTA, Versene, Sequestrene. Generally 5–10% Versene solutions are used. Alkaline solutions tend to hydrolyze protein to some extent (Cook and Ezra-Cohn, *J. Histochem.* **10**:560, 1962); hence solutions adjusted to between pH 6.5 and 7.5 are recommended. We (*J. Histochem.* **11**:662, 1963) have shown that in 5 μ sections there is no appreciable loss of the iron in cytosiderin, hemosiderin or enterosiderin during 7 days' exposure to 6% Versene at pH 7.5, and that the loss is scarcely appreciable at 4.5. Hence, neutral Versene decalcification would seem applicable to the study of iron bearing pigments in bone marrow.

Cook and Ezra-Cohn (*loc. cit.*) reported a somewhat less complete removal of calcium from ground unfixed bone by Versene than by hydrochloric or formic acid. But loss of protein nitrogen did not occur to any appreciable extent with Versene. Such loss was considerable with hydrochloric and formic acids from unfixed ground bone, but was reduced to a relatively minor amount in bone prefixed in formalin, especially if acid exposure was limited to the period of active calcium removal. In this connection the analyses of Cook and Ezra-Cohn are not closely enough spaced relative to the end of the active decalcification period.

Trott (*J. Histochem.* **9**:699, 1961) noted use of Versene at pH 7.2 by Schajowicz and Cabrini, and himself used a Versene solution at pH 7.5 for 7 days in the study of glycogen in rat jaw tissues.

For the demonstration of di- and triphosphopyridine nucleotide (NAD, NADP) linked dehydrogenases and the diaphorases and of succinic dehydrogenase in bones, Balogh (*J. Histochem.* **10**:232, 1962) decalcified fresh rat and mouse jaws and other bones, as well as $5 \times 5 \times 1$ mm blocks of cancellous and compact human bone, by a 3–5 day immersion at 4–10°C in 10% ethylenediaminetetraacetate in 0.1 M phosphate buffer, pH 7, readjusting to pH 7 with NaOH (or HCl) after addition.

On the other hand Cabrini and Rosner (*J. Histochem.* **11**:119, 1963) found it necessary to do these dehydrogenase formazan reactions in thin unfixed blocks, postfix in formalin and then decalcify and section by usual procedures. Among the fluids used for decalcifying was a 5% Versene at pH 7.

Tonna *et al.* (*J. Histochem.* **11**:720, 1963) used 10% disodium Versenate for decalcification of mouse femora.

General References. R. D. Lillie, *Am. J. Path.* **20**:291, 1944; R. D. Lillie, A. Laskey, J. Greco, H. J. Burtner and P. Jones, *Am. J. Clin. Path.* **21**:711, 1951.

Formulae for Decalcifying Fluids

1. **5% nitric acid.**

Concentrated (68–70%) nitric acid (sp. gr. 1.41)	50 cc
Distilled water	950 cc

Older directions called for tenfold dilution of the Pharmacopeial acid, sp. gr. 1.25, assay about 500 gm HNO_3 per liter (Lange). Later some of the German writers prescribed 75 cc of the 68% acid (sp. gr. 1.41) per liter, apparently neglecting the specific gravity in their computations. (Schmorl, 1907, 1928; Roulet, 1948; Romeis, 1932 but corrected in 1948.)

2. **Von Ebner's hydrochloric acid sodium chloride mixture.**

Concentrated hydrochloric acid (sp. gr. 1.19)	15 cc
Sodium chloride	175 gm
Distilled water	1000 cc

During decalcification add 1 cc of concentrated hydrochloric acid daily to each 200 cc of the above mixture, until decalcification is complete.

3. **Richman-Gelfand-Hill formic hydrochloric acid mixture.**

Concentrated formic acid (90%)	100 cc
Concentrated hydrochloric acid (38.8%, sp. gr. 1.19)	80 cc
Distilled water	820 cc

4. **5% formic acid** (essentially 1 N).

Concentrated formic acid (90–92%)	50 cc
Distilled water	950 cc

5. **Kristensen's fluid.**

1 N sodium formate (6.8%)	500 cc
8 N formic acid (see tables, p. 673)	500 cc

6. **Formalin formic acid, according to Schmorl.**

Formic acid (90%)	500 cc
Formaldehyde (40%)	50 cc
Distilled water	450 cc

Schmorl recommended this as working rapidly, without producing swelling. Nuclear staining was said to be well preserved.

7. **Evans and Krajian fluid** (*Arch. Path.* **10**:447, 1930, emended).

Sodium citrate crystals	10 gm
90% formic acid	25 cc
Distilled water	75 cc

8. **Evans and Krajian's fluid, Krajian's variant.**

85% formic acid	100 cc
95% ethanol or 99% isopropanol	100 cc
Sodium citrate crystals	20 gm
Trichloroacetic acid	1 gm
Distilled water	100 cc

9. **Molar HCl citrate buffer of pH 4.5.**

1 N hydrochloric acid	540 cc
1 M sodium citrate solution	460 cc

(29.4% of the dihydrate, or 35.7% of the $Na_3(CO_2)_3C_3H_4OH \cdot 5\frac{1}{2}$ H_2O)

10. **Lorch's citrate HCl buffer of pH 4.4.**

Citric acid crystals	14.7 gm
0.2 N sodium hydroxide	700 cc
0.1 N hydrochloric acid	300 cc
1% zinc sulfate	2 cc
Chloroform	0.1 cc

11. **Normal acetate buffer of pH 4.5**

Normal acetic acid	520 cc
Normal sodium acetate (8.2% anhydrous; 13.6% crystalline)	480 cc

Add 2 cc 1% zinc sulfate and 0.1 cc chloroform.

12. **Normal ammonium citrate citric acid buffer of pH 4.5.**

Normal citric acid (monohydrate 7%)	50 cc
Normal ammonium citrate (anhydrous 7.54%)	950 cc

Add 2 cc 1% zinc sulfate and 0.1 cc chloroform.

MATRIX STRUCTURE OF BONES AND TEETH

Ground sections of bones and teeth are sometimes required for the study of bone lamellae and canaliculi, and dentin tubules and enamel prisms. They are made from macerated and dried bone.

To macerate bones and teeth, saw into fairly thin pieces and soak in several changes of water over a period of several months. Then wash out and dry thoroughly in air. Then grind sections until nearly transparent between 2 pieces of pumice stone with water, or between 2 pieces of plate glass with powdered pumice and water. When sections are thin enough wash in water and dry.

White (cited from Lee) recommended cutting moderately thin slices of bone or tooth, presumably previously macerated and dried, and soaking in ether for 1 or 2 days. Then soak in collodion colored red with basic fuchsin for 2 or 3 days. Then transfer to 80% alcohol for another 2 or 3 days and finally grind down nearly to transparency by rubbing between 2 pieces of ground glass with water and pumice powder. Dry the surfaces and mount.

To mount ground sections, place on a slide a small fragment of solid balsam or other resin and heat until it just melts. Do the same with a coverglass. Place the ground section in the resin on the coverglass and press down the resin area on the slide on top.

Results: Lacunae and canaliculi are filled with air or with the colored collodion. Enamel requires preliminary etching with 0.6% hydrochloric acid alcohol or weak aqueous picric acid and mounting in solid camsal[1] which has a lower refractive index (1.478).

Bone matrix in paraffin or nitrocellulose sections of decalcified bone stains pink with hematoxylin eosin and azure eosin methods (pp. 217, 162). Remnants of cartilage in newly ossified bone are stained a deep purple with the latter. With Van Gieson's picrofuchsin (p. 540) bone matrix is a deep red. Osteoid tissue is similarly stained, contrasting with the pink to yellow of cartilage in fracture callus. Aniline blue and methyl blue collagen methods stain bone matrix only lightly.

Schmorl's thionin method is sometimes employed for the demonstration of lamellae and canaliculi in compact bone. Formalin fixation is recommended and should be followed by 6–8 weeks at 20°C or 3–4 weeks at 37°C in Müller's fluid (p. 55). Then wash 24 hours in running water and decalcify according to preference. Schmorl recommended direct transfer from Müller's fluid to hydrochloric acid alcohol: hydrochloric acid 2.5 cc, sodium chloride 2.5 gm, distilled water 100 cc, 95% alcohol 500 cc. When decalcification is completed, wash in several

---

[1] Camsal is an ordinarily liquid mixture of phenyl salicylate (salol) and camphor, in such proportion that a little camphor remains undissolved.

changes of 80% alcohol. Then dehydrate and imbed in paraffin or celloidin. Cut thin sections.

1. Bring to water as usual.
2. Stain 5 minutes in half-saturated aqueous (0.125%) thionin. Staining
   may be accelerated and intensified by addition of a drop or 2 of ammonia water to the thionin.
3. Rinse in water.
4. Differentiate 1–2 minutes in 95% alcohol.
5. Again rinse in water.
6. Transfer to concentrated aqueous phosphotungstic acid. Differentiation is completed in a few seconds, but longer exposure is harmless.
7. Wash 5–10 minutes in water until sections are sky blue. Longer washing is harmless.
8. Fix the color in a mixture of equal parts of concentrated formalin and
   water for 1–2 hours.
9. Dehydrate in 2 changes of 95% alcohol and 2 of 100% alcohol and clear
   in 1 change of equal parts 100% alcohol and xylene and 2 changes of
   xylene. For celloidin sections substitute 99% isopropyl alcohol for the
   100% ethyl alcohol in the 3 steps in which it is used.

Results: The walls of bone cavities and their processes are blue black;
cells are diffuse blue; nuclei, only little darker than cytoplasm. Nuclear
staining may be intensified by insertion of an alum hematoxylin stain
after the formalin step. The method is excellent for teeth. Bone matrix is
light blue. Cement lines between lamellae are readily seen. Fibrillar
structure is distinct.

Powers, Rasmussen and Clark (*Anat. Rec.* **111**:17, 1951) have adapted
the Romanes method (p. 614) for the demonstration of dentin tubules.
They recommend fixation in a modified Bouin fluid composed of 75 cc
saturated aqueous picric acid, 25 cc formalin (37% HCHO) and 1 gm
trichloroacetic acid; decalcification in 5% trichloroacetic acid in 50%
alcohol; and paraffin imbedding. Sections are deparaffinized, hydrated
and mordanted 18 hours in 1% (41.4 mM) aqueous cupric nitrate solution [$Cu(NO_3)_2 \cdot 3H_2O$] at 37°C, washed thrice in distilled water and
put through the Romanes procedure. The solution used in step 1 is
adjusted by addition of 16 drops (1 cc) of 1% ammonium hydroxide (a
1% dilution of 28% ammonia water?).

Lillie's method of silver impregnation (*Z. wiss. Mikr.* **45**:380, 1928)
with subsequent decalcification distinguishes osteoid tissue and new,
uncalcified bone lamellae from older calcified lamellae, and in denser
bone often gives a very sharp definition of lacunae and canaliculi. Gomori
has used a basically similar method with similar results, but his is somewhat more complicated (*Am. J. Path.* **9**:253, 1933).

Lillie's method:

1. Fix in 10% formalin for 2 days or more.
2. Wash thoroughly in several changes of distilled water.
3. Silver for 4–5 days at 37°C in 2–2.5% silver nitrate solution.
4. Wash thoroughly in distilled water.
5. Dacalcify in Ebner's sodium chloride hydrochloric acid mixture: concentrated hydrochloric acid 3 cc, saturated aqueous (35%) sodium chloride solution 100 cc, distilled water 100 cc. To this add 1 cc hydrochloric acid daily until decalcification is complete.
6. Wash out acid in 2–3 changes of half-saturated sodium chloride solution over 4–5 days. If the salt solution becomes acid to litmus, add a few drops of diluted ammonia water to neutralize.
7. Wash 18–24 hours in running water, harden 1–2 days in 80% alcohol, imbed in paraffin or nitrocellulose. Section and counterstain with hemalum and eosin or, better, with Weigert's iron hematoxylin and Van Gieson's picrofuchsin (p. 540).

Results: Thin trabeculae of bone are completely blackened; thicker bone shows black outer lamellae, with perhaps an unsilvered lamella or two adjacent to the peri- or endosteum, and deep lamellae respectively pink or red according to counterstain, with black lacunae and canaliculi. Calcified areas in cartilage and other calcium phosphate deposits also blacken. Dentin is blackened; enamel is partly blackened.

Actually, like the von Kóssa method, this demonstrates phosphates rather than calcium salts, but since soluble phosphates are first washed out, it is essentially calcium phosphate that is demonstrated by both methods.

Feeding of madder or of alizarin (C.I. No. 58000) has been used for the marking of newly formed bone. In place of the rather uncertain feeding procedure one may give perhaps 2 intraperitoneal injections weekly, of 200 mg per kg (in rats) of alizarin red S (C.I. No. 58005) over a period of several weeks. Rats given more frequent injections presented evidence of renal damage. At autopsy bone laid down during and shortly after the period of alizarin administration is found to be stained red (Highman, unpublished data).

Unfortunately this red color is extracted or decolorized by most decalcifying agents. Versene might be tried.

Tetracycline Fluorochrome Staining *in vivo.* Milch, Tobie and Robinson (*J. Histochem* 9:261, 1961) explain the specific golden yellow fluorescence of newly deposited calcium in bone, cartilage and calcifying neoplasms in tetracycline treatment as a chelation with Ca^{++} ions which they formulate as binding 2 moles of the drug *in vitro,* but in tissue they consider the Ca^{++} as bound covalently to 2 phosphate groups which are bound to collagen protein chains and chelate with the quinone oxygen of the drug by secondary valences. One might speculate that a Ca^{++} ion bound to only one phosphate radical could form a more effective ring chelate complex.

Technic. The technic is simple. Tissue from tetracycline treated patients is quickly frozen in petroleum ether with solid CO_2 or dry ice alcohol mixture and kept at $-20°C$ in a refrigerator until sectioned. Cryostat sections are prepared on a rotary microtome at 2–8 μ, cutting at $-15°C$. Sections are transferred directly to glass slides, caused to adhere by thawing with a finger on the back of the slide, removed from the cryostat and dried 30 minutes in an airstream. They are then mounted in glycerol and examined in 365 mμ light using a Corning 5840 2.25 mm filter in the light source and a Wratten 2A eyepiece filter to transmit blue and yellow light. Control hematoxylin eosin and alizarin red S stains are recommended.

Newly deposited calcium fluoresces golden yellow on a blue autofluorescence background (collagen).

Acid Phosphatase in Bone

For **acid phosphatase** in developing bone and cartilage Schajowicz and Cabrini (*Stain Techn.* **34**:59, 1959) compared fixations in slightly acid and neutral 10% formalin, Baker's chloral formalin,[1] acetone and 80% alcohol, decalcification in 5% Versene at pH 7 and in buffer mixtures of acetic acid and sodium hydroxide at pH 4.2.

Fixation for a maximum of 24 hours at 4°C in 10–20% neutral formalin or in Baker's chloral formalin was recommended. Longer periods and higher temperatures in neutral formalin occasioned progressive loss of enzyme activity. Baker's chloral formalin was well tolerated up to 15 days at 4°C. Alcohol destroyed the enzyme; acetone gave very irregular results.

Versene decalcification occasioned considerable loss of acid phosphatase. Acetic acid sodium acetate 0.05 M, pH 5, gave usable results, but better phosphatase activity was obtained with the citrate and formic citrate buffers at pH 4.2. Enzyme was preserved up to 15 days in pH 5 formic citrate mixtures. This buffer destroyed acid phosphatase at pH 2.6 and 3, but conserved it at 3.8, 4.2 and 5.

Paraffin imbedding, even for only 15 minutes *in vacuo*, was destruc-

[1] J. R. Baker II *et al.* (*J. Histochem.* **6**:244, 1958): 20cc 38% formaldehyde, 80 cc distilled water, 100 mg chloral hydrate, marble chips.

TABLE 18-1. FORMIC ACID SODIUM CITRATE BUFFERS

pH	2.6	3.0	3.8	4.2	5.0
20% sodium citrate	50	50	50	50	50
Formic acid	25	10	5	2.5	1
Distilled water	25	40	45	47.5	49

tive of enzyme. Hence frozen sections were used for either the 1950 Gomori lead sulfide or the Burton azo dye method.

I do not intend to suggest a return to the older methods of acid phosphatase demonstration but favor application of the newer methods to frozen sections prepared according to the Schajowicz-Cabrini technic.

ALKALINE PHOSPHATASE IN BONE

For studies of alkaline phosphatase distribution in calcified bone, fixation in 70% ethyl or isopropyl alcohol for 24 hours at about 20–25°C is recommended. Then decalcify at 0–5°C in a buffer mixture of pH 4.5 or higher, using 5–10 cc/100 mg bone and changing daily until oxalate tests for calcium are negative. Normal ammonium citrate + citric acid buffer is more effective than normal acetate buffer (formulae 10, 9, p. 633); the one dissolves 777 mg calcium as $Ca_3(PO_4)_2$ per 100 cc, the other dissolves 411 mg. Both decalcify considerably more rapidly than Lorch's mixture or the 0.1 M citrate and 0.1 M citrate and hydrochloric acid buffers (formula 8, and $\frac{1}{10}$ dilution of formula 7, p. 663, and the pH 4.5 mixture of the Horecker-Lillie buffer, p. 662), and appear to give adequate preservation of alkaline phosphatase activity. In the presence of an excess of bone, citrate buffers may give rise to copious calcium citrate precipitates, which are deposited on the surface of the specimen as well as on the bottom of the container. The acetate buffers remain clear. Formate buffers of pH 4.5 are relatively poor calcium solvents, and tartrate ion produces a highly insoluble calcium salt. Neither of these can be recommended for this special purpose.

If it becomes impractical to continue daily changes and observations for completion of decalcification, the process may be interrupted by washing briefly in water, 10–15 minutes, transferring to 80% isopropyl alcohol and storing at −20°C or −25°C in a deep freeze compartment until daily changes can be resumed. Then wash 10–15 minutes in water and return to the decalcifying fluid.

On completion of decalcification, wash overnight in running water and incubate 6 hours at 37°C in 1% sodium barbital solution containing 75 mg glycine per 100 cc to reactivate the enzyme. Wash 2–4 hours in running water to remove glycine. Dehydrate through ascending alcohols and clear in lead free gasoline or petroleum ether. A Technicon schedule (p. 73) may be used, but carriers and containers must be chemically free of metal and CO_3 ions. Infiltrate 10–15 minutes in paraffin at 58°C at 10–15 mm mercury pressure in a vacuum oven.

If a vacuum oven is not available, preparations may be infiltrated with paraffin in 20–30 minutes after dealcoholization with isopentane (B.P. 28°C), ethyl ether (B.P. 37°C) or a low boiling petroleum ether (Baker's special, B.P. 20–40°C). Or the usual 35–60°C petroleum ether may be used, but it will take longer to boil off. The specimens should be kept immersed in the paraffin by enclosing in wire gauze or in a Technicon capsule.

The paraffin sections are then handled for phosphatase demonstration according to the usual technics, as for soft tissues. See p. 317, or below, for Lorch's special method for simultaneous demonstration of phosphatase and preformed phosphates.

General References.

Lillie, Laskey, Greco, Burtner, and Jones. *Am. J. Clin. Path.* **21**:711, 1951.

R. W. Mowry, *Int. A. Med. Mus. Bull.* **30**:95, 1949.

I. J. Lorch, *Quart. J. Micr. Sci.* **88**:367, 1947.

A. J. Morse, *J. Dent. Res.* **24**:143, 1945.

Greep and Morse, *J. Am. Dent. As.* **36**:427, 1948.

Greep, Fisher, and Morse, *Science* **105**:666, 1947.

A. Zorzoli, *Anat. Rec.* **102**:445, 1948.

Lorch's Method for Alkaline Phosphatase and Preformed Phosphates (*Quart. J. Micr. Sci.* **88**:367, 1947).

1. Fix 12–24 hours in 80% alcohol, dehydrate in ascending alcohols and clear and infiltrate in paraffin. I suggest the petroleum ether-vacuum infiltration sequence, or see the variants on pp. 317, 320. Section at 8–10 μ. The method is applicable only to developing bones which may be sectioned successfully without decalcification.
2. Deparaffinize and hydrate as usual.
3. Immerse in 2% cobalt nitrate for 5 minutes.
4. Wash in 3–5 changes of distilled water, 1–2 minutes each.
5. Immerse for 30 seconds in freshly diluted, 1% ammonium sulfide.
6. Wash 5 minutes only in tap water.
7. Incubate 20 minutes to 15 hours at 37°C in this substrate:

2% calcium nitrate [Ca(NO$_3$)$_2$·4H$_2$O]	10 cc
2% magnesium chloride (MgCl$_2$·6H$_2$O)	10 cc
4% sodium β-glycerophosphate·5H$_2$O	10 cc
1% sodium barbital	70 cc
Ammonium sulfide	1 drop

8. Wash in 1% calcium nitrate.
9. Immerse for 10 minutes in saturated aqueous gallamine blue (C.I. No. 51045) buffered to pH 7 (I suggest Michaelis's Veronal sodium, p. 670).
10. Rinse 10–12 seconds in 0.5% sodium hydroxide.
11. Wash in water, dehydrate, clear and mount as usual. Interpose counterstain if desired: safranin, methyl green, neutral red, eosin or orange G.

Results: Sites of phosphatase activity are shown by purple calcium lake; preformed phosphates, by dark brown cobalt sulfide.

Barka and Anderson (1963) still speak of using the Lorch technic for alkaline phosphatase in calcifying bone, suggesting the glycine reactivation procedure of Greep *et al.* (*J. Am. Dent. A.* **36:**427, 1948). Some use of Versene (10% pH 5.5–7) has been made also.

Decalcification for alkaline phosphatase studies with 5% Versene or Sequestrene at pH 7, followed by reactivation of the enzyme in 1% sodium diethylbarbiturate, was recommended in 1956 by Schajowitz and Cabrini (*Stain Techn.* **31:**129, 1956). They compared 5% Versene, 5% Sequestrene (both adjusted to pH 7) and the pH 5 formic acid sodium citrate buffer of Greep *et al.* (p. 637) at a 5 day exposure, finding Sequestrene slightly inferior to the other 2, which were apparently about equal for this purpose.

The Allen and Freiman variant might be tried on frozen sections after short acetone fixation.

Albert and Linder sectioned young rat jaws after 80% alcohol fixation and imbedding in tropical ester wax without decalcification. Enzyme losses were decreased by the low melting point of this wax (47°C), and its hardness permitted section cutting.

Albert-Linder Bone Sectioning for Alkaline Phosphatase. (*Stain Techn.* **35:**277, 1960). Fix 2 hours in 80% alcohol and dehydrate 56 hours in several changes of absolute alcohol, all at 4°C. Clear 24 hours at 4°C in 2 changes of benzene. Infiltrate 2 hours *in vacuo* at 48–50°C in tropical ester wax (British Drug Houses, Inc.).

Cut blocks on a base sledge microtome using a Jung extra hard steel knife with a tool edged profile. Knife slant may vary between 45° and 90° to direction of cutting; tilt should be about 10°. Cut at normal speed.

Press a piece of Scotch tape larger than the section onto the block face before each cut. Lay pieces of tape sticky side up on glass plate. Coat each section with 2% celloidin and return to its place. Dry 30 minutes. Number sections with "brushing cellulose paint"; staple together in sequence and store at 4°C.

When ready to use dissolve off Scotch tape adhesive with several changes of chloroform. This hardens the celloidin, and the sections separate readily. The wax is removed at the same time. The sections are now transferred to 70% alcohol and can be handled as ordinary celloidin sections. The authors used Gomori's 1952 azo method; more recent methods are undoubtedly applicable. The Burstone and Barka variants seem applicable; and the procedure can probably also be used with the cobalt sulfide technics (p. 317).

Although no such procedure appears to have been tested as a whole, current trends in soft tissue alkaline phosphatase technics would indicate the advisability of trying alcohol or acetone freeze substitution at −70°C,

followed by pH 7 Versene or pH 5 formic acid sodium citrate decalcification, according to Schajowicz and Cabrini (p. 637), and frozen
sections according to the more recent soft tissue technics (Chapter 10).

PHOSPHORYLASE

Cobb (*A.M.A. Arch. Path.* **55**:496, 1953) reports a technic for the
histochemical localization of phosphorylase activity in young rat tibiae.
The bones from freshly killed rats were split lengthwise and frozen in
isopentane at 150°C. They were then desiccated *in vacuo* at —30°C
for at least 3 days. Next followed imbedding *in vacuo* for 15 minutes in
the chloroform soluble fraction of carnauba wax[1] and sectioning in
this very hard wax without decalcification. Sections were dewaxed in
chloroform.

Cobb's Phosphorylase Technic.

1. Dewax 10 minutes in chloroform, thus also partially inactivating the
   bone alkaline phosphatase.
2. Digest 90 minutes in amylase, saliva or diastase at 37°C to remove
   glycogen.
3. Soak overnight in distilled water to dissolve out all soluble bone salts.
4. Inactivate phosphoglucomutase by heating in a few drops of water in
   a moist chamber. (*In vitro* this enzyme resists heating at 65°C.)
5. Incubate 6 hours at 37°C in pH 5.9 acetate buffer containing a "high"
   concentration of glucose 1-phosphate and an unstated amount of
   barium chloride to precipitate liberated phosphate ions.
6. Fix glycogen overnight in 100% alcohol. Stain glycogen by the periodic
   acid Schiff procedure (p. 198). Cobb used the Hotchkiss A (?)
   variant. For controls omit steps 3–5 above. The excess over the controls represents glycogen newly formed as a result of phosphorylase
   activity.

Although I have not tried this method, and as published it lacks some
necessary details, the rationale seems good and the procedure is worthy
of trial. (See also Takeuchi, pp. 330–332).

GLYCOGEN

Glycogen also presents special problems in its preservation *in situ*
during decalcification procedures. Total losses have been reported during

[1] Carnauba wax is used industrially in furniture and floor waxes and should be
procurable through the makers of these products.

acid decalcification, and even Versene demineralization does not fully protect it (Trott, *J. Histochem.* 9:699, 1961; Schajowitz and Cabrini, *ibid.* 3:122, 1955).

Although 24 hour 25°C fixations in such fluids as acetic alcohol formalin, Rossman's and Gendre's fluids and the like seem to give about as full preservation of soft tissue glycogen as does freeze drying, the glycogen so precipitated remains relatively susceptible to aqueous extraction in the presence of acids. However, it was observed that in material primarily fixed in aqueous formalin deliberately acidified with acetic or formic acid the glycogen in muscle and marrow cells withstood decalcification much better.

This suggested (*J. Histochem.* 10:763, 1962) that glycogen could be preserved in tissue attached to bone during decalcification by achieving a more thorough fixation of the protein surrounding it or by prior imbedding in celloidin. Both these procedures should create semipermeable membranes surrounding the precipitated glycogen particles and thereby hinder re-solution and diffusion. In practice these procedures proved successful in preserving soft tissue glycogen in virtually undiminished amount during formic acid decalcification.

Decalcification Procedures for the Subsequent Demonstration of Labile Glycogen. (Lillie)

A. Celloidin procedure

1. Fix 24 hours at 25°C or 3–4 days at 5°C in acetic alcohol formalin or 6 hours at 60°C in methanol chloroform 65:35.
2. Complete dehydration with 95% and absolute alcohol and infiltrate 3 days in 1% celloidin in alcohol + ether (50:50).
3. Transfer to 80% alcohol overnight to harden celloidin.
4. Decalcify with daily changes of 5% formic acid in water, testing discarded fluid with 1% sodium oxalate for the presence of calcium ions. As soon as a negative test is obtained
5. Wash 6–8 hours in running water, dehydrate, clear, imbed and section in paraffin as usual.

B. Hard protein fixation procedure

1. Fix as above in acetic alcohol formalin or in Gendre's fluid (p. 58).
2. Transfer to Bouin's fluid for 3 days at 25°C.
3. Decalcify in daily changes of 10% formalin containing 5% formic acid, testing as above. When a negative oxalate test is obtained
4. Wash 8 hours in running water, dehydrate, clear, imbed and section in paraffin as usual.

Chapter 19

Various Special Procedures

VASCULAR INJECTIONS

The practice of vascular injection with colored masses has had wide application in the study of the circulatory system of various organs. The Berlin blue and carmine gelatin masses are classical. They serve well for gross preparations and those intended for clearing and study under low magnification. With both of these some color loss occurs during paraffin imbedding, and a carbon mass has been found more satisfactory for strictly histologic purposes.

Carbon Gelatin Mass. *Ashburn and Endicott,* in my laboratory, devised a carbon gelatin based on Mall's statement that he used such a mass for study of the circulation of the liver. This mass must be freshly prepared each time, though it might be kept frozen for a few days if desired. The carbon particles are apparently held back by the capillaries so that either the afferent or efferent vessels may be injected without filling the other. This technic has been used in the study of lobular relationships of destructive and cirrhotic processes in rat livers. The technic follows:

Dissolve 8 gm gelatin in 100 cc warm water. Sift animal charcoal through a 100 mesh sieve and suspend 20 gm of the sifted charcoal in the gelatin solution in a conical glass of perhaps 200 cc capacity immersed in a water bath at 45–50°C. While preparing the animal for injection keep the gelatin mass agitated with a small propeller type glass stirrer driven by a small electric motor. The propeller is directed downward and is kept fairly near the bottom of the conical glass.

Cannulae are made of glass with a slight bulbous enlargement on the end so that they can be tied in. It is preferable to have the opening on the side of the bulb, so as to avoid tears in the veins when introducing the cannula. At the same time, the opening must be distal to the constricted area about which the tie is made.

For injection of the hepatic veins, remove the thoracic and abdominal walls to expose the liver fully, tie off the vena cava below the liver, sever the portal vein and insert the cannula into the right atrium and thence downward into the inferior vena cava. Then pass a ligature around the vena cava and tie proximal to the bulbous end of the cannula. Then wash out the blood from the liver with warm saline solution from a 20–50 cc Luer syringe attached by a 15 cm (6 in.) length of thin walled rubber tubing to the cannula, carefully avoiding introduction of air. When clear saline solution flows from the portal vein, substitute another 10–20 cc Luer syringe filled with the warm carbon gelatin and inject. In changing the syringes, carefully avoid air bubbles. The surface of the liver blackens quickly. Gentle digital massage of the liver surface during injection facilitates both removal of blood and penetration by the mass.

Injection of the portal system is done in a similar manner, by placing the cannula in the portal vein below the liver and opening the inferior vena cava above it.

With larger animals, or human organs, some type of gravity perfusion apparatus with a heating arrangement to maintain temperature is required. A manometer can readily be attached to the injection system with a T tube, and the pressure can be regulated by varing the height of the reservoir of the gravity apparatus.

Some workers use 0.5% ammonium oxalate and 0.75% sodium chloride in the fluid used for washing out the blood before injection. This tends to prevent clotting. The inclusion of 0.2% sodium nitrite, in either the washing or injection fluid, will promote vascular dilation.

Ashton (*Brit. J. Ophth.* **34:**38, 1950) injects the retinal vessels with India ink. The long nerve end of the freshly enucleated eye is dipped in formalin for a few minutes. Then under a dissecting microscope, the optic nerve is cut across and a fine glass cannula is inserted into the isolated central artery. The vessels are first perfused for a few minutes with distilled water at about 500 mm mercury pressure. This perfusion is followed by one with 10% formalin, and then by the India ink. The eyeball is then immersed in formalin for 12 hours before opening. Although Ashton's procedure was intended for gross display of the retina, Ashburn's experience (p. 643) with the liver indicates that the material can be used for histologic purposes.

Fischer's Milk Method (*Zbl. allg. Path.* **13:**977, 1902). Since these carbon masses do not penetrate the capillaries, and this is perhaps their greatest virtue, it is necessary to resort to other methods for demonstration of the capillaries. One may wash out with salt solution as above and then inject with milk or cream, tie off both afferent and efferent vessels and fix in 7.5 cc formalin, 1.5 glacial acetic acid and 100 cc distilled water. Cut frozen sections and stain with Sudan III or IV (Fischer) or oil red O as usual (p. 457), and mount in Apáthy's gum syrup (p. 101). Or one may use one of the carmine or Berlin blue gelatin masses.

Carmine gelatin masses are made by dissolving carmine in water with heat and ammonia water, and then either first mixing with the gelatin solution and then neutralizing, or the converse. Overacidification with acetic acid is likely to occur and ruins the mass by producing a granular red precipitate. Mallory avoids this difficulty by driving off the excess ammonia by heat. I suggest the combination of gentle heat and blowing an air current over the surface of the carmine or carmine gelatin until ammonia is no longer detectable by odor or with moist litmus or nitrazine paper. Most of the directions for carmine gelatin masses are very vague as to the amounts of gelatin and of carmine in the final mixture. Robin alone among the authors cited in Lee prescribed 1 part gelatin and 7–10 parts of water for an aqueous gelatin mass, and 50 gm gelatin, 300 of water, and 150 of glycerol for a glycerol gelatin mass. He dissolved carmine in ammonia water and diluted it in glycerol and neutralized with acetic acid in glycerol, attaining perhaps a 3–4% stock solution of carmine, which was diluted with 3–4 volumes of either of the above masses.

Berlin blue masses we have generally found too pale for histologic use. Robin prescribed (A) 90 cc (?) saturated aqueous (28–30%) potassium ferrocyanide solution plus 50 cc glycerol; and (B) 3 cc (30 cc ?) Pharmacopoeial (French) ferric chloride solution (about 26%) plus 50 cc glycerol. These were mixed slowly, a few drops of hydrochloric acid were added, and the mixture was then combined with 3 volumes of one of his gelatin vehicles at 45–50°C. This is nearly a 15-fold excess of ferrocyanide. I suggest 17 gm crystalline potassium ferrocyanide, 85 cc distilled water and 50 cc glycerol for solution A above; and 30 cc U. S. or P. G. ferric chloride solution in B.

Or one may make a saturated aqueous "solution" of "soluble Berlin blue" at 60°C and mix with 3 volumes of 12% gelatin solution at the same temperature.

Since glycerol masses especially tend to cause contraction of vessels, it is well to add 0.1–0.2% sodium nitrite either to the preceding saline solution or to the mass itself or to both.

After injection with any gelatin mass, quickly cool the injected organs and fix in 10% formalin. With Berlin blue masses, avoid alkali, since this tends to convert the ferric ferrocyanide into ferric hydroxide and soluble alkali ferrocyanide. The inclusion of a little ferric chloride in the dehydrating alcohol is suggested by Romeis.

CORROSION TECHNICS

By substituting some such substance as rubber or neoprene latex for the injection mass and then digesting off the tissues with hydrochloric acid or artificial gastric juice, interesting casts of the vascular system may be obtained.

Duff and More (*J. Tech. Methods* **24**:1, 1944) used such a method on adult human kidneys. Kidneys as soon as possible post mortem are washed with tap water at 75 mm mercury pressure through a cannula tied into the renal artery. After 30 minutes' washing, the pressure is raised to 150 mm and washing is continued for several hours (until the kidney becomes uniformly pale) but not over 12–15 hours. Then, leaving the cannula in place, disconnect from the water faucet and place in a covered dish at 4°C for 6–12 hours to allow as much water to escape as possible. Then keep at 20–25°C for about 5 hours before injection with neoprene. Completely fill the tubing with the neoprene before connecting to the cannula. Inject with air pressure at 150 mm for 3½ minutes for normal kidneys. Injection of sclerotic kidneys may require 5 minutes' injection, or raising the pressure to 250 mm or warming the kidney to 60°C for 30 minutes before injection. Then disconnect and immerse the whole kidney in commercial hydrochloric acid at 56°C for 24–36 hours, agitating gently from time to time until all the renal tissue can be removed by gently washing the cast in warm water.

The cast maintains its form floating in water, but collapses when removed. Small fragments of the vascular tree may be teased apart and cut

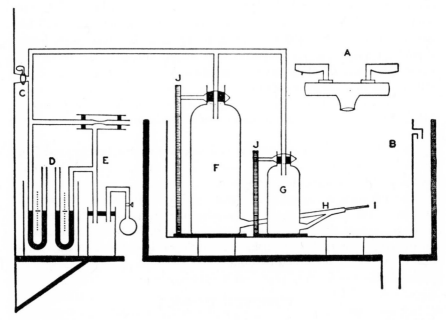

FIG. 19-1. Injection apparatus for metal corrosion preparations. Hot and cold water faucet A is over large sink B with a water bath containing kerosene reservoir F, metal reservoir G, Y-tube H with clamps (not shown) on each arm, cannula I, and ring stands J to support reservoirs. Air pressure enters from inlet C, is measured by manometers D, and controlled by a maximum-pressure Starling escape valve E.

off for microscopic study. The authors suggest Farrants's medium for examination under a coverglass of such fragments of the vascular tree. According to Lieb, neoprene casts should be stored in some mold inhibiting fluid (*J. Tech. Methods* **20**:48, 1940).

Similar corrosion methods have been used for injection of lungs through the bronchi, and simultaneous injection of the vascular system with neoprene latex of a different color can be done. Rigid plastics may be substituted for the latex.

McClenahan and Vogel (*Am. J. Roentgen.* **68**:406, 1952) use an alloy of bismuth (44.7), lead (22.6), indium (19.1), tin (8.3) and cadmium (5.3), designated as "Cerrolow 117,"[1] which melts at 47.2°C.

Arteries of organs to be injected are ligated before removal from the body to prevent access of air. The injection system is cleared of air, and the cannula is inserted into the artery and ligated in place under water. The organ is perfused with cool kerosene at 120–150 mm mercury pressure until the return flow is free of blood clots. The organ and the alloy reservoir are then warmed for about 30 minutes in a water bath at about 50°C. The organ is so oriented that the metal enters from the lowest point, so as to avoid entrapping kerosene; and perfusion with metal is carried on until no more kerosene emerges from the efferent veins by maintaining a pressure nearly equal to the antemortem maximum. The organ is then chilled with cold water while pressure is still maintained. When cold, the organ is transferred to 20% potassium hydroxide (15% NaOH should serve) and the soft tissue is corroded off over a period of 24 hours, with 2 changes of alkali and periodic gentle washing in water.

Large casts tend to sag at room temperature. Imbedding in clear plastic and cold storage are suggested as means of keeping casts undistorted.

RADIOAUTOGRAPHY

This procedure has had wide use in the past decade or so in a great variety of histologic research endeavors. By use of amino acids, nucleotides and other metabolites containing carbon 14 or hydrogen 3 (tritium) it has been possible to follow these substances in histologic location in protein and nucleic acid syntheses and other phases of metabolism. Specific proteins tagged with iodine 131 or sulfur 35 have been followed histologically on parenteral administration. The intestinal absorption of C^{14} labeled lactose has been examined; the fate of Fe^{59} fed in the food or parenterally injected has been studied. I^{131} thyroxine, H^3 noradrenaline, C^{14} carbon tetrachloride in liver necrosis have been scrutinized as to histologic and cytologic localization and changes therein in physiologic or pathologic processes. Cystine or methionine S^{35} and sodium sulfate S^{35} have been used for the study of sulfur and sul-

[1] Cerro de Pasco Copper Co., New York, N.Y.

fate turnover in proteins and in acid mucopolysaccharides. Zinc 65 has been fed to partially zinc deficient rats to help localize normal deposits of that metal.

The procedures of fastening a piece of dental film or 35 mm film to a slide with a rubber band or a strip of adhesive tape and treating slide and film separately after exposure have fallen largely into disuse, giving way to procedures in which the relation of film to section is permanently maintained. The procedures, relatively new 10 years ago, of coating with liquid emulsion and of application of prepared adhesive stripping film have become widespread, and each has undergone a number of modifications. For each I will cite a recent variation.

Liquid Emulsion Coating Technic, According to Kopriwa and Leblond (*J. Histochem.* **10:**269, 1962). This technic is generally credited to Leblond, the earliest reference cited by him and his associates being Bélanger and Leblond, *Endocrinology* **39:**8, 1946.

Fixation of tissue should be in accord with the special requirements for the specific tissue elements under study. Most ordinary fixations are suitable. Very thorough removal of mercury with iodine and of the iodine with cysteine should be practiced.

Routine paraffin sectioning is done; sections are deparaffinized and stained with alum hematoxylin if desired, or left unstained.

Collodionization. This step is perhaps preferably omitted for routine purposes. Messier and Leblond prescribed 2 dips into 1% collodion and drying overnight in a vertical position. The collodion film prevents 15–35% of the tritium beta particles from reaching the emulsion. Some stains, however, cause emulsion fogging if not covered.

Emulsion. Eastman NTB 2 bulk emulsion seems generally the most suitable. NTB 3 and the British Ilford K 5, which latter must be diluted after melting with an equal volume of triple distilled water to give the same consistency as NTB 2, also seem quite serviceable.

Coating. This is done in a photographic darkroom maintained at about 28°C (82.4°F) and 80% humidity, at about 1 meter (3 ft) from a Wratten safelight No. 2. Solid emulsion, stored in the refrigerator in the darkroom at 5°C, is scooped out with a porcelain spoon and deposited in a cylindrical staining jar which is standing in a 40–45°C water bath. In about an hour the emulsion is completely melted and free of bubbles. Warm slides bearing sections on a warm plate set at 40°C and dip in emulsion for 1–2 seconds. Drain excess back into jar and dry slides in vertical position for about 90–100 minutes with safelight turned off.

Exposure. Transfer slides to black plastic boxes containing a perforated metal capsule loaded with Drierite. Seal box with black adhesive tape, mark box with orange grease pencil identifying slides and date. Put box in cold room at 5°C, standing on end so that slides are horizontal with emulsion side down.

Exposure times vary with the isotope used, its state of decay if short lived, the amount present in the tissue and the substance in which incorporated. Previous published work with the isotope in use can be a fairly good guide, but in early experiments of an investigation it is well to try a series of exposure times designed to bracket the expected optimum.

Developing. This should be done in a separate photographic darkroom regulated at 17–18°C (about 63°F). Develop 2 minutes in Dektol (D-72), or 6 minutes in Dolmi (D-170) or 3 minutes in D-178. Fix in acid fixer with hardener or in 24% hypo for 10 minutes. Wash 15 minutes in running water at 17–18°C. Dehydrate in 95% alcohol, 2 changes of absolute alcohol, clear in cedar oil, wash in xylene and mount in balsam or synthetic resin.

It is to be noted that a considerable variety of stains may be applied to sections before coating, including hematoxylin eosin, the periodic acid Schiff reaction and Van Gieson's stain. Harris's hematoxylin and Bullard's are to be avoided. Apparently the mercuric oxide used in ripening is deleterious. Instead use a naturally ripened formula such as Boehmer's, Delafield's or Ehrlich's or an iodate formula, *e.g.*, Mayer's or Lillie's.

The Stripping Film Method. Stripping film Kodak England AR.10 seems to be preferred by some workers. Sections are prepared as for the coating technic, deparaffinized, stained as needed and brought to distilled water.

Film is cut in the darkroom to a size usually somewhat larger than the slide to be covered and placed face down on fresh distilled water for 2–3 minutes to swell the under plastic layer. The slide is then dipped into the water bath under the cut film, and the latter is picked up on it. Dry with fan at 20–25°C and store in black boxes as for the coating method (Pearse, 1960).

For Zn^{65} and other highly water soluble substances the method of Millar, Vincent and Mawson (*J. Histochem.* 9:111, 1961) seems applicable. Tissues were fixed in 9:1 methanol formalin, 4–5 μ serial (paraffin) sections were cut, Kodak autoradiographic permeable base 35 mm stripping film was used. Sections were dewaxed in dry chloroform and mounted on slides in the same.

A piece of film 10 cm long was cut from the roll, removed from the base and allowed to swell emulsion side down on distilled water. It was then transferred through 2 dry chloroform baths and mounted on the slide in the second bath with the aid of a stainless steel wire mesh fork holder with a space slightly wider than a 25 mm slide between the 2 lateral arms. The slide is brought up beneath the film between the fork arms of the film holder and the film is withdrawn from the holder on the slide. The slide and film were then washed in absolute alcohol, dried, stored, developed and mounted according to Pelc's method (*Internat. J. Appl. Radiol. Isotopes* 1:172, 1956). Instead the developer and fixer prescribed by the maker of the film should be used.

Fitzgerald (*J. Histochem.* 9:597, 1961) has avoided diffusion of water soluble materials in the preparation of radioautographs by using vacuum freeze desiccated cryostat sections or freeze substituted cryostat sections of immediately frozen experimental material. Stripping film is stripped and pressed down on the dry sections without prior wetting and exposed for the requisite period at $-20°C$. The preparations are then rehydrated either by exposure for several hours in the dark to an atmosphere of 80–90% humidity or by 5 minute immersion in formalin solution, followed by redrying before development. This improved adhesion of the stripping film to the glass slide. Development was done as usual with DK-50 for 3 minutes. Cytidine H^3 and thymidine H^3 were thus localized.

Baserga's Two Emulsion Procedure for H^3 and C^{14}. Utilizing the known shorter range of beta particles from H^3 (1.5 μ) as compared with that of the higher energy beta particles from C^{14} (60 μ), Baserga (*J. Histochem.* 9:586, 1961), in studies of the incorporation of thymidine H^3 into deoxyribonucleic acid and of uridine-2-C^{14} into ribonucleic acid, adapted the following technic from Joftes (*Lab. Invest.* 8:131, 1959).

1. Deparaffinize and hydrate 4 μ sections. In the darkroom
2. Dip in Eastman NTB_2 emulsion at 40°C (p. 649). Here it seems preferable to follow the latest method of Kopriwa and Leblond:
3. After 15 days, develop, fix, wash and stain with Mayer's hematoxylin.
4. Then dip 3 seconds in a diluted celloidin made by diluting Randolph Products celloidin imbedding solution A-4700 with 2 volumes of absolute alcohol + ether (50:50). Drain and dry. This is probably equivalent to 2–4% celloidin.
5. Dip again as before in Eastman NTB_2 emulsion.
6. Expose in dark another 15 days, develop, fix, wash, dehydrate and mount following the general directions of Kopriwa and Leblond.

The lower emulsion, immediately over the section, registers beta particle tracks both from the tritiated thymidine and from the radiocarbon labeled uridine; the upper emulsion contains tracks only from C^{14}.

Baserga regards this procedure of interposing a layer of celloidin between the 2 emulsion layers an improvement over that of Krause and Plaut (*Nature* 188:511, 1960), who used 2 layers of stripping film immediately superimposed.

Although other brands of nitrocellulose could undoubtedly be used, it would be necessary to determine experimentally the concentration which would yield a film of the required thickness to stop tritium beta particles and not materially impair the passage of the C^{14} particles.

Baserga's second report (*J. Histochem.* **10**:628, 1962) indicated that substitution of AR.10 stripping film in either or both of the stages gave poorer results and that the intermediary celloidin film was necessary and was superior to Permount, Formvar, polyvinyl alcohol and other substances. Additional H^3 and C^{14} compounds were used, with similar results.

MICROINCINERATION

The practice of microincineration, according to Lison, dates back over a century to Raspail in 1833, and has been reintroduced several times *de novo*. It was used by Virchow in 1847 for identification of iron in hemosiderin.

It is necessary to utilize some method of preparation of tissues which neither adds extrinsic mineral elements, as do chromates and mercuric salts, nor removes those mineral elements naturally present. Some have tried using frozen sections of unfixed fresh tissue, but these were difficult to prepare or to flatten on slides without some flotation procedure before the introduction of cryostat methods. The procedure of rapid freezing with liquid air (or easier, with one of the acetone carbon dioxide technics used for freezing blood plasma) followed by desiccation *in vacuo* at -35 to $-50°C$ and infiltration with paraffin directly after desiccation offers theoretically the best tissue preparation. Paraffin sections can then be cut and attached to appropriate slides as usual.

Fixation with 100% alcohol conserves most mineral elements well but gives indifferent to poor tissue fixation. The use of 10% formalin in alcohol is perhaps the best method. With 100% alcohol dehydration, clearing in benzene and paraffin infiltration it affords losses of water soluble salts perhaps as small as those from any other method.

The paraffin sections for incineration are to be floated on freshly filtered 95–100% alcohol on clean glass slides without albumen or other adhesive. Alternate sections should be prepared as usual for ordinary histologic examination and topographic comparison with the ashed sections. Sections should preferably be cut at 3–5 μ.

Place the slides on quartz plates or on slides in an electric furnace. Raise the temperature gradually at first, taking 10 minutes to reach 100°C; then more rapidly to 650°C, reaching this temperature in another 25 minutes. These are Scott's directions. Lison recommends the Schultz-Braun procedure of heating in flowing nitrogen until 500–530°C is reached, then admitting air for a few minutes to burn off the carbon. By this method, chlorides are said to be better preserved than at the higher temperatures, and the formation of not easily combustible partial oxidation products at lower temperatures is avoided.

When the oven is opened after incineration, remove the quartz plate and slides with heated forceps, to avoid rapid chilling and cracking of the glass. Then place the slides on an asbestos plate to cool. Cover the ashed section or *spodogram* (σπόδος ashes, γράμμα a drawing, a writing or a picture) with a coverglass and fasten down the edges with paraffin, petrolatum, sealing wax or a pyroxylin cement. Some sections may be sprayed with thin collodion (0.5–1% nitrocellulose in ether alcohol) for the purpose of making solubility tests and chemical reactions on the spodograms. This is not advised as the routine procedure, but see Fenton *et al.*, p. 653.

The first examination is to be made with oblique illumination from a strong light. Dark field condensers may also be used; and study under reflected light as practiced in mineralogic microscopy may be of value. Low magnifications are generally most profitable. Cell topography is often well maintained, but nuclei may not be evident.

Sodium and potassium chlorides, tricalcium and magnesium phosphates are preserved as such; carbonates are converted into oxides such as sodium, calcium and magnesium oxides. Dipotassium phosphate (K_2HPO_4) is converted into the pyrophosphate ($K_4P_2O_7$). Iron compounds appear as yellow to red ferric oxide (Fe_2O_3). Silica generally combines with calcium to form various silicates. Sulfur is either volatilized or converted into (or remains as) sulfates.

Identification of elements still remains difficult. Certain birefringent silica crystals remain identifiable. Silica appears as a white, doubly refractile crystalline mineral. It is insoluble in water. Calcium is seen as a white, singly refractile ash, almost insoluble in water. It responds to the gypsum and oxalate tests (p. 438). Magnesium is difficult to identify in the presence of calcium. Here the collodion technic, with some of the newer color reactions (Chapter 13), could be useful.

According to Alexander and Myerson, iron is present as yellow to red ferric oxide. It is to be distinguished from remaining carbon. The latter is black in direct transmitted light. Application of the HCl potassium ferrocyanide reagent (p. 407) to the collodionized ash gives the Prussian blue reaction, though the use of this test is not mentioned by these authors.

The papers of Scott (*Prot.* **20**:133, 1933; *Am. J. Anat.* **53**:243, 1933; *Anat. Rec.* **55**:75, 1933), of Cowdry (*Am. J. Path.* **9**:149, 1933) and of Alexander and Myerson (*Am. J. Path.* **13**:405, 1937) may be consulted. The last contains a bibliography of 124 titles, many of which deal with microincineration.

Erich Hintzsche's monograph *Das Aschenbild tierischer Gewebe und Organe*, Springer, Berlin, 1956 (149 pp.), should prove a valuable and comprehensive reference of more recent date.

Calcium Oxalate. Johnson (*J. Histochem.* **4**:404, 1956) demonstrated that by microincineration in a muffle furnace at 425–475°C calcium oxalate was converted to calcium carbonate. The carbonate could then be identified by gently applying dilute acid to the ash while under microscopic observation. Bubbles of CO_2 were evolved. If the preparations were heated to 600°C, $CaCO_3$ broke down to CaO and no gas was produced on addition of acid. As a further control it would be demonstrable that unheated preparations did not evolve gas on acid treatment.

Johnson later noted (*J. Histochem.* **6**:405, 1958) that calcium succinate, citrate, malonate and maleate also yield calcium carbonate on microincineration at 450°C, and that this may be demonstrated by evolution of CO_2 on acid treatment of the ash. However, pretreatment of sections with 2 *N* acetic acid removes such salts other than oxalate. Strontium and barium oxalates are also converted to carbonate by 450°C microincineration. Here Johnson noted that the Ca ash forms a red lake with alizarin red S and that those of Ba and Sr do not. It should be noted that 450°C microincineration leaves a considerable amount of unburned carbon.

Wolman and Goldring (*J. Histochem.* **10**:505, 1962) applied the von Kóssa reaction to the ash of preparations made by Johnson's method, thereby obtaining permanent preparations. It was necessary to compare serial sections, one not incinerated and one incinerated at 450°C and reacted by von Kóssa, and a third, incinerated but unsilvered. Only black deposits appearing in the silvered spodogram alone were considered as calcium oxalate. Wolman and Goldring sttae categorically that unashed calcium oxalate does not react to the von Kóssa test.

Johnson's method (*J. Histochem.* **12**:153, 1964) of *microincineration,* though less precise in temperature control than muffle furnace technics, can afford quite usable preparations without the more elaborate equipment required for the latter.

1. Cut 6–8 μ paraffin sections of material fixed in formalin, alcohol or other non-metal containing fixatives and mount on glass slides. Stain control preparations by appropriate usual histologic or histochemical methods.
2. Place slide in middle of an asbestos board and heat cautiously with the blue flame of a gas burner (Fisher or Meeker type), directing the flame downward on the slide and keeping it in motion to heat evenly. The section turns brown and then white. Continue heating, until it has almost disappeared.
3. Then cover slide with an inverted metal pan resting on the asbestos board. The pan heats up and slows the cooling of the slide, so that breakage of the glass from too rapid cooling is avoided.

Fenton, Johnson and Zimmerman (*J. Histochem.* **12**:153, 1964) have modified the foregoing technic by adding a specific histochemical reaction for iron after microincineration.

The microincinerated section, when cold, is gently dipped into a very thin parlodion or celloidin solution (dilute 1.5 cc 1% celloidin to 100 cc with an equal volume absolute alcohol ether mixture); remove slide at once and let dry in air.

Authors then apply a mixture of equal volumes of 5% potassium ferro-cyanide and 0.6 N hydrochloric acid and allow to act for 15 minutes. Wash in distilled water, dry in air or in oven and mount in Permount.

The reaction can also be watched in wet preparations.

Chapter 20

Buffers and Buffer Tables, Normal Acids and Alkalies

Since the previous edition we have expanded considerably our use of buffers, not only for staining procedures but also during fixation methods, in enzyme localization technics and in some decalcification procedures. Additional buffers in the acid and alkaline ranges have been found useful and are included here. Since the pH levels of buffer mixtures vary with their dilution, in a few cases figures for more than one dilution are included.

It is to be remembered that buffer mixtures are comparatively ineffective in preventing pH displacement when one of the salts is present in nearly pure form. The same phenomenon is observed with phosphates and citrates when the mixture is such that a mono- or dihydrogen salt would be crystallized in nearly pure form if the mixture were evaporated. Hence, where adjacent pH figures in any buffer series are relatively widely separated and no other contraindications exist, it is preferable to use a different buffer series if the desired pH level is approximated by a number of consecutive readings in the tables. Hence, closely spaced pH values in the tables are printed in boldface.

Due regard must be given to the effect of the buffer ions on the other ingredients of the solution in which they are used. For example, acid phosphate buffers precipitate thionin. Tartrates precipitate calcium salts, as do the less acid phosphate buffers. Acetates and citrates can be used in acid silver solutions. Formates and citrates reduce permanganate and chromate solutions, but acetates and phosphates can be used. (Acetic acid reduces permanganates and chromates slowly at 95–100°C.)

In the alkaline range buffers are less satisfactory because of their avidity for carbon dioxide from the laboratory air.

The salts and acids used should be of reagent grade—those specially made for buffer use when available. Particular note should be taken of the molecular weight specified on bottle labels. That weight should be used in preparing solutions, since some of the salts are available in a variety of states of hydration. It is often a matter of indifference whether

TABLE 20-1. FORMULAE AND MOLECULAR WEIGHTS OF COMMON BUFFER INGREDIENTS AND REAGENTS[1]

	Formulae	Molecular weights
Acetic acid[2]	CH_3COOH	60.05
Ammediol (2-amino-2-methyl-1,3-propanediol	$H_2N-\overset{\displaystyle CH_2OH}{\underset{\displaystyle CH_2OH}{\overset{\displaystyle \|}{\underset{\displaystyle \|}{C}}}}-CH_3$	105.140
Ammonia[2]	NH_3	17.032
Barbital sodium (sodium diethyl barbiturate)	$C_8H_{11}O_3N_2Na$	206.18
Borax	$Na_2B_4O_7 \cdot 10H_2O$	381.43
Boric acid	$B(OH)_3$	61.84
Cacodylic acid	$(CH_3)_2AsO_2H$	137.99
Citric acid, anhydrous	$C_3H_4(OH)(COOH)_3$	192.12
Citric acid, crystals	$C_3H_4(OH)(COOH)_3 \cdot H_2O$	210.14
γ-Collidine	$2,4,6(CH_3)_3C_5H_2N$	121.18
Ferric chloride anhydrous	$FeCl_3$	162.22
Ferric chloride crystals	$FeCl_3 \cdot 6H_2O$	270.32
Formic acid[2]	$HCOOH$	46.03
Glycine	NH_2CH_2COOH	75.07
Hydrochloric acid[2]	HCl	36.465
Maleic acid	$HOOCCH=CHCOOH$	116.07
Nitric acid[2]	HNO_3	63.016
Oxalic acid	$(COOH)_2$	90.038
Potassium acid phosphate	KH_2PO_4	136.09
Potassium chloride	KCl	74.553
Potassium hydroxide	KOH	56.104
Potassium phosphate tribasic	K_3PO_4	212.275
Sodium acetate	CH_3COONa	82.04
Sodium acetate, crystals	$CH_3COONa \cdot 3H_2O$	136.09
Sodium acid phosphate	$NaH_2PO_4 \cdot H_2O$	138.01
Sodium chloride	$NaCl$	58.448
Sodium citrate, crystals	$C_3H_4OH(COONa)_3 \cdot 5\frac{1}{2}H_2O$	357.18
Sodium citrate, granular	$C_3H_4OH(COONa)_3 \cdot 2H_2O$	294.12
Sodium formate	$HCOONa$	68.015
Sodium hydroxide	$NaOH$	40.005
Sodium oxalate	$Na_2C_2O_4$	134.004
Sodium phosphate, dibasic	Na_2HPO_4	141.98
Sulfuric acid[2]	H_2SO_4	98.082
Trihydroxymethylaminomethane ("tris")	$H_2NC(CH_2OH)_3$	121.14
Veronal sodium, Medinal (sodium 5,5-diethylbarbiturate)	$C_8H_{11}O_3N_2Na$	206.18

[1] Emended slightly from Lange, 1949.
[2] See special tables for preparation of normal solutions, pp. 672–673.

TABLE 20-2. pH STANDARD BUFFER SOLUTIONS AT 15–30°C

Molarity	Name	15°C	20°C	25°C	30°C	Grams per liter
0.05	Potassium tetraoxalate	1.67	1.68	1.68	1.69	12.71$KH_3(C_2O_4)_2 \cdot 2H_2O$
	Potassium acid tartrate	....	....	3.56	3.55	Shake excess salt with water at 25°C, decant
0.05	Potassium acid phthalate	4.00	4.00	4.01	4.01	10.21 $KHC_8H_4O_4(o)$
0.025⎫ 0.025⎭	$KH_2PO_4 + Na_2HPO_4$	6.90	6.88	6.86	6.85	3.40 KH_2PO_4 3.55 Na_2HPO_4
0.01	Borax ($Na_2B_4O_7 \cdot 10\ H_2O$)	9.27	9.22	9.18	9.14	3.81

Source: From Lange.

TABLE 20-3. ACID PHOSPHATES

HCl, cc	KH_2 PO_4, cc	pH values	
		1 M	0.1 M
30	20	0.69	1.53
29	21	0.75	1.56
28	22	0.81	1.63
27	23	0.90	1.66
26	24	0.98	1.71
25	25	1.05	1.77
24	26	1.12	1.80
23	27	1.23	1.84
22	28	1.35	1.89
21	29	1.43	1.94
20	30	1.52	2.00
19	31	1.61	2.05
18	32	1.70	2.10
17	33	1.76	2.15
16	34	1.82	2.23
15	35	1.92	2.27
14	36	2.02	2.31
13	37	2.11	2.38
12	38	2.20	2.44
11	39	2.29	2.50
10	40	2.38	2.56
9	41	2.45	2.63
8	42	2.52	2.70
7	43	2.62	2.79
6	44	2.72	2.89
5	45	2.85	3.02
4	46	3.00	3.14
3	47	3.17	3.23
2	48	3.32	3.44

Note: Use 1 N and 0.1 N HCl for acid component. See Table 20-25, KH_2PO_4, M.W. 136.09. Use 1 mol and 0.1 mol per liter, respectively.

TABLE 20-4. HCl SODIUM CITRATE BUFFER SERIES AT 1 M, 0.1 M, 0.01 M

HCl, cc	Na citr., cc	pH values			HCl cc	Na citr., cc	pH values		
		1 M	0.1 M	0.01 M			1 M	0.1 M	0.01 M
50	0	0.25	1.11	2.10	25	25	4.69	5.10	5.42
49	1	0.27	1.14	2.15	24	26	4.78	5.20	5.52
48	2	0.30	1.19	2.20	23	27	4.85	5.28	5.61
47	3	0.35	1.24	2.25	22	28	4.92	5.35	5.70
46	4	0.40	1.29	2.30	21	29	5.00	5.41	5.79
45	5	0.45	1.34	2.35	20	30	5.05	5.48	5.87
44	6	0.51	1.38	2.40	19	31	5.10	5.54	5.93
43	7	0.58	1.42	2.45	18	32	5.17	5.60	5.97
42	8	0.67	1.50	2.50	17	33	5.22	5.65	6.01
41	9	0.80	1.65	2.60	16	34	5.28	5.70	6.06
40	10	0.97	1.85	2.70	15	35	5.33	5.75	6.10
39	11	1.30	2.12	2.85	14	36	5.37	5.79	6.14
38	12	2.00	2.52	3.02	13	37	5.42	5.83	6.19
37	13	2.60	2.90	3.24	12	38	5.49	5.87	6.25
36	14	2.95	3.24	3.50	11	39	5.56	5.93	6.31
35	15	3.25	3.58	3.80	10	40	5.63	6.00	6.36
34	16	3.50	3.82	4.03	9	41	5.70	6.06	6.42
33	17	3.67	4.00	4.22	8	42	5.79	6.14	6.50
32	18	3.84	4.18	4.40	7	43	5.88	6.21	6.60
31	19	4.01	4.36	4.60	6	44	5.97	6.30	6.69
30	20	4.18	4.52	4.75	5	45	6.06	6.39	6.78
29	21	4.30	4.67	4.91	4	46	6.16	6.48	6.88
28	22	4.40	4.79	5.05	3	47	6.27	6.57	6.98
27	23	4.50	4.90	5.20	2	48	6.42	6.73	7.11
26	24	4.59	5.00	5.31	1	49	6.66	6.97	7.25
					0	50	7.17	7.51	7.82

Note: Sodium citrate is used at 357.18, 35.718 and 3.572 gm crystals per liter for 1 M, 0.1 M and 0.01 M, respectively. Granular sodium citrate, M.W. 294.12, contains less water; use 294.12, 29.412 and 2.941 gm/liter for 1 M, 0.1 M and 0.01 M.

a sodium or a potassium salt is used in a buffer mixture, providing that due account is taken of the change in molecular weight.

Distilled water is usually acid as prepared from block tin stills, and redistillation from glass does not seem to remedy this fault. Even freshly distilled or doubly distilled water boiled to expel carbon dioxide and cooled often gives pH levels between 5 and 6. However, the amount of acid present seems too small to affect seriously even hundredth-molar buffers, and we usually ignore the fact that fresh distilled water may measure pH 5.5. For most purposes singly distilled water of that pH level is quite satisfactory in buffers.

Buffers containing sodium citrate are particularly liable to mold growth. Strong stock buffers should be made up in 20–25% alcohol to

TABLE 20-5. SULFURIC ACID, ACID SODIUM PHOSPHATE BUFFER SERIES
FOR NILE BLUE STAINS

0.1 M solutions			0.1 M solutions			0.1 M solutions		
pH	H_2SO_4	NaH_2PO_4	pH	H_2SO_4	NaH_2PO_4	pH	H_2SO_4	NaH_2PO_4
1.1	50	0	2.1	36	14	3.1	13.5	36.5
1.2	48.5	1.5	2.2	34	16	3.2	11.5	38.5
1.3	47	3	2.3	31.5	18.5	3.3	10	40
1.4	45.5	4.5	2.4	30	20	3.4	8	42
1.5	44.5	5.5	2.5	28	22	3.5	6	44
1.6	44	6	2.6	25	25	3.6	5	45
1.7	42	8	2.7	23	27	3.7	3.5	46.5
1.8	40.5	9.5	2.8	20	30	3.8	2.5	47.5
1.9	39	11	2.9	18	32	3.9	1.5	48.5
2.0	37	13	3.0	15	35	4.0	0.5	49.5

Note: 0.2 M H_2SO_4, pH 0.87. 1% H_2SO_4 v/v, pH 0.9. See Table 20-25 for sulfuric acid; 0.1 M = 0.2 N. For 0.1 M $N_2H_2PO_4$, use 13.801 gm disodium phosphate per liter.

SOURCE: From *Stain Techn.* **31**:151, 1956.

inhibit this growth. When diluted 1:20 or 1:25 for use the alcohol concentration falls to an insignificant 1% or so.

In the acid range I have added a sulfuric acid, acid sodium phosphate series for Nile blue stains, Pearse's HCl sodium acetate series, an additional 0.01 M dilution series for the Walpole acetates, a cacodylate buffer from *Long's Handbook,* Gomori's tris HCl buffer from Pearse, 1960, Gancevici's K_3PO_4 HCl buffer in the 9.5–12.4 pH range, and have expanded the useful Michaelis Veronal HCl series by interpolation, to give closer readings. Holmes's borate series and Gomori's collidine hydrochloric acid series are retained from previous editions, for I have found occasional use for them. The McIlvaine series as given varies to some extent from that given by Clark, whose figures are based on the undiluted aqueous mixtures. The figures here are based on a 1:25 dilution of the stock 25% methanol solutions in distilled water, the concentration at which this buffer is used in azure eosin stains.

Data were determined on a Beckman pH meter, corrected to 25°C, and slightly smoothed. I am indebted to P. Jones for these measurements.

Tables based on Lange's data for density and grams per liter of the significant constituent are presented for the ready preparation of normal acid and ammonia solutions. For chemical titration procedures, these solutions must be standardized as usual, but for most histologic purposes they may be used as prepared.

TABLE 20-6. 0.1 *N* MALEIC
ACID + SODIUM HYDROXIDE,
LASKEY, 1951

1 *N* maleic acid	0.1 *N* NaOH	Distilled H$_2$O	pH
5	6	39	**1.83**
5	7	38	**1.87**
5	8	37	**1.89**
5	9	36	**1.90**
5	10	35	**1.94**
5	11	34	**1.98**
5	12	33	**2.00**
5	13	32	**2.02**
5	14	31	**2.08**
5	15	30	**2.10**
5	16	29	**2.15**
5	17	28	**2.20**
5	18	27	**2.22**
5	19	26	**2.28**
5	20	25	**2.30**
5	21	24	**2.38**
5	22	23	**2.42**
5	23	22	**2.49**
5	24	21	**2.55**
5	25	20	**2.62**
5	26	19	**2.70**
5	27	18	**2.75**
5	28	17	**3.05**
5	29	16	3.31
5	30	15	3.62
5	31	14	4.40
5	32	13	4.71
5	33	12	**4.91**
5	34	11	**5.00**
5	35	10	**5.15**
5	36	9	**5.27**
5	37	8	**5.34**
5	38	7	**5.45**
5	39	6	**5.50**
5	40	5	**5.59**
5	41	4	**5.62**
5	42	3	**5.68**
5	43	2	**5.73**
5	44	1	**5.75**
5	45	0	**5.83**

Note: 1 *N* maleic acid = 116.07
gm/liter. 0.1 *N* sodium hydroxide =
4 gm/liter.

TABLE 20-7. WALPOLE BUFFER,
1914, MODIFIED FROM PEARSE,
1960

1 N HCl	1 M NaAc	Distilled H$_2$O	pH
20	10	20	**0.65**
18	10	22	**0.75**
16	10	24	**0.91**
14	10	26	**1.07**
13	10	27	**1.24**
12	10	28	**1.42**
11	10	29	**1.71**
10.7	10	29.3	1.85
10.5	10	29.5	1.99
10.2	10	29.8	2.32
10.0	10	30	2.64
9.95	10	30.05	2.72
9.7	10	30.3	3.09
9.5	10	30.5	3.29
9.25	10	30.75	3.49
9.0	10	31	**3.61**
8.5	10	31.5	**3.79**
8	10	32	**3.95**
7	10	33	**4.19**
6	10	34	**4.39**
5	10	35	**4.58**
4	10	36	**4.76**
3	10	37	**4.92**
2	10	38	**5.20**

Note: In using this buffer other solutions added must replace part of the water, so that the 50 cc volume is not increased. 1 M sodium acetate = 82.04 gm/liter. For 1 N HCl, see Table 20-25.

TABLE 20-8. WALPOLE ACETATE
BUFFER

Acetic acid, cc	Sodium acetate, cc	0.2 M pH	0.01 M pH
20.0	0.0	2.696	3.373
19.9	0.1	2.804	3.420
19.8	0.2	2.913	3.477
19.7	0.3	2.994	3.503
19.6	0.4	3.081	3.523
19.5	0.5	**3.147**	**3.543**
19.4	0.6	**3.202**	**3.590**
19.2	0.8	**3.315**	**3.593**
19.0	1.0	**3.416**	**3.647**
18.5	1.5	**3.592**	**3.737**
18.0	2.0	**3.723**	**3.863**
17.0	3.0	**3.900**	**3.980**
16.0	4.0	**4.047**	**4.110**
15.0	5.0	**4.160**	**4.223**
14.0	6.0	**4.270**	**4.337**
13.0	7.0	**4.360**	**4.473**
12.0	8.0	**4.454**	**4.527**
11.0	9.0	**4.530**	**4.600**
10.0	10.0	**4.626**	**4.717**
9.0	11.0	**4.710**	**4.807**
8.0	12.0	**4.802**	**4.910**
7.0	13.0	**4.900**	**5.000**
6.0	14.0	**4.990**	**5.077**
5.0	15.0	**5.110**	**5.183**
4.0	16.0	**5.227**	**5.373**
3.0	17.0	**5.380**	**5.500**
2.0	18.0	**5.574**	**5.713**
1.0	19.0	5.894	6.003
0.5	19.5	6.211	6.227
0.0	20.0	6.518	6.777

Note: 1 N acetic acid, pH 2.2. 2 N acetic acid, pH 2. 0.2 M sodium acetate = 16.408 gm/liter; 0.01 M = 820 mg/liter. For acetic acid, see Table 20-26.

TABLE 20-9. HORECKER-LILLIE
BUFFER TABLE
(1:25 Dilution of
Solutions in 25% Alcohol)

pH	40 mM citric acid	40 mM sodium citrate
2.86	20	0
2.95	19	1
3.08	18	2
3.23	17	3
3.40	16	4
3.58	15	5
3.80	14	6
4.01	13	7
4.27	12	8
4.50	11	9
4.65	10	10
4.84	9	11
5.04	8	12
5.26	7	13
5.50	6	14
5.74	5	15
5.97	4	16
6.17	3	17
6.42	2	18
6.77	1	19
7.60	0	20
	$M/10$ 21.0	$M/10$ 29.4

Note: Stock buffer is made at 0.1 M; thus 21.014 gm citric acid, 35718 gm sodium citrate crystals = 29.412 gm granular in 250 cc ethanol + 750 cc distilled water. Final dilutions contain 1% alcohol.

TABLE 20-10. MCILVAINE-LILLIE
BUFFER TABLE
(1:25 Dilution of Stock 25%
CH_3OH Solution)

pH	0.04 M citric acid	0.08 M disodium phosphate
2.5	20.0	0
2.6	19.5	0.5
2.65	19.0	1.0
2.7	18.5	1.5
2.75	18.0	2.0
2.8	17.5	2.5
2.9	17.0	3.0
3.0	16.5	3.5
3.05	16.0	4.0
3.1	15.5	4.5
3.2	15.0	5.0
3.3	14.5	5.5
3.45	14.0	6.0
3.6	13.5	6.5
3.75	13.0	7.0
3.95	12.5	7.5
4.1	12.0	8.0
4.3	11.5	8.5
4.5	11.0	9.0
4.75	10.5	9.5
4.95	10.0	10.0
5.3	9.5	10.5
5.5	9.0	11.0
5.7	8.5	11.5
6.0	8.0	12.0
6.1	7.5	12.5
6.3	7.0	13.0
6.4	6.5	13.5
6.5	6.0	14.0
6.6	5.5	14.5
6.8	5.0	15.0
6.9	4.5	15.5
7.0	4.0	16.0
7.1	3.5	16.5
7.2	3.0	17.0
7.3	2.5	17.5
7.4	2.0	18.0
7.5	1.5	18.5
7.7	1.0	19.0
8.0	0.5	19.5
8.3	0	20.0

Note: The stock buffer is made at 0.1 M citric acid and 0.2 M Na$_2$HPO$_4$ in 25% methanol. 21.014 gm citric acid 28.396 gm Na$_2$HPO$_4$ in 250 cc methanol + 750 cc distilled water. Use 2 cc for 50 cc stain.

TABLE 20-11. CACODYLATE BUFFER, 0°C AND 25°C

	0°C				25°C		
pH	1 M cacodylic acid, cc	1 N NaOH, cc	Distilled H_2O, cc	pH	1 M cacodylic acid, cc	1 N NaOH, cc	H_2O, cc
5.2	513	50	437	5.2	522	50	428
5.4	342	50	608	5.4	348	50	602
5.6	235	50	715	5.6	238	50	712
5.8	166	50	784	5.8	169	50	781
6.0	124	50	826	6.0	125	50	825
6.2	96.3	50	853.7	6.2	97.2	50	852.8
6.4	79.2	50	870.8	6.4	79.8	50	870.2
6.6	68.5	50	881.5	6.6	68.8	50	881.2
6.8	61.6	50	888.4	6.8	61.9	50	888.1
7.0	57.4	50	892.6	7.0	57.5	50	892.5
7.2	54.6	50	895.4	7.2	54.7	50	895.3

Note: Ionic strength, 0.05. Cacodylic acid 137.99 gm/liter = 1 M $(CH_3)_2AsO_2H$ recrystallized from warm alcohol (from Long's *Biochemists' Handbook*). Sodium hydroxide, M.W. 39.999, or essentially 40 gm/liter.

TABLE 20-12. SÖRENSEN'S PHOSPHATES[1]

	Dry salt mixtures[2] for field use				Phosphates at 0.1 M, 0.067 M, 5 mM				
pH	mg Na$_2$H PO$_4$ +	mg NaH$_2$ PO$_4$ ·H$_2$O	mg Na$_2$H PO$_4$ +	mg KH$_2$ PO$_4$	KH$_2$ PO$_4$ or Na H$_2$PO$_4$ ·H$_2$O, cc	Na$_2$H PO$_4$, cc	0.1 M	0.067 M	5 mM
5.3	27	973	27	973	50	0	4.41	4.47	4.77
5.4	33	967	33	967	48	2	5.31	5.42	5.63
5.5	41	959	42	958	47	3	5.53	5.60	5.81
5.6	52	948	53	947	46	4	5.67	5.74	5.95
5.7	66	934	67	933	45	5	5.78	5.83	6.06
5.8	82	918	84	916	44	6	5.86	5.91	6.14
5.9	102	898	103	897	43	7	5.94	5.99	6.22
6.0	126	874	128	872	42	8	6.02	6.07	6.30
6.1	155	845	156	844	41	9	6.08	6.14	6.36
6.2	190	810	193	807	40	10	6.12	6.19	6.42
6.3	230	770	232	768	39	11	6.17	6.24	6.47
6.4	273	727	275	725	38	12	6.23	6.28	6.51
6.5	323	677	326	674	37	13	6.28	6.32	6.56
6.6	382	618	385	615	36	14	6.33	6.37	6.61
6.7	439	561	442	558	35	15	6.37	6.41	6.65
6.8	498	502	502	498	34	16	6.41	6.45	6.68
6.9	558	442	561	439	33	17	6.45	6.49	6.72
7.0	618	382	621	379	32	18	6.49	6.53	6.75
7.1	672	328	676	324	31	19	6.53	6.56	6.79
7.2	726	274	728	272	30	20	6.55	6.59	6.82
7.3	773	227	775	225	29	21	6.58	6.63	6.86
7.4	812	188	815	185	28	22	6.61	6.68	6.91
7.5	845	155	847	153	27	23	6.65	6.72	6.95
7.6	873	127	875	125	26	24	6.70	6.76	7.00
7.7	897	103	898	102	25	25	6.76	6.81	7.05
7.8	917	83	918	82	24	26	6.81	6.86	7.09
7.9	934	66	935	65	23	27	6.84	6.91	7.13
8.0	949	51	949	51	22	28	6.87	6.94	7.16
					21	29	6.89	6.96	7.18
					20	30	6.91	6.98	7.20
					19	31	6.94	7.01	7.22
					18	32	6.97	7.03	7.25
					17	33	7.00	7.05	7.28
					16	34	7.02	7.07	7.31
					15	35	7.06	7.11	7.34
					14	36	7.10	7.15	7.38
					13	37	7.14	7.20	7.41
					12	38	7.19	7.24	7.45
					11	39	7.24	7.28	7.51
					10	40	7.30	7.33	7.59
					9	41	7.36	7.40	7.65
					8	42	7.42	7.47	7.70
					7	43	7.49	7.54	7.75
					6	44	7.57	7.61	7.80
					5	45	7.65	7.69	7.87
					4	46	7.73	7.77	7.96
					3	47	7.81	7.85	8.05
					2	48	7.92	7.97	8.15
					0	50	8.98	8.93	8.73

[1] The mixtures on this page were made by P. Jones, and read electrometrically on a Beckman pH meter. Readings are corrected to 25°C and slightly smoothed. Phosphate buffers above 8 and below 5.3 are considered unreliable for histological use and readings are omitted.

[2] The dry salt mixtures calculated from Sörensen 0.067 M data. They are to be dissolved in rain water at 1 % concentration, *ca.* 0.070 M; if higher dilutions are used, pH values may be approximated from the next table.

	gm/liter		mg/liter
	0.1 M	0.067 M	5 mM
KH$_2$PO$_4$	13.509	9.006	675
NaH$_2$PO$_4$H$_2$O	13.801	9.201	690
Na$_2$HPO$_4$	14.198	9.465	710

TABLE 20-13. OXALATE BUFFER[1]

0.1 M oxalic acid	0.1 M sodium oxalate	pH
25	0	**1.34**
24	1	**1.40**
23	2	**1.45**
22	3	**1.50**
21	4	**1.55**
20	5	**1.65**
19	6	**1.71**
18	7	**1.80**
17	8	**1.89**
16	9	**1.99**
15	10	**2.12**
14	11	**2.36**
13	12	**2.59**
12	13	**2.88**
11	14	**3.22**
10	15	**3.35**
9	16	**3.51**
8	17	**3.61**
7	18	**3.73**
6	19	**3.92**
5	20	**4.05**
4	21	**4.18**
3	22	**4.37**
2	23	4.58
1	24	4.95
0	25	7.02

TABLE 20-14. OXALATE + FECL$_3$[1]

0.1 M Na oxalate	0.1 M FeCl$_3$	pH
25	0	7.0
24	1	4.92
23	2	4.6
22	3	4.27
21	4	3.7
20	5	2.3
19	6	**1.9**
18	7	**1.88**
17	8	**1.80**
16	9	**1.75**
15	10	**1.70**
14	11	**1.60**
13	12	**1.59**
12	13	**1.55**
11	14	**1.51**
10	15	**1.49**
9	16	**1.48**
8	17	**1.44**
7	18	**1.40**
6	19	**1.38**
5	20	**1.36**
4	21	**1.33**
3	22	**1.32**
2	23	**1.30**
1	24	**1.28**
0	25	**1.24**

[1] Oxalic acid, M.W. 90.038. 0.1 M = 9,004 gm/liter. Sodium oxalate, M.W. 134.004. 0.1 M = 13.4 gm/liter.

[1] Ferric chloride, FeCl$_3$·6H$_2$O, M.W. 270.32. Use 27.032 gm/liter for 0.1 M.

TABLE 20-15. LASKEY III:3:51[1]

1 N NaOH	Dist. H_2O	1 N glyc.	pH 0.5 N	pH 0.1 N
0.5	19.5	20	8.30	8.15
1	19	20	8.60	8.50
2	18	20	8.85	8.75
3	17	20	9.10	8.95
4	16	20	9.40	9.30
5	15	20	9.52	9.40
6	14	20	9.64	9.55
7	13	20	9.73	9.65
8	12	20	9.80	9.78
9	11	20	9.90	9.88
10	10	20	9.98	9.99
11	9	20	10.04	10.00
12	8	20	10.12	10.09
13	7	20	10.22	10.18
14	6	20	10.28	10.22
15	5	20	10.40	10.33
16	4	20	10.50	10.48
17	3	20	10.65	10.60
18	2	20	10.90	10.85
19	1	20	11.20	11.12
19.5	0.5	20	11.48	11.30

(Glycine + NaOH column group header above "1 N NaOH", "Dist. H_2O", "1 N glyc.")

These are made as stock 1 N solutions from which dilutions are made as required.

[1] Glycine, M.W. 75.07. Use 75.07 gm/liter. NaOH, M.W. 39.999. Use 40 gm/liter.

TABLE 20-16. SÖRENSEN'S GLYCINE NACL NaOH[1]

Glycine NaCl (0.1 N each)	N/10 NaOH	pH levels at 18°C	24°C	30°C
95	5	8.58	8.45	8.32
90	10	8.93	8.79	8.67
80	20	9.36	9.22	9.08
70	30	9.71	9.56	9.42
60	40	10.14	9.98	9.83
55	45	10.48	10.32	10.17
51	49	11.07	10.90	10.74
50	50	11.31	11.14	10.97
49	51	11.57	11.39	11.22
45	55	12.10	11.92	11.74
40	60	12.40	12.21	12.03
30	70	12.67	12.48	12.29
20	80	12.86	12.66	12.47
10	90	12.97	12.77	12.57

[1] For 0.1 N use: Glycine, M.W. 75.07, 7.507 gm/liter; NaCl, M.W. 58.448, 5.845 gm/liter; NaOH, M.W. 39.999, 4.00 gm/liter.

SOURCE: Cited from Clark.

TABLE 20-17. GOMORI'S "TRIS
MALEATE" BUFFER[1]

1 M maleic acid	1 M (CH₂OH)₃ C-NH₂	0.5 N NaOH	Water	pH
5	5	1	39	**5.08**
5	5	2	38	**5.30**
5	5	3	37	**5.52**
5	5	4	36	**5.70**
5	5	5	35	**5.88**
5	5	6	34	**6.05**
5	5	7	33	**6.27**
5	5	8	32	**6.50**
5	5	9	31	**6.86**
5	5	10	30	**7.20**
5	5	11	29	**7.50**
5	5	12	28	**7.75**
5	5	13	27	**7.97**
5	5	14	26	**8.15**
5	5	15	25	**8.30**
5	5	16	24	**8.45**

[1] Tris maleate = trihydroxymethylamino-methane. 1 M = 121.14 gm/liter. Maleic acid, 1 M = 116.07 gm/liter. Sodium hydroxide, 0.5 N = 20 gm/liter.
SOURCE: *Proc. Soc. Exp. Biol. & Med.* **68**:354, 1948.

TABLE 20-18. GOMORI'S TRIHY-
DROXYMETHYLAMINOMETHANE +
HYDROCHLORIC ACID: "TRIS"
HCl (0.05 M)

pH	Tris 0.2 M[1]	HCl 0.1 N[2]	Distilled water
7.19	10	18	12
7.36	10	17	13
7.54	10	16	14
7.66	10	15	15
7.77	10	14	16
7.87	10	13	17
7.96	10	12	18
8.05	10	11	19
8.14	10	10	20
8.23	10	9	21
8.32	10	8	22
8.41	10	7	23
8.51	10	6	24
8.62	10	5	25
8.74	10	4	26
8.92	10	3	27
9.10	10	2	28

[1] For 0.2 M tris, use 24.228 gm/liter.
[2] For 0.1 N HCl, see Table 20-25.
SOURCE: Modified, from Pearse, 1960.

TABLE 20-19. SÖRENSEN'S BORATE BUFFERS

0.1 N HCl, cc	Borate,[1] cc	0.1 N NaOH, cc	pH levels	
			20°C	30°C
475	525		**7.61**	**7.58**
450	550		**7.93**	**7.89**
425	575		**8.13**	**8.09**
400	600		**8.27**	**8.23**
350	650		**8.49**	**8.44**
300	700		**8.67**	**8.61**
250	750		**8.79**	**8.72**
200	800		**8.89**	**8.83**
150	850		**8.99**	**8.92**
100	900		**9.07**	**9.01**
50	950		**9.15**	**9.08**
	1000		9.23	**9.18**
			22°C	30°C
	1000		**9.21**	**9.15**
	900	100	**9.33**	**9.29**
	800	200	**9.46**	**9.43**
	700	300	**9.63**	**9.59**
	600	400	**9.91**	**9.86**
	500	500	**10.99**	**10.91**
	400	600	**12.25**	**12.13**

[1] Borate is 12.404 gm boric acid and 100 cc 1 N sodium hydroxide diluted to 1 liter with distilled water.

TABLE 20-20. GOMORI'S γ-COLLIDINE HYDROCHLORIC
ACID BUFFER

pH at 25°C[1]	100 cc portions			40 cc portions		
	Collidine + HCl[2]	0.1 N HCl[3]	Dist. water	Collidine + HCl[2]	0.1 N HCl[3]	Dist. water
6.45	30	40.0	30.0	12	16	12
6.62	30	37.5	32.5	12	15	13
6.80	30	35.0	35.0	12	14	14
6.92	30	32.5	37.5	12	13	15
7.03	30	30.0	40.0	12	12	16
7.13	30	27.5	42.5	12	11	17
7.22	30	25.0	45.0	12	10	18
7.31	30	22.5	47.5	12	9	19
7.40	30	20.0	50.0	12	8	20
7.49	30	17.5	52.5	12	7	21
7.57	30	15.0	55.0	12	6	22
7.67	30	12.5	57.5	12	5	23
7.77	30	10.0	60.0	12	4	24
7.88	30	7.5	62.5	12	3	25
8.0	30	5.0	65.0	12	2	26
8.18	30	2.5	67.5	12	1	27
8.35	30	0.0	70.0	12	0	28

[1] At 37°C subtract 0.08 from recorded pH values for 25°C.

[2] Collidine HCl: Dissolve 24.236 gm γ-collidine in 200 cc 0.1 N HCl + 1000 cc distilled water. This gives the equivalent of the usually prescribed 25 cc 0.2 M collidine and 5 cc 0.1 N HCl to help dissolve it in each 30 cc portion above. The values for 0.1 N HCl are correspondingly reduced by 5 cc in the above table.

[3] For 0.1 N HCl, see Table 20-25.

TABLE 20-21. MICHAELIS VERONAL SODIUM HCl (40 cc)[1]

pH	0.1 N HCl[2]	0.1 M Veronal sodium[3]	pH	0.1 N HCl[2]	0.1 M Veronal sodium[3]
6.4	19.6	20.4	**8.1**	10.3	29.7
6.5	19.5	20.5	**8.2**	9.2	30.8
6.6	19.4	20.6	**8.3**	8.2	31.8
6.7	19.3	20.7	**8.4**	7.1	32.9
6.8	19.1	20.9	**8.5**	6.1	33.9
6.9	18.8	21.2	**8.6**	5.2	34.8
7.0	18.6	21.4	**8.7**	4.4	35.6
7.1	18.2	21.8	**8.8**	3.7	36.3
7.2	17.8	22.2	**8.9**	3.1	36.9
7.3	17.3	22.7	**9.0**	2.6	37.4
7.4	16.8	23.2	**9.1**	2.2	37.8
7.5	16.1	23.9	**9.2**	1.9	38.1
7.6	15.4	24.6	**9.3**	1.5	38.5
7.7	14.5	25.5	**9.4**	1.0	39.0
7.8	13.5	26.5	**9.5**	0.8	39.2
7.9	12.4	27.6	9.6	0.6	39.4
8.0	11.4	28.6	9.7	0.4	39.6

[1] Recalculated on a 40 cc volume and interpolated arithmetically from the table on p. 454 in the second edition of this book.

[2] For 0.1 N HCl, see Table 20-25.

[3] For 0.1 M Veronal sodium, use 20.618 gm/liter.

TABLE 20-22. HOLMS'ES ALKALINE BUFFER FOR SILVER SALTS

pH	0.2 M H_3BO_3[1]	0.05 M $Na_2B_4O_7 \cdot 10H_2O$[2]
7.4	18	2
7.6	17	3
7.8	16	4
8.0	14	6
8.2	13	7
8.4	11	9
8.7	8	12
9.0	4	16

[1] 0.2 M boric acid = 12.4 gm/liter.

[2] 0.05 M borax = 19.0 gm/ liter. 1% Borax is pH 9.11 at 25°C.

TABLE 20-23. HCl + 2-AMINO-2-METHYLPROPANE-1,3-DIOL (AMMEDIOL) BUFFER[1]

Ionic strength 0.05				Ionic strength 0.1				Ionic strength 0.2			
pH	1 N HCl[2]	1 M Ammediol[3]	Water	pH	1 N HCl[2]	1 M Ammediol[3]	Water	pH	1 N HCl[2]	1 M Ammediol[3]	Water
8.2	50	61.7	888.3	8.2	100	120.9	779.1	8.2	200	239	561
8.4	50	68.2	881.2	8.4	100	133.7	766.3	8.4	200	260	540
8.6	50	79.0	871	8.6	100	154	746	8.6	200	294	506
8.8	50	95.9	854.1	8.8	100	183	717	8.8	200	348	452
9.0	50	122.1	827.9	9.0	100	229	671	9.0	200	441	359
9.2	50	164	786	9.2	100	303	597	9.2	200	606	194
										2 M	
9.4	50	232	718	9.4	100	424	476	9.4	200	437	363
										2 M	
9.6	50	338	612	9.6	100	626	274	9.6	200	652	148
						2 M					
9.8	50	511	439	9.8	100	478	422	9.8			
						2 M					
10.0	50	790	160	10.0	100	764	136	10.0			

[1] Ammediol, M.W. 105.140; Ammediol HCl, M.W. 141.605. The solubility of ammediol is 250 gm/100 cc distilled water, according to the *Merck Index*.

[2] For 1 N HCl, see Table 20-25.

[3] For 1 M Ammediol, use 105.14 gm/liter.

SOURCE: Long, 1961, p. 35.

TABLE 20-24. TRIPHOSPHATE HCl BUFFER, pH 9.5–12.4

pH	K_3PO_4 1 M[1]	HCl 1 N	H_2O
9.5	40	24.5	35.5
10.0	40	23.5	36.5
10.5	40	22.0	38.0
11.0	40	19.0	41.0
11.5	40	12.0	48.0
12.0	40	5.5	54.5
12.4	40	0.75	59.25

[1] 1 M K_3PO_4 = 212.28 gm/liter. Solubility at 25°C, 1931 gm/liter. The sodium salt Na_3PO_4. 12 H_2O requires 380.14 gm/liter for 1 M and would approach saturation at 45°C; hence it cannot be substituted.

SOURCE: Gancevici, *Arch Rouman. Path. Exp. Microbiol.* **21**:191, 1962.

TABLE 20-25. TABLES FOR PREPARATION OF NORMAL SOLUTIONS
OF SULFURIC, HYDROCHLORIC AND NITRIC ACIDS FROM
THE USUAL CONCENTRATED ACIDS

Sulfuric Acid

Specific gravity	% H_2SO_4, w/w	gm H_2SO_4 per liter	Normality	Vol. = 49.04 gm for 1 N sol.,[2] cc
1.8337	95	1742	35.51	28.2
1.8355	96	1762	35.93	27.86
1.8364	97	1781	36.31	27.6
1.8361	98	1799	36.68	27.3
1.8342	99	1816	37.03	27.1
1.8305	100	1831	37.34	26.8

Hydrochloric Acid

Specific gravity	% HCl, w/w	gm HCl per liter	Normality	Vol. = 36.47 gm for 1 N sol.,[2] cc
1.1789	36	424.4	11.64	86.0
1.1837	37[1]	438.0	12.01	83.3
1.1885	38	451.6	12.38	80.8
1.1932	39[1]	465.4	12.75	78.4
1.1980	40	479.2	13.14	76.2

Nitric Acid

Specific gravity	% HNO_3, w/w	gm HNO_3 per liter	Normality	Vol. = 63.02 gm for 1 N sol.,[2] cc
1.4048	68	955.3	15.16	66.0
1.4091	69	972.3	15.43	64.9
1.4134	70	989.4	15.70	63.8
1.4176	71	1006	15.96	62.7
1.4218	72	1024	16.25	61.6

[1] Figures for 37% and 39% HCl are interpolations.

[2] Figures in Column 5 are calculated from Lange's data as given in the first 3 columns. Where assay figures are stamped on printed concentrated acid labels this figure should be used. Grams per liter is at 20°C.

To prepare normal acid solutions measure the amount specified in Column 5 into a 1 liter volumetric flask and then add distilled water up to the liter mark. These instructions are intended to be sufficiently accurate for histologic purposes.

If the normal solutions are to be used for quantitative chemical work they must be standardized as usual for that purpose.

TABLE 20-26. VOLUME EQUIVALENTS OF MOLAR WEIGHTS

Formic acid				Acetic acid				Ammonia			
Per cent assay	Specific gravity, 20°C	Gm acid per cc	Molar volume, cc	Per cent assay	Specific gravity, 20°C	Gm acid per cc	Molar volume, cc	Per cent assay	Specific gravity, 20°C	Gm NH_3 per cc	Molar volume, cc
84	1.1929	1.002	45.93	90	1.0661	0.9595	62.59	24.0	0.9101	0.2184	78.0
		1.009	45.61			0.9644	62.27		0.909	0.2212	77.0
85	1.1953	1.016	45.30	91	1.0652	0.9693	61.95		0.908	0.2240	76.0
		1.023	45.00			0.9742	61.64	25.0	0.9070	0.2268	75.1
86	1.1976	1.030	44.70	92	1.0643	0.9792	61.33		0.906	0.2296	74.2
		1.036	44.41			0.9840	61.03		0.905	0.2323	73.3
87	1.1994	1.043	44.12	93	1.0632	0.9888	60.73	26.0	0.9040	0.2350	72.5
		1.050	43.84			0.9935	60.44		0.903	0.2378	71.6
88	1.2012	1.057	43.56	94	1.0619	0.9982	60.16		0.902	0.2405	70.8
		1.063	43.29			1.0026	59.90	27.0	0.9010	0.2433	70.0
89	1.2028	1.070	43.02	95	1.0605	1.007	59.63		0.900	0.2460	69.3
		1.077	42.75			1.0115	59.37		0.899	0.2487	68.5
90	1.2044	1.084	42.48	96	1.0588	1.016	59.11	28.0	0.8980	0.2514	67.8
		1.090	42.21			1.0205	58.85		0.897	0.2542	67.0
91	1.2059	1.097	41.94	97	1.0570	1.025	58.59		0.896	0.2569	66.3
		1.104	41.68			1.0295	58.32		0.895	0.2596	65.6
92	1.2078	1.111	41.42	98	1.0549	1.034	58.08	29.0	0.8940	0.2622	64.9
		1.118	41.16			1.038	57.85		0.893	0.2649	64.3
93	1.2099	1.125	40.91	99	1.0524	1.042	57.63	30.0	0.8920	0.2676	63.7
		1.132	40.66			1.046	57.41	35.28[1]	0.8805	0.3106	54.8
94	1.2117	1.139	40.41	100	1.0498	1.050	57.19				
		1.146	40.16								
95	1.2140	1.153	39.92								

[1] At 15.6°C in British literature "0.880 ammonia."
SOURCE: Calculated from Lange, with interpolations.

References

G. S. Walpole: *J. Chem. Soc.* **105**:2501, 1914.

B. L. Horecker and R. D. Lillie: Unpublished data, Sept., 1943.

W. M. Clark: *The Determination of Hydrogen Ions,* 3d ed. Baltimore, The Williams & Wilkins Company, 1928.

L. Michaelis: *J. Biol. Chem.* **87**:34, 1930.

W. Holmes: *Anat. Rec.* **86**:163, 1943.

G. Gomori: Personal communication.

C. Long: *Biochemist's Handbook,* D. Van Nostrand Company, Inc., Princeton, N.J., 1961.

A. G. E. Pearse: *Histochemistry,* 2 ed., Little, Brown and Company, Boston, 1960.

N. A. Lange: *Handbook of Chemistry,* 10th ed., McGraw-Hill Book Company, New York, 1961.

Index